Environmental Change & Challenge

Fifth Edition

Environmental Change & Challenge

A Canadian Perspective

Philip Dearden
Bruce Mitchell

OXFORD UNIVERSITY PRESS

Oxford University Press is a department of the University of Oxford.
It furthers the University's objective of excellence in research, scholarship, and education by publishing worldwide. Oxford is a registered trade mark of Oxford University Press in the UK and in certain other countries.

Published in Canada by Oxford University Press
8 Sampson Mews, Suite 204, Don Mills, Ontario M3C 0H5 Canada

www.oupcanada.com

First Edition published in 1998
Second Edition published in 2005
Third Edition published in 2009
Fourth Edition published in 2012

Library and Archives Canada Cataloguing in Publication
Dearden, Philip, author
Environmental change & challenge : a Canadian perspective / Philip Dearden, Bruce Mitchell. — Fifth edition.

Includes bibliographical references and index.
ISBN 978-0-19-901514-6 (paperback)

1. Environmental management—Canada—Textbooks. 2. Human ecology—Canada—Textbooks. 3. Nature—Effect of human beings on—Canada—Textbooks. 4. Global environmental change—Textbooks. I. Mitchell, Bruce, 1944-, author II. Title. III. Title: Environmental change and challenge.

GF511.D42 2016 333.70971 C2016-901419-3

Cover image: Paul Souders/Getty Images
Part- and Chapter-opening photos: Part A: Andrew Smith/EyeEm/Getty Images; Chapter 1: © Scott Stulberg/Corbis; Part B: Paul Zizka/Getty Images; Chapter 2: © Yi Lu/Viewstock/Corbis; Chapter 3: © Chris Harris/All Canada Photos/Corbis; Chapter 4: © Ashley Cooper/Corbis; Part C: Andrew Burton/Getty Images; Chapter 5: Michael Wheatley/Getty Images; Chapter 6: Keith Douglas/Getty Images; Part D: andriko lozowy/Getty Images; Chapter 7: © Paul Souders/Corbis; Chapter 8: Yva Momatiuk & John Eastcott/Getty Images; Chapter 9: © Tim Fitzharris/Minden Pictures/Corbis; Chapter 10: CAVALIER Michel/hemis.fr/Getty Images; Chapter 11: Klaus Lang; Chapter 12: Paul Nicklen/Getty Images; Chapter 13: Michael Wheatley/All Canada Photos; Chapter 14: KAREN BLEIER/AFP/Getty Images; Part E: Thomas Koehler/Photothek via Getty Images; Chapter 15: Tobias Ackeborn/Getty Images.
Design elements: Contents Overview/Domestic Guest Statement/Index image: © iStock/shaunl; International Guest Statement: © iStock/martinhosmart; Detailed Contents/About the Authors/chapter endmatter/References: © iStock/Andrey Danilovich; Preface/Features/Perspectives on the Environment/Glossary: © iStock/AntonCheckotkin; Acknowledgments/Environment in Focus/Appendix: © iStock/sbayram.
Chapter 9 opening quote: © 2015 by Jean-Sébastien Landry and Navin Ramankutty; licensee MDPI, Basel, Switzerland. This article is an open access article distributed under the terms and conditions of the Creative Commons Attribution License http://creativecommons.org/licenses/by/4.0/).

Oxford University Press is committed to our environment.
This book is printed on Forest Stewardship Council® certified paper which contains a minimum of 10 per cent post-consumer waste and comes from responsible sources.

Printed and bound in Canada

2 3 4 — 20 19 18

CONTENTS OVERVIEW

DETAILED CONTENTS

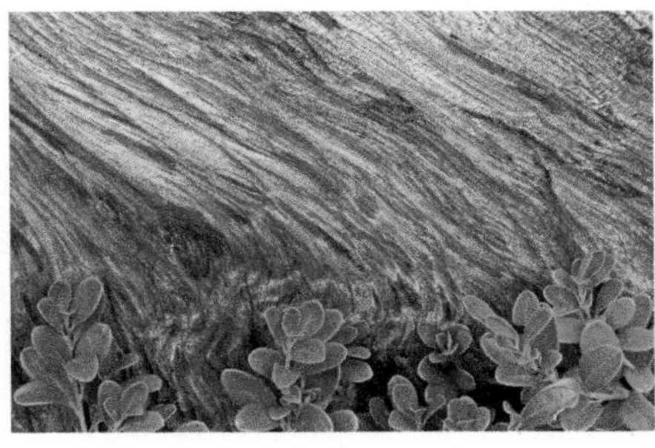

CHAPTER EIGHT Oceans and Fisheries 240

CHAPTER NINE Forests 284

CHAPTER TEN Agriculture 326

CHAPTER THIRTEEN Urban Environmental Management 446

CHAPTER FOURTEEN Endangered Species and Protected Areas 477

PART E *Environmental Change and Challenge in Canada* 524

CHAPTER FIFTEEN Making It Happen 526

PREFACE

When we wrote the first edition of *Environmental Change and Challenge* almost two decades ago, it was already becoming very obvious that the two themes of "change" and "challenge" were going to be major defining characteristics of the twenty-first century. However, the speed and magnitude with which change has occurred was often unanticipated. And with that rapid change have come massive challenges.

Scientists in the mid 1990s were well aware of global climate change, but the speed of change was expected to be a concern for the next rather than this generation. The Arctic Ocean was predicted to be ice-free in 50 to 100 years. However, following the colossal ice losses over the last couple of years as positive feedback loops kicked in, that prediction has been revised to within the next few years.

The challenges created by these and other changes will be profound and global. Sea levels will rise, communities will be flooded, ocean currents will change, rainfall patterns will alter, crops will fail, and billions of lives will be affected. As we prepared this fifth edition, Canadians in Atlantic Canada had experienced record snowfalls in the winter of 2015, while during the same period Quebec and Ontario experienced record-setting cold temperatures and British Columbia and much of Alberta had well-above-average temperatures. Drought caused Alberta to declare the agricultural sector a disaster in the summer of 2015 and thousands of people succumbed to heat exhaustion in India. In addition, plunging oil prices in the second half of 2014 and through 2015, as well as the turmoil and resulting migrant crisis in the Middle East in Syria, Iraq, and Libya remind us that we must deal with change, uncertainly, complexity, and, often, conflict.

The reality of these changes is difficult for many people to believe, since it counters many of our most deep-seated beliefs. Treaties were signed with First Nations for "as long as the rains fall, as long as the rivers flow, as long as the winds blow" because these were the immutable constructs of nature that were reliable. The Earth was also conceived as being so large that the impact of humans was trifling in comparison. Photos of our lonely planet floating through space taken from spacecraft helped to dispel this myth.

A fundamental change has taken place over the past couple of decades in the relationship between humans and our fragile planet. No longer is the planet a vast and wild place where change occurs on a geological time scale driven by natural forces; it has, in fact, become the "greenhouse" of the greenhouse gas analogy in which wild nature is replaced by human constructs, and even the vast atmosphere and oceans reflect human desires as they become increasingly choked by the industrial wastes of a consumer society.

There has never been a more critical time when humans should know how the planet works and especially about the processes that drive our life-support system. But environmental management is not only about managing natural systems; it is also about managing humans and our impacts on these systems. This book was written with these twin goals in mind: that students should gain a basic appreciation of how the planet works and also understand the impacts of humanity on these systems, the challenges created, and potential solutions.

The book is also focused primarily on Canada. Canada is a huge and beautiful country, one of the most magnificent places on Earth. Our geography, people, history, and political culture are different from those of the US and Europe. Canadians can and should also play a major role in what happens globally in terms of the environment. We are the world's second-largest country in terms of area. We are also a rich country. In general, our citizens have a high quality of life and value the environment, but we also create some of the highest per capita impacts in the world in terms of carbon dioxide emissions, water use, and waste production. Changes need to take place. And those changes need to take place far more quickly than is currently the case. Our "leaders" have often been willing to make those changes only if they perceive support for them. That support hinges on having a well-informed and active populace.

We believe it is critical that university students leave our universities when they graduate with a greater understanding of the planetary ecosystems that support life and of their impacts on ecosystems, as well as an awareness of what society and individuals can do to help improve the situation. If all university graduates came out thus informed and acted on this knowledge to create change in their own lifestyles and society, the prognosis for the future would be a little more optimistic.

This book was written for students taking a first course in environment to impart an understanding of the biosphere's function and to link basic environmental management principles to environmental and resource problems in a Canadian context. The book provides both a basic background for those who will go on to specialize in fields other than environment and a broad platform upon which more detailed courses on environment can build later.

Part A (Chapter 1) provides an overall introduction to environment, resources, and society and the role of science, both social and natural, in helping us to understand the relationship among them. This relationship is illustrated in more detail by a case study, the Northern Gateway pipeline from Alberta to the northwest coast of British Columbia. We also provide a global and national context for environmental management and describe some approaches for assessing current progress in dealing with environmental challenges. If we do not know how we are doing, we can hardly judge with any degree of accuracy the severity of the problem or map out suitable strategies to address the problem.

Part B (Chapters 2–4) provides a basic primer on the environmental processes that constitute the Earth's life-support system. Primary emphasis is on energy flows, biogeochemical cycles, and biotic responses, with reference to Canadian examples wherever possible. A strong emphasis is placed both here and in subsequent sections on making explicit links between these principles and examples illustrating the principles in action.

Part C (Chapters 5 and 6) reviews different approaches, processes, and products that should characterize high-quality resource and environmental planning and management. Some refer to such attributes as elements of "best practice." Our hope is that by the end of these two chapters, you will be able to develop a mental checklist of the attributes you would expect to see used in planning and management and that you would advocate either as a team member addressing resource and environmental issues or as a member of civil society.

Part D (Chapters 7–14) takes the basic science of Part B and the management approaches of Part C and puts them together by focusing on environmental and resource management themes: climate change, oceans and fisheries, forests, agriculture, water, minerals and energy, urban environmental management, and endangered species and protected areas. In each chapter, we provide an overview of the current situation in Canada and the main management challenges. Selected international examples also are provided. Text boxes highlight particular case studies of interest and also illustrate the connectivity among the different themes.

The final section (Chapter 15) concludes the book with views from three perspectives—global, national, and personal. Here we emphasize solutions and the actions that individuals can take in moving towards a more sustainable society and introduce the "Law of Everybody," suggesting that if everyone took a few conservation actions, they would add up to a massive contribution to the overall changes required. We question the ways in which values are taken into account in much environmental decision-making and also the way in which development progress is measured. The Happy Planet Index, for example, is one international indicator that has been suggested as an alternative to measure progress that takes into account not only level of human well-being but also the costs of achieving that well-being.

In preparing the fifth edition, we have given particular attention to four aspects. First, throughout the book we have updated information and insights to reflect events and research since the fourth edition was published in 2012.

Second, we have arranged for many guest statements to be written by new authors, or to have previous authors write brand-new guest statements, or to have previous authors update their guest statements. As a result, of the total of 30 guest statements in the fifth edition, 17 are new guest statements from new authors, three are new guest statements from authors who had contributed guest statements to the fourth edition, and 10 are revised guest statements from authors from the fourth edition.

Third, we have incorporated "integrative case studies" throughout the book, to highlight the importance of taking an ecosystem or holistic approach to resource and environmental management issues. Examples are the Northern Gateway pipeline in Chapter 1, the decline of the cod fishery in Chapter 8, the Sydney Tar Ponds remediation initiative in Chapter 11, and a generic "water-energy-food" nexus example in Chapter 15.

Fourth, to highlight that we each should take responsibility for our actions, and become contributors to solutions, either as individuals or as members of Canadian society, we have refreshed the "What You Can Do" boxes in each chapter, and also have sought to highlight opportunities through which you can "make a difference."

Change and challenge are main themes of this book, and fundamental changes are required in the way by which society manages itself to meet the challenges that lie ahead. We hope that this book will help in some small way to contribute to producing the more sustainable future that must evolve over the next few years and encourage you, the reader, to become part of making this future a reality.

As we go to press in late 2015 a new federal government had been elected in October 2015. This government is promising a very different way of approaching its responsibilities, including appointing a new Minister, a Minister of Environment and Climate Change. The mandate of responsibilities for this Minister can be seen at http://pm.gc.ca/eng/minister-environment-and-climate-change-mandate-letter and obviously contrasts relative to the preceding Government. We encourage you to read this mandate, compare it with some of the political statements in the text, and help the new government stay true to this mandate.

Philip Dearden
Bruce Mitchell

FEATURES

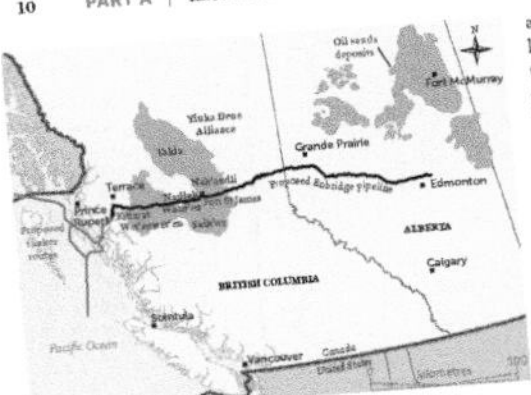

Current Changes and Challenges

Coverage of current events—including the Northern Gateway pipeline debate, the 2014 flooding in Calgary and Toronto, the dramatic decline in bee populations, and the 2014 IPCC report and responses to it—illustrates environmental changes and challenges happening every day all over the world.

288 PART D | Resource and Environmental Management in Canada

more than 50,000 hectares. More than one-third of Canada, however, is naturally treeless, and most of it occurs in the North. Together, Quebec, NWT, Ontario, and British Columbia account for almost two-thirds of the country's boreal forest. Canada clearly has a major international role to play in forest conservation and management.

Deforestation is the permanent conversion of forests to other land uses. In Canada the main process is conversion to agricultural land, with conversion to oil and gas use being the next main factor and the most rapidly growing. Forest degradation by unsustainable harvesting practices is another issue. Overall, the annual rate of deforestation is falling, dropping from 64,000 hectares in 1990 to around 50,000 hectares by 2013 (Natural Resources Canada, 2014a). However, it should be noted that this is an amount being lost each and every year.

Canada is also crucial to maintenance of global intact forest landscapes (IFLs). These are landscapes large enough to retain native **biodiversity** and contain no signs of fragmentation by logging and infrastructure such as roads, mining, and oil or gas development. Such areas are key for biodiversity protection as well as for ecosystem service provision. In fact, recent research shows that even small amounts of tree removal can have very significant effects on ecosystem service provision (Zhang et al., 2014). A recent global monitoring assessment of causes of IFL degradation (World Resources Institute, 2014) found that:

- Since 2000, 8.1 per cent of IFLs have been degraded.
- Almost 95 per cent of the world's remaining IFLs are in the tropical and boreal regions.
- The largest areas of IFL degradation have been found in the Northern boreal forest belt of Canada, Russia, and Alaska (47 per cent) and tropical forest regions such as the Amazon (25 per cent) and Congo (9 per cent) basins.
- Just three countries—Canada, Russia, and Brazil—together contain 65 per cent of the world's remaining IFLs. These countries also accounted for over half of all IFL degradation with road building, often linked to logging and extractive industries, being a key driver. Other drivers vary

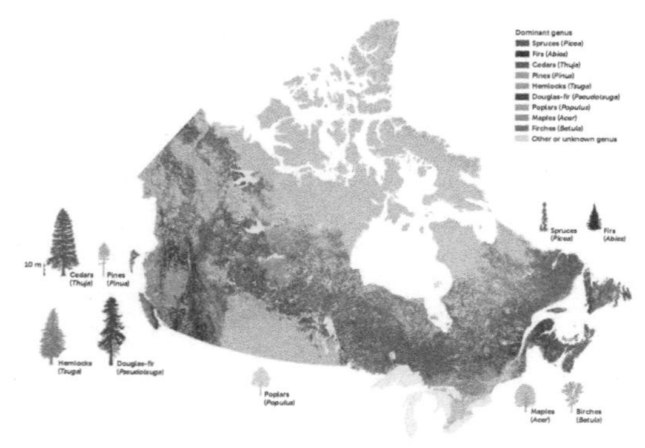

FIGURE 9.2 | Forest composition in Canada.

Fresh National and Global Perspectives

"Guest Statement" features, including 20 entirely new or revised statements, highlight the work of engaged scientists making a difference in Canada and internationally in areas such as food security, endangered species conservation, environmental protection by indigenous peoples, flood management, and disaster risk reduction.

Revised Art Program

From carefully chosen images that present the issues in living colour to detailed figures and tables that provide the most up-to-date data, the revised art program complements and augments the discussion in every chapter.

16 PART A | Introduction

Our home, planet Earth.

insects to the great blue whale—are on board planet Earth, we are mainly concerned with those who seem to be having the greatest impact on the system—humans, or *Homo sapiens*. This species, along with a few others such as rats and cockroaches, has experienced a staggering increase in population numbers over the past century.

The steep curve of population increase, shown in Figure 1.2, coincides with the time that humans learned how to exploit the vast energy supplies of past *photosynthetic* activity lain down as coal and oil in the Earth's crust. Until then, energy supplies had been limited by daily inputs from the sun. The discovery of this new treasure house of energy allowed humans to increase food supplies dramatically and improve

Perspectives on the Environment

The Potential of Youth

Our world is home to 1.8 billion young people between the ages of 10 and 24, and the youth population is growing fastest in the poorest nations. Within this generation are 600 million adolescent girls with specific needs, challenges and aspirations for the future.

Never before have there been so many young people. Never again is there likely to be such potential for economic and social progress. How we meet the needs and aspirations of young people will define our common future.

Source: UNFPA (2014: ii).

and greatly speed up the processing and transportation of materials (see Chapters 2 and 12 for more discussion on this). More than 7.3 billion humans now draw upon the planetary life-support system for sustenance; before the Industrial Revolution, there were fewer than a billion. Another result of increased energy consumption is the pollution that now chokes this life-support system and is causing unprecedented human-induced changes in global climate.

An estimated 4.3 people are born every second around the world. By April 2015 the Earth supported over 7.3 billion people. For a sense of how rapidly population growth is occurring, check the population "worldometer" (see "Worldometers" in "Related Websites" at the end of this chapter) which provides a live count of population increase. The United Nations forecasts an increase to 9.6 billion people by 2050 and 10.9 billion by 2100 (UN Population Division, 2014), representing more than 80 million additional people per year to feed. This scenario assumes that replacement-level fertility rates are maintained. A high-variant scenario, which assumes slightly higher fertility rates, places global population at 10.9 billion by mid-century and 16.6 billion by the end of the twenty-first century. Very small differences in fertility assumptions can make a large difference in population levels. The figures quoted above represent an increase from those made only a couple of years before, as fertility rates seem to be declining more slowly than had been projected earlier, and death rates are falling rapidly in some regions. In fact, the fertility rates in 15 high-fertility sub-Saharan countries have increased by more than 5 per cent, rather than declining as predicted.

Much of the projected increase will occur in less developed countries, where populations in the UN's medium scenario are predicted to grow by 33 per cent between 2005 and 2050, compared to only 2.4 per cent in developed countries (Figure 1.3). By 2050, according to a UN forecast, the populations of the world's 50 least developed countries will increase by 56 per cent. China's massive population (just over 1.4 billion in 2015) would continue to grow until 2030, when economic growth would trigger reductions in fertility, and level out at around 1.47 billion. India (1.28 billion in 2015) is predicted to overtake China as the most populous country on Earth by 2030 and continue to grow until 2060, when it would peak at 1.7 billion people. Nigeria (182 million in 2015) would also experience rapid growth, with the population increasing to 288 million, while that of Bangladesh (160 million in 2015) would reach 254 million. Almost all of the additional 3... billion people from now to 2100 will enlarge the populatio... of developing countries. From 2013 to 2100, eight countri... are expected to account for over half of the world's project... population increase: Nigeria, India, the United Republic ... Tanzania, the Democratic Republic of Congo, Niger, Ugan... Ethiopia, and the United States of America, listed accord... to the size of their contribution to global population gro...

68 PART B | The Ecosphere

case, the predator is often smaller than the prey and gains its nourishment from the prey over a more extended time period that may lead to the eventual death of the host. This may cause the death of the parasite too, although some parasites, such as dog fleas and mosquitoes, can readily switch hosts. Tapeworms, ticks, lamprey, and mistletoe are all examples of parasites.

Not all relationships between species are necessarily detrimental to one of the species. Mutualism is the term used to describe situations in which the relationship benefits both species. These benefits may relate to enhanced food supplies, protection, or transport to other locations. The relationship between the nitrogen-fixing bacteria and their host plants, described in Chapter 4, is an example of such a relationship that results in enhanced nutrition for both species. Other examples include the relationship between flowering plants and their pollinators, which results in the transport of pollen to other plants, and the protection offered by ants to aphids in return for the food extracted from plants by the aphids. Box 2.7 describes another example. Interactions that appear to benefit only one partner but do not harm the other are examples of **commensalism**. The growth of **epiphytes**, plants that use others for support but not nourishment, is one example.

This Amazonian bromeliad is growing as a epiphyte high on the branches of a tree.

Keystone Species

Species with a strong influence on the entire community are known as **keystone species**. They are named after the final wedge-shaped stone laid in an arch. Without the keystone, all the other stones in the arch will collapse. In Canada, our national symbol, the beaver, is a good example of such a

ENVIRONMENT IN FOCUS

BOX 2.7 | Nemo: One Complicated Fish!

Clownfish are one of the world's most recognized fish, well known through the character of Nemo in the Disney film *Finding Nemo*. Living in a mutualistic relationship with sea anemones, they are fiercely territorial and protect the anemones from butterfly fish, which feed on anemone tentacles. It is thought that the clownfish themselves may have developed immunity to the butterfly fish stings through co-evolution, a process discussed in more detail in Chapter 3. The clownfish also excrete a large amount of ammonia, which fuels an increase in photosynthetic microscopic algae that in turn provide the anemones with energy in exchange for somewhere to live. The anemones also benefit from the food scraps brought by the clownfish.

The complicated life of the clownfish does not stop there. They are sequential hermaphrodites, meaning that if the female dies, the largest male changes sex and takes on the female role, and the largest juvenile grows more quickly and becomes the breeding female. The male fish takes most care of the eggs, guarding and fanning them until they hatch.

Native to the waters of the Pacific and Indian Oceans, the fish are omnivores and feed primarily on zooplankton. Their populations have come under greater stress since their popularization in the Disney movie, due to demands from the aquarium trade, and are thought to make up almost half of the global aquarium trade, with only half of that trade being supplied by breeding. Clownfish are now rare in some areas where they were previously plentiful due to this trade.

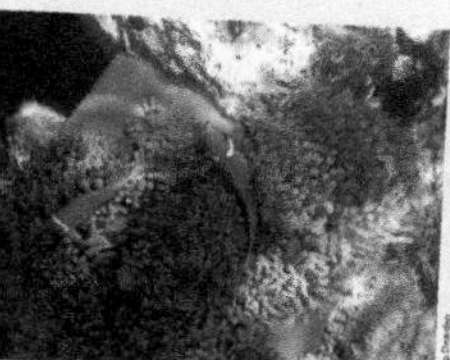

Clownfish seek the shelter of their anemone off the Maldives.

Fascinating Examples and Perspectives

"Environment in Focus" boxes reveal how concepts, approaches, and theories are applied in a variety of real-world contexts, while "Perspectives on the Environment" boxes provide insightful, thought-provoking quotations from respected researchers and thinkers in the field.

Emphasis on Solutions

Explorations of global, national, and personal solutions suggest actions that can be taken to move towards more sustainable ways of living.

CHAPTER FOURTEEN | Endangered Species and Protected Areas 521

ENVIRONMENT IN FOCUS

BOX 14.13 | What You Can Do: Supporting Protected Areas

1. Visit parks and other protected areas often throughout the year. Enjoy yourself. Tell others that you have enjoyed yourself, and encourage them to visit.
2. Always follow park regulations regarding use. Feeding wildlife, for example, may seem kind or harmless, but it can lead to death of the animal.
3. If you have questions regarding the park's management or features, do not be afraid to ask. A questioning public is a concerned public.
4. Many park agencies have public consultation strategies relating to topics ranging from park policy to the management of individual parks. Let them know your interests so that you can be placed on the mailing list to receive more information.
5. Join a non-governmental organization, such as the Canadian Parks and Wilderness Society or Nature Canada, with a strong interest in parks issues.
6. Many parks now have cooperating associations in which volunteers can help with various tasks. Find out whether a park near you has such an organization.
7. Write to politicians to let them know of your park-related concerns.

Summary

1. Extinction levels have reached unprecedented levels. There are several reasons why we should be concerned. Life-supporting ecosystem processes depend on ecosystem components. As we lose components through extinction, these processes become more impaired. We also derive many useful and valuable products from natural biota, including medicines. In addition to these utilitarian reasons, there are ethical and moral reasons why we should be concerned about species extinction.
2. Many factors are behind current declines. The underlying factor is human demand as population and consumption levels grow. Much attention has concentrated on the tropics because of the high biodiversity levels and high rates of destruction there. However, Canada has experienced 13 extinctions and 22 extirpations since European colonization.
3. Main pressures causing extinction include overharvesting, predator control, and habitat change. Habitat change includes not only physical changes (e.g., conversion of habitat into agricultural land) but also those caused by chemicals and the introduction of alien species.
4. Not all species are equally vulnerable to extinction. Species with specialized habitat requirements, migratory species, species with insular and local distributions, species valued by humans for commercial reasons, animal species with a large body size, species needing a large home range, species not effective as dispersers, and species with low reproductive potential tend to be the most vulnerable.
5. Canada is party to several international treaties for the protection of biodiversity, including the legally binding Convention on Biological Diversity. None of the CBD goals set for 2010 were met, including the overriding mission of slowing down the rate of biodiversity loss.
6. As a signatory to the CBD, Canada was required to introduce legislation to protect endangered species. In 2002, the federal government passed the Species at Risk Act (SARA).
7. The Committee on the Status of Endangered Wildlife in Canada (COSEWIC) is responsible for determining the status of rare species and categorizing them as extinct, extirpated, endangered, threatened, or vulnerable. As of 2014, 721 species had been classified as at risk. The Committee's assessment is the first step in the process for protecting a proposed species at risk under SARA.
8. For species listed under SARA, recovery and management plans must be developed and implemented, unless the minister responsible feels that recovery is not "feasible." By 2013, only 56 out of 221 plans had been completed.
9. Protected areas are one of the key strategies to combat the erosion of biodiversity, both internationally and in Canada. Protected areas fulfill many roles in society, including species and ecosystem protection, maintenance of ecological processes, and as places for recreation and spiritual renewal, aesthetic appreciation, tourism, and science and education in natural outdoor settings.
10. There are many different kinds of protected areas in Canada, including national and provincial parks, wilderness areas, tribal parks, wildlife refuges, ecological reserves, and regional and municipal parks. The amount of protection given to ecosystem components varies among these different types.

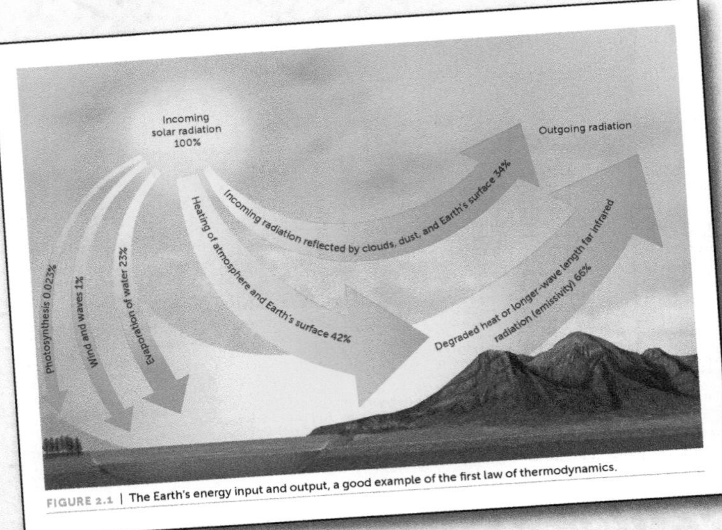

FIGURE 2.1 | The Earth's energy input and output, a good example of the first law of thermodynamics.

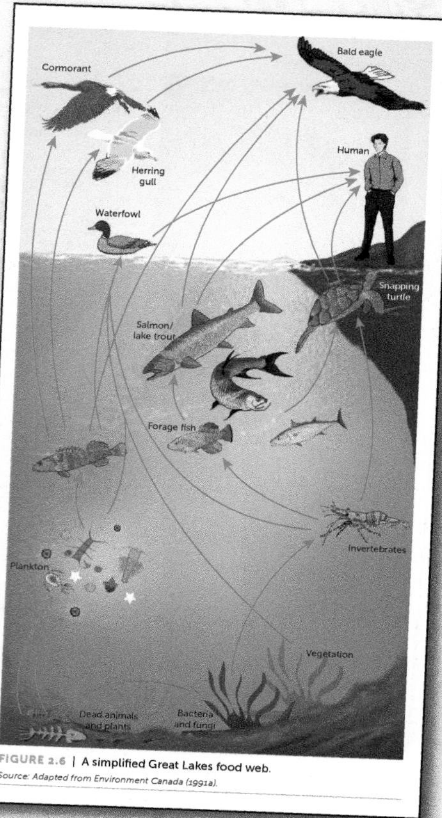

FIGURE 2.6 | A simplified Great Lakes food web.
Source: Adapted from Environment Canada (1991a).

Primer on Scientific Concepts

Thorough coverage of the environmental processes that form the Earth's life-support systems helps readers understand essential scientific concepts and recognize the importance of taking a holistic, scientifically informed approach to environmental issues.

PART C

Planning and Management: Perspectives, Processes, and Methods

Plans are nothing; planning is everything.

—Dwight D. Eisenhower

The chapters in Part B focused mainly on the natural science pertinent to resources and the environment in Canada. In the following two chapters, Part C, attention is given to planning and management related to perspectives, processes, and methods that can be applied in resource and environmental management. A key point needs emphasis. Often, it is inappropriate to think that humans "manage" the environment or natural resources. Instead, we usually attempt to manage the *interaction* between humans and the environment. This is why resource and environmental management involves more than application of "science" or "technical expertise." It also requires sensitivity to various—and often different—values, interests, needs, and wants.

Chapter 5 focuses on perspectives regarding planning and management of natural resources and environments, while Chapter 6 considers processes and methods. Together, they provide an overview of concepts, approaches, and methods to inform the subsequent discussions in Part D on management of various resources.

Chapter 5 begins by considering the concept of *best practice*. It then examines the importance of *context* for a problem-solving situation and the need to be able to design solutions to fit specific situations. The unique characteristics of a given place and time suggest that it is best to develop approaches and solutions specific to a situation. However, when this is done, a potential problem is that some people may perceive other people or regions receiving preferential treatment, since different arrangements are being applied to them. As a result, there often is pressure to use the same or a similar approach in all places, regardless of differences among them. Thus, debate arises over the merits of using a

Coverage of Environmental Planning and Management

In-depth coverage of the philosophies, processes, and products that characterize the best approaches to environmental planning and management remains a strong feature in the fifth edition.

Robust Online Ancillary Suite

The fifth edition of *Environmental Change and Challenge* is supported by a wide range of supplementary items for students and instructors alike, all designed to enrich and complete the learning and teaching experiences.

For the Student

Available at **www.oupcanada.com/DeardenMitchell5e**.

- A **mobile study room**—where students can access study support tools on their tablets, smartphones, or PCs—includes activities, quizzes, science links, and multimedia to enhance the material found in each chapter.

For Instructors

The following instructors' resources are available to qualifying adopters. Please contact your OUP Canada sales representative for more information.

- An **instructor's manual**, **PowerPoint slides**, and an **image bank** make classroom presentation of material more engaging and relevant for students.
- A **test generator** allows instructors a wide array of options for sorting, editing, importing, and distributing questions.

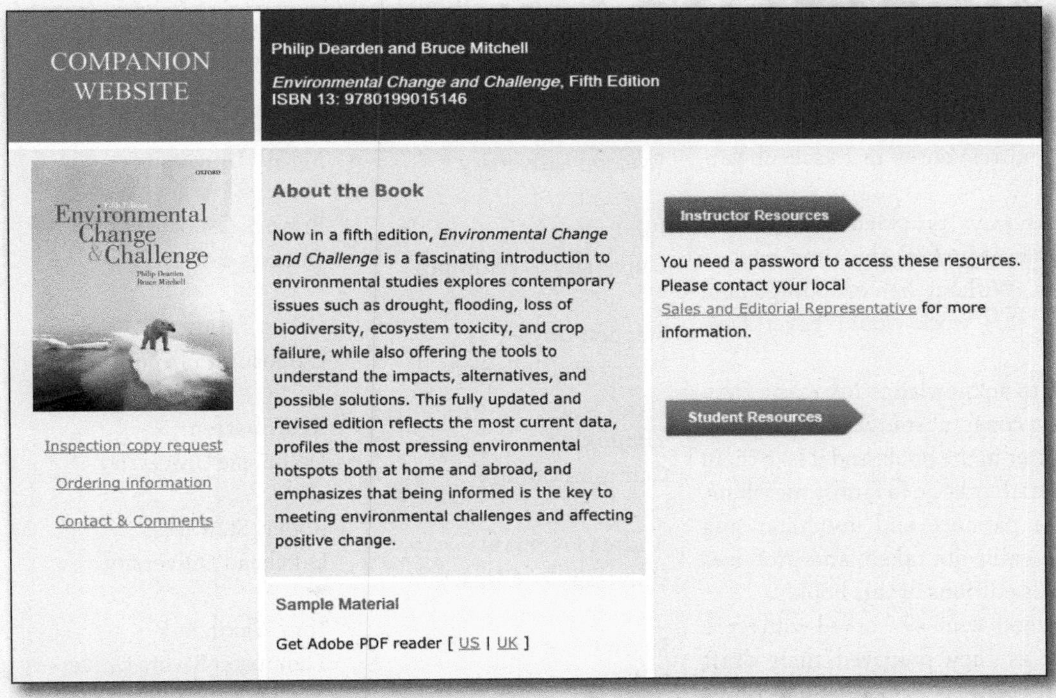

www.oupcanada.com/DeardenMitchell5e

ACKNOWLEDGEMENTS

Bruce Mitchell gratefully acknowledges the research assistance provided by Janette Kingsbury for the fifth edition. Janette provided support in a variety of ways, and was especially systematic in identifying and verifying sources, which contributed to enhancing the final product.

Robert Gibson, University of Waterloo, and Bram Noble, University of Saskatchewan, provided valuable advice and insight related to strategic environmental assessment, especially regarding instances of best practice in Canada.

Tanya Collier MacDonald of the Cape Breton Tar Ponds Agency provided information about the ongoing remediation work as well as photographs related to the tar ponds.

Colleagues Paul Parker in Geography and Environmental Management and Roland Hall in Biology, both at the University of Waterloo, provided photographs which enhance the text.

Aimee McKee took the head-and-shoulders photograph accompanying the personal information for Bruce in the "About the Authors" section. He admires her skill and patience regarding that photograph.

Dan McCarthy in the School of Environment, Resources and Sustainability, University of Waterloo, provided three photographs showing challenges and responses in Kaschechwan, Ontario related to flooding.

Joan Mitchell in numerous ways provided support and encouragement, allowing Bruce Mitchell the time needed to work on the fifth edition. Without her encouragement and constructive comments, this work would never have been completed.

Philip Dearden would like to acknowledge his many first-year students who have been a constant source of inspiration and energy for the subject matter in the book, and it is to them that I dedicate the book. Special thanks go to family members, including dog Max, for their patience and understanding on home tasks uncompleted, walks not taken, and promises unfulfilled through the various editions of this book.

The authors of guest statements who we worked with were enthusiastic and committed as they prepared their draft statements, and then revised them in light of suggestions. They have added depth and breadth beyond what could have been provided from the two co-authors of this new edition, and we are most grateful that they agreed to prepare their individual statements.

We are both indebted to Jodi Lewchuk of Oxford University Press, who worked with us in her role as developmental editor for the fourth edition, and continued with us as work began on the fifth edition. After she was promoted to acquisitions editor, we had the good fortune to have Peter Chambers take on the developmental editor's role, and he was diligent and systematic with constructive advice as the new manuscript was prepared and then revised. We also had the pleasure of interacting with Leslie Saffrey who served as the copy editor for the fifth edition. Leslie was constructive and thorough in her copy editing, and her suggestions resulted in the manuscript being much improved. We also express our appreciation to Lisa Ball for her careful and helpful work during the production and printing phases of the fifth edition. We appreciate the time taken by our guest contributors to provide statements that help diversify and enliven the text.

Thanks also to the many reviewers whose comments have proved invaluable over the years. In addition to those who provided anonymous feedback on this fifth edition, the authors and publisher thank the following reviewers, whose thoughtful comments and suggestions have helped to shape all the editions of this text:

Darren Bardati
Bishop's University

Michael Bardecki
Ryerson University

Bill Buhay
University of Winnipeg

Stephen Doyle
Okanagan College

Tim Elkin
Camosun College

Andrea Freeman
University of Calgary

Susan Gass
Dalhousie University

Leslie Goodman
University of Manitoba

Johanne Kristjanson
University of Manitoba

Robert McLeman
University of Ottawa

Barbara Jean McNicol
Mount Royal College

T. Meredith
McGill University

Brian S. Osborne
Queen's University

Hilary Sandford
Camosun College

Kate Sherren
Dalhousie University

Robert Stewart
Lakehead University

Tom Waldichuk
Thompson Rivers University

Barry Weaver
Camosun College

Jennifer Weaver
University of Toronto
Mississauga

Ann P. Zimmerman
University of Toronto

ABOUT THE AUTHORS

Philip Dearden

I grew up in Britain. Even though home was in one of the wilder parts of Britain, I was always struck with the biological impoverishment of my homeland and dreamed of living in a country where wild nature still existed. My dream was realized when I first came to Newfoundland as a graduate student in the early 1970s. Since that time I have travelled all over Canada, and most of the rest of the world, and have a strong appreciation of the beauty and grandeur of the Canadian landscape.

My main interest is in conservation, and I have taught courses and undertaken research on this topic, based at the University of Victoria, for over 35 years. Throughout this period, I have taught large introductory classes in society and environment and loved every minute of it. I have a strong belief that the power of individual actions can help to make a better environmental future and that we need to support NGOs working in this area. I have held many positions in the Canadian Parks and Wilderness Society, including chair of the British Columbia chapter, and am currently a trustee emeritus.

My main field of research is conservation and protected areas, and I maintain active research programs in Canada, Asia, and Africa on this topic. Current topics include community-based approaches to dugong conservation in Thailand, designing climate-change resistant marine protected area networks in Thailand, developing optimal approaches for whale shark watching in the Philippines, scaling up marine protected area networks in the Philippines, and developing community-based approaches to conservation around the Serengeti in Tanzania. I am a member of the IUCN's World Commission on Protected Areas and have advised many international bodies on protected area management. Author of more than 220 articles and eleven books and monographs, including (with Rick Rollins and Mark Needham) *Parks and Protected Areas in Canada: Planning and Management* (fourth edition, Oxford, 2016), I have also been recognized for excellence in teaching with an Alumni Outstanding Teacher Award and Maclean's Popular Professor recognition at the University of Victoria. I am Leader of the Marine Protected Area Research Group at the University of Victoria (https://mparg.wordpress.com/) and enjoy sailing, hiking, and skiing whenever I get the opportunity.

Bruce Mitchell

I was born and raised in Prince Rupert, a small community on the northwestern coast of British Columbia whose economy was strongly based on natural resources, especially forests and fish. Consequently, from an early age, I became aware of the importance of "natural resources" and the "environment." As a graduate student, I focused on water resources, having become aware of how critical this resource is for natural systems and humankind. I never forgot the observation that an adult of average health in average living conditions could expect to live not more than about 72 hours without potable water of sufficient quantity and quality. This and the vulnerability created from droughts and floods suggested that water was, and continues to be, a key resource at local and global scales.

As a high school student and an undergraduate, I worked summers as a shoreworker in a fish-processing plant and then as a deckhand on a troller fishing mainly for salmon. That experience provided first-hand experience with a resource-harvesting industry. But, more importantly, it made me aware of how knowledgeable people who had not finished their formal education in the school system could be. This experience showed me that "local knowledge" is a remarkable source of understanding and insight. This became a lifelong lesson: experiential knowledge deserves respect, and those pursuing science should continuously look to such knowledge to complement and enhance what they believe they know based on science.

Studying geography provided me with a foundation to understand natural systems, as well as the way in which humans interact with or use them. As time passed, I became more and more convinced that many "natural resource and environmental problems" were often "people problems." I also became aware of the concept of "wicked problems," those which are ill defined, with no single correct solution and for which solutions often cause other, sometimes even greater, challenges. As a result, I focused my attention towards planning and management, always mindful of the need to draw upon scientific research and local knowledge.

I have published over 160 articles and book chapters, 32 books and monographs, and 34 reports and commentaries; have served as President of the Canadian Water Resources Association; have been a visiting professor at 12 universities in various countries; and received the Award for Scholarly Distinction from the Canadian Association of Geographers as well as a Distinguished Teacher Award from the University of Waterloo. I am a Fellow of the Royal Society of Canada and a Fellow of the International Water Resources Association; have been awarded the Massey Medal from the Royal Canadian Geographical Society; and am a honorary professor at four Chinese universities.

As a faculty member, I have conducted research in Canada as well as in other countries, such as Australia, China, Indonesia, and Nigeria. Working in other countries has made me aware of how important it is to understand the ecological, economic, social, and political contexts within which management of natural resources and the environment occurs. It also has convinced me that, while many problems are formidable and even intimidating, again and again it has been possible to make progress in ameliorating, if not totally resolving, them. Thus, I believe we should and can be positive. With competence, determination, discipline, and integrity, we can contribute to resolving problems and to creating opportunities for a better future.

Environmental Change & Challenge

PART A
Introduction

On Spaceship Earth, there are no passengers; we are all members of the crew.

—Marshall McLuhan

The relationship among environment, resources, and society is one of the most important challenges, if not the most important challenge, facing humans on Earth. For many of Earth's human inhabitants, this relationship is an ongoing reality as they try to meet their everyday needs for food, water, and shelter. They do not need to be reminded of how important it is. To ignore the relationship is to perish.

For others, usually urban dwellers in developed countries, this reality seems distant. Food comes from the supermarket, water is piped into homes, work and home environments have controlled temperature through central heating and air conditioning. Not until disruptions occur in these delivery systems—caused by floods, tsunamis, droughts, ice storms, earthquakes, hurricanes, insect infestations, or similar forces of nature—do many people realize that they, too, depend on the environment for survival, as has been true since before the dawn of human civilization.

This first section introduces some basic concepts regarding the relationship among environment, resources, and society and the ways by which we try to understand complex natural and socio-economic systems. There are many ways of knowing about environment. Here we concentrate mainly on the contribution of the natural and social sciences.

Science, especially environmental science, is becoming an increasingly collaborative undertaking. This collaboration involves not only workers from one discipline but those from many disciplines coming together to contribute their understanding of a particular phenomenon. An understanding of acid precipitation, for example, necessarily requires the input of chemists, biochemists, climatologists, geologists, hydrologists, geographers, biologists, health specialists, economists, and political and legal experts, to name a few. Each discipline has its own expertise and methods of approach, and they can be combined in different ways to yield more effective answers to environmental problems. Even with the use of science, there can be high levels of uncertainty and conflict. How we can try to deal with uncertainty and change is one of the main themes of this book, and this is illustrated in the case study of the Northern Gateway pipeline in Chapter 1.

Chapter 1 considers two concepts relating to a vision for the future: sustainable development and resilience. Sustainable development, popularized in 1987 with the publication of ***Our Common Future***, the report of the World Commission on Environment and Development, has provoked much debate and disagreement, since different groups interpret it in ways that favour their values and interests. Despite conflicting views about what sustainable development means, it frequently appears in policies related to the environment and natural resources. Thus, it is important to have a critical appreciation of its strengths and limitations. Resilience is the second concept proposed as a guiding concept for development and environment in the future. Resilience has been gaining in popularity in many areas of the scholarly and scientific literature over the last decade, but what does it really mean, and how can it be enhanced? Our intent here is to ensure that you understand what both these concepts mean, what they offer, and what their weaknesses are.

Needless to say, the global situation is infinitely more complex than sustainability or resilience alone. The next section of Chapter 1 provides an overview of the global situation with regard to environment and society. What are some of the main trends pointing to future directions? Although disagreements exist about the rate and severity of environmental change, few claim that overall conditions are improving. One indicator, the Living Planet Index, suggests that overall we have lost more than 50 per cent of the ecological health of the Earth since 1970.

However, there is good news. Predictions of global population, for example, are slightly lower than previously—9.15 billion people by the year 2050. One important dimension that has only shown growth, however, is resource use, fuelled mainly by the demands of consumers in developed countries—we are reminded of the old comic strip ***Pogo*** in which the title character, a possum living in a swamp, famously proclaimed, "We have met the enemy, and he is us." If there is one fundamental message that we would like to convey, it is that the power of individuals to make decisions on a daily basis can reduce these pressures. Canadians have much to contribute in this regard, since we are among the most profligate consumers of energy and water in the world and are also among the most prolific producers of waste. Our society has developed into one of the most wasteful on the planet. Only we can turn that around.

The jurisdictional and governance arrangements for environmental management in Canada constitute one critical factor influencing our relationship with the environment and resources. Such arrangements are rarely taken into account by scientists and environmentalists, but they can be the most important factor when considering how and when a particular problem is going to be addressed. Canada is a large country, and the various levels of government are complex and often work poorly together.

Whether the context is global, national, or regional, we are interested in measuring our progress in addressing environmental change. As noted earlier, however, the situation is very complex, with far more variables, interactions, and changes than we can possibly measure. The following section of the first chapter provides some background on how we try measuring progress through the use of indicators and outlines the various kinds of indicators and their strengths and weaknesses.

The chapter ends with the presentation of a simple framework that summarizes the process of environmental management. Throughout the book, we return to this framework to illustrate deficiencies in understanding or lack of connection between different elements of the framework.

Part A provides an overall introduction to environmental change and challenge with reference to the global, national, and regional levels. Most of the remainder of the book concentrates on Canada, although we consider global aspects throughout the book and return to a global perspective in the final chapter. Part B provides an overview of the main environmental processes we need to be familiar with to understand many environmental problems. Part C discusses some of the dimensions and best practices of various aspects of resource management. This is followed by Part D, in which we discuss various thematic aspects of resource management, such as fisheries, water, and climate change. The final section, Part E, draws together some of these themes, returns to global and national summaries of current trends, and points out some of the things that individuals can do to effect change for the better in the environment of tomorrow.

CHAPTER ONE

Environment, Resources, and Society

Learning Objectives

- To appreciate different perspectives related to environment and resources
- To understand different approaches to analyzing complex environmental and socio-economic systems
- To understand the implications for change, complexity, uncertainty, and conflict relative to environmental issues and problems
- To learn about various aspects that must be addressed to bring "science" to bear on environmental and resource problems
- To understand the significance of sustainable development and resilience
- To appreciate the concept of "wicked problems"
- To understand the nature of human population growth
- To appreciate the impacts of overconsumption on global ecosystems
- To understand relevant jurisdictional and governance arrangements in Canada
- To recognize that Canada's natural environment and society are part of a global system
- To describe different ways of tracking progress among nations on environmental matters over time

Introduction: Change and Challenge

The year 2014 was the hottest year in global history, and halfway through 2015 climate scientists are already predicting that 2015 will be hotter. Nine of the 10 hottest years in global records have occurred since 2000. The odds of this happening at random are about 650 million to 1. Every year so far in the twenty-first century has been in the top 20 warmest years on record. The globe is definitely warming. Interestingly, Canada experienced its coolest year in the last 18 years in 2014. As you will discover in Chapter 7, global climate change is a very complex phenomenon; some areas will consistently warm, others cool, and still others oscillate as conditions change. 2014 was, however, the thirty-eighth year in a row that the world was warmer than the twentieth-century average. It is likely that you and most other people in the world today have never lived in a cooler-than-average year.

Natural systems change. They have always changed and will always change. There is strong evidence, discussed later, that human activities have become a main driving force behind environmental change. Whatever the reason, it seems that changes are happening more abruptly and with greater magnitude than previously. They threaten societal well-being, and society must respond—and respond thoughtfully and deliberately.

Changes also occur as a result of shifts in human values, expectations, perceptions, and attitudes, which may have implications for future interactions between societies and natural systems. The value of the world economy has increased more than sixfold in the past 35 years. This increase was not merely the result of population growth; the chief cause has been increased **consumption**. Expectations have changed. Things seen as luxuries 50 or 60 years ago, such as TVs and automobiles, can now be found in some of the most remote societies on Earth.

John Lehmann/The Globe and Mail/CP

The muddy brown slopes of Cypress ski hill in West Vancouver in January 2015. Due to unseasonably warm weather, only 6 of 30 runs were able to open.

Perspectives on the Environment

On Change

There is nothing wrong with "change," if it is the right direction.

—Winston Churchill, British prime minister (1940–5, 1951–5)

There is nothing more certain and unchanging than uncertainty and change.

—John F. Kennedy, president of the United States (1961–3)

Changes in natural and human systems generate challenges. If we wish to protect the integrity of biophysical systems yet also ensure that human needs are satisfied, questions arise about how to determine ecosystem integrity and how to define basic human needs. Such questions force us to think about conditions both *today* and in the *future*. Such questions also remind us that an understanding of environmental and resource systems requires both natural and social sciences. Neither alone provides sufficient understanding and insight to guide decisions. Finally, such questions pose fundamental challenges as to whether we can realistically expect to manage or control natural systems or whether we should focus on trying to manage human interactions with natural systems.

In this chapter, we begin by explaining what we mean by "environment," "resources," and "society" and then consider alternative ways to understand systems, issues, and problems. A case study of the Northern Gateway pipeline proposal illustrates opportunities and challenges regarding resource and environmental systems as well as the importance of using both science and social science to inform public decisions and policy-making. The case study vividly demonstrates that decisions are often made in the context of changing conditions, incomplete knowledge and understanding, conflicting interests and values, trade-offs, and uncertainty.

These conditions apply not only to the Northern Gateway proposal or, indeed, to Canada generally but also to the global stage. In this context, we provide an overview of some major environmental trends and the main issues that arise. There is no doubt that human population growth is a stress on this planet, but so are the consumption patterns of the more affluent sectors of society. These factors are leading to unprecedented changes in global systems. Of particular concern are the challenges posed by **global climate change**. It is important that we appreciate the role that Canada plays in global

© Design Pics Inc/Alamy Stock Photo

Flooding followed by drought has significantly reduced the grain crop growing in this field in Manitoba.

environmental change—both as the second-largest country on Earth and as a source of major carbon resources, such as our forests and oil reserves. The decisions made by Canada regarding these resources have global implications. Therefore, you need to understand the governance aspects of environmental management in Canada to appreciate how decisions are made and how stakeholders such as you can become more involved.

The changes taking place are very complex. It is important that we grasp the essence of major changes and act accordingly. One way of doing this is to use the various **indicators** that measure environmental change and response, and we discuss the ways in which these indicators, such as ecological footprints, are used. We conclude the chapter by identifying some key considerations regarding how scientific understanding and insight can be used to inform resource and environmental management and decisions.

Defining Environment and Resources

The **environment** includes the atmosphere, hydrosphere, **cryosphere**, lithosphere, and **biosphere** in which humans, other living species, and non-animate phenomena exist. As an analogy, the environment is the habitat or home on which humans and others depend to survive. In contrast, **resources** are more specific and are normally thought of as such things as forests, wildlife, oceans, rivers and lakes, and minerals and petroleum.

Some consider resources to be only those components of the environment with utility for humans. From this perspective, coal and copper were part of the environment but were not resources until humans had the understanding to recognize their existence, the insight to appreciate how they could be used, and the skills or technology to access and apply them. In other words, in this perspective, elements of the environment do not become resources until they have value for humans. This is considered an **anthropocentric view** in the sense that value is defined relative to human interests, wants, and needs.

In contrast, another perspective sees resources as existing independently of human wants and needs. On that basis, components of the environment, such as temperate rain forests and grizzly bears, have value regardless of their immediate value for people. This perspective is labelled as **ecocentric** or **biocentric** because it values aspects of the environment simply because they exist and accepts that they have the right to exist.

In this book, we are interested in resources both as they have the potential to meet human needs and with regard to their own intrinsic value. Whichever category is emphasized, we often encounter change, complexity, uncertainty, and conflict. For example, different attitudes at different times may lead to an area being logged or used for mining or designated as a protected area. People and other animals drink water to live, and at the same time urban areas may compete with farmers for access to water. An area of significant value for its biodiversity or ecological integrity may be designated as a national or provincial park—but then might change into an ecosystem of less intrinsic value to humans as a result of ecological processes. For instance, if a fire sweeps through an old-growth forest, the question arises as to whether the fire should be allowed to burn because it is a natural part of ecosystem processes or whether humans should intervene to put it out.

Thus, recognizing anthropocentric and biocentric perspectives does not automatically resolve all the problems that scientists and managers face when dealing with the environment and resources. However, being aware of such viewpoints helps us to understand the positions that individuals or groups take with regard to what is appropriate action. You may wish to consider whether your perspective is more anthropocentric or biocentric. Does understanding your fundamental perspective help you to appreciate why your view about the right thing to do regarding a resource situation sometimes conflicts with what others would like to see happen?

Three Waves Regarding Approaches to Environmental Management

Different views emerge, dominate, and evolve related to how environmental management is interpreted. In that context, it has been suggested that **three waves** of thinking have occurred. The value of such "waves" is that they allow us to appreciate what dominant views influence outlooks at any given time and to consider what might be done to cause a shift in thinking if we conclude the dominant view is not sufficient.

The first wave emerged during the late nineteenth century, when those concerned about the environment sought to inventory and protect, and, when possible, extend places viewed as valuable for present and future generations. This wave focused on rediscovering and protecting wilderness areas, and the outcome often was the creation of parks and refuges. People associated with the first wave were characterized as "conservationists" with a primary aim to protect existing environments.

The second wave has been characterized as "environmental activism," and began in the early twentieth century. A key goal was to identify and highlight environmental degradation and urge governments and the private sector to reduce the damage. Furthermore, this wave questioned prevailing ideals of growth and progress with little regard to environmental constraints or limits. As with the first wave, those in the second wave advocated a new direction for societies. A key difference was that those in the second wave argued for significant shifts in basic values. Outcomes during the second wave included establishment of statutes, policies, and environmental protection agencies or ministries to protect endangered places and species.

The third wave emerged in the latter decades of the twentieth century. In addition to highlighting environmental degradation and pollution, its champions called for repair and remediation with a goal to achieve sustainable development. A dominant concern for this wave has been the emergence of global climate change as a fundamental force that drives many environmental changes. During this wave, activists have sought to create international coalitions to create pressure on national governments and also to work to resolve localized environmental problems. A feature of the third wave is building positive solutions, rather than primarily criticizing, as well as believing that the current generation has responsibilities and obligations to future generations. Underlying concepts and values have been drawn from deep ecology, ecofeminism, social ecology, environmental justice, and indigenous peoples. An overall commitment is to repair environmental damage and create a path toward sustainability.

Some, such as Ari Santas (n.d.), have argued that a fourth wave is needed. Do you agree? If so, what should be the building blocks for a fourth wave? If you disagree, what are your reasons?

Philip Dearden

Frazer Harrison/Getty Images

Anyone who has been up close to a manta ray will never forget such a sight or dispute the right of such species to survive. However, a purely anthropocentric resource view will tend to look at their value more in terms of making money as material for bags, wallets, shoes, and jewellery, like the bracelet pictured here. This manta is alive and well at Komodo Island, Indonesia.

Alternative Approaches to Understanding Complex Natural and Socio-economic Systems

In this book, we examine many complex systems, and our understanding of these systems is often based on the knowledge derived from more than one discipline. As an individual, you should be aware of what insight you can contribute from a disciplinary, interdisciplinary, and/or transdisciplinary base and what knowledge you offer to others, from various disciplines, as part of a team. Systems have environmental, economic, and social components. The environmental component alone can be subdivided into aspects requiring expertise in disciplines such as biology, zoology, chemistry, geology, and geography. However, while humans have organized knowledge into disciplines for convenience and manageability, the "real world" is not organized in that way, nor does it recognize disciplinary boundaries. As an individual, you can approach research from a disciplinary or cross-disciplinary perspective, so it is important to understand alternative ways of creating and applying knowledge. These alternative ways include at least the following:

1. *Disciplinary.* Disciplinary understanding is organized around the concepts, theories, assumptions, and methods associated with an academic discipline. Disciplines reflect a belief that specialization will result in in-depth understanding, and this is correct. However, since systems of interest to environmental scientists and managers have many components, the danger of a disciplinary approach is that important connections with parts of the system not considered by a disciplinary specialist will not be taken into account. Some disciplines

are broader than others and more open to interaction with other disciplines. Geography is one such example, where the discipline specializes in synthesizing knowledge from many disciplines to understand differences among places.

2. *Multidisciplinary*. To obtain the in-depth insight of the disciplinary specialist but also gain the benefits of a broader view by drawing on specialists from various disciplines, the multidisciplinary approach emerged. In this approach, different specialists examine an issue, such as biodiversity, from their disciplinary perspectives, such as biology, economics, and law. The specialists work in isolation, or only with others from the same discipline or profession, and provide separate reports, which are submitted to one person or group, which then synthesizes the findings and insights. In this manner, both depth and breadth are achieved through synthesis of the findings of different specialists *after* they have completed their analyses.
3. *Cross-disciplinary*. While specialists in a multidisciplinary team work in isolation from one another, in cross-disciplinary research a disciplinary specialist "crosses" the boundaries of other disciplines and borrows concepts, theories, methods, and empirical findings to enhance his or her disciplinary perspective. However, while in this approach the specialist deliberately crosses disciplinary boundaries to borrow from other disciplines, he or she does not actively engage with specialists from the other disciplines but simply draws on their ideas, approaches, and findings. This approach allows the investigator to make connections throughout an investigation that would not occur in a disciplinary or multidisciplinary approach, and this can be very positive. At the same time, it can also involve misunderstanding of the borrowed material; using theories, concepts, and methods out of context; and overlooking contradictory evidence, tests, or explanations in the discipline from which the borrowing is done.
4. *Interdisciplinary*. To overcome the limitations of the previous three approaches, interdisciplinary investigations involve disciplinary specialists crossing other disciplinary boundaries and engaging with other specialists *from the very beginning* of a research project. The objective is to achieve the benefits of both depth and breadth, as well as synthesis or integration, *from the outset* rather than at the end of the process, as occurs in the multidisciplinary approach. This approach requires more time than the second and third approaches, because a team of disciplinary specialists must meet at the start and then regularly throughout a study. In addition, the approach requires respect, trust, and mutual understanding among the disciplinary specialists, since it is common for one disciplinary specialist to question basic beliefs or assumptions that another specialist takes for granted. The approach also requires patience, because disciplinary specialists have to be prepared to learn the jargon of other specialists so that clear communication can occur. Finally, an interdisciplinary approach requires team members to have considerable self-confidence and a willingness to acknowledge the weaknesses of their disciplines, since their disciplinary views will inevitably be challenged by others.
5. *Transdisciplinary*. A transdisciplinary approach extends the interdisciplinary perspective by seeking a holistic understanding that crosses or transcends boundaries of many disciplines. Furthermore, the problem or issue is usually not viewed as in the domain of any one discipline or profession. An example is "health informatics," which brings together concepts and methods from medical and information sciences. Another attribute of transdisciplinarity is a commitment to include stakeholders while defining research problems and objectives and when developing strategies to collect evidence. Particular attention is given to engaging with people who could be affected by the outcomes from the research. A Charter of Transdisciplinarity was adopted at the First World Congress of Transdisciplinarity in 1987 (see http://inters.org/Freitas-Morin-Nicolescu-Transdisciplinarity), and a handbook was published in 2008 (Hirsch Hadorn et al., 2008).

   The same weight is given to the perspectives from each discipline or profession. This approach, as with interdisciplinarity, can be challenging given the specialized vocabularies associated with different expertise and the potential to be overwhelmed by huge volumes of data and insights, some of which may be contradictory. Brown, Harris, and Russell (2010) provide further insight about this approach.

Science-Based Management of Resources and Environment

In this book, we consider how understanding and insight from science can be used to inform management and decision-making. The nature of science is discussed in more detail in the introduction to Part B. Mills et al. (2001) provide five guidelines for contributions by scientists for effective management of resources and the environment.

1. *Focus the science on key issues, and communicate it in a policy-relevant form*. If science is to have value for managers, it must address pertinent management issues, and research must be conceived in a manner relevant to such issues. This stipulation does not preclude scientific research from addressing basic or fundamental

questions. However, to be perceived as relevant to the needs of managers, scientific work must be focused on and be timely to the needs of managers. In that regard, while scientists can provide important input into establishing management goals, this task is properly in the domain of the value-laden process of decision-making and is not part of scientific research per se.

2. *Use scientific information to clarify issues, identify potential management options, and estimate consequences of decisions.* A basic challenge for managers is to determine whether a problem has been defined in an appropriate manner. Sometimes, because of complexity and uncertainty, managers may be unaware of questions that should be asked. In that regard, science, by helping to clarify relations and trends in systems, can clarify known issues and identify issues previously overlooked or unknown. Science can also help to calculate the implications of different options related to an issue or problem.
3. *Clearly and simply communicate key scientific findings to all participants.* While it is important for scientists to publish their results in peer-reviewed journals, if their work is to be relevant for managers then scientists must also share their findings in forums and formats accessible and understandable to non-specialists.
4. *Evaluate whether or not the final decision is consistent with scientific information.* Making relevant scientific information available and accessible is necessary but not sufficient. It must be considered and incorporated into decision-making. One way of ascertaining whether that is happening, and of putting pressure on decision-makers to do so, is to conduct systematic and formal evaluations of decisions to determine to what extent they have relied on science.
5. *Avoid advocacy of any particular solution.* There is much debate regarding this guideline, since some scientists believe that they should be advocates for solutions when their knowledge leads them to a preferred conclusion. Others maintain that if scientists and their evidence and interpretations are to be credible, they should not be seen to favour any particular solution. For example, if a scientist is a known advocate of the use of herbicides and pesticides to enhance agricultural production, would that person's evidence supporting the use of herbicides and pesticides be viewed as credible? Even if scientists can separate their basic values from their scientific understanding, there is a danger that they will be perceived to favour a particular viewpoint, leaving doubt in some people's minds as to whether data, interpretations, conclusions, and recommendations from such a scientist have been "contaminated" by those values.

The dilemma, of course, is that nobody is value-free or value-neutral, so to suggest that scientists can or should be value-free or "objective" is difficult to sustain. However, there is a difference between being perceived to be open-minded in defining a problem or identifying alternative solutions and being known to uphold a particular view or position and consistently producing findings that support only that one view or position. A further complication occurs when there is insufficient evidence to support a conclusion and scientists are asked to provide a professional opinion. In such situations, the scientist will be viewed as more credible if he or she has no record of advocating a particular perspective.

Perspectives on the Environment

Professional Judgement

Since there seldom is time to conduct new research in the middle of a major policy debate, there always will be holes, sometimes big ones, in the science information. The scientists will be asked to at least hypothesize relations that might fill those holes, and that will require significant personal judgement. Often, tight time frames will not permit the sort of multiple rounds of peer review that are desirable and typical in the science arena. In these circumstances, faith in the objectivity and independence of the scientists is particularly important.

—Mills et al. (2001: 14)

War on Science?

The five points in the previous section identify ideal attributes of science related to management of resources and the environment. A note of realism needs to be injected here, however, as it is not inevitable that everyone will enthusiastically look to science to advance understanding and develop solutions. Indeed, Turner (2013) has argued that in Canada what can be characterized as a "**war on science**" had occurred, as some government leaders strove to control science, especially when its findings challenged or led to questions about their government's priorities, policies, or programs. Such tension between political leaders and scientists is not a recent phenomenon (Hutchings et al., 1997; Wagner, 2001), but such tension increased in the last decade at a national level in Canada.

Characteristics of the war on science include:

1. Closing or sharply reducing funds for government units or organizations whose research has produced findings that question or could be used to challenge government initiatives. Examples include the elimination of the long-form census by Statistics Canada in 2010, the closing of the federal National Roundtable on the Environment and the Economy, the withdrawing of federal funding from

the Experimental Lakes Area in northwestern Ontario, and the budget cutbacks that led to termination of the Polar Environment Atmospheric Research Laboratory (PEARL), all in 2012, with PEARL receiving new funding in May 2013.
2. Not allowing government scientists to publish their research findings in journal articles or to present them at conferences unless the material has first been reviewed and approved by the relevant minister's office.
3. When government scientists make a conference presentation or are interviewed by the media, having a spokesperson from the relevant minister's office accompany them and determine which questions can be answered. This approach was highlighted at the International Polar Year conference in 2012, when each Environment Canada scientist was accompanied by a media person who listened to responses and answered follow-up queries him- or herself. Another example occurred in the autumn of 2010, when an Environment Canada scientist was not allowed to discuss with journalists his paper related to ozone layer research which already had been published in an international journal.
4. Discrediting or raising questions about research findings that challenge a government's priorities, policies, or programs.

Turner (2013: 35) characterized the above initiatives as reflecting an attitude of "wilful blindness," meaning the government's determination not to allow science or social science data collection or research that might lead to questions about government policies. He concluded that such an approach places low value on "evidence-based" policy and instead is guided mainly by ideology or values. Further examples can be found in Hutchings et al. (1997), who provide specific details of what they term "bureaucratic interference" with government science related to fisheries research and management regarding the collapse of the cod fishery in the northwest Atlantic (see Chapter 8), and to declines in the Pacific salmon fishery as water in the Nechako River in British Columbia was diverted to meet the needs of an ALCAN aluminum plant in Kitimat.

In the international journal *Nature*, an editorial (2012: 6) criticized the Canadian federal government's approach to science research, and indicated its approach contrasted sharply to new policy by the United States federal government. For example, the National Science Foundation in the US has stipulated that scientists can express their views as long as they make it clear they are providing a personal opinion and are not speaking on behalf of their agency. In contrast, O'Hara (2010: 501) commented that climate change scientists at Environment Canada were barred from having interviews with journalists from national or international media unless they were first pre-approved by their minister's office. The rationale? To avoid causing surprises for the minister.

One view of the interaction between government and science.

Raeside Cartoons

The Northern Gateway Proposal

One of the highest-profile issues relating to the role of science, policy, and environmental decision-making in Canada for several decades is the proposal to build a pipeline from the oil sands of Alberta to the BC coast to enable access to Asian markets (Mitchell, 2015: 3–10). The proposal has many international ramifications, including the large increases in global CO_2 emissions and global warming that will result from the oil extraction, transport, and consumption. It has national implications, including the scale of the project, the transprovincial issues raised, the federal jurisdictions involved, and the involvement with global trade. It also raises provincial, regional, and local concerns over the place-specific impacts of the infrastructure required. There are also important ethical issues related to the rights of Aboriginal peoples and to whether, no matter what the monetary benefits, we should be making a major contribution to furthering the negative impacts of the world's primary environmental problem.

The Northern Gateway project is a 1,177-kilometre oil pipeline proposed by Enbridge, a Canadian energy company, extending from the oil sands of northern Alberta to Kitimat on British Columbia's north coast. This large project involves two parallel pipelines with capacity for 525,000 barrels of bitumen daily, and is estimated to cost an initial $6.65 billion. Such a pipeline would reduce the reliance of Alberta oil on an increasingly self-sufficient US market (see Chapter 7).

The federal government strongly supported the project, claiming that it would benefit all Canadians. The key cabinet member, Minister of Natural Resources Joe Oliver, also dismissed environmental concerns. In an open letter in early 2012, he asserted that the federal government "... would stand up to environmental and other radical groups that would seek

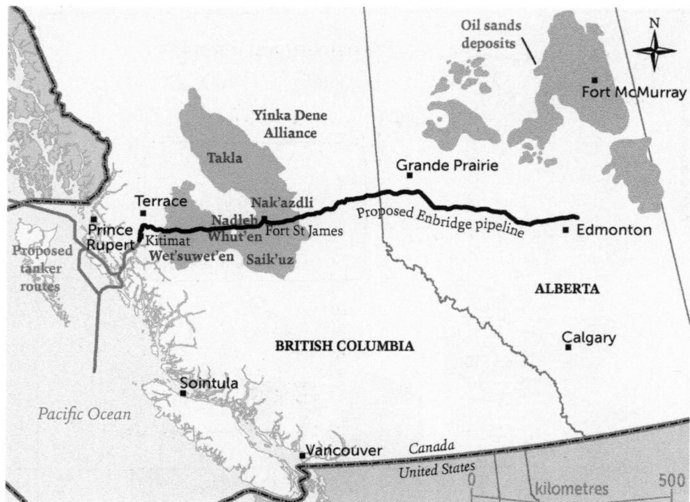

FIGURE 1.1 | **The routing of the proposed pipeline, showing crossing of Aboriginal territories and tanker routes.**
Source: Unist'ot'en Camp, http://unistotencamp.com/wp-content/uploads/2009/03/energy_enbridge_pipeline_tanker_routes_yinkadene_feb2012.jpg.

to block this opportunity to diversify our trade." In addition, he stated that critics intended to "hijack" the environmental assessment hearings, in order "to achieve their radical ideological agenda." Oliver commented that there could be no doubt about the ideology of such opposition groups. They intended to "stop any major project no matter what the cost to Canadian families in lost jobs and economic growth. No forestry. No mining. No oil. No gas. No more hydro-electric dams" (Oliver, 2012).

The statement provides an interesting comparison between political and scientific perspectives on resource decision-making. Both groups were in favour of taking a broader approach to the pipeline assessment, but to the politicians, opposition to this one pipeline was likened to opposition to all resource developments, a view few Canadians would support. In contrast, many scientists felt that the total impact of the pipeline should be considered, including the burning of the oil by Enbridge's customers, rather than just the effects of transporting the oil from Alberta to the Pacific Ocean. They also called for an assessment where the cumulative impacts of all the resource developments would be taken into account, rather than just on a case-by-case basis (Palen et al., 2014). Unfortunately, the politically appointed federal panel reviewing the proposal would discuss neither of these two perspectives, causing widespread speculation that the federal government had already decided the outcome.

There was a lot of concern about the pipeline in British Columbia because it would cross sensitive environments, including many rivers with spawning grounds for salmon, as well as landslide-prone areas and the Great Bear Rainforest. In addition, BC would shoulder most of the costs arising from any spills from the pipeline. The pipeline also would cross the lands of over 50 Aboriginal bands. Many of them were opposed to the pipeline, due to worries that spills would trigger major negative environmental impacts and thereby threaten the bands' livelihood. In contrast, some bands were supportive, especially because of jobs to be created by the project. The BC government specified five requirements to be met before it would support the proposal (British Columbia, 2012):

1. Successful completion of an environmental review process.
2. World-leading marine oil-spill response, prevention, and recovery systems for BC's coastline and ocean to manage and mitigate risks and costs from heavy-oil pipelines and shipments.
3. World-leading practices for land oil-spill prevention, response, and recovery systems to manage and mitigate risks and costs of heavy-oil pipelines.
4. Address legal requirements regarding Aboriginal and treaty rights, and provide First Nations with opportunities, information and resources to participate in and benefit from a heavy-oil project.
5. British Columbia receives a fair share of the fiscal and economic benefits of a proposed heavy-oil project that reflects the level and nature of risk borne by the province, the environment, and taxpayers.

Although initially the Alberta government rejected the BC government's arguments, it subsequently agreed to all five conditions.

The federal government established a National Energy Board panel in late 2009 to examine the Northern Gateway pipeline proposal and report before the end of 2013. The prime minister stated that such a panel indicated the federal

© Chris Darimont

Pooley Creek in British Columbia, one of the ecologically sensitive areas near the proposed pipeline route.

government would make its decision based on science rather than politics. Some became skeptical of this pronouncement, however, when in mid 2012 it became apparent that Fisheries and Oceans Canada had not completed an environmental assessment of all the pipeline's proposed river crossings (Moore, 2012). Acknowledging this problem, Fisheries and Oceans Canada stated that, if the pipeline were approved, it would continue its studies during the subsequent regulatory permitting phase. The department spokesperson also acknowledged that different conclusions could be drawn based on the scientific data. This point was illustrated by reference to two river crossings by the pipeline. Fisheries and Oceans Canada had concluded the risk of negative environmental impacts was medium to high. In contrast, scientists employed by Enbridge concluded the risk was low (Moore, 2012). A different concern was the risk of spills from tankers moving oil through BC coastal waters, after loading oil at the Kitimat terminal. This issue was not included in the terms of reference of the National Energy Board panel's review. More significantly, the federal government had previously authorized tanker traffic along the BC coast.

In December 2013, the Enbridge Northern Gateway Project Joint Review Panel (2013a; 2013b) published its two-volume report. It recommended approval by the federal government of the proposed pipeline, subject to 209 conditions. The conditions, which would be enforced by the National Energy Board, include requirements for Enbridge Northern Gateway to:

- Develop a marine mammal protection plan
- Prepare a caribou habitat restoration plan
- Develop a training and education monitoring plan
- Prepare an enhanced marine spill trajectory and fate modelling
- Develop a research program on the behaviour and cleanup of heavy oils
- Conduct pre-operations emergency response exercises and develop an emergency preparedness and response exercise and training program

In mid June 2014, six months after it received the Joint Review Panel's recommendation, the government of Canada (2014c) announced that, "After carefully reviewing the report, the Government accepts the independent Panel's recommendation to impose 209 conditions on Northern Gateway pipeline's proposal." The government (2014c) further commented that:

> Moving forward, the proponent must demonstrate to the independent regulator, the NEB, how it will meet the 209 conditions. It will also have to apply for regulatory permits and authorizations from federal and provincial governments. In addition, consultations with Aboriginal communities are required under many of the 209 conditions that have been established and as part of the process for regulatory authorizations and permits. The proponent clearly has more work to do in order to fulfill the public commitment it has made to engage with Aboriginal groups and local communities along the route.

Raeside Cartoons

The scope of the science undertaken by federal agencies for the National Energy Board review was called into question by many scientists.

The government noted that the cost of the project had risen to at least $7.9 billion. The prime minister and other spokespersons for the Conservatives insisted that the approval decision was based on "science and evidence." However, others were more skeptical. For example, Ditchburn (2014: A6) noted that in June 2014, ". . . 300 scientists and scholars signed an open letter urging Harper to reject the review panel's "flawed" findings, including its failure to consider the impact of greenhouse-gas emissions from Alberta's oil-sands."

After the approval announcement, a group of First Nations' leaders announced they would work collectively in ". . . a new push to halt the project through the courts, in public campaigns, and—if necessary—by protests on the land" (Cryderman, 2014: A8). Their main worries included the possibility of spills from oil tankers in coastal waters and loss of wildlife. Two dozen First Nations also stated that they would be using all available legal means to oppose the pipeline project. A significant challenge for the government regarding First Nations in British Columbia is that most have never signed treaties with the Crown, and many land claims are still not settled.

Christy Clark, premier of British Columbia, commented that as of June 2014 Enbridge had satisfied just one of the conditions stipulated by the BC government, which was to pass a federal environmental review. Since the BC government must issue up to 60 authorizations before the pipeline can proceed, it has a key role in the overall decision-making process.

Given the scale and breadth of opposition to the project, the costs that are now estimated to be significantly higher than $8 billion, and the global collapse in oil prices in late 2014 and early 2015, it could be that Enbridge has won the battle but lost the war. There is no current statement from Enbridge on this issue, but it may well be content with record $1 billion earnings in 2014, double its 2013 earnings, and decide not to pursue the pipeline further at this time. Nonetheless the proposal provides many insights about resource decision-making, uncertainty, change, and the role of science in Canada.

Wicked Problems

The Northern Gateway project is also a good example of what has been termed a "wicked problem" (Rittel and Webber, 1973). Churchman (1967: B141) introduced the concept and explained that **wicked problems** are ill-defined, with incomplete and/or contradictory information or interpretations, many stakeholders with values in conflict, and an overall system and related issues that are uncertain and confusing. Churchman cautioned that, as a result of such features, solutions could trigger new problems worse than the initial symptoms.

A practical characteristic of wicked problems is that usually a single obviously correct solution does not exist. Instead, managers and decision-makers have choices among various options, each having strengths and limitations as well as uncertainties. As a result, to assess options, attention must be given to recognizing the different values and priorities of various stakeholders and to finding a solution that will achieve as many benefits as possible while minimizing disadvantages, including the likelihood of causing major new problems or exacerbating existing ones. A realist also will recognize that undoubtedly the outcome will involve some winners and losers and that not everyone will be thrilled with the outcome. Regarding those who do not get what they hoped for, it then becomes essential to explain the rationale for the course taken, and, to the extent possible, provide assistance to those who become disadvantaged.

To what extent does the Northern Gateway project represent a wicked problem? What might a set of options look like, to try to meet the concerns of those fundamentally opposed to such a project?

Sustainable Development and Resilience

The previous sections have highlighted that we usually have choices but that choosing the right action is often difficult because of changing conditions, uncertainty, complexity, and conflicting views. Many believe that a key element in making choices is a clear sense of where we want to go. What is the desirable future that we want to create? Without a clear sense of direction, it is challenging to know what matters deserve priority and how to resolve trade-offs when conflicts occur. The concept of "vision" often comes up in regard to establishing a clear direction, and is discussed in Chapter 5.

In this section, however, we introduce two concepts—sustainable development and resilience—often pointed to as representing the kind of future to which we should aspire.

Sustainable Development

Sustainable development emerged in the late 1980s through the work of the World Commission on Environment and Development. In directing us to pursue development that meets the needs of the present without compromising the ability of future generations to meet their own needs, sustainable development stipulates that we consider both intra- and intergenerational equity. However, sustainable development offers a major challenge, since it requires a re-examination of and shift in current values, policies, processes, and practices.

Sustainable development entails three strategic aspects. At one level, it presents a vision or direction regarding the nature of future societies. In sustainable societies, attention is given to meeting basic human needs, achieving equity and justice for present and future generations, realizing self-empowerment, protecting the integrity of biophysical systems, integrating environmental and economic considerations, and keeping future options open. At a second level, sustainable development emphasizes a system of governance and management characterized by openness, transparency, decentralization, and accessibility. It accepts the legitimacy of local or indigenous knowledge and seeks to incorporate such understanding with science-based knowledge when developing strategies and plans. It also recognizes that conditions change

Perspectives on the Environment

Sustainable Development

Sustainable development is development that meets the needs of the present without compromising the ability of future generations to meet their own needs. It contains within it two key concepts:

- the concept of "needs," in particular the essential needs of the world's poor, to which overriding priority should be given; and
- the idea of limitations imposed by the state of technology and social organization on the environment's ability to meet present and future needs.

—WCED, World Commission on Environment and Development (1987: 43) and much uncertainty exists. Thus, it is necessary to be flexible and adaptable, thereby allowing for policies and practices to be modified as experience accumulates. At a third level, and related to specific places or resource sectors, sustainable development seeks to ensure that economic, environmental, and social aspects are considered together and that trade-offs are visible and transparent to those affected.

The concept of sustainable development has generated both enthusiasm and frustration. The enthusiasm comes from those who believe that it provides a compelling vision for the twenty-first century, one with more attention to longer-term implications of development and to balancing economic, social, and environmental considerations. The phrase "think globally and act locally" reminds us that while ultimately the planet is a single system in which actions in one part often have implications for other parts, resolution of problems also requires significant action at the local level, thereby stimulating self-empowerment, partnerships, and cooperative approaches to management and development (see Chapter 6).

The frustration has come from those who believe that "sustainable development" is so vague that it can be defined in ways to suit different and often conflicting interests. Thus, developers like the concept because they can argue that growth must continue if basic human needs are to be met and if standards of living are to continue to rise. In contrast, environmentalists support the concept because they can use it to argue that environmental integrity must be given priority if there is to be long-term and equitable development.

How do you think such incompatibilities and tensions can be reconciled?

A related concept, developed by J. Elkington (1994) in the 1990s, is **triple bottom line** (TBL or 3BL), also referred to as the 3Ps (people, planet, and profit). Used by both for-profit and not-for-profit sectors, the TBL approach goes beyond the conventional business focus on profits, return on investment, and shareholder value to incorporate attention to both environmental and social aspects (Slaper and Hall, 2011: 4). TBL has the same challenge as sustainability, however. As Slaper and Hall (2011: 4) observe, the challenge is not how to define TBL, but how to measure it because economic or financial, social and environmental components do not have common measurement units.

Resilience

Walker and Salt (2006: 1) define **resilience** as "the ability of a system to absorb disturbance and still retain its basic function and structure." However, they observe that resource management "best practice" normally focuses on optimizing particular goods or services from a natural resource system. Such optimization is usually achieved by taking specific components from the system through controlling other components. An example would be to increase crop production by using herbicides or pesticides to control organisms detrimental to such increased production, as discussed in Chapter 10. The ultimate goal is to move a system into some ideal state and sustain it in that state.

The dilemma, they note, is that reaching and sustaining an ideal state assumes that future changes in the system will be minor, incremental, and linear. In contrast, reality is often the opposite. Systems are frequently altered through "lurching and non-linear" changes. And, as we strive to use resource systems efficiently, one outcome can be that desirable redundancies are eliminated, since the goal is to retain only features with immediate value. The ultimate outcome is a drastic reduction in resilience. This perspective about resilience fundamentally challenges the goal of aiming for "sustainable development," as defined earlier. In the view of Walker and Salt,

> . . . the more you optimize elements of a complex system of humans and nature for some specific goal, the more you diminish that system's resilience. A drive for an efficient optimal state outcome has the effect of making the total system more vulnerable to shocks and disturbances.
>
> . . .
>
> The bottom line for sustainability is that any proposal for sustainable development that does not explicitly acknowledge a system's resilience is simply not going to keep delivering goods (or services). The key to sustainability lies in enhancing the resilience of social-ecological systems, not in optimizing isolated components of the system. (2006: 9)

Do you think "resilience" provides an alternative or is complementary to "sustainable development"? If you conclude that either of these two concepts contains major flaws, what alternative "vision" would you propose to help guide us toward a desirable future condition? As you reflect on your view, consider the ideas provided by Ryan Plummer in the accompanying "Domestic Guest Statement" about resilience.

The question of sustainable development and Canada's progress will be reviewed in a later section. The next section provides a quick snapshot of the global context for environmental management in the face of increasing human pressures.

The Global Picture

Our home, planet Earth, is different from all the other planets we know. As it hurtles through space at 107,200 kilometres per hour, an apparently infinite supply of energy from the sun fuels a life-support system that should provide perpetual sustenance for Earth's passengers. Unfortunately, this seems not to be the case. Organisms are becoming extinct at rates

DOMESTIC GUEST STATEMENT

Some Reflections on Social-Ecological Resilience | *Ryan Plummer*

I landed at the Arlanda airport and took the high-speed "eco-friendly" train, the Arlanda Express, into Stockholm, Sweden. After dropping my bags at the Mornington Hotel, I immediately went to Stockholm University, the site of Resilience 2008. Enthusiasm about resilience was clearly apparent as I entered the Aula Magna and registered for the conference. The eagerness in the air continued and intensified over the next several days as approximately 600 people engaged with the idea of resilience. This first major international conference on resilience was just one of the seminal events that made 2008 "the year resilience was put on the map." The Stockholm Resilience Centre, host of the conference, was in its start-up phase, with an investment of 205 million SEK (about Cdn$31 million in 2014) to build a world-leading research centre.

While 2008 may have been the year that resilience was put on the map, ideas about resilience date back to the 1970s. Ecology was not the only discipline in which researchers were interested in resilience, as the term and concept emerged at the same time in psychology. Since that time, an integrative and complex systems perspective has developed. Social-ecological resilience has become central to current scholarship and practice because it acknowledges the interconnections or linkages between humans and Nature. Resilience thinking, an organizing framework in the context of dynamic social-ecological systems, is informed by three central ideas: (1) resilience—the capability of a system to absorb disturbances and reorganize, while keeping the same identity; (2) adaptability—the capability of stakeholders to influence resilience; and (3) transformability—the ability to develop into a different kind of system when/if the present system is untenable. Popular science publications by the Stockholm Resilience Centre provide an excellent introduction to resilience and applying resilience thinking (see Stockholm Resilience Centre in "Related Websites" at the end of this chapter).

Canada is a vibrant place for resilience research. It builds on an established record of studying the environment in Canada and occurs throughout the country in diverse contexts. Research associated with resilience encompasses a wide range of topics. Examples include multi-level governance, adaptive co-management, regime shifts, social innovation, learning, networks, scenario development and modelling, and co-production of knowledge (a collaborative problem-solving process in which stakeholders draw upon multiple knowledge sources to develop a shared understanding), many of which are discussed in later chapters.

Application of resilience thinking is still relatively recent, but there is a growing interest about putting resilience concepts into practice in Canada. For example, threats to aquatic systems across Canada prompted a team of researchers and partners to study how resilience thinking could be implemented in watershed stewardship in Canada. The team focused on the Hammond River watershed in New Brunswick and the Cowichan River watershed on Vancouver Island, British Columbia. Participant concerns regarding stewardship and issues experienced in these watersheds are evident in many places in Canada. The research team developed a workshop by drawing upon work by the Resilience Alliance (a consortium of institutions, organizations, and individuals with a shared interest in resilience; see Resilience Alliance in "Related Websites" at the end of this chapter) and scholars internationally. The workshop was delivered to the stewardship groups to introduce resilience thinking and demonstrate how it could be applied to their respective watersheds. As the participants worked through the resilience exercises, they identified values of and threats to the watershed at multiple scales, explored options to address known disturbances, and contemplated trade-offs in preparing for surprises. Resilience thinking adds to previous watershed planning exercises by getting stakeholders to think deeply about the linkages between social and ecological systems, roles of system dynamics and interconnections between scales, and responses (capacity for adaptation and transformation) to both known and unknown disturbances. To learn more about the resilience analysis workshop in the Cowichan watershed see POLIS Water Sustainability Project in "Related Websites" at the end of this chapter.

Ryan Plummer

Chinook salmon capture on the Cowichan, where the salmon have supported First Nation livelihoods for centuries. In 2014 the runs were severely threatened by unprecedented drought that saw the river almost run dry. These kinds of threats are likely to be more prevalent in the future as a result of climate change and emphasize the importance of enhanced resilience for both natural and human systems.

Resilience is a proliferating discourse in Canada. It is receiving considerable attention from scholars, practitioners, policy-makers, and even the media. Nevertheless, it is important to also think critically about the concept. Resilience has several meanings. Care is required in defining the term and understanding the concept. The manner in which resilience is framed and the possibility and appropriateness of measuring it raise questions about its usefulness for evaluation.

Ryan Plummer

Ryan Plummer, PhD, is a professor at Brock University in St. Catharines, where he is also the director of the Environmental Sustainability Research Centre and of the Sustainability Science and Society graduate program. As well, he is a senior research fellow at the Stockholm Resilience Centre (Sweden). His program of research broadly concerns the governance and resilience of social-ecological systems.

unsurpassed for at least 65 million years. These extinctions cover all life forms and probably represent the largest orgy of extinction ever in the 4.5-billion-year history of the planet. Our seas are no longer the infinite sources of fish we thought they were. Our forests are dwindling at unprecedented rates. Even the atmosphere is changing in composition and making the spectre of significant climatic change a reality. Every raindrop that falls on this planet bears the indelible stamp of the one organism bringing about these changes—you and us. Awareness of the dominant influence of humans on planetary processes has led scientists to consider formal designation of a new epoch, the **Anthropocene**, in the Earth's evolution (Box 1.1).

Concern over this situation led to the request by UN Secretary-General Kofi Annan in 2000 to assess the relationship between planetary ecosystems and the demands placed on them by human activity. Between 2001 and 2005, the **Millennium Ecosystem Assessment** examined the consequences of ecosystem change for human well-being and established the scientific basis for actions needed to enhance the conservation and sustainable use of ecosystems and their contributions to human well-being. Some 1,360 experts from 95 countries were involved in the assessment and concluded that environmental degradation was occurring faster than at any time in the past, that many of the changes are non-linear, and once they start, the processes of degradation will increase rapidly. These positive feedback loops are discussed more extensively in Chapter 4 and throughout the rest of the book. Since the landmark UN assessment, many subsequent scientific papers have documented the continuing trend of rapid environmental degradation described in the MEA, and these papers are also referenced in subsequent chapters.

Population

One main variable that affects our impact on the planetary life-support system is the number of passengers being supported. Although countless billions of passengers—from

ENVIRONMENT IN FOCUS

BOX 1.1 | The Anthropocene

The International Union of Geological Sciences (IUGS) characterizes the epoch that started about 11,700 years ago, after the last major ice age, as the Holocene, meaning "entirely recent." However, some scientists, including Eugene Stoermer and Nobel laureate Paul Crutzen, have recently proposed that a better term for today is the "Anthropocene," from *anthro*, meaning "human," and *cene* meaning "new." The rationale is that in the recent past and today, humans are significantly altering the atmosphere through greenhouse gas emissions, which cause climate change; causing serious pollution of oceans; and triggering extinctions of animal and plant species. As a result, proponents of the term "Anthropocene" argue that it better captures the era in which we live because people have become a dominant force influencing the global environment.

The IUGS uses a series of terms (Quaternary, Tertiary, Cretaceous, Jurassic, Triassic, etc.) to characterize different periods in the Earth's evolution, and argues that any geological epochs within a period (e.g., Holocene and Pleistocene, both within the Quaternary period) must be defined with reference to new boundaries in rock strata. Those who support that view argue that the Anthropocene has no such definitive benchmark to indicate when it began as an epoch and therefore is inappropriate. Supporters of the Anthropocene concept acknowledge the difficulty in setting a start date, but argue that it began during the early 1800s, driven by the Industrial Revolution. The key point, they argue, is that the Anthropocene highlights that humans are significantly affecting the planet in its entirety.

The IUGS has assembled a working group of scientists to determine by 2016 as to whether the Holocene is over and a new epoch to be called the Anthropocene has started within the Quaternary period.

What are your thoughts about the appropriateness of Anthropocene as a new epoch? What value could it have in reminding people that humans have become a major force in shaping the evolution of our environment and planet?

Our home, planet Earth.

insects to the great blue whale—are on board planet Earth, we are mainly concerned with those who seem to be having the greatest impact on the system—humans, or *Homo sapiens*. This species, along with a few others such as rats and cockroaches, has experienced a staggering increase in population numbers over the past century.

The steep curve of population increase, shown in Figure 1.2, coincides with the time that humans learned how to exploit the vast energy supplies of past *photosynthetic* activity lain down as coal and oil in the Earth's crust. Until then, energy supplies had been limited by daily inputs from the sun. The discovery of this new treasure house of energy allowed humans to increase food supplies dramatically and improve and greatly speed up the processing and transportation of materials (see Chapters 2 and 12 for more discussion on this). More than 7.3 billion humans now draw upon the planetary life-support system for sustenance; before the Industrial Revolution, there were fewer than a billion. Another result of increased energy consumption is the pollution that now chokes this life-support system and is causing unprecedented human-induced changes in global climate.

An estimated 4.3 people are born every second around the world. By April 2015 the Earth supported over 7.3 billion people. For a sense of how rapidly population growth is occurring, check the population "worldometer" (see "Worldometers" in "Related Websites" at the end of this chapter) which provides a live count of population increase. The United Nations forecasts an increase to 9.6 billion people by 2050 and 10.9 billion by 2100 (UN Population Division, 2014), representing more than 80 million additional people per year to feed. This scenario assumes that replacement-level fertility rates are maintained. A high-variant scenario, which assumes slightly higher fertility rates, places global population at 10.9 billion by mid-century and 16.6 billion by the end of the twenty-first century. Very small differences in fertility assumptions can make a large difference in population levels. The figures quoted above represent an increase from those made only a couple of years before, as fertility rates seem to be declining more slowly than had been projected earlier, and death rates are falling rapidly in some regions. In fact, the fertility rates in 15 high-fertility sub-Saharan countries have increased by more than 5 per cent, rather than declining as predicted.

Much of the projected increase will occur in less developed countries, where populations in the UN's medium scenario are predicted to grow by 33 per cent between 2005 and 2050, compared to only 2.4 per cent in developed countries (Figure 1.3). By 2050, according to a UN forecast, the populations of the world's 50 least developed countries will increase by 56 per cent. China's massive population (just over 1.4 billion in 2015) would continue to grow until 2030, when economic growth would trigger reductions in fertility, and level out at around 1.47 billion. India (1.28 billion in 2015) is predicted to overtake China as the most populous country on Earth by 2030 and continue to grow until 2060, when it would peak at 1.7 billion people. Nigeria (182 million in 2015) would also experience rapid growth, with the population increasing to 288 million, while that of Bangladesh (160 million in 2015) would reach 254 million. Almost all of the additional 3.7 billion people from now to 2100 will enlarge the population of developing countries. From 2013 to 2100, eight countries are expected to account for over half of the world's projected population increase: Nigeria, India, the United Republic of Tanzania, the Democratic Republic of Congo, Niger, Uganda, Ethiopia, and the United States of America, listed according to the size of their contribution to global population growth.

Perspectives on the Environment

The Potential of Youth

Our world is home to 1.8 billion young people between the ages of 10 and 24, and the youth population is growing fastest in the poorest nations. Within this generation are 600 million adolescent girls with specific needs, challenges and aspirations for the future.

Never before have there been so many young people. Never again is there likely to be such potential for economic and social progress. How we meet the needs and aspirations of young people will define our common future.

Source: UNFPA (2014: ii).

ENVIRONMENT IN FOCUS

BOX 1.2 | Population and Exponential Growth

Population change is a result of the interaction between births and deaths. The **crude birth rate (CBR)** minus the **crude death rate (CDR)** will yield the **crude growth rate (CGR)**, all usually expressed as per thousand of the population per year. In this way, populations of different countries, regardless of their size, can be compared. The figures are known as "crude" because they give no insights into factors such as age and sex ratios, figures that are very important for understanding future potential growth. If CBR and CDR are equal, a zero population growth will result if the effects of migration are excluded.

In 1798, a British clergyman, Thomas Malthus, pointed out that population growth was geometric or **exponential** (i.e., 2, 4, 8, 16, 32, 64, and so on), whereas the growth in food supply was arithmetic (i.e., 1, 2, 3, 4, 5, and so on). This phenomenon, said Malthus, would inevitably lead to famine, disease, and war. Such a viewpoint was not popular in his day, when population growth was considered very beneficial. For many years, the Malthusian view was ignored. The opening up of new lands for cultivation in North America and the southern hemisphere and later the development of Green Revolution techniques (Chapter 10) allowed food supplies to increase rapidly.

Increasing numbers of experts, watching the decline in food supplies per capita over the past few years (see Chapter 10) and the increase in population, particularly in less developed countries, now feel that the Malthusian spectre is quite real. More than 80 million people are added every year to the population in less developed countries, compared to about 1.6 million in more developed countries. Figure 1.2 illustrates how global population has grown over the centuries and millennia.

On the other hand, some pundits, particularly economists, feel that more population simply furnishes more resources—human resources—upon which to build increases in wealth for the future. Indeed, there are concerns that some developed countries will start losing population in the future and that this will have a negative impact on their economies. For example, Japan is predicted to lose 20 per cent of its population by 2050, with declines also expected to take place in Germany, Russia, and Italy. In both the US and Canada, the trend is predicted to move in the opposite direction, largely as a result of immigration. By 2050, it is estimated that Canada's population (35.7 million in 2014) will have increased to 37 million through immigration, despite a fertility rate of 1.5 children per woman.

Political leaders in some of the less developed countries experiencing the most rapid population growth rates have argued that population growth per se is not a problem and that the main problem is overconsumption in the more developed countries. This distributive concern is echoed by women's groups—also wary of coercive birth control programs—who think that most progress can be achieved by improving the status of women. Women with more education usually have smaller, healthier families, and their children have a better chance of making it out of poverty. Yet two-thirds of the world's 876 million people who can neither read nor write are women, and a majority of the 115 million children not attending school are girls. Women who have the choice of delaying marriage and child-bearing past their teens also have fewer children than teen brides. Yet more than 100 million girls will be married before their eighteenth birthday during the next decade.

However, starting with the landmark 1994 International Conference on Population and Development (ICPD) at which 179 governments adopted a forward-looking, 20-year Program of Action, remarkable progress has been made on achieving consensus on approaches to population control. The ICPD Program of Action, sometimes referred to as the Cairo Consensus, recognized that reproductive health and rights, as well as women's empowerment and gender equality, are cornerstones of population and development programs. Furthermore, at the 2005 World Summit, the largest-ever gathering of world leaders reaffirmed the need to keep gender equality, HIV/AIDS, and reproductive health at the top of the development agenda.

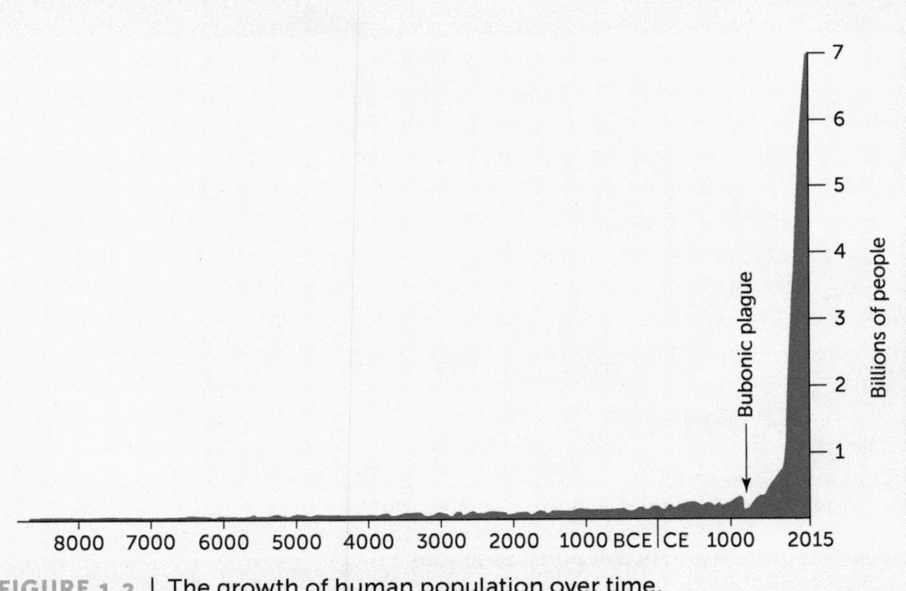

FIGURE 1.2 | The growth of human population over time.

AP Photo/Rajesh Kumar Singh/CP

The symbolic 7 billionth human is born. At the Community Health Centre in Mall, about 45 kilometres from Lucknow in India's most populous state of Uttar Pradesh, father and mother look on their newborn daughter, Nargis. Born on 31 October 2011, Nargis is the symbolic 7 billionth human presently on Earth.

Philip Dearden

Age structure is an important demographic variable. Shown here are three generations of Moken ("Sea Gypsies") from Myanmar. The Moken are a society still in the high equilibrium stage of the demographic transition. They have no access to modern health care, but as this changes in the future, population will expand as mortality rates decline.

For the US, much of this growth will come from immigration, although very high birth levels prevail among some sectors of the US population. In contrast, the combined populations of more developed countries will change only minimally, rising from 1.25 billion in 2013 to 1.28 billion by 2100. Most of that growth will come from immigration from less developed countries.

The different trajectories of the developed and developing countries are epitomized by Nigeria and Japan (almost 127 million in 2015). In Japan, the birth rate is slightly more than one child per woman. Fourteen per cent of the Japanese population is younger than 15, and 21 per cent is older than 65. In contrast, 44 per cent of Nigeria's population is younger than 15, with only 3 per cent over 65. A typical Nigerian woman gives birth to six children over her lifetime. About nine out of 10 people between the ages 10 and 24 now live in less developed countries.

Population age structure is also important. If two countries have similar populations but differing age structures, they will have dramatically different future population growth. Population age structure is usually represented as a population pyramid (Figure 1.4), and the shape gives information

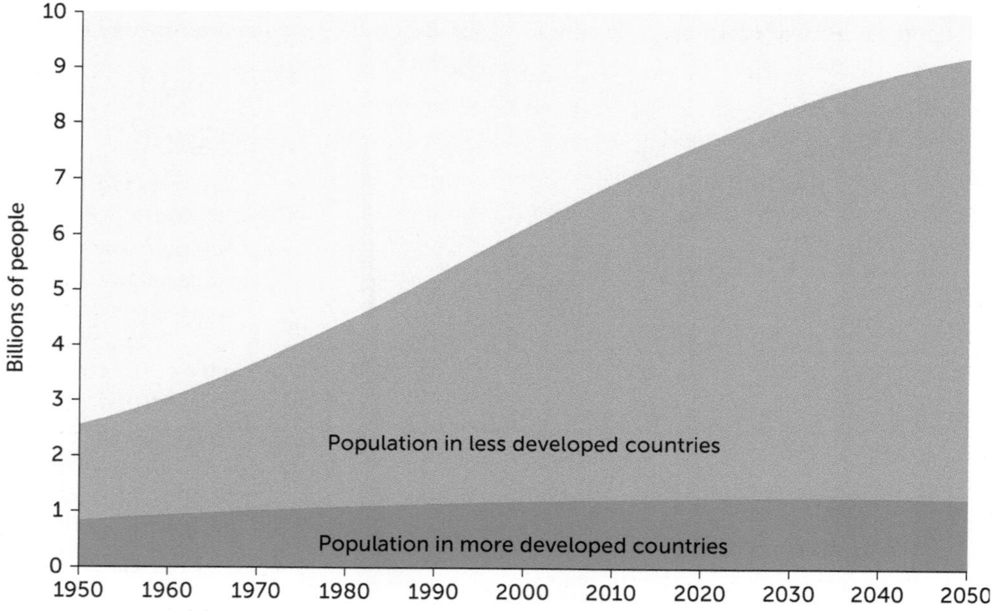

FIGURE 1.3 | World population growth and projections, 1950–2050.

Source: UN Population Division (2007b).

Philip Dearden

Women's group in Haryana. Empowering and educating women is one of the major steps toward lowering birth rates in many developing countries. Women's groups in some parts of India, such as here in Haryana, are having a major role in this transformation.

about birth and death rates as well as life expectancy. It also reveals the number of dependants: young dependants (aged below 15) and elderly dependants (those over 65). Dependants rely on the economically active for economic support. Many less developed countries have a high number of young dependants, while many developed countries have a growing number of elderly dependants. In the more developed regions, 23 per cent of the population is already aged 60 years or over, and that proportion will reach 32 per cent in 2050 and 34 per cent in 2100. In developed countries as a whole, the number of older persons has already surpassed the number of children, and by 2050 the number of older persons in developed countries will be nearly twice the number of children. Developing countries are also experiencing population aging. In developing countries as a whole, 9 per cent of the population today is aged 60 years or over, and this proportion will more than double by 2050, reaching 19 per cent that year, and triple by 2100, reaching 27 per cent. Globally, the number of persons aged 60 or over will more than triple by 2100, increasing from 841 million in 2013 to 2 billion in 2050 and close to 3 billion in 2100.

A population with a high number of young dependants and a low life expectancy has a very triangular pyramid. A population with a falling birth rate and rising life expectancy is reflected in a population pyramid with fairly straight sides. Generally, the shape of a country's population pyramid changes from a triangular to a barrel-like shape with straighter edges as the country develops and passes through the demographic transition discussed below. In fact, places experiencing an aging population and a very low birth rate may have a population structure that looks a little like an upside-down pyramid.

Human reproductive age is usually between 15 and 44 years. The larger the number of people in this age bracket, the greater the potential for population increase. **Total fertility rates** represent the average number of children each woman has over her lifetime. If the fertility rate is 2.0, then theoretically this will lead to stable populations as children replace their parents. If the rate is higher than 2.0, it will lead to population growth; if lower, the population declines. However, because of infant mortality, particularly in less developed countries, the **replacement-level fertility** is calculated as higher than 2.0.

The largest generation in history—1.8 billion people—is now between the ages of 10 and 19, and the child-bearing decisions by this generation will be critical. Current projections are predicated upon global fertility declines from 2.53 children per woman in 2005–2010 to 2.24 children per woman in 2045–2050 and 1.99 children per woman in 2095–2100. If fertility were to remain half a child above this level, world population would reach 10.9 billion by 2050 and 16.6 billion by 2100. However, if it were to fall half a child below the projection, this would lead to a population of 8.3 billion by mid-century and 6.8 billion by the end of the century. And

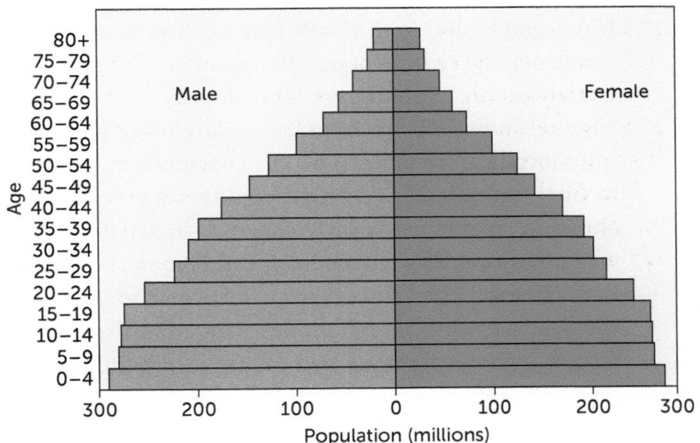

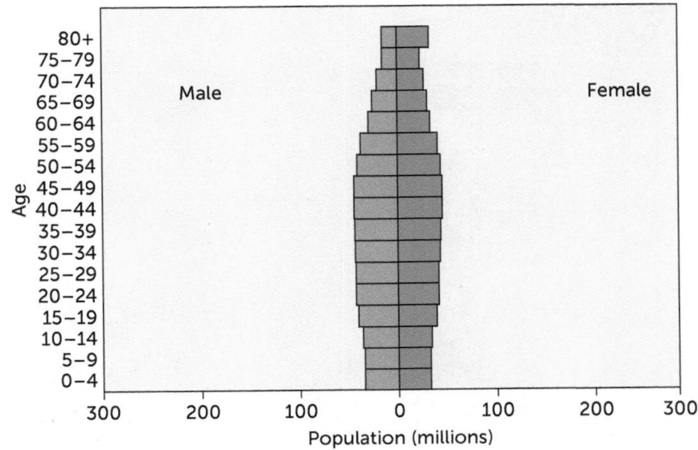

FIGURE 1.4 | Population pyramids for developing (top) and developed (bottom) countries.

Source: UN Population Division (2007b).

although the average annual global population growth rate has fallen from more than 2 per cent, where it was from the 1950s to the 1990s, to less than 1.3 per cent today, that rate is being applied to a much larger and still increasing population. Furthermore, after early declines in fertility rates, the rates in many countries have now reached a plateau.

The tragedy of HIV/AIDS, although having a strong impact on some countries, will not have a significant impact on global population. HIV reached a peak over the past decade in most countries highly affected by the epidemic; a growing number of them are reaching and maintaining lower levels. However, in southern Africa, the region with the highest prevalence of the disease, life expectancy fell from 62 years in 1990–1995 to 52 years in 2005–2010 and is only recently beginning to increase. Life expectancy in the region is not expected to recover to the level where it was in the early 1990s until 2030.

Another important consideration is the speed of the **demographic transition** in each country. Demographers, those who study population structure and growth, have noted a relationship between economic growth and population that occurs in four main phases (Figure 1.5):

1. *High equilibrium.* Both death and birth rates are high, resulting in very little population growth. This situation usually occurs in pre-industrial societies.
2. *High expanding.* Advances in health care result in declining mortality rates but show no concomitant decrease in birth rates, leading to high population growth. This situation occurs in the early stages of industrialization when some benefits of technology and industrial society are starting to be felt but are insufficient to outweigh the desire to have large families. Large families are an advantage in underdeveloped countries, providing more labour to generate family income. Lacking the pension systems of more advanced societies, parents need to have someone to look after them as they age. Large families also compensate for the high rate of child mortality in pre-industrial societies.
3. *Low expanding.* Birth rates start to fall as the benefits of increased income begin to erode the advantages of having large families. In Western societies, where the cost of raising children is high, having large families is no longer an overall economic benefit.
4. *Low equilibrium.* Birth rates and death rates are in balance as a result of the decline in birth rates.

What the future holds in terms of population growth depends on the reproductive decisions taken by today's children, such as these Maasai children in Loliondo, Tanzania, as they grow up.

As with most simplified models, the model can be criticized because of its generality, being largely based on European experience, and not taking a full range of cultural factors into account. Moreover, a fifth phase to the model is emerging in some nations, illustrated in Figure 1.5, as total populations fall.

Historically, the decline in death rates (the **epidemiological transition**) in most developed countries was relatively slow. Discoveries about the causes of disease and how they could be countered were made in conjunction with growing interest and investments in science. For example, in the late 1800s, Louis Pasteur and others discovered the main infectious agents and the means by which they were transmitted. Vaccines were created, and whole populations became immune to diseases such as typhoid and smallpox. By the 1930s, antibiotics such as penicillin were being developed. These medications led to cures for many other ailments. Sanitation improved, as did nutrition. However, these innovations took time, and the decline in crude death rates was gradual in the developed world. In contrast, these innovations were made available in many less developed countries all at once, often leading to a precipitous decline in death rates without a corresponding decrease in birth rates.

Some countries travel through this sequence more quickly than others, with rapid economic development followed by

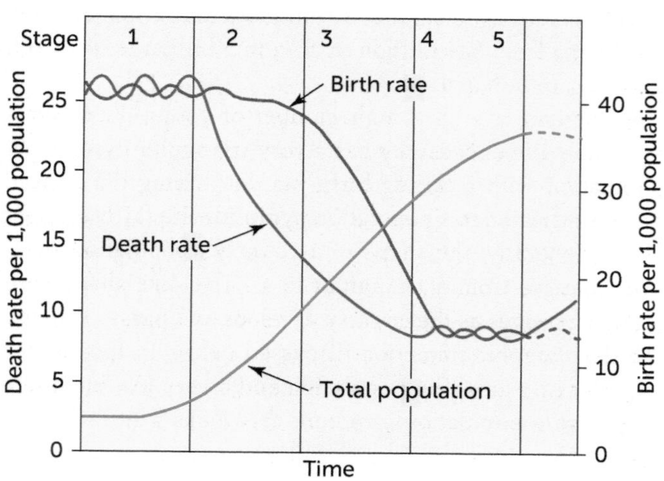

FIGURE 1.5 | The demographic transition.

corresponding adjustments in birth rates. Thailand is a prime example, where a fertility rate of 6.4 in 1960 fell to 1.8 in 2009, with economists forecasting further reductions, leading to a future labour shortage. However, not all countries adjust as rapidly as Thailand. In Thailand, a Buddhist country, there are no religious obstacles to reducing family size, women play a major role in household decision-making, education is valued for both sexes, and there has been a latent demand for effective contraception and effective means to distribute contraceptive devices. These conditions often do not exist in many countries.

Another component of population growth, and one particularly important to Canada, is **migration**. Migration often occurs in tandem with the demographic transition, and three main types have been noted: first, rural to rural migration, which can produce direct impacts on natural resources, often through agricultural expansion; second, rural to urban migration, which is generally associated with increased patterns of energy use as well as meat and dairy consumption; and third, international migration, often accompanied by remittances sent home, that may fuel further resource consumption in some areas. Canada is projected by the UN to be the second-largest recipient of international migration in the world, after the US, up to the year 2050.

Many scholars also feel that forced **environmental migration**, already significant in some areas of the world, will become an increasingly important phenomenon. It seems likely, too, that adaptation planning and funding under the UN Framework Convention on Climate Change will eventually include the development of strategies for resettling populations from highly vulnerable areas such as small island states. A recent review of environmental migration found that the most frequently studied environmental phenomena are (in decreasing order of significance): drought, land degradation, flooding, access to contextually significant natural resources, sea-level rise, other natural disasters, agricultural productivity, and deforestation, and that most subsequent migrations involve subsistence farmers moving short distances across relatively porous international boundaries (Obokata et al., 2014).

Recognition that the demographic transition was important in stabilizing population growth and that economic development was a main driving force behind the transition was also a factor in the drive to industrialize the world promoted by many global organizations, such as the World Bank and the United Nations. Furthermore, a strong relationship was seen between some indicators of environmental degradation and economic growth, sometimes known as a **Kuznet curve**, after the economist who first theorized this relationship (Figure 1.6). As economic growth increases, so does environmental degradation—until a threshold is reached. After that point, so it has been claimed, the wealth generated by increased industrial activity is sufficient to pay for environmental services (e.g., pollution control) that poorer countries cannot afford. Thus, the goal of development planning was to help countries reach that threshold so that they could enjoy the benefits of increased wealth while not succumbing to environmental degradation. For some aspects, such as pollution control, this relationship seems to hold. However, it is less reliable for other components, such as biodiversity conservation for which irreversible thresholds exist, and also for some countries, especially small crowded ones.

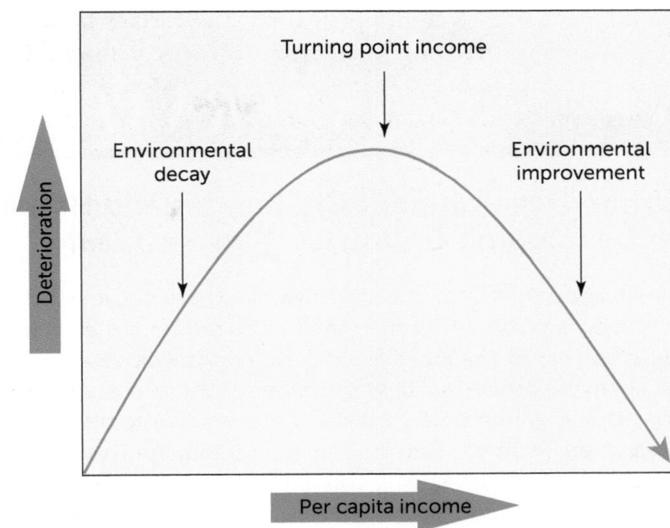

FIGURE 1.6 | The theoretical relationship between environmental degradation and environmental deterioration.

Unfortunately, the relationship among society, stages of development, and economic growth is more complex than these models allow. In particular, they ignore one of the most (and many scientists would argue the single most) important factors—the impact of consumption on the capability of planetary ecosystems to continue to provide life-support services.

Consumption

The Earth's passengers do not all have the same impact on the life-support system. Some passengers—those in first class—get special meals, three times a day, wine included; those in the economy section are lucky if they get one meal and must buy their own water, if it is even available. The richest 20 per cent of the world's population are responsible for more than 75 per cent of world consumption, while the poorest 20 per cent consume less than 2 per cent (World Bank, 2008). In terms of metal use, for example, the 15 per cent of the global population in the US, Canada, Japan, Australia, and Western Europe account for 61 per cent of aluminum use, 60 per cent of lead, 59 per cent of copper, and 49 per cent of steel. The average North American uses 22 kilograms of aluminum a year, the average African less than 1 kilogram. Rural populations are significantly poorer than urban populations,

INTERNATIONAL GUEST STATEMENT

Urban Development Challenges and Human Living Conditions in Cities in Developing Countries | *Peter Adeniyi*

Urban conditions tend to become worse where public policy and programs do not secure needs required for sustainable development at the local level. These needs include access to adequate shelter, security of property tenure, sustainable means of livelihood, safe drinking water and waste disposal, a clean environment, and a sense of community. This is the situation in most developing countries where urban development plans are directed at regeneration and physical transformation of slums and blighted areas with little regard to needs of the poorest occupants.

The prevalence of slums and blighted areas in cities of developing countries can be explained in two ways. First, planning efforts are outpaced by sprawling expansion, which breeds an ever-evolving urban sprawl with no guided growth trajectory. People build houses and wait for the roads, water, drainage, or electricity to come. The environment, aesthetics, and common facilities are an afterthought. High-risk areas such as flood plains, waste dumpsites, wetlands, and so on are occupied by informal settlements constructed with every conceivable material (raffia palms, nylon, pre-used corrugated iron sheets). The few available municipal basic services are provided through individual and communal efforts. Second, planned residential developments soon become degraded due to a population that has increased beyond the carrying capacity of the limited old and decaying infrastructure. In some cases these neighbourhoods are close to zones of major commercial activities, and their re-densification often leads to degradation of the formal housing stock and an upsurge of informal housing development on any available open space. Supply and utilization of basic urban services become inefficient and, over time, a once planned and livable neighbourhood becomes a rundown slum.

Many Nigerian cities exemplify the two scenarios. A study by the Federal Ministry of Lands, Housing and Urban Development (FMLHUD, 2014) in three cities—Kaduna (north), Aba (southeast) and Oshogbo (southwest)— reveals that deficiencies in infrastructure and basic services and an inability to generate employment create serious challenges for managing slum areas. The infrastructure deficiencies and lack of access to basic municipal services often intensify other composite vulnerabilities. For example, in Aba, a poor drainage system combined with poor management of waste exacerbates flooding, which, in turn, aggravates human health risks.

Every stage and kind of slum formation, from infancy to consolidation, maturity, and gradual degradation of formal housing, and every variety of informal housing development is found in these cities. Almost all environmental indicators (building appearance, number of people living in a building, road and drainage conditions, waste disposal, noise and air pollution, and so on) receive negative ratings. Supply of public utilities (such as water and electricity) is either in poor condition or completely absent. Access to employment is described as critical, and access to shelter, security, and the conditions of public schools, health care, and transportation are poor. A large proportion of the population depends on pure water ("treated" water packaged and sold in small polyethylene sachets). In some neighbourhoods, a majority of dwellers do not feel they ever have enough water for their households' daily needs. However, social assets and networks are very strong in these slums. A large percentage belongs to

Olumuyiwa Olayinka Adeniyi

Agharandu Road, Ohazu Community, Abia State, Nigeria.

Olumuyiwa Olayinka Adeniyi

Dump, Unguwan Sanusi Community, Kaduna State, Nigeria.

at least one social group (religious, tribal, trade, and landlords' or residents' associations). A significant percentage is willing to volunteer their professional services, personal labour, and finance and thereby mobilize community members to support government efforts.

Well-targeted investments in programs to improve urban environmental conditions and basic infrastructure are essential for the cities of developing countries to achieve their full potential. Provision of basic urban services remains a precondition to address the key challenges and aspirations of city dwellers, but governments in developing countries do not have enough capacity to mobilize the enormous resources required to deliver. A partnership with development partners, private investors, and the communities is vital. In Nigeria, various short-, medium-, and long-term strategies have been outlined to revitalize identified slums and blighted areas. These range from immediate interventions, such as provision of potable drinking water, rehabilitation of roads, and clearance of drainage ditches and waste dumps, to longer-term investments in the design and provision of municipal infrastructures and policy implementation options that encourage slum dwellers to leverage existing asset bases and networks to sustain outputs. The strategies are expected to be achieved through synergy among various stakeholders comprising governments at all levels, private investors, development partners, and the communities. This inclusive participatory arrangement would seem to provide a sustainable platform for mobilizing resources to improve the living conditions of the teeming slum dwellers and to prevent future development of urban slums in the developing world.

Olumuyiwa Olayinka Adeniyi

Peter Olufemi Adeniyi, an Emeritus Professor at the University of Lagos, Nigeria, specializes in remote sensing, geographic information systems, and resource appraisal. He has served as Vice-Chancellor, Federal University of Technology, Akure, Nigeria (2002–2006); Head and National Coordinator of Rural Development Data in the then Directorate of Food, Roads and Rural Infrastructure (DFRRI); and Chairman, Committee on National Inventory of Community-Based Infrastructural Facilities in Nigeria. He is currently the Chairman of the Presidential Technical Committee on Land Reform and a member of the Africa Technical Advisory Group on Land Governance Assessment Framework.

and one of the main drivers of future consumption will be the increased urbanization of global populations (Chapter 13). In the above "International Guest Statement," Peter Adeniyi highlights challenges created by greater urbanization in developing nations.

Energy consumption is also very unequally distributed, with the people in the wealthiest countries using 25 times more per capita than the world's poorest people. More than a third of the global population does not have access to electricity, but demands are growing. There are also large differences in energy consumption among developed countries, with the average Canadian and American consuming 2.4 times as much energy as the average person in Western Europe.

Canadians are among the top per capita consumers of energy in the world, with an even larger electricity consumption rate than Americans (Figure 1.7). Each Canadian consumes as much energy as 60 Cambodians. Government policies encourage us to be wasteful by subsidizing energy production, and we as individuals normally do not resist. Energy is a good index of our planetary impact, reflecting our ability to process materials and disrupt the environment through pollution such as acid precipitation (Chapter 4) and the production of greenhouse gases (Chapter 7). However, as shown in Figure 1.8, there is no direct relationship between electricity consumption and human development. In other words, it is possible to have high standards of living without excessive energy consumption, as exemplified by many European countries. Canada has yet to make this transition.

Perspectives on the Environment

Urbanization

In 2008, the world reached an invisible but momentous milestone: for the first time in history, more than half its human population, 3.3 billion people, live in urban areas. By 2030, this number is expected to swell to almost 5 billion. Many of the new urbanites will be poor. Their future, the future of cities in developing countries, the future of humanity itself all depend very much on decisions made now.

Source: United Nations Population Fund (2007b).

Although much is being done throughout the world to curb population growth, as seen in this signboard in Vietnam encouraging couples to have only one child, consumption knows no bounds (and we are continuously exhorted to buy more). "I want that" is the slogan of our times.

Both photos Philip Dearden

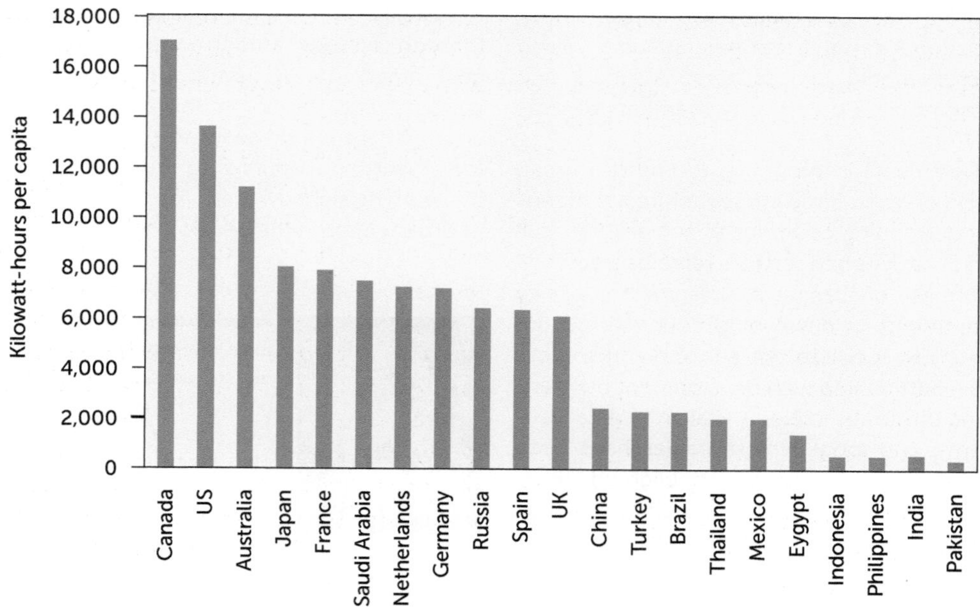

FIGURE 1.7 | Annual electricity consumption per capita.
Source: World Bank World Development Indicators (2014).

Obviously, very different kinds of passengers share our planet, and the differences among them have grown rather than diminished as a result of increased wealth over the past 20 years. **Gross national product (GNP)** is an index used by economists to compare the market value of all goods and services produced for final consumption in an economy during one year. Over the past two decades, the planetary GNP has risen by $47 trillion, but only 15 per cent of this increase has trickled down to the 80 per cent of the passengers in the economy section of the spaceship. The rest has made the rich even richer.

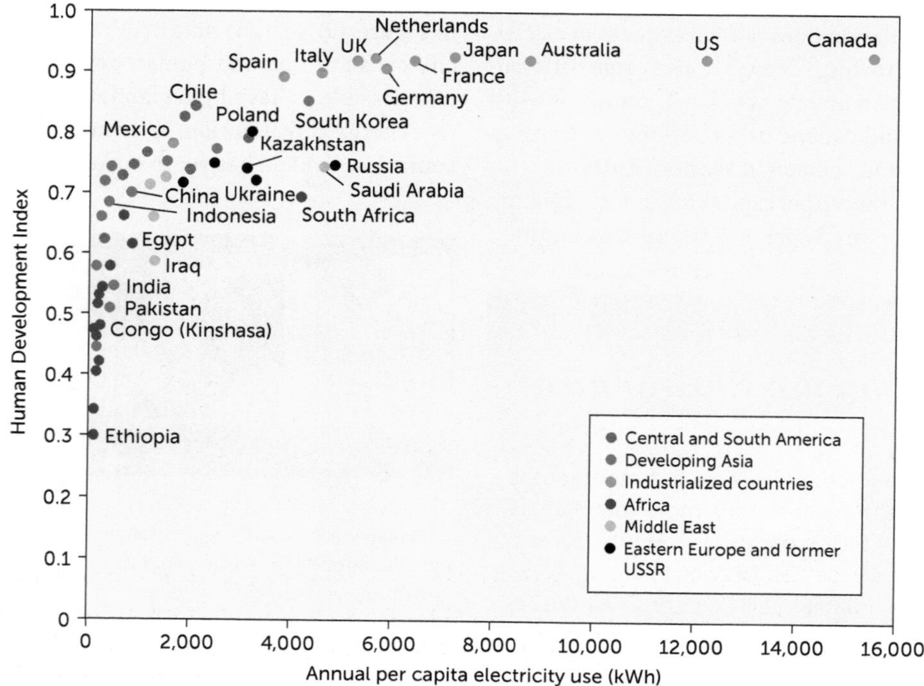

FIGURE 1.8 | The relationship between energy use and the Human Development Index.
Source: UNDP (2005).

Global poverty is a major challenge to planetary survival. Living in extreme poverty (less than $1 a day) means not being able to afford the most basic necessities. An estimated 8 million people a year die from absolute poverty. Moderate poverty, defined as earning about $1 to $2 a day, enables households to just barely meet their basic needs but still forgo many of the things—education, health care—that many others take for granted. The smallest misfortune (e.g., a health issue, job loss) threatens survival.

However, progress is being made with the first Millennium Development Goal target—to cut the 1990 poverty rate in half by 2015—being achieved five years ahead of schedule, in 2010. However, 17 per cent of people in the developing world, 1 billion people, still live at or below $1.25 a day, compared with 1.91 billion in 1990. Progress has also been made at higher poverty lines, with 2.2 billion people living on less than US $2 a day, the average poverty line in developing countries. That is only a slight decline from 2.59 billion in 1981.

Nine Planets??

The stresses on the planetary life-support system are a consequence of overconsumption and the resulting pollution, as well as overpopulation and the resulting poverty. Together, they create pressure on the **planetary carrying capacity** at many different scales. Although in the past many cultures violated the carrying capacities of their local environments with dire results, never before have we approached these limits at a global scale.

Clear evidence indicates that critical thresholds are being reached and surpassed. Rockström and his colleagues (2009) have looked at the scale of these changes and propose that nine main planetary processes shown in Figure 1.9 need to be taken into account. Change in these is often non-linear, and when certain thresholds are crossed there may be sudden and irreversible change with enormous consequences for the Earth as the home of humanity. Their work identifies thresholds for each of climate change; rate of biodiversity loss (terrestrial and marine); interference with the nitrogen and phosphorus cycles; stratospheric ozone depletion; ocean acidification; global freshwater use; change in land use; chemical pollution; and atmospheric aerosol loading.

Three of these system processes have already exceeded the safe operating zones: rate of biodiversity loss (see Chapter 14), climate change (see Chapter 7), and interference with the nitrogen cycle (see Chapter 4). The implications of these changes are discussed in more detail in the chapters indicated. What is interesting about this approach is the perspective of setting scientifically determined biophysical preconditions for human development and the need to stay within those

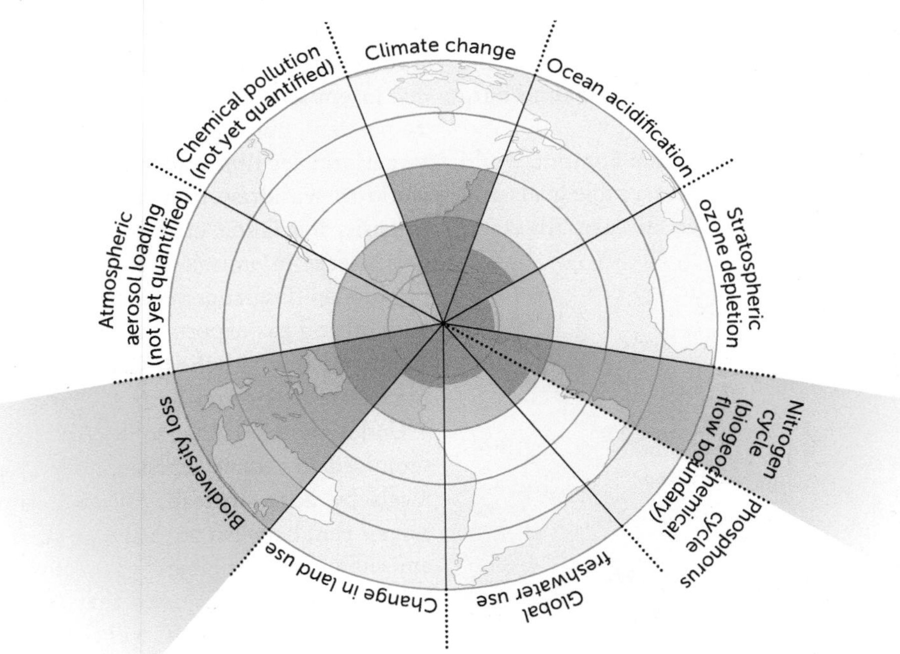

FIGURE 1.9 | Beyond the boundary. The inner green shading represents the proposed safe operating space for nine planetary systems. The red wedges represent an estimate of the current position for each variable. The boundaries in three systems (rate of biodiversity loss, climate change, and human interference with the nitrogen cycle) have already been exceeded.

Source: Rockström et al. (2009: 427). Copyright © 2009, Rights Managed by Nature Publishing Group

boundaries. Violating these boundaries will result in a noted loss in the resilience of the Earth in its ability to produce the goods and services necessary to support humanity.

Jared Diamond, a geographer at UCLA, has written a fascinating book on why past societies collapsed and what we can learn from their experiences. Appropriately, the book is titled *Collapse* (2005), and we strongly recommend it. Diamond suggests that four main reasons explain why societies fail to make corrections to prevent societal collapse. They may not anticipate the problem; they may fail to appreciate the severity of the problem even though they are aware of it; they may appreciate the problem but neglect to address it; and they may perceive the problem as a serious threat, try to solve it, and fail. Diamond explores examples of all these situations. However, his main message is to alert us to how we can forestall such a collapse in modern society. At the heart of Diamond's analysis is the role of environmental degradation in causing societal collapse. One of his most sobering conclusions is that many of the societies that collapsed were very successful and collapse seemed impossible, yet it happened with frightening rapidity.

There have been many warnings about the impact of environmental degradation on society in the future, spanning back to Rachel Carson's *Silent Spring* (1962) of a half-century ago and including the famous *Limits to Growth* study of the early 1970s (Meadows et al., 1972) through to the report of the World Commission on Environment and Development in 1987 (WCED, 1987). Some of the trends were highlighted at the Earth Summit in Rio de Janeiro in 1992 and at the World Summit on Sustainable Development in Johannesburg 10 years later.

In 2000, at the United Nations Millennium Summit, world leaders agreed to a set of time-bound, measurable goals and targets for combatting poverty, hunger, disease, illiteracy, environmental degradation, and discrimination against women. Placed at the heart of the global agenda, the eight objectives, now called the Millennium Development Goals (MDGs), aim to improve human well-being. These goals are

1. Eradicate extreme poverty and hunger
2. Achieve universal primary education
3. Promote greater gender equality and empower women
4. Reduce child mortality
5. Improve maternal health
6. Combat HIV/AIDS, malaria, and other diseases
7. Ensure environmental sustainability
8. Develop a global partnership for development

Under each of the MDGs, countries agreed to targets to be achieved by 2015. Many of the regions facing the greatest challenges in achieving these targets coincide with regions facing the greatest problems of ecosystem degradation. Progress on individual MDGs is discussed in several chapters while overall progress is summarized in Chapter 15. The use of indicators is discussed in greater detail later in this chapter.

The evidence for and causes of global climate change are discussed in more detail in Chapter 7, along with Canada's response. However, the implications of climate change are very severe for Canada, with temperature increases over the land about double the global average. Canada has the second-highest per capita emissions of greenhouse gases in the world. Canada agreed under the Kyoto Protocol to target a 6 per cent cut in emissions by 2012. Instead, emissions increased by 29 per cent, putting the country 35 per cent above its Kyoto target and leading Canada to be the only country in the world to withdraw from the treaty. While greenhouse gas intensity has fallen, efficiency gains have been swamped by an increase in emissions from an expansion in oil and gas production (Englander et al., 2013). Net emissions associated with oil and gas exports have more than doubled since 1990. This compares with the UK's reduction of 23 per cent over the same time period and Germany's reduction of 22 per cent.

Under the Copenhagen Accord signed in 2009, Canada promised to reduce emissions by 17 per cent below 2005 levels by 2020. Instead, however, emissions increased by 1.5 per cent between 2012 and 2013, driven mainly by rising emissions from the oil and gas sector.

Scientists have suggested that an overall increase in temperatures in excess of 2°C will cause runaway environmental damage and that emissions need to be kept under 450 parts per million carbon dioxide emission equivalents (Ce) to avoid this consequence. More recent modelling suggests that 2°C was an optimistic threshold, with 1.5°C being more realistic. Nonetheless, to put emissions in perspective: considering the overall planetary carrying capacity and using the suggested annual allowable emission ceiling of 14.5 gigatonnes (Gt) CO_2, if emissions were frozen at the current level of

Philip Dearden

Families in Lesotho are still large, but the planetary impact of this entire family will be a fraction of that of one Canadian child.

29 Gt CO_2, to stay below the threshold we would need two planets. However, emissions are not equally distributed. In Ethiopia, for example, the average per capita carbon footprint is 0.1 tonnes, compared to 20 tonnes in Canada. The per capita increase in emissions since 1990 for the United States (1.6 tonnes) is higher than the total per capita emissions for India in 2004 alone (1.2 tonnes). The overall increase in emissions from the United States exceeds sub-Saharan Africa's total emissions. If every person living in the developing world had the same carbon footprint as the average for high-income countries, global CO_2 emissions would rise to 85 Gt CO_2, a level that would require six planets. With a global per capita footprint at Canadian and US levels, we would need nine planets to sustain this level of emissions, and hence the title for this section. As a global community, we are running up a large and unsustainable carbon debt, but the bulk of that debt has been accumulated by the world's richest countries.

In terms of addressing the situation, a global perspective is obviously necessary, although responsibilities clearly differ. For example, a 4 per cent cut would be generated in global emissions if a 50 per cent cut were initiated in CO_2 emissions for South Asia and sub-Saharan Africa. A similar cut in high-income countries would reduce emissions by 20 per cent. Equity must also play a role. An average air-conditioning unit in Florida emits more CO_2 in a year than a person in Afghanistan or Cambodia is responsible for during his or her lifetime. A European dishwasher emits as much CO_2 in a year as the total carbon footprint of three Ethiopians. What kind of role do you think Canada and Canadians should assume to shoulder their share of global responsibility?

Other important global perspectives on Canada should be kept in mind. Our land is vast, about 13 million km², and our population small, about 35.7 million people in 2014 (Figure 1.10). Population density is 0.04 people per hectare, compared to Bangladesh at eight people per hectare. Canada would have to have a population of more than 8 billion to equal this density. Immigration, rather than natural increase, is the most important factor in population growth in Canada. Migrants made up 21 per cent of the total Canadian population by 2011. Are more people good for Canada when we consider that there is more to Canada than just the economy? Does Canada have a moral obligation to accept migrants from overcrowded countries elsewhere or from countries generating "environmental refugees" as a result of environmental stress in their home countries? These are some of the important questions that policy-makers—and you—must consider.

In terms of numbers alone, Canada is not overpopulated compared to virtually any other country. Canada is the second-largest country in the world in terms of area and includes 20 per cent of the world's wilderness, 24 per cent of its wetlands, 10 per cent of its forests, and almost 7 per cent of its renewable fresh water and has the longest coastline in the world. However, as discussed above, it is not simply numbers of people but rather the impact of those people that is critical. Canadians are among the world's top producers per capita of industrial and household garbage, hazardous wastes, and greenhouse gases (Box 1.3). Some point to the size of the country, the cold in winter, and the heat in summer as the reasons behind our remarkable energy consumption, but it is clear that Canadians can contribute substantially to reducing impacts on the planetary life-support system. We offer suggestions on some of the ways that you can help contribute to the needed changes throughout the text, and we return to this theme in Chapter 15.

Changes in environmental directions for Canada require changes in policies and legislation and the strict implementation of those changes. It is therefore important for you to appreciate the jurisdictional arrangements for environmental management in Canada, the topic of the next section.

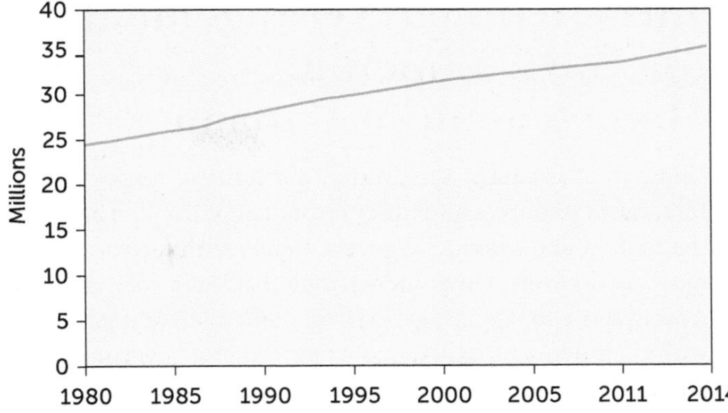

FIGURE 1.10 | Population growth in Canada, 1980–2014.

Source: Statistics Canada, CANSIM database, Table 051–0001, cansim2.statcan.gc.ca.

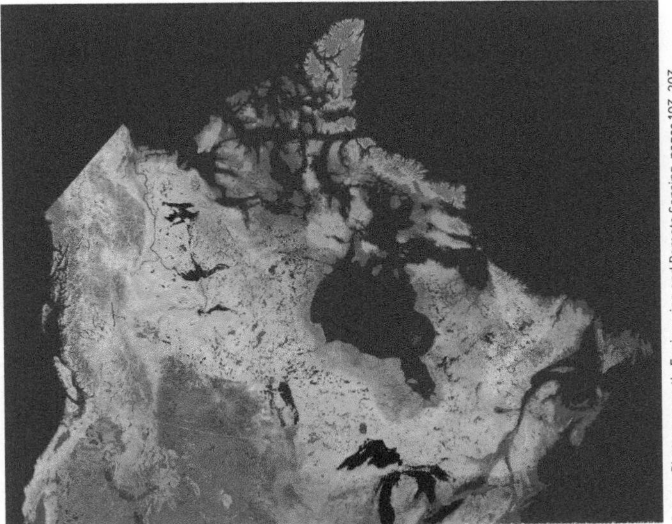

Satellite image of Canada (processed at the Canada Centre for Remote Sensing, Earth Sciences Sector, Natural Resources Canada).

Source: Photogrammatic Engineering and Remote Sensing, pages 193-203, Vol. 63/2. Natural Resources Canada, 1997.

Jurisdictional Arrangements for Environmental Management in Canada

Under the Canadian Constitution, authority or responsibility for natural resources and the environment is divided between the federal and provincial governments, with territorial and municipal governments increasingly having a role. As well, Aboriginal peoples are increasing their role commensurate with their being recognized as a new order of government. In addition, Canada is involved in bilateral arrangements with the United States to address environmental problems such as air pollution and to deal with shared water bodies such as the Great Lakes and the Columbia River, as well as in multilateral arrangements with other nations or international organizations regarding resources such as fisheries, migratory birds and animals, and minerals on or under the ocean floor.

Federal, Provincial, and Municipal Roles

Canada is a federated state, with power and authority shared between federal and provincial governments and with municipal governments receiving their power and authority from provincial legislatures. Ownership and control of all Crown lands and natural resources not specifically in private ownership is given to the provinces, under section 92A of the Constitution Act, 1867, except for the Canadian North (north of 60 degrees latitude), where the federal government has proprietary rights to land and resources until the territories receive such power, and for resources found on or under seabeds off the coasts of Canada (some provinces, however, have challenged this right).

Legislative authority is mixed between the federal and provincial governments and often becomes a significant source of conflict. The federal government has jurisdiction over trade and commerce, giving it substantial authority over both interprovincial and export trading of resources (oil and natural gas, water). Alberta, Saskatchewan, and British Columbia, which have oil and natural gas, often object to the federal government becoming involved in setting prices and determining buyers, arguing that such matters are within provincial authority because of their responsibility for property and civil rights, as well as because these resources are under provincial control. The federal government has used its legislative authority for navigation and shipping and for fisheries to create water pollution regulations—even though water within provinces falls within the jurisdiction of the provinces. Thus, ambiguities and inconsistencies exist regarding jurisdiction over resources and the environment. One consequence is that it has been difficult to establish *national approaches* (combined federal and provincial) to deal with resource and environmental issues.

In the early to mid 1990s, many provincial governments began to download selected responsibilities, which they had traditionally held, to municipalities. The provinces argued that downloading was consistent with the principle of **subsidiarity**, which stipulates that decisions should be taken at the level closest to where consequences are most noticeable. While such an argument is rational, the primary motive for downloading often was the desire of provincial governments to shift the cost of many responsibilities to lower levels of government to reduce provincial debts and deficits. Whatever the motivation, the outcome is that municipalities have become much more significant players in natural resource and environmental management, since in many instances provinces have withdrawn from related management activities.

Effective partnerships exist between provincial and municipal governments. Among the best and most enduring examples are the Ontario conservation authorities, watershed-based organizations established by statute in 1946 to manage many renewable resources within river basins. Individual authorities were established when two or more municipalities in a watershed petitioned the provincial government to establish one. When a majority of the

ENVIRONMENT IN FOCUS

BOX 1.3 | Canada Facts

- We generate about 383 kilograms of solid waste per capita per year, ranking seventh in the world.
- We generate almost six tonnes of hazardous waste for each US$1 million of goods and services produced; Japan generates less than a quarter of a tonne.
- We have one of the highest per capita uses of water in the world, about 15 m³ per day, roughly three times that of Sweden and Japan.
- We are among the highest per capita energy consumers in the world.
- We use our cars nearly 10 per cent more than residents of other industrialized countries.
- We emit 2 per cent of the world's greenhouse gases with 0.5 per cent of the world's population and rank second in global production of greenhouse gases per capita.

municipalities in a watershed agreed that they would work collaboratively, the province established a conservation authority. Today, 36 authorities exist, primarily in the more settled parts of the province.

While the provincial government would not impose a conservation authority, it provided a strong incentive for local governments to form one by offering funds not available to municipalities on their own but available after a conservation authority was established. This cost-sharing arrangement was a powerful stimulus for municipalities to agree to establish authorities, and for many years the cost-sharing was fifty–fifty between the province and the municipalities. However, in the mid 1990s, the Ontario government significantly reduced its proportion of the funding to the conservation authorities as part of a drive to reduce government activities and costs. Another challenge in the reallocation of responsibility to municipal governments is the variable degree of competence to deal with resource and environmental matters. There is significant variation among municipalities and other local-level governments in technical expertise and required data, funding capability, leadership, community awareness and engagement, and ability to implement, monitor, and enforce solutions related to resource and environmental management. Often, the provincial governments have downloaded responsibility to local governments without having determined whether they had the necessary competence to take it on.

Monitoring Progress toward Sustainable Development

In 1997, the Office of the Auditor General began reporting on progress by 24 federal government departments and agencies regarding sustainable development. Brian Emmett, the commissioner of the Environment and Sustainable Development, observed in his 1997 report that Canadians expected governments to provide strong leadership and a clear vision and to lead by example through fostering a culture of environmental protection and sustainable development within federal organizations. The commissioner also stated that few quick solutions were available for environmental problems and that progress would require persistence, patience, and focused effort. The challenge was characterized as a "long journey" requiring systematic change if a real difference were to be realized for present and future generations (Commissioner of the Environment and Sustainable Development, 1997).

Looking to the future, the commissioner wrote that many environmental problems and sustainable development issues were "difficult to manage" as well as "scientifically complex" and involved long time frames. Furthermore, he noted, rarely do they fit tidily within one department's or government's mandate or jurisdiction. He highlighted three major aspects where improvement was necessary:

- Federal government agencies' performance often fell well short of stated objectives. As a result, an *implementation gap* existed, since policy direction too often was not translated into effective action. Issues surrounding implementation challenges are addressed in Chapter 6.
- Many pressing issues transcended departmental mandates and governmental jurisdiction. Consequently, *lack of coordination and integration* was frequent. The need was to manage "horizontal issues," or those involving shared responsibility.
- There was often inadequate information about the benefits of environmental programs. Therefore, a strong need existed to resolve *inadequate performance review* processes so that both senior managers and parliamentarians could know what was being accomplished.

The commissioner's fall report in 2009 focused on one aspect—ensuring high-quality information to design, implement, and monitor environmental management programs. In the words of the commissioner, Scott Vaughan, "Informed decision-making is at the heart of sound policy-making. The environmental programs of the federal government need science-based environmental information that is timely, robust, and accessible in ways that both identify patterns of environmental degradation and help programs concentrate on the most urgent environmental problems" (Commissioner of the Environment and Sustainable Development, 2009).

The commissioner emphasized two major challenges: (1) individual environmental monitoring programs must accurately track environmental quality, and (2) the many environmental programs scattered among agencies "can and should work in tandem to provide a composite or cumulative picture." Having examined numerous individual programs, the commissioner concluded that many do work as intended. The commissioner concluded, however, that, "Unfortunately, other systems are incomplete, out-of-date, or non-existent."

The commissioner's reports from 1999 onwards can be found at the link in "Related Websites" at the end of this chapter. The reports are referred to in many chapters throughout the book as a main source of objective evaluation on federal government environmental programs, and will be returned to in the concluding chapter.

Given the attention by the commissioner to the need for timely, robust, and accessible environmental information, in the next section we examine practices for tracking environmental conditions, with particular attention to the role of indicators.

Measuring Progress

From the foregoing discussions, you will appreciate that the environmental situation is often so complex that many, including many decision-makers, give up on trying to make sense of it. However, if we do not understand the problem and whether it is getting better or worse, we cannot implement effective management strategies. One of the goals of science is to provide understanding of complex problems. And one way of doing this is through the use of indicators.

Ecological footprints are the demands that humans place on nature in terms of supplying materials and disposing of wastes. They provide simple indicators to enable comparisons among regions, countries, municipalities, and individuals. On a global scale, only 1.7 hectares are available for each person, and this amount is shrinking every year, largely as a result of population growth. Yet the collective average global footprint is 2.6 hectares per person, with a North American average double that of Europeans and seven times greater than that of Asia or Africa. Globally, humans are consuming the natural resources of 1.5 planets. To provide for everyone at Canadian standards would require 3.5 Earths, not just one. Estimates suggest that by 2030, less than 0.9 hectare will be available per person at a global scale.

Figure 1.11 shows the main components of the ecological footprint and how they have changed over time. The footprint overall has more than doubled since 1961. Carbon is the main source of humanity's increasing footprint. Carbon grew from 36 per cent of the footprint in 1961 to 53 per cent by 2010. Clearly, to reduce footprints to more sustainable levels, energy consumption has to be a main concern. Figure 1.11 also shows the amount of biologically productive area—cropland, pasture, forest, and fisheries—available to meet humanity's needs, the **biocapacity**. Since the late 1980s, the ecological footprint had exceeded the Earth's biocapacity, as the latter declines as a result of overuse. Manifestations of this overuse—pollution, climate change, biodiversity collapse,

When you have your morning cup of coffee or tea with sugar, your ecological footprint is reaching out to the tropics where coffee beans, tea leaves, and sugar are grown. Tea plantation, Sri Lanka (top). Sugarcane fields, South Africa (bottom).

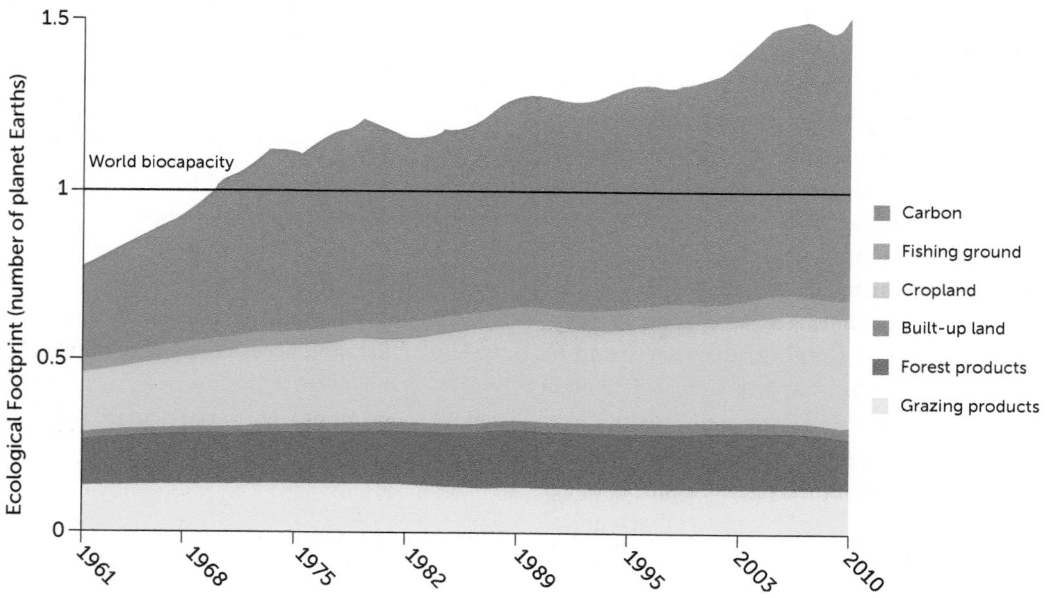

FIGURE 1.11 | World ecological footprint, 1961–2010.

Source: WWF 2014. ® "WWF" and "World Wildlife Fund" are WWF Registered Trademarks. © 1986 Panda Symbol WWF.

ENVIRONMENT IN FOCUS

BOX 1.4 | What You Can Do: Getting Started on Reducing Your Impact

Every chapter in the text includes a "What You Can Do" feature at the end, reflecting our belief in the role of personal engagement with the challenges discussed in the text. Many of the suggestions relate to reducing your own ecological footprint and are brought together in the final chapter.

An excellent way for you to get started on examining your own environmental impact is to calculate your personal footprint, that of your household, your friends, your dog . . . and see what improvements can be made over this term, over the next year, and over your life. Several footprint calculators are available on the Web (e.g., see "Global Footprint Network" in "Related Websites" at the end of this chapter).

and water stress—are discussed throughout the book. The challenge is to devise effective strategies to reduce the footprint below biocapacity before the ecological debt becomes insurmountable (Figure 1.12).

Some countries have ecological demands greatly in excess of their capabilities, and they import ecological capital from elsewhere to make up for this deficit. Although trade between nations is to be expected, this excess of ecological footprint over capacity allows some nations to live beyond their ecological means. Canada has one of the largest available ecological capacities (14.24 hectares per capita); we also have one of the largest ecological footprints per capita and now rank eleventh in the world.

Within Canada there are also significant differences. A study undertaken for the Federation of Canadian Municipalities (Wilson and Anielski, 2005) examined the ecological footprints of 20 municipalities. The Canadian average was 7.25 hectares per capita, compared with a global average of 2.6 hectares per person. Perhaps not surprisingly, the largest footprints in Canada were both in oil-driven Alberta, with Calgary being top (9.86) closely followed by Edmonton (9.45). Sudbury, Ontario, had the lowest footprint (6.87), largely attributable to efforts of the public works engineer in charge of heating and sewage. He introduced many innovative programs, especially related to using local energy sources, such as the power of the wind, the sun, and the Earth's heat, that have reduced both the cost of heating and resource consumption. It is a striking example of how the initiative and energy of one person can make a significant improvement in planetary resource use.

Indicators such as ecological footprints are not new. For many years, doctors have used body temperature, measured easily by thermometer, as one indicator of the health of the human body. Gross domestic product has been used as an indicator of economic performance, as has the Dow Jones industrial average. These indicators tell us something of the current state of a particular system, but they do not help us to understand why the system is in that state. Over the past 25 years, there has been growing awareness of the need to develop indicators that would gauge the health of other aspects of societal well-being, including the environment. Indicators are often used to provide information on environmental problems that enables policy-makers to evaluate their seriousness, to support policy development and the setting of priorities by identifying key factors that cause pressure on the environment, to monitor the effects of policy responses, and to raise public awareness and generate support for government actions. Box 1.5 describes one framework that helps to develop

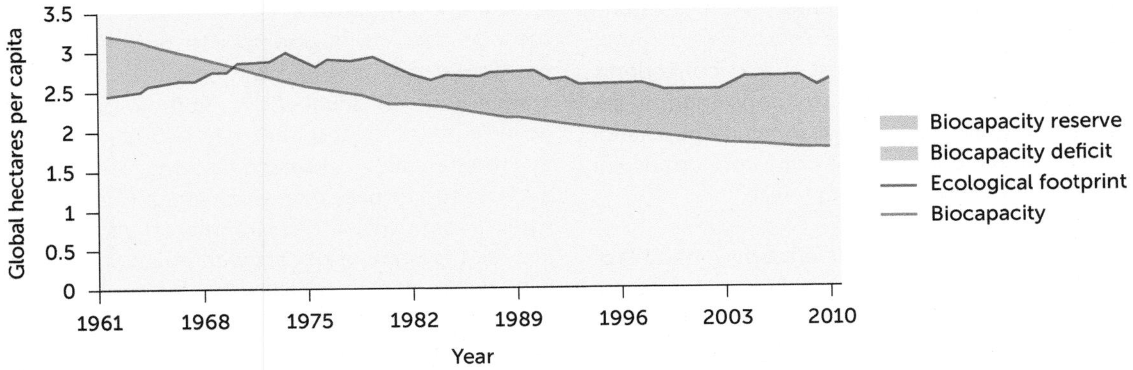

FIGURE 1.12 | Trends in ecological footprint and biocapacity per person between 1961 and 2010.

Source: WWF (2014). ® "WWF" and "World Wildlife Fund" are WWF Registered Trademarks. © 1986 Panda Symbol WWF.

causal linkages between indicators—the Drivers-Pressures-State-Impact-Response framework, or DPSIR (Figure 1.13).

One example of the DPSIR approach is the joint Environment Canada–US Environmental Protection Agency series of indicators on the state of the Great Lakes (Environment Canada, 2003b), which is broken down into pressure, state, and response indicators. It is interesting to note that two of the richest nations in the world found that there was insufficient data on many of the 80 desired variables. On the basis of the 43 indicators used, the conclusion is that the overall trend is "mixed"—i.e., some indicators show improving conditions, others deterioration.

Another example of the DPSIR framework is from the Commission for Environmental Cooperation (CEC), which was established under the North American Free Trade Agreement to examine environmental challenges in North

ENVIRONMENT IN FOCUS

BOX 1.5 | The DPSIR Indicator Framework

The most widespread framework for classifying environmental indicators is the Drivers-Pressures-State-Impact-Response (DPSIR) framework developed by the Organisation for Economic Co-operation and Development (OECD) and adopted by all European Union countries, the US, Canada, Australia, Japan, and many developing countries (e.g., Malaysia) and international organizations (such as the Commission on Sustainable Development of the UN, the United Nations Environment Programme, and the World Bank). The framework, as shown in the figure below, is popular because of its organization around key causal mechanisms of environmental problems.

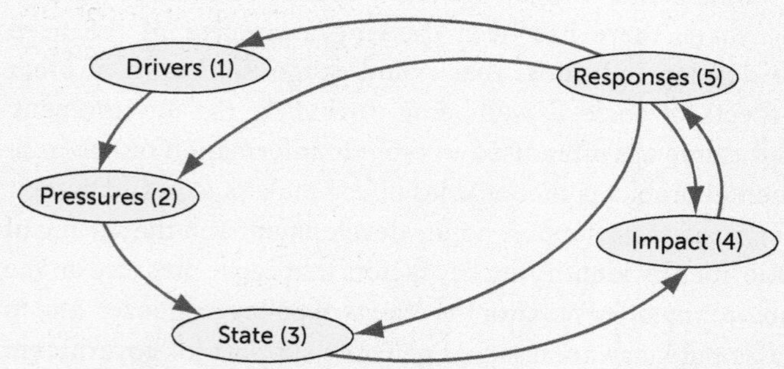

FIGURE 1.13 | The DPSIR Indicator's framework.

Driving forces (1) Drivers are the underlying forces causing environmental change. They describe social, demographic, and economic developments in societies and corresponding changes in lifestyles, overall levels of consumption, and production patterns. Examples of drivers include population pressures and the demand for various consumer goods and services (e.g., cars, red meat, increasing travel).

Pressure indicators (2) These indicators are the pressures on the environment resulting from the drivers. Examples include emission of pollutants, use of resources, use of land for roads, water withdrawals, deforestation, and fisheries catches. Initial interest in these indicators focused further down the causal chain in the state indicators, described below. However, there is now widespread realization that state indicators are mere reflections of changes further up the chain, prompting much greater interest in drivers and pressures. One example of the link between drivers and pressures can be found in a driver such as the number of cars. Not only can we address the driver (by seeking to limit the number of cars through better public transportation, raising the price of gas, or imposing special taxes, licensing fees, or tolls on people who insist on driving their cars into downtown urban areas during the daytime), but we can also try to reduce the pressure by making vehicles more fuel efficient and less polluting.

State indicators (3) State indicators describe the quantity and quality of physical phenomena (e.g., temperature), biological phenomena (e.g., fish stocks, extinctions), and chemical phenomena (e.g., CO_2 concentrations, phosphorus loading) and tell us the current state of a particular environmental system. They are often tracked over time to produce a trend.

Impact indicators (4) The changes in the state of the environment described by the state indicators result in societal impacts. For example, a rise in global temperatures (a state indicator) has an impact on crop productivity, fisheries value, water availability, flooding, and so on.

Response indicators (5) Response indicators measure the effectiveness of attempts to prevent, compensate for, ameliorate, or adapt to environmental changes and may be collective or individual efforts, both governmental and non-governmental. Responses may include regulatory action, environmental or research expenditures, public opinion and consumer preferences, changes in management strategies, and provision of environmental information. Examples include the number of cars with pollution control or houses with water-efficient utilities, the percentage of waste that communities and households recycle, use of public transport, and passage of legislation. Response indicators are critical to assessing the effectiveness of policy interventions but are often the most difficult to develop and interpret.

America. It produced a report that looks ahead to 2030 and assesses how the drivers, pressures, states, and impacts will change (CEC, 2011). Virtually all areas of the environment will come under increasing pressure. Three areas of prime concern are continued and accelerated warming, particularly in the Arctic, continued loss of terrestrial biodiversity, and persistence of elevated levels of ground-level ozone in urban areas. Again, though, particular attention is drawn to the lack of adequate information and understanding in many areas, which prevents making assessments with confidence.

The federal government produces a suite of indicators, the Canadian Environmental Sustainability Indicators (see "Related Websites" at the end of this chapter), to track progress toward meeting the goals and targets of the Federal Sustainable Development Strategy (FSDS). Information is provided in three main categories: air quality; freshwater quality and availability; and nature protection, and these are discussed in more detail in the relevant chapters.

One issue difficult to resolve in reporting on environmental change is the degree of aggregation of information included in an indicator. An almost infinite amount of information could be collected on environmental systems (Figure 1.14). Much of this information might be useful for understanding the basic nature of the system while not being necessary for decision-making. Research scientists and line agencies may be involved in the routine collection of such data, and without such data, meaningful indicators cannot be constructed. At a higher level of sophistication, these raw data may form an *integrated database*, such as the integration of social and biophysical data as a basis for integrated watershed management planning. However, synthesis of these data into indicators is often most useful to decision-makers, and indicators themselves may show greater or lesser degrees of aggregation, especially in a spatial sense. The Canadian Environmental Sustainability Indicators are examples of the kind of indicators in which there is some spatial aggregation for the whole country.

Higher levels of thematic aggregation produce *indices*. Simple indices are composed mainly of similar indicators. The well-known Dow Jones industrial average, for example, combines changes in market processes for 30 blue-chip stocks listed on the New York Stock Exchange. The **Living Planet Index**, created by the World Wildlife Fund (WWF) is an example of a widely used index (WWF, 2014) that quantifies the overall state of planetary ecosystems. It tracks over 10,000 populations of 3,038 vertebrate species—fish, amphibians, reptiles, birds, mammals—around the world and shows a decline of 52 per cent between 1970 and 2010 (Figure 1.15). Separate indices are produced for terrestrial, marine, and freshwater species, and the three trends are averaged to create an aggregated index. Although vertebrates represent only a fraction of known species, it is assumed that trends in their populations are typical of biodiversity overall.

Composite indices, such as the ecological footprint, are often the most useful for decision-makers and represent the highest level of aggregation. Although few in number, they incorporate many, often very different sub-variables. The Human Development Index, created by the United Nations Development Programme; the Environmental Sustainability Index of the United Nations; and GNP are other examples of aggregate indices.

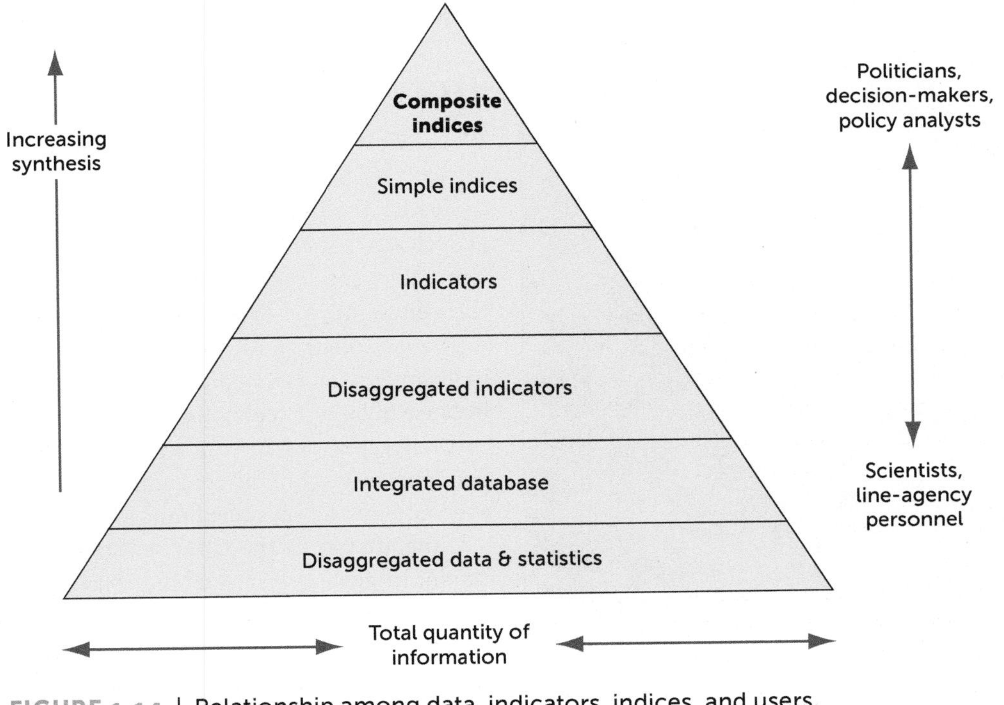

FIGURE 1.14 | Relationship among data, indicators, indices, and users.

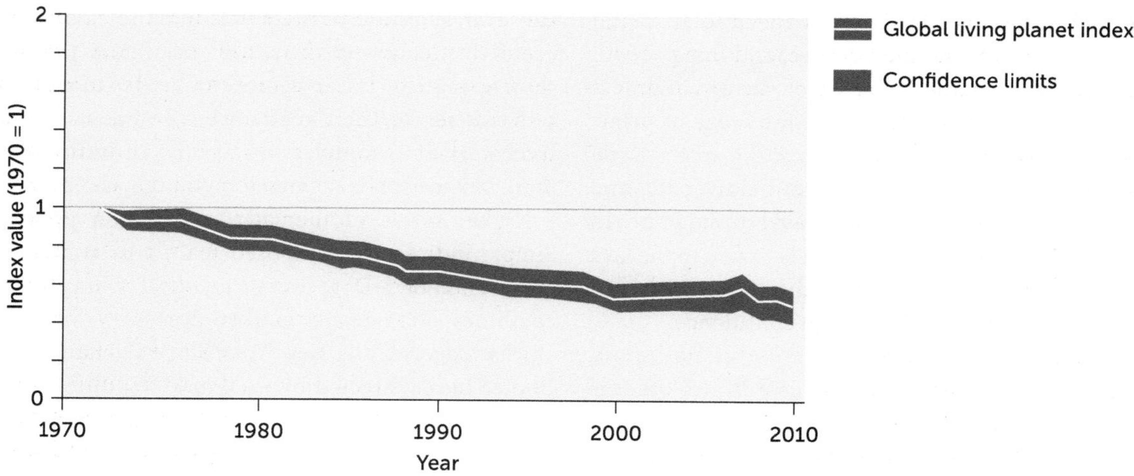

FIGURE 1.15 | The Living Planet Index, 2014.

Source: WWF (2014). ® "WWF" and "World Wildlife Fund" are WWF Registered Trademarks. © 1986 Panda Symbol WWF.

The Canadian Index of Wellbeing (CIW) encompasses eight different categories of well-being: living standards, healthy populations, community vitality, democratic engagement, time use, leisure and culture, education, and environment. Based at the University of Waterloo, the CIW aims to produce a composite index with a single number that moves up or down like the Toronto Stock Exchange or Dow Jones Industrial, giving a quick snapshot of whether Canadians' overall quality of life is getting better or worse.

Philip Dearden

Even if we could determine the value of insect pollinators to Canada's agriculture adequately, money could never buy the services they provide.

Composite indices are highly attractive because they convey a lot of information and are useful for making macro-level policy decisions. However, these highly aggregated indicators also carry risks. They often tell us what is happening at the macro level but add little in terms of explaining why. They may mask the complex detail that decision-makers require to make informed decisions. Composite indices must be highly transparent and capable of disaggregation to facilitate understanding of why change is occurring.

Indicators provide some basis for assessing change and comparison among countries, but they raise questions about the role of science in environmental decision-making. This aspect is discussed in more detail in the next section.

Implications

We are violating global thresholds related to the carrying capacity of the life-support system of the planet. We have ceased to live off the interest and are often consuming the capital at such a rate that it threatens the future viability of the system. Many species reach such carrying capacity limits with their environment, overshoot them, and have their numbers drastically reduced by environmental factors, as discussed in Chapter 3. So far, we have been able to avoid this process because of human technological ability, which has increased carrying capacities. But can we continue to increase our numbers and our habits of consumption indefinitely? Or must even humans accept some limits to activities and numbers?

If the answer to the latter question is yes, then identification, in general terms, of the changes needed is not that difficult. We need to balance birth and death rates, restore climatic stability, protect our atmosphere and waters from excessive pollution, curb deforestation and replant trees, protect the remaining natural habitats, and stabilize soils.

The challenge, however, is charting a course to fulfill these objectives. Before its demise, the Soviet Union had possibly the most stringent and comprehensive environmental protection regulations in existence and yet still ended up as one of the most polluted environments on Earth. The regulations were simply not enforced. The secret is charting a course that not only addresses the goals mentioned above but is actually able to achieve these goals.

In this book, we aim to provide some background as to how this can be achieved, with particular reference to the Canadian situation. In this chapter, we started by discussing the characteristics of the "environment" and "resources." We also examined different approaches to understanding complex systems and considered issues related to the use of "science" in decision- and policy-making. The case study of the Northern Gateway proposal illustrates the complexity of many environmental challenges. They are characterized by uncertainty, rapid change and conflict, and the need to appreciate both the scientific and the technical aspects of a problem and the social dimensions. This book attempts to provide an introduction to both of these aspects. Part B outlines some of the main processes of the *ecosphere*, the basic functionings of the planetary life-support system, and the ways in which we are disrupting them. Part C details some of the main planning and management approaches that have evolved within the Canadian context to address environmental challenges. Part D provides a thematic assessment of the challenges associated with particular activities such as fisheries, forestry, agriculture, wildlife use, water, energy production, and mineral extraction.

Figure 1.16 illustrates the relationship among these aspects. Natural systems form the basis of all human activity. A system is a recurring process of cause-and-effect pathways. You are in the educational system. You use the transportation system to go to your college or university, which is warmed by a heating system. Systems are composed of sets of things—e.g., educational institutions, buses, heating components—that are all related and linked together in some sort of functional way. Between these different components there is a flow of material, such as students, passengers, or heat, subject to some driving force—a thirst for knowledge, the need to get somewhere, or the need to be warm. Systems are generalized ways of looking at these processes.

Natural systems range in scale from the giant atmospheric and oceanic circulation systems to the processes underway in a single living cell. The pollination of a flower by a bee, the melting of a glacier, and the biological fixation of nitrogen from the atmosphere are all parts of such systems. These systems are infinitely complex, and there is a great deal of uncertainty as to how they function. One of the goals of natural science is to try to understand this complexity. We do this by constructing simplified models of how we think they work (e.g., Figure 1.16, Box 1). The models presented in Chapters 2 and 4 on how energy flows through the biosphere and on the nature of biogeochemical cycles are examples of these kinds of simplified representations of natural systems.

We do not know all the facts relating to these systems. We do not know all the components, let alone their functional relationships (Figure 1.16, Box 2). Many species, especially insects, still await discovery, even in well-explored temperate countries such as Canada. Of those we do know about, we have to select those we think are important and worth representing in our simplified models. Only recently, for example, have we become aware of the critical role played by various lichens in the circulation and retention of nitrogen in temperate rain forests (Chapter 4). Furthermore, not all characteristics are

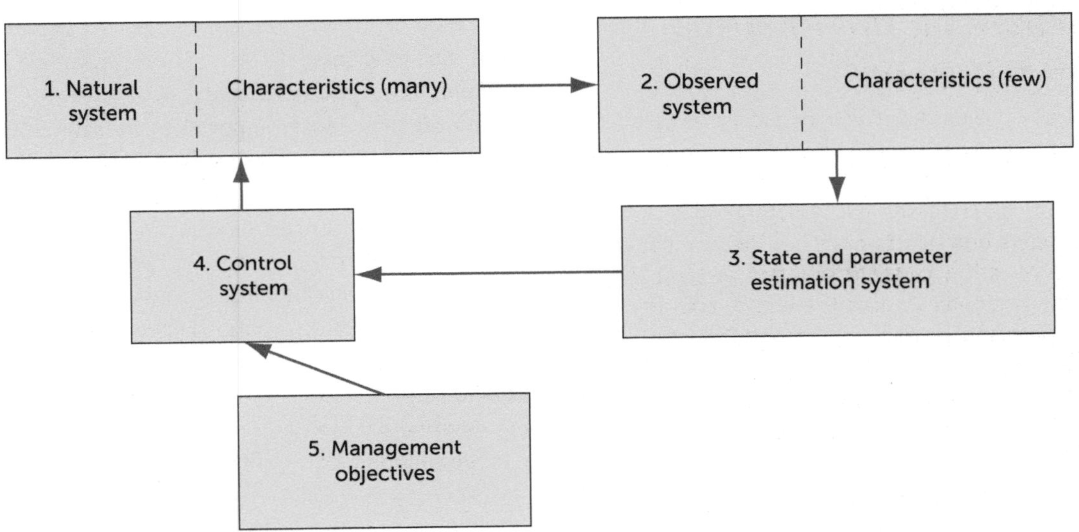

FIGURE 1.16 | Simplified model of interaction of biophysical and social systems in resource management.

measurable, even if we are aware of their existence. Thus, our simplified models are fraught with uncertainty.

On the basis of these models, we estimate the status of a given system (Figure 1.16, Box 3). How many fish spawn in a certain river? What proportion of the landscape supports commercial tree growth? What soil characteristics are suitable to support a given crop? If we understand the current status of the system, we can also start to ask what will result if certain parameters are changed. What would happen to the system, for example, if we took a certain number of fish from the river before they spawned, if we removed tree growth from a portion of the landscape, or if we grew a given crop in the same soil for a particular time period? In other words, we try to assess the impact of various changes to the system. Formal processes of impact assessment have arisen in many jurisdictions. They assess not only the impact on natural systems but the impact on social systems as well, as described in Chapter 6.

On the basis of this understanding, we try to replace natural systems with control systems in which the main decision regulators are humans rather than nature (Figure 1.16, Box 4). Instead of natural forces determining the number of fish that reach the spawning grounds, or the age of trees before they are replaced by other trees, or what species will grow in a particular location, people make these decisions as we modify the environment to our own advantage. These control systems are considered under topics such as forestry, water, energy, and agriculture in Part D of the book. And as control measures are introduced, we are increasingly appreciating that we may make natural and social systems less resilient, and therefore increase their vulnerability when significant or sudden changes occur.

Perspectives on the Environment

When Science Meets Art

The moral I labor toward is that a landscape as splendid as that of the Colorado Plateau can best be understood and given human significance by poets who have their feet planted in concrete—concrete data—and by scientists whose heads and hearts have not lost the capacity for wonder. Any good poet, in our age at least, must begin with the scientific view of the world; and any scientist worth listening to must be something of a poet, must possess the ability to communicate to the rest of us his sense of love and wonder at what his work discovers.

Source: Abbey (1977: 87).

Control systems are implemented on the basis of the social, economic, technological, and management constraints of a society (Figure 1.16, Box 5). These factors influence the demands for various outputs from the system and the speed of extraction. The environmental management strategies discussed in Part C of the book outline some main approaches to mediating between the social and economic demands of the society and the productive capacity of the system. As with the natural system, these strategies are characterized not only by complexity and uncertainty but also by *conflict* among different societal groups regarding the rate of outputs and distribution of benefits. Simply deciding which groups in society have a legitimate interest in a particular environmental issue is quite complex, as described in Chapter 5. Various dispute resolution mechanisms (Chapter 6) have emerged to address the conflicts arising from resource allocation decisions.

As we can already see, the challenges faced in environmental management are complex indeed, and consequently it is necessary to employ an integrated approach, such as the ecosystem approach described in Chapter 5, to understand this complexity. Both natural and social systems are fraught with uncertainty, making an adaptive approach (Chapter 6) a necessity, with strong adherence to the *precautionary principle*, as discussed in Chapter 5. Furthermore, our present predicament is largely the result of modification of natural systems before we had invested the time and effort—or had sufficient data or scientific expertise—to understand the consequences of our actions, especially related to the concept of resilience. The fisheries on both the Pacific and the Atlantic coasts of Canada are in trouble (see Chapter 8) because our simplified system models were inadequate as a basis for decision-making. However, in some instances, even when the long-term implications of an activity on the future viability of a resource are understood, the activity continues for political and economic reasons. The overharvesting of timber (Chapter 9) is a good example.

Perhaps the most important message underlying the environmental challenges we face is the need for fundamental changes in the way we view our relationship with nature, as discussed earlier in this Chapter regarding anthropocentric and biocentric/ecocentric perspectives, as well as later in Chapter 15. Changes in outlook and approach must take place at all levels, from international agencies such as the World Bank, through national and regional governments, to household and individual initiatives. Part of the goal of this book is to motivate you to become more involved in making these changes happen, both locally and globally.

Summary

1. The environment is the combination of the atmosphere, hydrosphere, cryosphere, lithosphere, and biosphere in which humans, other living species, and non-animate phenomena exist.
2. Some consider resources to be only those components of the environment of utility to humans. This view is considered to be anthropocentric; value is defined relative to human interests, wants, and needs. Another, contrasting perspective is that resources exist independently of human wants and needs. This view is ecocentric or biocentric; aspects of the environment are valued simply because they exist, and they have the right to exist.
3. Environmental and resource issues can be approached from disciplinary, multidisciplinary, cross-disciplinary, interdisciplinary, and transdisciplinary perspectives. Each provides a different basis or model for viewing the world. We should strive for interdisciplinary and transdisciplinary approaches in order to understand complex systems.
4. For a science-based approach to management of resources and the environment, we should (a) focus the science on key issues and communicate it in a policy-relevant form; (b) use scientific information to clarify issues, identify potential management options, and estimate consequences of decisions; (c) clearly and simply communicate key scientific findings to all participants; (d) evaluate whether or not the final decision is consistent with scientific information; and (e) be aware of the balance between scientists providing technical information and interpretation, and being advocates for particular approaches or solutions.
5. Following the change of government after the federal election in mid October 2015, Prime Minister Trudeau indicated that the Liberal federal government would work to ensure scientific evidence and conclusions were systematically drawn upon when developing policy. What changes do you think would be most effective in facilitating greater attention to scientific understanding of issues when the federal government takes decisions?
6. The Northern Gateway is a multi-billion dollar pipeline proposal to transport oil from Alberta to the BC coast for sale in Asia. The process of decision-making helps illustrate some of the challenges with aligning political and scientific perspectives on resource management issues.
7. Many environmental challenges of today can be considered "wicked problems": they are characterized as being ill-defined, with incomplete and/or contradictory information or interpretations, having many stakeholders with values in conflict, and having an overall system and related issues that are uncertain and confusing.
8. Having a vision of or sense of direction toward a desirable future condition is essential for planning and management. In that regard, sustainable development has been proposed as an appropriate ideal to characterize what societies should aspire to.
9. Resilience, or "the ability of a system to absorb disturbance and still retain its basic function and structure," challenges some of the basic assumptions underlying sustainable development.
10. On the global scale, there is undeniable evidence of unprecedented environmental degradation as a result of human activities. Such is the scale of influence of human activities that a new geological epoch, the Anthropocene, has been proposed to characterize current times. Growing global population is a continuing challenge, as are the consumer demands of people in the wealthier countries.
11. An estimated 4.3 people are born every second around the world. By 2015, there were more than 7.3 billion people on Earth. The United Nations forecasts an increase to 9.6 billion people by 2050, representing more than 80 million additional people per year to feed.
12. Conditions continue to deteriorate in many poorer countries. The richest 20 per cent of the world's population is responsible for more than 75 per cent of world consumption, while the poorest 20 per cent consume less than 2 per cent.
13. The eight Millennium Development Goals adopted by the United Nations in 2000 aim to improve human well-being by reducing poverty, hunger, and child and maternal mortality; by ensuring education for all; by controlling and managing diseases; by tackling gender disparity; by ensuring environmental sustainability; and by pursuing global partnerships. Under each of the MDGs, countries agreed to targets to be achieved by 2015.
14. In order to stay below the threshold level of what scientists predict would be runaway change, and if emissions were frozen at the current level, we would need the absorptive capacity of two planets.
15. Canada is one of the most privileged countries, covering some 13 million km^2 and with a population of over 35 million people. However, our environmental impacts are considerable. Our per capita consumption of water and energy is among the highest in the world. We also have some of the highest production per capita of waste products, including greenhouse gases.
16. Canada has the second-highest per capita emissions of greenhouse gases in the world. Canada agreed under the Kyoto Protocol to target a 6 per cent cut in emissions. Instead, emissions have increased by 29 per cent, and the country is 35 per cent above its Kyoto target.
17. Responsibility for the environment and natural resources is divided between the federal and provincial governments, with the territories and municipalities taking on increasingly important roles. Aboriginal peoples also

are much more involved. The shared responsibility often requires collaboration and partnerships, which can create tensions because of differing interests and perspectives.

18. Indicators are one way by which science can assist decision-makers to appreciate current trends. There are different kinds of indicators with different levels of complexity. Decision-makers often want few indicators that contain the most information to be able to understand the situation. Indicators that combine many different elements are called composite indices.

19. The Living Planet Index shows a reduction of more than 50 per cent overall in biodiversity of the planet since 1970. Ecological footprints show the extent of human demand on global ecosystems. These "footprints" measure the area of biologically productive land and water needed to provide ecological resources and services—food, fibre, and timber; land on which to build; and land to absorb carbon dioxide (CO_2) released by burning fossil fuels.

20. A comparison of humanity's ecological footprint with biocapacity (the amount of biologically productive area—cropland, pasture, forest, and fisheries—available to meet humanity's needs) shows that since the late 1980s, the ecological footprint exceeds the Earth's biocapacity by more than 50 per cent. Canadians have a very high ecological footprint, but Canada also has a very high biocapacity.

21. The main challenge for humanity is to implement effective strategies to ensure that the ecological footprint falls below biocapacity as soon as possible.

Key Terms

Anthropocene
anthropocentric view
biocapacity
biosphere
consumption
crude birth rate (CBR)
crude death rate (CDR)
crude growth rate (CGR)
cryosphere
demographic transition
ecocentric (biocentric) values
ecological footprint
environment
environmental migration
epidemiological transition
exponential growth
global climate change
gross national product (GNP)
indicators
Kuznet curve
Living Planet Index
migration
Millennium Ecosystem Assessment
planetary carrying capacity
population age structure
replacement-level fertility
resilience
resources
subsidiarity
sustainable development
three waves
total fertility rates
triple bottom line
war on science
wicked problems

Questions for Review and Critical Thinking

1. What information is available in your municipality or province regarding environmental hazards?

2. If you had been hired to provide recommendations related to the Northern Gateway project, what information would you have needed to make a decision about the potential risk to ecosystem and human health? Could you place a monetary value on any potential risk?

3. What is your opinion about the validity and value of the concept of Anthropocene?

4. Do you find the idea of "three waves" helpful to understand the evolution of thinking by environmentalists? Do you believe we are now in an era of a "fourth wave"? If so, what are the characteristics of such a wave?

5. How do you react to the comment that there had been a "war on science," and that the federal government had been actively taking action to limit and circumscribe the contribution of science in management of natural resources and the environment?

6. Following the change of government after the federal election in mid October 2015, Prime Minister Trudeau indicated that the Liberal federal government would work to ensure scientific evidence and conclusions were systematically drawn upon when developing policy. What changes do you think would be most effective in facilitating greater attention to scientific understanding of issues when the federal government takes decisions?

7. What are the characteristics of "wicked problems"?

8. What is the distinction between sustainable development and resilience? How does the concept of resilience challenge the goals of sustainable development? Which do you believe makes a better basis for imagining a desirable future state: sustainable development or resilience?

9. Outline the main arguments for considering population growth as a threat to global carrying capacity or as a building block for future economic growth.
10. What moral obligations, if any, do Canadians have to assist people in the developing world whose standards of living do not meet basic human needs?
11. Is population growth or environmental degradation the major problem in the less developed countries? Which is cause, and which is effect?
12. What are indicators used for? What are the main types of indicators? Are there any indicators used by your province or municipality that give insight into environmental changes?
13. What are some of the main initiatives of Canadian governments to address environmental problems?
14. What is a system? Outline the components of a system that you use on a regular basis.
15. What are the top three things you would do if you were the prime minister of Canada to contribute toward achieving global sustainability and resilience?

Related Websites

Canadian Environmental Sustainability Indicators
www.ec.gc.ca/indicateurs-indicators/default.asp?lang=En&n=47F48106-1

Canadian Index of Wellbeing
https://uwaterloo.ca/canadian-index-wellbeing/

Canadian Sustainability Indicators Network
www.csin-rcid.ca

Canada–United States Collaboration for Great Lakes Water Quality (Selection of indicators for Great Lakes)
www.binational.net

Fraser Basin Council: Sustainability Indicators
www.fraserbasin.bc.ca/comm_indicators.html

Global Footprint Network
www.footprintnetwork.org/en/index.php/GFN/page/personal_footprint/

Living Planet Index
www.wwf.panda.org/about_our_earth/all_publications/living_planet_report/living_planet_report_graphics/lpi_interactive/

National Round Table on the Environment and the Economy (NRTEE)
http://collectionscanada.gc.ca/webarchives2/20130322140948/http:/nrtee-trnee.ca/

Office of the Auditor General, Commissioner of the Environment and Sustainable Development, *Reports on the Environment and Sustainable Development*
www.oag-bvg.gc.ca/internet/English/parl_lp_e_901.html

Resilience Alliance
www.resalliance.org

Stockholm Resilience Centre
www.stockholmresilience.org

United Nations Environment Programme: Global Environment Outlook
www.unep.org/geo/geo4/media/index.asp

Sustainable Communities Online (Community-based indicators)
www.sustainable.org

United Nations Population Fund
www.unfpa.org

Worldometers
www.worldometers.info/world-population/

Worldwatch Institute
www.worldwatch.org

Further Readings

Note: This list comprises works relevant to the subject of the chapter but not cited in the text. All cited works are listed in the References at the end of the book.

Brown, V., J.A. Harris, and J.Y. Russell. 2010. *Tackling Wicked Problems Through the Transdisciplinary Imagination*. London: Earthscan.

Hacking, T., and P. Guthrie. 2008. "A framework for clarifying the meaning of the Triple Bottom-Line, integrated, and sustainability assessment," *Environmental Impact Assessment Review* 28, 1: 73–89.

McDowell, L.S. 2012. *An Environmental History of Canada*. Vancouver: University of British Columbia Press.

Mulrennan, M.E. 2015. "Aboriginal peoples in relation to resources and environmental management," in B. Mitchell, ed., *Resource and Environmental Management in Canada*, 5th edn, Don Mills, ON: Oxford University Press, 55–83.

Savitz, A. 2006. *The Triple Bottom Line*. San Francisco: Jossey-Bass.

Tam, C.-L., 2015. "Canada's role in global sustainability: Successes, failures, and opportunities," in B. Mitchell, ed., *Resource and Environmental Management in Canada*, 5th edn, Don Mills, ON: Oxford University Press: 30–54.

Williston, B. 2012. *Environmental Ethics for Canadians*. Don Mills, ON: Oxford University Press.

Worldwatch Institute. 2011. *Vital Signs: The Trends That Are Shaping Our Future*. New York: W.W. Norton.

Go to www.oupcanada.com/DeardenMitchell5e to access additional learning tools on your smartphone, tablet, or PC.

PART B
The Ecosphere

The human brain now holds the way to our future. We have to recall the image of the planet from outer space: a single entity in which air, water, the continents are interconnected. That is our home.

—David Suzuki

The first section of the book provided an overview of the global and Canadian situations regarding the relationship between humans and the Earth. As the Canadian communications theorist Marshall McLuhan noted, we are not passive bystanders in this interaction. We are members of the crew, helping direct what happens to our planet. As crew members, we need to have some idea of the workings of our "Spaceship Earth," particularly of the nature of its life-support system. Part B will provide this overview. Here we describe the natural systems through simplified models, following the conceptual framework outlined in Chapter 1 (Figure 1.13). This will provide the background you need to understand many of the environmental challenges facing society today.

Most of what follows is derived from just one form of environmental knowledge—natural science (see Box B.1). Through natural science we try to understand and find order in nature so that we can accurately predict the outcome of given changes that may occur. An important underlying assumption is that patterns in nature can be discerned if we approach things in the right manner and with the right tools. The *scientific method* lays the foundation for how scientists approach this task. An important assumption of the scientific method is that different scientists will obtain the same results if they repeat the experiment or observations in the same manner as the original observations. This is one reason why scientists must give detailed descriptions of their methodology and attempt to be as objective as possible. What use would a thermometer be, for example, if its readings of temperature varied according to who took the measurement?

Although the scientific method is designed to minimize the effects of scientists on the phenomenon they are studying, it is a myth to believe that science is "objective." Scientists work in a social environment and are greatly influenced by their peers and by society. The research topics selected and the way research questions are framed are key components of the scientific method and yet are heavily influenced by

ENVIRONMENT IN FOCUS

BOX B.1 | Traditional Ecological Knowledge

Most of the concepts presented in this book are the result of the "scientific approach" to understanding different phenomena. There are other approaches, however, and one gaining increasing attention is **traditional ecological knowledge (TEK)**. The scientific community now understands that indigenous peoples often have detailed knowledge of their local environments, which is not surprising for peoples gaining their sustenance directly from that environment. Indigenous peoples tend to undertake the same kinds of tasks as Western scientists, such as classification and naming of different organisms and studies of population dynamics, geographical distributions, and optimal management strategies. Unlike Western science, however, this knowledge is rarely recorded in written form but is handed down orally from generation to generation.

Interest in TEK has been spurred by increasing industrial interest in northern regions and the potential impact of resource extraction on Native communities. Inevitably, this has given rise to discussions about which form of ecological knowledge, Western or traditional, is the "best." In reality, both have their advantages and disadvantages. Modern science is informed by developments around the world but is limited in its knowledge of changes over time in a particular place, an area where traditional knowledge is particularly rich. Scientists tend to concentrate on information that can be tested by replication and to ignore idiosyncratic and individual behaviour that is given substantial weight by indigenous hunters.

A graphic example of these differences came to light in March 2008. Scientists from the Department of Fisheries and Oceans (DFO; now Fisheries and Oceans Canada) claimed that the bowhead whale populations in the eastern Arctic were so low—about 5,000 animals—that the species was listed as threatened under the Species at Risk Act, discussed in Chapter 14. However, for many years the Inuit had claimed that there were far more animals and that the hunting quota of one whale every two years should be increased. As a result of new scientific information, this latter claim was found to be correct, and DFO scientists expanded their estimates to 14,400. That is nearly 300 per cent higher than the Ministry's earlier estimate and roughly equal to the 11,000 whales thought to have frequented waters such as the Davis Strait and Lancaster Sound during the nineteenth century, when whales were vigorously hunted for their blubber as the main source of lamp oil. This example highlights that there is no "best" form of knowledge and illustrates the potential for traditional knowledge and conventional science to complement one another. A similar dispute is now occurring over polar bear numbers, although it appears that, in this case, a scientific approach is providing a more accurate picture of the state of the natural system (see Figure 1.16).

Management systems also differ between indigenous and scientific approaches. The traditional system is self-regulating, based on communal property arrangements. Conservation practices, such as rotation of hunting areas, were commonly practised. However, the system is not infallible, especially with the onslaught of outside influences and commercialization. There are examples around the world where indigenous peoples have hunted species to extirpation within their homelands. Similarly, the modern system of private property rights and state allocation of harvesting rights does not always work. This was recognized all too clearly with the complete collapse of the North Atlantic cod fishery in the middle of the twentieth century: if scientists and policy-makers had given more credence to the local ecological knowledge of inshore fishers in Newfoundland outport communities, the destruction of the fishery might have been averted. Scientists and indigenous peoples are now realizing the benefits offered by the two systems of knowledge and management approaches and are trying to use both through co-management arrangements.

GomezDavid/iStockphoto

There is considerable dispute between scientists and indigenous peoples about the numbers of polar bears remaining.

the individual scientist. Despite the fact that social biases and values influence science, it is important to maintain as value-free an approach as possible and to ensure that biases are explicit and documented.

Scientists collect data or ***facts*** (observations widely accepted as truthful) about the environment and then try to make some order out of those facts. This order is called **theory**. The theory of natural selection, first outlined by Charles Darwin and Alfred Russel Wallace in 1858, is a good example. When there is universal acceptance of the theory, a **scientific law** may be established. A scientific law represents the most stringent form of understanding and lays down a universal truth that describes in all cases what happens in certain circumstances. In the next two chapters, you will be introduced to some of these laws. They are useful because they provide firm blocks upon which we can build our scientific understanding.

The scientific method links, with minimum error, the testing of hypotheses with the existing body of knowledge. It prescribes a series of steps that, over time, scientists have found are most likely to provide understanding about phenomena under study, irrespective of the observer undertaking the observations or experiment. The process starts with a question often derived either from observations of the environment or from existing literature. A **hypothesis** is generated to explain the phenomenon of interest, and experiments or observations are designed to disprove the hypothesis. If the hypothesis is not rejected, then additional experiments may be designed in further efforts to disprove it. If all efforts fail, the hypothesis becomes incorporated into theory and is accepted as a valid answer to the question. However, natural scientists do not have to follow one scientific method. Many important scientific insights have come about through quite irregular approaches. Nonetheless, it is wise to learn from previous experience and to know the kinds of procedures usually followed in any given area of inquiry.

That said, we should not feel that any of the hypotheses, theories, or even laws advanced by science are beyond question. The whole purpose of **science** is to ask questions, and science advances by continually changing and modifying previous knowledge. "Be kind to scientists (and teachers!) but ruthless in your questions" is not a bad dictum. Debate and disagreement in science are normal. In the following chapters, for example, ideas on some topics are changing rapidly, and even some concepts (e.g., keystone species, climax vegetation) are being questioned by some scientists. This active debate is often misunderstood by those outside the academic community. It can also be used for political purposes to support inaction on measures that might be unpopular, such as limits on industrial emissions to reduce acidic precipitation. Debate and dispute, however, are signs of the vitality and strength of scientific thinking—and of the urgent need to get closer to truth—rather than the converse.

When we think of science, we often tend to think of it within the context of natural and physical sciences, and most of the next three chapters focus on this understanding of "science." However, social science is also critical to understanding and addressing environmental management. Just as natural scientists hope to provide greater understanding of the natural world, social scientists address the same need for social dimensions. How can we understand how individuals think, how to change their behaviour, how governments and the economy operate, and how legislation is formed and enforced? What can we learn from societies elsewhere, and how they have interacted with their environmental surroundings in the past? These are the kinds of questions that we look to disciplines such as geography, anthropology, history, psychology, sociology, political science, and economics to address.

The methods of social science can also have much in common with the natural sciences, with hypothesis testing as a means of building theory and establishing laws that will help provide a generic understanding of seemingly disparate events. Yet the great variability in social systems, the difficulties with isolating and controlling many of the variables under study in a social context (as opposed to natural phenomena or laboratory work), and the challenges of repeatability (it is often impossible to duplicate the circumstances for repeated experiments) make adherence to strict scientific procedures impossible. These difficulties make it necessary for social scientists to apply a very broad range of approaches to gaining social understanding. Thus, although theory formation is a critical part of the social sciences, the formulation of universal laws is very rare.

Furthermore, although both natural and social scientists strive for **quantitative** (numerical) data because of the precision that numbers provide, **qualitative** (non-numerical) data are sometimes all that can be obtained or even all that can or should be sought, depending on the particular research question. A case in point: Over many years, federal fisheries' scientists tended to dismiss the qualitative data from inshore Newfoundland fishers as "anecdotal" and chose to rely largely on their own estimates of stock biomass, which were based on offshore data from the trawler fishery and from their own survey boats. As it turned out, the anecdotal observations and warnings based on generations of knowledge and experience were far more accurate than the quantitative data the scientists chose to believe. Both kinds of data are important. For example, if someone tells you that the weather was "cool," that does not convey as much information as telling you that the temperature was −25°C. Data on the beauty of a certain landscape is less amenable to quantitative assessment, although some scientists have developed numerical ways of approaching such problems!

The three chapters in Part B provide a basic overview of the principal processes that maintain the planetary life-support system. A simple model of the planet would look like the layers of an onion (Figure B.1). We are most concerned with the outer layer, the **ecosphere**, which consists of three main layers:

- The **lithosphere**, which is the outer layer of the Earth's mantle and the crust. It contains the rocks, minerals, and soils that provide the nutrients necessary for life.

- The **hydrosphere**, which contains all the water on Earth. Water in a frozen state is referred to as the **cryosphere**, a very important component for much of Canada.
- The **atmosphere**, which contains the gases surrounding the lithosphere and hydrosphere. It can be further divided into four main sub-layers. The innermost layer, or **troposphere**, contains 99 per cent of the water vapour and up to 90 per cent of the air and is responsible for our weather. Two gases, nitrogen (78 per cent) and oxygen (21 per cent), account for 99 per cent of the gaseous volume. This layer extends on average to about 17 kilometres before it gives way to the second layer, the **stratosphere**, wherein lies the main body of ozone that blocks out most of the ultraviolet radiation from the sun. At about 50 kilometres from the Earth's surface is the **mesosphere** and above that the **thermosphere**. As distance from Earth increases, the pressure and density of the atmosphere decreases as it melds into space.

These three layers combine to produce the conditions necessary for life in the ecosphere, which stretches from the depths of the ocean trenches up to the highest mountain peaks, a layer some 20 kilometres in width, no larger in scale than the peel of an apple, which contains some 30 million different kinds of organisms. The following chapters impart some idea of the main environmental processes of the ecosphere and describe how human activities interrupt these processes.

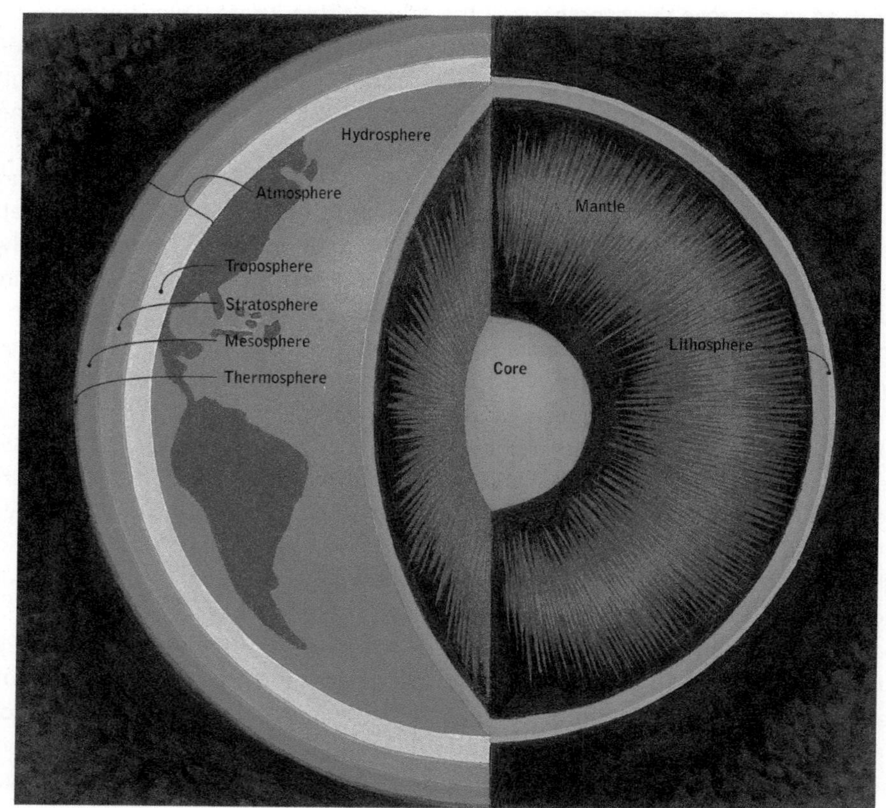

FIGURE B.1 | A simplified model of the Earth showing the ecosphere.

Key Terms

atmosphere
cryosphere
ecosphere
hydrosphere
hypothesis
lithosphere
mesosphere
qualitative
quantitative
science
scientific law
stratosphere
theory
thermosphere
traditional ecological knowledge (TEK)
troposphere

CHAPTER TWO

Energy Flows and Ecosystems

Learning Objectives

- To know the nature of energy and the laws governing its transformation
- To understand the way energy flows through the ecosphere and links ecosystem components
- To outline the main influences on the structure and nature of ecosystems
- To understand the nature and importance of biodiversity
- To appreciate the Canadian context for biodiversity and approaches and challenges with biodiversity conservation in Canada
- To understand the ecological implications associated with the loss of biodiversity
- To learn the importance of reducing energy use in society

Introduction

The annual arrival of the capelin to the beaches of Newfoundland to spawn on the first full moon of June had long been a bounty—not only for many animal species but also for the settlers who collected the fish for consumption and application to their gardens as fertilizer. The capelin is a small fish of the North Atlantic and an important food supply for many other species, including cod, salmon, halibut, mackerel, seals, various whale species, and many species of seabirds such as puffins and murres. In the late 1970s and early 1980s, the numbers of fish coming to spawn declined markedly.

Normally, 80 to 90 per cent of the Atlantic puffin's diet consists of capelin. In the early 1980s, scientists noticed capelin declined to 13 per cent of their diet, resulting in severe malnutrition of puffin chicks and subsequent declines in the population owing in part to starvation. Their numbers fell as a direct result of the removal of their food base, the capelin. The energy flow between the species had been interrupted by the opening of an offshore capelin fishery that had removed the capelin from the food chains that nourish many other marine species. The puffins were a noticeable victim of

Kenneth Canning/iStockphoto

The colourful bill is the most striking feature of the Atlantic puffin, which breeds among the rocks of sea islands.

© All Canada Photos/Rolf Hicker

Spawning capelin on a beach in Newfoundland.

this appropriation, but other species feeding on the capelin suffered the same consequence. These species in turn would affect the abundance of other species at all levels in the food web, since the numbers of some species are controlled mainly by their predators. This example illustrates the importance of understanding how energy links species and flows through ecosystems. Changing the energy available at one part of the food chain will have repercussions throughout the ecosystem.

Reading this book, taking notes in class, even snoozing at home all require energy. That energy comes ultimately from the **radiant energy** of the sun and is transformed into chemical energy in the form of food supplies before being converted to mechanical energy in the form of physical exertion and activity. In this chapter, you will gain an appreciation of energy in relation to such transformations, how energy flows through ecosystems, and the ecosystem consequences that result. You also will be introduced to the main factors that control the structure and composition of ecological communities and how these interact to produce the biodiversity of our planet.

Energy

Energy is the capacity to do work and is measured in calories. A **calorie** is the amount of heat necessary to raise one gram or one millilitre of water one degree Celsius (°C), starting at 15 degrees. Energy comes in many forms: radiant energy (from the sun), chemical energy (stored in the chemical bonds of molecules), as well as heat, mechanical, and electrical energy. Energy differs from matter in that it has no mass and does not occupy space. It affects matter by making it *do* things—work. Energy derived from an object's motion and mass is known as **kinetic energy**, whereas **potential energy** is stored energy that is available for later use. The water stored behind a dam is potential energy that becomes kinetic energy as it pours over the dam. The gas in a car is potential energy before it is poured into the engine to create mechanical energy for propulsion.

Most of the energy available for use is termed **low-quality energy**, which is diffuse, dispersed at low temperatures, and difficult to gather. The total energy of all moving atoms is referred to as **heat**, whereas temperature is a measure at a particular time of the average speed of motion of the atoms or molecules in a substance. The oceans, for example, contain an enormous amount of heat, but it is very costly to harness this energy for use. They have high heat content but low temperature. On the other hand, **high-quality energy**, such as a hot fire or coal or gasoline, is easy to use, but the energy disperses quickly. It is important that we match the quality of the energy supply to the task at hand. In other words, the aim is not to use high-quality energy for tasks that can be undertaken by low-quality supplies. Heating space, such as your house, for example, requires only low-temperature heat, yet many homes are heated through the conversion of high-quality energy sources that entail significant energy losses in generation, transport, and application. Nuclear energy, which involves high-quality heat at several thousand degrees converted to high-quality electricity transmitted to homes and used in resistance heating, is very inefficient. The most efficient way to provide space heating is to have super-insulated houses and passive solar heating. Examples of energy savings in buildings and the progress being made in this area are discussed in more detail in Chapter 13.

All organisms, including plants, require energy for growth, tissue replacement, movement, and reproduction. To gain a comprehensive perspective on life, we must understand energy and how it is transformed and used. Box 2.1 provides an introductory definition of life.

Laws of Thermodynamics

Two laws of physics (or physical laws) describe the way in which trillions of energy transformations per second take place all over the globe. They are known as the *laws of thermodynamics*. The first one, the **law of conservation of energy**, tells us that energy can neither be created nor destroyed; it is merely changed from one form into another (nuclear is a form of potential energy—the energy is simply held in the nucleus of an atom). Organisms do not create energy; rather, they obtain it from the surrounding environment. When an organism dies, the energy of that organism is not "lost." It flows back into the environment and is transformed into different types of energy, the total sum of which adds up to the original amount. Similarly, we all know that most cars obtain their energy from gasoline. As the fuel gauge goes from full to empty, this does not indicate that energy has been consumed; it has merely been transformed from chemical energy into other forms of energy, including the mechanical energy to move the car.

The second law of thermodynamics, the **law of entropy**, tells us that when energy is transformed from one form into another, there is always a decrease in the quality of usable energy. In any transformation, some energy is lost as lower-quality, dispersed energy that is dissipated into the surrounding environment, often as heat. The amount of energy lost varies depending on the nature of the transformation. In a coal-fired generating station, for example, 35 per cent of the coal's energy at most is converted into electricity. The rest is given off as waste heat to the environment.

In a car, only about 10 per cent of the chemical energy of the gasoline is actually converted into mechanical energy to turn the wheels. The remainder is dispersed into the environment. Put your hand onto the hood of a car that has just stopped running. The heat you feel is a result of this second law of energy or the law of entropy. **Entropy** is a measure of the disorder or randomness of a system. High-quality, useful energy has low entropy. As energy becomes dispersed through transformation, the entropy increases.

For organisms, the second law is particularly important because they must continuously expend energy to maintain themselves. Whenever energy is used, some of that energy is lost to the organism, creating a need for an ongoing supply that must exceed these losses if the organism is to survive. If losses exceed gains for an extended period of time, then the organism dies.

There are many other important ramifications of this law. It tells us, for example, that energy cannot be recycled. As it flows through systems, it is continuously degraded. We think of "advanced" societies as being energy consumers. Large dams and nuclear power stations, for example, are visible signs of a modern economy. As we become more economically developed, we find new ways to transform energy. Cars, telephones, electric can openers, blenders, microwaves, hot tubs, computers, and smartphones are all energy transformers. Yet as more energy is transformed, more is dispersed into the atmosphere because entropy increases. This dispersion can be likened to a bar of soap in a bowl of water. As the soap is used over time, it dissolves into the water, making it less and less useful. Similarly, as energy is used it gradually disperses into the atmosphere, becoming less useful.

All photos courtesy Philip Dearden

For many people, such as villagers in India, biomass is the main form of energy. It can take many forms ranging from wood (a) through to dried buffalo feces (b), which are burned to cook food and, in some places, heat houses. These energy sources are ancient and depend on photosynthesis from the sun. Modern technology is now helping to capture the sun's energy in new and exciting ways, such as these solar cells in a remote village in western Thailand (c).

ENVIRONMENT IN FOCUS

BOX 2.1 | What Is Life?

We have asserted that energy is essential for all life, but what is life? Living organisms have a number of common characteristics, including:

- They use energy to maintain internal order.
- They increase in size and complexity over time.
- They can reproduce.
- They react to their environment.
- They regulate and maintain a constant internal environment.
- They fit the biotic and abiotic requirements of a specific habitat.

We think we have a fairly good idea of what constitutes life, but there is still a lot of debate as to how life developed on Earth. More than 85 years ago, two scientists proposed a theory, called the Big Bang Theory, which explained the origin of the universe as the result of a massive explosion that occurred some 15 billion years ago. The solar system came from the resulting matter. As the chunks of matter grew in size, they heated up. As the Earth cooled, warm seas formed, and precipitation helped to create a nutrient-rich environment. Over time, the continuous bombardment of this nutrient-rich soup by high energy levels from the sun created chemical reactions producing simple organic compounds, such as amino acids. Scientists have managed to recreate several organic compounds necessary for life from inorganic molecules by bombarding them with energy.

Over billions of years, larger organic molecules came to be synthesized until the first living cells, probably bacteria, developed between 3.6 and 3.8 billion years ago. These cells passed through several stages over billions of years, with increasingly complex development. This activity took place in the ocean environment, protected from ultraviolet (UV) radiation. Between 2.3 and 2.5 billion years ago, a major change occurred when photosynthetic bacteria developed that emitted oxygen into the atmosphere as they manufactured carbohydrates from the carbon dioxide in the atmosphere. Over time, the oxygen reacted with the abundant and poisonous methane in the atmosphere, reducing levels of this gas and leading to the atmosphere we know today. Some oxygen was also converted to ozone in the lower stratosphere, which protected evolving life from UV radiation and allowed the emergence of life from deeper to shallower waters and eventually onto land itself.

Life holds many surprises. For example, in 2014 scientists reported on the deepest (thus far) drilling exercise into the crust of the Earth. A giant drill was lowered from a Japanese ship through more than 1,000 metres of ocean before drilling through a record-breaking 2,446 metres of rock beneath the sea floor into an ancient coal bed. In the samples, the scientists found a microbe community that was thriving despite having no light, no oxygen, barely any water, and very limited nutrients. The microbes have very low energy requirements and digest carbon compounds from the coal. Scientists are now trying to figure out how they got there. Were they always there and buried with the original organic materials or did they somehow bore their way down afterward? If such life can survive on Earth, can it survive on other planets? Are there implications for global climate change that are not fully understood as the microbes take in hydrocarbons and expel methane, a greenhouse gas, as a waste product?

As we learn more about life, things get increasingly complicated. To try to simplify the vast array of life on Earth, biologists recognize five main kingdoms. The simplest kingdom (#1) consists of *monerans,* single-celled micro-organisms that include bacteria and photosynthetic blue-green bacteria. The genetic material of monerans is not contained within a nuclear envelope. They are known as *prokaryotic* and were the first to evolve. The other four kingdoms (#2 to #5) all have nuclei and a high degree of internal structure; they are known as *eukaryotic*. The *protists* (#2) comprise a large variety of unicellular and multi-cellular species such as algae, protozoans, slime moulds, and foraminifera. Kelp species, found in abundance around much of Canada's coastline, are multi-cellular algae of this kingdom. The kingdom consists of 14 phyla (the primary subdivision of a taxonomic kingdom) with more than 14,000 species described. *Fungi* have their own kingdom (#3), one that evolved relatively recently, some 400 million years ago. This kingdom includes both fungi, such as mushrooms, which are multi-cellular, and yeasts, which are unicellular. All fungi are heterotrophs and mostly digest dead organic matter or act as parasites. Many are asexual. They are key components of the biogeochemical cycles described in Chapter 4.

The remaining two kingdoms (#4, #5) will be most familiar to you. The *plantae* (#4) are mostly photosynthetic, although there are some exceptions as described later in Box 2.4. Unlike algae, plants are always multi-cellular. They dominate terrestrial ecosystems and contain two main groups, the *bryophtyes* and *vascular* plants. Bryophytes, such as mosses and liverworts, are restricted to moist environments because they lack a waxy cuticle to cover their foliage. They also lack vascular tissues. Vascular plants are very complex and have vascular tissues in their stems to convey water and nutrients. There are a further nine divisions within the vascular plants, including ferns, conifers, and flowering plants. It is estimated that there are more than 235,000 species of flowering plants. Other divisions, such as the ginkgo, have only one surviving species.

The final kingdom (#5) is the *animalia,* which are heterotrophic, multi-cellular organisms that have the ability to move. They ingest their food and digest it within their bodies. Most reproduce sexually. This is the largest kingdom, mostly because of the vast numbers of insects. Insects are examples of the *invertebrates*, having no backbone. *Vertebrates*, on the other hand, have backbones and include amphibians, fish, birds, reptiles, and mammals. There are about 4,500 species of mammals. Mammals feed their young with milk, are homeotherms (i.e., they can regulate their body temperatures at a constant level), are hairy, and have a four-chambered heart. This book is mainly about the impacts of one mammal, humans, on the rest of life on this planet.

Some of the principal transformations that have to take place to achieve a sustainable society are to view high energy consumption as undesirable; to reduce energy waste; and to switch from the non-renewable sources of energy that now dominate (coal and oil particularly) to renewable sources, such as those discussed in Chapter 12. Until the Industrial Revolution, the speed of processing raw materials was limited by the energy available, supplied largely by human and animal labour combined with wood, wind, and water power. These sources were in turn limited by the input of solar energy over a relatively short time period. The use of coal, and later oil, to fuel steam engines removed these limitations and made accessible a vast storehouse of potential energy created by the sun over millions of years through the remains of compressed plants. Acid rain, greenhouse gases, climatic change, and many other environmental problems result directly from this transformation of the energy base of society from a renewable to a non-renewable one. In geological terms, we have released the energy input of millions of years in the blink of an eye—the past 250 years. Many current environmental problems are a result of this increase in entropy.

Energy Flows in Ecological Systems

Energy is the basis for all life. The source of virtually all this energy is the sun. More than 150 million kilometres away, the sun, a giant fireball of hydrogen and helium, continuously bombards the Earth with *radiant energy*. This energy, although it is only about 1/50 millionth of the sun's output, fuels our life-support system, creates our climate, and powers the cycles of matter discussed in Chapter 4. About a third of the energy received is reflected by the atmosphere back into space (Figure 2.1). Of the remainder, about 42 per cent provides heat to the Earth's surface, 23 per cent causes

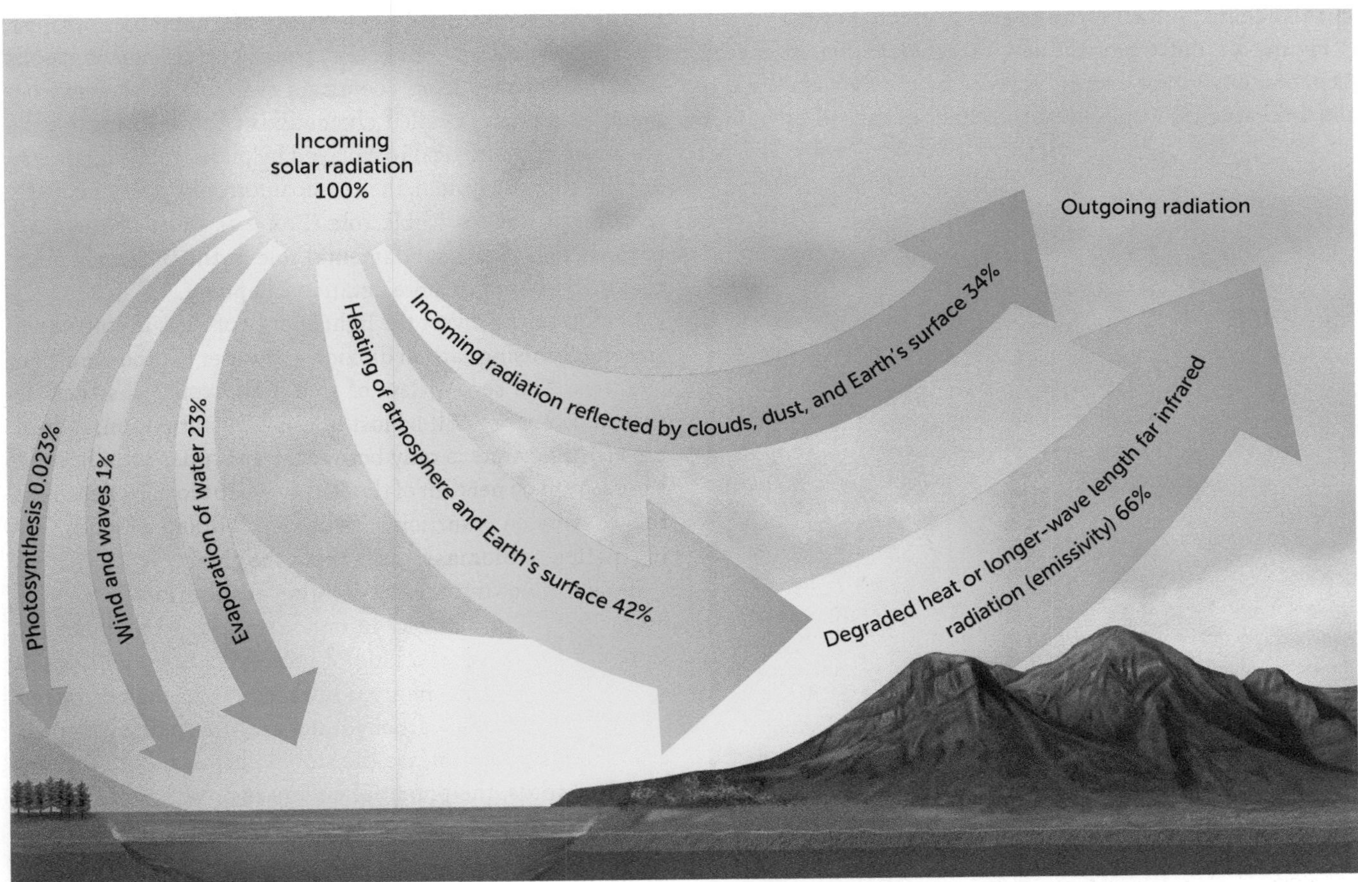

FIGURE 2.1 | The Earth's energy input and output, a good example of the first law of thermodynamics.

Plants that grow on the forest floor have differing strategies to obtain enough light to survive. Most, such as many ferns, can survive on relatively low light levels. Some, such as the devil's club shown here, grow very large leaves (over 40 centimetres wide for the devil's club) in order to expose as much photosynthetic surface as possible to the low light levels. The devil's club is a member of the ginseng family and well known among indigenous peoples in western North America for its medicinal properties.

evaporation of water, and less than 1 per cent forms the basis for our ecological systems. When we think of solar energy, it is important to remember not just the direct heat from the sun but also these indirect forms of energy created by heat input.

Figure 2.1 illustrates the law of conservation of energy. The total amount of energy received by the Earth is equal to the total amount lost. One of the changes caused by human activity is delaying the loss of heat to space by trapping it in the atmosphere through increased levels of heat-trapping gases such as carbon dioxide and methane. The mechanisms and implications of global climate change are discussed more fully in Chapter 7.

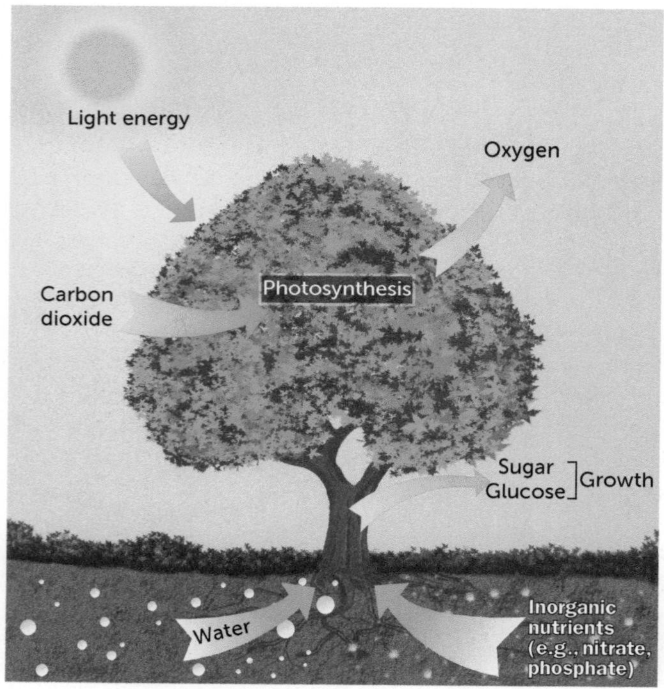

FIGURE 2.2 | The process of photosynthesis.

Producers and Consumers

The sun's energy is transformed into matter by plants through the process of **photosynthesis** (*photo* = light, *synthesis* = to put together). Through this process, plants combine carbon dioxide and water, using energy from the sun, into high-energy carbohydrates such as starches, cellulose, and sugars (Figure 2.2). Green pigments in the plants, called **chlorophylls**, absorb light energy from the sun. Photosynthesis also produces oxygen, some of which is used by plants in various metabolic processes. The rest goes into the atmosphere. Hundreds of millions of years of evolution have served to produce the oxygen in the atmosphere that we depend on for life.

Organisms with the ability to capture energy and manufacture matter are known as **autotrophs** (*auto* = self, *trophos* = feeding) or **producers**. All other organisms obtain their energy supply through eating other organisms and are known as **heterotrophs** (*heter* = different) or **consumers**. There are two kinds of autotrophs, **phototrophs** and **chemoautotrophs**. Phototrophs obtain their energy from light; chemoautotrophs gain their energy from chemicals available in the environment, in a process called chemotaxis. Although most of us are aware of the critical role played by phototrophs (plants) in our life-support system, the chemoautotrophs play an equally critical yet not so visible role (Box 2.2). Most of them are bacteria and play a fundamental role in the biogeochemical cycles, discussed in more detail in Chapter 4.

Phototrophs convert the light energy of the sun into chemical energy, using carbon dioxide and water to produce carbohydrates. The second law of thermodynamics instructs us that some energy will be lost in this transformation; indeed, the efficiency rate is only between 1 and 3 per cent. In other words, 97 to 99 per cent of the energy will be lost. Nonetheless, this conversion is sufficient to produce billions of tons of living matter, or **biomass**, throughout the globe.

Besides photosynthesis, **cellular respiration** is another essential energy pathway in organisms. In both plants and animals, this involves a kind of reversal of the photosynthesis process in which energy is released rather than captured. High-energy organic carbohydrates are broken down through a series of steps to release the stored chemical bond energy. In other words, the potential energy is now realized as kinetic energy in the way described above. This produces the inorganic molecules, carbon dioxide, water, heat (because of the law of entropy), and energy that can be used by the organism for various purposes, such as growth, feeding, seeking

Animals as different as the caterpillar and the elephant are on the same trophic level.

shelter, communicating with one another, producing seeds, and maintaining basic physiological functions such as constant body temperature and breathing. Since we are unable to obtain energy from photosynthesis or through chemotaxis, this is how we, and all other organisms unable to fix their own energy, get our energy supplies.

For cellular respiration to occur, most organisms must have access to oxygen or they will die. Such organisms are known as **aerobic** organisms. Some species, **anaerobic** organisms, such as some bacteria, can survive even without oxygen. This makes them useful in the breakdown of organic wastes, such as sewage.

ENVIRONMENT IN FOCUS

BOX 2.2 | Deep-Sea Life

We often think of the deep-sea floor as a biological desert. In the 1970s, however, scientists discovered that rich biological communities were supported at hydrothermal vents on the sea floor, mainly bacteria that derive their energy from sulphide emissions. Similar kinds of chemoautotrophic-based communities were discovered on whale skeletons found at depth, nourished by sulphides produced as the carcasses decay. Discoveries of fossils suggest that dead whales may have provided dispersal stepping stones for these communities for more than 30 million years. The question then becomes—what was the impact on these communities when whales were virtually eliminated from the oceans by whalers? Scientists do not yet have the answer to this question.

However, we do know that the biodiversity of the sea floor is much greater than imagined and may equal that of shallow-water tropical reefs. The deep-sea trenches are thought to be especially rich in microbe biodiversity because they serve as collecting grounds for organic matter, made up of dead animals, algae, and other microbes, sourced from the surrounding areas. The trenches cover only a small area of the ocean but have a disproportionate importance on the marine carbon balance, a topic discussed in more detail in Chapter 8. In addition to microbes, other deep-sea forms of life have been discovered: an expedition to the deepest trench in the world, the Mariana Trench, east of the Philippines, photographed a new species of snail fish at 8,143 metres deep. The white translucent fish has broad wing-like fins and an eel-like tail and slowly glides over the bottom. The sea floor also contains many other habitats, including cold seeps, seamounts, submarine canyons, abyssal plains, other oceanic trenches, and asphalt volcanoes, sure to contain a large number of **endemic species**, with total numbers perhaps as high as 10 million.

Although seemingly far removed from human activities, deep seabeds are threatened by many of them, including pollution, mining, shipping, military operations, and climate change. Deep-sea bottom trawling is a major concern and very damaging to seamounts and the cold-water corals they sustain. These habitats are home to several commercial

Continued

bottom-dwelling fish species. Seamounts are also important spawning and feeding grounds for species such as marine mammals, sharks, and tuna, which makes them very attractive fishing grounds. Deep-sea fish are particularly vulnerable to large-scale fishing activities because of their long life cycles and slow sexual maturation. Lack of information on deep-sea environments and their species makes it difficult to establish whether sustainable fisheries can take place.

One way to protect such environments is by establishing marine protected areas (MPAs), as discussed in Chapters 8 and 14. Canada has designated Sable Gully, the largest underwater canyon in eastern Canada, as an MPA. The gully is located approximately 200 kilometres off the coast of Nova Scotia at the edge of the Scotian Shelf, where the sea floor suddenly drops by more than 2 kilometres. More than 70 kilometres long and 20 kilometres wide, this area is home to many interesting and unusual species. The gully is a productive ecosystem that supports a diversity of marine organisms. The world's deepest-diving whale, the bottlenose whale, is a "vulnerable" species, according to the Committee on the Status of Endangered Wildlife in Canada, that lives in the gully year round. Fin whales and northwest Atlantic blue whales, both also classified as "vulnerable" (Chapter 14), make use of the gully throughout the year. Deep-sea corals are a significant feature of the benthic fauna in the area, and nine species are confirmed to live in the gully. MPA regulations prohibit disturbing, damaging, destroying, or removing any living marine organism or habitat within the gully. The MPA contains three management zones, providing varying levels of protection based on conservation objectives and ecological sensitivities. The regulations also control human activities in areas around the gully that could cause harm within the MPA boundary.

Food Chains

Some of the energy captured by autotrophs is subsequently passed on to other organisms, the consumers, by means of a **food chain** (Figure 2.3). **Herbivores** eat the producers and are in turn the source of energy for higher-level consumers, or **carnivores** (Box 2.3). Decomposers will feed on all these organisms after they die. Each level of the food chain is known as a **trophic level**. A giant Douglas fir tree on the Pacific coast and a minute Arctic flower on Baffin Island are on the same trophic level—autotrophs. Herbivores, on the second level, range in size from elephants to locusts. The role in energy transformation, rather than the size of the organism, is the important factor in determining trophic level.

Some organisms, such as humans, raccoons, sea anemones, and cockroaches, are **omnivores** and can obtain their energy from different trophic levels. When we eat vegetables, we are acting as **primary consumers**; when we eat beef, we are at

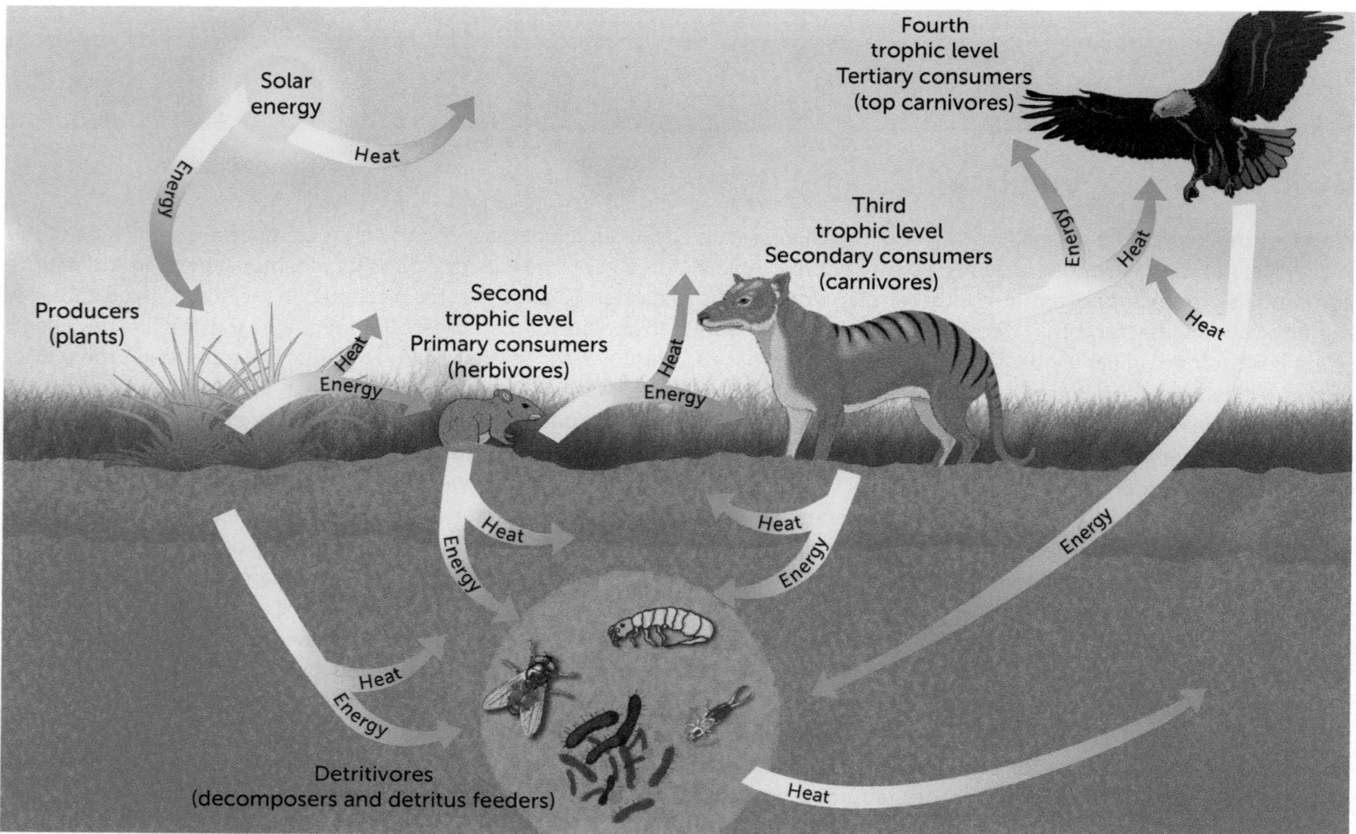

FIGURE 2.3 | A food chain.

ENVIRONMENT IN FOCUS

BOX 2.3 | Carnivorous Plants

Not all plants are autotrophs. Carnivorous plants, such as the pitcher plant, the floral emblem of Newfoundland and Labrador, gain their energy from ingesting the bodies of insects that become trapped in their funnel-shaped leaves. The plant, which grows in boggy areas across Canada, has no photosynthetic surfaces. Instead, the leaves act as "pitchers" to hold a soapy liquid from which a hapless insect cannot escape. The plant may be aided in the decomposition of dead insects by other insects that have developed immunities to the decomposing enzymes produced by the plant. The plant plays host to several insects that seem to thrive on the environment it provides. This is an example of **mutualism** in which both species benefit from a relationship.

Pitcher plant godrick/iStockphoto

The carnivorous pitcher plant, the provincial flower of Newfoundland and Labrador, grows in abundance in eastern Canada.

the second trophic level, acting as **secondary consumers**; and when we eat fish that have derived their energy from eating smaller organisms, we may be **tertiary consumers** at the top of the food chain. The level at which food energy is obtained has some important implications, to be discussed later.

We tend to concentrate on these **grazing food chains**, but equally important are the **decomposer food chains** (Figure 2.4). Overall, some 80 per cent of the annually produced plant biomass cycles through the detritus chain rather than being consumed by herbivores. These chains are based on dead organic material or **detritus**, which is high in potential energy but difficult to digest for the consumer organisms described above. However, various species of micro-organisms, bacteria, and fungi are able to digest this material as

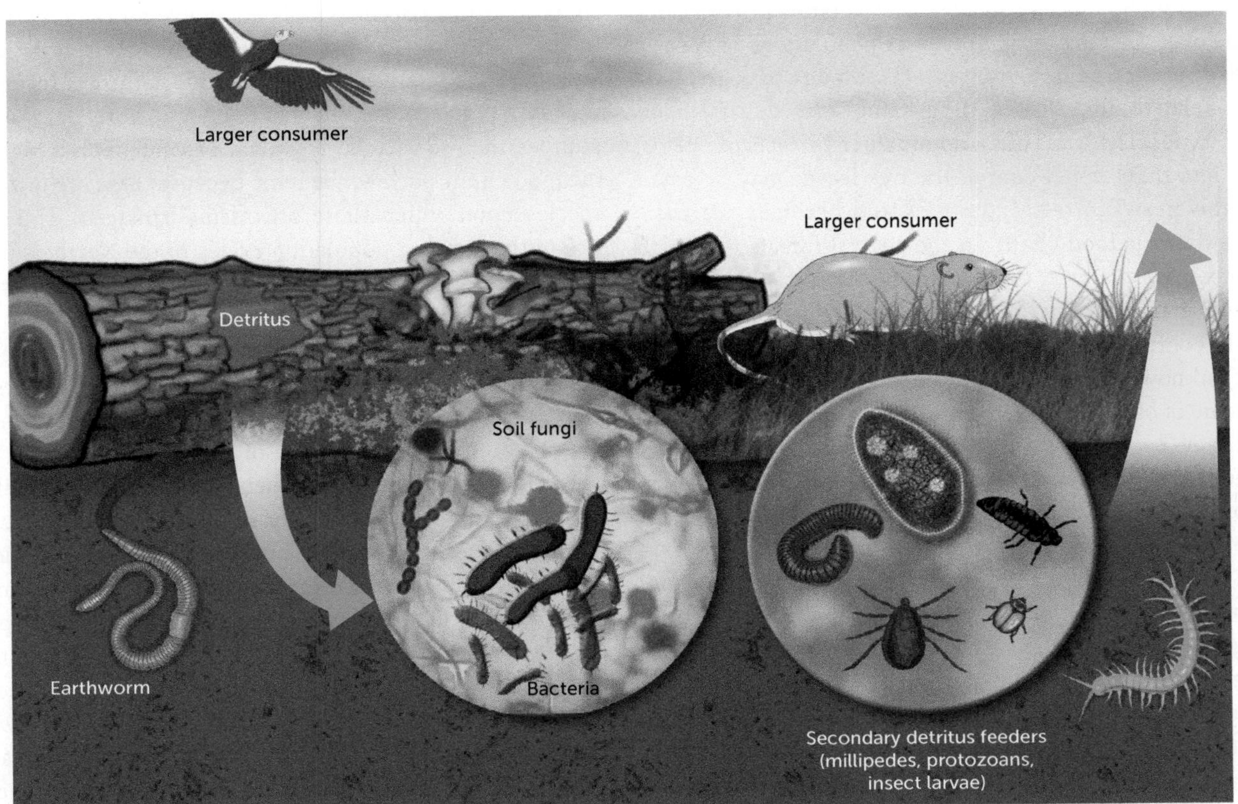

FIGURE 2.4 | Detritus-based food chain.

their source of energy. Indeed, many large grazing animals such as cows and moose have such bacteria in their stomachs to help break down the cellulose in plant material. These decomposers (or saprotrophs) derive their energy from dead matter (*sapro* = putrid). They are joined by consumers such as earthworms and marsh crabs, known as detritivores, which may consume both plant and animal remains.

A decomposer food chain plays an integral role in breaking down plant and animal material into products such as carbon dioxide, water, and inorganic forms of phosphorus and nitrogen and other elements. For example, fungi that consume simple carbohydrates, such as glucose, first break down dead wood. Following this phase, other fungi, bacteria, and organisms such as termites break down the cellulose that is the main constituent of the wood. Were it not for these organisms, wood and other dead organisms would accumulate indefinitely on the forest floor.

As will be discussed in more detail in Chapter 4, detritus plays a major role in ecosystem processes as a source of nutrients and within and between ecosystem transfers of energy and matter. Overall plant biomass exceeds animal biomass by a factor of 10, and hence plant biomass has received a lot of attention in this regard. However, in certain ecosystems animal detritus is a main factor in nutrient supply, and scientists are only beginning to understand the importance of, for example, dead salmon to the health of west coast rain forests in British Columbia. When these nutrient flows are reduced, through large-scale fishing, for example, the repercussions are felt throughout the ecosystem as vegetative growth rates decline over the long term, as well as populations of species higher on the food chain, from insects through to bears.

The relative importance of grazing and detrital food chains varies. The latter often dominate in forest ecosystems, where less than 10 per cent of the tree leaves may be eaten by herbivores. The remainder dies and becomes the basis for the detritus food chain. In the coastal forests of British Columbia, for example, there are some 140 different species of birds, mammals, and reptiles through which energy can flow. In contrast, more than 8,000 known species, as well as many unknown, are involved in breaking down the soil litter. The same is often true in freshwater aquatic systems, where there may be relatively little plant growth but abundant detritus from overhanging leaves and dead insects. However, the converse is true in marine ecosystems (see Box 2.4), where 90 per cent of the photosynthetic **phytoplankton** (*phyto* = plant, *plankton* = floating) may be grazed by the primary consumers, the **zooplankton**.

In general, ecological theory suggests that the more species in the ecosystem, the more alternative pathways are available for energy flow, and the better able the ecosystem is to withstand stress and thereby be resilient. In the Arctic, for example, a simple food chain might be phytoplankton to zooplankton to cod to ringed seal to polar bear. All these species heavily depend on the species at the preceding trophic level. Were one of these species to be drastically reduced in number or made extinct, the chances of the role of that species being compensated for by other species is low, and the whole food chain might well collapse. This situation can be compared to that at the other extreme, such as a tropical forest, where there are many times more species and the chance of other species combining to fulfill the ecological role of a depleted one is much higher. This situation is sometimes referred to as **ecological redundancy** or **functional compensation**, and it assumes that a given role in an ecosystem can be played by more than one species. A competing idea is that species can be likened to the rivets holding an airplane together. Just as the loss of species through extinction increasingly endangers an ecosystem—or the planet as a whole—so the likelihood of the plane in flight disintegrating increases as rivets are lost because no rivets can replace them. In practice, however, many factors are involved, such as the relative degree of specialization of the various organisms. In some ecosystems there may be examples of functional compensation; others will tend more toward rivet-popping. In general, functional compensation will help build resilience, but care must be exercised before generalizing the theory to all ecological systems.

Rarely are food chains organized in the simple manner shown in Figure 2.3. Usually, there are many competing organisms and energy paths representing **food webs** rather than simple food chains (Figure 2.6).

The number of species increases from the poles to the tropics as conditions become more amenable for life (Figure 2.7). In the Arctic, for example, there are relatively few species and therefore relatively few alternative pathways for energy flow. If a prey species, such as the Arctic hare, decreases in number, then so will the organism dependent on it higher in the food chain, such as the lynx, because there are few other species upon which these organisms can feed. This gives rise to the familiar population cycles in the North as predator numbers closely reflect the availability of dominant prey species (Figure 2.8).

Some ecosystems seem to be dominantly controlled by prey populations (**bottom-up control**) whereas others are more influenced by predators (**top-down control**). In the latter, predators restrict the size of the prey population. This seems to occur, for example, when wolves control deer, elk, or moose populations. Conversely, in some systems, the quality of available forage limits the number of herbivores, which in turn limits the number of predators. The predator numbers are essentially limited by the energy flow through the previous trophic levels. If herbivore populations fall as a result of disease or lack of forage, this will result in a drop in predator populations because of a lack of food. Ecosystems in which controls are dominantly bottom-up tend to have marked limits on plant productivity through abiotic factors, such as low nutrient supply, lack of water, and similar factors, or very

ENVIRONMENT IN FOCUS

BOX 2.4 | Oceanic Ecosystems

From space, the Earth appears to be a blue, not a green, planet, reflecting the fact that 71 per cent of the Earth's surface is covered by oceans. Life originated in this blueness, perhaps 3.5 billion years ago, and only came onto land some 450 million years ago. Hence, much of our biological ancestry lies within these waters. Although we know about more different species on land than in the oceans, the number of phyla, distinguished by differences in fundamental body characteristics, is higher in the oceans. Of the 33 different animal phyla, for example, 15 exist exclusively in the ocean, and only one is exclusively land based. We share the same phylum as the fishes, the chordata, characterized by a flexible spinal cord and complex nervous system.

Through their photosynthetic activity, the early bacteria that started in the oceans helped to create the conditions under which the rest of life evolved. Current photosynthetic activity is no less important to our survival.

Scientists estimate that the phytoplankton in the sunlit or **euphotic zone** of the oceans (10 metres to 200 metres in depth) produce between one-third and one-half of the global oxygen supply. In doing so, they also extract carbon dioxide from the atmosphere. Some 90 per cent of this is recycled through marine food webs, but some also falls into the deep ocean as the detritus of decaying organisms and is stored as dissolved carbon dioxide in deep ocean currents that may take more than 1,000 years to reappear at the surface. The oceans contain at least 50 times as much gas as the atmosphere and are playing a critical role in helping to delay the so-called greenhouse effect, discussed in more detail in Chapters 7 and 8.

These phytoplankton, so important to atmospheric regulation, are also the main autotrophic base for the marine food web. From tiny zooplankton through to the great whales, almost every marine animal has phytoplankton to thank for its existence. Phytoplankton flourish best in areas where ocean currents return nutrients from the deep ocean back to the euphotic zone. This occurs in shallow areas, such as the Grand Banks near Newfoundland, where deep ocean currents meet the coast or where two deep currents meet head on. Such areas are the most productive in what is generally an unproductive ocean, and they are the best sites for fisheries. Ninety per cent of the marine fish catch comes from these fertile nearshore waters. Unfortunately, these waters are also the sites of greatest pollution. The blueness of most of the rest of the ocean is a visible sign of the low density of phytoplankton. That is why the sea is blue, not green.

Given the importance of plankton in marine ecosystems, it is disconcerting that scientists predict reductions in biomass

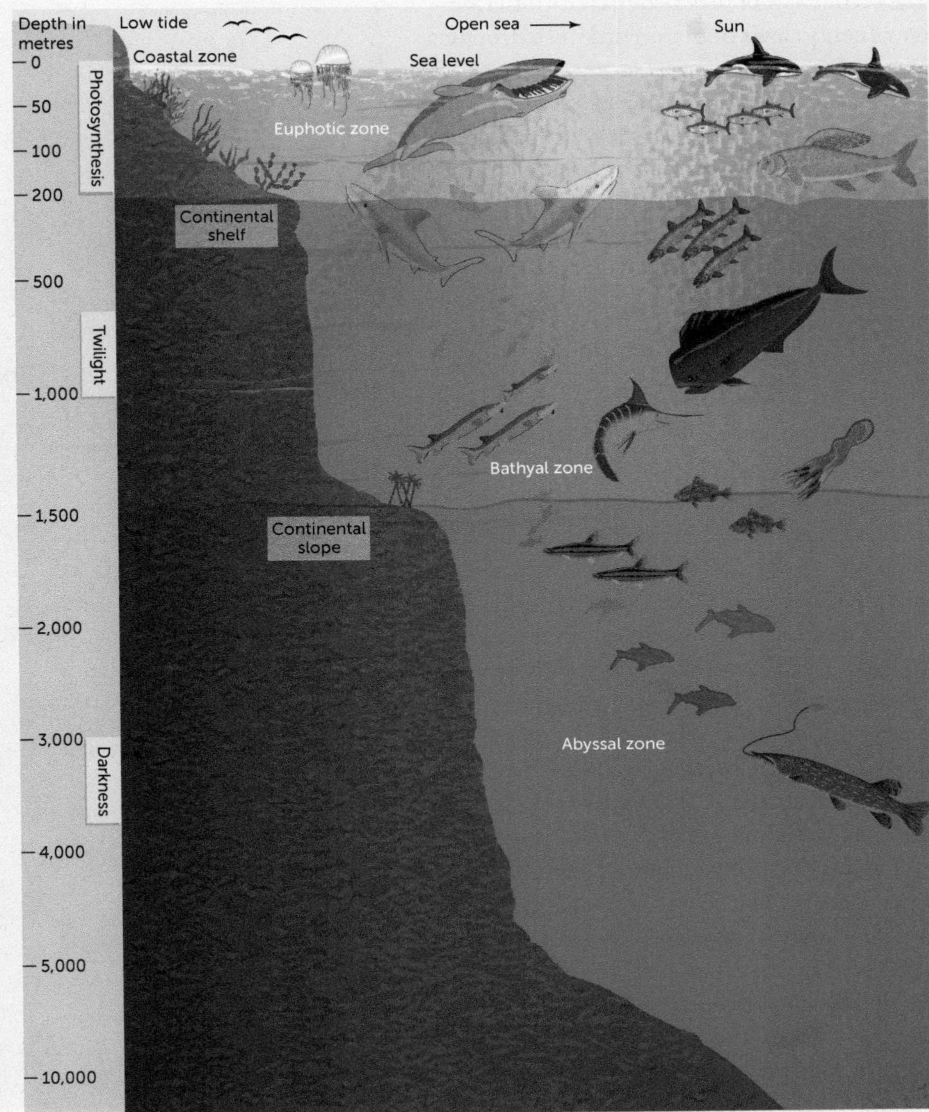

FIGURE 2.5 | Key elements of marine ecosystems.

Continued

as a result of increasing ocean temperatures associated with global climate change. If temperatures rise the predicted 2°C by 2080, this will cause greater oceanic stratification and affect nutrient supply to the plankton, resulting in an estimated 6 per cent decline in phytoplankton and an 11 per cent decline in zooplankton. The trophic amplification will be duplicated through the food webs and have serious consequences for marine ecosystem productivity. The changes are expected to be especially apparent in tropical oceans, where many poor people depend on fishing for their sustenance.

close relationships between a specific plant, a herbivore, and a carnivore. Ecosystems reflecting top-down control typically lack these features. However, as with most ecological phenomena, these are general guidelines—most ecosystems contain elements of both top-down and bottom-up control.

Biotic Pyramids

The second law of thermodynamics describes how energy flows from trophic level to trophic level, with a loss of usable energy at each succeeding transformation. In natural food chains, the **energy efficiency**—the amount of a system's total energy input that is transformed into work or some other usable form of energy—may be as low as 1 per cent. In general, we expect about 90 per cent of the energy to be lost at each level (Figure 2.9). Similar losses may be experienced in biomass and numbers of organisms at each trophic level. This explains why there are fewer secondary than primary consumers and fewer tertiary than secondary. Carnivores must always have the lowest numbers in an ecosystem in order to be supported by the energy base below. The case of the Atlantic puffins, described in the introduction to this chapter, provides a good example. The biomass of carnivores (puffins) could no longer be supported by the energy from the preceding trophic level, the capelin. Species at the very top of the food chain are known as **apex predators** (see the "International Guest Statement" by Anak Pattanavibool) and are especially vulnerable to changes that occur at lower trophic levels.

Some ecosystems, however, may display an inverted **biomass pyramid**. In natural grasslands such as those in southern Saskatchewan, the dominant species, such as grasshoppers, are small-bodied and do not have a large biomass. In contrast, many herbivores in this system, such as antelope and mule deer, are large bodied and long lived, with a large total biomass. The same situation exists in the oceans,

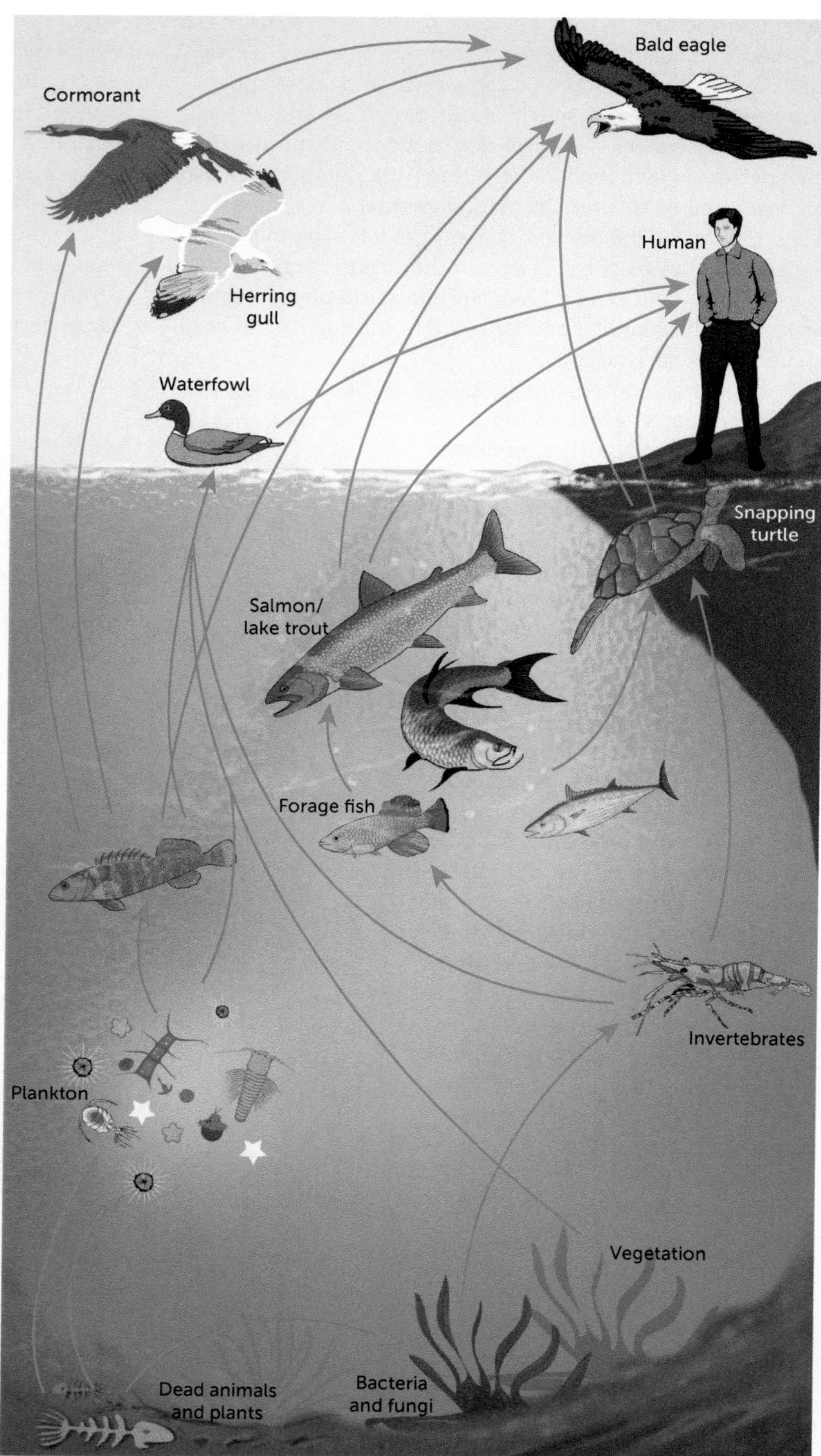

FIGURE 2.6 | A simplified Great Lakes food web.

Source: Adapted from Environment Canada (1991a).

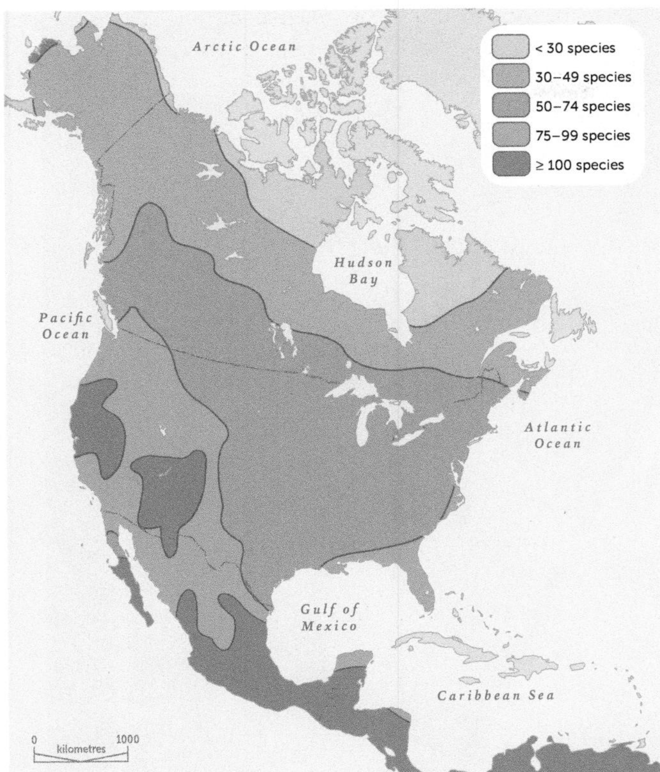

FIGURE 2.7 | The number of mammal species per latitude.

Source: After Simpson (1964).

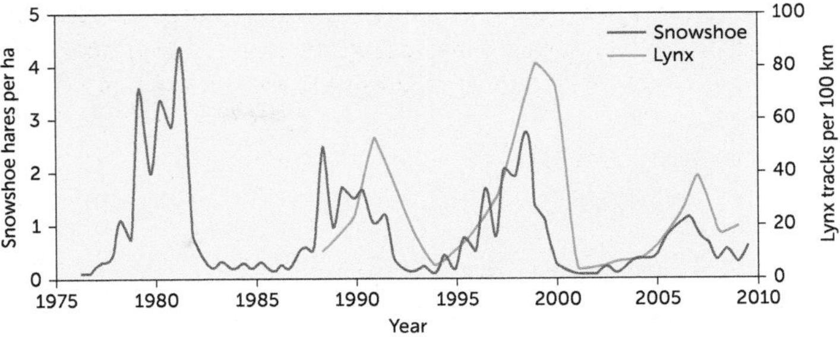

FIGURE 2.8 | Snowshoe hare and lynx cycles, boreal forest, Kluane, Yukon.

Source: Federal, Provincial, and Territorial Governments of Canada (2010: 101).

discussed in more detail in Chapter 8. However, in both cases, the productivity of the plant base is much greater than that of the herbivores.

Several reasons exist for the low energy efficiencies of natural food chains. First, not all the biomass at each trophic level is converted into food for the next trophic level. Many organisms have developed characteristics to avoid being eaten by something else. For example, many plant species have thorns or produce secondary chemicals to deter herbivores. Others have low nutritive levels. Generally, only between 10 and 20 per cent of the biomass of one trophic level is harvested by the next level. Furthermore, of that which is consumed, not all is digested. Humans, for example, are not well equipped to break down and consume the bones or fur of animals, nor are they equipped, compared to moose and other members of the deer family, to break down woody tissue. The proportion of ingested energy actually absorbed by an organism is the **assimilated food energy.** Finally, as cellular respiration occurs to liberate energy for the growth, maintenance, and reproduction of the organism, energy is further released as heat.

The longer the food chain, the more inefficient it is in terms of energy transformation, reflecting the second law of thermodynamics. An Arctic marine food chain that starts from the producers (phytoplankton) to primary consumers (zooplankton) that are subsequently grazed by the largest animals ever to exist on Earth (whales) is very efficient because it is so short, with only three energy transformations in which energy is lost. Longer food chains involve a proportionately larger loss of energy because of the greater number of energy transformations. Entropy dictates that long food chains with five or six trophic levels, such as that supporting a killer whale, are very scarce.

The energy pyramid also has important implications for humans. For example, it takes between 8 and 16 kilograms of grain to produce 1 kilogram of beef. This means that more land must be cultivated to provide people with a diet high in meat as opposed to a diet based on grains. Since humans are one of the species that can access food energy at several different trophic levels, in terms of energy efficiency it would be better to operate as low on the food chain as possible—that is, as primary consumers or vegetarians. This topic is discussed in more detail in Chapter 10.

Productivity

Productivity in ecosystems is measured by the rate at which energy is transformed into biomass, or living matter, and is usually expressed in terms of kilocalories per square metre per year. In terrestrial ecosystems, the large majority of production comes from vascular plants, with much smaller amounts from algae, mosses, and liverworts. In the oceans, most production comes from algae, although some vascular plants, such as sea grasses, have been found to have very high rates of production and sequestration of carbon. **Gross primary productivity (GPP)** is the overall rate of biomass production, but there is an energy cost to capturing this energy. This cost, cellular respiration (R), must be subtracted from the GPP to reveal the **net primary productivity (NPP).** This is the amount of energy available to heterotrophs.

All ecosystems are not equal in their ability to fix biomass. Light levels, nutrient availability, temperature, and moisture, among other factors, regulate the rates of photosynthesis (see Box 2.5). The most productive ecosystems per unit area are **estuaries**, swamps and marshes, and tropical rain forests (Figure 2.10). Recent data indicate that the temperate rain forests, such as those in the Pacific Maritime ecozone, are just as

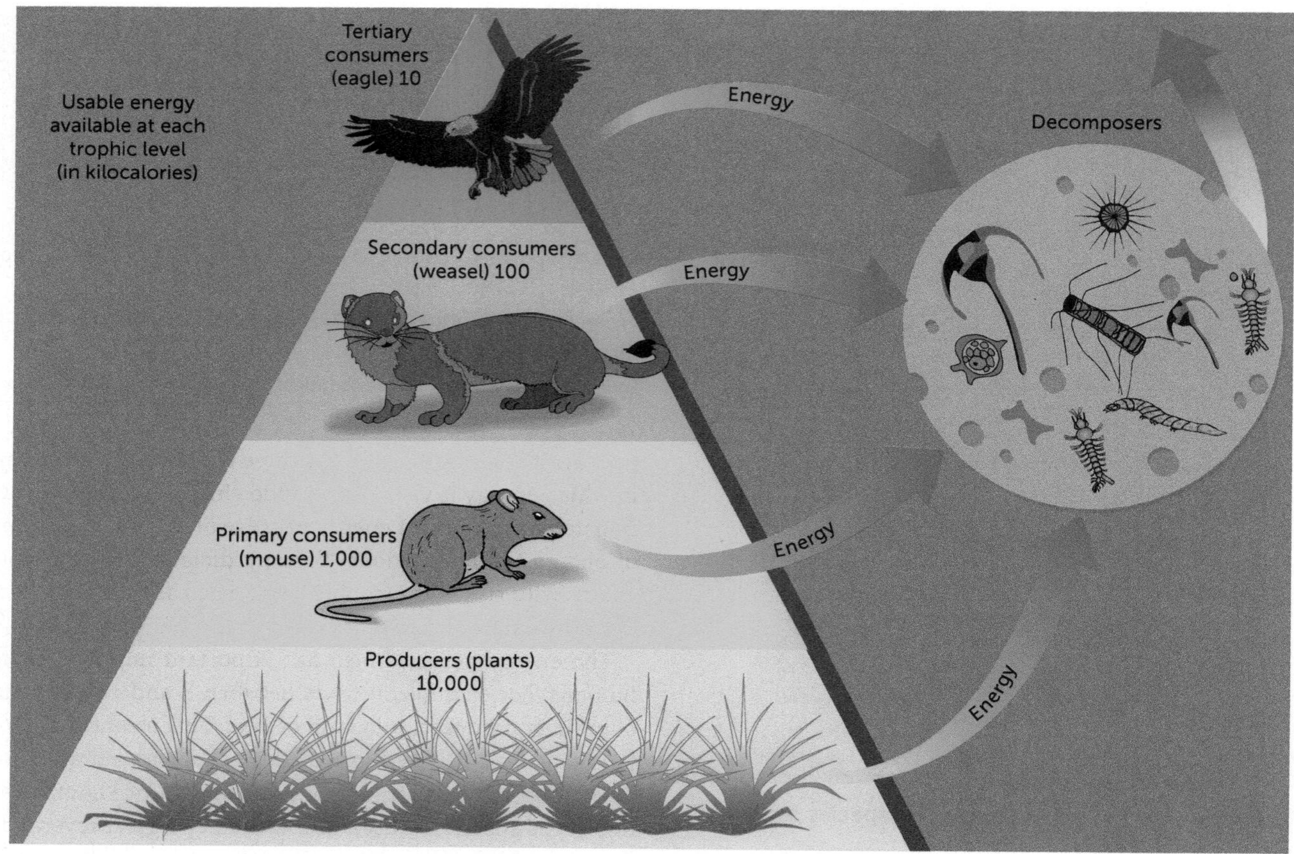

FIGURE 2.9 | Generalized pyramid of energy flow.

Apex Predators and Tiger Conservation in Thailand | *Anak Pattanavibool*

Apex predators are at the top of the food chain. They are vulnerable to any changes in the trophic levels below them, but can also exert a controlling influence on all trophic levels. Their influence on other trophic levels is often recognized as a **trophic cascade**. One of the best-known examples is the reintroduction of wolves into Yellowstone National Park, which resulted in changes in behaviour of their main prey species, the elk, which in turn resulted in changes in the vegetation of the park. The same relationship has been noted in Banff National Park with the decline in wolf populations having impacts throughout the ecosystem.

As super-predators, when no other species preys upon them except humans, apex predators often come into conflict with humans. In marine ecosystems, apex predators are often considered to be at or above the fourth trophic level. However, in terrestrial ecosystems, the third trophic level is where the big cats, wolves, crocodiles, and hyenas are located. The polar bear is the largest terrestrial predator, but an equally iconic apex predator is the tiger. Long the recipient of international funding and conservation attention, the tiger continues to decline in range and abundance.

The tiger is the pride of Asia's natural heritage. They used to roam across Asia from the Middle East to Southeast Asia and from the Russian Far East south to Indonesia. They are endangered because of the clash with human civilizations and exploitation. At the beginning of the twentieth century, approximately 100,000 tigers existed across Asia. By 2010 the global population had declined to about 3,500 individuals. The habitat remaining is only 7 per cent of its historical range. Most breeding populations are in the Indian subcontinent, including India, Nepal, and Bangladesh. In Southeast Asia, breeding populations are restricted to either very large or well-protected landscapes (Walston et al., 2010).

In Thailand, an estimated 200–250 wild tigers are scattered in protected areas, which cover about 25 per cent of the country's land area. Most of the remaining tigers exist in small numbers in heavily fragmented landscapes. Only one place in Thailand, as detailed below, now contains a breeding population of over 100 tigers.

Tigers face three major threats: (1) direct poaching for tiger body parts and traditional Chinese medicines; (2) poaching of their main prey species, particularly sambar, gaur, and banteng; and (3) habitat alteration from forest to agricultural landscapes. In Thailand, most primary forests have been fragmented. Furthermore, poaching still penetrates deep inside many protected areas. Tigers and other large animals have therefore been either wiped out or severely depleted from many protected areas due to poaching and fragmentation (Lynam, 2010). Tigers will survive in ecologically functioning numbers only in areas with strong law enforcement. In India, tigers remain only in well-guarded national parks. The extirpation of tigers from famous Indian tiger reserves in the early 2000s (e.g., Sariska and Panha National Parks) happened mainly because of inadequate protection. Biologists are now finding out just how hard it is to reintroduce tigers once they are extirpated from an area.

In Thailand, the situation is desperate. Half of the country's tiger population exists in a large (18,000 km^2) and well-guarded forest landscape named the Western Forest Complex (WEFCOM). More than 2,000 guards are stationed in over 200 locations to protect the area. However, the large number of guards will not guarantee the safety of tigers and other wildlife. Many times they lack the capacity and law enforcement training to cope with the poaching pressure. Therefore, a program has been created to monitor the performance of park guards. Currently, park guards in WEFCOM use a "Smart" patrol system, which involves a suite of implementation components necessary for effective law enforcement, including strategic planning, adequate training, sufficient staff levels, equipment and other resource needs, standardized law enforcement (LEM) protocols, and full integration of LEM data into an adaptive management cycle where results are used systematically to improve management practices. An effective Smart patrol promotes "good governance" and "best practice" by empowering park guards to engage fully in decision-making processes with park managers (Department of National Parks, Wildlife and Plant Conservation, 2013).

Wildlife scientists now use camera traps as a reliable method to count tigers, based on the fact that each individual tiger has a unique stripe pattern. With this technology, scientists can estimate the number of tigers more precisely and reliably than previously. In WEFCOM, the tigers are now monitored annually with camera trapping and capture analysis, a methodology that has revealed about 100 tigers.

Courtesy Anak Pattanavibool

Tigers at Huai Kha Khaeng Wildlife Sanctuary.

Very few species can have as great an impact on conservation policy and actions as tigers. Since 2010, global leaders from governments, non-governmental organizations (NGOs), and various other organizations have met several times to discuss how to save and recover tigers. Each of the 13 tiger-range countries has completed national tiger action plans. India and Nepal have proved their intent to recover tiger populations by significant improvement in protected area management and enforcement. In Thailand's WEFCOM, tiger numbers in the core area have been gradually increasing, and there is evidence that tigers have dispersed into other protected areas on the perimeter. This recovery pattern confirms the importance of preserving habitat for future use.

An additional challenge for WEFCOM is that it is located on the border with Myanmar. Both countries need to work together to reduce impacts from future development projects (e.g., roads, dams) that will fragment the tiger habitat. People have to understand the long-term benefits of conserving tigers as a key part of the ecosystem for this and future generations.

Courtesy Anak Pattanavibool

Dr Anak Pattanavibool is director of the Wildlife Conservation Society in Thailand and a lecturer in the Department of Conservation at Kasetsart University in Bangkok.

productive as the tropical forests. Other ecosystems are more limited because of deficiencies in one or more of the characteristics noted above. A desert, for example, lacks water, the Arctic lacks heat, and the ocean lacks nutrients.

In Canada some of our most highly industrialized and polluted lands are adjacent to estuaries. These sites are highly desirable with access to both ocean transport and fresh water. Many industries were preferentially located at these sites when there was little realization of the critical ecological role played by estuaries. However, one estuary, the Musquash in the Bay of Fundy, should experience reduced degradation in the future. It has been declared a marine protected area under Canada's Oceans Act (Chapter 8), and one of the main characteristics noted for its designation was its high productivity. It

ENVIRONMENT IN FOCUS

BOX 2.5 | The Iron Experiment

The village of Old Massett on Haida Gwaii was thrust onto the international stage in 2012 as it made headlines in international newspapers and received condemnation from UN bodies. The source of the unwanted fame was an experiment conducted there, designed by a US entrepreneur and implemented by the Haida Salmon Restoration Corporation to boost the productivity of the Pacific Ocean off Haida Gwaii at a time when juvenile salmon were in the area. They did this by dumping into the ocean more than 100 tonnes of iron dust, made up of iron sulphate fertilizer and iron oxide, over about 1 km^2 about 300 kilometres west of the islands.

Iron is often a dominant limiting factor in oceanic ecosystems, and adding iron was expected to produce a phytoplankton bloom (which it did, of about 10,000 km^2,) and have repercussions throughout the food chain that would produce more food for the juvenile salmon and improve their survival rate. It was also hoped that the experiment would generate funds by capturing carbon in a developing international carbon market. Carbon is soaked up by the phytoplankton, and other organisms feed off the plankton, die, sink to the ocean's bottom, and sequester the carbon. But the international carbon trading market has yet to develop adequately to permit this kind of trading.

Unfortunately, there are many other scientific complications from this sequence, complications not taken into account, and national and international scientists were unanimous in condemning the experiment. Delegates in a meeting of the United Nations' International Maritime Organization publicly condemned the experiment as "irresponsible." The experiment violated international anti-dumping laws, and there were calls for the perpetrators to be prosecuted, but in the end no action was taken.

is among the few remaining ecologically intact estuaries in a region that has seen extensive modification of its salt marshes.

Between 1985 and 2006, primary productivity increased markedly on over 22 per cent of Canada's vegetated surface and declined on only 1 per cent (Federal, Provincial, and Territorial Governments of Canada, 2010). The main growth areas are in the North, where global climate change has been most strongly felt and where successional processes, as discussed in the next chapter, appear to be accelerating. Similar trends have occurred globally, where increases in tropical productivity are attributed to reduced cloud cover.

Humans take about 40 per cent of terrestrial NPP for their own use. The remainder supports all the other organisms on Earth, which in turn maintain the environmental conditions

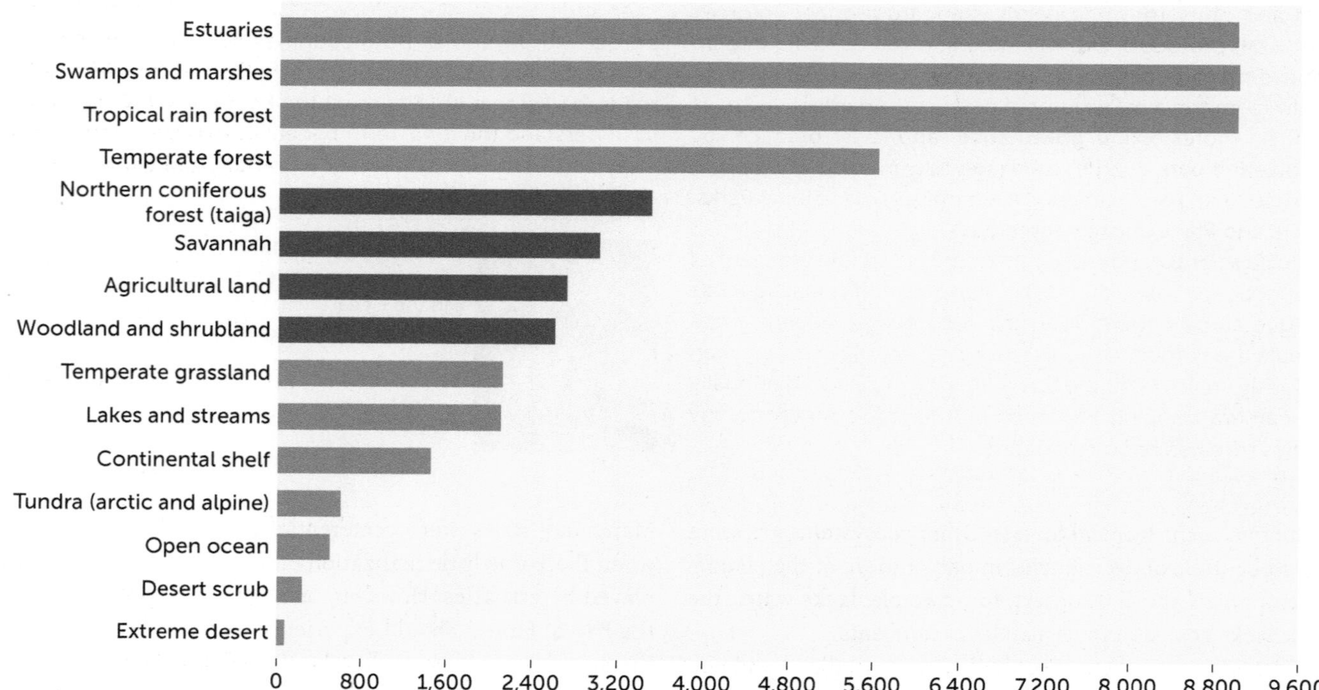

FIGURE 2.10 | Estimated annual average net productivity of producers per unit of area in principal types of life zones and ecosystems. Values are given in kilocalories of energy produced per square metre per year.

Estuaries are among the most productive ecosystems. Unfortunately, they are also very convenient sites for industrial activity, such as the log boom storage seen here in Campbell River, British Columbia, which inhibits productivity.

that keep us alive. The human population is projected to increase by about 40 per cent over the next 50 years, as discussed in Chapter 1. It is highly doubtful that the Earth's systems could withstand a concomitant increase in the amount of NPP being appropriated for human use—another illustration of the carrying capacity challenge we face.

In addition to primary productivity, we can measure **net community productivity (NCP)**, including heterotrophic and autotrophic respiration. Measurements indicate that as communities mature, although GPP and NPP rise, an increasing proportion of their energy is devoted to heterotrophic respiration. In mature communities, the amount of respiration may be sufficient to account for all the energy being fixed by photosynthesis. There is thus no net gain, leading to some foresters' characterization of such communities as "decadent" because they are mainly interested in the productivity of the autotrophs.

Over time, natural systems mature toward maximization of NCP. On the other hand, humans are often concerned with maximizing NPP. This is an example of the decision regulators discussed in Chapter 1. Natural forest system decision regulators may allow trees to achieve ages of several hundred to more than a thousand years before they die. The control system exerted by forest management determines that the life of the trees will be that which maximizes NPP, before considerable amounts of energy become devoted to heterotrophic respiration (Figure 2.11). The age of the trees in systems managed for forestry will hence be much younger than in natural systems.

Auxiliary energy flows allow some ecosystems and sites to be especially productive. For example, tidal energy in an estuary is a form of auxiliary energy flow that helps to bring in nutrients and dissipate wastes so that organisms do not have to expend energy on these tasks and can devote more energy to growth. Agriculture, as discussed in Chapter 10, relies extensively on the inputs of auxiliary energy in the form of pesticides, fertilizer, tractor fuel, and the like to supplement the natural energy from the sun to augment crop growth. In many cases, this subsidy, mostly derived from fossil fuels, exceeds the amount of energy input from the sun. Without this subsidy, productivity would be much reduced. There is a cost to the subsidy, however, in terms of high energy costs and the environmental externalities created as the subsidy disperses into the environment in the form of pollution.

Ecosystem Structure

The energy flows described above are all part of the ecosphere. The ecosphere can be broken down in size to smaller units. At the smallest level is the individual **organism**. A group of individuals of the same species is a **population**. The populations in a particular environment are known as a **community**. The **ecosystem** is a collection of communities interacting with the physical environment. However, ecosystems represent a somewhat abstract conceptualization of the

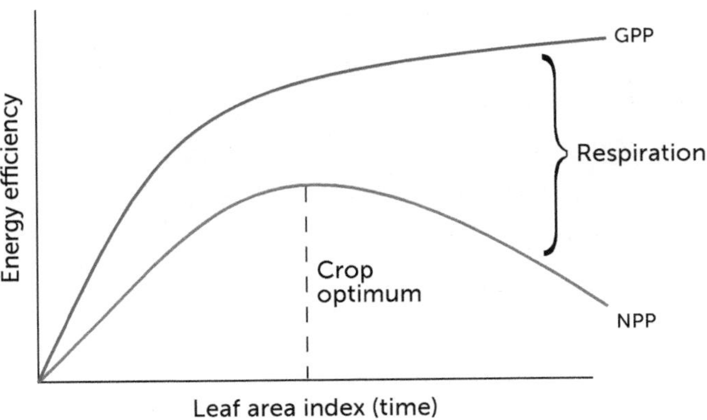

FIGURE 2.11 | The general relationship between productivity and time as a forest matures. Foresters might consider the optimal stage of the forest to be at maximum NPP, even though GPP continues to increase over time.

environment that can range greatly in scale. Because of the highly interactive nature of the relationship between organisms and their environment, it is often difficult to define precisely the boundary of an ecosystem. Ecosystems are open systems and exchange material and organisms with other ecosystems. Ecosystems and communities thus provide useful abstractions for the study of the environment but should not be taken as precise categories that will be agreed upon by all scientists.

Similar ecosystems can be grouped together as ecozones, representing their dominant vegetation and animal communities. The main ecozones in Canada are shown in Figure 2.12. In turn, these can be grouped into the largest classification of life forms, **biomes**, based upon dominant vegetation and adaptations of other organisms to that particular environment. Globally, six main biomes are recognized: marine, freshwater, forest, grassland, desert, and tundra. Canada has as many biomes as any country in the world. The main factors that control biome distribution are water availability and temperature. Figure 2.13 summarizes how these factors influence biomes on the global scale.

Abiotic Components

The food chains described above constitute the living or **biotic components** of ecosystems. **Abiotic components** play an important role in determining how these biotic components are distributed. Important abiotic factors include light, temperature, wind, water, and soil characteristics such as pH, soil type, and nutrient status. All these factors influence different organisms in various ways. The interaction among these characteristics and the organisms and between the organisms themselves determines where each organism can grow and how well it may grow.

Soils are critical in determining the vegetation growth of an area (Box 2.6). Soil is a mixture of inorganic materials such as sand, clay, and pebbles; decaying organic matter such as leaves; water; and air. This mixture is home to billions of micro-organisms that are continuously modifying and developing the soil. In the absence of these organisms, Earth would be a sterile rock pile rather than a rich life-supporting environment. Most of these organisms are in the surface layer of the soil, and one teaspoon may contain hundreds of millions of

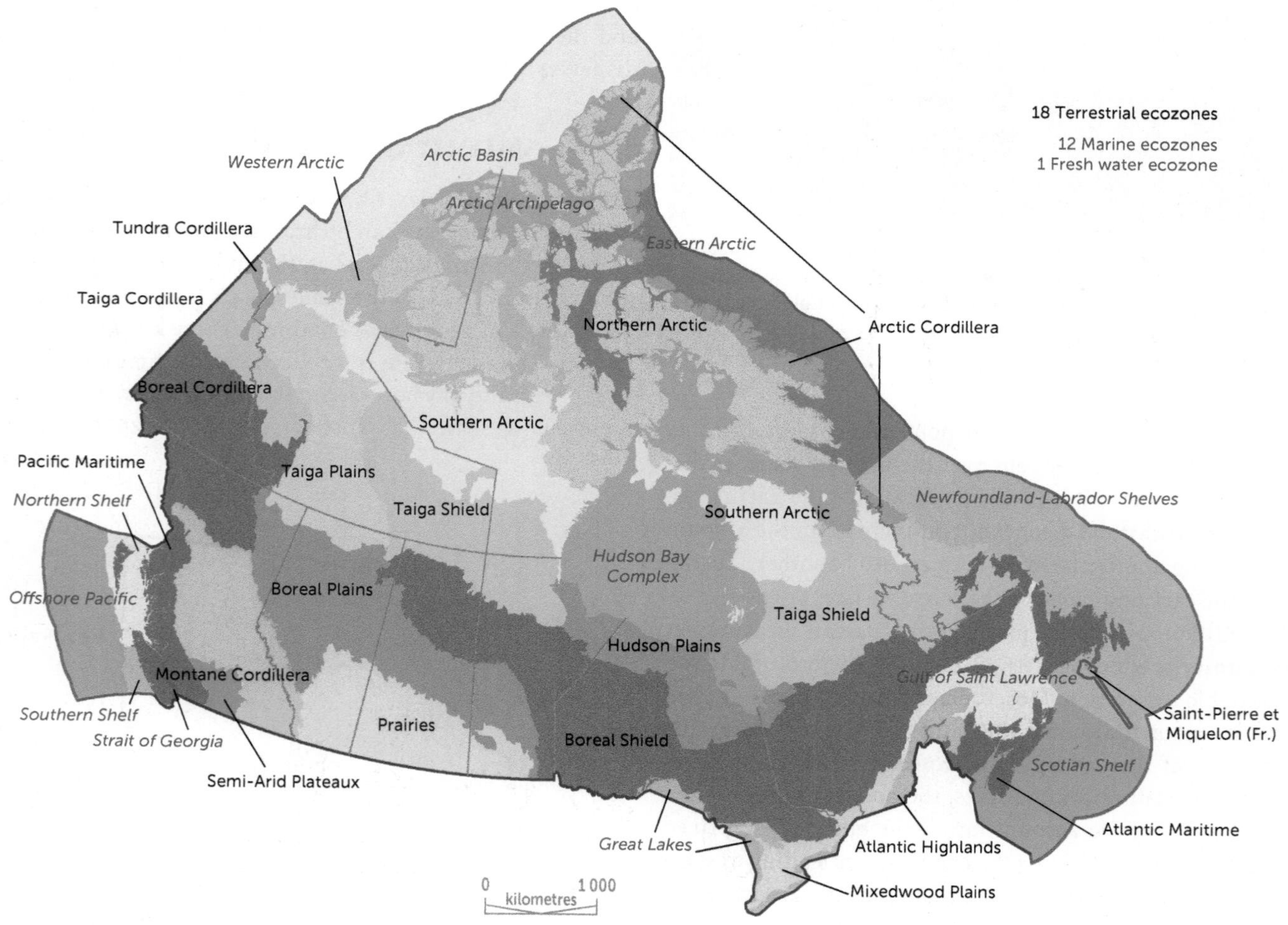

FIGURE 2.12 | Ecozones of Canada.

Source: Adapted from CCEA. http://ccea.org/Downloads/shapefiles/CA_ecozones_1M_v5_final_map%20v20140213.pdf

Average rainfall (centimetres per year)

120
110
100
90
80
70
60
50
40
30
20
10
0

Northern coniferous forest
Deciduous forest
Tropical rain forest
Polar grassland (tundra)
Temperate grassland
Tropical grassland (savannah)
Cool desert
Temperate desert
Tropical desert

Cool
Temperate
Hot

Average temperature

FIGURE 2.13 | Influence of temperature and rainfall on biome.

Philip Dearden

Philip Dearden

Tropical deserts are extreme environments with the hottest temperatures combined with the lowest precipitation in the world, resulting in no vegetation growth over wide areas. Animals that live there have special adaptations to these conditions. One example is the smallest canid in the world, the fennec fox, found in the North Sahara, and often sold as pets to visitors. The fox is nocturnal to avoid the heat of the day and has many internal adaptations to withstand the searing heat. The large ears help dissipate heat but are also crucial to the acute hearing of the fox which can hear the movements of prey species hiding under the sand. The fox is listed on the International Union for Conservation of Nature's Red List of endangered species (see Chapter 14).

bacteria, algae, and fungi. In addition, many larger species—roundworms, mites, millipedes, and insects—play vital roles in this complex ecology.

Most soils form from the **parent material** where they are found. This may originate from the weathered remains of bedrock or where sediments have been deposited from elsewhere by water, ice, landslides, or wind. Over centuries, ongoing physical and chemical weathering and organic activities modify this mixture. As the parent material breaks down, inorganic elements such as calcium, iron, manganese,

ENVIRONMENT IN FOCUS

BOX 2.6 | Soils in Canada

Just as we can define ecozones, soil scientists can define soil zones that group together soils that are relatively similar in terms of their measurable characteristics. A glance at the soil map of Canada (Figure 2.14) will reveal a close resemblance to the ecozone map, since at this scale both tend to reflect the gross climatic and geological conditions of the region. The Canadian System of Soil Classification includes nine orders, the largest category of classification:

Brunisols cover 8.6 per cent and are brown soils found mainly under forests.

Chernozems cover 5.1 per cent, occur under grasslands, and are some of the most productive soils.

Cryosols are the dominant soils in Canada, covering some 40 per cent of the country's land mass, and are found in association with permafrost.

Gleysols cover only 1.3 per cent and are found in areas that are often waterlogged.

Luvisols cover 8.8 per cent and occur in a wide variety of wooded ecosystems. They have higher clay content than brunisols.

Organics cover 4.1 per cent of Canada, and are formed in wetland ecosystems where decomposition rates are slow.

Podzols are found beneath heathlands and coniferous forests, are relatively nutrient poor, and cover 15.6 per cent of Canada.

Regosols cover less than 1 per cent of Canada and vary little from their parent material.

Solonets are saline soils, covering 0.7 per cent of Canada, and are found mostly in grassland ecosystems.

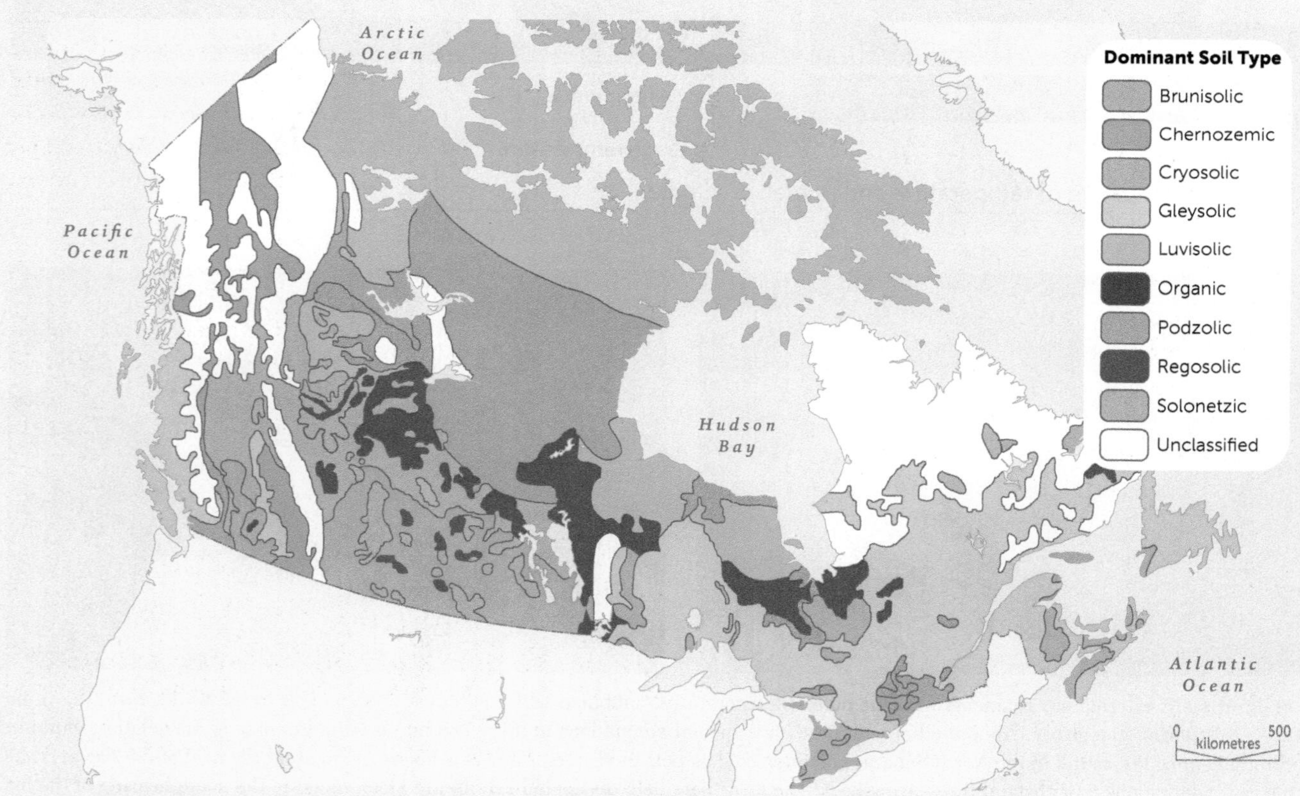

FIGURE 2.14 | Soil zones of Canada.

and phosphorus (Chapter 4) are released. The amount of nutrients in the material and the speed of breakdown are major influences on the fertility of the resulting soil; for example, hard rocks such as granite break down slowly and yield few nutrients. Different soils will thus result, depending on the location. These various processes result in different layers forming in the soil, called **soil horizons.** A view across these horizons is called a **soil profile**. Figure 2.15 shows a generalized profile. However, not all soils have all these different horizons.

Time is also a critical factor in soil development. Soils that have been exposed to millions of years of chemical and physical weathering, such as many tropical soils, have often lost their entire nutrient content. Conversely, where **glaciation** has scraped all the soil away, as in much of Canada as recently as 10,000 years ago, the hard rocks, such as the granite of the Canadian Shield, have had little opportunity for weathering. They are also infertile. However, soils can be very fertile where retreating ice sheets deposited large quantities of clay rich in nutrients, as on the Prairies.

Soils also differ in their texture, or sizes of different materials. Clay is the finest, followed by silt, sand, and then gravel, the coarsest. Soils that contain a mixture of all these with decomposed organic material, or **humus**, are called **loams** and often make the best soils for vegetation growth. Texture is a main determinant of **soil permeability**, or the rate at which water can move through the soil. Water moves very slowly through soils composed mainly of the smallest particles, clay, and the soil easily becomes waterlogged. On the other hand, the large spaces between particles of sand or gravel lead to rapid drainage, and the soils may be too dry to support good vegetation growth. Plants obtain their nutrient supply necessary for growth from ions dissolved in the soil water, and so permeability is critical.

Soil has many different chemical characteristics. One of the most important is the pH value (see Chapter 4), measuring the acidity/alkalinity of the soil, which helps to determine which minerals are available and in what form. Different plants have different mineral requirements. The pH is influenced by many factors including the parent material, type of vegetation, and hydrology. Atmospheric deposition can also be significant, both from natural and human sources. Even in relatively pristine areas, such as the southern Rocky Mountains, the deposition of nitrates and sulphates from the atmosphere is enough to have detrimental impacts on the sensitive alpine ecology (Wasiuta et al. 2015). At the other end of the landscape scale, on agricultural lands, farmers often try to change the acidity of their soils, for example, by adding lime if the soil is too acidic or sulphur if the soil is too alkaline.

Just as the laws of thermodynamics explain energy flows, some principles help us to understand how organisms react to different abiotic influences. The first of these is known as the **limiting factor** principle. This principle tells us that all

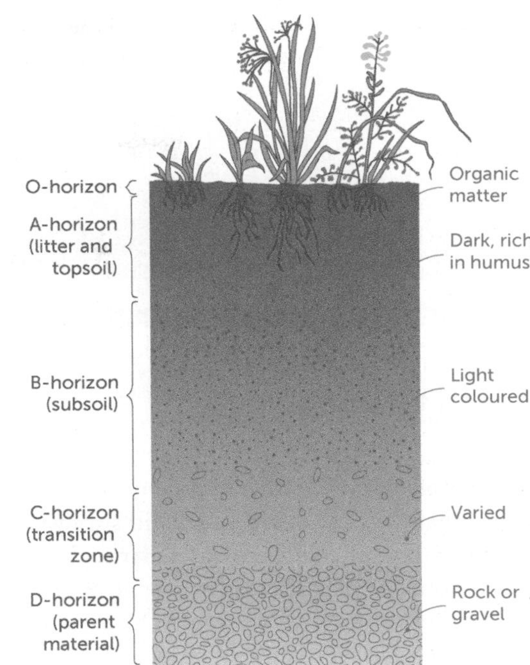

FIGURE 2.15 | Generalized soil profile.

factors necessary for growth must be available in certain minimum quantities if an organism is to survive. Thus, a surplus of water will not compensate for an absence of an essential nutrient or adequate warmth. In other words, a chain is only as strong as its weakest link. The weakest link is known as the **dominant limiting factor**. A major goal of agriculture is to remove the effect of the various limiting factors. Thus, auxiliary energy flows are employed to ensure that a crop has no competition from other plants (weeding), or that water supply is adequate (irrigation), or that the plant has optimal nutrient supply (fertilizer) (Chapter 10).

In northern climates, vegetation structure is very simple, as both low temperature and low rainfall result in growth conditions in which few species can survive. In the short Arctic summer, however, areas of tundra are ablaze with brightly coloured flowers, such as these mountain avens and oxytropis on Victoria Island, Nunavut.

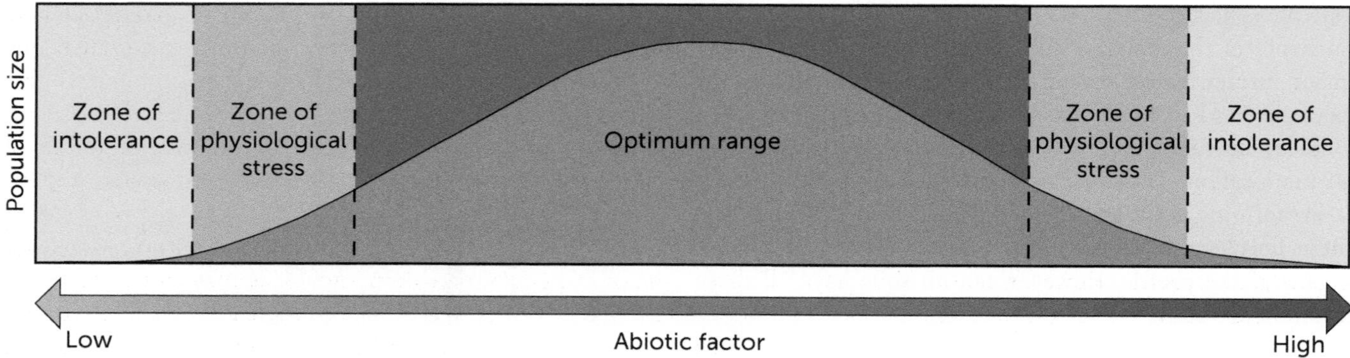

FIGURE 2.16 | Range of tolerance.

The corollary of the above is that all organisms have a range of conditions that they can tolerate and still survive. This is known as the **range of tolerance** for a particular species. This range is bounded on each side by a zone of intolerance for which limiting factors are too severe to permit growth (Figure 2.16). There may, for example, be too much or too little water. As conditions improve for the particular factor, certain individuals within the population can tolerate the conditions, but because the conditions still are not optimal, relatively few individuals can exist. This is known as the **zone of physiological stress.** Still further amelioration creates a range where conditions are ideal for that species, the **optimum range.** Here, in theory, barring other factors, there will be the highest population of the particular organism.

Water availability is often the critical factor that determines differences between communities. Where precipitation exceeds about 1,000 millimetres per year, for example, trees will usually dominate the landscape if other factors are suitable. Below 750 millimetres, precipitation falls short of the range of tolerance for trees, and grasses will dominate because they have a tolerance for water stress in the order of 100 millimetres per year. Below that level, even grasses run into their zone of intolerance, and cacti, sagebrush, and other drought-resistant species dominate.

Organisms react not to just one abiotic factor, such as water availability, but to all the factors necessary for growth. Sometimes the optimal range for one factor will not overlap with the optimal range for other factors; the organism is thus in the zone of physiological stress for that factor, which would become the dominant limiting factor. Organisms may also be out-competed for a particular factor in their optimum range by another organism with a greater tolerance to that environmental factor and again be forced into a zone of physiological stress. In other words, the simple single-factor model represented in Figure 2.13 is more complicated because numerous abiotic and biotic influences must also be taken into account. The model does, however, provide a useful conceptual tool to help understand the spatial distribution of organisms.

Philip Dearden

The panda is a classic example of a specialist species.

BlueMaxphoto/Thinkstock

Some species, such as the black bear, are very adaptable and have a relatively broad range of tolerance. On the Pacific coast, black bears are frequent scavengers of the intertidal zone, where many items are considered potential food. The year-round availability of an abundant and varied food source results in very large individuals.

Biotic Components

Other species also have an important role in influencing species distributions and abundance. Species interact in several ways, including in competition for scarce environmental resources. Each species needs a specific combination of the physical, chemical, and biological conditions for its growth. This is known as the **niche** of that species. Where the species lives is known as the **habitat**.

The **competitive exclusion principle** tells us that no two species can occupy the same niche in the same area. Most species have a *fundamental niche*, representing the potential range of conditions that they can occupy, as well as a narrower *realized niche*, representing the range actually occupied. The physical conditions for growth exist throughout the fundamental niche, but the species may be out-competed in parts of this area through the overlapping requirements of other species. **Specialist** species have relatively narrow niches and are generally more susceptible to population fluctuations as a result of environmental change. Many endangered species are specialists. The panda is a classic example of such a specialist, with a total concentration on one plant, bamboo, as a source of food. Whenever the bamboo supply falls, as it does after it flowers, this specialist species has few suitable alternative sources of food. Historically, when bamboo was abundant this did not particularly matter, because the pandas simply moved to a new area. However, as the animals have become increasingly restricted to smaller and more isolated reserves, it has become a major problem.

In Canada, specialist species include many of the endangered species discussed in later chapters, such as the burrowing owl and the whooping crane. **Generalist species**, on the other hand, like the black bear and coyote, may have a very broad niche, where few things organic are not considered a potential food item. Such generalist species have adapted most successfully to the new environments created by humans.

Competition

Intraspecific competition occurs among members of the same species, whereas **interspecific competition** occurs between different species. Both forms of competition result from demands for scarce resources. Intraspecific competition occurs particularly where individual species densities are very high. Interspecific competition occurs where species niches are similar. Competition may be reduced through **resource partitioning** in which the resources are used at different times or in different ways by species with an overlap of fundamental niches. Hawks and owls, for example, both hunt for similar types of prey but at different times, since owls are mainly nocturnal.

Intraspecific competition may lead to the domination of specific areas by certain individuals; the area is known as a **territory** and may be aggressively defended against intruders. Grizzly bears establish such territories, which may be as large as 1,000 km^2 for dominant males, although the possibility of defending such a large territory from intruders at all times is remote. During the breeding season, male robins establish and defend nesting territories, the boundaries of which are advertised in song. This kind of behaviour aims to establish sufficient resources for breeding pairs to be successful. Ultimately, intraspecific competition contributes to regulation of population size in areas where favourable habitat is limited, since those individuals unable to defend territories are outcast to less favourable areas where their likelihood of success is limited.

Biotic Relationships

There are other kinds of relationships between species besides competition. In predation, for example, a **predator** species benefits at the expense of a **prey** species. The lynx eating the hare and the osprey eating the fish are familiar examples of this kind of relationship, although in a broader sense we should also consider the herbivore eating the plant. Predation is a major factor in population control and usually results in the immediate death of the prey species. A predator must be able to overwhelm and kill prey on a regular basis without getting hurt. Usually, predators are bigger than their prey and often target weaker members of the prey population to avoid getting injured. They may also hunt as a group to improve the likelihood of a kill and minimize the possibility of a debilitating injury.

One theory that addresses the relationship between the benefit of making a kill and feeding against the cost of the energy expended to make the kill is **optimal foraging theory**. The theory recognizes that there is a point of compensation between the benefit of obtaining the prey and the costs of doing so and that the predator's behaviour adjusts to optimize the benefits. It may be more worthwhile, for example, to hunt a smaller prey more often, even though it will result in less food intake, if the smaller prey can be dispatched with little fear of injury and eaten quickly so that another predator cannot steal it. Optimal foraging theory also suggests that as one type of prey becomes scarce, most predators will switch prey if they can. Several examples of this kind of behaviour are discussed within the marine context in Chapter 8.

Prey species have evolved many strategies to avoid being transferred along the food chain. Some plants develop physical defences such as thorns, while others may evolve chemical defences such as poisons to deter their predators. The chemicals manufactured by plants provide the raw material for many of our modern medicines, such as aspirin, which comes from willows. Animal species employ a wide variety of predator avoidance strategies ranging from camouflage, alarm calls, and grouping to flight.

A special kind of predator–prey relationship is **parasitism**, where the predator lives on or in its prey (or host). In this case, the predator is often smaller than the prey and gains its nourishment from the prey over a more extended time period that may lead to the eventual death of the host. This may cause the death of the parasite too, although some parasites, such as dog fleas and mosquitoes, can readily switch hosts. Tapeworms, ticks, lamprey, and mistletoe are all examples of parasites.

Not all relationships between species are necessarily detrimental to one of the species. Mutualism is the term used to describe situations in which the relationship benefits both species. These benefits may relate to enhanced food supplies, protection, or transport to other locations. The relationship between the nitrogen-fixing bacteria and their host plants, described in Chapter 4, is an example of such a relationship that results in enhanced nutrition for both species. Other examples include the relationship between flowering plants and their pollinators, which results in the transport of pollen to other plants, and the protection offered by ants to aphids in return for the food extracted from plants by the aphids. Box 2.7 describes another example. Interactions that appear to benefit only one partner but do not harm the other are examples of **commensalism**. The growth of **epiphytes**, plants that use others for support but not nourishment, is one example.

Philip Dearden

This Amazonian bromeliad is growing as a epiphyte high on the branches of a tree.

Keystone Species

Species with a strong influence on the entire community are known as **keystone species**. They are named after the final wedge-shaped stone laid in an arch. Without the keystone, all the other stones in the arch will collapse. In Canada, our national symbol, the beaver, is a good example of such a

ENVIRONMENT IN FOCUS

BOX 2.7 | Nemo: One Complicated Fish!

Clownfish are one of the world's most recognized fish, well known through the character of Nemo in the Disney film *Finding Nemo*. Living in a mutualistic relationship with sea anemones, they are fiercely territorial and protect the anemones from butterfly fish, which feed on anemone tentacles. It is thought that the clownfish themselves may have developed immunity to the butterfly fish stings through co-evolution, a process discussed in more detail in Chapter 3. The clownfish also excrete a large amount of ammonia, which fuels an increase in photosynthetic microscopic algae that in turn provide the anemones with energy in exchange for somewhere to live. The anemones also benefit from the food scraps brought by the clownfish.

The complicated life of the clownfish does not stop there. They are sequential hermaphrodites, meaning that if the female dies, the largest male changes sex and takes on the female role, and the largest juvenile grows more quickly and becomes the breeding female. The male fish takes most care of the eggs, guarding and fanning them until they hatch.

Native to the waters of the Pacific and Indian Oceans, the fish are omnivores and feed primarily on zooplankton. Their populations have come under greater stress since their popularization in the Disney movie, due to demands from the aquarium trade, and are thought to make up almost half of the global aquarium trade, with only half of that trade being supplied by breeding. Clownfish are now rare in some areas where they were previously plentiful due to this trade.

Philip Dearden

Clownfish seek the shelter of their anemone off the Maldives.

DOMESTIC GUEST STATEMENT

Landscape Ecology | *Chris Malcolm*

The key to successful environmental resource management is an understanding of the ecological relationships between and among the many environmental components that exist in space and time. These components are connected in a hierarchy from the micro-scale (energy and nutrient flows), through the meso-scale (organisms, populations, and communities), to the macro-scale (ecosystems and the biosphere). For example, in eastern North American deciduous forests, one year's production of acorns by oak trees, termed masting, can influence the prevalence of Lyme disease, spread by black-legged ticks, two to three years later. A good production of acorns attracts white-footed mice and white-tailed deer. The deer spend up to 40 per cent of their time in the forest in high mast years and only 5 per cent in low mast years, a spatial pattern of habitat selection based on differential acorn production on a temporal scale. The mice host a bacterium, *Borrelia burgdorferi*, which they spread to the ticks, which both increase in numbers as the mice population grows and spread to the deer that spend more time in proximity to the mice. As the deer move about, in and out of the forest, they expand the range of the ticks. The ticks carrying *Borrelia burgdorferi* can cause Lyme disease if they come into contact with humans. Further complicating this relationship, the mice often eat the pupae of gypsy moths, which control the moth population. If the moths outbreak, however, they feed on oak tree leaves, reducing acorn production and ultimately the potential for Lyme disease (Jones et al., 1998).

There are a number of approaches to understanding relationships across space and time at various scales. Various terms describe the meso-scale approach, including "landscape ecology," "landscape connectivity," "spatial ecology," and "ecological integrity." "Landscape" is the common term at this scale, although it does not have a universal definition, which can make the development of management policies with respect to landscape-scale phenomena confusing. However, those who study wildlife movements generally define "landscape" as a heterogeneous area of land composed of a mosaic of habitat types. Landscapes come in the form of the patchwork of tundra, permafrost lakes, spruce krumholtz, bogs, and fens of the Subarctic; the glaciated network of kettle lakes, granite outcrops, and coniferous forests of the boreal Canadian Shield; or the transition of temperate rain forest to rocky tidal pools and kelp forests on British Columbia's west coast.

Landscape ecology is the science of studying and attempting to improve the relationships between spatial patterns and ecological processes on a multitude of spatial scales and organizational levels (Wu and Hobbs, 2007). **Landscape connectivity** is the degree to which the landscape facilitates or restricts movement between and among habitat patches (Taylor et al., 1993). Landscape connectivity can further be divided into **structural** and **functional connectivity**. Structural connectivity focuses solely on the physical relationships between habitat patches such as fragmentation, corridors, or distances between them, while functional connectivity includes the behavioural responses of organisms to structural connectivity. *Spatial ecology* has a decided geographical emphasis that examines how the spatial arrangements of organisms, populations, and landscapes influence ecological dynamics (Collinge, 2010). *Ecological integrity* describes a natural system in which the interconnected web of components and processes, from nutrient and energy flows to populations of species within complex communities, are intact and functioning. Ecological integrity tends to be an idealized concept, as gaining a holistic understanding of a landscape through one of the other approaches described above is extremely difficult!

As an ecological biogeographer, I, along with my students, have been examining patterns of movement within fish populations at the landscape scale. We have been examining functional connectivity for northern pike, both in regard to natural and anthropogenic structure. In the southern portion of Riding Mountain National Park, Manitoba, Clear and South Lakes are separated by a narrow sand barrier bar several metres wide. Clear Lake is a large, deep, mesotrophic lake (see Chapter 4), while South Lake is small, shallow, and eutrophic. Northern pike spawning habitat in Clear Lake is rare and poor in quality, while South Lake provides prime spawning habitat. However, the pike can only enter South Lake if the spring melt breaks through the barrier bar, creating a temporary corridor.

Courtesy Chris Malcolm

Measuring pike from the Little Saskatchewan River.

Continued

This does not occur every year. In the spring, prior to spawning, we placed VHF transmitters on 40 northern pike in Clear Lake and watched as 39 of them entered South Lake when a corridor opened in the barrier bar. We placed micro-VHF transmitters in the oviduct of 19 of the 40 pike, which would be expelled with eggs. We relocated 15 of the micro-transmitters, all in South Lake. We were able to demonstrate that the northern pike population in Clear Lake depends on a natural, ephemeral connectivity to South Lake; one that requires conservation of the landscape in a manner to allow this process to continue.

As anthropogenic habitat fragmentation increases, there is a pressing need to understand its impact on connectivity. The Little Saskatchewan River, in southwestern Manitoba, was divided into five disjunct stretches by a series of dams and weirs between 1820 and 1960. These barriers impeded upstream movement of fish. Between 1992 and 2004, fishways were constructed around three of the dams. Again using VHF telemetry, we discovered that connectivity up and down the river is extremely important. Pike routinely climb fishways and fall back down over dams, often more than once a year. They also show site fidelity outside of the spawning season, repeatedly returning to the same location within days or weeks, although it might require travelling back and forth around a dam. We even recorded two pike that swam 120 kilometres upstream! Landscape genetics, the study of how landscape features influence population genetics, has revealed to us that there is no significant genetic variability in northern pike within the river system. This connectivity within the Little Saskatchewan River would not have occurred during the period between dam and fishway construction.

Sometimes it is not functional connectivity but the dynamic nature of limiting factors related to connectivity of habitat components that affects wildlife habitat selection. Back in Clear Lake, 30 metres deep, lives a small benthic fish, the slimy sculpin (*Cottus cognatus*). In early summer, like many other temperate lakes, Clear Lake stratifies into two thermal layers. The epilimnion, a warmer upper layer, remains connected to mixing processes at the surface, which help to maintain dissolved oxygen levels. The hypolimnion, a lower colder layer, does not mix with the epilimnion; it becomes disconnected from the surface oxygen source, and dissolved oxygen levels decline over the summer. Dissolved oxygen is a limiting factor for fish presence, which in turn can be used to measure ecological health. In cooperation with Parks Canada, my students and I have discovered that during the summer, dissolved oxygen levels in the hypolimnion of Clear Lake can decline to a level at which slimy sculpins must move out of their preferred habitat in the deepest water. Are these low levels of dissolved oxygen natural or anthropogenically enhanced? Have dissolved oxygen levels always dropped to levels that require slimy sculpins to move to areas of higher oxygen concentrations, or have humans contributed to lower levels by perhaps increasing eutrophic processes in Clear Lake?

One of the wonderful yet problematic aspects of ecological research at the landscape scale is the great expanse of unknown causal relationships. There's so much to learn, so many mysteries to solve! But at the same time, natural resource management is fraught with difficult decisions and controversy in the face of the unknown.

Courtesy Chris Malcolm

Chris Malcolm (right) is an Associate Professor in Geography at Brandon University.

species (Box 2.8). Beavers can have a profound impact on their environments through the dams they build that raise and lower water levels. This, in turn, affects the limits of tolerance of other species in the community that may suddenly find themselves submerged under a beaver pond or facing lower water levels downstream. Different species will have different reactions to this change, depending on, for one thing, their range of tolerance relating to water. However, when a keystone species is removed, there is generally a cascading effect throughout the ecosystem as other species are affected. The same species may be a keystone in some communities and not in others, depending on the community composition in that particular locale.

It is especially significant when a keystone species is removed from an area, or **extirpated**, by human activity. Such changes may take some time before they become obvious. Changes to soil characteristics caused by the extermination of major herbivores, such as bison from the prairie, may take centuries before they become noticeable and are generally not reversible. The same is true for the other large grazers, such as the great whales (discussed in Chapter 8), which have been decimated over the last couple of centuries.

Biodiversity

Over billions of years, interaction between the abiotic and biotic factors through the process of evolution, discussed in more detail in the next chapter, has produced many different life forms. **Biodiversity** is the sum of all these interactions, and high biodiversity is often taken as an indicator for healthy ecosystems.

Biodiversity is usually recognized at three different levels:

1. **Genetic diversity** is the variability in genetic makeup among individuals of the same species and the ultimate source of biodiversity at all levels. In general, genetic diversity in a population increases the ability to avoid inbreeding and withstand stress.
2. A species is a group of life forms that resemble one another and can interbreed successfully. **Species diversity** is the

ENVIRONMENT IN FOCUS

BOX 2.8 | Canada's National Symbol—The Beaver

The beaver is found all the way from Mexico to the Arctic and from Vancouver Island to Newfoundland. However, the beaver is mostly associated with the northern woods and their waterways, where it is well known for its water engineering. Many different species of beaver could once be found throughout the northern hemisphere. A Eurasian counterpart remains in small populations, but it is the North American beaver that has flourished and become one of the continent's most successful mammals. It also played a critical role, as did the sea otter on the west coast, in attracting the European colonial gaze to the resources of North America.

The beaver is a rodent—the second-largest in the world. All rodents are distinguished by their sharp incisor teeth, designed to gnaw though bark, crack nuts, or attack any other edible vegetable matter in a similarly efficient manner. The success of this strategy is attested to by the proliferation of rodents, which make up nearly 40 per cent of all mammal species. The specialty of the beaver, of course, is its ability to fell trees (some as large as a metre in diameter), which can then be used as food and as building material for its familiar dams and lodges. Trees, particularly hardwoods such as poplars, are felled close to the water's edge so that they can be dragged into the water, which is the beaver's preferred medium. With their broad flat tails, sleek coats, and powerful webbed hind feet, beavers are well equipped for their aquatic construction activities. Their dams impede the flow of water, giving them greater access to trees, and the ponds created by the dams make them less vulnerable to terrestrial predators. They can use the ponds as a low-energy way of transporting food to their lodges, which, surrounded by water, are virtually impregnable to predators.

Probably no other animal except humans has the ability to cause such a radical and deliberate change to the environment, which is why beavers are sometimes termed "system engineers." Beaver dams benefit not only beavers but also other water-oriented organisms, such as waterfowl, otters, muskrats, and frogs and other amphibians. With an estimated population of more than 60 million prior to European settlement in North America, their ecological impact on the landscape would have been substantial. Although they were trapped out of large areas, they are now starting to recolonize as a result of conservation activities. Of course, this is good news; there are, however, unanticipated consequences.

iStockphoto/Thinkstock

Reaching up to 32 kilograms and 1 metre long, the beaver is the largest rodent in North America.

When beavers create their shallow ponds, they also create ideal habitat for vegetation decay and the subsequent release of methane, a potent greenhouse gas. In fact, scientists have calculated that as beaver populations have recovered since 1900 they have caused a 200-fold increase in methane emissions (Whitfield et al., 2014). With increasing populations into the future, beaver-generated methane could become a factor in global warming.

Who would have thought?

total number of species in an area and is also known as *species richness*.

3. **Ecosystem diversity** is the variety of ecosystems in an area. Some ecosystems are more vulnerable to human interference than others. Estuaries and wetlands, for example, are highly productive but are often used for industry and agriculture. As these ecosystems are replaced by human-controlled ecosystems, natural diversity at the landscape level is reduced.

Scientific knowledge of biodiversity is primitive. There may be up to 100 million species, although most scientific estimates suggest between 5 million and 20 million, of which we have identified some 1.8 million (Figure 2.17). Some

Perspectives on the Environment

Genetic Diversity

Genetic diversity is nature's insurance policy. It increases biological productivity, assures ecological resilience and creates options for future innovation. An outcome of enhanced genetic resources and adaptive potential means maintaining the full complement of genetic diversity of all species in situ and ex situ (wild and domestic) as well as the full geographic distribution of species necessary to ensure adaptive potential.

—Government of Canada (2014)

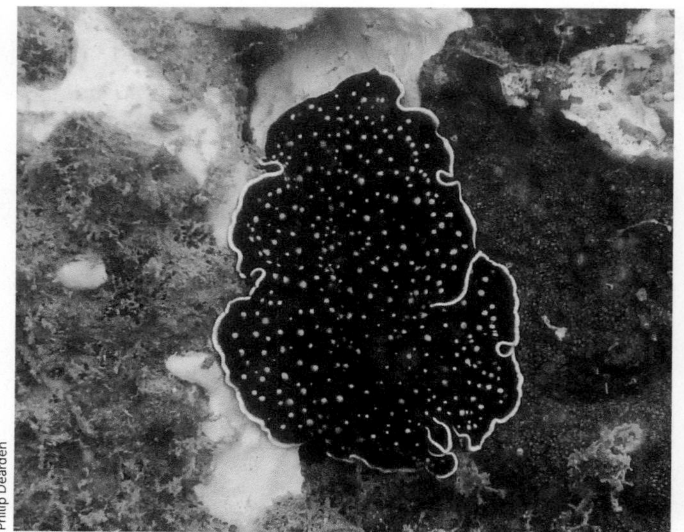

There are many amazing creatures in the ocean, such as this gold-spotted flatworm (left) and nudibranch (right), and many more to be discovered.

56 per cent of these species are insects, 14 per cent are plants, and just 3 per cent are vertebrates such as mammals, birds, and fish. Even new mammals are still being discovered, such as the giant muntjac and the saola discovered on the borders of Vietnam and Laos in the last 20 years. However, most species awaiting discovery are probably tropical invertebrates, bacteria, and fungi. We also know relatively little about the ocean (Chapter 8). Only about 15 per cent of described species are from the oceans. Most biologists agree that there are fewer species to be found there than on land. On the other hand, there are 32 phyla in the oceans, compared with only 12 on land.

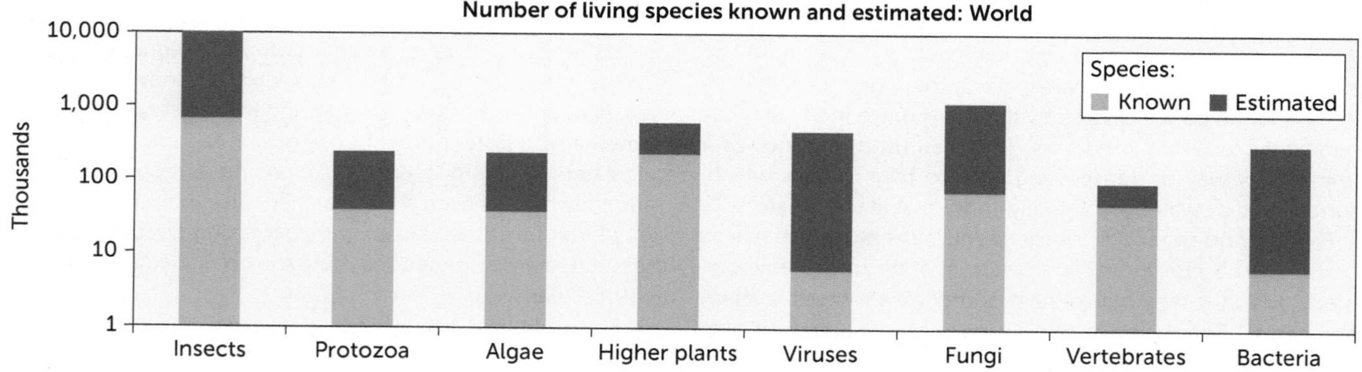

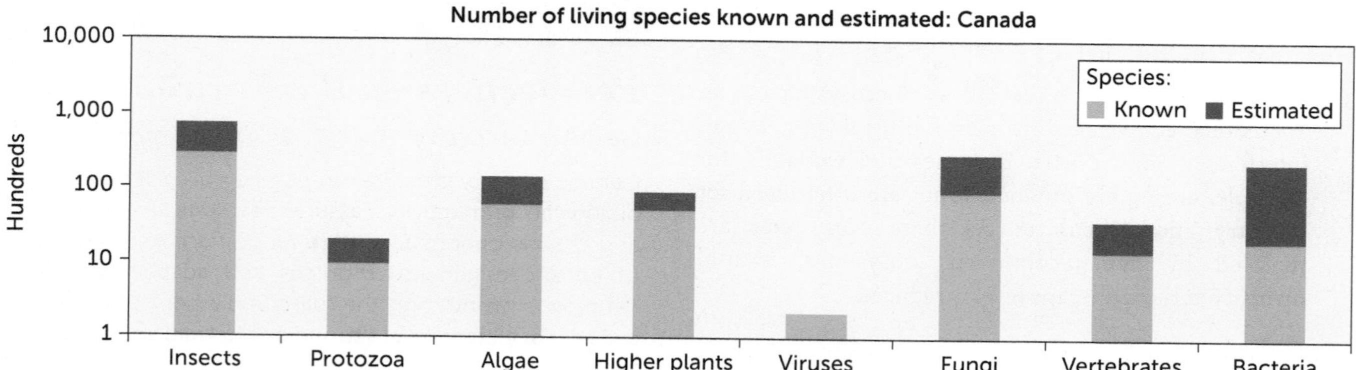

FIGURE 2.17 | Numbers of known and estimated living species in the world and in Canada.

Source: B. Groombridge (1992: 17). Reprinted with kind permission of Springer Science and Business Media B.V.

Species identification is only the first building block in biodiversity. We also need to understand the differences in genetic diversity within species and how species interact in ecosystems to really understand how the life-support system of the planet works. Even at the species level our knowledge is limited, but we do know that biodiversity is declining at unprecedented rates as a result of human pressures and has been identified as the most stressed of all planetary systems. Extinction as an ecological process is considered in more detail in the next chapter, and the main reasons behind these declines and possible solutions are considered in Chapter 14.

Biodiversity in Canada

Biodiversity is not evenly distributed around the world. Some biomes, mainly tropical forests, are extremely diverse (Box 2.9). In temperate latitudes there is much less diversity. Overall, as discussed earlier, species numbers decline in a gradient from the tropics to the poles. Latin America, for example, is home to more than 85,000 plant species. North America has 17,000, of which only 4,000 occur in Canada. Several reasons have been advanced to account for the latitudinal gradient in species richness, but the primary cause appears to be the effect of solar radiation (i.e., temperature) that increases evolutionary speed at lower latitudes. For this reason most **biodiversity hot spots**, areas with high numbers of endemic species, are found mainly in tropical forest areas.

Estimates suggest that Canada has more than 140,000 different species (Box 2.10), of which about half have been named. The taxonomic groups containing the most numbers of species are shown in Figure 2.18. Although the groups represented in this graph are not as well known as other groups, such as birds and mammals, they undertake key functions in ecosystems, often functions that we are only just becoming aware of and that support the more familiar and larger organisms. Beneficial insects, for example, fertilize flowers and control pests; crustaceans provide food for fish; bacteria recycle nutrients; and fungi are essential for bread, beer, and penicillin. The Canadian Endangered Species Conservation Council provides five-year assessments of the status of more than 7,000 species in Canada (Chapter 14).

Another important element of biodiversity is the concept of **endemism**. Endemic species are ones found nowhere else on Earth. In Canada, we have relatively few endemic species compared, for example, to southern Africa, where some 80 per cent of the plants are endemic, or southwest Australia, where 68 per cent are endemic. In Canada, there are approximately 54 endemic species of vascular plants, mammals, freshwater fish, and molluscs. Examples include the Vancouver Island marmot (Canada's only endangered endemic mammal species), the Acadian whitefish, and 28 species of plants in the Yukon. Reasons for our low endemism include the recent glaciation over most of the country, which effectively wiped out localized species, and the wide-ranging nature of many of our existing species. In terms of protecting biodiversity, it is especially important that endemic species are given consideration.

Perspectives on the Environment

Biodiversity

The survival, security, and well-being of Canadians directly depend upon the health, resilience, and productive capacity of natural systems. Beyond providing the necessities of life, Canada's natural wealth is a cornerstone of the Canadian economy, the foundation for Canada's natural resource sectors, and the key to continued growth in sectors such as agriculture, ecotourism, and recreation. Biodiversity also serves as the basis for the emerging bio-based economy, including the genomics, biotechnology, and pharmaceutical industries. Many Aboriginal communities, particularly in the North, depend on the sustainable harvesting of biological resources from intact ecosystems for their livelihoods, food, and cultural and ceremonial needs. These communities also have interests and are involved in the commercial uses of biodiversity and the emerging bio-based economy. Biodiversity is the foundation of the spiritual and cultural connection that many Canadians have with nature.

—Government of Canada (2014b: 10)

The **Convention on Biological Diversity** is a legally binding international agreement that seeks a global response to

Most of the world's species are insects, and many more await discovery.

ENVIRONMENT IN FOCUS

BOX 2.9 | The Tropical Forests

Charles Darwin, who described the mechanisms of evolution in *On the Origin of Species* (1859), originated most of his ideas while in the tropics. It was in the tropics—where life is sped up through high energy inputs and abundant moisture, where adaptation is at its most complex and intricate, and where the struggle for survival is most dramatic—that evolution could most readily be appreciated.

The diversity of the tropical forests is astounding—estimates suggest that at least half of the world's species are within the 7 per cent of the globe's surface covered in tropical rain forest. For example: in 100 square metres in Costa Rica, researchers found 233 tree species; one tree in Venezuela was home to at least 47 different species of orchids; there are 978 different species of beetles that live on sloths; and more than 1,750 different species of fish live in the Amazon basin. In general, the rain forests of South America are the richest in species, followed by Southeast Asia and then Africa. Several factors account for this abundance.

1. Tropical rain forests have been around for more than 200 million years, since the time of the dinosaurs and before the evolution of the flowering plants. It is thought that at that time there was just one gigantic landmass, before continental drift started to form the continents as we now know them. The vegetation of many areas was subsequently wiped out by succeeding glacial periods, which had minimal impact on the rain forests. Hence, evolutionary forces and speciation have had a long time to operate in the tropics.
2. Over the long period of evolution, there is a kind of positive feedback loop. As more species have developed and adapted, it has caused further adaptations as more species seek to protect themselves from being eaten and also to improve their harvesting of available food supplies. It is thought, in particular, that plant diversity has been partly the result of the need to adapt defences against the myriad insects that graze on them. As the plants develop their defences, insects adapt to the new challenge. The very high biodiversity of these groups is due to the speed of these evolutionary processes. In a system where most plants are immune to most insects but highly susceptible to a few, it pays to be a long way from a member of your own species. Successful trees are hence widely distributed, which allows more opportunity for speciation to occur.
3. The tropics receive a higher input of energy from the sun than other areas of the globe. Not only are they closer to the sun, but they also have little or no winter. The flux in solar input at the equator between the seasons is 13 per cent, but at 50 degrees latitude, the variation is 400 per cent.
4. Tropical rain forests receive a minimum of 2,000 millimetres of precipitation evenly distributed throughout the year. Moisture is therefore not a limiting factor, allowing for continuous growth. There is a strong correlation between diversity and rainfall.
5. Tropical rain forests are the most diverse ecosystems that have evolved on Earth. They are also characterized by examples of co-evolution and mutualism in which two species are absolutely co-dependent on one another. More than 900 species of wasp, for example, have evolved to pollinate the same number of fig tree species; each wasp has adapted to just one species of fig. Should anything destroy one species's food supply in such a finely tuned system, then the co-dependent species will also meet its demise.

While the evolutionary process has benefited from most of these characteristics, the soils in tropical areas have suffered. They have been exposed to weathering processes for a very long time, with no renewal and remixing from glaciation. The warm temperatures and abundant moisture are perfect for chemical weathering to great depths, and most tropical soils have long since had their nutrients washed out. A fundamental difference between tropical and temperate ecosystems is that in the tropics, unlike more temperate climes, most of the nutrients are stored in the biomass and not in the soils. When tropical vegetation is removed—by logging, for example—this removes most of the nutrients.

danishkhan/iStockphoto

Species that evolved among the complexity of tropical forests have developed many adaptations to protect themselves. The camouflage of the leaf insect pictured here gives it some protection from predators.

the challenges of biodiversity degradation and implement programs to counter this trend and to use biodiversity sustainably and equitably. When the Convention was signed in 1992, Canada offered to host the Secretariat in Montreal, signifying Canada's strong support. Unfortunately, subsequent governments have been less supportive, and Canada has moved from being a world leader in this field to being more commonly seen as an obstruction to achieving greater progress.

Under the Convention, each country must produce a biodiversity strategy outlining the steps it will take to reverse declines in biodiversity. At the Nagoya Conference of the Parties to the Convention in 2012, each signatory nation committed to meeting several goals and targets (known as the **Aichi Targets**), and were tasked with setting national targets and action that would meet these goals by 2020 (Table 2.1). The table is useful as it has implications for many subsequent chapters in this book related to agriculture, forestry, and protected areas, for example, and the targets for protected areas are considered in more detail in Chapter 14.

The Office of the Auditor General has undertaken several audits of Canada's progress on biodiversity protection and concluded:

> Environment Canada has been leading the development of Canada's 2020 goals and targets under the Convention, resulting in four draft goals and 19 related draft targets covering a range of important topics, from creating protected areas to sustainably using biodiversity. However, most of the 19 draft targets are not sufficiently specific and key actions for achieving the targets have not been developed. Without details on key actions that need to be taken, it is not clear how Canada will meet its biodiversity targets by 2020. (Office of the Auditor General of Canada, 2013: 8)

As part of this process, in 2010 Canada produced the first assessment of biodiversity from an ecosystem perspective. Although there were some positive trends—for example, the amount of land in protected areas (see Chapter 14) has increased and populations of some marine mammals appear to be improving—the overall findings are not encouraging. In particular the report suggested action is urgently needed to address key findings:

> These findings include loss of old forests, changes in river flows at critical times of the year, loss of wildlife habitat in agricultural landscapes, declines in certain bird populations, increases in wildfire, and significant shifts in marine, freshwater, and terrestrial food webs. Some contaminants recently detected in the environment are known to be increasing in wildlife. Plant communities and animal populations are responding to climate change. Temperature increases, shifting seasons, and changes in precipitation, ice cover, snowpack, and frozen

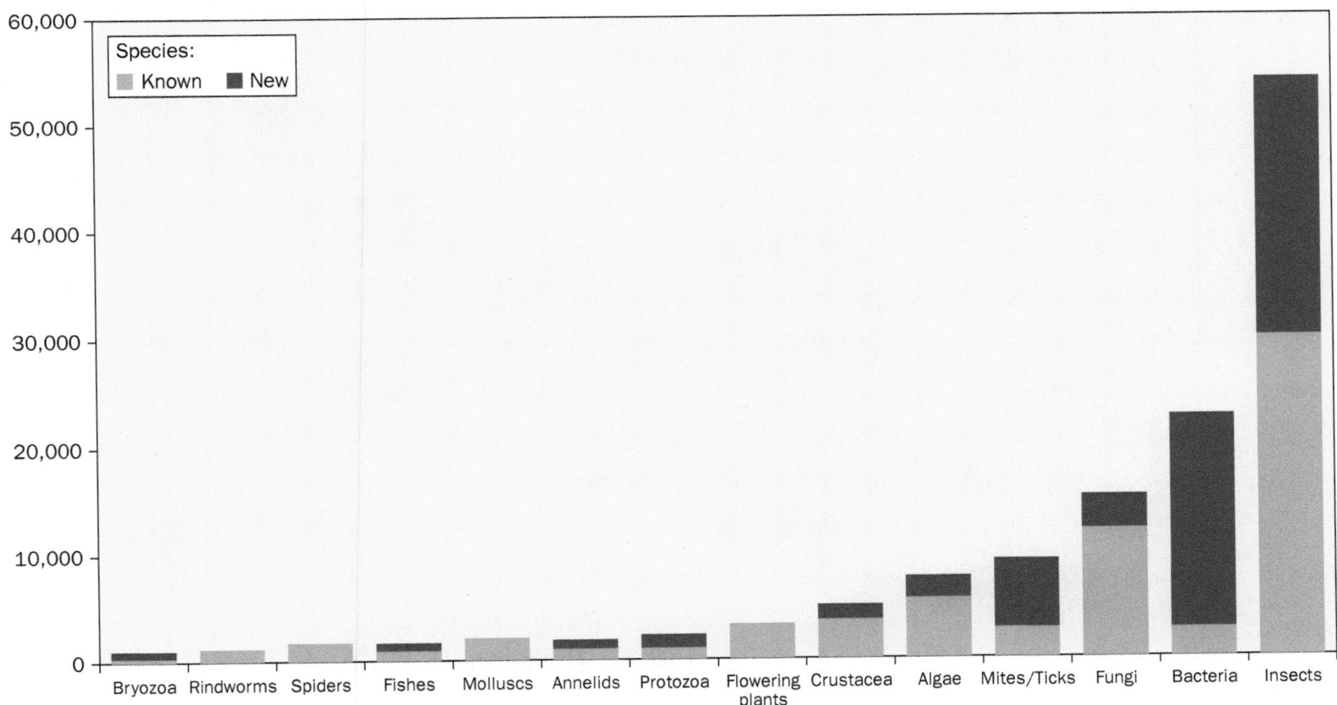

FIGURE 2.18 | Groups with the most species in Canada (excluding viruses).

Source: Mosquin et al. (1995: 58).

ENVIRONMENT IN FOCUS

BOX 2.10 | Carolinian Canada

Carolinian Canada is the wedge of land stretching from Toronto west to Windsor that contains 25 per cent of the country's human population. It also contains the highest number of tree species in the country, as the mixing zone between the eastern deciduous forests to the south and mixed coniferous-deciduous forests to the north. Its location in the southernmost part of the country, with the mediating effects on climate of the southern Great Lakes, allows semi-tropical tree species such as the cucumber and sassafras to spread up into this land of ice and snow. After Vancouver and Victoria, Windsor ranks as the third-warmest city in Canada, and it is the most humid city in the country. It is little wonder that in summer the humidity and lush vegetation can give the appearance of a much more southern location.

Besides the distinctive vegetation, the Carolinian zone also supports a noteworthy bird population. Point Pelee is one of the top birding spots in North America. Not only do migrating birds (exhausted from crossing Lake Erie northward in spring) rest here, but it is also part of the Carolinian forest and the nesting habitat for many species unusual for Canada, particularly warblers. Of the 360 bird species seen, about 90 stay to nest, and in spring there may be 25 to 30 different warblers spotted on a good day. In the fall, the birds are joined by thousands of monarch butterflies as they pause here before heading south on their 3,600-kilometre journey to the Gulf of Mexico for the winter.

Point Pelee is a national park. Most of the rest of the Carolinian forest is not so well protected and is heavily fragmented by agriculture and urban development. It is estimated that close to 40 per cent of Canada's rare, threatened, and endangered species are primarily Carolinian. The Carolinian Canada Program, started in 1984, has coordinated the efforts of government agencies and private landowners to try to protect the remaining forest. About half of the 38 targeted sites have some degree of protection, but biologists still worry that these fragments are too small and isolated to be capable of protecting this most diverse area of Canada.

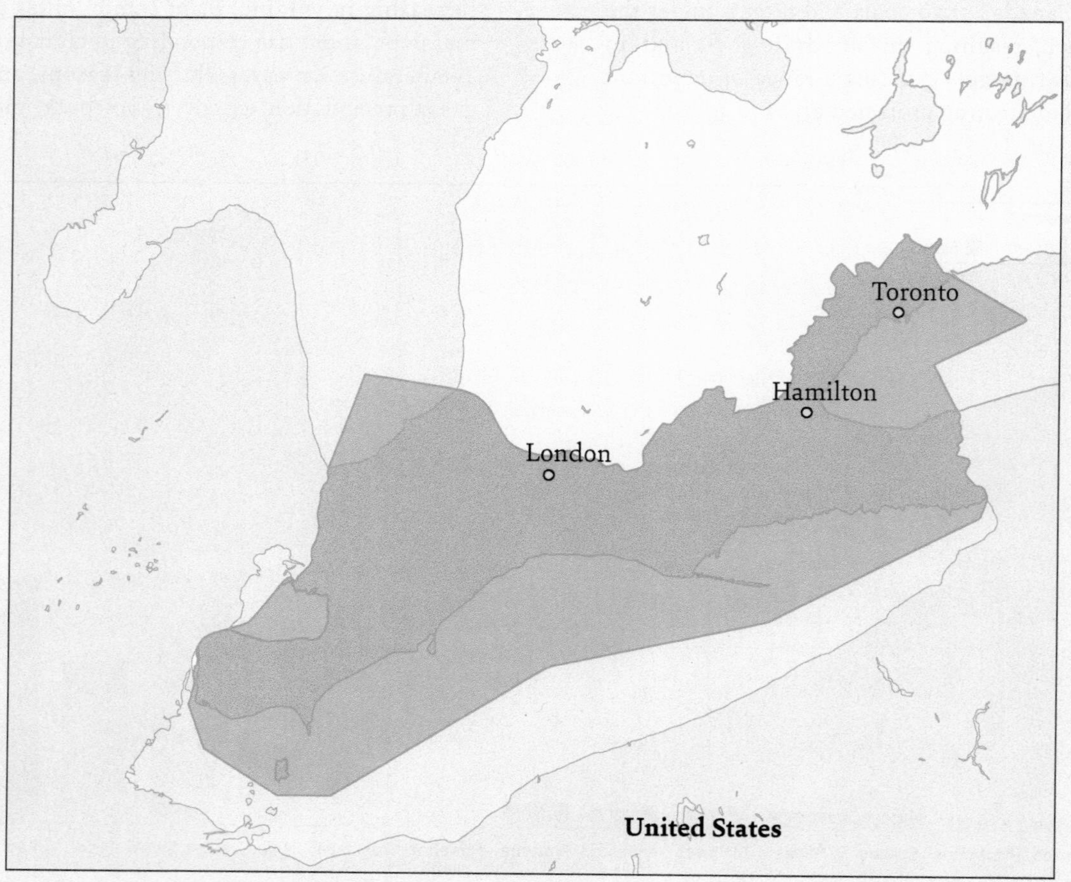

FIGURE 2.19 | Carolinian Canada.

ground are interacting to alter ecosystems, sometimes in unpredictable ways.

Some key findings identify ecosystems in which natural processes are compromised or increased stresses are reaching critical thresholds. Examples include: fish populations that have not recovered despite the removal of fishing pressure; declines in the area and condition of grasslands, where grassland bird populations are dropping sharply; and fragmented forests that place forest-dwelling caribou at risk. The dramatic loss of sea ice in the Arctic has many current ecosystem impacts and is expected to trigger declines in ice-associated species such as polar bears. Nutrient loading is on the rise in over 20 per cent of the water bodies sampled, including some of the Great Lakes where, 20 years ago, regulations successfully reduced nutrient inputs. This time, causes are more complex and solutions will likely be more difficult. Lakes affected by acid deposition have been slow to recover, even when acidifying air emissions have been reduced. Invasive non-native species have reached critical levels in the Great Lakes and elsewhere. (Federal, Provincial, and Territorial Governments of Canada, 2010: 1)

TABLE 2.1 | Biodiversity Goals and Targets for Canada

Goal A. By 2020, Canada's lands and waters are planned and managed using an ecosystem approach to support biodiversity conservation outcomes at local, regional and national scales.

1. By 2020, at least 17% of terrestrial areas and inland water, and 10% of coastal and marine areas, are conserved through networks of protected areas and other effective area-based conservation measures.
2. By 2020, species that are secure remain secure, and population of species at risk listed under federal law exhibit trends that are consistent with recovery strategies and management plans.
3. By 2020, Canada's wetlands are conserved or enhanced to sustain their ecosystem services through retention, restoration and management activities.
4. By 2020, biodiversity considerations are integrated into municipal planning and activities of major municipalities across Canada.
5. By 2020, the ability of Canadian ecological systems to adapt to climate change is better understood, and priority adaptation measures are underway.

Goal B. By 2020, direct and indirect pressures as well as cumulative effects on biodiversity are reduced, and production and consumption of Canada's biological resources are more sustainable.

6. By 2020, continued progress is made on the sustainable management of Canada's forests.
7. By 2020, agricultural working landscapes provide a stable or improved level of biodiversity and habitat capacity.
8. By 2020, all aquaculture in Canada is managed under a science-based regime that promotes the sustainable use of aquatic resources (including marine, freshwater and land based) in ways that conserve biodiversity.
9. By 2020, all fish and invertebrate stocks and aquatic plants are managed and harvested sustainably, legally and applying ecosystem-based approaches.
10. By 2020, pollution levels in Canadian waters, including pollution from excess nutrients, are reduced or maintained at levels that support healthy aquatic ecosystems.
11. By 2020, pathways of invasive alien species introductions are identified, and risk-based intervention or management plans are in place for priority pathways and species.
12. By 2020, customary use by Aboriginal peoples of biological resources is maintained, compatible with their conservation and sustainable use.
13. By 2020, innovative mechanisms for fostering the conservation and sustainable use of biodiversity are developed and applied.

Goal C. By 2020, Canadians have adequate and relevant information about biodiversity and ecosystem services to support conservation planning and decision-making.

14. By 2020, the science base for biodiversity is enhanced and knowledge of biodiversity is better integrated and more accessible.
15. By 2020, Aboriginal traditional knowledge is respected, promoted and, where made available by Aboriginal peoples, regularly, meaningfully and effectively informing biodiversity conservation and management decision-making.
16. By 2020, Canada has a comprehensive inventory of protected spaces that includes private conservation areas.
17. By 2020, measures of natural capital related to biodiversity and ecosystem services are developed on a national scale, and progress is made in integrating them into Canada's national statistical system.

Goal D. By 2020, Canadians are informed about the value of nature and more actively engaged in its stewardship.

18. By 2020, biodiversity is integrated into the elementary and secondary school curricula.
19. By 2020, more Canadians get out into nature and participate in biodiversity conservation activities.

Source: Government of Canada (2014b: 91).

© Getty/Jared Hobbs

The Vancouver Island marmot is Canada's only endangered endemic mammal species.

The report notes that biodiversity and ecosystem monitoring is deficient in Canada, and that "relevant ecosystem-level information is less available than decision-makers may realise" (Federal, Provincial, and Territorial Governments of Canada, 2010). Others feel that decision-makers are very happy that there is such little information available, as it reduces the pressure on them to respond to the detrimental changes that are taking place. This lack of adequate biodiversity monitoring is also highlighted in an independent and comprehensive assessment of the state of biodiversity information in Canada (Hyde et al., 2010). Without an effective biodiversity information monitoring system, Canada will be unable to respond to questions relating to ecosystem health, species at risk, invasive species, and changes in species distributions and abundance as they are affected by environmental changes such as climate change. Unfortunately, rather than rectify this situation, the federal government has responded with increasingly severe budget cuts to Environment Canada, as reported by the Auditor General (2013), such that the department believes that it can no longer lead the next national *Ecosystem Status and Trends* report, which was due in 2015. Canada is obviously experiencing considerable challenges in meeting its international obligations to counter biodiversity decline.

Implications

The above discussion points to important implications for society and species distributions:

- All of the Earth's inhabitants are interlocked in environmental systems that depend on one another for survival. Perturbations in part of the system have impacts on other parts of the system.
- The basic scientific laws that govern the transformation of matter and energy dictate that, sooner or later, society must transform itself from a throwaway society built on processing ever-increasing matter and energy flows to one in which energy efficiencies are improved and matter flows are reduced.
- A species may have a wide range of tolerance to some factors but a very narrow range for others.
- Species with the largest ranges of tolerance for all factors tend to be the most widely distributed. Cockroaches and rats, for example, enjoy virtually global distribution.

ENVIRONMENT IN FOCUS

BOX 2.11 | What You Can Do: Learning about Your Local Ecosystems

This chapter has laid a foundation of environmental understanding of how ecosystems work in terms of energy flow and organization. In that context, there are things that individuals can do:

1. Learn about the ecosystems and species in your own area and the factors that influence their distribution and abundance.
2. Understand the main biodiversity challenges in your area.
3. Determine how you can get engaged with resolving these challenges.
4. Be relentless in your search for government information. The government has some very competent environmental scientists (although much fewer than previously) and is required by international conventions to produce various reports. In many cases, these reports are not as complimentary to government programs as the government might wish, and they are not widely available. Search them out, and be critical.
5. Search for and review reports from other stakeholder perspectives, such as NGOs, foundations, and the private sector.

- Many weed and pest species are successful because of their large range of tolerance. Eurasian water milfoil, a significant nuisance in many waterways in Canada, is an alien that can grow in conditions from Canada to Bangladesh.
- Response to growth factors is not independent. Grass, for example, is much more susceptible to drought when nitrogen intake is low.
- Tolerance for different factors may vary through the life cycle. Critical phases often occur when organisms are juveniles and during the time of reproduction.
- Some species can adapt to gradually changing conditions for some factors, up to a point. However, after this **threshold** of change is reached, the population will collapse.

The loss of biodiversity also has enormous implications, as discussed further in Chapter 14. Before the rise of biodiversity as a concept, the human-induced extinctions of species were normally viewed as tragic, isolated events. However, biodiversity has helped us reframe the problem and acknowledge the systematic nature of the process as well as the implications for ecological processes overall as genetic, species, and landscape impoverishment occurs at ever-increasing rates. Such is the concern over biodiversity loss that an international treaty, the Convention on Biological Diversity, is attempting to mobilize global responses to the problem. However, international progress, as well as that by the government of Canada on biodiversity protection, has been slow.

From this discussion, it should be apparent that ecosystems are complicated. A complex set of interrelationships exists among organisms and between organisms and their environment. A change in part of this matrix will often result in corresponding changes throughout. Humans are now such a dominant influence on global environmental conditions at all scales that significant changes are underway as a result of human activities. There is considerable uncertainty as to how ecosystems and the entire life-support system of this planet will react to these changes. Yet even under natural conditions, ecosystems are not static. The next chapter will focus on how ecosystems change over time.

Summary

1. Energy is the capacity to do work. Energy comes in many forms, including radiant energy (from the sun), chemical energy (stored in chemical bonds of molecules), and heat, mechanical, and electrical energy. Energy differs from matter in that it has no mass and does not occupy space.
2. Understanding energy flows is critical to an understanding of the ecosphere and environmental problems. The laws of thermodynamics explain how energy moves through systems. The first law states that energy can be neither created nor destroyed but merely changed from one form to another. The second law informs us that at each energy transformation, some energy is converted to a lower-quality, less useful form.
3. Energy is the basis for all life. Through the process of photosynthesis, certain organisms transform carbon dioxide and nutrients in the presence of radiant energy from the sun into organic matter. This matter forms the basis of the food chains by which energy is passed from trophic level to trophic level. At each transference, the second law of thermodynamics dictates that some energy is lost, typically as much as 90 per cent.
4. Productivity is a measure of the abilities of different communities to transform energy into biomass. The most productive communities are found in estuaries, wetlands, and rain forests.
5. The ecosphere is the thin, life-supporting layer of the Earth characterized by interactions between the biotic and abiotic components. It can be further subdivided into communities, ecosystems, and biomes.
6. The concepts of limiting factors and range of tolerance help us to understand the interaction between the biotic and abiotic components of the ecosphere.
7. Each species needs a specific combination of physical, chemical, and biological conditions for its growth. This is the niche of that species.
8. The principle of competitive exclusion tells us that no two species can occupy the same niche in the same area at the same time.
9. Species compete for scarce resources in any given habitat. However, there are many other forms of relationship between species, such as predation, parasitism, mutualism, and commensalism.
10. Species with a strong influence on the entire community are known as keystone species.
11. Biodiversity involves the variety of life at three different scales: genetic, species, and landscape. Estimates suggest that Canada has more than 140,000 species, of which about half have been named.
12. The progress of the government of Canada in implementing its biodiversity strategy has been very slow and it is highly unlikely that Canada will meet the 2020 legally binding obligations under the international Convention on Biological Diversity.

Key Terms

abiotic components
aerobic
Aichi targets
anaerobic
apex predators
assimilated food energy
autotrophs
biodiversity
biodiversity hotspots
biomass
biomass pyramid
biomes
biotic components
bottom-up control
calorie
carnivores
cellular respiration
chemoautotrophs
chlorophylls
commensalism
community
competitive exclusion principle
consumers
Convention on Biological Diversity
decomposer food chain
detritus
dominant limiting factor
ecological redundancy
ecosystem
ecosystem diversity
endemic species
endemism
energy
energy efficiency
entropy
epiphytes
estuary
euphotic zone
extirpated
food chain
food webs
functional compensation
functional connectivity
generalist species
genetic diversity
glaciation
grazing food chains
gross primary productivity (GPP)
habitat
heat
herbivores
heterotrophs
high-quality energy
humus
interspecific competition
intraspecific competition
keystone species
kinetic energy
landscape connectivity
landscape ecology
law of conservation of energy
law of entropy
limiting factor
loams
low-quality energy
mutualism
net community productivity (NCP)
net primary productivity (NPP)
niche
omnivores
optimal foraging theory
optimum range
organism
parasitism
parent material
photosynthesis
phototrophs
phytoplankton
population
potential energy
predator
prey
primary consumers
producers
radiant energy
range of tolerance
resource partitioning
secondary consumers
soil horizons
soil permeability
soil profile
specialist
species diversity
structural connectivity
territory
tertiary consumers
theory
threshold
top-down control
trophic cascade
trophic level
zone of physiological stress
zooplankton

Questions for Review and Critical Thinking

1. What are the main biotic and abiotic components of ecosystems?
2. How do the laws of thermodynamics apply to living organisms?
3. How do the laws of thermodynamics apply to environmental management?
4. What are chemoautotrophs, and what role do they play in ecosystem dynamics?

5. On what trophic level is a pitcher plant? Why? Are there plants on the same trophic level in your area? What are they, and where do they grow?

6. In what kinds of ecosystems do detritus food chains dominate?

7. What roles do phytoplankton play in maintaining ecospheric processes?

8. What are the management implications of recognizing concepts such as specialist, generalist, and keystone species? Can you think of any examples in your area?

9. What is optimal foraging theory?

10. What do you think the dominant limiting factors are for plant communities in your area?

11. Draw a cross-section across (E–W) and down (N–S) your province or territory, and show the main environmental gradients and the vegetational response.

12. What are some of the main transformations that have to take place in society to reflect the implications of the laws of thermodynamics and law of conservation of matter?

13. How does genetic diversity help to protect a species from extinction?

14. What is endemism, and why does Canada have relatively few endemic species?

15. What progress is Canada making on implementing its biodiversity strategy?

Related Websites

Biodivcanada.ca
www.biodivcanada.ca

Convention on Biological Diversity: Canada
www.cbd.int/countries/?country=ca

Further Readings

Note: This list comprises works relevant to the subject of the chapter but not cited in the text. All cited works are listed in the References at the end of the book.

Hocking, M.D., and J.D. Reynolds. 2011. "Impacts of salmon on riparian plant diversity," *Science* 331: 1609–12.

Hodges, K.E., and A.R.E. Sinclair. 2003. "Does predation risk cause snowshoe hares to modify their diets?" *Canadian Journal of Zoology* 81: 1973–85.

Krebs, C.J., et al. 2003. "Terrestrial trophic dynamics in the Canadian Arctic," *Canadian Journal of Zoology* 81: 827–43.

Mills, E.L., et al. 2003. "Lake Ontario: Food web dynamics in a changing ecosystem (1970–2000)," *Canadian Journal of Fisheries and Aquatic Sciences* 60: 471–90.

Predavec, M., C.J. Krebs, K. Dannell, and R.J. Hyndman. 2001. "Cycles and synchrony in the collared lemming (*Dicrostonyx groenlandicus*) in Arctic North America," *Oecologia* 126: 216–24.

Go to www.oupcanada.com/DeardenMitchell5e to access additional learning tools on your smartphone, tablet, or PC.

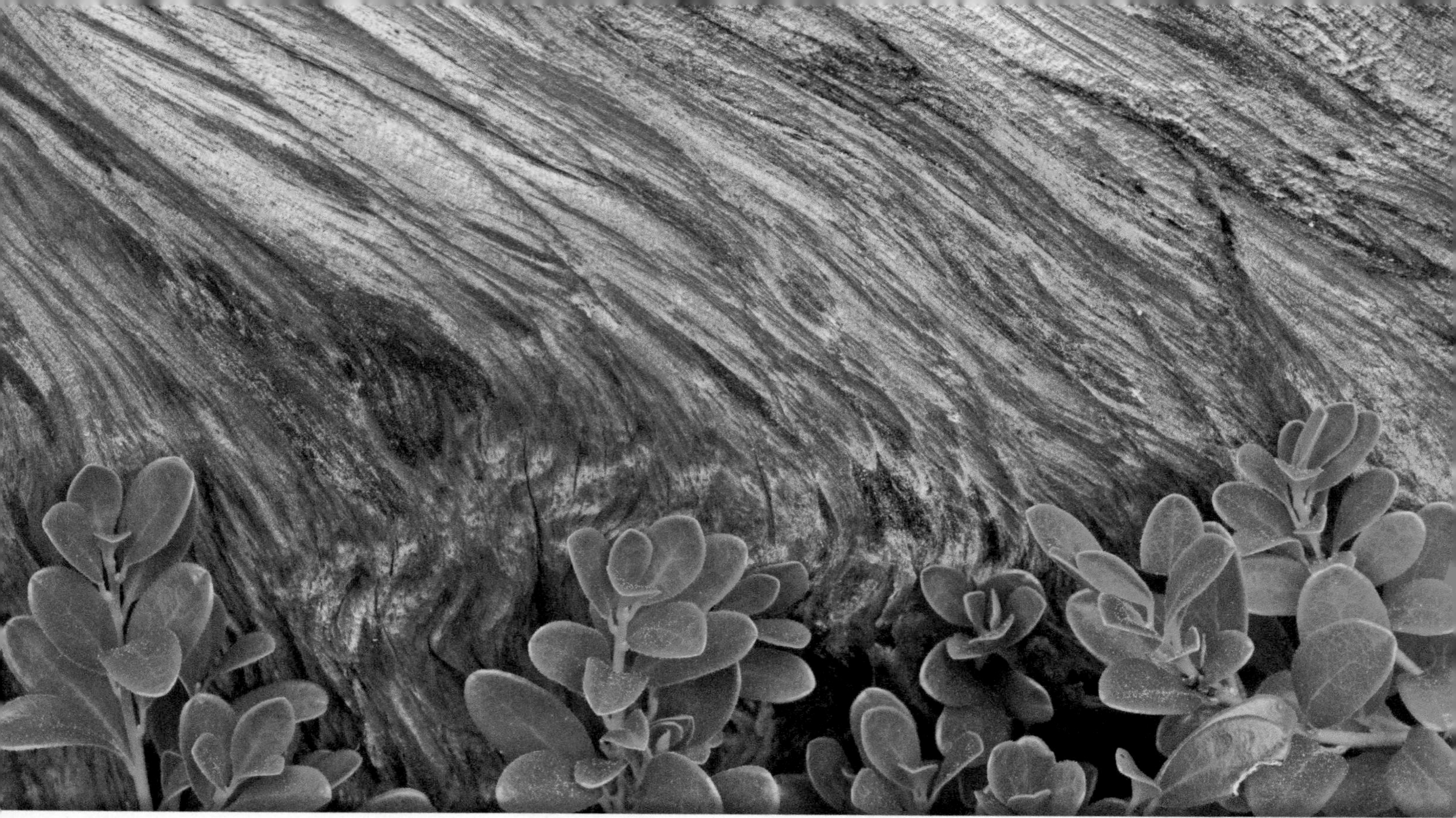

CHAPTER THREE

Ecosystems Are Dynamic

Learning Objectives

- To understand the nature of ecosystem change and its implications for society and environmental management
- To understand the process of primary and secondary succession and the ways in which humans alter these processes
- To appreciate the role of disturbance such as fires, insect infestations, and major storms as often being an integral and natural part of healthy ecosystem function
- To explore the impact and management of invasive species
- To recognize the main factors affecting species population growth
- To appreciate the nature of evolution and extinction
- To appreciate some of the implications of global climate change on species distributions and abundance

Introduction

Communities and ecosystems change over time. The rate of change depends on the factors driving change, the response of individual **species**, how species interact with one another, and how they respond collectively and individually to their abiotic environment from an ecosystem perspective. Part of the response of the species making up these systems, in the case of plants, is related to their range of tolerance to such factors as the amount of light, nutrients, and soil type, discussed in Chapter 2. For animals, the response may be related to the type, distribution, and availability of food resources or the potential for predation. Some changes are very rapid, such as those caused by a forest fire. Others, such as climate change under natural conditions, occur over long time periods and allow communities to adjust slowly to the new environment. Unfortunately, the speed of change now occurring as a result of greenhouse gas emissions is faster than any previously experienced, and many species will be unable to adapt at this speed. As vegetation communities change, so do the heterotrophic components dependent on plants for food. Similarly, if the components of the food web change, it may well cause a change in vegetation.

In this chapter, we examine aspects of change in ecosystems, starting with the process of ecological succession, and then discuss the concept of ecosystem function and its dynamic characteristics. Next we examine the role of a species' population growth and how and why it varies. Last, we look at the role of longer-term change in the processes of evolution and extinction and their effects on biodiversity and ecosystem function. The impact of humans on these processes is often to alter their natural function relative to a time when humans were far less populous on Earth.

Ecological Succession

Ecological succession is a relatively slow process. It involves the gradual replacement of one assemblage of species by another as environmental conditions change over time. Some of these changes are created by the species themselves, and others occur more indirectly. We divide succession into two basic types, with some additional variants. **Primary succession** is the colonization of a previously unvegetated surface, such as when a glacier retreats or a landslide removes all traces of the vegetation of the previous ecosystem (Figure 3.1). Little or no soil exists, and the first species to occupy the area, known as *primary colonizers*, must be able to withstand high variability in temperatures and water availability and highly limited nutrients. Few species can tolerate such conditions.

Lichens are typically the first colonizers because they can establish on bare rock surfaces that are virtually devoid of nutrients and can hold water (Box 3.1). Over time, lichens, in combination with other physical and chemical processes, break down rocks. Their biomass traps water and nutrients. Over centuries, their accumulating biomass and alteration of the environment make it possible for other species to colonize; mosses most often follow. Mosses grow faster than lichens, resulting in yet greater accumulation of biomass and the beginnings of soil. The lichens are eventually out-competed by the faster-growing mosses.

The next stage in successional advance is typically invasion by herbaceous plants such as grasses and species that we

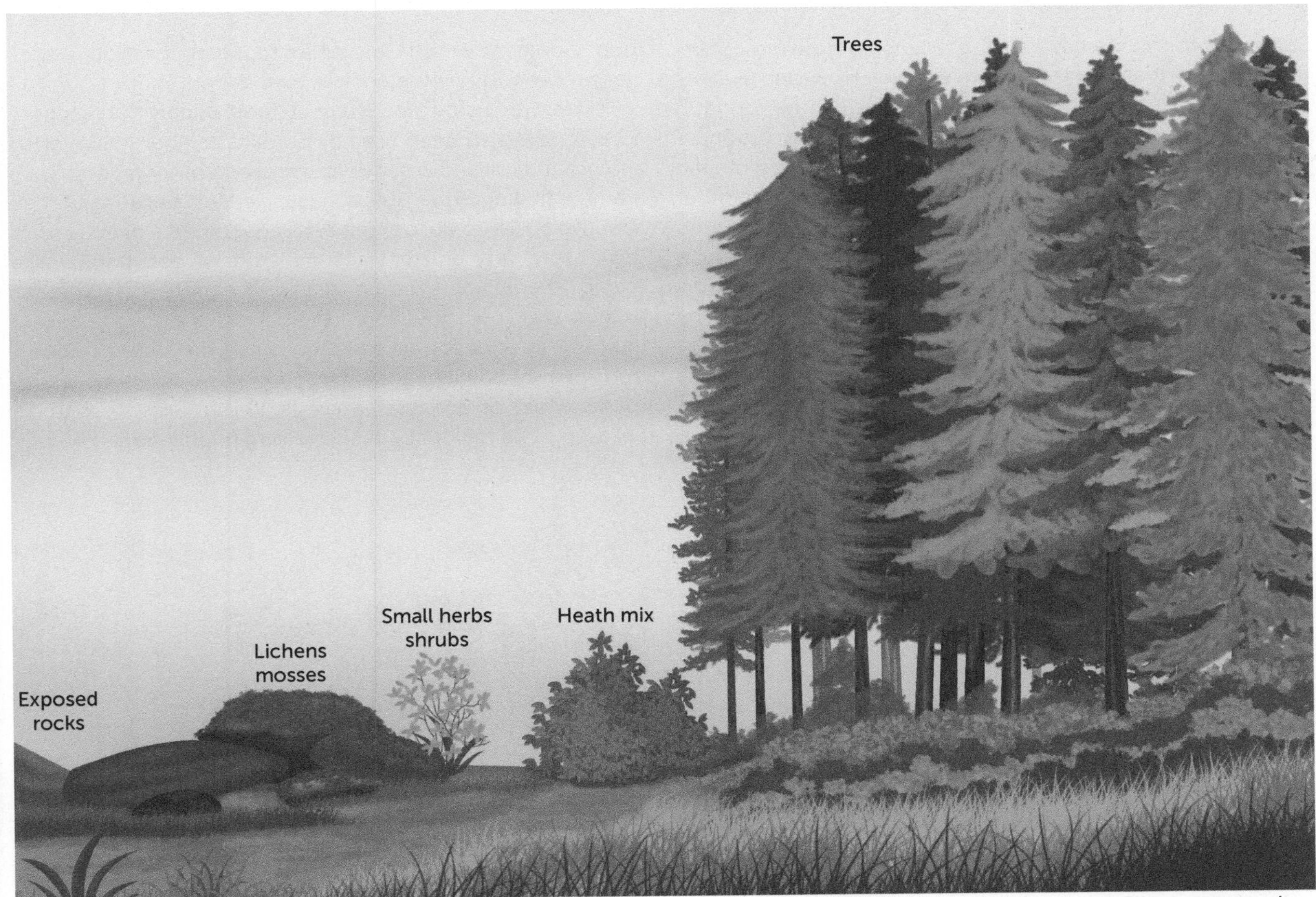

FIGURE 3.1 | A general model of primary succession over time, from a bare rock surface to a forest community.

Only 10,000 years ago, most of Canada was covered in a thick layer of ice. The Kaskawulsh Glacier in Kluane National Park, Yukon, is a remnant of this time.

often think of as "weeds." Most of these species are annuals or biannuals. Such species are able to colonize a wide range of habitats and have reproductive strategies to disperse widely. Dandelions and fireweed are good examples. While some plant species physically disperse into the habitat patch, others are already present in the form of seeds lying dormant in the soil, sometimes for decades! These seeds germinate when environmental conditions, such as the availability of light, become favourable for growth. The seeds that lie "in wait" are said be part of the soil **seed bank**.

Over time, these early herbaceous species create an environment conducive for the next successional stage to establish, which includes hardy shrubs and light-tolerant trees that in turn further ameliorate conditions until shade-tolerant tree species become established. Examples of light-tolerant ("sun-loving") trees are birch, oak, and trembling aspen. Species

ENVIRONMENT IN FOCUS

BOX 3.1 | Lichens

Some environments have such challenging growing conditions that virtually nothing can survive. However, lichens are one of the few types of organism that can be found in such places. Lichens are partnerships, part of an evolutionary mutualistic relationship between fungi and photosynthetic algae such that each benefits from the presence of the other (Box 2.1). The fungi are able to cling to rocks or trees with their filaments and to retain water. In turn, the algae produce food for both groups of species through photosynthesis. This may include the fixing of nitrogen from the atmosphere by cyanobacteria, as discussed in the next chapter. This combination is able to survive intense cold and drought and has been evolving for more than a billion years, making lichens one of the most primitive of living organisms. Individual lichens may be more than 4,000 years old. Over centuries, sufficient growth of lichens may occur so that the thinnest of soils is produced, allowing other species able to tolerate harsh conditions to colonize. Lichens are therefore very important primary colonizers.

More than 18,000 species of lichens have been described throughout the world, and undoubtedly many others have yet to be discovered. They have different life forms—dust, crust, scale, leaf, club, shrub, and hair. The best known in Canada include the leafy variety found growing on trees, an encrusting variety that grows on rocks and sometimes trees, and the so-called (and misnamed) reindeer mosses found throughout northern Canada.

Not only are lichens important agents of succession, but some species rely on them for food. A couple of species are found not in early successional environments but in old-growth forests, and these lichens constitute the main winter food supply for British Columbia's mountain caribou, a species precariously on the brink of extinction.

Besides providing an essential food supply for caribou, lichens have also been used by humans as flour (when dried and ground up) and as a dye for wool and other fabrics. They are now finding other uses as well. Lichens, because of their adaptive ability to absorb mineral requirements directly from the air, are very efficient accumulators of pollution. Unlike many other plant species, they concentrate pollutants to exceed their own tolerance levels and hence are excellent indicator species for air pollution, since they will be absent from heavily polluted areas. Wong and Brodo (1992) documented that of 465 species of lichen in Ontario, with 52 believed to be regionally extinct owing to pollution.

Orange lichens surround a pool in Precambrian rock on Georgian Bay, south of Philip Edward Island, Ontario.

Fireweed, seen here growing in Yukon, is a common herb in early successional sites throughout Canada.

The term "treeline" is used to describe areas where vegetation communities dominated by trees give way to those dominated by other types of vegetation, such as herbs and grasses. Rarely, however, is there a sharp line; rather, there is usually an ecotone, where patches of both tree- and grass-dominated communities exist together.

that can establish in the shade include western hemlock and western red cedar, which we typically find in old-growth forests. In areas where precipitation and temperature are adequate, trees typically dominate the final stage of this successional process, with fewer species in the understorey. Each stage along the way is known as a **seral** stage.

In the first half of the twentieth century, it was believed that vegetation would ultimately reach a well-defined, stable stage known as the **climax community** and that this final successional stage was in equilibrium with the environment. However, equilibrium conditions are rare and **disturbances** (such as fires, insect infestations, floods, ice storms) are so common that most ecological systems never reach a stable climax stage. Disturbances are relatively discrete events in time and space (such as floods) that alter the structure and function of populations, communities, and ecosystems. Many agents of disturbance are natural and integral parts of the healthy functioning of ecosystems. This is contrary to our intuitive sense that phenomena such as fires, floods, and windstorms are harmful to ecosystem health.

An example of a major disturbance currently unfolding is the mountain pine beetle invasion affecting more than 18 million hectares of forest in British Columbia and Alberta; this invasion is now poised to move further east across Canada. The beetles have killed and are killing millions of trees and thus are preventing these forests from achieving or maintaining a state of climax. As such, they are "setting back the successional clock" to an environment represented by early successional states. The pattern of recovery following this disturbance will depend on the features of the species themselves, the nature of interactions among species, and many unpredictable factors. Thus, ecosystems and landscapes are dynamic, interacting in complex ways, often unpredictable, over large space–time scales.

Succession is not an inevitable linear progression. It is a guideline to help understand the changes that may take place in ecological communities. In some instances—in recently glaciated terrain, for example—very hardy species of trees, such as willows and alders, may become established in favoured sites with little previous colonization having occurred. **Cyclic succession** may also occur where a community progresses through several seral stages but is then returned to earlier stages by natural phenomena such as fire (Box 3.2) or intense insect attack. The different seral stages are not discrete but may blend from one into another. These blending zones tend to be the areas with the highest species diversity, since they contain species from more than one community. They are known as **ecotones** and occur as relatively richer zones between communities.

Sand dune succession is another common form of primary succession in which the primary colonizers are not lichens but grasses that have the ability to withstand not only the high variability in temperature and water but also the continuously shifting sand. The grasses help to stabilize the sand until mat-forming shrubs invade. Later, conditions may become suitable for hardy trees such as pines that may in turn be replaced by other tree species such as oaks.

Climax is a relative rather than an absolute stage. Communities do not change up to the climax and then cease to change. However, the nature of the species assemblage is more constant over time once a **mature community** is established. Even in mature communities, future changes in pathogens, predation, and climate will generate ongoing changes.

The climax vegetation for most areas is strongly influenced by the prevailing climate and is therefore known as a **climatic climax**, but even the climate changes. Scientists are detecting a northern extension of the tree line in the Arctic as a result of global climate change and warming temperatures. In the

ENVIRONMENT IN FOCUS

BOX 3.2 | Fire Management and Ecosystem Change

In many areas, fire is a natural occurrence that has a profound impact on plant and animal communities. In some communities, it may be the dominant agent of disturbance, and if suppressed by human interference, those communities may change significantly in species composition. Fire has been used as a tool to manipulate ecosystems to produce desired effects, such as removing forests to facilitate agriculture, burning grasslands to generate new grass growth, and herding animals so that they can be more readily hunted. Fire is used in forest management: hazard reduction for silviculture, insect and disease control, wildlife habitat enhancement, and range burning.

Fire has several important ecological and social implications:

- It favours the growth of certain species over others. Some species are fire-resistant (such as the Douglas fir), while the heat from fire may aid in the germination of other species. For example, lodgepole pine seeds can only be released from their cones when sufficiently high temperatures melt the resin that once held the cone tightly shut. The phenomenon is termed **serotiny**. Fire may result in the death of other species.
- At moderate levels of intensity and frequency, it tends to increase the diversity of species in a community. Fire releases nutrients from the biomass into the soil and atmosphere; some may be lost from the site, while the remainder help to stimulate growth of some species—for example, the pine seedlings mentioned above.
- It stimulates the growth of various grasses and herbs that provide fodder for herbivores, which may in turn increase carnivore populations.
- Soil temperatures are increased not only during the fire but also afterwards—the site has a lower albedo and is more open to the sun. This also influences chemical and biological properties of the soil, stimulating microbial activities and enhancing decomposition.
- Highly intense or very frequent fires may cause sufficient nutrient impoverishment of a site to preclude further growth of trees, and the vegetation may become dominated by grasses and low shrubs. Many of the heathlands of Northern Europe were created in this manner, and clear-cutting and fire in nutrient-poor black spruce forests in Canada can have the same effect.

Early concepts of forestry and conservation encouraged policies of total fire suppression, with little attention given to the role of fire in various ecosystems. This mindset led to unanticipated changes in some ecosystems. For example, in the absence of fires, as a result of fire suppression, lodgepole pine seeds cannot grow (as explained above) and thus establish what otherwise would be a forest dominated by that species. Instead, these ecosystems with an altered fire regime may be dominated by species such as trembling aspen. Further, fire-suppression results in the accumulation of organic debris such as dead trees. If and when fire occurs, this debris will help fuel a fire such that the fire will jump from the forest floor to the canopy. Often, these fires are so intense and spread over such a large area that they cannot be controlled. Managers of protected areas such as parks now realize that if fire is a natural part of an ecosystem, fire-suppression policies are altering the ecosystem in unnatural ways. This has led to **prescribed burning** programs in many parks, such as Banff National Park (Chapter 14). A decision on whether or not fire should be suppressed should reflect knowledge of an ecosystem's natural fire regime. The regime includes factors such as the frequency, intensity, and size of this agent of disturbance. Such knowledge enables managers to mimic the regime, thus maintaining the natural state of the ecosystem. Some fires may be ecologically appropriate. Others may result from human carelessness or lack of ecological understanding. Furthermore, we cannot ignore the potentially destructive effects of fires on human livelihoods.

Global warming (see Chapter 7) will result in more frequent and intense fires. The burning of millions of tons of carbon that is biologically fixed in the biomass of the trees releases carbon dioxide, further exacerbating the buildup of greenhouse gases in the atmosphere. This is an example of a **positive feedback loop**. The hotter it gets, the drier it gets, the more fires we have, the more carbon dioxide is released, and the warmer it gets. Scientists predict that temperature rise associated with global warming will be in the order of 4–6°C within 40 years for the boreal forest biome. They also predict lower rainfalls. This will lead to greater drying of the land surface

A 2009 road closure through the Saskatchewan Valley in Alberta's Banff National Park allows for a forest-fire controlled burn.

and, again, increased frequency and area of fire. Overall, forest ecosystems will show a high degree of disturbance not typical of that which they experience as part of their natural fire regime. Species dependent on old-growth ecosystems, such as woodland caribou, will be put under increasing pressure. Caribou are highly dependent on the forest for lichens, which form the major part of their winter diet and grow only in forests more than 150 years old.

DOMESTIC GUEST STATEMENT

How Will Forests Respond to Rising Atmospheric Carbon Dioxide?

Ze'ev Gedalof and Aaron Berg

As humans, we tend to think about global environmental change in terms of temperature and precipitation, or the frequency of hurricanes, or the persistence of drought. For plants, though, global environmental change includes the very composition of the atmosphere. Changing levels of ground-level ozone (O_3), carbon dioxide (CO_2), and reactive nitrogen (nitrogen compounds that support growth) have the potential to affect all aspects of plant growth—from growth rates, to distributions, to reproductive success. Given the huge number of variables involved and the uncertainty regarding future greenhouse gas emissions and climate projections, the task of predicting these effects is extremely challenging. By necessity, most scientists focus on only one or two variables at a time and study short-lived organisms growing in controlled environments. Understanding the effects of increasing CO_2 is especially important, as it is the most rapidly accumulating greenhouse gas and is involved directly in photosynthesis. Specifically, increasing CO_2 should increase the growth rates of trees due to two possibly complementary processes: First, direct CO_2 fertilization may occur because higher partial pressure of CO_2 increases the rate of CO_2 reactions with rubisco (a plant enzyme) during photosynthesis, thus inhibiting photorespiration. Second, increasing water-use efficiency may occur due to reduced stomatal conductance (the rate of passage of carbon dioxide entering or water vapour exiting through the stomata of a leaf), leading to greater drought tolerance.

Scientists have developed many tools for studying the effects of elevated CO_2 on plant growth. While much has been learned from these studies, the inferences that can be made about forests are limited. For example, while closed growth chambers allow for a high degree of control over environmental conditions, they can be used to study only small plants and seedlings, and there are typically few interspecific interactions, damaging agents, or climatic variations included in experiments. Open-top chambers allow for more natural conditions to be simulated, but are similarly restricted to studying small organisms. More recently, the development of the Free Air CO_2 Enrichment (FACE) sites has allowed large, natural ecosystems to be studied by providing a slow continuous supply of CO_2 from the upwind side of the site. The extremely high costs of FACE technology has meant that most of the 35 studies undertaken to date have focused on agriculturally important species, and only three have studied unmanaged forests. Furthermore, the FACE studies have been brief and, like virtually all CO_2 enrichment studies, have applied an abrupt change in CO_2 levels rather than the gradual increase that has occurred over the past 150 years (Klironomos et al., 2005). Because many tree growth processes occur over years and decades—including foliage retention in evergreen species, root versus shoot growth, reproduction cycles, and carbohydrate storage—trees could respond differently to abrupt increases in CO_2 than to gradual increases.

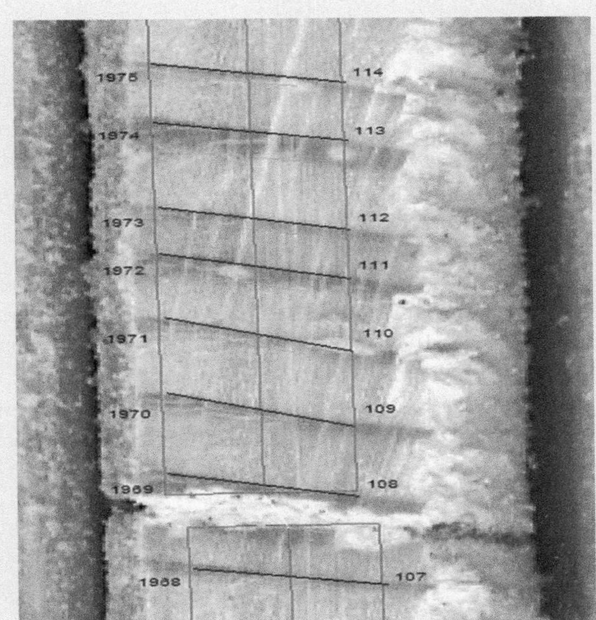

FIGURE 3.2 | A typical core sample from a conifer species. The black lines show annual ring boundaries, and the light blue lines show subseasonal anatomical differences. There is a small crack in the core in the middle of the 1969 growth ring.

Source: Courtesy Ze'ev Gedalof and Aaron Berg (2010).

Continued

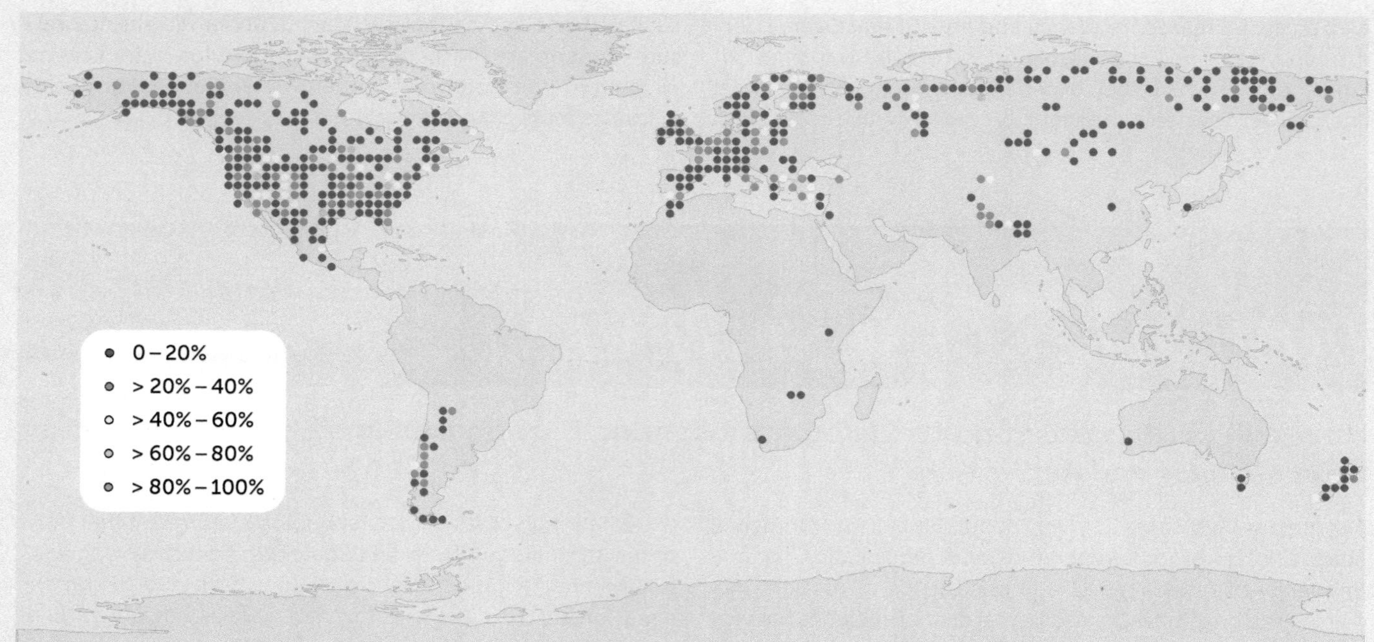

FIGURE 3.3 | **The global distribution of the tree-ring data sites and the proportion of sites (rounded to the nearest degree of latitude by longitude), showing unexplained increases in growth over the twentieth century.**

Source: Adapted from Gedalof and Berg (2010).

An alternative to these experimental approaches is to use natural history methods to examine how trees have responded to the observed increases in atmospheric CO_2 over the past century (Gedalof and Berg, 2010). In most temperate regions of the globe, trees produce annual growth rings that can be used to reconstruct the history of growth rates over the lifetime of the tree (Figure 3.2). While many factors contribute to the growth rates of trees, including site productivity, tree age, climatic variability, disturbance, and competition, most of these factors can be modelled mathematically or be averaged by using many samples and many sites.

Using this approach, we asked the question: Is there an increasing trend in the growth of trees over the past century that cannot be explained by these other competing explanations? To answer this question we used the International Tree Ring Data Bank (NOAA, n.d.), a publicly accessible archive containing data on the annual growth rates of tens of thousands of trees worldwide. Using statistical models, we removed the variability in growth that could be explained by factors unrelated to CO_2. While we cannot control all causes of variability in growth rates, the large sample size we used suggests that these other effects should average out. While our analysis lacks the precision of the three natural FACE forest experiments, the fact that we analyzed over 2,300 sites allows even a small signal to emerge from the noise of the data. What we found is both surprising and interesting: approximately 20 per cent of trees worldwide show an unexplained increasing trend in growth (Figure 3.3)—about four times what one would expect by chance. There is no obviously discernable spatial pattern to the sites where growth is increasing, and no species is more likely than any other to show increasing growth rates. What this implies is that while CO_2 fertilization is clearly a locally important phenomenon, based on the CO_2 increases observed over the past century it is not universal.

This finding is important because it shows that forests cannot be relied on to accelerate their growth in response to rising atmospheric CO_2 and thereby slow down the rate of atmospheric accumulation. Second, those trees able to take advantage of rising CO_2 will have a competitive advantage over those that cannot—suggesting that future competitive interactions may be surprising. Finally, and most importantly, there is still a lot to learn about how rising atmospheric CO_2 will affect forests and forested ecosystems. It is an exciting time to work in the field of forests and global change.

Ze'ev Gedalof is an associate professor in the Department of Geography at the University of Guelph, and is director of the Climate & Ecosystem Dynamics Research (CEDaR) laboratory.

Aaron Berg is an associate professor in the Department of Geography at the University of Guelph, and is a co-director of the University of Guelph Centre for Hydrogeomatics.

western and High Arctic, there has been an increase in willow, with dwarf birch increasing in the eastern Arctic (Myers-Smith et al., 2011). There can be important implications of such changes for other species. For example, as taller shrubs begin to dominate over larger areas they may shade out the earlier seral stage species, such as the lichens. Lichens are the main food supply for endangered caribou species, and these successional changes may have implications for the future health of the caribou.

In some areas, other factors such as soil conditions may be more important than climate in determining community composition and structure. These are known as **edaphic climaxes** (Box 3.3).

In addition to primary succession, successional processes occur on previously vegetated surfaces such as abandoned fields or avalanche tracks, or following a fire, where soil is already present. This process is known as **secondary succession.** The earlier soil-forming stages of primary succession are not repeated, so the process is much shorter, with the dispersal characteristics of invading species being a main factor in community composition. Annual weeds again dominate the community until perennial weeds, such as goldenrod, start to become established. Where conditions are suitable, the community will eventually be invaded by shrub and ultimately tree species. A major challenge for agriculture and forest managers is to prevent this natural recolonization by species that may not yield the required products. As a result, chemical herbicides, as discussed in greater detail in Chapters 9 and 10, are often used to arrest secondary succession.

Similar kinds of processes also occur in aquatic environments. Here, the natural aging is called eutrophication (*eu* = well, *trophos* = feeding) as nutrient supplies increase over time with inflow and the growth and decay of communities. The process can be relatively rapid in shallow lakes, because the nutrients (one of the auxiliary energy flows discussed in Chapter 2) promote increased plant growth that leads to more biomass and nutrient accumulation. The lake becomes shallower over time, with less surface area of water, and the aquatic communities may eventually be out-competed by marsh and ultimately terrestrial plants. This process is another example of a positive feedback loop (the shallower the lake gets, the stronger the forces become to make it shallower), discussed in more detail in the next section. Eutrophication may also constitute a significant management problem, since the species being replaced often have higher values to humans than the species replacing them. This problem is discussed in more detail in Chapter 4.

Philip Dearden

Sand dunes are a good place to observe the successional changes over time, as shown here. Over time and with increasing distance from the sea, the communities change to those in later seral stages representing the buildup and colonization of the sand.

Indicators of Immature and Mature Ecosystems

As successional changes take place in communities, several trends emerge. For example, annual net primary productivity declines as the slower-growing species establish, and diversity increases as more specialized species come to dominate the community and more finely subdivide the resources of the particular habitat. However, the increase in diversity will not continue indefinitely, according to the **intermediate disturbance hypothesis** (Figure 3.4). This hypothesis suggests that ecosystems subject to moderate disturbance generally maintain high levels of diversity compared to ecosystems that experience low or high levels of disturbance. Under low levels, competitive exclusion by the dominant species reduces diversity. With high disturbance, only those species tolerant of the stress can persist. Disturbance occurs at different scales, from small scale such as that associated with a gap created in a forest when a tree falls over from death or windthrow, to large scale associated with widespread fire.

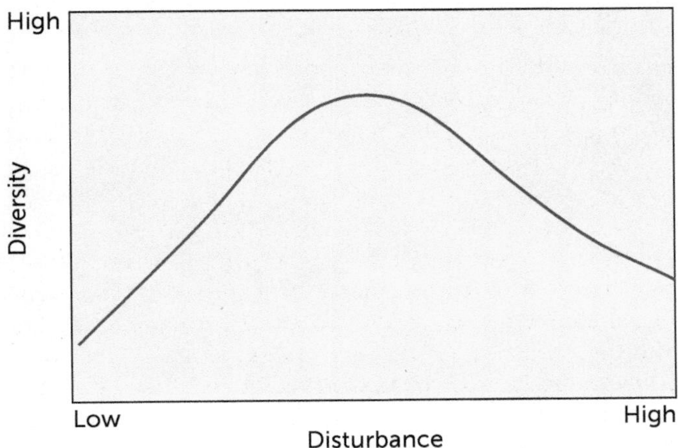

FIGURE 3.4 | The intermediate disturbance hypothesis.

Certain differences between mature and immature systems are generic (Table 3.1). In general, mature ecosystems tend to have a high level of community organization among many larger plants and have a well-developed trophic structure. Decomposers dominate most food chains, with a high efficiency of nutrient cycling and energy use. Net productivity is low. Immature ecosystems tend to have the opposite of these characteristics.

ENVIRONMENT IN FOCUS

BOX 3.3 | Edaphic Climax: Table Mountain, Newfoundland

The west coast of Newfoundland (as with most of the rest of the island) is dominated by the boreal forest (Chapter 9). In Gros Morne National Park (Figure 3.5), however, and at other locations on the west coast, this greenery (white spruce, paper birch, balsam fir) is punctuated by practically treeless orange-coloured outcrops that bear little if any similarity to the surrounding vegetation. These outcrops result from the distinctive chemical composition of the bedrock, known as serpentine. Along with three other serpentine outcrops in western Newfoundland, the Table Mountain massif in Gros Morne was formed on the floor of the Atlantic Ocean millions of years ago and rafted up to its present position through the process of continental drift.

Serpentine is characterized by high levels of nickel, chromium, and magnesium and low levels of calcium. Most species of the surrounding forests cannot tolerate these conditions; if they grow at all, they are stunted. Instead, the serpentine is host to relict communities of tough Arctic-alpine species that have survived since the retreat of the glaciers and have not been displaced through the process of succession such as the Arctic-alpines on the surrounding bedrock. These serpentine communities are edaphically driven, where the underlying geology is more important than climate in determining plant cover.

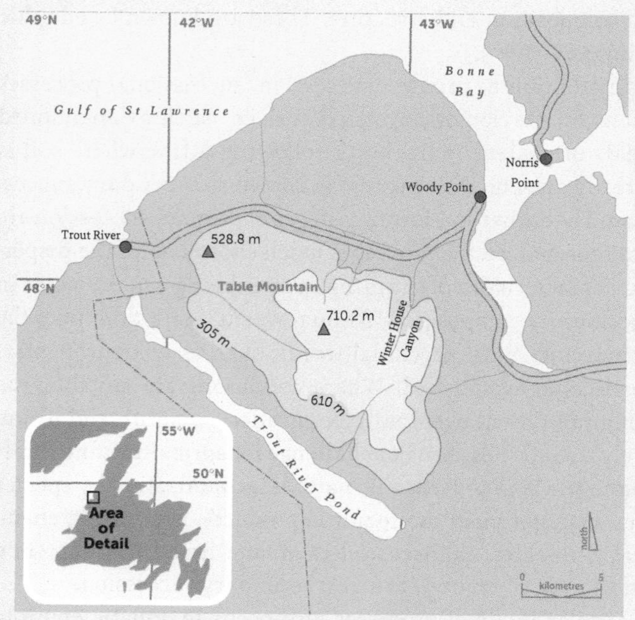

FIGURE 3.5 | Location of Table Mountain.

The difference between the dominant vegetation of the edaphic climax of outcrops in Newfoundland's Gros Morne National Park and the surrounding boreal forest can be clearly seen along the geological boundary.

The inhospitable soil chemistry has allowed rare species, such as this *Lychnis alpina*, to continue to grow in the area as relicts from the ice age.

TABLE 3.1 | Characteristics of Immature and Mature Ecosystems

Characteristic	Immature Ecosystem	Mature Ecosystem
Food chains	Linear, predominantly grazer	Web-like, predominantly detritus
Net productivity	High	Low
Species diversity	Low	High
Niche specialization	Broad	Narrow
Nutrient cycles	Open	Closed
Nutrient conservation	Poor	Good
Stability	Low	Higher

Source: Modified from Odum (1969). Copyright © 1969 by the American Association for the Advancement of Science.

Effects of Human Activities

Humans influence ecological succession. Many activities are directed toward keeping certain communities in early seral stages. In other words, humans seek to maintain the characteristics of the immature ecosystems, shown in Table 3.1, as opposed to those of the mature ecosystems that would result if natural processes were allowed to proceed. Agriculture, for example, usually involves large inputs of auxiliary energy flows to ensure that succession does not take place as weeds try to colonize the same areas being used to grow crops. The same can be said for commercial forestry. Maintaining ecosystems in early successional stages has several implications:

- The productivity of early successional phases is often higher than later phases.
- Nutrient cycling, discussed in more detail in the next chapter, is often more rapid in early stages. Trees, for example, not only hold nutrients in their mass for a longer time than herbaceous plants, but also maintain relatively low temperatures in soils. High temperatures result in more rapid breakdown of organic material and release of nutrients to the environment. Water uptake and storage by plants is also much reduced. Consequently, disturbance may result in a significant loss of nutrient capital from a site through losses in soil water to streams.
- Overall biodiversity tends to be reduced.
- The species most adversely affected are often highly specialized ones at higher trophic levels.
- The species that benefit most are usually pioneer species (weeds and pests) that have broad ranges of tolerance and efficient reproductive strategies for wide dispersal.

Changing Ecosystems

In the early 1970s, residents of the Okanagan Valley in British Columbia noticed excessive weed growth in some of the lakes in the valley. Several popular beaches were becoming unusable because of the weeds, and the invasion was spreading rapidly. This was of considerable concern to the residents, not only because of the impact on their recreational

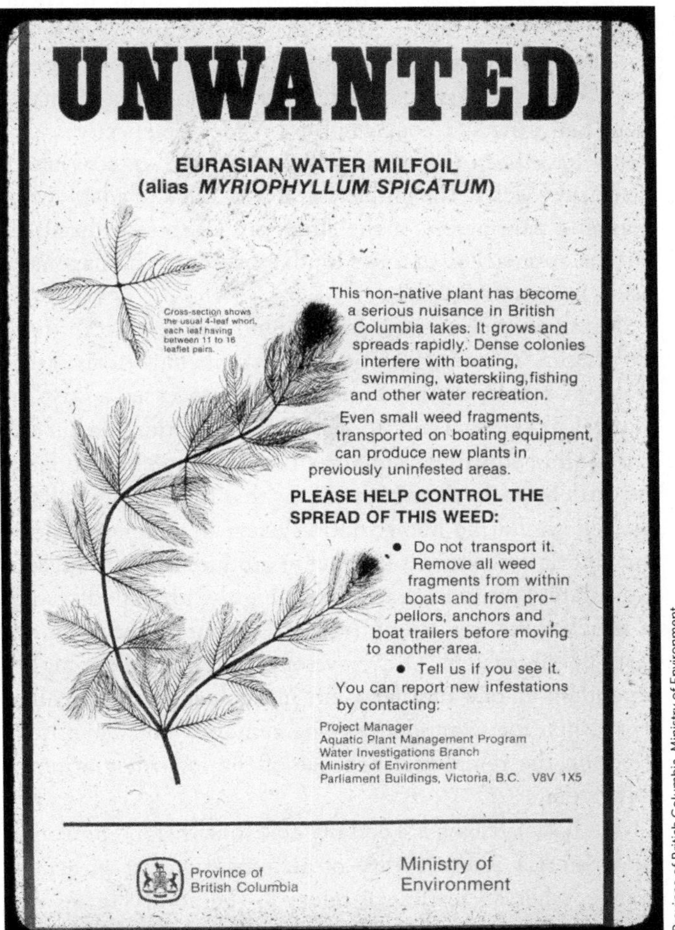

Province of British Columbia, Ministry of Environment

Signs warning of the spread of Eurasian water milfoil were placed at boat-loading ramps throughout BC but did little to stem the colonization. In the tourist economy of the Okanagan Valley, where resorts rely on water-based activities to attract clientele, considerable conflict arose among different stakeholders regarding the most appropriate means of controlling the spread of milfoil.

activities but also because of the impact on the economy of this tourist area, for which water-based recreation was the main attraction.

The culprit was Eurasian water milfoil, which arrived in the area in the 1970s and, over the next couple of decades, would spread not only to all the lakes in the Okanagan but also to many other lakes in southern BC and other provinces. The government spent significant amounts of money trying to control the spread of the species but to no avail. Originating in Eurasia, the milfoil had reached the eastern shores of this continent probably a century ago and since that time had spread across the continent, replacing native aquatic plants in many water bodies.

This ecological event, the spread of a Eurasian plant into North America, also illustrates the dynamic relationship among the biophysical, socio-economic, and management systems that is the main focus of this book. In BC, for example, the dependence of local economies such as that of the Okanagan Valley on water-based tourism triggered a strong response to milfoil that involved the use of the chemical 2,4-D. This created considerable conflict among different stakeholders regarding the relative impact of the plant versus that of the control mechanism. Critics claimed that management had failed to consider the broader perspectives that would have been included had they adopted an ecosystem-based approach to the problem and had failed to adapt to the changing parameters of the situation. Chapter 6 discusses various approaches to these kinds of resource management issues in greater detail.

Situations such as this are common. We tend to think of ecosystems as having relatively constant characteristics, of being in a balance in which internal processes adjust for changes in external conditions. It is not a static state but one of **dynamic equilibrium**. James Lovelock (1988) postulated the **Gaia hypothesis**, which claims that the ecosphere itself is a self-regulating homeostatic system in which the biotic and abiotic components interact to produce a balanced, constant state. This is an example of a highly integrated system in which there is a strong interaction among the different parts of the system. Other systems may not be so highly dependent on one another. Cells in a colony of single-celled organisms, for example, may be removed and have little effect on the remainder because of the low integration of the system.

Not all ecosystems are equally able to withstand perturbations. **Inertia** is the ability of an ecosystem to withstand change, whereas **resilience** refers to the ability to recover to the original state following disturbance (see Chapter 1). Ecosystems can have low inertia and high resilience or any combination thereof. In terms of human usage, it is best to work with systems that have both high inertia and high resilience. This means that they are relatively difficult to disturb and, even when disturbed, will recover quickly. Such systems are relatively stable. The best growth sites for forestry—alluvial sites in nutrient-rich areas at low elevations—would fit into this category. In contrast, many tropical and Arctic sites of low inertia and low resilience are readily disturbed and recover only very slowly, if at all.

Ecosystems are continuously subject to change, and equilibrium exists only in a dynamic form. In some cases, as with the milfoil described above, this is obviously true. The milfoil invasion involved the replacement of various native aquatic species with a mono-specific stand of the alien species. Similar effects are common with other non-native invaders, such as Scottish broom, purple loosestrife (Box 3.4), sea lamprey, and zebra mussels.

Invasive Alien Species

Organisms found in an area outside their normal range, such as Eurasian water milfoil and purple loosestrife, are considered **alien species**. The UN **Convention on Biological Diversity** defines "alien species" as a species introduced outside its normal past or present habitat. Many species transported to a new environment do not survive. However, others multiply rapidly, out-compete native species, change native habitats, and become **invasive** alien species. Characteristics that make plant species more likely to be a successful invasive alien include being a fast-growing generalist with an ability to alter growth form to suit different conditions, being a fast reproducer able to reproduce both sexually and asexually with a good dispersal mechanism, and being associated with humans.

Invasive species are second only to habitat destruction as a leading cause of biodiversity loss. Globally, invasive alien species are responsible for almost 40 per cent of all animal species extinctions for which the cause is known. On islands, they are often the main cause of extinctions, since there is little opportunity for the indigenous species to escape. Twenty-two per cent of species listed as endangered in Canada are in such a perilous state because of the effects of invasive species in their respective habitats (Venter et al., 2006).

In Canada, some 12 per cent of the 11,950 species assessed in *Wild Species 2010: The General Status of Species in Canada* are not native, and their numbers are increasing (Figure 3.6). Some of them—Dutch elm disease, purple loosestrife, leafy spurge, Japanese knotweed, green crabs, spiny water fleas, gypsy moths, carp, rainbow trout, starlings, domestic (feral) cats, and rats—are among the world's most serious invasive species problems. More than 500 species of alien plants in Canada have developed into agricultural weeds. They cost farmers millions of dollars every year to control, costs that we all pay when purchasing grains, vegetables, and fruit grown in Canada.

One example is the various species of knapweed introduced into Canada and the US from the Balkan states, probably in

ENVIRONMENT IN FOCUS

BOX 3.4 | Purple Loosestrife: Alien Invader

Purple loosestrife was inadvertently introduced to North America from Europe more than a century ago. Ocean-going ships typically carry ballast water—that is, water to balance their cargo load in heavy seas—taken on in the originating port. When the ship reaches calm water near its destination, this ballast and everything in it, including biological organisms, is discharged. An aggressive invader of aquatic systems, the purple loosestrife arrived in ballast and has spread through thousands of hectares of wetlands in Quebec and Ontario. In Manitoba, it ranks among the most serious noxious weeds. It is estimated that an additional 190,000 hectares of wetland habitat in North America is invaded by purple loosestrife each year. After its woody root systems have become established, native plants and the animals that depend on them for food are forced out.

Whiteway/iStockphoto

Growing along the banks of a stream, purple loosestrife grows aggressively in aquatic systems and has been a problematic invader of native species habitats in Ontario, Quebec, and Manitoba.

At the University of Guelph, experiments with the *Galerucella pusilla* beetle have showed promising results in controlling this invader plant. The beetles have a voracious appetite for purple loosestrife. They eat the metre-high plant at such a rate that the plant's capacity to produce seed (about 2.5 million per plant per year) is reduced by 99 per cent. Thus, use of the beetles to control purple loosestrife is promising, since previous control efforts that relied on physical removal, burning, mowing, and spraying produced negligible results. However, the beetles also forage on native plant species. Manitoba has initiated a biological control program using the highly host-specific weevil *Nanophyes marmorates*, which is showing promise for controlling loosestrife.

Sources: www.purpleloosestrife.org; www.ducks.ca/purple.

shipments of alfalfa. The diffuse knapweed causes the most problems; it has a wide range of tolerance and a very effective seed dispersal system that it has used to colonize vast areas of rangeland in western Canada. It is also **allelopathic**—that is, it can directly inhibit the growth of surrounding species through production of chemicals in the soil. The species displaces native species and considerably reduces the carrying capacity of the rangelands. Cattle will eat it only as a last resort, and the nutritive content is less than 10 per cent of that of the displaced native species. Initial control efforts relied on chemical sprays. A more integrated approach is now being taken, using biological control and attempting to limit its spread through stricter controls on vehicular access to rangelands, one of the main means of seed distribution as seeds ride on vehicle tires.

Besides plants, many other species have proved troublesome. Two fungi, chestnut blight and Dutch elm disease, for example, have had significant impact on the landscape of central and eastern Canada. Both attack native trees that at one time were conspicuous parts of the deciduous forests. The American chestnut was attacked by an Asian pathogenic fungus that was introduced on stocks of Japanese chestnuts during the past century and the elm by a European fungus transmitted between trees by beetles. More than 600,000 elm trees were killed in Quebec alone, and 80 per cent of Toronto's elms died within one year in the 1970s.

Another fungus, the white pine blister rust, illustrates the complexity of the impact of invasive species. The fungus, originating in Eurasia, attacks five-needled pines and causes extensive mortality. Whitebark pine is a key component of the subalpine ecosystems of the Canadian Rockies. It has a mutualistic relationship (Chapter 2) with Clark's nutcracker,

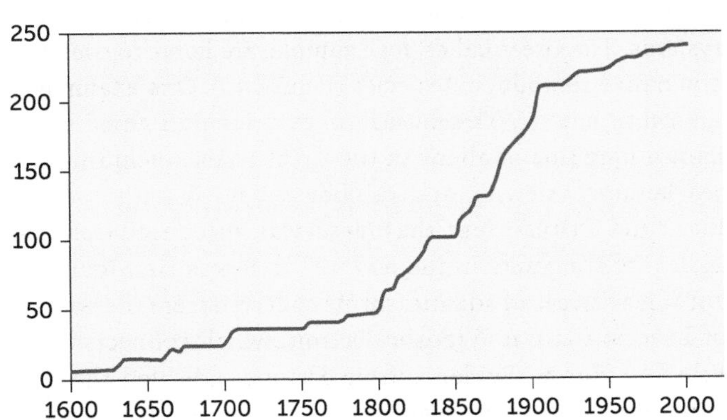

FIGURE 3.6 | Invasive non-native plants in Canada.

Source: Federal, Provincial, and Territorial Governments of Canada (2010: 54). © Environment Canada, 2010

a crow-like bird that caches the seeds for forage during the winter. Unlike those of many pines, the whitebark cones are opened not by fire but by animal activity. The seeds cannot be carried by wind and rely on the nutcracker for dispersal. The bird caches the seeds in forest openings for easy retrieval, creating perfect conditions for germination of the seed. However, the birds, while remarkable in their ability to remember hundreds of cache sites, invariably "forget" some. These seeds may then germinate, resulting in the establishment of seedlings. Beyond the mutualistic relationship between these species in that both benefit, it is important to note that the seeds of the pine are too heavy to disperse very far, which means that the nutcracker is a keystone species, as discussed in Chapter 2. When keystone species are lost in an ecosystem, that system is subject to significant change. Stuart-Smith et al. (2002) measured mortality rates of the pine in excess of 20 per cent in some areas of the national parks as a result of fungus attack. There is concern that if mortality rates increase, it will lead to population declines of the Clark's nutcracker.

Often, invasive species have been deliberately introduced by humans and can have much the same impact as species introduced accidentally. One example is the introduction of Sitka black-tailed deer into Haida Gwaii as a food source for local people in the late nineteenth century. In the absence of predators such as wolves and cougars, the deer populations and distribution expanded rapidly. However, because of the nature of the archipelago, some islands were colonized early, others later, and others not at all. This created ideal conditions for scientists to study the impact of the deer over different time periods. Stockton et al. (2005) found that vegetation cover exceeded 80 per cent in the lower vegetation layers on islands without deer. This contrasted with 10 per cent for islands that had supported deer for longer than 50 years. Overall plant species richness was similar, but at the plot level it was reduced by 20 to 50 per cent on islands that had had deer for more than 50 years. In general, these results show the potential of seemingly innocuous species to greatly simplify ecosystems.

Many of the most serious invasions occur in aquatic ecosystems. The Great Lakes, for example, are home to over 185 non-native reproducing species (Figure 3.7). One example is the zebra mussel. The mussel, named for its striped shell, joins a long line of aliens in the Great Lakes, including the sea lamprey, alewife, and rainbow smelt. A native of the Black and Caspian Seas, the mussel was introduced from the ballast of freighters in the mid 1980s. It was first found in 1988 in a sample of aquatic worms collected from the bottom of Lake St Clair at Windsor–Detroit, which connects lakes Erie and Huron. Evidence from Europe indicated that the species was an aggressive colonizer, able to displace most native species. In a short time, it displaced 13 species from Lake St Clair and caused the near-extinction of 10 species in western Lake Erie.

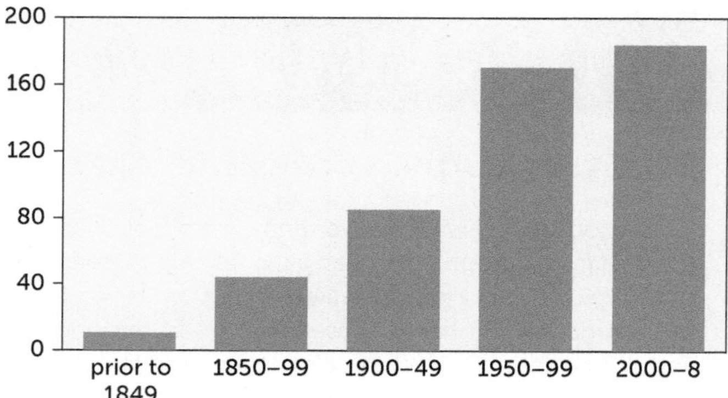

FIGURE 3.7 | Trends in non-native species in the Great Lakes.

Source: Federal, Provincial, and Territorial Governments of Canada (2010: 52). © Environment Canada, 2010

The mussel usually grows in the top 3 to 4 metres of the water, although it can live as deep as 30 metres. By the end of 1988, the mussel had colonized half of Lake St Clair and two-thirds of Lake Erie at densities as high as 30,000 per m^2. On one occasion, a density of 600,000 per m^2 was recorded.

© Jim West/Alamy Stock Photo

Zebra mussel infestations like this one have been clogging water intakes in the Great Lakes since the invasive species was first discovered in Lake St Clair in 1988.

The mussel has now spread throughout the Great Lakes, where it appears capable of colonizing any hard surface. It has encrusted water intakes and discharges, severely reducing their efficiency and necessitating significant expense to remove it. Water flow through intakes may be reduced by as much as 50 per cent. Many different approaches are being undertaken to screen out the mussel, but it appears to be able to pass through most physical barriers. At the moment, chlorination is the most common measure, but this raises problems related to the potential formation of toxic organochlorines. Ontario Power Generation has spent more than $20 million on installing and maintaining chlorine applicators at its Great Lakes and inland facilities and another $13 million on research to reduce chlorine use. Estimates of the damage to all Great Lakes utilities range from $200 to $500 million per year. The mussel also colonizes spawning sites for other fish, with as-yet undetermined impact on their populations or the $4.5 billion fishing and tourism industry in the region.

Impacts on the population levels of other species are likely to come about more indirectly through effects on food chains. The mussel is a filter-feeder that removes phytoplankton from the water, thereby affecting all the species higher in the food chain, such as walleye, bass, trout, and perch. In the Great Lakes, for example, there was a marked reduction in the body size of whitefish following the colonization by the mussel. The linking factor seems to be the collapse of the amphipod *Dipoeria*, a major food source for whitefish. In some European locations, invasion by the mussel has led to clearer water as a result of the removal of phytoplankton. These changes may benefit some species, even fish species. Bottom-feeders, such as carp and whitefish, and invertebrates, such as crayfish, may benefit as more nutrients are returned to the lake bottoms, in the form of either dead mussels or mussel feces.

However, the mussel does not remove all species of phytoplankton equally. This is creating problems with blooms of blue-green algae, such as the toxic *Microcystis aeruginosa*, that are not ingested by the mussel. Some scientists believe that the algae may be primarily responsible for Lake Erie's 500- to 1,000-km^2 dead zone, which had mostly been attributed to chemical pollutants.

It remains to be seen whether species higher in the food chain, such as waterfowl, can help to control the spread of the mussel. Already, numbers of some of these species, which stop over to feed during their migration, appear to have risen considerably. Realistically, it appears that the ducks may have some impact, as they have had in Europe, but that the infestation will be too large and the number of ducks too small for the problem to be controlled in this manner. Furthermore, once a species becomes established, it is difficult to prevent further spread. Despite major efforts in the US to stop the spread of the zebra mussel, it was found for the first time in early 2008 in Lake Mead in the desert near Las Vegas, about 2,000 kilometres from the Great Lakes.

In 2005 another deadly invader suddenly appeared in the Great Lakes: viral haemorrhagic septicemia, or VHS, dubbed the "Ebola virus for fish." Great Lakes fish have little immunity to it, and it has led to massive die-offs as they become infected. The virus is one of the world's most dreaded fish diseases, normally found only in salt water, and one of the first foreign pathogenic microbes to become established in the Great Lakes. The virus has been identified in 19 species, and in the St Lawrence River hundreds of thousands of round gobies have succumbed to the disease. Gizzard shad die-offs from VHS in Lake Ontario west of Rochester and in Dunkirk Harbor on Lake Erie also have been reported.

Yet another threat—the Asian bighead carp—has arrived. The carp has a voracious appetite, eating up to 20 per cent of its body weight in plankton every day and reaching almost a metre in length. The carp escaped from fish farms in the southern US in the 1990s and invaded the Illinois and Mississippi River systems. Only a canal in Chicago that connects to Lake Michigan, protected by an electric fence, prevents the fish from entering the Great Lakes. Biologists believe it is only a matter of time before the carp enters the lakes, which would lead to the demise of the entire fishery. One possible means of entrance is through the live fish trade. Carp are brought live from fish farms in the US to Asian markets and restaurants in Toronto, and the water subsequently is discarded into the drainage system, along with any fingerlings (young fish). Since 2005, the importation of live carp into Ontario has been illegal but, despite the threat of large fines, some entrepreneurs continue to take that risk.

As noted earlier, many invasive aquatic species, including the zebra mussel, arrive in their new habitat courtesy of ocean freighters, which take on water for ballast in one part of the world and release it in another. More than 3,000 species are being transported around the world every day through this process. Given the magnitude of these introductions, it is inevitable that some of these species will not only find a tolerable home in their new location but also explode into great numbers.

In 2004, an international convention to prevent the potentially devastating effects of the spread of harmful aquatic organisms carried by ballast water was adopted by the International Maritime Organization, the United Nations agency responsible for the safety and security of shipping and the prevention of marine pollution from ships. All ships must have a Ballast Water and Sediments Management Plan, keep records of their use of ballast, and follow standard procedures to manage ballast water.

Canada has legislation and programs that ostensibly deal with the problem of invasive species, especially those that may damage agricultural and forest crops or pose a danger to human health. Under the terms of the United Nations Convention on Biological Diversity, discussed in Chapter 14, Canada is also committed to containing invasives that threaten biodiversity. In 2006, the previously voluntary ballast measures became mandatory under the Ballast Water Control and Management Regulations. All ships arriving from beyond the exclusive economic zone (EEZ) and entering waters under Canadian jurisdiction must undertake one of the following: exchange their ballast water, treat their ballast water, discharge their ballast water to a reception facility, or retain their ballast water on board (Figure 3.8).

Hyperabundance

Introduced species are not the only ones that attain undesirable numbers in some ecosystems. Native species may do the same. This often occurs where natural habitats have been disturbed and species, particularly predatory species, have been removed. Prey species, previously controlled by natural factors, may become hyper-abundant, becoming pest species and presenting considerable management challenges.

One example is the double-crested cormorant that nests on islands in Lake Erie. These large, migratory water birds nest in colonies and return to the place they were hatched to breed. The cormorant experienced a rapid population drop in the 1960s caused primarily by pesticides such as DDT; consequently, it was targeted for protection and its populations have rebounded. Today, ecologists have recognized that the bird colonies are threatening rare vegetation. The cormorant is associated with broken tree branches, foliage stripped for nests, and guano deposits that threaten vegetation health. Middle Island is one of the few forested islands remaining in the region, and in an effort to preserve the rare plant species there, Point Pelee National Park staff have begun to cull the birds that nest on the island. Species culls are one response to hyper-abundant species and are often controversial. If you were a park manager—what would you do? Which criteria would you use to help reach a decision?

Species Removal

Just as the introduction of species to new habitats can disturb ecosystem function, so can the removal of species from food webs. The reduction or removal of some species, the so-called keystone species discussed in the previous chapter, may be particularly disruptive. One well-known example relates to the extirpation of the sea otter from the Pacific coast.

When explorer James Cook anchored at Nootka Sound on the west coast of Vancouver Island in 1778, he reported that the fur of the sea otter "is softer and finer than that of any others we know of; and, therefore, the discovery of this part of the continent of North America, where so valuable an article of commerce may be met with, cannot be a matter of indifference." Indeed, it was not. The British, seeking trading goods to barter with the Chinese in exchange for tea, discovered that sea otter pelts were in great demand in China and thus made every effort to ensure that the west coast became British (rather than Spanish or Russian!) Columbia.

The sea otter is a large seagoing weasel of the outer coasts, flourishing in giant kelp beds. It lacks a protective layer of blubber but has a very fine fur that traps air and insulates it from the cold Pacific waters. It also needs a lot of food (up to 9 kilograms per day) to fuel the fast metabolism that counteracts energy loss to the environment. Favourite prey are sea urchins, crabs, shellfish, and slow-moving fish.

The otter was easy to catch, and Russian, American, and Spanish hunters, aided by local Native populations, finished

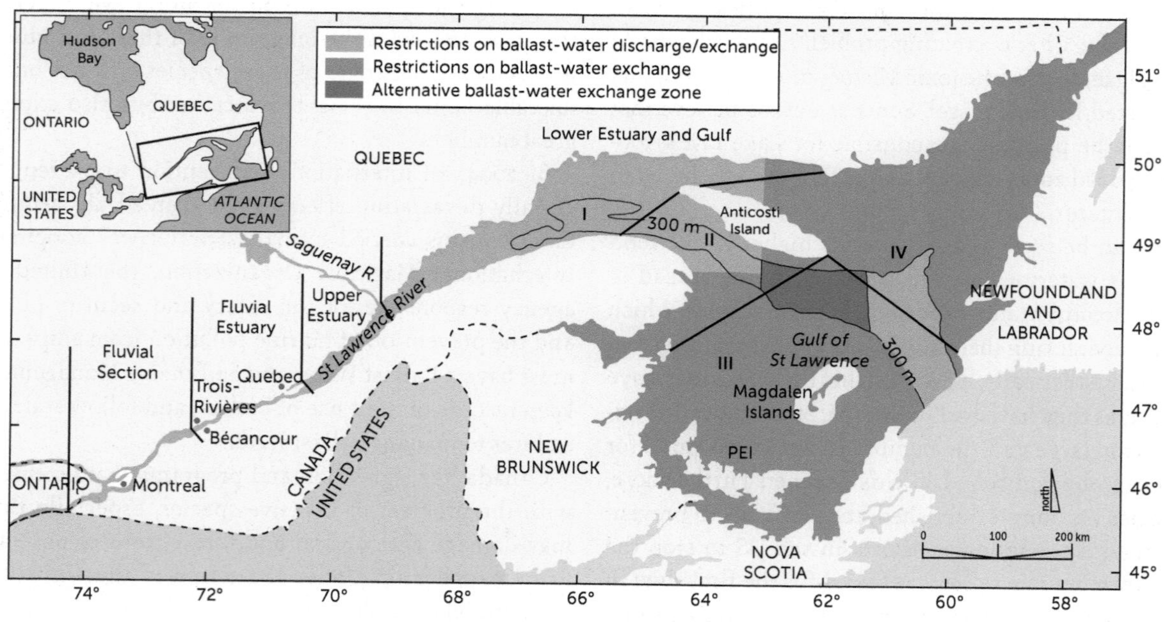

FIGURE 3.8 | Areas for ballast water control on the east coast.

off what the British had begun. Within 40 years, populations were reduced from more than half a million to 1,000–2,000. On the coast of British Columbia, it is likely that it was completely extirpated. However, relict populations remained around Monterey in northern California and in the Aleutian Islands. Individuals from this latter population were reintroduced to the coast of British Columbia, where expanding populations thrive again.

Scientists discovered the otter's key role in maintaining ecosystems after studying two groups of islands off Alaska. They noticed that although the two groups were very similar in terms of location and physical conditions, one group had much more life—bald eagles, seals, kelp beds, and otters—than the other. The otter plays a critical role in controlling sea urchin populations (Estes et al., 1989). Sea urchins are voracious eaters of kelp (large, brown seaweed) which plays a major role in coastal ecosystems providing food and habitat for many other species. Diatoms, algae, and microbes grow on the fronds of the kelp, along with colonies of filter-feeding bryozoans and hydroids. Predators abound. Fish come to feed off the colonists or to seek protection from open-water predators such as seals, sea lions, and killer whales. When overgrazed by sea urchins, this productive habitat disappears. The urchins eat through the holdfasts that anchor the kelp to the ocean floor, and the kelp is soon washed away into the open ocean or onto land. As the kelp disappears, so do the species dependent on it. On the two island groups in Alaska, one group had managed to escape the fur rampage that eliminated the otter elsewhere, and this one displayed the rich coastal community that should extend all along the outer coast of the North Pacific. Otter populations, through their control of the urchin populations, are therefore critical to maintaining the productivity of the entire community, right up to bald eagle populations. The fact that the fashion tastes of Chinese mandarins 200 years ago, met by traders from the other side of the world who wanted to enjoy afternoon tea, are still reflected in bald eagle populations 7,000 kilometres away on the BC coast indicates the complex interactions between biophysical and human systems.

Feedback

Feedback is an important aspect of maintaining stability in ecosystems whereby information is returned into a system as a result of change. Feedback initiates responses that may exacerbate (positive feedback) or moderate (**negative feedback**) the change. There is, for example, considerable debate regarding the role of feedback loops in global climate change, as discussed in Chapter 7. One positive feedback loop that may have a strong influence in Canada is the effect of increased temperatures in the North. It would increase the area of snow-free land in summer and is known as **polar amplification**. Snow has a high **albedo**; in other words, it reflects rather than absorbs much of the incoming radiation. As temperatures rise, the area covered in snow will be replaced by areas free of snow, uncovering rocks and vegetation with lower albedo values. This will cause more heat to be absorbed, which in turn will contribute to global warming. A similar situation with regard to forest fires was noted in Box 3.2.

On the other hand, negative feedback loops may also be in operation and counteract such positive feedback loops. One of them has to do with the possible role of phytoplankton in global warming. Phytoplankton produce a gas called dimethyl sulphide. When seawater interacts with the gas, sulphur particles formed in the atmosphere serve as condensation nuclei for cloud droplets. As the planet heats up, the productivity of the phytoplankton should increase, leading to an increase in the amount of gas and cloud droplets produced. This will have the effect of increasing cloud cover and reflecting solar radiation away from the planet, which could lead to cooling of the Earth. However, scientists feel that this cooling will be offset by the overall impact of global warming, as discussed in Chapter 7.

Almost all the examples in this chapter can be used to illustrate some aspect of feedback mechanisms. The allelopathic quality of the diffuse knapweed, for example, shows a positive feedback loop that promotes the spread of the species. The more the species spreads, the more conditions are created into which only it can spread. The sea otters produce a negative feedback loop in the sea urchin–kelp relationship. If the urchins become too numerous and overgraze the kelp beds, increases in otter populations will help to reverse this imbalance. When this negative feedback loop was removed from the system, there was nothing to maintain the dynamic balance of the system.

Similar examples of feedback loops occur at all scales, even down to the regulation of temperatures in individual organisms. Sometimes these feedback messages can be rapid, as

Philip Dearden

Sea otters.

in the case of organism thermoregulation. In other cases, there can be considerable delay between the stimulus for change and the resulting feedback response. Unfortunately, as the example of the positive feedback loop and snowmelt described above indicates, sometimes the delay between the stimulus and the response may be so long that we are not conscious of it. By the time we are aware, it may be too late to try to moderate the stimulus, and a powerful positive feedback loop may already, albeit slowly, have been set in motion. This is one reason why many scientists support immediate actions to reduce emissions of greenhouse gases (see Chapter 7), even though we do not yet have a clear understanding of all the relationships involved.

We are also becoming more aware of the chaotic nature of many systems in which a slight perturbation becomes greatly enhanced by positive feedback. The so-called **butterfly effect**, for example, traces how the turbulence of a butterfly flapping its wings in South America might, through cascading effects on airflows, influence the weather in North America (Hilborn, 2004). Further research has revealed the existence of similar phenomena in many different systems in which very small changes can have a great influence on outcomes.

Synergism

Synergism is another important characteristic that may influence change in ecosystems. A synergistic relationship occurs when the combined effect of two or more separate entities is greater than the sum of their individual effects. One example is the problem of acid deposition, discussed in Chapter 4. The effects of acid deposition are often exacerbated by the presence of other pollutants, such as ground-level ozone. Individually, both these forms of pollution may cause a certain amount of damage to an ecosystem. In combination, however, their effects are magnified.

Ecological Restoration

Many ecosystem changes result from human activities, and these changes may have a negative impact on ecosystem components and functions. However, this does not mean that severely damaged ecosystems have to stay that way, and restoration ecology has developed as a field of study and practice to help repair environmental damage. This book contains many examples, ranging from remediation of the Sydney Tar Ponds discussed in Chapter 11 and reclamation of the areas around Sudbury rendered treeless by acid rain (Chapters 4 and 13) to efforts to reintroduce endangered species into national parks (Chapter 14). The goals of these efforts vary enormously—from merely stabilizing an area with a self-maintaining cover of vegetation, as in the reclamation of many industrial sites, to efforts to restore areas to their pre-disturbance condition. One of the common difficulties in the latter situation is ascertaining the nature of the original ecosystem. Restoration ecologists are now concentrating more on trying to restore natural processes in an area rather than reintroducing components. However, **ecological restoration** is very challenging and costly, and there is widespread agreement that it is better to avoid degrading ecosystems in the first place rather than to try restoring them afterwards. Aerin Jacob provides an insightful "International Guest Statement" in the following section that illustrates some challenges related to disturbance, species removal, hyperabundance, and ecological restoration based on her work in Kibale National Park in Uganda.

Population Growth

The number of individuals in a species is known as the **population**. When calculated on the basis of a certain area, such as the number of sea otters per hectare, it becomes **population density**. The number of organisms in a population is important, because low numbers will make a species more vulnerable to extinction. Changes in population characteristics are known as population dynamics.

Populations change as a result of the balance among the factors promoting population growth and those promoting reduction. The most common response is through adjustments in the birth and/or death rates to the factors shown in Figure 3.9, although emigration and immigration can be important factors in some species. As long as births are more numerous than deaths, then a population will increase exponentially over time (Figure 3.10) until the environmental resistance of the factors shown in Figure 3.9 begins to have an inhibiting effect that will serve to flatten out the curve.

The **carrying capacity** of an environment is the number of individuals of a species that can be sustained in an area indefinitely, relative to given resource supply and demand. Most species will grow rapidly in numbers up to this point and then fluctuate around the carrying capacity in a dynamic equilibrium (Figure 3.11). The carrying capacity is not one fixed figure, however, but will vary along with changes in the other abiotic and biotic parts of the ecosystem. In the puffin–capelin example in Chapter 2, the carrying capacity of the North Atlantic waters to support the puffin population was severely reduced as a result of a reduction in their food supply caused by competition from another organism, humans. Management inputs, such as provision of supplementary feeding or other habitat requirements, are often used to change the capacity of an area to meet human demands.

Organisms that demonstrate the kind of S-shaped growth curve of Figure 3.11 are *density-dependent*, and as the population density increases, the rate of growth decreases. In other words, the larger the population, the lower the growth rate. This view is in accord with the equilibrium view of ecosystems discussed earlier, but populations can still crash as a result of the dynamic nature of carrying capacities, as

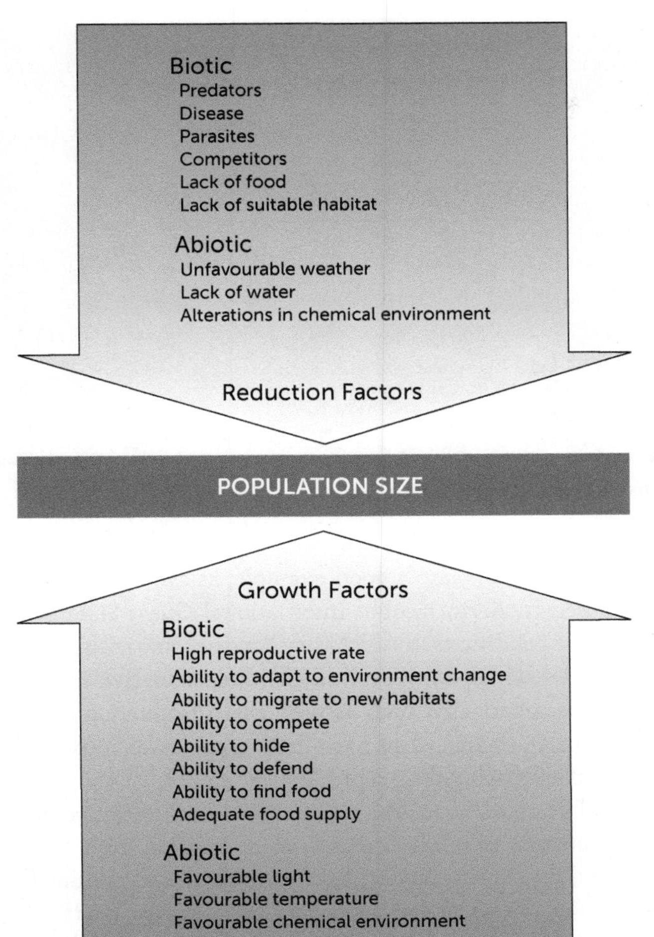

FIGURE 3.9 | Factors affecting population growth.

discussed above. Some organisms, however, are *density-independent*, and the population operates with a positive feedback loop—the more individuals in the population, the more that are born, and the population grows at an increasing rate to demonstrate a J-shaped curve. At some point, this population meets environmental resistance, causing the population to crash back to, or below, the carrying capacity. The algae blooms on ponds in the late spring or early summer are a result of this kind of growth. In reaction to the increased nutrient availability after winter, spectacular growth can occur until this food supply is exhausted and the population crashes. The dramatic and economically damaging increase in the numbers of the mountain pine beetle in BC is another example. Ecologists now accept that given the absence of cold winters because of climate change, the population will only reach its limit when it has exhausted its food supply (Chapter 9).

In some locations in Europe, this is what has happened with the zebra mussel discussed earlier. Mussel populations soared to a peak and stayed there for a few years before exhausting the food supply and crashing to between 10 and 40 per cent of the highest numbers. However, in other locations, such as Sweden, the expected crash has yet to occur.

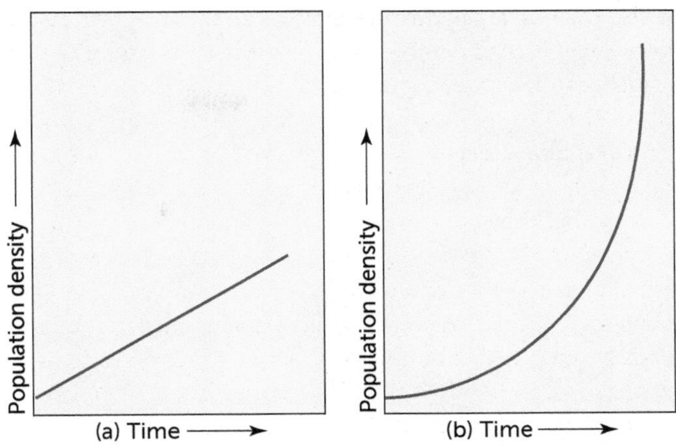

FIGURE 3.10 | Arithmetic (a) and geometric (b) growth patterns.

Given the enormous food supplies of the Great Lakes and the low numbers of predators such as waterfowl, it may be a very long time before any natural population crash happens there.

The capacity of species to increase in number is known as their **biotic potential**, the maximum rate at which a species may increase if there is no environmental resistance. Different species, however, have different reproductive strategies. Some species, such as the zebra mussel, are known as **r-strategists**, which produce large numbers of young early in life and over a short time period but invest little parental energy in their upbringing. Most of their energy is spent on reproduction, and they have few resources left to devote to maintaining a longer lifespan. Such species are usually small and short-lived and can respond to favourable conditions through rapid

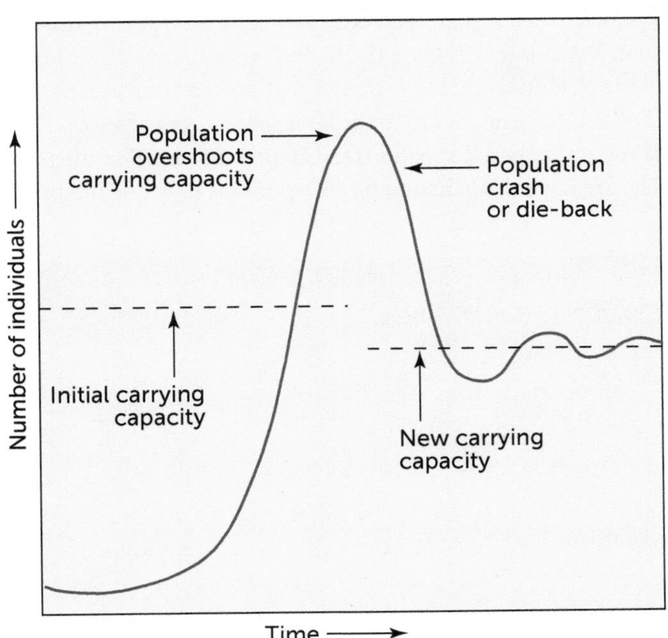

FIGURE 3.11 | Carrying capacity and population growth rates.

AndamanSE/Thinkstock

Lingbeek/iStockphoto

Jellyfish and the Pacific white-sided dolphin are good examples of marine r and K species respectively.

reproduction. They are opportunists, and their reproductive strategy is essentially based on quantity. Such species tend to dominate the early seral stages of the successional process.

K-strategists, on the other hand, produce few offspring but devote considerable effort to ensuring that these offspring reach maturity. Their strategy is based on quality. Individuals live longer and are usually larger. Populations of K-strategists often reach the carrying capacity of an environment and are relatively stable compared to r-strategists, which may experience large variations in population size. Table 3.2 summarizes the characteristics of these different strategists.

Examples of r-strategists include insects, rodents, algae, annual plants, and fish. A mature female codfish, for example, may produce more than 9 million eggs in one season. However, fewer than 5 per cent of these offspring may mature and last the first year. Most K-strategists are larger organisms, such as the larger mammals (including humans). Their lower biotic potential and lesser ability to disperse often means that they are more restricted to the later seral stages of succession. Many endangered species (see Chapter 14) are K-strategists. The great whales (Chapter 8), with perhaps only one offspring every three years, are a good example, as are the elephants discussed in Aerin Jacob's "International Guest Statement." When the conditions to which they have become accustomed, and under which they evolved their reproductive strategy, change dramatically, such as with the introduction of new predators (humans), they have little capacity to respond in terms of increasing their reproductive rate.

In addition to the factors outlined above, chance also plays an important role in determining population size. Severe winters, disease outbreaks, fires, droughts, and similar factors often have a major impact on populations. Peary caribou, for example, exist north of the 74th parallel by digging under the snow to feed on vegetation. In 1974–5, heavy snows and freezing rains led to high mortality as the herd starved, unable to reach their food source. Unfortunately, these are the very same weather conditions predicted to become more common as a result of global climate change. In 1993, there were more than 3,000 Peary caribou on Bathurst Island in the High Arctic. By 1997, as a result of repeated bad winters, the number was down to 75, although 2015 surveys show about double that number.

TABLE 3.2 | Characteristics of K-Strategists and r-Strategists

K-Strategists	r-Strategists
Late reproductive age	Early reproductive age
Few, larger young	Many, small young
More care of young	Little care of young
Slower development	Rapid development
Greater competitive ability	Limited competitive ability
Longer life	Shorter life
Larger adults	Smaller adults
Live in generally stable environments	Live in variable or unpredictable environments
Emphasis on efficiency	Emphasis on productivity
Stable populations usually close to carrying capacity	Large population fluctuations usually far below carrying capacity

INTERNATIONAL GUEST STATEMENT

The Roles of Elephants and Logging in Tropical Rain Forest Dynamics | *Aerin Jacob*

Tropical rain forests are often called pristine, evoking images of ecosystems untouched since time immemorial. However, they are anything but stagnant. Tropical rain forests are affected by a wide range of interacting factors, including natural events such as volcanic eruptions, fire, and disease, and human influences such as technology, resource extraction, and war. Although people have affected tropical rain forests for millennia, the extent and intensity of our current impacts are much greater than ever before. Depending on the number, severity, and direction of interacting factors, the effects on plant and animal communities can be direct or indirect, be predictable or unpredictable, and have short- or long-term consequences.

In Kibale National Park, a biodiversity hotspot in western Uganda, a combination of human activities and elephant behaviour triggered an ecological chain reaction that hinders, if not completely suppresses, natural forest regeneration. Forests in this region used to be extensive, with lowland forests connected to montane and alpine forests. Large animals, including elephants, moved freely throughout the landscape; in the 1900s, the colonial government described Uganda as "literally over-run with elephants—big, dangerous, destructive beasts" (Jacob, 2014: 21). To separate wildlife from the growing human population, over 40,000 elephants were shot between 1927 and 1958. Expanding agriculture confined remaining herds to increasingly fragmented protected areas, where ivory poaching in the 1970s and 1980s reduced their numbers by a further 80 per cent. In Kibale, surviving animals concentrated near the relative safety of research stations. Although their global and regional populations were severely reduced, in some parts of the park elephants became locally hyper-abundant, which affected forest dynamics.

Capable of moving long distances and dispersing seeds and nutrients over vast areas, elephants tend to prefer clearings and disturbed areas over mature forest. Locally, their foraging disturbs forest structure and affects the growth of individual trees—making elephants unpopular with the timber industry. Commercial, mechanized logging took place in Kibale during the 1960s, with the degree of subsequent forest recovery depending on the intensity and incidental damage resulting from the harvest. The removal of many canopy-level trees creates unnaturally large gaps in the forest—sometimes bigger than a football field—and changes the microclimate of the forest floor. Freed from dense shade, a thick layer of sun-loving shrubs and vines grows quickly in these gaps. This almost impenetrable tangle of herbaceous vegetation smothers tree seedlings and saplings, provides ground cover for insects and rodents that eat seeds and seedlings, and attracts browsing elephants that trample seedlings and eat or break saplings. Any young tree that somehow escapes the insects, rodents, and elephants then has to contend with increased windthrow. Thus, a positive feedback is created between the herbaceous tangle and elephants that slows or stops secondary succession.

As K-strategists, elephants have slow population growth rates (or low biotic potential). Nevertheless, in the absence of factors regulating growth, their population will grow at its maximal rate. Given that Kibale has been relatively well protected since the early 1990s, we wanted to know how the effects of the elephant population on the forest had changed over time. Because it is difficult and dangerous to directly study elephants by following them on foot through thick forest, from 1996 to 2008 we indirectly estimated their relative abundance by counting the number of trails they made as they moved through vegetation. This count was used to compare elephant abundance in logged and unlogged forest over time. Two patterns emerged: first, the relative abundance of elephants had increased over the last two decades, and second, they were particularly fond of heavily logged forest (Omeja et al., 2014).

While on the surface it appears that elephants eat anything in their path, they are actually selective feeders, preferring foods low in certain defensive compounds and high in energy, protein, and minerals (Rode et al., 2006). Grasses and shrubs make up a large portion of their diet, as well as the leaves, twigs, and branches of small trees and bark from large trees (Omeja et al., 2014). It is possible that the populations of preferred tree species might decrease over time, thereby forcing elephants to change their dietary preferences. However, many tree species can tolerate some degree of damage, so

Rafael Reyna and Colin Chapman

Family group of elephants caught on a camera trap in Kibale National Park, Uganda.

Continued

elephant browsing is not always fatal. Using long-term data on elephant diets and the tree community, we tested whether the abundance of preferred tree species changed. We found that the populations of tree species were not related to the proportion of trees damaged by elephants, nor that elephants shifted their dietary preferences to become more selective feeders.

However, two things remain unknown. First, we do not know how global environmental change might affect the situation. In recent years, climatic changes in western Uganda include an increase in temperature and more erratic rainfall (Jacob, 2014). Such climatic changes can affect the primary productivity and nutritional chemistry of plants, increasing the amounts of fibre and defensive compounds and decreasing the amount of protein in leaves. If nutritional chemistry of their native foods changes, elephants could alter their dietary preferences and might increasingly turn to crop-raiding to meet their nutritional needs (Rode et al., 2006). Today, elephants leave the park only to raid adjacent farms; human–elephant conflict remains one of the highest priority concerns for local people. Second, we still do not know how to restore heavily logged forest. Even when the elephant population was drastically reduced by poaching, heavily logged areas did not recover. Because tropical trees are very long lived, we might not see the negative effects of removing elephants from the ecosystem for decades or centuries to come.

Decisions about how to manage forests should reflect knowledge of the ecosystem's natural disturbance regimes (e.g., frequency, intensity, extent). Therefore, we should concentrate on managing logging that mimics natural forest dynamics, including using low-impact methods to reduce incidental damage, keeping canopy gaps small and far apart, and harvesting large trees.

Aerin Jacob is an ecologist and conservation scientist working in tropical and temperate ecosystems. She is a post-doctoral fellow at the University of Victoria.

Evolution, Speciation, and Extinction

When Charles Darwin published his *On the Origin of Species* in 1859, he started a thought revolution that has seeped into virtually every realm of human ideology. His ideas challenged the static beliefs of many fields with the concept of evolution and the mechanisms by which change can occur. He postulated that over the long term, populations adapt to changing conditions through **evolution**, a change in the genetic makeup of the population over time. This can be achieved through mutations passed on to subsequent generations, eventually creating new species. Within any population, some variation in the genetic composition also may predispose a certain segment of the population to adapt to certain conditions. If change occurs to favour those conditions, then the part of the population genetically better adapted to the new conditions will be more successful. In this way, over time, **natural selection** can lead to changes in the characteristics of a population. Darwin's ideas crystallized following his famous expedition to the Galapagos Islands (Box 3.5).

Phyletic evolution is the process in which a population has undergone so much change that it is no longer able to interbreed with the original population, and a new species is formed. This is the process of **speciation**. It can happen as a result of geographical isolation, when a single population becomes fragmented by a geographical feature, such as a mountain range or a water body, and the populations evolve separately from one another. If conditions differ in the respective environments of the different breeding groups, then natural selection will favour those individuals best suited to those conditions. Another example occurs when part of a population adapts better to a new food source. It is better for these individuals to mate with similar individuals to enhance the ability to exploit that food source, and over time this process might create sufficient differences that they become a different species. Sometimes the effects of these influences may combine.

The evolution of the polar bear from the grizzly bear is one example. It is thought that the polar bear evolved as a separate species from the grizzly bear between 343,000 and 479,000 years ago. Bears with characteristics that helped them hunt seals on ice flows, such as lighter-coloured fur and greater strength, would be relatively more successful in the Far North rather than in the rest of the range, where a brown pelt and greater mobility are advantages. Polar bears also developed genes that helped them process very fatty diets. In this way, a single bear species became two bear species through adaptation to different environments and the process of natural selection. This process of local adaptation and speciation is known as *adaptive radiation*. However, instances of interbreeding between the two species have recently come to light.

Genetic diversity helps to protect species from extinction. The resilience of a species depends partly on the magnitude of the environmental change, how rapidly it takes place, and the capacity of the species' gene pool to respond to these changes. In general, the broader the gene pool, the greater the capacity to adapt to change. Peripheral populations, or populations at the edge of their range (see the "tails" in Figure 2.16), may be especially important as their genetic composition may differ from that of the core population. Canada has many peripheral populations, such as the northern spotted owl (see Chapter 9).

ENVIRONMENT IN FOCUS

BOX 3.5 | The Galapagos Islands

The Galapagos are one of the most famous island groups in the world, and one of the most isolated. The two characteristics are linked. They are rightly famous as the crucible where naturalist Charles Darwin made the observations that he developed in his famous *On the Origin of Species*, and it was the islands' isolation both from the mainland and each other that allowed these characteristics to develop so that they were so noticeable. Darwin's theory now provides the basis for our understanding of life on Earth, explaining the diversity of life.

Situated on the equator, over 900 kilometres from Ecuador, the volcanic Galapagos are surrounded by the swirling cold Humboldt ocean current bringing a mix of species, (some more associated with the Antarctic, such as the Galapagos penguins), many other sea birds feeding on the rich nutrient base, and some of the largest aggregations of sharks on the planet. However, the Galapagos are better known for their land animals such as iguanas. The iguanas differ in morphology and colour from island to island. Darwin noticed there were variations within the same species, and between islands—most famously the mockingbirds or "Darwin's finches"—but did not understand the significance of these variations until he returned to England and started to describe his collection. Other scientists informed him that the "Darwin's finches" were not finches at all, and that what he had thought were different varieties of one species, were, in fact different species that had evolved to exist in different habitats on different islands. Some were seed-eaters, some were cactus-eaters, some were insectivores, some ate ticks from tortoises, and two drank blood from seabirds. Each had developed a specialized bill shape to assist in its search for its particular food.

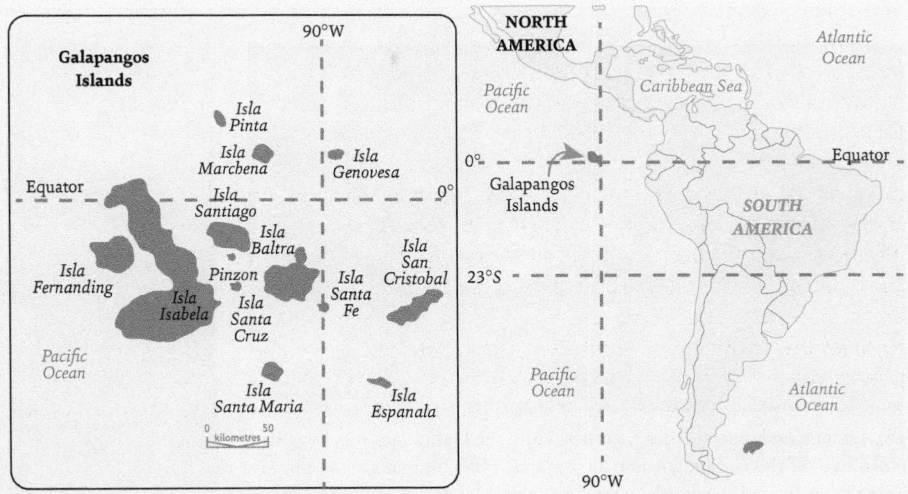

FIGURE 3.12 | The Galapagos Islands.

It took Darwin many years to refine his ideas and he did not publish *On the Origin of Species* until 1859, almost 30 years after his visit to the Galapagos, wherein he laid out his theory in the introduction:

> As many more individuals of each species are born than can possibly survive; and as, consequently, there is a frequently recurring struggle for existence, it follows that any being, if it vary however slightly in any manner profitable to itself, under the complex and sometimes varying conditions of life, will have a better chance of surviving, and thus be naturally selected. From the strong principle of inheritance, any selected variety will tend to propagate its new and modified form. (p. 5)

Now we celebrate the Galapagos for their many endemic species. The islands were made into a national park by the Ecuadorian government in 1959, and they are recognized as one of the most important UNESCO World Heritage Sites.

Many famous species inhabit the Galapagos. One is the world's largest species of tortoise, which varies from island to island in the shape of its shell. Unfortunately, the most famous one, "Lonesome George," the last tortoise found on Pinta Island in 1971, died in 2012 without any progeny. The Galapagos host the world's only seagoing iguana. Food being scarce on land, these iguanas are adapted to feeding on marine algae up to 9 metres below the surface of the sea. Darwin did not like them: "The black Lava rocks on the beach are frequented by large (2–3 ft [60–90 cm]), disgusting clumsy

Philip Dearden

The endemic Galapagos hawk, the top predator on the islands, eats the placenta of a newborn Galapagos sea lion.

Continued

Lizards. They are as black as the porous rocks over which they crawl & seek their prey from the Sea. I call them 'imps of darkness.' They assuredly well become the land they inhabit." (Darwin, 2001: 494). Also living in the islands is the world's only species of flightless cormorant, the Galapagos sea lion, the Galapagos fur seals, and many other endemic species.

The top predator in the islands is the Galapagos hawk, meaning that many species have no natural predators, so they are quite tame and allow people to approach to very close distances. Tourism is strictly controlled to try to maintain these characteristics and protect this unique laboratory of nature for all time.

Philip Dearden

Two famous endemic species together! Here the Galapagos mockingbird picks lice off the Galapagos marine iguana. The iguanas are not merely being friendly with each other; they are cold-blooded reptiles and crave the heat that togetherness brings.

Philip Dearden

The endemic giant tortoise.

It is important to protect these small populations, as discussed in Chapter 14, for their unique genetic properties that increase the resilience of the species to change and that may be crucial for future reintroductions.

Changes in the abiotic environment are not alone in promoting evolutionary change. Species may also change through **co-evolution**, whereby changes in one species cause changes in another. Each species may become an evolutionary force affecting the other. A typical case is a prey species evolving to be more effective in avoiding a predator. In turn, the predator may evolve more efficient hunting techniques to detect the prey. Many such relationships have evolved in the tropical forests, especially between specific plants and animals, because of the long period of evolutionary change that has taken place in such environments. Canada has many examples as well, particularly relating to pollination in which various insects, birds, and bats have evolved to pollinate flowering plants, and, in turn, a great diversity of plant shapes, sizes, and colours have developed as a direct response to the activities of the pollinators.

The processes of evolution described above have always been thought to take place very slowly. However, biologists have identified processes occurring much more quickly as a result of human activities in a process known as **contemporary evolution** (Darimont et al., 2009). One of the main pressures for contemporary evolution is human harvesting of prey populations. In established fisheries, once fish enter targeted age classes, predation by humans occurs at rates two to three times higher than that of natural predators, often exceeding 50 per cent (Stokes and Law, 2000). Fisheries have hence selected for the survival of certain fish, usually small fish. For example, the average weight of groundfish on the Scotian Shelf (southwest of Nova Scotia) declined by 66 per cent between 1970 and 1995 (Leggett and Frank, 2008). These smaller fish produce fewer and less viable eggs, leading scientists to formulate the Big Old Fat Fecund Female Fish (BOFFFF) hypothesis. These old fish are irreplaceable in that they not only contain more eggs but also proportionately more viable eggs. As BOFFFFs are harvested, fish populations have increasingly greater difficulty in achieving replacement population, and a negative feedback loop sets in.

Our predation of terrestrial vertebrates, especially ungulates (for example, cows, pigs, and deer), is also well developed (Darimont et al., in press). Fa et al. (2002) estimated that human predators kill more than 5 million tonnes of wild mammals in neotropical and Afrotropical forests per year. Gauthier et al. (2001) reported that half of the adult mortality of North American snow geese results from hunting. Collins and Kays (2011) showed that large and medium-sized mammals are more likely to die as a result of human activity than to natural causes, with hunting being the main cause of mortality. Human predation induces micro-evolutionary change because we are replacing natural predators as dominant agents of selection.

Traditional harvesting strategies have often concentrated on taking the oldest and largest members of a population. For example, we shoot the largest ram and catch the largest fish, letting the others go so that they can grow larger and

Philip Dearden

Many tropical orchids are products of co-evolution. The flower has evolved to imitate the female wasp of the species that pollinates the flower. The male is deceived into thinking that the flower is a female wasp, flies into the flower, and in so doing picks up pollen that is subsequently taken to the next imitator; thus pollination occurs.

Perspectives on the Environment

Defaunation

We live amid a global wave of anthropogenically driven biodiversity loss: species and population extirpations and, critically, declines in local species abundance. Particularly, human impacts on animal biodiversity are an under-recognized form of global environmental change. Among terrestrial vertebrates, 322 species have become extinct since 1500, and populations of the remaining species show 25% average decline in abundance. Invertebrate patterns are equally dire: 67% of monitored populations show 45% mean abundance decline. Such animal declines will cascade onto ecosystem functioning and human well-being. Much remains unknown about this "Anthropocene defaunation"; these knowledge gaps hinder our capacity to predict and limit defaunation impacts. Clearly, however, defaunation is both a pervasive component of the planet's sixth mass extinction and also a major driver of global ecological change.

—Dirzo et al. (2012: 401).

be harvested later. However, research is indicating that individuals do not have equal capacity to become large and that by eliminating the largest, we are systematically selecting for smaller individuals in the future. In general, individuals' size and growth rates decline, while reproductive investment increases and individuals become reproductively mature at smaller sizes and earlier ages. This is happening with many different species as average sizes continue to decline. Other features may also be influenced by human hunting. For example, Jachmann et al. (1995) reported an increase in tusklessness among African elephants. Tuskless males increased in the population from approximately 1 per cent in the early 1970s to about 10 per cent in 1993, and tusklessness among females rose from 10.5 per cent in 1969 to roughly 38 per cent in 1989 following intense poaching that targeted individuals with ivory-bearing tusks. These trends have since been confirmed at many locations in Africa. The number of tuskless female elephants in Zambia's South Luangwa National Park and adjacent Lupande Game Management Area, for example, increased from 10.5 per cent in 1969 to 38.2 per cent in 1989, the peak of the "ivory wars," as a result of illegal hunting for ivory. Two of the best-known large tuskers on the African continent, Mountain Bull and Satao, were both killed for their ivory deep inside national parks in Kenya in 2014. Many conservationists now wonder whether this tuskless evolutionary trend may be the only way to save Africa's elephants in the long run.

Extinction is the opposite of evolution and represents the elimination of a species that can no longer survive under new conditions. The fossil record suggests that perhaps close to 99 per cent of the species that have lived on Earth are extinct. The fact that we may still have up to 50 million species, more than have ever existed before, indicates that speciation has exceeded the extinction level. However, speciation takes time. Even for r-strategists, it may take hundreds or thousands of years; for K-strategists, it may take tens of thousands of years. Evidence suggests that in recent times, human activities have strongly tipped the scale in favour of extinction over speciation (Box 3.6), as discussed in Chapter 14. Table 3.3 gives some examples of species that at one time existed in Canada but are now extinct.

Extinction, like speciation, is not a smooth, constant process but one punctuated by relatively sudden and catastrophic changes. It appears that multi-cellular life, for example, has experienced five major and many minor mass extinctions. Scientists think that the age of the dinosaurs, a remarkably successful dynasty that relegated mammals to minor ecological roles for more than 140 million years, was brought to an end 65 million years ago by the impact of a large extraterrestrial object. And then the mammals took over. Perhaps the dinosaurs, through the processes of evolution and speciation, managed to out-compete the mammals for a long period and, were it not for the chance impact of the asteroid might still be the dominant animal life. However, this chance occurrence not only led to the demise of the cold-blooded dinosaurs but also favoured the survival of the rodent-like mammals with their smaller body size, less specialization, and greater numbers. Small body size was likely a sign of the mammals' inability to challenge the dinosaurs during the normal evolutionary process; however, small body size became a positive feature favouring survival under the new conditions.

TABLE 3.3 | Some Canadian Vertebrate Species Now Extinct

Species	Distribution	Last Recorded	Probable Causes
Great auk (*Alca impennis*)	Canada, Iceland, UK, Greenland, Russia	1844	Hunting
Labrador duck (*Camptorhynchus labradorius*)	Canada, US	1878	Hunting, habitat alteration
Passenger pigeon (*Ectopistes migratorius*)	Canada, US	1914	Hunting, habitat alteration
Deepwater cisco (*Coregonus johannae*)	Canada, US	1955	Commercial fishing, introduced predators
Longjaw cisco (*Coregonus alpenae*)	Canada, US (Great Lakes)	1978	Commercial fishing, introduced predators

ENVIRONMENT IN FOCUS

BOX 3.6 | Humans and Extinction

Extinction is a natural process. Scientists estimate the average rate of species extinction by examining the fossil record, which suggests that extinctions among mammals occur at the rate of about one every 400 years and among birds one every 200 years. Current extinction rates are difficult to estimate, because we do not have a full inventory of species and so we do not know what we are losing. Based on current rates of habitat destruction for tropical forests, estimates range as high as 100,000 extinct species per year. Many of these extinct species are likely to be undescribed arthropods (invertebrate animals with an external skeleton, a segmented body, and jointed appendages, such as insects and spiders), since these make up the majority of species in tropical forests. The most recent and sophisticated assessments, based on detailed historical assessments rather than on models, suggest that extinction rates across all species groups range from 1 to 5 per cent becoming extinct since 1800 (Hambler et al., 2011). Some groups show rates that are double or triple this range, such as amphibians. If one group had to be selected as a proxy for overall species loss, it would be birds.

More than 22,000 species are listed as threatened on the Red List of the World Conservation Union (IUCN, 2014). Fewer than 10 per cent of the world's species have undergone status assessments, yet more than 30 per cent of amphibians, 23 per cent of mammals, and 12 per cent of birds are threatened, according to the IUCN. Overall, however, corals are declining most rapidly (Figure 3.13). Species at risk of extinction are discussed in more detail in Chapter 14.

Scientists have known for many years that, during and after the last Ice Age (approximately the last 100,000 years), there was a mass extinction of large mammals with Africa losing 18 species; Europe, 19; Asia, 38; Australia and the surrounding area, 26; North America, 43; and South America, 62. Although there was a loss of habitat for many species during the Ice Age, the extinctions affected all climate zones and cold-adapted species as much as other species, and there had been no corresponding losses in earlier ice ages. Researchers have now mapped all these extinctions against the expansion of

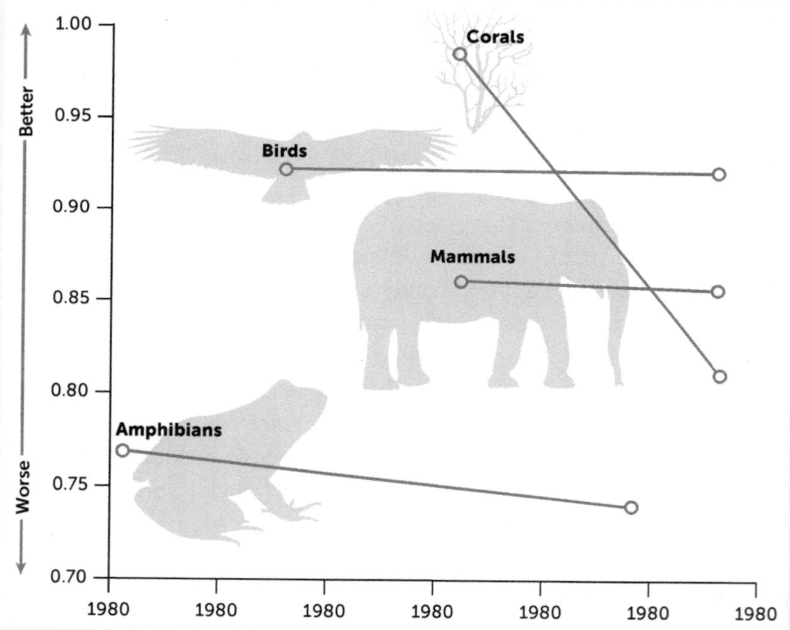

FIGURE 3.13 | The Red List Index shows the rate of change toward extinction over time of various species groups on IUCN's Red List. If a group were stable in number in the least-threatened category, there would be a horizontal line over time with an index of 1. An index of 0 would indicate that all listed species in that group had become extinct. The graph shows that, overall, amphibians are closest to extinction; however, corals are showing the most rapid decline.

Source: Bubb et al. (2009).

humans and found that there is a much stronger correlation of extinction with human presence than with climate. It seems that, even in these early times, humans evolved as a super-predator capable of driving many other species to extinction. For example, in North America the extinctions included ten species of horse, four of camel, two of bison, a native cow, four elephant species, the sabre-toothed tiger, four "antelopes," and the American lion. No such extirpations were associated with the same period in Eurasia. The period also saw a substantial in-migration of humans from the Asian continent, who began to prey on animals unfamiliar with, and therefore not adapted to, human hunting. This hunting, combined with the environmental stresses experienced through habitat alteration and repercussions through the food chain, was sufficient to extirpate these species. Researchers (Waters et al., 2015) have recently discovered direct evidence of prehistoric hunting on horses and camels in Alberta about 13,300 calibrated years before present (yBP).

Charles Kay (1994) studied the subsequent impact of Native Americans on ungulate populations before the onset of European influences. He concludes that even then, humans were the main limiting factor on ungulate populations in the intermountain West and that elk in particular were over-exploited. The people had no effective conservation strategies and hunted to maximize their individual needs, irrespective of environmental impacts. Thus, the image of North America as a vast wilderness unaffected by human activities before the coming of the Europeans appears to be a myth. Even that mightiest symbol of the wild, the grizzly bear, was apparently under pressure from Aboriginal hunters in Alaska (Birkedal, 1993).

It seems difficult to believe that what we now consider primitive weapons, such as this spear and other hunting tools of the Orang Asli peoples of Malaysia, may have enabled humans to hunt many other species to extinction.

There are other examples of the non-random impact of mass extinction on life. The features that make some species successful during ordinary times may be completely unrelated to the new conditions, making life's pathway somewhat chaotic and unpredictable rather than the smooth path that evolutionary theory might suggest.

Impacts of Global Change

Global climate change will have profound impacts on the numbers and distributions of species in the world. Overall, climate is the main determinant of the patterns of life. Changes in temperature and precipitation (discussed in more detail in Chapter 7), will have a profound effect on these patterns. In general, there will be a poleward shift of life zones. The east-to-west orientation of the main terrestrial ecozones of Canada, shown in Figure 2.12, is likely to be replaced by a predominantly north–south pattern. Prairie ecozones will expand and forested ecozones will contract as precipitation levels fall. Species dependent on grasslands will increase their range; those dependent on forests will contract.

Already, there are many documented examples of species range changes in response to climate change. For example, egg-laying, flowering, and spawning are occurring earlier for many species, in some cases disrupting delicate cycles that ensure that insects and other food are available for young animals. Tree swallows across North America advanced egg-laying by as much as nine days from 1959 to 1991. Unfortunately, the hatchlings are now emerging before major insect hatches, and as a result populations of tree swallows are declining because of chick starvation. These types of

Paleontologists work at a dig site of a fossilized dinosaur at Alberta's Dinosaur Provincial Park. More species of extinct dinosaurs have been found and identified at this World Heritage Site than anywhere else in the world.

ENVIRONMENT IN FOCUS

BOX 3.7 | The Burgess Shales

Burgess Shales fossils in the foreground at the Burgess Shales World Heritage Site in Yoho National Park, British Columbia.

Harvard paleontologist Stephen Jay Gould called the Burgess Shales in British Columbia's Yoho National Park the single-most important scientific site in the world. The reason for this superlative is the extensive bed of fossils high on the flanks of Wapta Mountain. They are fossils from the Cambrian era, some 530 million years ago, when there was a great flourishing of diverse life forms. The special feature of the site is that the fossils from this era are preserved in great detail, even down to the soft body parts, such as stomach contents.

The story revealed is one of great diversity at a time when all but one phylum of animal life made a first appearance in the geological record. The site also contains many body patterns for which there are no current counterparts. Thus, it seems as though life could be characterized as three billion years of unicellularity, followed by this enormously diverse Cambrian flowering in a brief five-million-year period, and a further 500 million years of variations on the basic anatomical patterns set in the Cambrian period. Why, or how, this flowering took place is uncertain. It would seem to require a combination of explanations. First, there was literally an open field available for colonization—an environment ripe to support life but with little life in it. Therefore, species did not have to be particularly good competitors to survive. Virtually anything could survive. Since this time, even after mass extinctions, sufficient species have remained as pretty tough competition for any newcomers. Second, it seems as though the early multi-cellular animals must have maintained flexibility for genetic change and adaptability that declined as greater specialization arose and organisms concentrated on refining the successful designs that had already evolved. Furthermore, we have little idea why most of these early experiments in life died out and yet others remained. There seem to be no common traits shared by the survivors to indicate that they were the victors of Darwinian strife. Perhaps just the lucky ones survived.

Gould, in his fascinating book *Wonderful Life*, suggests that these findings challenge our established view of evolution as an inevitable progression over time from the primitive and few to the sophisticated and many. They also radically challenge our view of ourselves as being the logical end point of evolutionary change, the rightful inheritors of the Earth. In Gould's words: "If humanity arose just yesterday as a small twig on one branch of a flourishing tree [of evolution], then life may not, in any genuine sense, exist for us or because of us. Perhaps we are only an afterthought, a kind of cosmic accident, just one bauble on the Christmas tree of evolution" (Gould, 1989: 44). In other words, we should be humble!

changes are expected to continue, and it is predicted that the drought in the Prairie Potholes region (southeastern Alberta and northeastern Montana to southern Manitoba and western Minnesota) will lead to significant reductions in the populations of 14 species of migratory waterfowl; 30 to 50 per cent fewer prairie ponds will hold water in spring by 2060, with an associated 40 to 50 per cent decline in the numbers of ducks settling to breed in the area.

There are interesting human dimensions to range changes for some species. The white-footed mouse, for example, is a prime host for the pathogen that causes Lyme disease. The mouse is expanding its range northward into Quebec as a result of mild winters, and Roy-Dufresne et al. (2015) predict that by the end of 2015 it will have colonized a further 3 degrees of latitude northward, with consequent implications for human health.

Other changes are also taking place, such as in **phenology**, or the ways in which climate affects the seasonal patterns of plants and animals. Bloom time for plants, for example, is influenced by temperature, and rising temperatures associated with global climate change will be reflected in the timing of flowers. Between 2001 and 2012, for example, the first bloom time of 19 Canadian plants moved forward an average of nine days (Gonsamo et al., 2013). These changes in phenology can lead to mismatches in the timing of dependent species. In an oceanic example, the breeding success of Cassin's auklet, a seabird, off the northern tip of Vancouver Island reflects ocean temperatures, as populations of their main zooplankton prey peak earlier than chick arrival in warm years (Hipfner, 2008). Seabirds that rely on zooplankton prey are particularly vulnerable to these mismatches, as zooplankton are short-lived species with a limited window of peak abundance, as discussed in Chapters 2 and 8.

Spring migration is also occurring earlier and fall migration later for many species. For example, 25 migratory bird species are arriving in Manitoba earlier than they did some 60 years ago; only two are arriving later. However, as usual, there are complications. Short-distance migrants are migrating earlier because they can read the local cues that conditions in their destination are right for them. However, migrating birds in Costa Rica have few cues to tell them that conditions in Canada are right for their return. Consequently, they arrive at their normal time only to find that the food supply has already waned.

Some species will be able to adapt to these rapid changes; others will not. For example, the quino checkerspot butterfly, found in California and Mexico in very restricted distributions, was a prime candidate for extinction a decade ago, as expanding urban areas caused its habitat in California to decline to two small colonies, and temperatures further south in Mexico became too hot for the caterpillar's food plant to survive. However, completely unexpectedly, the butterfly turned up in a new, cooler, higher-altitude habitat in California and now lays its eggs on a completely different plant type. Had this habitat also been destroyed, this adaptation strategy would not have been available, highlighting the importance of protecting areas as insurance against future climate change.

Notwithstanding such rapid adaptations (and undoubtedly there will be many more surprises), extinctions will occur because some species are incapable of adjusting at such rapid rates. Already, the US has listed the polar bear as threatened under the Endangered Species Act as a result of rapid melting of the sea ice that the bears depend on for hunting seals. Canadian scientists are reporting similar findings, with underweight bears being reported in a number of locations (Rode et al., 2012; Stirling and Derocher, 2012).

Scientists predict that 9 to 52 per cent of all terrestrial species (up to 1 million plants and animals) will be on an irreversible path to extinction by 2050. These figures appear to be supported by past temperature changes. Mayhew et al. (2008) analyzed the fossil record for the past 520 million years against estimates of low-latitude sea-surface temperature for the same period. They found that global biodiversity (the richness of families and genera) is related to temperature and has been relatively low during warm "greenhouse" phases, while during the same phases the extinction and origination rates of taxonomic lineages have been relatively high.

These changes will affect marine ecosystems as much as, if not more than, terrestrial ecosystems. Migratory whales, for example, will face shrinking crucial Antarctic foraging zones, which will contain less food and be farther away. Levels of global warming predicted over the next 40 years will lead to winter sea-ice coverage of the southern ocean declining by up to 30 per cent in some key areas. Migratory whales may need to travel 200 to 500 kilometres farther south to find the "frontal zones" that are their crucial foraging areas. The affected migratory whale species will include the blue whale, the Earth's largest living creature, and the humpback whale, only now coming back from the brink of extinction after populations were decimated by commercial whaling, mainly during the first half of the twentieth century.

Both species build up the reserves that sustain them throughout the year in the frontal zones, which host large populations of their primary food source, krill. Shrinking ice-covered areas affect krill production in two ways: sea ice is a refuge for krill larvae in winter and an area of intense algal blooms on which the krill feed in summer. Krill is so fundamental to the southern ocean ecosystem that the impact will not be confined to whales but will also affect seals, seabirds, and penguins as well as fisheries productivity. Frontal zones are areas where water masses of different temperatures meet. They are associated with upwelling of nutrients supporting large plankton populations on which species such as Antarctic krill feed. As frontal zones move southward, they also move closer together, reducing the overall area of foraging habitat available. Since the krill depends on sea ice, less sea ice is also expected to reduce the abundance of food for whales in the feeding areas (Tynan and Russell, 2008).

Implications

This chapter emphasizes that ecosystems are dynamic entities that change over time. Without such change, we would not have evolved, and the dinosaurs would not have become extinct. The main implication is that we should accept and try to understand the nature of these changes and be able to distinguish between those essentially the result of natural processes and those that are the result of human activities. We cannot impose static management regimes on dynamic ecosystem processes without causing ecological disruption. A visible reminder of this was the fire-suppression policy characteristic of many national park services, which often ignored the natural role of fire in these ecosystems. When fires did start in such ecosystems, the buildup of fuel was often so great as to cause a major and very damaging fire, as happened in Yellowstone National Park in the US in 1988. Most park services have abandoned such practices for a more dynamic approach that tries to mimic the role of natural fires through prescribed burning programs.

Unfortunately, the temporal and spatial scales of ecosystem change are often so great that they are very difficult to observe in the human lifespan. This limitation has been recognized as the **shifting baselines** phenomenon, where

ENVIRONMENT IN FOCUS

BOX 3.8 | What You Can Do: Caring for Your Ecosystem

It may seem that, with all the complexities of ecosystem change, an individual can do little to influence the situation. However, this is far from the case, since many changes are brought about by individuals, and the sum total of their actions adds up to the tremendous changes described in this chapter. Specific actions that you can take include:

- Minimize your contribution to global warming. The many ways of doing this are outlined in Chapter 7.
- Avoid the actions that speed up eutrophication processes: polluting waterways, using excessive fertilizer on your garden, and using phosphate-based detergents and other nutrient additives.
- Buy produce from organic farmers, who do not use chemical additives.
- Do not introduce new species into the environment either deliberately by releasing them or inadvertently by, for example, transporting their seeds or fragments.
- Join or start a campaign to eradicate an alien invasive species.
- Get to know the local flora and fauna in your area so that you can recognize alien invasive species.
- All change is not bad. Join a group that is trying to change an ecosystem for the better (sometimes called ecological restoration).

every generation sets the baseline for change at the beginning of their own existence, rather than from the beginning of human-induced change. We do not realize how full the skies of the Prairies must have been with migrating waterfowl prior to the development of intensive agriculture, for example, because we were not there to witness it. Scientists are only now beginning to unravel the mysteries of some of these dynamic interactions between the different components of the ecosphere. There are complicated feedback loops and synergistic relations. In some cases, positive feedback loops are strengthened and accelerate undesirable changes that underlie some of the most serious environmental challenges facing humanity, such as global warming. Global climate change will place considerable stress on many species in terms of their limits of tolerance. This will lead to changes in range and abundance, and some species will become extinct. Climate change will also influence the functioning of ecosystems, the characteristic ways in which energy and chemicals flow through the plants, herbivores, carnivores, and soil organisms that are the living components of ecosystems, as described earlier in this chapter. Productivity will change; in some places it will increase, in others decline. Food webs will be disrupted as predators and prey react differently to the changing conditions. When faced with such dynamic ecosystem changes, we must use equally dynamic thinking to confront the challenges of the future.

One manifestation of such dynamic thinking is efforts to reverse defaunation through the assisted translocation of species. Humans have a long history of moving other species around, but rarely for conservation reasons. In the future this may have to become a major aspect of efforts to maintain global biodiversity. Species may be translocated to other areas to reinforce dwindling populations of the same species, or to replace populations that have been extirpated. However, thinking has now progressed beyond such measures to consider moving species outside their normal range, for example, in anticipation of future climate change or to replace extinct species that played a similar ecological role. Alternatively "de-extinction" may be considered, whereby extinct species are brought back to life using clonal technologies of synthetic biology. In **rewilding**, the goal is not to reintroduce one species but rather to restore the ecological processes that underlie natural systems, complete with their ecological components. Whatever the approaches taken, they are all very complex and expensive. The first priority must be to protect the remaining natural systems from the ongoing degradation from human activities that appears to be unstoppable. This is discussed more fully in Chapter 14.

Summary

1. Ecosystems change over time. The speed of change varies from very slow, over evolutionary time scales, to rapid, caused by events such as landslides and volcanic eruptions.
2. Ecological succession occurs as a slow adaptive process involving the gradual replacement of one assemblage of species by another as conditions change over time.

Primary succession occurs on surfaces not previously vegetated, such as surfaces exposed by glacial retreat; secondary succession occurs on previously vegetated surfaces, such as abandoned fields. Fire is an important element in ecosystem change. Some ecosystems, such as much of the boreal forest, have evolved in conjunction with periodic fires. Fire suppression in such ecosystems can be detrimental to these natural processes.

3. Ecosystems tend toward a state of dynamic equilibrium in which the internal processes of an ecosystem adjust for changes in external conditions. Not all ecosystems are equal in their ability to withstand perturbations. Inertia is the ability of an ecosystem to withstand change; resilience is the ability to recover to the original state following disturbance. Both contribute to the stability of the system.
4. Important causes of ecosystem change include the introduction of alien species and the removal of native keystone species.
5. Feedback mechanisms exist in ecosystems that may either exacerbate (positive feedback loops) or mitigate (negative feedback loops) change.
6. Population change occurs as a result of the balance between factors promoting growth (e.g., increase in birth rates or reduction in death rates) and those promoting reduction (e.g., declines in birth or survival rates or increase in death rates).
7. Different species have different reproductive strategies. K-strategists produce few offspring but devote considerable effort to ensuring that these offspring reach maturity. In comparison, r-strategists produce large numbers of young starting early in life and over a short time period and devote little or no energy to parental care.
8. Populations adapt to changing conditions over the long term through evolution. Evolution results in the formation of new species as a result of divergent natural selection responding to environmental change. This is speciation. Extinction results in the elimination of species that can no longer survive under new conditions.
9. Although evolution can take thousands of years, scientists now detect evolutionary changes on the scale of tens of years as a result of humans acting as predators on a massive scale.
10. Global climate change will have a significant impact on the distribution and abundance of species. Some will flourish. Others will decline. Some will become extinct.
11. The concept of shifting baselines makes it difficult for individuals to grasp the scale of changes that have taken place in the environment prior to their existence.
12. Efforts to reverse defaunation will increase as biodiversity declines continue, and assisted translocation of species and rewilding will become established parts of environmental management approaches.
13. Every effort needs to be made to maintain the current extent of global natural ecosystems to minimize the need for these complex and expensive management approaches.

Key Terms

albedo
alien species
allelopathic
biotic potential
butterfly effect
carrying capacity
climatic climax
climax community
co-evolution
contemporary evolution
Convention on Biological Diversity
cyclic succession
disturbances
dynamic equilibrium
ecological restoration
ecological succession
ecotones
edaphic climaxes
evolution
extinction
Gaia hypothesis
inertia
intermediate disturbance hypothesis
invasive
K-strategists
mature community
natural selection
negative feedback
phenology
polar amplification
population
population density
positive feedback loop
prescribed burning
primary succession
resilience
rewilding
r-strategists
secondary succession
seed bank
seral
serotiny
shifting baselines
speciation
species
synergism

Questions for Review and Critical Thinking

1. What are different kinds of succession? Can you identify different seral stages in your area?
2. What is an edaphic climax? Can you find some local examples and identify the dominant limiting factor?
3. How does the concept of succession relate to environmental management?
4. How important was fire in the development of vegetation patterns in your region? Is there a fire management plan in your region? If so, what are its management goals?
5. Identify the main non-native plant and animal species in your region. What effect are they having on the local ecosystems? What are the implications for management?
6. Can you think of any other examples of negative and positive feedback loops in the ecosphere besides those mentioned in the text?
7. Are K-strategists or r-strategists most vulnerable to environmental change?
8. What is co-evolution? Can you think of any examples of co-evolution among species in Canada?
9. What place in Canada has been called the most important scientific site in the world, and why?
10. What are the implications of global climate change on species distributions and abundance?
11. How far should we go in species de-extinction? What are some of the challenges that such an approach brings?
12. What is "rewilding"? Why do we need it?
13. Some of the best-known rewilding schemes relate to the Prairies. Find out what has been suggested. Do you think this is feasible?

Related Websites

Hinterland Who's Who: Invasive Alien Species in Canada
www.hww.ca/en/issues-and-topics/invasive-alien-species-in.html

Invasive Species
www.invadingspecies.com

www.oag-bvg.gc.ca/internet/English/parl_cesd_200803_06_e_30132.html

www.imo.org/ourwork/environment/ballastwatermanagement/Pages/Default.aspx

globallast.imo.org

www.invasivespeciesinfo.gov/international/canada.shtml

IUCN Red List of Threatened Species
www.redlist.org

The Rewilding Institute
http://rewilding.org/rewildit/

Further Readings

Note: This list comprises works relevant to the subject of the chapter but not cited in the text. All cited works are listed in the References at the end of the book.

Butchart, S.H.M., et al. 2010. "Global biodiversity: Indicators of recent declines," *Science* 328: 1164–8.

Environment Canada and US Environmental Protection Agency. 2009. *State of the Great Lakes 2009*. Ottawa and Washington: Governments of Canada and the United States of America.

Gould, S.J. 2002. *I Have Landed: The End of the Beginning in Natural History*. New York: Harmony Books.

McNeely, J.A. 2001. *The Great Reshuffling: Human Dimensions of Invasive Alien Species*. Gland, Switzerland: World Conservation Union.

Martin, T.G., P. Arcese, and N. Scheerder. 2011 "Browsing down our natural heritage: Deer impacts on vegetation structure and songbird populations across an island archipelago," *Biological Conservation* 144: 459–69.

Noonburg, E.G., B.J. Shuter, and P.A. Abrams. 2003. "Indirect effects of zebra mussels (*Dreissena polymorpha*) on the planktonic food web," *Canadian Journal of Fisheries and Aquatic Sciences* 60, 11: 1353–68.

Quammen, D. 1988. *The Flight of the Iguana: A Sidelong View of Science and Nature*. New York: Touchstone Books.

Go to www.oupcanada.com/DeardenMitchell5e to access additional learning tools on your smartphone, tablet, or PC.

CHAPTER FOUR

Ecosystems and Matter Cycling

Learning Objectives

- To understand the nature of matter
- To be able to describe why human intervention in biogeochemical cycles is a fundamental factor behind many environmental issues
- To learn the main components and pathways of the phosphorus, nitrogen, sulphur, and carbon cycles
- To be able to identify the main components of the hydrological cycle and the nature of human intervention in the cycle
- To understand the causes, effects, and management approaches to eutrophication and acid deposition

Introduction

The collapse in the Atlantic puffin population, described in Chapter 2, was a result of human interference with energy flow through the ecosystem. There are implications, however, for other aspects of ecosystem functioning. Puffins and most other seabirds play an important role in recycling nutrients, particularly phosphorus, from marine to terrestrial ecosystems. If these systems are disturbed, then the efficiency of the recycling mechanisms can be greatly reduced. Since the phosphorus cycle has very limited recycling capabilities from aquatic to terrestrial systems, the impact of interfering with it in this way could be substantial. This chapter explains how matter, such as phosphorus, cycles in the ecosphere and some of the implications of disturbing these cycles. The most critical environmental challenges facing the Earth, such as global warming, acid deposition, and the spread of dead zones in the ocean, result from cycle disturbance. Consequently, it is critical that you understand the nature of biogeochemical cycles if you are to fully appreciate the nature of these problems and their potential solutions.

This chapter is divided into three sections. First, it describes four biogeochemical cycles. Second, it outlines and explains the hydrological cycle. Finally, it examines the environmental consequences of human actions on these cycles and highlights a few of the important ways you can be a part of the effort to mitigate these changes.

Matter

Everything is either matter or energy. However, in contrast to the supply of energy, which is virtually infinite, the supply of matter on Earth is limited to that which we now have. **Matter**, unlike energy, has mass and takes up space. Matter is what things are made of and is composed of the 92 natural and 17 synthesized chemical elements such as carbon, oxygen, hydrogen, and calcium. *Atoms* are the smallest particles that still exhibit the characteristics of the element. Subatomic particles include *protons*, *neutrons*, and *electrons*, which have different electrical charges. At a larger scale, the same kinds of atoms can join together to form molecules. When two different atoms come together, they are known as a **compound**. Water (H_2O), for example, is a compound made up of two hydrogen atoms (H) and one oxygen atom (O). Four major kinds of organic compounds—carbohydrates, fats, proteins, and nucleic acids—make up living organisms.

Matter also exists in three different states (solid, liquid, and gas) and can be transformed from one to another by changes in heat and/or pressure. At the existing temperatures at the surface of the Earth, we have only one representative of the liquid state of matter, water. We can also readily see water in its other two states as ice (solid) or vapour (clouds).

Just as the laws of thermodynamics explain energy flow, the **law of conservation of matter** helps us to understand how matter is transformed. This law tells us that matter can be neither created nor destroyed but merely transformed from one form into another. Thus, matter cannot be consumed so that it no longer exists; it will always exist but in a changed form. When we throw something away, it is still with us, on this planet, as matter somewhere. There *is* no "away." However, what we do with that matter is very important, as outlined by Jutta Gutberlet in the "International Guest Statement" on recycling in Brazil. All pollution stems from this law. The huge "Superstacks" on large smelters such as at Inco in Sudbury, Ontario, do not dispose of waste (see Chapter 12); they just disperse those wastes over a much larger area. The matter dispersed is the same and ultimately falls as acid deposition somewhere else. The same is true for all the wastes that we wash down our sinks. They do not disappear but collect in larger water bodies and create pollution problems.

Subic/iStockphoto

According to the law of matter, emissions from stacks such as these do not simply disappear but end up somewhere else, often with undesirable consequences, such as acid deposition or global warming.

MOF/iStockphoto

Water is the only substance that occurs in all three phases of matter at the ambient temperatures of the Earth's surface.

Biogeochemical Cycles

For millions of years, matter has been moving among different components of the ecosphere. These cycles are as essential to life as the energy flow described in Chapter 2. About 30 of the naturally occurring elements are a necessary part of living things. These are known as **nutrients** and may be further

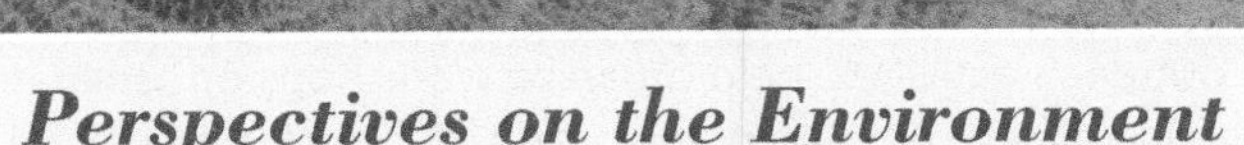

Perspectives on the Environment

We know from studies of chemistry that our bodies are reorganized star-dust, recycled again and again, so that, truly, our bones are of corals made.

—Rowe (1993)

classified into **macronutrients**, which are needed in relatively large amounts by all organisms, and **micronutrients**, required in lesser amounts by most species. About 97 per cent of organic mass is composed of six nutrients: carbon, oxygen, hydrogen, nitrogen, phosphorus, and sulphur. These nutrients are cycled continuously among different components of the ecosphere in characteristic paths known as **biogeochemical cycles.**

Action-Oriented Research on Community Recycling in São Paulo, Brazil

Jutta Gutberlet

With more than half of the world's population already living in urban spaces, increased generation of solid waste is a serious concern most cities have to deal with. Avoiding the generation of waste and managing the waste appropriately are therefore critical aspects in making communities more sustainable. Non-existent or improper waste disposal arrangements generate health risks and cause harm to the environment, finally also affecting our climate. In the global South, according to UN-HABITAT (2010), more than 828 million, or 33 per cent of the urban population, resides in poor neighbourhoods, often not covered by regular collection of household waste. Under these circumstances, informal sector recyclers and community-based organizations, such as associations or cooperatives, are vital players in waste management.

The recyclable material embedded in household waste is a vital resource for informal waste collectors, organized recyclers, and micro-recycling entrepreneurs. Being able to access these materials represents a basic need to the commons. Greater resource efficiency can be achieved by following the four R's—rejecting, reducing, reusing, and recycling materials—while landfilling and incinerating waste reiterates prevailing unsustainable exploitation and the waste of natural resources. A cyclic approach integrating production, consumption, and final destination, as demanded by industrial ecology, life-cycle studies, material flow, and ecological footprint analysis is necessary for building more sustainable cities. Thus integrating the informal recycling sector and improving working conditions and livelihoods of waste collectors and recyclers are important steps toward resource recovery, particularly in the context of the global South.

My research aims to contribute to building more sustainable, healthier, and more inclusive communities, and to challenging the prevailing growth-oriented economic development. The focus is on understanding alternatives related to waste generation, selective waste collection, and recycling. The research methodology is participatory and action oriented.

Since 2005 I have been working within the Participatory Sustainable Waste Management (PSWM) program, which started as a bilateral research project in the metropolitan region of São Paulo, Brazil, and is hosted by the Community-Based Research Laboratory (CBRL) at the University of Victoria (www.pswm.uvic.ca). The program helps recycling cooperatives to become more resilient and public policies more inclusive. The program encompasses strategies and community activities focused on the empowerment of the participants, by improving the working conditions in the recycling cooperatives, working toward a fair income for the resource recovery service, diminishing health risk factors, promoting inclusive public policies, and building environmental awareness as steps toward co-production in waste management.

Participatory sustainable waste management means "solid waste recovery, reuse and recycling practices with organized and empowered recycling co-ops supported with public policies, embedded in solidarity economy and targeting social equity and environmental sustainability" (Gutberlet, 2009: 171). The PSWM program puts in practice this approach, which facilitates cyclical use of resources, generates livelihoods, and provides opportunities for human development and empowerment through cooperative recycling. Selective waste collection means recovering resources, sparing virgin materials and diminishing environmental degradation and biodiversity loss, and ultimately caring for current and future generations. Selective waste collection happens worldwide, particularly in the global South, where this activity generates work and employment among the most vulnerable population. Improving their working conditions and expanding the activity ultimately also translates into stronger local economies and overall reduced social vulnerability, adding to more sustainable communities.

In Latin America, Asia, and Africa, in particular, an extensive informal sector is involved in collecting and separating recyclable materials from the waste stream (Gutberlet, 2012,

Continued

2008a; Scheinberg et al., 2010; Wilson et al., 2012). In Brazil, for example, there are approximately 600,000 individuals involved in this activity. Yet most of these recyclers (*catadores*) remain extremely poor and marginalized.

The research my graduate students and I undertake has revealed diverse ways in which these informal collectors are redefining waste as a resource and has underscored the difficulties encountered in accessing recyclable materials and receiving fair pay for the service of collection and separation. Many of the organized groups are collaborating in regional networks, engaging in collective commercialization and other activities strengthening this social movement. Past research has contributed to increase the level of organization among the *catadores*, which is bringing positive change toward community-led recycling as a poverty reduction strategy that also improves environmental health in many cities in Brazil. We have investigated the potential for integrating organic waste management with urban agriculture, thereby further reducing the volume of waste on landfills and returning valuable nutrients to depleted soils (Yates and Gutberlet, 2011). The majority of the organized recyclers in Brazil, and particularly their leaders, are women. The activity provides them with opportunities for income generation and, most important, it allows for their capacity-building and collective engagement. Cooperative recycling contributes to the human development of those who are impoverished and socially excluded from society. As part of the PSWM program, researchers engage in community outreach activities, help organize workshops or seminars, produce video documentaries, and conduct participatory and action-oriented research interventions in Brazil and other countries (Tremblay and Gutberlet, 2011). These activities help increase the awareness among governments and communities about waste co-production issues and the need to decrease waste generation. Overall the research illustrates the value of source separation in reducing waste. Lessons have been shared about the ways in which to inform policymakers on sustainable and socially responsible waste management, both by way of academic publications and (more effectively) through video documentaries, reports, booklets, and other more accessible forms of information dissemination. Video is an important tool for empowering participants and informing the public and local governments about the work of the recyclers and their livelihood concerns.

A major current threat to informal and community recycling is related to privatization and corporate approaches in waste management, particularly with the introduction of waste-to-energy incineration technology (Gutberlet, 2010). Municipalities are tempted by an apparently quick solution to their waste crisis, and sometimes they buy into this technology, most often locking into long-term contracts (30 or more years). Not only does this form of waste management cause environmental hazards, but it also dismisses the fact that resource recovery and recycling are more socially and environmentally friendly, generate employment, and contribute to resource conservation. The research described here builds on participatory epistemologies opposing these current trends and demonstrates the social, environmental, and economic value in cooperative recycling. The findings contribute to designing inclusive solid waste policies that propel community building and disseminate more sustainable lifestyles.

Jutta Gutberlet

Selective waste collection at the cooperative Coopercata in Mauá, Brazil.

Courtesy Jutta Gutberlet

Jutta Gutberlet is an associate professor of geography at the University of Victoria. She directs the Community-Based Research Laboratory and undertakes research primarily in South America on community-based waste treatment.

Figure 4.1 shows a generalized model of such a cycle. Like all the subsequent diagrams of cycles in this chapter, it exemplifies the types of simplifying models that scientists construct to try to represent the vast complexity of Earth processes, as described in Chapter 1 and illustrated in Figure 1.16. Nutrients can be stored in the different compartments shown in Figure 4.1 for varying amounts of time. In general, there is a large, relatively slow-moving abiotic pool that may be in the atmosphere or the lithosphere and is chemically unusable by the biotic part of the ecosystem, or is physically remote. There is a more rapidly interacting exchange pool between the biotic and abiotic components. Nutrients move at various speeds from the biotic to the abiotic pools. For example, very rapid exchange takes place through respiration as carbon and oxygen move rapidly between the biotic and atmospheric components. The elements that now make up your body have undergone millions of years of recycling through these various compartments. You are a product of recycling!

Ecosystems also vary substantially in terms of the speed of cycling and the relative proportion of nutrients in each compartment. Some systems have nutrient-poor soils, for example, and have developed different mechanisms to store nutrients

Slash-and-burn agriculture helps transfer nutrients from the biomass to the soil to increase agricultural productivity. It is a common agricultural practice in the tropics, where most of the nutrients are in the biomass and not in the soil. This photograph shows such fields cut in the forest in the Cardamom Mountains of Cambodia. The soils rapidly lose fertility owing to the burning of the biomass, and they are then abandoned for secondary succession to occur.

in other compartments. Tropical forest ecosystems are classic examples. Most of the nutrients are stored in the biomass as opposed to the soil system (Table 4.1). When leaves fall to the ground, they are rapidly mined for nutrients by plant roots before those nutrients have a chance to be leached out of the system. This is why the root zone of trees in the tropical forest is generally very shallow. There is no point in going deep to find nutrients; they must be harvested as quickly as possible from leaf-fall on the surface. In contrast, many temperate forests have soils of high fertility. Removal of the nutrients in the biomass, through logging for example, does not remove as high a proportion of the site nutrient capital as removal in tropical ecosystems. This is discussed in more detail in Chapter 9.

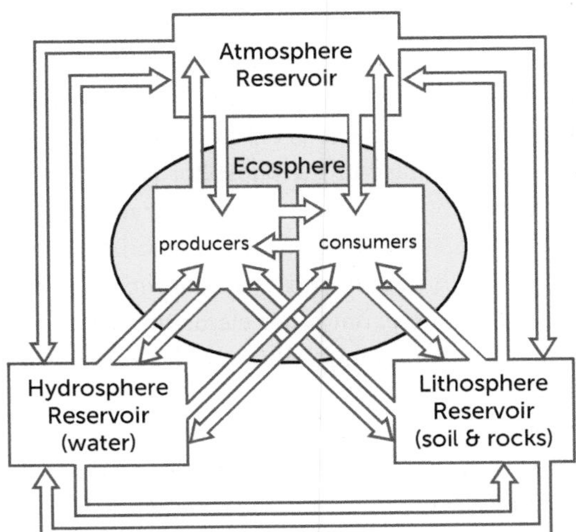

FIGURE 4.1 | Each nutrient is stored and released by components of the Earth's systems. Different nutrients follow slightly different paths through the systems and are stored and released at different rates.

Speed of cycling may also change within a cycle, depending on the nutrient of concern and the time of year. For the carbon cycle, for example, there is greater uptake of CO_2 in spring and summer as deciduous trees grow leaves. In fall, there is a correspondingly greater release as the leaves fall off and decompose (see Box 4.1). On average, a carbon dioxide molecule stays in the atmospheric component of the cycle from five to seven years. This is known as the *residence time*. It takes, on average, 300 years for a carbon molecule to pass through the lithosphere, cryosphere, atmosphere, hydrosphere, and biotic components of the carbon cycle. By way of contrast, it may take a water molecule two million years to make a complete cycle. The speed of cycling is influenced by such factors as the chemical reactivity of the substance. Carbon, for example, participates in many chemical reactions. It also occurs as a gas. In general, a gaseous phase allows for a speeding up of a cycle, because gas molecules move more quickly than molecules in the other states of matter.

Cycles can be classified according to the main source of their matter. **Gaseous cycles**, as the name would suggest, have most of their matter in the atmosphere. The nitrogen cycle is a good example. **Sedimentary cycles**, such as the phosphorus and sulphur cycles, hold most of their matter in the lithosphere. In general, elements in sedimentary cycles tend to cycle more slowly than those in gaseous cycles, and the elements may be locked into geological formations for millions of years.

Under natural conditions, recycling rates between components achieve a balance over time in which inputs and outputs are equal. Human activity serves to change the speed of transference between the different components of the cycles. Many of our pollution problems result from a human-induced buildup in one or more components of a cycle that cannot be effectively dissipated by natural processes. It is similar to when you consume more alcohol than your body can effectively process and you wake up with a headache.

TABLE 4.1 | Approximate Distributions of Carbon and Nitrogen in Temperate and Tropical Rain Forests

	Tropical Rain Forest (%)	Temperate Rain Forest (%)
Carbon in vegetation	75	50
Carbon in litter and soil	25	50
Nitrogen in biomass	50	6
Nitrogen in biomass above ground	44	3

ENVIRONMENT IN FOCUS

BOX 4.1 | The Decomposers

In Chapter 2, attention was drawn to the importance of decomposer organisms and detritus food chains. These are the main means by which nutrients in the biotic component of the ecosphere are returned to the abiotic so that plants can once again use them. Photosynthesis has been described as the process of making a complicated product out of simple components; decomposition is the reverse process of making simple components out of that complicated product.

Decomposer organisms such as fungi may attack leaves that are still on the plant; the fungi release products such as sugars, which are then washed to the ground by rainfall. Once leaves fall to the ground, they are broken down progressively by various groups of organisms. Larger organisms such as earthworms, slugs, snails, beetles, ants, and termites help to break up the leaf material initially. Many gardeners are fully aware of the ability of slugs, for example, to devour green leaves in great quantities.

Fungi and heterotrophic bacteria further break down the organic matter, releasing more resistant carbohydrates, followed by cellulose and lignin. The humus—the organic layer in the soil—is composed mainly of products that can resist rapid breakdown. A chemical process, oxidation, is mainly responsible for the decay of this material.

As everyone who has witnessed leaf decay in autumn knows, the process can occur quite rapidly. The speed varies depending on the environment. Warm environments tend to promote more rapid microbial activity. Leaf decay in the tropics takes place in a matter of weeks. In the boreal forest, however, where conditions are cold and the leaves, such as spruce and pine needles, quite resistant, **recycling** of the nutrients held in the leaves may take decades. Overall, the average recycling time for organic material in the wet tropics is five months; in the boreal forest, it is 350 years. The high amounts of lignin found in leaves of needle-leafed trees help to protect the trees against freezing conditions but offer little food value to decomposers, so decay is slow. In comparison, deciduous trees, such as maple, have a high reward for decomposers: high nitrogen levels and little protective lignin, so they decay very quickly. However, researchers are now discovering that the slow breakdown of organic matter in the boreal forest also plays a major role in global carbon storage. As the forests are removed through logging and other activities, not only does the supply of leaves disappear, but the built-up carbon is released through either burning associated with these activities or the higher ground temperatures resulting from the reduced amount of shade.

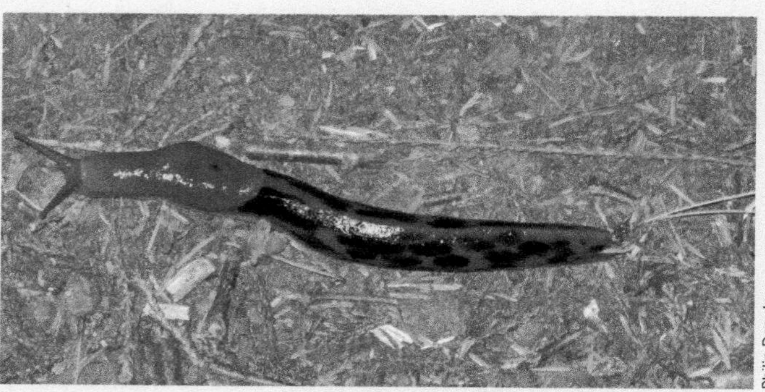

Philip Dearden

Slugs play an important role in breaking down vegetable matter. In the wet west coast forests, the biomass of slugs is greater than that of any other animal in the ecosystem.

In addition to the biogeochemical cycles, some attention will be given in this chapter to the hydrological cycle. This cycle is critical to all other cycles, since water plays a major role in the mobilization and transportation of materials. The energy for this, as with all other aspects of the cycles, ultimately comes from the sun. Photosynthesis powers the biotic aspects of the cycles, and atmospheric circulation, fuelled by the sun's energy, controls the water power that is so important for weathering and erosion processes.

Sedimentary Cycles

Sedimentary cycles mobilize materials from the lithosphere to the hydrosphere and back to the lithosphere. Some, such as sulphur, may involve a gaseous phase, while others, such as phosphorus, do not. These cycles rely essentially on geological uplift over long periods to complete the cycle. Human actions interfere with the speed at which many of these cycles occur and can result in serious environmental problems. The lack of a gaseous phase in the phosphorus cycle means that the cycle is missing one potential route for more rapid recycling, which can lead to problems when mobilization rates are increased through human activity. Phosphorus and sulphur will be discussed here, but other elements, such as calcium, magnesium, and potassium, follow similar pathways.

Phosphorus (P)

Phosphorus, a macronutrient incorporated into many organic molecules, is essential for metabolic energy use. It is relatively rare on the Earth's surface in relation to biological demand, so it is essential that phosphorus cycles efficiently between components. Many organisms have devised means of storing this element preferentially in their tissues, and phosphorus moves very readily within plants from older tissues to more active growth sites. Deciduous trees may recirculate up to 30 per cent of their phosphorus back to their more permanent components before the leaves fall, in an effort to preserve the nutrient.

Under natural circumstances, phosphorus is a prime example of a nutrient held in a tight circulation pattern between the biotic and abiotic components. Replenishment rates through weathering and soil availability are limited; thus, the amount retained by the biomass is quite critical. The residence time of phosphorus in terrestrial systems can be up to 100 years before it is leached into the hydrosphere. Phosphorus is often the dominant limiting factor (Chapter 2) in freshwater aquatic systems and for plant growth in terrestrial soils. Agricultural productivity relies heavily on augmenting this supply (auxiliary energy flow) through fertilizer application. Gruber and Galloway (2008) suggest that both the nitrogen and the carbon cycles in the ocean are ultimately controlled by phosphorus and, since these cycles are key to the global warming response, the phosphorus cycle will be a main determinant of global futures.

Box 4.2 outlines the impact humans have on the phosphorus cycle.

The availability of phosphorus in the soil is influenced by soil acidity. Acidity is measured on the pH scale, which is discussed in more detail later in this chapter. Below pH 5.5, for example, phosphorus reacts with aluminum and iron to form insoluble compounds. Above pH 7, the same thing happens in combination with calcium. Obviously, things that change soil pH, such as acid precipitation, can have a critical effect on phosphorus availability. This is an example of the kind of synergistic reaction discussed in Chapter 3, in which the combination of either high or low pH values with low phosphorus availability, as a result of chemical reactions, can have a stronger effect than the sum of the two individually.

Rocks in the Earth's crust are the main reservoir of phosphorus (Figure 4.2). Geological uplift and subsequent weathering (Box 4.3) make phosphorus available in the soil, where it is taken up by plant roots. Phosphate ions are the main source of phosphorus for plants and are released from slowly dissolving minerals such as iron, calcium, and magnesium phosphates. Many higher plants have a mutualistic relationship with soil fungi, or mycorrhizae, which helps them gain improved access to phosphorus in the soil. Once incorporated into plant material, the phosphorus may be passed on to organisms at higher trophic levels.

The Head-Smashed-In UNESCO World Heritage Site in southern Alberta is rich in phosphorous, as Native peoples used the 11-metre-high cliff to kill stampeding bison by driving them off the edge. The decomposed bones left large deposits of this macronutrient behind.

Animal wastes are a significant source of phosphorus and return to the soil. All organisms eventually die, and the organic material is broken down by the decomposer food chains. This may take some time, since a considerable amount of the phosphorus is within animal bones. In the past, farmers have used concentrated sources of animal bones, such as

ENVIRONMENT IN FOCUS

BOX 4.2 | Human Impacts on the Phosphorus Cycle

Humans intervene in the phosphorus cycle in several ways that serve to accelerate the mobilization rate:

- Mining of phosphate-rich rocks for fertilizer and detergent production, creating excessive runoff into aquatic environments
- Biomass removal, leading to accelerated erosion of sediment and solutes into streams
- Concentration of large numbers of organisms such as humans, cattle, and pigs, creating heavy burdens of phosphate-rich waste materials
- Removal of phosphorus from oceanic ecosystems through fishing, with the phosphorus returned to fresh water and ultimately the marine system through the dissolution of wastes

The major implication of all these interventions is for excessive phosphorus accumulation in freshwater systems, resulting in eutrophication. Human activity is now estimated to account for about two-thirds of the phosphorus reaching the oceans. The environmental impact of this nutrient enrichment will be discussed in more detail later.

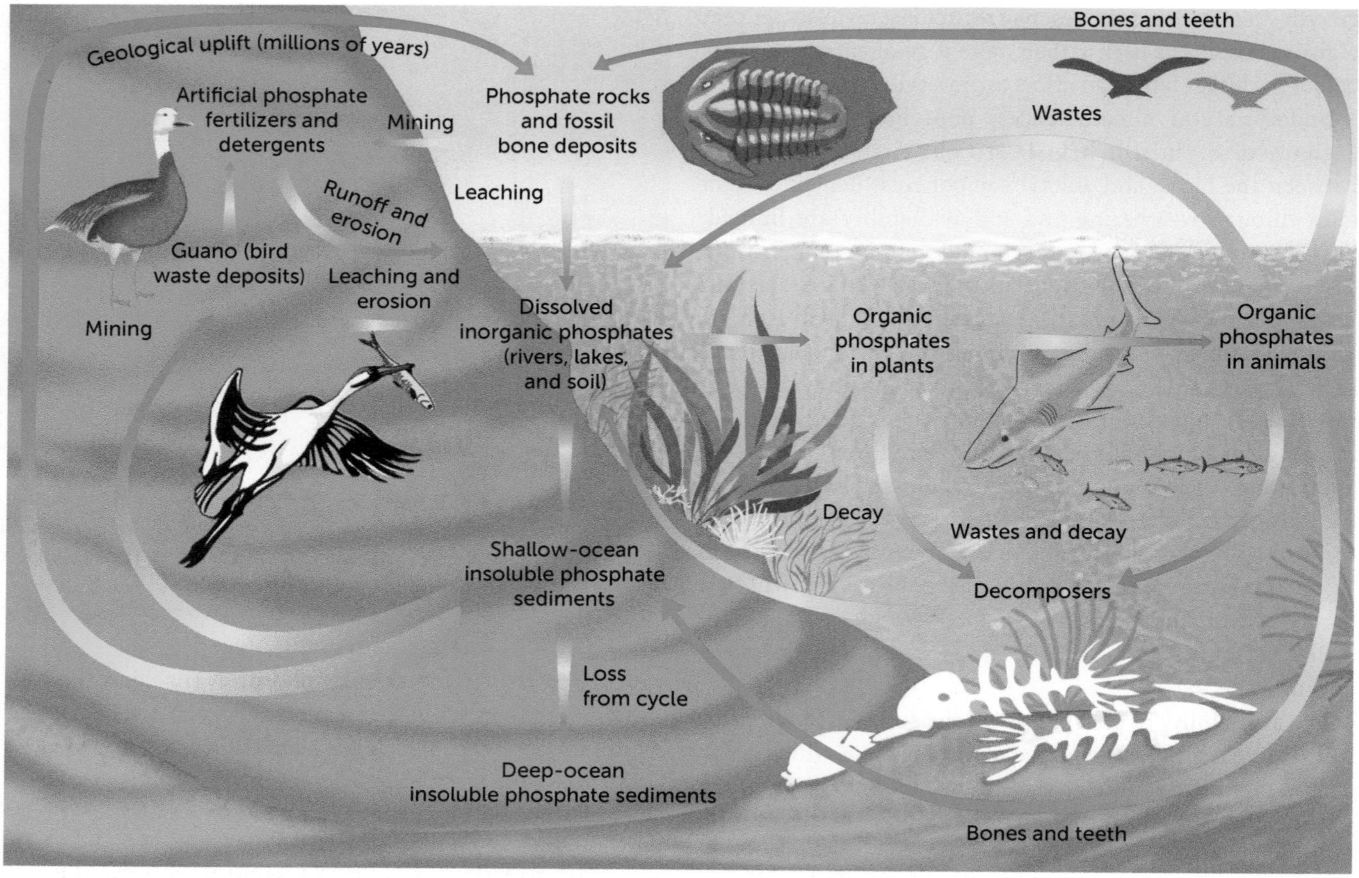

FIGURE 4.2 | The phosphorus cycle.

the bison jumps used by indigenous peoples on the Prairies, as a source of phosphate fertilizer.

Following breakdown in the soil, the phosphorus is then either taken up again by plants or removed by water transport. Bacteria mineralize the returned organic phosphorus into inorganic forms so that plants can take it up once more. Most of the water transport occurs in particulate form by streams, which is one reason to be concerned about excessive sedimentation occurring through land-use activities such as logging and agriculture, as described in Chapters 9 and 10.

Stream transport ultimately ends up in the ocean. Estuaries have such high productivities, as discussed in Chapter 2, in part because of this nutrient input from upstream. The circulation patterns within estuaries tend to trap nutrients, but some phosphorus finds its way into the shallow ocean areas of the coastal zone. It may be fixed in biomass by phytoplankton or other aquatic plants in the euphotic (*eu* = well, *photos* = light) zone and once again incorporated into the food chain. The coastal zones, with this plentiful supply of nutrients and photosynthetic energy from the sun, cover less than 10 per cent of the ocean's surface but account for more than 90 per cent of all ocean species.

Beyond the coastal zone and the continental shelves, water depth increases into the open ocean. Phosphorus and other nutrients that have not been incorporated into food chains, plus elements from the death of oceanic organisms, filter through to the bathyal and ultimately the abyssal zones (see Figure 2.5). Here, uptake by organisms is extremely limited, and the nutrients must either be moved back to the euphotic zone by upwelling currents or wait to be geologically uplifted over millions of years to move into another component of the cycle. Where such upwellings occur, such as off the west coasts of Africa and South America, plentiful fisheries

Philip Dearden

The nutrients that have sustained this salmon are now being recycled.

ENVIRONMENT IN FOCUS

BOX 4.3 | Weathering, the Rock Cycle, and Plant Uptake

The weathering of the rocks of the Earth's crust plays an important role in supplying long-term inputs to biogeochemical cycles. Weathering is part of the **rock cycle** whereby rocks that have been uplifted are eroded into different constituents. The rock cycle involves the transformation of rocks from one type to another, such as when volcanic rocks are eroded and washed into the ocean. Over millions of years, the resulting sediments are turned into sedimentary rocks. In turn, these sedimentary rocks may be compressed within the Earth's crust and altered by heat and pressure before once more being uplifted through the process of continental drift.

Weathering involves numerous different processes. In Canada, mechanical weathering involves the physical breakup of rocks as a result of changing temperatures. The action of water is important. Chemical processes, such as hydration and carbonation, further the process by removing elements in solution. Secondary clay minerals are produced from primary rock minerals by hydrolysis and oxidation. These clays are very important in terms of holding the nutrients in the soil. The soil can be thought of as a giant filter bed in which each particle is chemically active. As water percolates through, containing many different nutrients in solution, some of these nutrients are held by the clays and become available for plant uptake.

Plants constantly lose moisture from their leaves. This creates a moisture gradient within the plant that serves to draw water up to replace what has been lost. Water moves from the roots, and more nutrient-laden water is taken in by the roots. It is the job of the roots to keep the plant supplied with water. As nutrients are removed from the soil water around the plants, new nutrients move within the soil water to replace them.

© David Parker/Science Photo Library

These sedimentary rocks have been compressed and folded as part of the rock cycle.

are found because of the combination of high nutrient and energy levels. Some fish species, such as salmon, are **anadromous**, spending part of their lives in salt water and part in fresh water, where they die after spawning. When they die, the nutrients they have collected during their ocean phase are returned to the freshwater system, resulting in a significant input of nutrients, including phosphates (Chapter 8).

Two other recycling mechanisms also occur. One is the biotic one described earlier as marine birds, such as puffins, cormorants, and other fish-eating birds, return phosphorus to land in the form of their droppings, representing the phosphorus that has concentrated through the marine food chain. This phosphorus, known as **guano**, constitutes the largest source of phosphorus for human use and is heavily mined for fertilizer production. A small amount of phosphorus is also returned to land through the atmosphere as sea spray.

Sulphur (S)

Like phosphorus, sulphur is a sedimentary cycle, but it differs from phosphorus in two important ways. First, it has an atmospheric component and therefore better recycling potential. Sulphur is not often a limiting factor for growth in aquatic or terrestrial ecosystems. Second, like most of the other cycles but unlike phosphorus, it has strong dependencies on microbial activity. Sulphur is a necessary component for all life and a building component of proteins.

Most sulphur is found in sedimentary rocks such as pyrite-rich shales and evaporite rocks and in seawater. Sulphur is not available in the lithosphere and must be transformed into sulphates to be absorbed by plants. Bacteria are critical here, changing sulphur into various forms in the soil (Figure 4.3). The exact form depends on factors such as the presence (**aerobic**) or absence (**anaerobic**) of oxygen, which is usually a reflection of the relationship of the particular site of transformation to the water table and the presence of other elements such as iron. From these microbial transformations by chemoautotrophs (discussed in Chapter 2), gases such as hydrogen sulphide (H_2S) may be released directly into the atmosphere (giving the familiar "rotten egg" smell we associate with marshlands), or sulphate salts (SO_4^{2-}) may be produced. Through their roots, plants can then absorb the sulphates, sulphur enters the food chain, and the same processes occur as in the biotic components of the other cycles.

The complexity of these cycles is illustrated further by some of the interactions that occur between cycles. For example, the phosphorus cycle benefits when iron sulphides

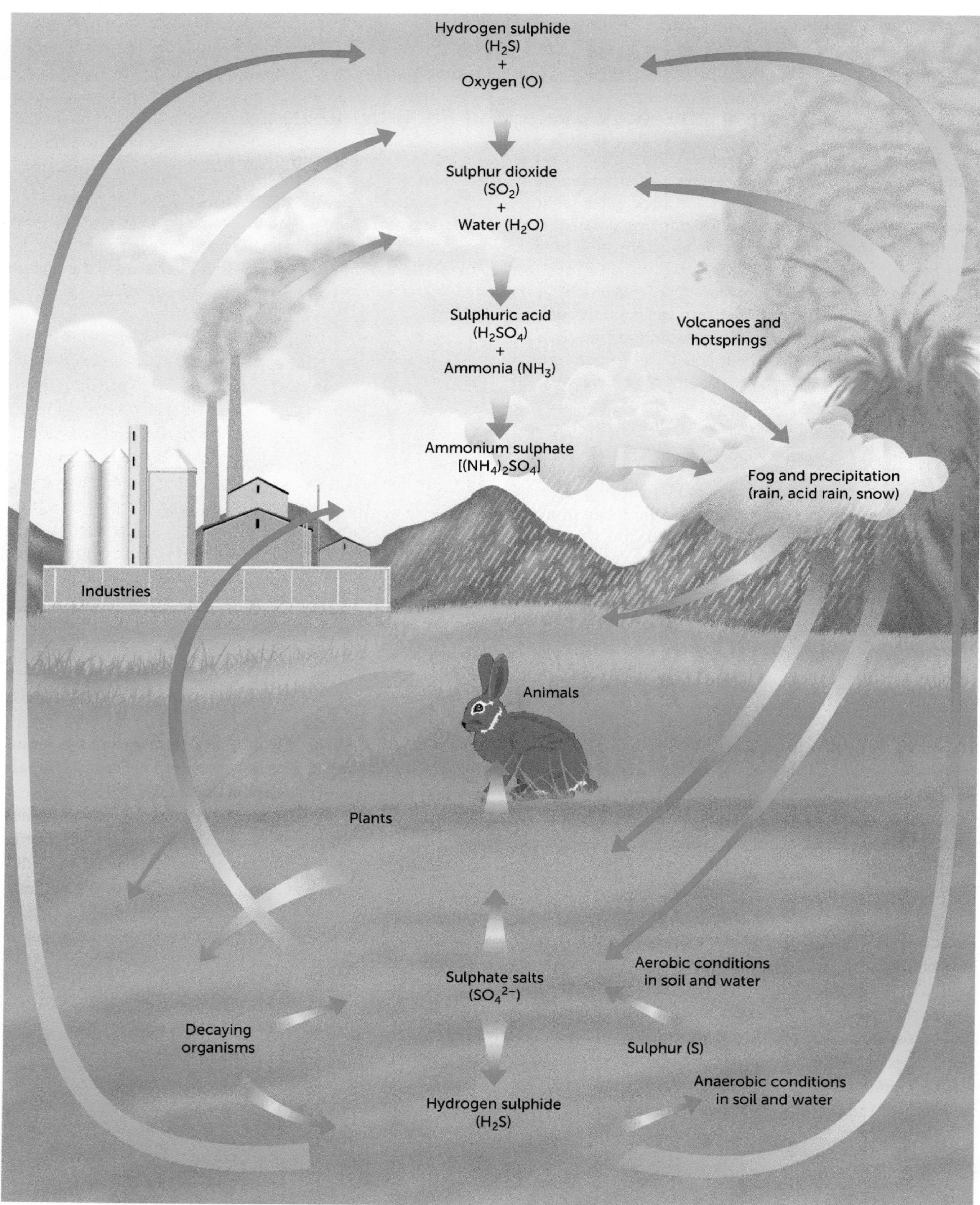

FIGURE 4.3 | The sulphur cycle.

are formed in sediments and phosphorus is converted from insoluble to soluble forms, where it becomes available for uptake. There are also important interactions with global climate change. For example, rising temperatures and reduced rainfall in many areas of the Canadian North are causing more frequent drying out of extensive peat beds. When these peat beds are re-wet, they emit three to four times as much SO_2 as do continually wet peat beds and hence add to the acid deposition described later in this chapter.

The upward movement of the gaseous phase of the sulphur cycle is also important, since sulphur is also returned to the atmosphere, albeit usually for a short time, thereby shortening the long sediment uplift time that characterizes the phosphorus cycle. This is fortunate, because average ocean residence times are quite long and sulphur is continually lost to the ocean floor. From the upper reaches of the oceans, sulphur can be returned to the atmosphere by phytoplankton or photochemical reactions. However, unlike phosphorus, a relatively small proportion of sulphur is fixed in organic matter, and availability is not usually a problem. As with phosphorus, human intervention in the sulphur cycle (Box 4.4) is significant.

Gaseous Cycles

Nitrogen (N)

Nitrogen is a colourless, tasteless, odourless gas required by all organisms for life. It is an essential component of chlorophyll, proteins, and amino acids. The atmosphere is more than 78 per cent nitrogen gas (N_2) and also contains other forms of gaseous nitrogen such as ammonia (NH_3), nitrogen dioxide (NO_2), nitrous oxide (N_2O), and nitric oxide (NO). Excess quantities of these other forms are involved in many of our most challenging environmental problems, such as acid deposition, ozone depletion, and global climate change (Box 4.5).

Nitrogen cycles between the atmosphere and the lithosphere, with the most important interactions occurring at the atmosphere–lithosphere interface through biological activity. Nitrogen can also collect in the hydrosphere and result in environmental problems such as eutrophication. Most organisms cannot gain access to nitrogen from the atmosphere. The nitrogen is instead obtained from the soil as nitrates. The main way in which the atmospheric reservoir is linked to the biotic components of the food chain is through **nitrogen fixation** and **denitrification**, both mediated through microbial activity (Figure 4.4). The historical record shows a close coupling between the speed of these processes and atmospheric CO_2 levels.

Nitrogen Fixation

Biological nitrogen fixation occurs as bacteria transform atmospheric nitrogen into various forms. Chemotropic bacteria consume atmospheric nitrogen (N_2) to obtain the energy required to fuel their metabolic processes and convert atmospheric nitrogen into nitrates or compounds such as ammonia gas (NH_3) and ammonium salts (NH_{4+}). The most important nitrogen fixers are bacteria of the *Rhizobium* family that grow on the root nodules of certain plants, such as members of the pea or legume family (e.g., peas, beans, clover, alfalfa). The bacteria and roots of the plant communicate through chemical stimuli that result in the bacteria infecting root cells. Once infected, the cells swell into the nodules that you can see on the roots of the peas or beans in your garden. In a remarkable example of co-evolution, the plant and bacteria exist in a mutualistic relationship where the plant supplies the products of photosynthesis to the relationship, and the bacteria transform the atmospheric nitrogen into nitrates. It is one of the few known examples of two organisms cooperating to make one molecule.

Nitrates and ammonium salts are both readily absorbed by plants and create rich soils that support plant production. Nitrogen is quickly depleted from the soil and, along with phosphorus, is often a limiting factor in terrestrial soils, which explains why farmers grow crops such as alfalfa and

ENVIRONMENT IN FOCUS

BOX 4.4 | Human Impacts on the Sulphur Cycle

Human industrial activities are the main source of sulphur gases in the atmosphere. Humans intervene in the sulphur cycle mainly through

- The burning of sulphur-containing coal, largely to produce electricity
- The smelting of metal ores that contain sulphates

Almost 99 per cent of the sulphur dioxide and about one-third of the sulphur compounds reaching the atmosphere come from these activities. These sulphur compounds react with oxygen and water vapour to produce sulphuric acid (H_2SO_4), a main component of acid deposition, as discussed later in this chapter.

clover as part of a crop rotation to help build up nitrates in the soil. About one-half of the nitrogen circulating in agricultural ecosystems comes from this source. The increasing cost of fertilizer worldwide has focused more attention on biological nitrogen fixation as a part of meeting the global food challenges of the future (see Chapter 10). Through genetic engineering, for example, it may be possible to inject other crops, such as cereals, with similar symbiotic unions between plants and nitrogen-fixing bacteria. However, it may not be that simple. For example, research indicates that species involved in nitrogen fixation may also be particularly susceptible to phosphorus deficiencies, given their high P and energy requirements.

Some wild species such as alder, lupines, and vetch have similar bacteria associated with them and hence play a valuable role when they act as primary colonizers in the successional process or when they help to recolonize sites that have been logged (Chapter 9) or otherwise disturbed. These relationships are mutualistic in that both organisms gain. The plant receives enhanced nutrient supply, and the bacteria find a home in which the plant supplies them with various sugars.

Other bacteria and algae that fix nitrogen are not attached to specific plants. These free-living nitrogen-fixing microorganisms are particularly important in the Arctic and within the ocean. These free-floating relationships are not as efficient at fixing nitrogen from the atmosphere as vegetative relationships. Estimates suggest that in terrestrial ecosystems, about twice the amount of nitrogen is fixed by mutualistic relationships as by these free-floating relationships.

Nitrogen is also made available through atmospheric fixation that occurs largely during thunderstorms. Lightning causes extremely high temperatures that unite oxygen and nitrogen to form nitric acid (HNO_3), which is subsequently carried to earth as precipitation and converted into nitrates (NO_3^-). These nitrates can then be taken up by plant roots. Estimates on the importance of atmospheric fixation vary, but 10 per cent of total fixation would be a maximum figure, and most estimates place it at about only 5 per cent.

Mineralization, or Why Compost Matters

Although nitrogen-fixing bacteria are an important source of nitrates within soil, most physical nitrogen (e.g., nitrates and ammonium salts) comes from the breakdown of existing biomass by decomposer food chains. In fact, nitrogen is tightly circulated in most ecosystems between the dead and living biomass.

Once fixed in the soil, nitrogen is incorporated into plant matter and then moved through the food chain. **Mineralization** is the process by which decomposing biomass (i.e., dead plants) is converted back to ammonia (NH_3) and ammonium salts (NH_{4+}) by bacterial action and returned to the soil. This process highlights the importance of compost in agricultural production and is explored more fully in Chapter 10. Primarily, mineralization does not produce nitrates directly, but rather indirectly through another process known as nitrification.

Nitrification and Denitrification

Chemotrophic bacteria, such as *Nitrosomonas* and *Nitrobacter*, convert ammonia and ammonium salts into nitrites and then into nitrates. Other bacteria—anaerobic bacteria—reverse the nitrogen-fixing process and convert nitrates into

ENVIRONMENT IN FOCUS

BOX 4.5 | Human Impacts on the Nitrogen Cycle

Humans disrupt the nitrogen cycle in many ways:

- Chemical fixation to supply nitrates and ammonia as fertilizer. The amount fixed is greater than that produced by natural processes. The Millennium Ecosystem Assessment (2005) predicts large increases in the future (Figure 4.5), and Gruber and Galloway (2008) predict that humans will double the turnover rates of the nitrogen cycle of the entire Earth. Rockström, with 29 other leading scientists (Rockström et al., 2009), analyzed the safe operating boundaries of the major global systems and found that three of these were already well past those safe boundaries, as can be seen in Figure 1.9. Disruption of the nitrogen cycle was one of these. The main impacts are through runoff of excess fertilizer (contributing to eutrophication) and denitrification (contributing to climatic change). Agricultural fertilizers are implicated in both. Eutrophication will be discussed in more detail in the next section. Denitrification transforms nitrogen fertilizers into nitrous oxide, a greenhouse gas (Chapter 7), and is also involved in the catalytic destruction of the ozone layer. Health concerns also are related to excessive nitrate levels from fertilizers running into water supplies (Box 4.9). The role of agriculture in the nitrogen cycle is discussed in more detail in Chapter 10.
- Removal of nitrate and ammonium ions from agricultural soils through the harvesting of nitrogen-rich crops
- High-temperature combustion, which produces nitric oxides (NO) that combine with oxygen to produce nitrogen dioxide (NO_2), which reacts with water vapour to form nitric acid (HNO_3), a main component of acid deposition

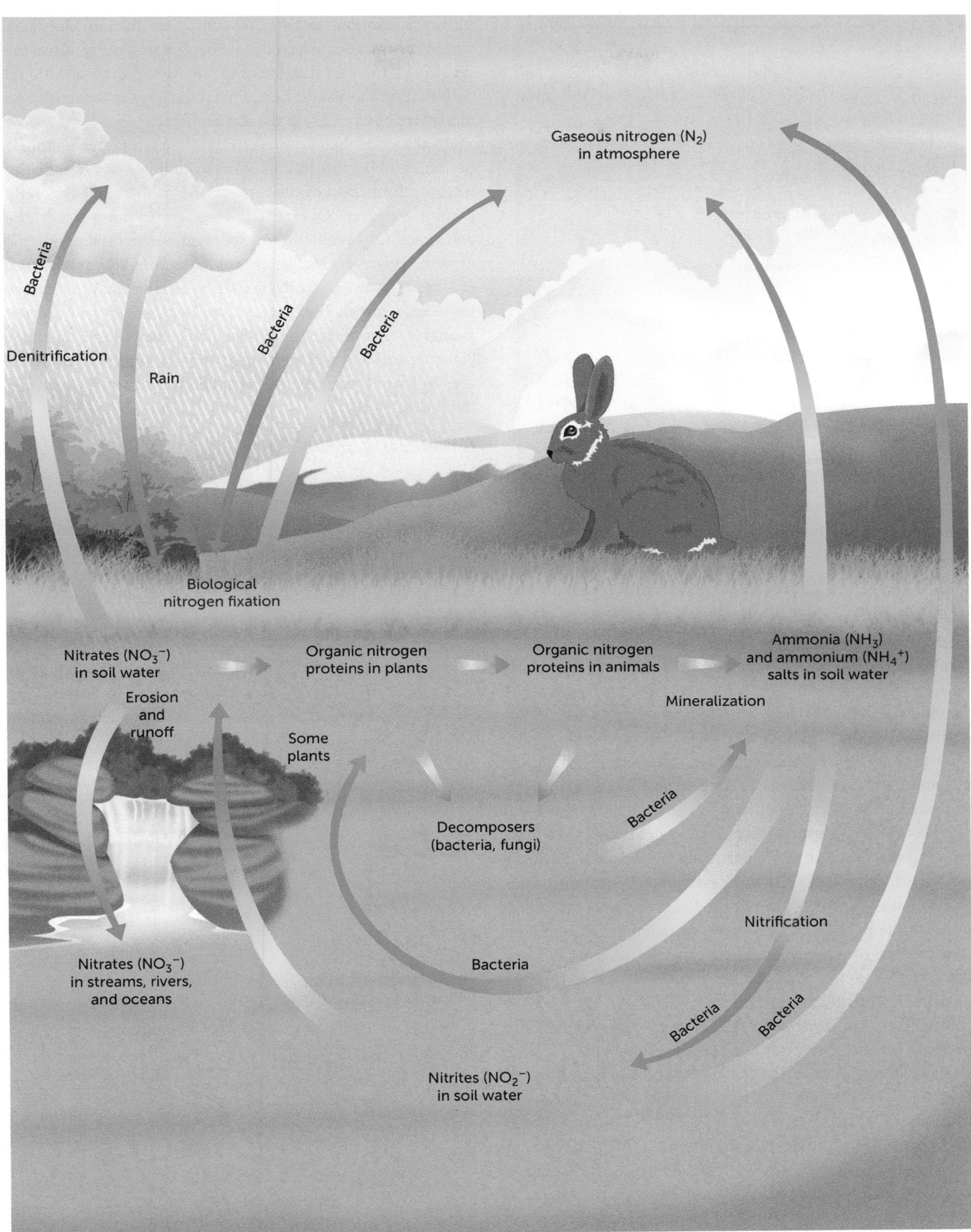

FIGURE 4.4 | The nitrogen cycle.

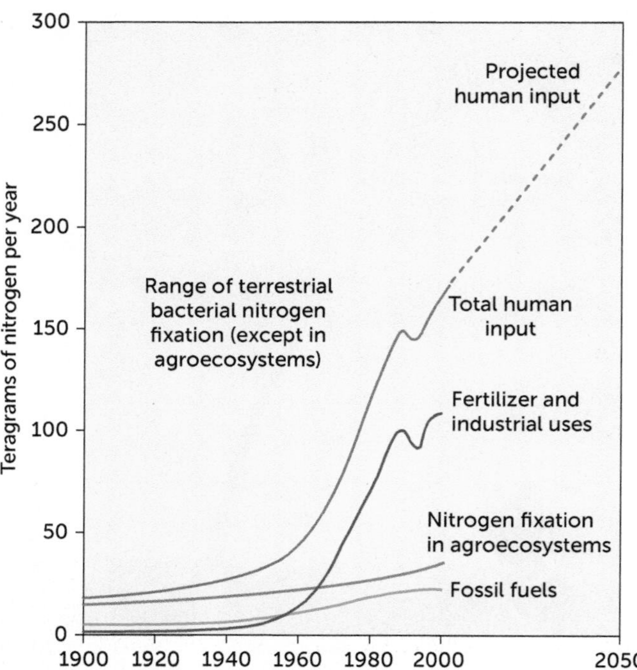

FIGURE 4.5 | Global trends in the creation of reactive nitrogen on Earth by human activities, with projections to 2050.

Source: Millennium Ecosystem Assessment (2005).

nitrogen gas, returning it to the atmosphere (Figure 4.4). Denitrification occurs in anaerobic conditions, especially where large amounts of nitrates are available, such as on flooded agricultural fields.

Nitrates are highly soluble in water, and if not held tightly they may be lost to the ecosystem by surface runoff and become a major contributor to the problem of eutrophication, as discussed in more detail later in the chapter. Ammonia is also susceptible to loss by soil erosion, since it tends to adhere to soil particles. Like phosphorus, nitrogen is often a limiting factor for growth. When excessive concentrations occur in water, it is a major contributor to the process of eutrophication. Unlike phosphorus, however, nitrogen is not immobilized in deep-ocean sediments but has an effective feedback mechanism to the atmosphere from the ocean through microbial denitrification.

Scientists are trying to understand the relationship between the nitrogen cycle and the major elements of global climate change, such as the carbon cycle. They know for certain, based on historical records, that the cycles are closely linked but are still unsure as to the direction and magnitude of changes that might be expected in the future and whether the nitrogen cycle will form a positive or negative feedback loop with rising atmospheric carbon levels (Figure 4.6). On the one hand, ocean acidification resulting from the ocean's taking up anthropogenic CO_2 might lead to an increase in the C/N uptake ratio of marine phytoplankton and enhanced nitrogen fixation. If this happens, the marine biosphere would act as a negative feedback for climate change, since the resulting enhanced fixation of carbon would draw additional carbon from the atmosphere, thus reducing the accumulation of anthropogenic CO_2 in the atmosphere.

On the other hand, current climate–carbon cycle models used for making projections of Earth's climate do not consider nitrogen limitation of the terrestrial biosphere but generally assume a strong CO_2 fertilization effect. In other words, the additional CO_2 available will act to stimulate further organic growth. However, the latter would require the availability of large quantities of nitrates, since nitrates are a necessary ingredient for all life, as discussed earlier. If they are not available, then nitrogen will become a major limiting factor (Chapter 2). Thus, nitrogen limitation will significantly affect the ability of the terrestrial biosphere to act as a CO_2 sink in the future.

Carbon (C)

Although carbon dioxide gas (CO_2) constitutes only 0.03 per cent of the atmosphere, it is the main reservoir for the carbon that is the building block for all necessary fats, proteins, and carbohydrates that constitute life. Plants take up carbon dioxide directly from the atmosphere through the process of photosynthesis and at the same time emit oxygen. The carbon becomes incorporated into the biomass and is passed along the food chain. Residence times can vary greatly, but older forests constitute a significant repository for carbon for centuries. Respiration by organisms transforms some of this carbon back into carbon dioxide (Figure 4.7), and the cellular

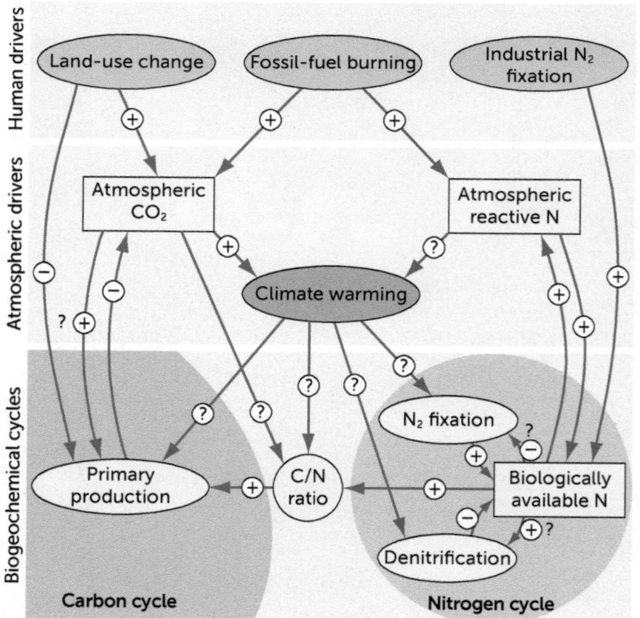

FIGURE 4.6 | Nitrogen–carbon–climate interactions.

Source: Gruber and Galloway (2008). Copyright © 2008. Rights managed by Nature Publishing Group.

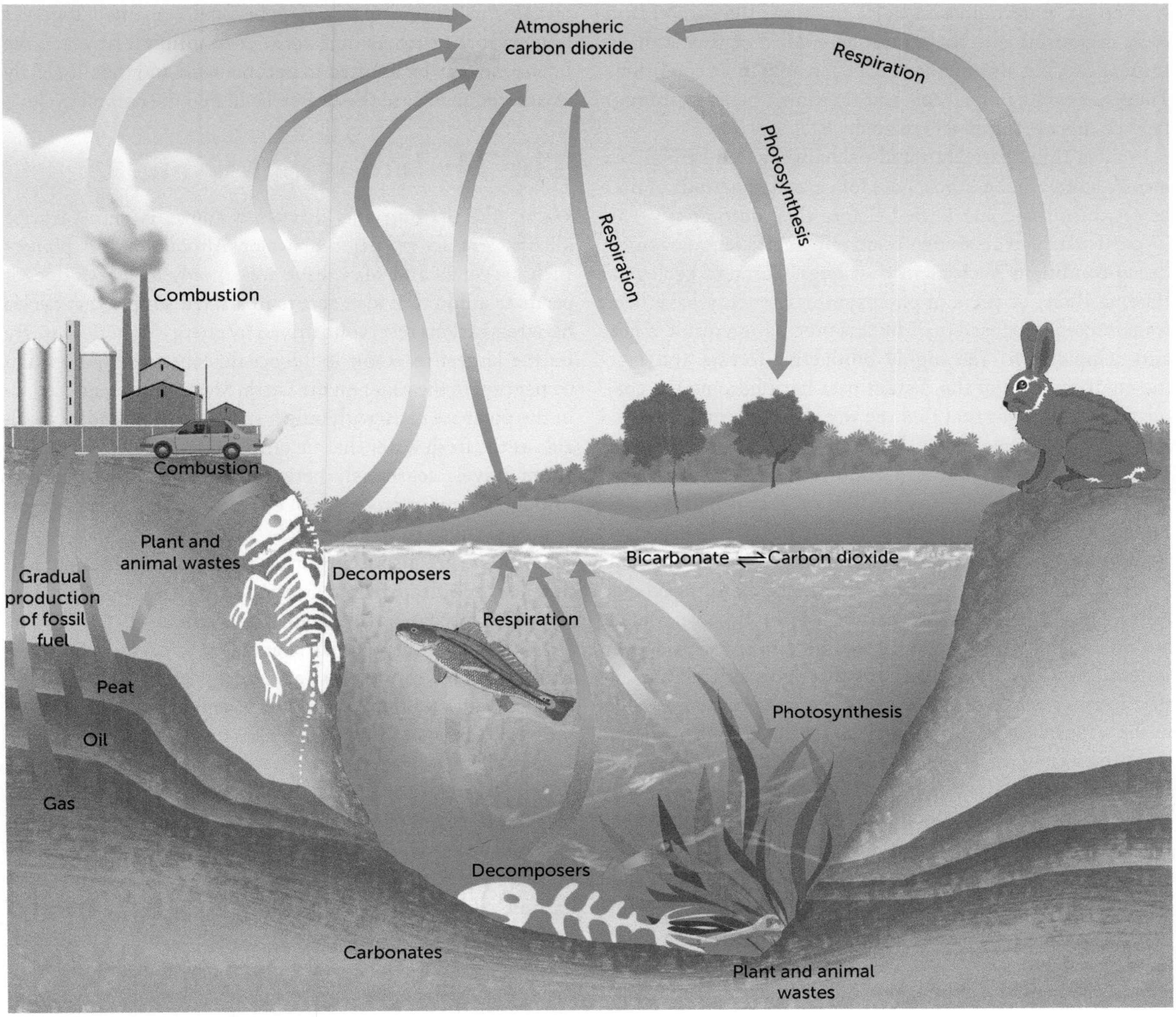

FIGURE 4.7 | The carbon cycle.

© AP Photo/Jeff Gentner/CP

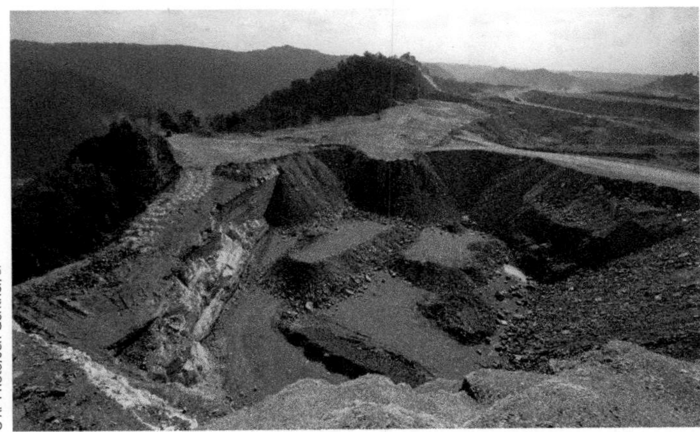

Large amounts of carbon are stored in the lithosphere, such as in these coalbeds, the product of millions of years of photosynthetic activity.

Philip Dearden

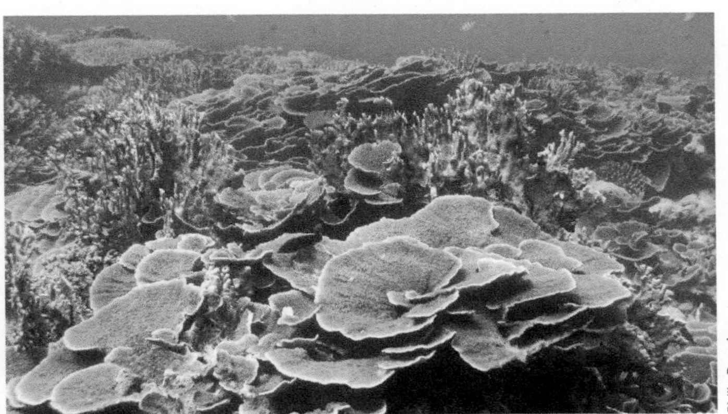

Coral reefs, such as this reef in the Andaman Sea at Koh Surin, Thailand, store large amounts of carbon from the remains of thousands of years of coral growth.

respiration of decomposers helps to return the carbon from dead organisms into the atmosphere. Most of this is in the form of CO_2 but also methane (CH_4) in anaerobic conditions. Thus, the cycling of carbon and the flow of energy through food chains are intimately related.

Besides this relatively rapid exchange, some carbon can also be stored in the lithosphere for extended periods of time as organisms become buried before they decompose. This is particularly true under relatively inefficient anaerobic decay conditions such as in peat bogs. Through geological time, millions of years of photosynthetic energy have been transformed into fossil fuels by this process as a result of heat and compression. The highly productive forests and marine environments of the distant past have become the coal, oil, and natural gas that fuel the world's economy today (see Box 4.6). Scientists predict that there will be a positive feedback loop between increased atmospheric CO_2 and the terrestrial and marine elements of the cycle that will serve to further increase atmospheric CO_2.

Some of the carbon dioxide is dissolved into the shallower ocean before re-entering the atmosphere. Residence time is in the order of six years in these shallower waters but much longer (up to 350 years) when mixed with deeper waters. These residence times are now of considerable scientific interest because of the rising levels of carbon dioxide in the atmosphere and the potential for the oceans to absorb these increases (see Chapter 8). Recent predictions show that increased carbon dioxide within the atmosphere will also have a positive feedback loop with the carbon concentrations in the ocean and that the oceans' storage capacity for carbon may be decreasing. Some of these predicted changes are discussed in more detail in the "Domestic Guest Statement" by Kirsten Zickfeld.

Large amounts of carbon are stored for much longer periods in the ocean. When marine organisms die, their shells of calcium carbonate ($CaCO_3$) become cemented together to form rocks such as limestone. Over millions of years, the limestone may be uplifted to become land and then is slowly weathered to release the carbon back into the carbon cycle.

The Hydrological Cycle

Water, like the nutrients discussed above, is necessary for all life. You are 70 per cent water. Although other planets such as Venus and Mars have water, only on Earth does it occur as a liquid. It also occurs in a fixed supply that cycles between various reservoirs driven by energy from the sun. By far the largest reservoir is the ocean, containing more than 97 per cent of the water on the Earth. Most of the rest is tied up in the polar ice caps, with only a small amount readily available as the fresh water that sustains terrestrial life (Table 4.2). Water travels ceaselessly between these various reservoirs through the main processes of evaporation and precipitation known as the **hydrological cycle** (Figure 4.8).

Scientists are also discovering more about a little-known water source deep in the Earth's crust. The world's oldest water was discovered in Canada 2.4 kilometres below the surface in a deep mine and has been dated to between 1 billion and 2.5 billion years old. Estimates suggest that there may be as much as 11 million km³ of such deep water, more than all the world's rivers, swamps, and lakes put together.

The average residence times in the other global reservoirs vary greatly (Table 4.2). In the deep ocean, it may take 37,000 years before water is recycled through evaporation into the atmosphere, whereas once in the atmosphere, average residence time is in the order of 9 to 12 days. These figures have special relevance with regard to the effects of pollution. Although many major rivers have suffered from critical pollution incidents, the flushing action of rivers, combined with the short residence time of the water, means that

ENVIRONMENT IN FOCUS

BOX 4.6 | Human Impacts on the Carbon Cycle

As human populations have increased, two major changes to the carbon cycle have occurred:

- Natural vegetation, usually dominated by tree growth, has been replaced by land uses, such as urban and agricultural systems, that have reduced capacity to uptake and store carbon.
- For the past 200 years or so, human activity, particularly industrial activity, has mobilized large amounts of fossil fuels from the lithospheric component of the cycle to the atmospheric component. Estimates suggest that this mobilization represents the release of one million years of photosynthetic activity every year. The concentration of carbon dioxide in Earth's atmosphere now exceeds 390 parts per million (ppm), which is more than 90 ppm above the maximum values of the past 740,000 years, if not 20 million years. Furthermore, increasing CO_2 has driven an increase in the global oceans' average temperature by 0.74°C and in sea level by 17 centimetres. Human impacts are discussed in more detail in Chapter 7.

DOMESTIC GUEST STATEMENT

Feedbacks between the Carbon Cycle and Climate | *Kirsten Zickfeld*

Combustion of fossil fuels such as oil, gas, and coal and changes in land use presently release 10 billion metric tons of carbon into the atmosphere. About half of this carbon is taken up by **carbon sinks** on land and in the ocean, whereas the other half remains in the atmosphere, leading to the rise in atmospheric carbon dioxide (CO_2) concentrations. The primary process contributing to the uptake of CO_2 on land is the fertilization of vegetation by CO_2. Vegetation is more productive in a CO_2-enriched atmosphere if water and other nutrients are not limiting plant growth. Other processes contributing to the terrestrial sink of CO_2 are the regrowth of forest on land that was previously cleared for agriculture, primarily in temperate regions of the northern hemisphere, and nitrogen fertilization of natural ecosystems. Humans are supplying large amounts of nitrates through fertilizers, which make their way into natural ecosystems, stimulating plant growth. In the ocean, the primary process contributing to uptake of CO_2 from the atmosphere is the dissolution of CO_2 in seawater and the subsequent transport of CO_2 to deeper waters by ocean circulation, which removes the CO_2-rich water from contact with the atmosphere.

How will the carbon sinks evolve as the Earth's climate warms, affecting the geographic distribution and functioning of ecosystems and ocean circulation? This is one of the research questions we explore in the Climate Research Laboratory at Simon Fraser University in Vancouver. Specifically, we are investigating how uptake of anthropogenic CO_2 by carbon sinks on land and in the ocean changes as global warming progresses. To explore this question we use sophisticated "Earth-system models," which simulate key processes in the main components of the climate system—atmosphere, hydrosphere, lithosphere, cryosphere, and biosphere—and the exchanges of mass (including CO_2) and energy between these components.

Simulations with Earth-system models suggest that the fraction of human-induced CO_2 emissions taken up by carbon sinks will decrease as the climate warms, providing for a positive feedback: weakening of the carbon sinks will lead to an increase in atmospheric CO_2, thereby enhancing the atmospheric greenhouse effect and causing further warming (Zickfeld et al., 2011). Several processes contribute to the weakening of carbon sinks in a warmer climate. As temperature increases, the decomposition of organic matter in soils speeds up, releasing more CO_2 into the atmosphere. Temperature also affects the productivity of plants. In regions where temperature is at or above the optimum temperature for plant growth, as is in the tropics, warming will decrease productivity. In regions where temperature is below the optimum temperature, as in the high latitudes of both hemispheres, warming will benefit plant productivity. The net global effect of warming on plant productivity will depend on the balance between these two processes. Most Earth-system models indicate that the decrease in productivity in the tropics will dominate, reducing the capacity of land ecosystems to absorb CO_2. Some models even suggest that land ecosystems may turn into a source of CO_2 to the atmosphere under moderate to high levels of warming (Zickfeld et al., 2013).

Large amounts of organic matter are preserved in the permanently frozen soils (permafrost) of the northern hemisphere. Due to the cold conditions, these organic matter pools are removed from decomposition by fungi and heterotrophic bacteria. As the climate warms and the soil thaws, these pools become available to decomposition, releasing CO_2 and methane (if the decomposition occurs under anaerobic conditions such as in waterlogged soils) into the atmosphere. Large amounts of organic matter and hence carbon are stored in permafrost soils, providing for a potentially large positive feedback on atmospheric CO_2 (MacDougall et al., 2012). Scientists currently debate how quickly the carbon will be released and how much will be released as CO_2 or as methane, which is a more powerful greenhouse gas than CO_2.

The ability of CO_2 to dissolve in seawater is temperature dependent and decreases as seawater warms (this effect is similar to the one we experience when opening a bottle of soda left to heat in the sun: the CO_2 gushes out). Due to this effect, the capacity of the ocean to take up and store CO_2 decreases in a warmer climate (Zickfeld at al., 2011). There is also another effect that contributes to the weakening of the oceanic carbon sink: in a warmer climate, waters at the sea surface will warm more rapidly than deeper waters. Warm waters are less dense and more buoyant and therefore float on top of colder and denser waters. This increased stratification of the ocean inhibits transport of CO_2-rich waters from the sea surface to the deep ocean, leaving these waters in contact with the atmosphere for a longer time and reducing the flux of CO_2 into the ocean (Zickfeld et al., 2008).

Earth-system models agree that the net effect of global warming is a weakening of the carbon sinks both on land and in the ocean, but differ widely in simulating the magnitude of this effect. All models indicate that the ocean uptake of anthropogenic CO_2 will continue in the future, even under scenarios entailing large amounts of warming. The future evolution of the land carbon sink is much more uncertain: most models suggest that land ecosystems will continue to

Continued

take up anthropogenic CO_2 in the future, but some models suggest that land ecosystems will turn into a source of CO_2 to the atmosphere (Zickfeld et al., 2013). Incomplete representation of processes in models, interactions with other nutrient cycles such as the nitrogen cycle, and land-use changes make the future evolution of the land carbon sink in a changing climate particularly hard to predict.

Kirsten Zickfeld

Kirsten Zickfeld is an associate professor in the Department of Geography at Simon Fraser University and director of the Climate Research Laboratory. She and her students undertake research on the effects of human activities on the climate system, climate feedbacks, and tipping points.

a relatively rapid recovery is often possible. This is not the case, however, with groundwater pollution, especially deep groundwater pollution.

Residence times are also changing in response to temperature changes associated with global climate change. An obvious change is related to rapid melting of ice caps. There are some interesting and unexpected outcomes. For example, researchers in the Selwyn Mountains in the Northwest Territories found 700-year-old caribou feces containing a frozen plant virus being released from the melting glaciers. The cryogenically preserved virus is scientifically exciting but also raises interesting questions about what other unknown viruses may emerge from melting ice caps.

The hydrological cycle involves the transport of water from the oceans to the atmosphere, through terrestrial and subterranean systems, and back to the oceans, all fuelled by energy from the sun. Eighty-six per cent of the water in the atmosphere is evaporated directly from the oceans' surface. The remainder comes from evaporation from smaller water bodies, from the leaves of plants (**transpiration**), or from the soil and plants (**evapotranspiration**). As it evaporates, water leaves behind accumulated impurities. The most common dissolved substance in the ocean is sodium chloride, or table salt, which also contains many other elements in trace amounts. Evaporation acts as a giant purification plant until further pollutants are encountered in the atmosphere.

Once in the atmosphere, the water vapour cools, condenses around tiny particles called **condensation nuclei**, forms clouds, and is precipitated to the earth as rain, snow, or hail.

TABLE 4.2 | Global Water Storage

Reservoir	Average Renewal Rate	Percentage of Global Total
World oceans	3,100 years	97.2
Ice sheets and glaciers	16,000 years	2.15
Groundwater	300–4,600 years	0.62
Lakes (freshwater)	10–100 years	0.009
Inland seas, saline lakes	10–100 years	0.008
Soil moisture	280 days	0.005
Atmosphere	9–12 days	0.001
Rivers and streams	12–20 days	0.0001

The warmer the air is, the more water it can hold. Moisture content can be expressed in terms of **relative humidity**, the amount of moisture held compared to how much could be held if fully saturated at a particular temperature. At a relative humidity of 100 per cent, the air is saturated, and cloud, fog, and mist form. Clouds are moved around by winds and continue to grow until precipitation (Box 4.8) occurs and the water is returned to the Earth.

About 76 per cent of precipitation falls into the ocean. The remainder joins the terrestrial part of the cycle in ice caps, lakes, rivers, groundwater, and transport between these compartments. Gravity moves water down through the soil until it reaches the water table, where all the spaces between the soil particles are full of water. This is the **groundwater** (Box 4.9). Lakes, streams, and other evidence of surface water occur where the land surface is below the water table. Surface water is a major factor in sculpting the shape of the surface of the Earth. At greater depths, the groundwater may penetrate to occupy various geological formations, known as aquifers.

As mentioned in Box 4.9, water is unique in that at the ambient temperatures and pressure of the Earth's surface, it is the only substance that exists in all three phases of matter (solid, liquid, vapour). Water is stored in all three forms within the hydrological cycle and moves among these forms by the processes shown in Figure 4.12. **Sublimation** is the process for direct transfer between the solid and vapour phases of matter, regardless of direction. This explains why on sunny winter days when the air is dry, snowbanks may shrink without any visible melting. About 75 per cent of the world's fresh water is stored in the solid phase, and it may stay in this phase for a long time. Measurements in the Antarctic, for example, indicate that some of the ice is more than 100,000 years old.

Although over the short term there are relatively constant amounts of water in the different storage compartments, over the long term these amounts can change markedly. For example, large amounts of water are evaporated from the oceans and precipitated on land as snow during glacial periods. Over time, the snow accumulates and builds ice fields that may be more than a kilometre thick. This effectively removes water from the oceanic component, causing the sea level to fall. During glacial times, then, the area of land will increase relative to the ocean, and the area of Earth's surface covered by ice may increase by up to 300 per cent.

ENVIRONMENT IN FOCUS

BOX 4.7 | Some Important Properties of Water

Water has several properties that make it unique:

- Water is a molecule (H_2O) that can exist in a liquid, gaseous, or solid state.
- These molecules have a strong mutual attraction, promoting high surface tension and high capacity to adhere to other surfaces; these properties allow water to move upward through plants.
- Water has a high heat capacity, meaning that it can store a great deal of heat without an equivalent rise in temperature; this is the reason why the oceans have such a moderating influence on climate.
- It takes a lot of heat to change water from liquid to gaseous form; this is why evaporation results in a cooling effect.
- Few solids do not undergo some dissolution in water; this allows water to carry dissolved nutrients to plants, but it also means that water is easily polluted.
- Unlike other substances, when water passes from a liquid to a solid state, it becomes less rather than more dense; this is why ice floats on top of liquid water and permits aquatic life to exist in cold climates.

Most of these properties spring from the fact that although the water molecule is electrically neutral, the charges are distributed in a bipolar manner. In other words, a positive charge is at one end of the molecule, and a negative charge is at the other. This means that water molecules have a strong attraction for each other and also explains why water is such a good solvent, since the charges increase the chemical reactivity of other substances.

In a more contemporary example, pumping rates of groundwater more than doubled from 1960 to 2000, largely due to agricultural demands. Much of this water is evaporated and then precipitated and eventually reaches the ocean. Researchers have calculated that 25 per cent of the current rise in sea level is a result of this reallocation of water from the ground into the ocean (Wada et al., 2010). This illustrates well how human activities are making planetary cycles acyclic

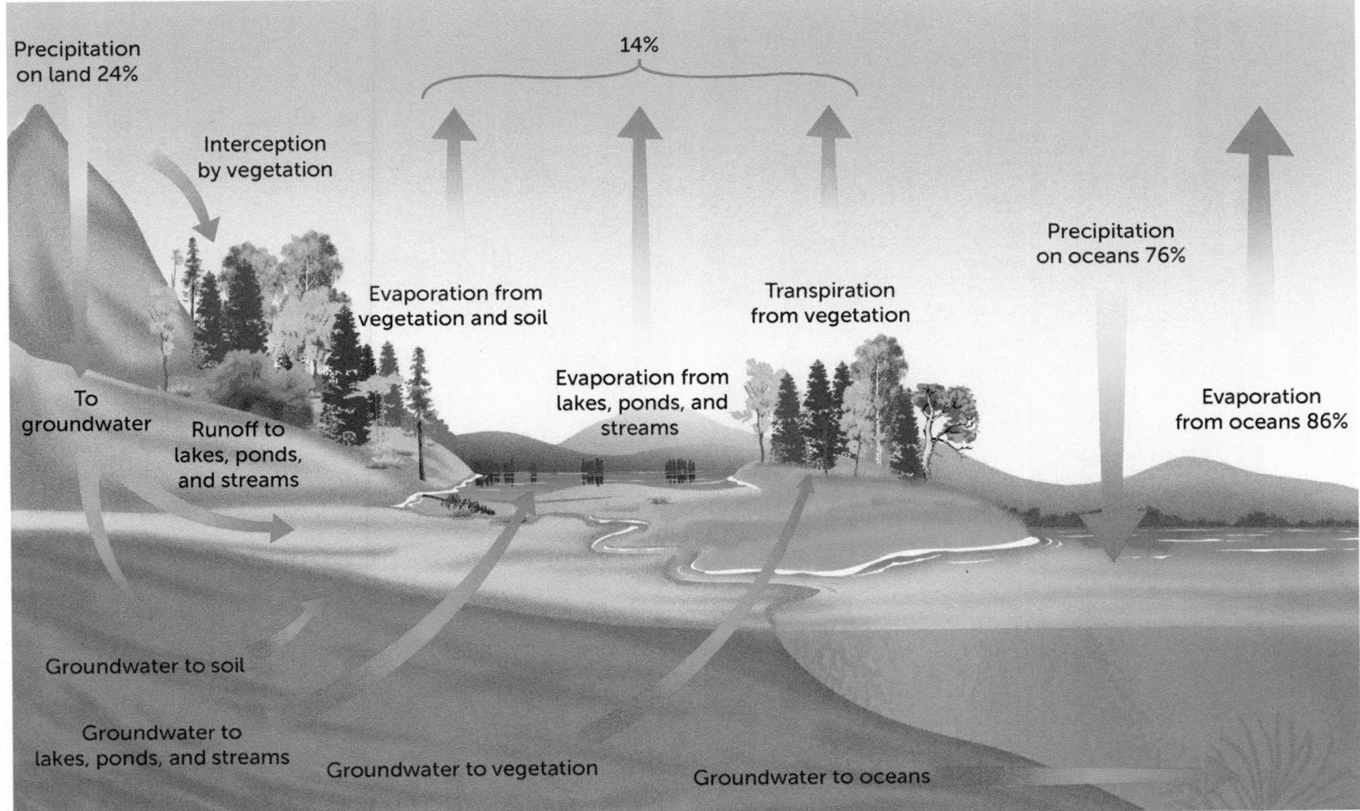

FIGURE 4.8 | The hydrological cycle. Water moves through the hydrological cycle as a liquid, as a vapour, and as snow.

ENVIRONMENT IN FOCUS

BOX 4.8 | Precipitation

Precipitation occurs in several forms: rain, snow, hail, dew, fog, and rime ice (frost). It occurs when the accumulated particles of condensed water or ice in clouds become large enough that they overcome the uplifting air currents and fall to earth as a result of gravity. Some of this precipitation may never reach the ground. Lower air layers may be warmer and drier, and re-evaporation may occur as the precipitates pass through these layers—an excellent example of the speed of some of these mini-cycles that occur as parts of the larger Earth cycles.

Distribution of precipitation is one of the main factors influencing the nature and location of global biomes and the ecozones of Canada. In Canada, precipitation varies from almost none in the Arctic to more than 3,000 millimetres annually on the west coast (Figure 4.11).

Differences in precipitation occur for various reasons. At the global scale, heating of equatorial regions causes air to rise. As it rises, it cools and condenses, clouds form, and precipitation occurs. As a result, equatorial regions tend to have consistent high rainfall. Where this air falls as it cools, over subequatorial regions, it tends to be dry, such as in the Sahara Desert.

In Canada, much of the precipitation comes from low-pressure systems, large cells of rising air that form along the boundary between warm and cold air masses. The main factor influencing relative precipitation levels in Canada is moisture-laden winds crossing the ocean and being forced to rise as a result of mountain barriers. The most extreme example occurs with westerlies coming across the Pacific and meeting the Western Cordillera, thus creating the highest precipitation levels in the country. As the air warms up in its descent from the mountains, it can hold more moisture, and precipitation levels fall considerably to produce a **rainshadow effect** that accounts for the small amounts of precipitation across the Prairies, with as little annual precipitation as 300 to 400 millimetres. Precipitation levels rise again in central Canada because of disturbances bringing moisture from the Gulf of Mexico and Atlantic Ocean. In southern Ontario, precipitation increases to 800 millimetres, and more than

Desert-like conditions occur in some areas of Canada, largely due to rainshadow effects. Although we associate the Fraser River with the high rainfalls of the west coast (left), the interior of British Columbia, like the Middle Fraser Canyon depicted on the right, is quite dry.

1,000 in the lee of the Great Lakes, a major source of moisture for downwind localities. In Atlantic Canada, exposure to maritime influences increases once more, with up to 1,500 millimetres of precipitation falling annually on the south coast of Newfoundland.

The Arctic is very dry because the prevailing winds from the north are very cold and therefore have little capacity for carrying moisture, they pass over terrain that has relatively few sources of water evaporation (sources often remain frozen for a proportion of the year), and there is an absence of low-pressure systems in winter. Topography is also an important determinant of whether the precipitation falls as snow or rain.

More localized precipitation may be produced by convection as warmer and lighter air rises, and cooler, heavier air sinks. This mechanism is important for localized storms in summer when the air is heated by the warm ground and may send columns of moist, warm air to great elevations, resulting in thunderstorm activity.

through the rapid mobilization of matter from one storage compartment to another.

In Canada, the solid phase of water is particularly important. Canada may have up to one-third of the world's fresh water but most of it is held in a solid state. Compared to the surface supply in Canada, the country's 100,000 glaciers contain more than 1.5 times the volume of fresh water. Most of this is in the Arctic, where summer air temperatures have risen markedly due to global climate change. These glaciers and ice caps are the largest contributor to global sea level rise outside Antarctica and Greenland (Gardner et al., 2011; Sharp et al., 2011). Glaciers in southern BC and the Rocky Mountains (Place, Helm, and Peyto glaciers) have melted at an even faster rate than reference glaciers in the High Arctic (Figure 4.9; see also Chapter 7).

There may be critical threshold rates of melting for ice, after which melt occurs very rapidly, as illustrated by recent events at Ward Hunt Lake, Canada's most northerly lake (Paquette et al., 2015). After relatively stable ice conditions from 1950 to 2007, the lake ice thinned remarkably. In 2008 the lake became ice free in summer for the first time and was again in 2011. The mean number of melting degree days went from 80.4 in 1996–2007 to 136.2 in 2008–12, illustrating this very rapid change. Ice decay was accelerated by feedback effects from heat advection through warm inflows, and the perennial ice disappeared.

Permafrost melting from the same increases in temperature will also have considerable implications for the hydrological cycle as well as for the overall landscape. The thawing will create more ponds and wetlands with an associated change in vegetation, as is already documented in northern Quebec (Thibault and Payette, 2009). One of these changes is the replacement of sphagnum moss–dominated communities by wetter ones dominated by sedge. The sedge is more biodegradable than the sphagnum and, as it decays, tends to release increasingly more methane rather than carbon (Hodgkins et al., 2015). Methane is a more potent greenhouse gas than carbon dioxide, and this shift will create another positive feedback loop, leading to more warming and more thawing. In other areas where cooler conditions prevail, there will be an increase in the depth of the active layer (the layer that freezes and unfreezes every year), leading to collapse of some sites with draining of lakes and lowering of water tables (Woo et al., 2006).

More than 95 per cent of Canada is snow covered for part of the winter. Spring melt is hence a critical part of the hydrological cycle in Canada as water moves from the solid to liquid

Water in the solid phase of ice may be in the Lowell glaciers of the St Elias range in western Yukon for thousands of years before melting and flowing to the ocean.

Relative humidity is high most of the year in Atlantic Canada and produces some beautiful atmospheric effects.

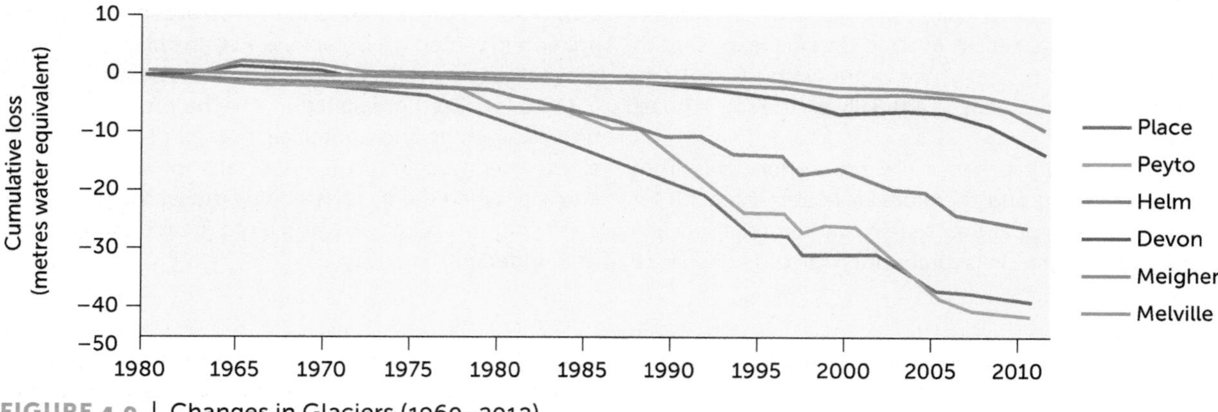

FIGURE 4.9 | Changes in Glaciers (1960–2012)
Source: Geological Survey of Canada (2013).

phase. This creates a runoff regime for many Canadian rivers, characterized by low late-winter flows and high spring melt flows that slowly diminish over the summer into the winter lows as water becomes stored in the solid phase once more. This marked seasonality is one of the reasons why Canada has developed considerable expertise in the construction of water storage facilities, one of the many human impacts on the hydrological cycle (Box 4.10).

Canada also has abundant storage of fresh water in lake systems, covering almost 8 per cent of the area of the country. These lakes are regularly replenished by river flow that contains approximately 7 per cent of the total river discharge in the world (Table 4.3). However, these river discharges are also changing as a result of global climate change. For example, Environment Canada reports that of its monitoring sites, lowest annual flow increased significantly at 51 sites and decreased significantly at 27 sites. The sites with increased minimums occurred in northwest Canada and the Arctic, whereas decreased flow sites were mainly in eastern and Atlantic Canada and across southern Canada from BC to the Prairies. Aquatic biodiversity is affected by these changes in relation to spawning times and other aspects of the life cycle.

About 75 per cent of the rivers and 60 per cent of the discharge in Canada drain north to the Arctic Ocean (Figure 4.13), whereas 90 per cent of the Canadian population lives within 300 kilometres of the US border, creating the potential for water deficits in this water-rich country (see Chapter 11).

As water demands grow, we have become increasingly dependent on groundwater sources. Once they become polluted with agricultural biocides or industrial wastes, however, they may be unsuitable for human use for centuries. The importance of this is underscored by the fact that Canada is estimated to have 37 times the amount of water in underground sources as in surface sources and one-quarter of the Canadian population relies on groundwater for domestic use, while some communities, such as Fredericton, New Brunswick, are almost totally dependent on groundwater.

Biogeochemical Cycles and Human Activity

Despite the apparent sophistication of human society, the humble fact remains that society could not exist without biogeochemical cycles and those unpretentious bacteria that make them work. Yet all the cycles are susceptible to perturbations by human activity. Such is the scale of human actions that the major transfers taking place between some of the reservoirs in the cycles are human induced. Some of the most notable and difficult environmental challenges now faced by society spring from these transfers. The purpose of this section is to discuss two of them in more detail: eutrophication and acid deposition. A third example, global climatic change—largely resulting from disruptions in the carbon and nitrogen cycles—is of such significance that Chapter 7 is devoted to it.

Eutrophication

Eutrophication is a natural process of nutrient enrichment of water bodies that leads to greater productivity. In an assessment of safe limits for stressing global systems, Rockström et al. (2009) found that of the nine main systems, three were already stressed above these limits. The nitrogen cycle is one of these three, and the phosphorus cycle is also rapidly approaching its planetary boundaries, although some scientists feel that phosphorus is already well over its limit in freshwater ecosystems. Furthermore, an assessment of water-based pollutants in North America found that of the 256 pollutants released to water, just two—nitrate compounds and ammonia—made up 90 per cent of the total discharge (Commission for Environmental Cooperation, 2011). Given this volume, it is little surprise that eutrophication of global water bodies is an increasing challenge.

Phosphorus and nitrogen are often the two main limiting factors for plant growth in aquatic ecosystems. Systems with

ENVIRONMENT IN FOCUS

BOX 4.9 | Groundwater

Groundwater is found within spaces between soil and rock particles and in crevices and cracks in the rocks below the surface of the Earth. Above the water table is the unsaturated zone where the spaces contain both water and air. In this zone, water is called soil moisture. Groundwater moves the same way as surface waters, downhill, but rarely as quickly, and not at all through impermeable materials such as clay. Permeable materials allow the passage of water, usually through cracks and spaces between particles. An **aquifer** is a formation of permeable rocks or loose materials that contains usable sources of groundwater. They vary greatly in size and composition. Porous media aquifers consist of materials such as sand and gravel in which the water moves through the spaces between particles. Fractured aquifers occur where the water moves through joints and cracks in solid rock. If an aquifer lies between layers of impermeable material, it is called a confined aquifer, which may be punctured by an artesian well, releasing the pressurized water to the surface. If the pressure is sufficient to bring water to the surface, the well is known as a flowing artesian well.

Areas where water enters aquifers are known as recharge areas; discharge areas are where the water once more appears above ground. These discharge areas can contribute significantly to surface water flow, especially in periods of low precipitation. Groundwater, of course, is a very significant part of the Canadian water supply. Dependencies range from 100 per cent in Prince Edward Island to 17 per cent in Quebec, with Ontario having the largest total consumption.

One example of the interaction between groundwater and biogeochemical cycle disruption is contamination of the groundwater of the Abbotsford Aquifer in the Lower Mainland of BC. Agriculture is the main land use. Changes in agricultural products over the past 30 years have led to high concentrations of nitrogen. These changes include a shift in animal production from locally fed dairy/beef cattle to poultry production based on outside feed. Crops have changed from grass and hay to raspberry production, which requires less nitrogen. Poultry manure is used to fertilize the raspberries. Nitrogen use is less than one-half of that produced. The remainder infiltrates to the groundwater. Of 2,297 groundwater samples taken over the years, 71 per cent have exceeded the maximum level specified in the *Guidelines for Canadian Drinking Water Quality* of 10 milligrams per litre (mg/L), with some as high as 91.9 mg/L. This is cause for concern. These nitrates may be transformed to nitrites in the digestive systems of babies, which in turn may lead to an oxygen deficiency in the blood, known as methemoglobinemia, or blue-baby syndrome. High nitrate levels have also been linked to cancer.

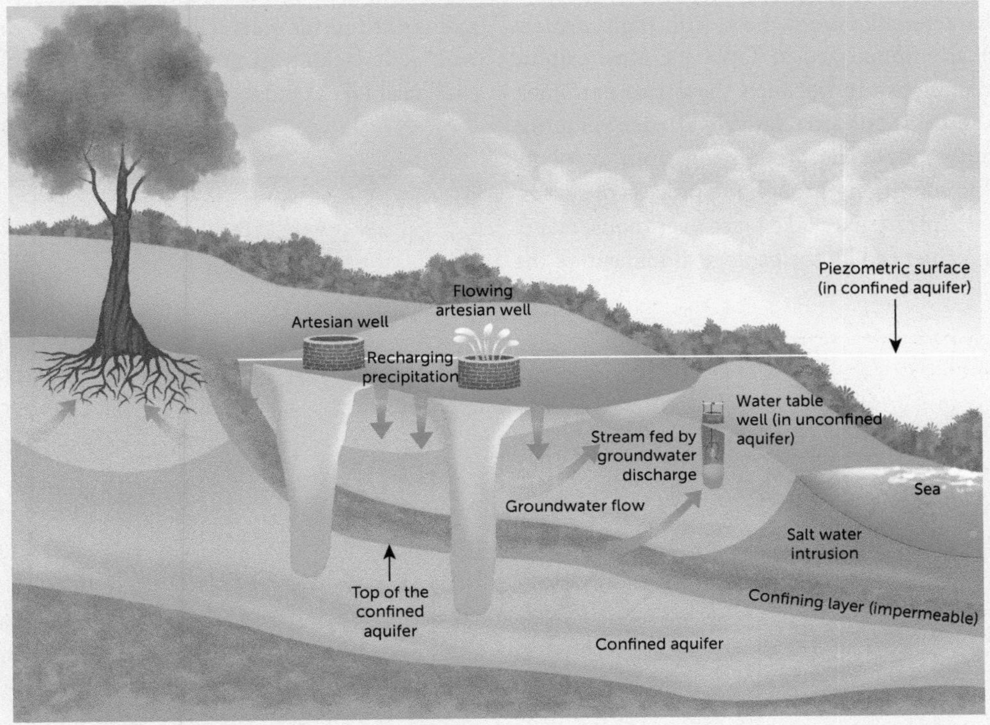

FIGURE 4.10 | Groundwater flow.

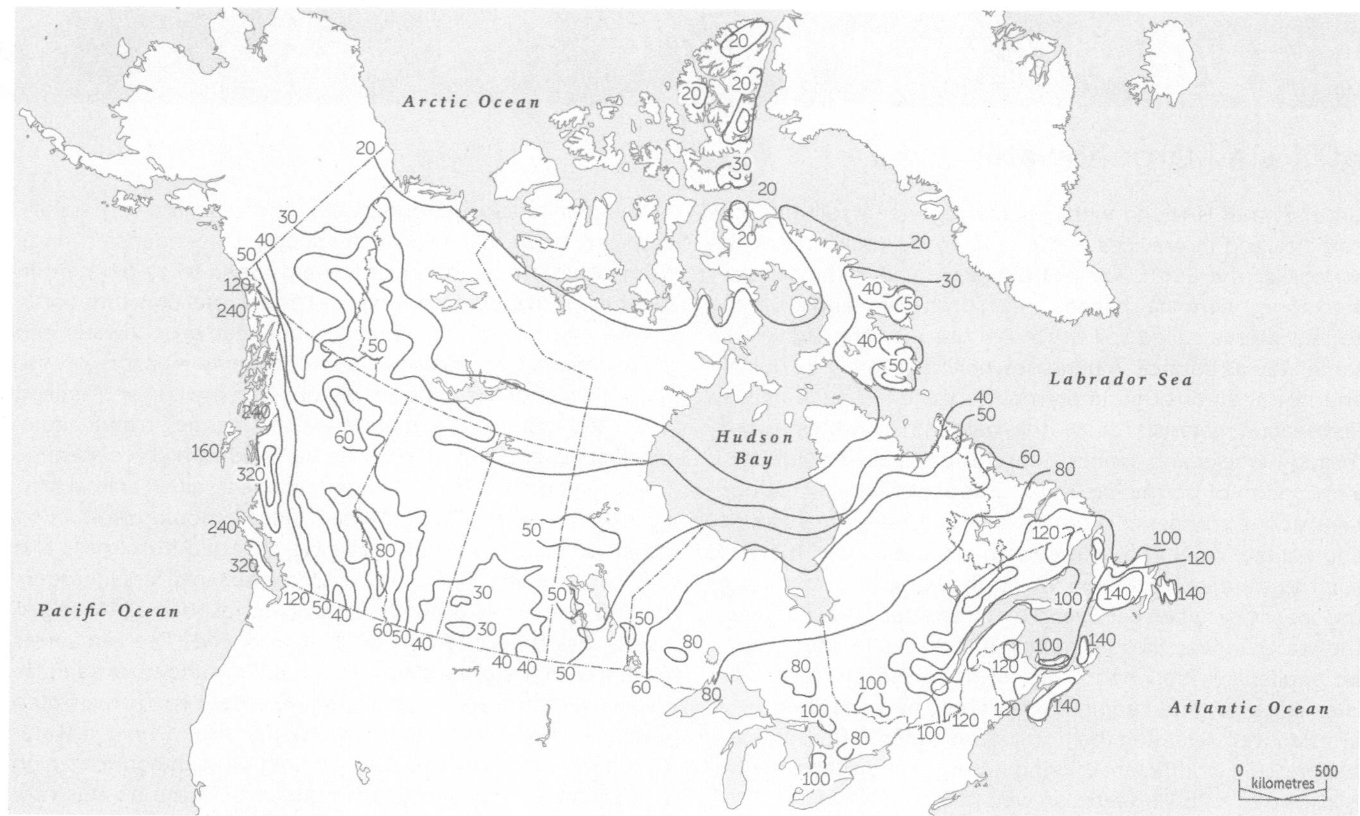

FIGURE 4.11 | Average annual rain and snow for Canada (cm).
Source: Adapted from Phillips (1990: 210).

relatively low nutrient levels, **oligotrophic** ecosystems, have quite different characteristics from those with high nutrient levels (**eutrophic**), as summarized in Table 4.4. **Mesotrophic** bodies have characteristics in between these two extremes. Natural terrestrial ecosystems are relatively efficient in terms of holding nutrient capital. The progression from an oligotrophic to eutrophic condition, through the process of succession discussed in Chapter 3, may take place over thousands of years. This rate is influenced by the geological makeup of the catchment area and the depth of the receiving waters. Catchments with fertile soils will progress more quickly than those with soils lacking in nutrients. Depth is important, because shallower lakes tend to recycle nutrients more efficiently.

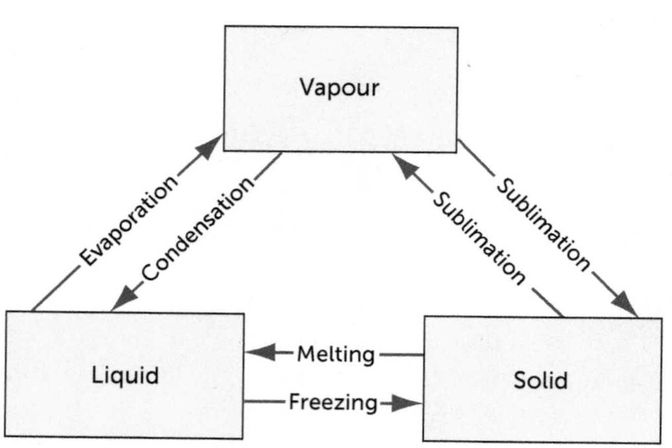

FIGURE 4.12 | Changes of phase in the hydrological cycle.

TABLE 4.3 | Mean Annual Stream Discharge to the Oceans for Selected Canadian Rivers

River	Watershed Area (km^2)	Discharge (m^3s^{-1})
Saguenay	90,100	1,820
St Lawrence	1,026,000	9,860
Churchill	281,300	1,200
Nelson	722,600	2,370
Albany	133,900	1,400
Koksoak	133,400	2,550
Yukon (at Alaska border)	297,300	2,320
Fraser	219,600	3,540
Columbia (at Washington border)	154,600	2,800
Mackenzie	984,195	10,800

Source: Briggs et al. (1993: 206).

ENVIRONMENT IN FOCUS

BOX 4.10 | Human Impacts on the Hydrological Cycle

Human activities also affect the hydrological cycle. Changes include:

- The storage and redistribution of runoff to augment water supplies for domestic, agricultural, and industrial uses
- The building of storage structures to control floods
- The drainage of wetlands
- The pumping of groundwater
- Cloud seeding
- Land-use changes such as deforestation, urbanization, and agriculture that affect runoff and evapotranspiration patterns
- Climatic change caused by interference with biogeochemical cycles

What Causes Eutrophication?

Cultural eutrophication (eutrophication caused by human activity) speeds up the natural eutrophication process through the addition of phosphates and nitrates to the water body. As lakes become shallower as a result of this input, nutrients are used more efficiently, productivity increases, and eutrophication progresses. This is a classic example of a positive feedback loop, with change in the system promoting even more change in the same direction. Additional phosphates and nitrates come from many different sources (Table 4.5), and in accordance with the law of conservation of matter discussed earlier, they do not simply disappear but accumulate in aquatic ecosystems. In total, between 8.5 and 9.5 tonnes of phosphorus find their way into the ocean from the 20 million tonnes mined in the world each year. This is approximately eight times the natural amount.

What Are the Effects?

This enrichment promotes increased growth of aquatic plants, particularly favouring the growth of floating phytoplankton over **benthic** plants rooted in the substrate. As the benthic plants become out-competed for light by the phytoplankton, they produce less oxygen at depth. Oxygen is critical for the maintenance of more diverse, oxygen-demanding fish species such as trout and other members of the salmonid family, which also start to decline in number. The oxygen produced by photosynthesis by the phytoplankton tends to stay in the shallower water, escaping back to the atmosphere rather than replenishing supplies at greater depths.

Oxygen depletion is further exacerbated by the decay of the large mass of phytoplankton produced. Dead matter filters to the bottom of the lake where it is consumed by oxygen-demanding decomposers. Once broken down, nutrients may be returned to the surface through convection currents and provide more food for more phytoplankton and algae. Blue-green algae replace green algae in eutrophic lakes, which further exacerbates the problem, since most blue-green algae are not consumed by the next trophic level, the zooplankton.

These effects of oxygen depletion in a water body also occur whenever excess organic matter is added. Under natural conditions, water is able to absorb and break down small amounts of organic matter, with the amount depending on the size, flow, and temperature of the receiving water body. The greater the size and flow and the lower the temperature, the greater the ability to absorb organic materials and retain oxygen levels.

When organic wastes are added to a body of water, the oxygen levels fall as the number of bacteria rises to help break down the waste. This is known as the **oxygen sag curve** (Figure 4.14) and is measured by the **biological oxygen demand (BOD)**, the amount of dissolved oxygen needed by aerobic decomposers to break down the organic material in a given volume of water at a certain temperature over a given period. At the discharge source, the oxygen sag curve starts to fall, and there is a corresponding rise in the BOD. As distance from the input source increases and the bacteria digest the wastes, then the oxygen content returns to normal, and the BOD falls.

Major sources of nitrates and phosphates, such as runoff from feedlots and sewage discharge, also contain large amounts of oxygen-demanding wastes. Heat is another source of oxygen stress. The overall result is a progression to a less useful and less healthy water body. The composition of the fish species changes to those less dependent on high oxygen levels, species that are generally less desirable for human purposes. Populations of waterfowl may fall as aquatic plants die off. The water becomes infested with algae, aquatic weeds, and phytoplankton, making swimming and boating unpleasant and giving off unpleasant odours. Water treatment for domestic or industrial purposes becomes more expensive.

What Can We Do about It?

The main way to control eutrophication is to limit the input of nutrients into the water body (Table 4.5). Domestic and animal wastes must be treated to remove phosphates. Advanced treatment can remove up to 90 per cent of these wastes. More difficult problems occur with diffuse, **non-point sources,**

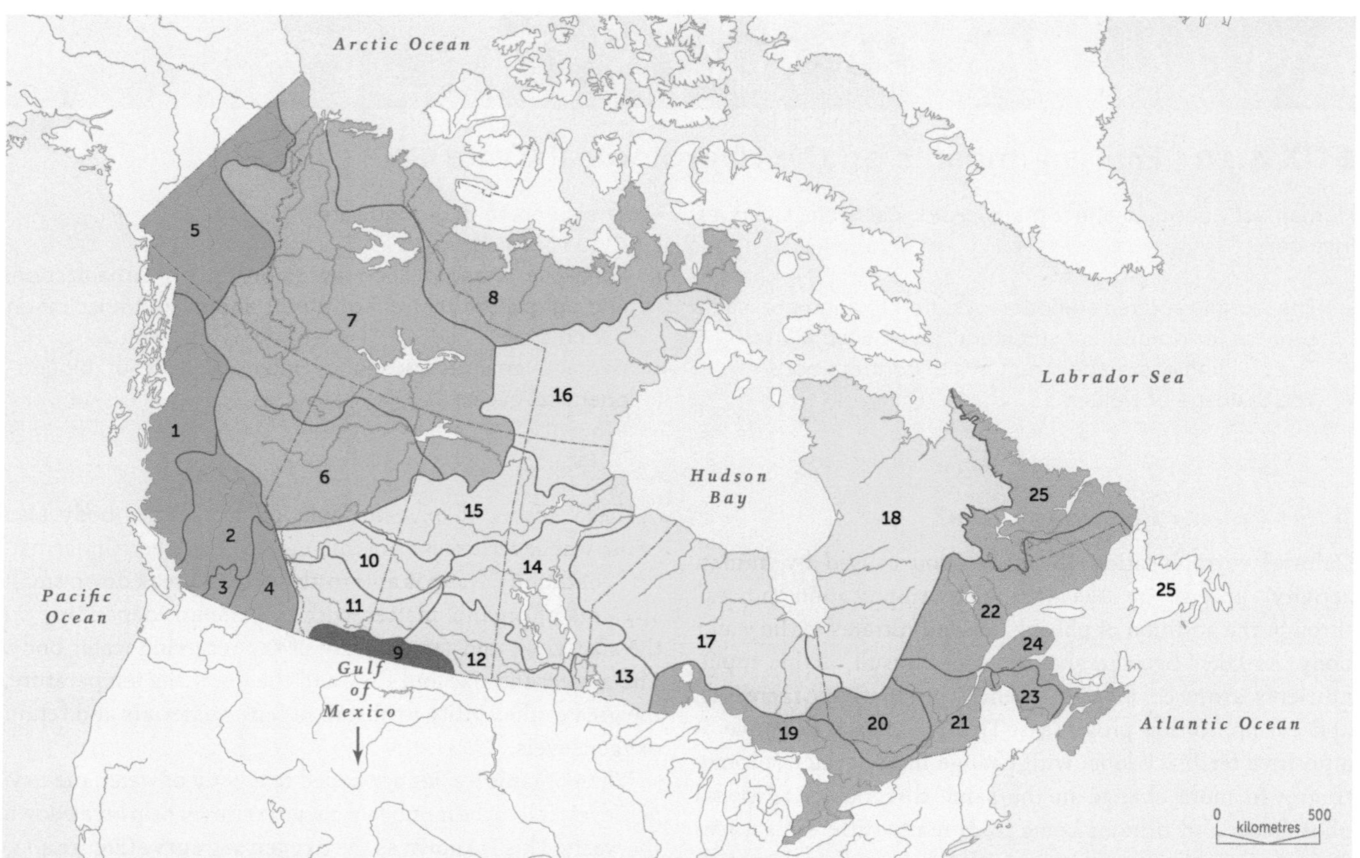

Ocean Basin Region		River Basin Region	Area In 000s km²
Pacific	1	Pacific Coastal	352
	2	Fraser-Lower Mainland	234
	3	Okanagan-Similkameena	14
	4	Columbiaa	90
	5	Yukon	328
Arctic	6	Peace-Athabasca	487
	7	Lower Mackenzie	1,300
	8	Arctic Coast-Islands	2,025
Gulf Of Mexico	9	Missouria	26
Hudson Bay	10	North Saskatchewan	146
	11	South Saskatchewana	170
	12	Assiniboine-Reda	190
	13	Winnipega	107
	14	Lower Saskatchewan-Nelson	363
	15	Churchill	298
	16	Keewatin	689
	17	Northern Ontario	394
	18	Northern Quebec	950
Atlantic	19	Great Lakesa	319
	20	Ottawa	146
	21	St Lawrencea	116
	22	North Shore-Gaspe	403
	23	St John-St Croixa	37
	24	Maritime Coastal	114
	25	Newfoundland-Labrador	376
Canada			9,974

FIGURE 4.13 | Drainage regions of Canada.

a. Canadian portion only; area on US side of international basin regions excluded from total.

Source: Environment Canada (1985: 35).

TABLE 4.4 | Characteristics of Oligotrophic and Eutrophic Water Bodies

Characteristic	Oligotrophic	Eutrophic
Nutrient cycling	low	high
Productivity (total biomass)	low	high
Species diversity	high*	low
Relative numbers of "undesirable" species	low	high
Water quality	high	low

*Lakes that are extremely non-productive (e.g., high mountain lakes) will have low species diversity.

TABLE 4.5 | Main Nutrient Sources Contributing to Cultural Eutrophication

Runoff from	fertilizers (N and P)
	feedlots (N and P)
	land-use change, such as cultivation, construction, mining natural sources
Discharge of	detergents (P)
	untreated sewage (N and P)
	primary and secondary treated sewage (N and P)
Emissions from	internal combustion engines (dissolved nitrogen oxides)

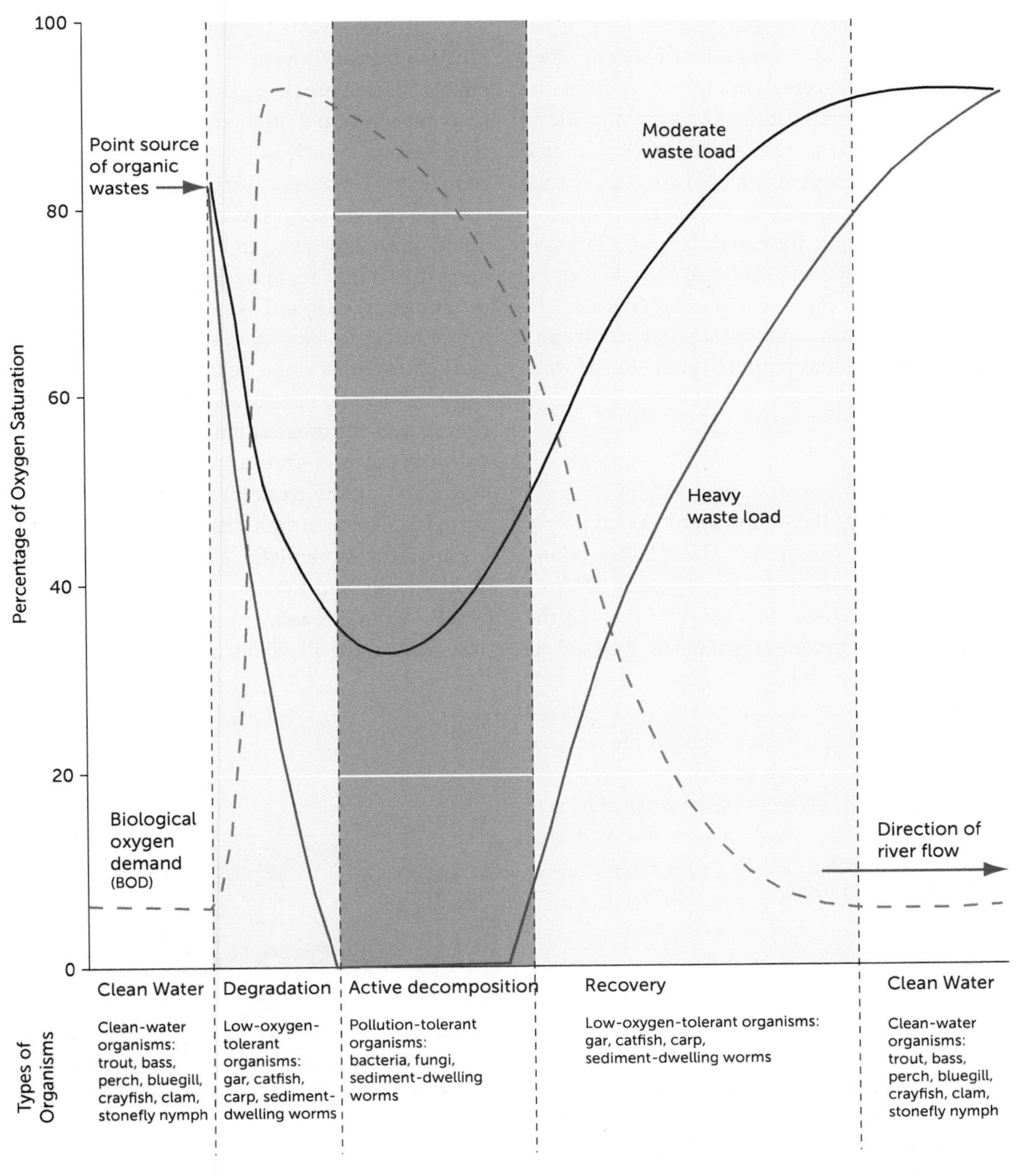

FIGURE 4.14 | Oxygen sag curve and biological oxygen demand (BOD).

such as runoff from urban areas and agricultural land. Such flows really have to be controlled at the source, since they enter the water body, by definition, in so many different locations. In the past, measures to control water pollution have been largely directed toward **point sources** of pollution, or single discharge points, such as effluent discharges from sewage plants or industrial processes. By and large, because of the high visibility of such sources, they are easy to identify and monitor, and pollution from such sources has fallen as a result. Increasing attention is now being directed toward the non-point sources (see Chapter 11).

Eutrophication used to be considered a problem of smaller water bodies, but now entire areas of the world's largest water bodies, the oceans, are becoming so eutrophic they are being described as "dead zones." More than 200 such zones have been recognized, some as large as 70,000 km^2. One of the largest and best-known areas is in the Gulf of Mexico, which receives all the excess fertilizers brought down from the Mississippi watershed. However, similar areas are now found in the waters off every continent, and researchers expect that their number and size will increase as global climatic change generates greater rainfall and greater runoff in many areas.

Eutrophication was thought to have been largely addressed through pollution control some 25 years ago. Now it is apparent that the challenge is still there, but at a larger scale. The next section explores one of Canada's most notable eutrophication challenges, Lake Erie, and points to some of the ways to address the problem.

Lake Erie: An Example of Eutrophication Control

In all parts of the country, there are many examples of eutrophic lakes. The best-known are the Great Lakes, where phosphorus levels are an issue in the open waters of three of the four Canadian Great Lakes. Phosphorus levels in the middle of Lake Superior and in the eastern basin of Lake Erie currently meet water quality objectives. Phosphorus levels in Lakes Huron and Ontario and in Georgian Bay are below water quality objectives, and above objectives in the western and central basins of Lake Erie (Dove and Chapra, 2015).

Lake Erie is a particularly well-known case because of its size and importance. Lake Erie is the second-smallest and also the shallowest of the Great Lakes, which collectively contain almost 20 per cent of the world's fresh water. Erie has experienced considerable changes in fish species composition since the early explorers described a highly diverse community. Gone are the lake sturgeon, cisco, blue pike, and lake whitefish as the human population in the basin increased and water quality declined. Some 11 million people live in the Erie drainage basin, and 39 per cent of the Canadian and 44 per cent of the American shore is taken up by urban development. There is also considerable industrial use around the shore and intensive agricultural use throughout the basin.

In the past, up to 90 per cent of the bottom layer of the central zone of the lake became oxygen-deficient in the summer. Huge algae mats more than 20 metres long and a metre deep became common. Beaches were closed. The natural eutrophication that might have taken thousands of years was superseded by cultural eutrophication within the space of 50 years.

In 1972, Canada and the US signed the Great Lakes Water Quality Agreement to try to come to grips with this problem. The signing of the 1985 Great Lakes Charter, in which the two countries agreed to take a cooperative and ecosystem-based approach to the lakes, further strengthened international efforts (See also Chapter 11). Since the 1970s, phosphorus controls, implemented under the Canada Water Act, have led to significant reductions in the phosphorus concentration of the water (Figure 4.15). Phosphate-based detergents were banned and municipal waste treatment plants upgraded.

These measures have led to improvement of water quality, but significant problems still remain. The controls are largely on point-source pollution, discharges that have a readily identifiable source, such as waste treatment plants and industrial complexes. However, much of the remaining nutrient load comes from non-point sources, such as runoff from agricultural fields, lawn fertilizer, and construction sites that are much more difficult to regulate. Figure 4.15 shows that phosphorus levels meet the Great Lakes Water Quality Agreement objective for total phosphorus in the offshore regions of the eastern basin, but not in some nearshore areas, and the central and western basin do not always meet objectives. The greatest frequency and the greatest magnitude of guideline exceedances are observed in the western basin of Lake Erie. The levels of nitrite and nitrate concentrations have also been rising, leading to increased eutrophication as a result of other nutrients.

Important synergistic effects between increasing phosphorus loads and invasive species can exacerbate the problem. For example, zebra mussels (Chapter 3) are filter-feeders that remove the phosphorus from the water and convert it

Jason Lugo/iStockphoto

Animal feedlots are a major source of nutrients, such as phosphates and nitrates, which speed up eutrophication.

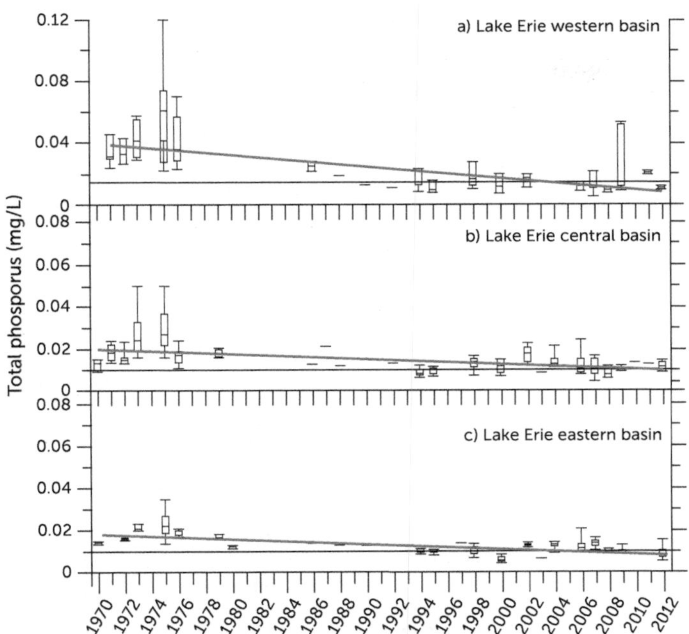

FIGURE 4.15 | Long-term trends of total phosphorus in Lake Erie: (a) western basin, (b) central basin and (c) eastern basin. Data are spring, surface values from offshore stations (≥10 m in western basin, ≥ 22 m in central basin, and ≥ 30 m in eastern basin). Box and whisker plots show the distribution of the individual measurements (boxes show median, 25th, and 75th percentiles and whiskers indicate the minimum and maximum values). Linear temporal trends are shown in red; basin-specific objectives (1978 Great Lakes Water Quality Agreement) are shown as black horizontal lines.

Source: Environment Canada; *1978 Great Lakes Water Quality Agreement; Great Lakes Surveillance*, Environment Canada, unpublished data. Courtesy A. Dove.

into a form easily usable for aquatic plants and algae to grow. They selectively feed on edible algae, giving opportunity for expanded blooms of the toxic blue-green algae *Microcystis.* The latter can be toxic to animals, including humans, and also is not a preferred food for zooplankton and therefore affects the base of the food chain, particularly for fish larvae (Vanderploeg et al., 2009). This has led to the interesting situation in which some areas in the centre of the Great Lakes, particularly in Huron and Ontario, are phosphorus deficient and hence limit fish growth, whereas there is an excess of phosphorus in the littoral area related to the concentrating effect of the zebra mussels and growth of *Microcystis.*

Scientists have also found that the amount of water flowing into Lake Erie is a major influence on the size and severity of the dead, oxygen-deficient zone that forms in the Lake every summer (Yuntao et al., 2015). The extreme drought of 2012, for example, led to the largest dead zone ever recorded. Previously, it had been thought that phosphorus levels were primarily responsible, but now it seems that meteorological factors, particularly precipitation, can have a major effect. Very large inflows are associated with large algae blooms, whereas small inflows create larger dead zones, calling for management that pays greater attention to these factors.

Acid Deposition

In 1966, fisheries researcher Harold Harvey was puzzled to find that the 4,000 pink salmon he had introduced to Lumsden Lake in the La Cloche Mountains southwest of Sudbury, Ontario, the previous year had all disappeared. Their passage upstream and downstream of the lake had been blocked. To unravel the mystery, he began to take more measurements of the lake and look into its history. The results were startling—not only had the salmon disappeared but many other species of fish indigenous to the lake had gone missing as well (Table 4.6). The reason soon became apparent. Between 1961 and 1971, Lumsden Lake had experienced a hundredfold increase in the acidity of its waters, as had many other lakes in the same region (Table 4.7). The changes had shifted the lakes outside the limits of tolerance of the species, as discussed in Chapter 2. The indigenous fish species, and many of the species upon which they depended for food, simply could not tolerate the new conditions and perished. They were victims of the effects of **acid deposition.**

What Is Acid Deposition?

Acids are chemicals that release hydrogen ions (H+) when dissolved in water, whereas a base is a chemical that releases hydroxyl ions (OH−). When in contact, acids and bases neutralize each other as they come together to form water (H_2O). Acidity is a measure of the concentration of hydrogen ions in a solution and is measured on the pH scale, which goes from 0

TABLE 4.6 | Disappearance of Fish from Lumsden Lake

1950s	Eight species present
1960	Last report of yellow perch
1960	Last report of burbot
1960–5	Sport fishery fails
1967	Last capture of lake trout
1967	Last capture of slimy sculpin
1968	White sucker suddenly rare
1969	Last capture of trout and perch
1969	Last capture of lake herring
1969	Last capture of white sucker
1970	One fish species present
1971	Lake chub very rare

Source: H. Harvey, unpublished speech, based on Beamish and Harvey (1972). Reprinted with the author's permission.

to 14 (Figure 4.16). The midpoint of the scale, pH 7, represents a neutral balance between the presence of acidic hydrogen ions and basic hydroxyl ions. The pH scale is logarithmic. A decrease in value from pH 6 to pH 5 means that the solution has become 10 times more acidic. If the number drops to pH 4 from pH 6, then the solution is 100 times more acidic.

Precipitation, as either snow or rain, tends to be slightly acidic, even without human interference, because carbon dioxide in the atmosphere combines with water to form carbonic acid. Generally, "clean" rain has a pH value of 5.6. Acid rain is defined as deposition that is more acidic than this, and in Canada rainfall has been recorded with pH levels much lower. *Acid deposition* is a more generic term that includes not only rainfall but also snow, fog, and dry deposition from dust.

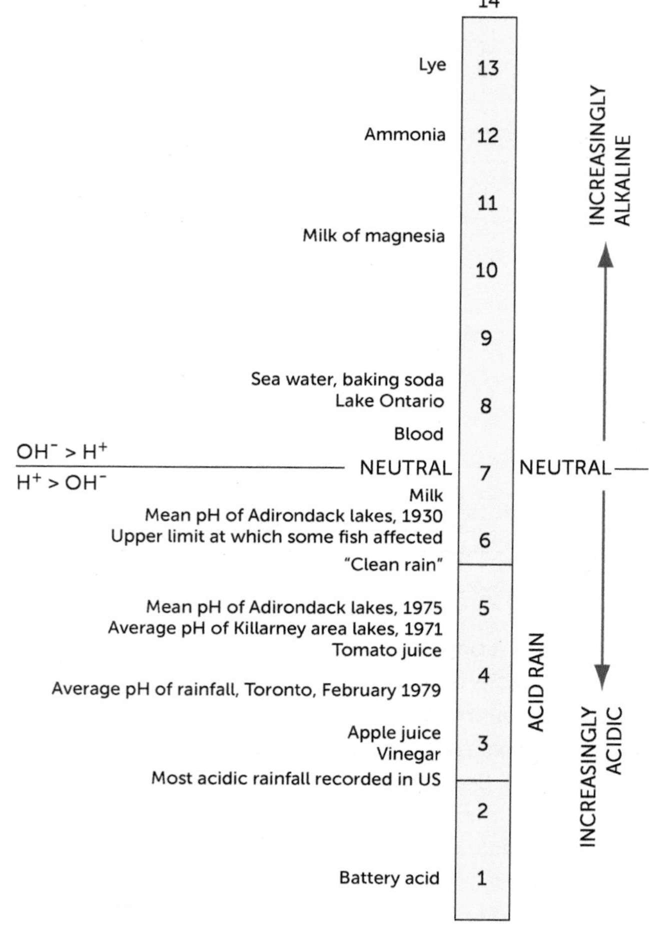

FIGURE 4.16 | The acid (pH) scale.

What Causes Acid Deposition?

The increases in acidity reflected in the pH levels of the lakes listed in Table 4.7 are due to human interference in the sulphur and nitrogen cycles. The largest sources are the smelting of sulphur-rich metal ores and the burning of fossil fuels for energy. These processes change the distribution of the elements between the various sources shown in Figures 4.3 and 4.4, and consequently, natural processes are inadequate to deal with the buildup of matter. Increased amounts of sulphur and various forms of nitrogen are ejected into the atmosphere, where they may travel thousands of kilometres before being returned to the lithosphere as a result of depositional processes. Human activities account for more than 90 per cent of the sulphur dioxide and nitrogen oxide emissions in North America.

Excessive sulphur is produced when ore bodies, such as copper and nickel, are roasted (smelted) at high temperatures to release the metal. Unfortunately, such ores often contain more sulphur than metal, and the sulphur is released into the atmosphere as a waste product of the process. A similar effect is created when sulphur-containing coal is burned as the energy source in power plants. In Canada, the smelting of metal ores accounts for most sulphur emissions (Figure 4.17). In the US, electrical utilities are the largest source, accounting for 70 per cent of emissions. The effects of these emissions became obvious fairly early on around smelting plants such as those at Inco in Sudbury and in Trail, BC. Trees were destroyed over large areas. Now there are very encouraging signs of rehabilitation, as discussed in Chapter 13.

These obvious signs of ecological damage were ignored for many years. However, as the ecological implications became better known, industry began to build higher stacks to eject the waste further into the atmosphere. Inco, for example, built a 381-metre "Superstack" in 1972 (see also Chapter 13). At the local scale, this improved matters somewhat but merely served to create problems elsewhere, especially in Quebec, as entire air masses became acidified and dropped their acid

TABLE 4.7 | Lake Acidification in the La Cloche Mountains, 1961–71

Lake	pH 1961	pH 1971
Broker	6.8	4.7
David	5.2	4.3
George	6.5	4.7
Johnnie	6.8	4.8
Lumsden	6.8	4.4
Mahzenazing	6.8	5.3
O.A.S.	5.5	4.3
Spoon	6.8	5.6
Sunfish	6.8	5.6
Grey (1959)	5.6	4.1
Tyson (1955)	7.4	4.9

Source: H. Harvey, unpublished speech, based on Beamish and Harvey (1972).

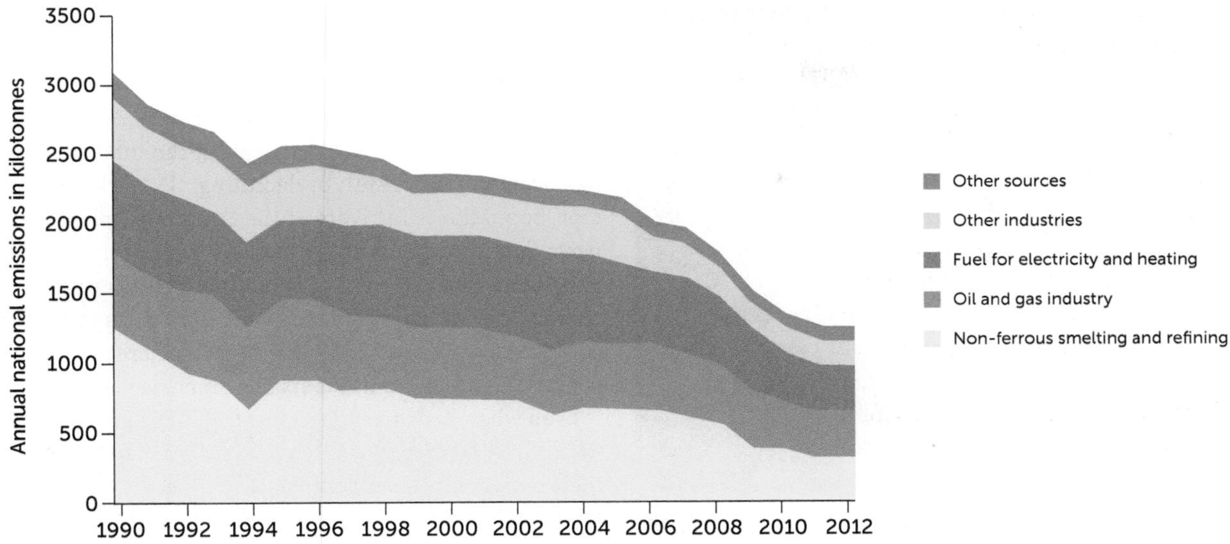

FIGURE 4.17 | Sulphur oxide emissions and their sources, 1990–2012.

Source: Environment Canada (2015c). © Her Majesty The Queen in Right of Canada, as represented by the Minister of Environment, 2015. The Environment Canada data is available online, at no cost, by visiting http://www.ec.gc.ca

burdens over a larger area. Weather patterns are not random, and so acidified air masses tend to travel in the same kinds of patterns. In central and eastern Canada, as air masses travel from southwest to northeast, they bring a heavy pollution burden from the heavily industrialized Ohio Valley in the US, which falls mostly in Canada. It is estimated that approximately half of the sulphate falling in Canada originates in the US.

These point sources of pollution are, however, easier to monitor and control than the other main source of acids—nitrogen emissions. The highest emissions come from various means of transport as a result of high-temperature combustion, followed closely by emissions from the oil and gas industry (Figure 4.18). Two main factors account for the decline in nitrogen emissions: a reduction in emissions from transportation, due to cleaner technology and fuels, and a reduction in emissions from electricity generation as a result of regulation and domestic and international agreements.

What Are the Effects of Acid Deposition?

Aquatic Effects

The effects of acid deposition on the fish of Lumsden Lake and other aquatic ecosystems are one visible sign of some of the impacts of acid deposition. Other species are also affected as the pH of the water body declines. Indeed, as can be seen in Figure 4.19, fish are often not the most sensitive species and are really more of an indicator of the damage that has already

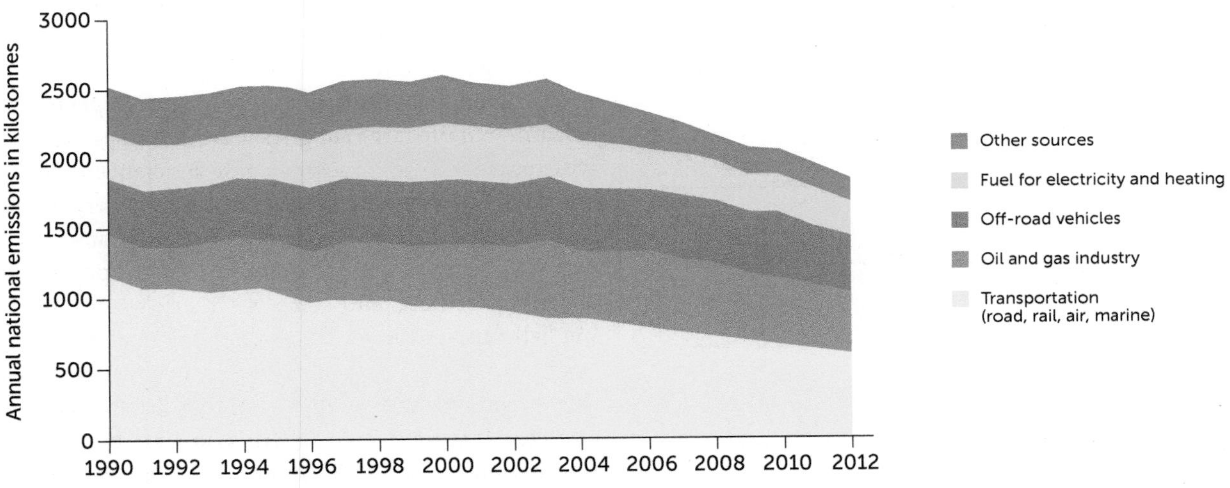

FIGURE 4.18 | Nitrogen oxide emissions and their sources, 1990–2012.

Source: Environment Canada (2015b). © Her Majesty The Queen in Right of Canada, as represented by the Minister of Environment, 2015. The Environment Canada data is available online, at no cost, by visiting http://www.ec.gc.ca

A handful of the jelly-like *Holopedium* species that are becoming the dominant plankton in some lakes in eastern Canada as a result of calcium deficiencies caused by acid rain.

occurred. As insects such as mayflies are eliminated, species higher in the food chain that feed on them become affected through food depletion. The same is true of fish-eating birds such as loons, whose young have been shown to have a lower chance of survival on acidified lakes because of starvation.

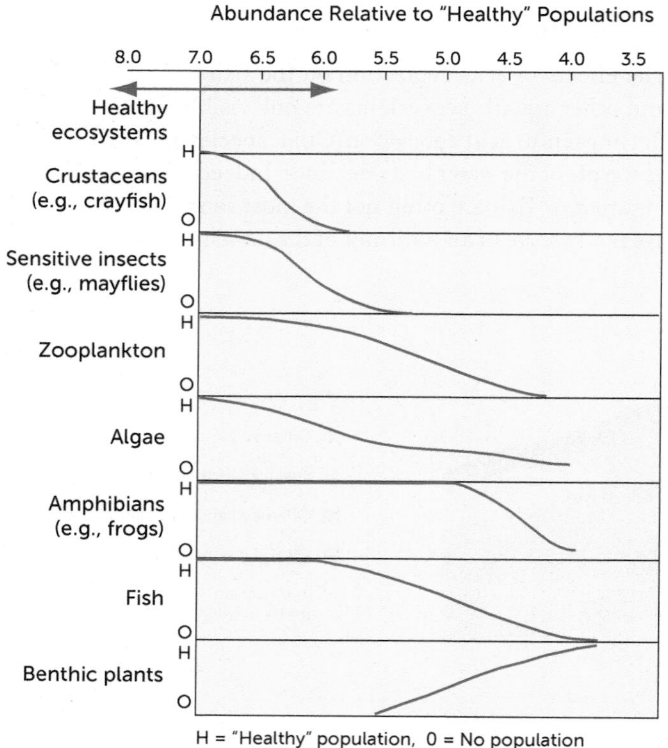

FIGURE 4.19 | Sensitivity of various aquatic organisms to pH level.

Source: Environment Canada (1991b).

Unfortunately, some of these impacts appear permanent. Examination of historical angling records in Nova Scotia, for example, indicates that of 60 main salmon rivers, 13 runs of salmon are extinct and a further 18 are virtually extinct. It is estimated that more than half of the total salmon stock has been lost as a result of declining pH levels. Atlantic salmon populations in rivers of the Southern Upland region of Nova Scotia continue to be severely negatively affected and will likely become extinct if adult survival rates remain at current low levels and pH recovery continues to be delayed. Interestingly, in northern Nova Scotia, where acid deposition is much less, salmon numbers have increased recently.

Even where fish manage to survive, they may be grossly disfigured, with twisted backbones and flattened heads, because their bones have been deprived of the necessary nutrients for strength. Reproductive capacities may be sufficiently impaired to lead to eventual population declines. Generally, the time of reproduction is the most sensitive part of the life cycle. The critical factor is often the lower pH level of the water as the snow melts. At this time, the buildup of acids over the winter can result in even higher acidity than experienced through the rest of the year. This pulse of acidity is called **acid shock**, and it may also be one of the causes of stress on amphibious creatures, such as frogs, that often use small temporary pools of water for breeding in the spring following runoff. At Lumsden Lake, for example, spring runoff produced a pH as low as 3.3, more than 100 times more acidic than the 1961 levels.

More acidic water and the subsequent food chain effects are not the only concern. Other chemical changes also occur. The increased acidity, for example, releases large amounts of aluminum from the terrestrial ecosystem into the rivers and lakes. Here it forms a toxic scum, lethal to many forms of aquatic life.

The full implications of what some of these changes mean over the long term are only just coming to light. In eastern Canada, for example, acid rain has removed many nutrients from already nutrient-deficient watersheds. Calcium is one such nutrient, and it turns out that a dominant species of the zooplankton and subsequent food chain, *Daphnia*, requires calcium in quite large supplies to be able to grow its protective exoskeleton. In the new calcium-deficient environment, it can no longer compete against another species, *Holopedium*, with lower calcium requirements, that is now displacing *Daphnia*. Unfortunately, *Holopedium* relies upon a slimy gel to repel predators, and some of Ontario's lakes are becoming "jellified" as a result of the doubling in abundance of the species since the 1980s (Jeziorski et al., 2014). Not only does this provide an unpleasant swimming experience, but there are fears that the plankton will also start to clog filtration systems on water supply intakes. In addition, *Holopedium* has relatively low nutrient content compared with *Daphnia* and therefore fewer nutrients will be passed along to the next trophic level.

Terrestrial Effects

Terrestrial effects of acid deposition first became visible around emission sources, such as at Trail, BC, and Sudbury, Ontario, as trees began to die. Before joining the soil, the acids eat away at the sensitive photosynthetic surfaces of the leaves. Broad-leaved trees, such as sugar maples, the source of Quebec's $400-million annual maple syrup industry, are particularly susceptible because of the large surface area of their leaves.

Once in the soil, the acids leach away the nutrients required for plant growth, leading to nutrient deficiencies. The high levels of aluminum released by the acids also help to inhibit the uptake of nutrients. The bacteria so critical to the workings of many biogeochemical cycles are also adversely affected and cause changes in natural soil processes. Decomposition and humus formation are retarded. Soil contains many organisms involved in the critical ecological functions of biogeochemical cycling and energy flow. There may be more than 100 million bacteria and several kilometres of fungal hyphae in a single gram of healthy soil. Mycorrhizal fungi are very important for the growth of many plants because they help to transport nutrients from the soil water into the roots. Research on Jack pine, undertaken to understand the potential impact of increased acidity on these mutualistic relationships, found that changes in calcium-to-aluminum ratios caused by increased acidity influenced the succession of mycorrhizal fungi on tree root systems. The actual physical contact of the acids with the plant roots can also inhibit growth and lower resistance to disease. The long-term effects of these kinds of changes on tree growth, the ecological health of the community, and forest yields are still highly uncertain, but they are not going to be beneficial.

Eastern Canadian watersheds now exhibit releases of sulphur from soils in excess of deposition. Two internal catchment sources, sulphate desorption and release via decomposition of organic matter, are the likely causes of the budget imbalance. The release of this extra sulphur acts as an additional acid load for soils and downstream waters and may be partly retarding the recovery of surface waters in eastern Canadian forested watersheds. However, increased nitrogen deposits are not a problem, since most areas are nitrogen deficient and the increased inputs act as fertilizer.

Damage from acid deposition is now visible over much wider areas than those surrounding sources of high emissions. Extensive areas of damage have been recorded in Europe and in the eastern United States. At these larger scales, it is often difficult, however, to single out one cause, such as acid deposition. It is likely that other factors—climate change and other pollutants, such as high levels of ozone brought about by excessive nitrogen oxides—are also important in placing stress on these communities in synergistic reactions.

The smelter at Trail, BC, caused extensive damage to the surrounding vegetation.

The impact on plant life is not restricted to natural ecosystems. Significant changes can also occur on agricultural lands as direct damage to crops or more indirect changes through changes to soil chemistry. The growth of crops such as beets, radishes, tomatoes, beans, and lettuce is inhibited, and biological nitrogen fixation is diminished at a pH of 4. In central and eastern Canada, 84 per cent of the most productive agricultural lands receive more than the 20 kilograms of acid deposition per hectare. In some areas, the application of lime to the soil has become a routine agricultural procedure in an attempt to neutralize the acids by adding more basic ions.

Heterotrophs can also be affected. As the forest cover diminishes, so does the habitat for many species. Toxic metals such as cadmium, zinc, and mercury, released from the soil by the acids, may be concentrated by certain species of plants and lichens and accumulated in the livers of species eating them, such as moose and caribou.

Loons, with their beautiful coloration and haunting cries, are a wilderness symbol for many Canadians, but their breeding success has been reduced by the effects of acid rain.

Ecosystem Sensitivity

Not all ecosystems are equally sensitive to the effects of acid deposition. The **critical load** is the maximum level of acid deposition that can be sustained in an area without compromising ecological integrity. Some areas have a high capacity to neutralize the excess acids because of the high base capacity of the bedrock and soils. For example, the Prairies are not as sensitive to the effects of acid deposition, because underlying carbonate-rich rocks, deep soils, and other factors combine to provide high **buffering capacity**. On the other hand, areas with difficult-to-weather rocks with low nutrient content (e.g., granite) and with thin soils following glaciation often have very low buffering capacities. Much of central and eastern Canada and coastal British Columbia fit within this category (Figure 4.20). The provinces most vulnerable to acid deposition in terms of amount of area ranked as highly sensitive are Quebec (82 per cent), Newfoundland and Labrador (56 per cent), and Nova Scotia (45 per cent). The spatial coincidence of low buffering capacities and high deposition rates explains why most attention in Canada has centred on the central and eastern parts of the country.

Socio-economic Effects

The environmental effects described above have socio-economic implications, and there are also direct effects of acid deposition on human health. In aquatic ecosystems, for example, declines in fish populations have implications for those involved in fishing, whether commercially, for subsistence food, or for sport. The impacts of acid deposition on tree growth and the forest industry are also of considerable concern. Some studies indicate that tree growth reductions of up to 20 per cent might be experienced. Estimates of the market value of lost wood production resulting from acid rain are in the hundreds of millions of dollars in Nova Scotia and New Brunswick. The full effects, however, are likely to be much greater than this. Research indicates that a time lag of some 20 to 30 years is likely before the effects of acid rain are reflected in reduced tree growth.

Many values, however, are difficult to express in monetary terms. Thousands of Canadians, for example, maintain lakeside cottages. It is challenging to ascribe a value to the changes that might occur as the lakes become devoid of life. Common loons, for example, are for many the quintessential symbol of the Canadian wilderness, yet populations have been found to be quite sensitive to lake acidification. Below pH levels of 4.5, loons do not seem able to find enough food to feed their young. However, as a result of emissions regulations in Canada and the US, overall improvements in the capacity of many lakes to support aquatic biota are being observed. For instance, a general increase in the number of breeding fish-eating water birds (such as loons) has been observed in lakes in Ontario, Quebec, and Newfoundland, particularly those near reduced emission sources. At the same time, algae, invertebrates, and water-bird food chains in many lakes in this region continue to show acidification impacts (i.e., direct effects of acidification, metal toxicity, loss of prey species, and reduced nutritional value of remaining prey), particularly in lakes and rivers where fish communities have been affected.

The human-built environment, as well as the natural environment, is damaged by acid deposition. The acids eat away at certain building materials. The effects have been most damaging in Europe, with its many old monuments, but such effects can also be seen on the Houses of Parliament and nearby statues in Ottawa. Estimates suggest that acid rain causes over $3 billion worth of damage to the human-built environment in Canada every year.

The most direct impact on human health may arise from inhalation of airborne acidified particles, which can impair respiratory processes and lead to lung damage. There are significant relationships between air pollution levels in southwestern Ontario, for example, and hospital admissions for respiratory illnesses. Comparative studies between heavily polluted areas in Ontario and less polluted areas in Manitoba found diminished lung capacity in about 2 per cent of the children in the more polluted areas. Further studies have confirmed this relationship, although whether high sulphate or ozone levels are responsible has yet to be conclusively determined. Calculations by the US government suggest that southern Ontario has been saving more than $1 billion per year in health costs since 2010 as a result of efforts to reduce emissions in the US.

Humans can also be affected by ingesting some of the products of acid rain. Regarding drinking water, for example, in some areas where older delivery systems are still in place, the increased acidity of water can corrode pipes and fittings and result in elevated levels of lead in the water supply. This is one reason why in certain areas, such as Victoria, BC, it is recommended that schools flush their water fountains early in the morning to spill the water that has been held overnight and that might show elevated lead levels.

Acidified water may also hold other substances in solution that are deleterious to human health. Excess levels of aluminum have already been noted. When metals such as mercury, chromium, and nickel are leached from the substrate into water, they may be taken up and concentrated along the food chain and eventually cause a human health problem.

What Can We Do about It?

One of the main challenges associated with acid deposition is that it is not limited to the areas generating the emissions and causing the problem. In Canada, more than half of the acid deposition originates in the US. To address such problems, international efforts are required, as is a greater concern on the part of individuals (see Box 4.11).

Canada has addressed the problem through national, bilateral, and multilateral efforts. In 1983, the Canadian Council

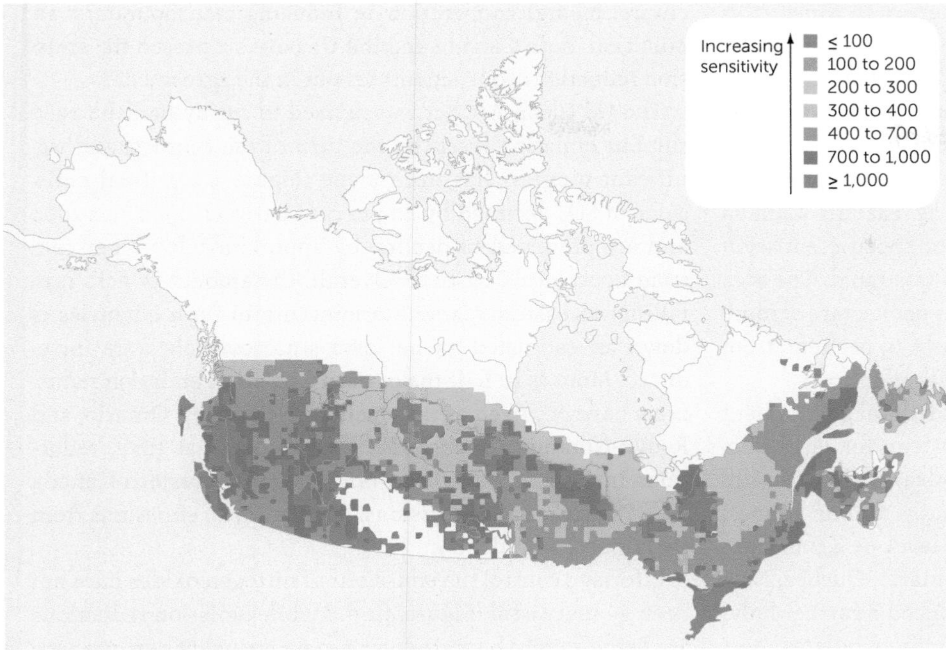

FIGURE 4.20 | Sensitivity of terrain to acidity. Critical load index, 2008; yellow through red categories are considered acid-sensitive terrain.

Source: Federal, Provincial, and Territorial Governments of Canada (2010: 68). © Environment Canada, 2010

FIGURE 4.21 | Areas where the critical load has been exceeded in the Boreal Shield. Number of units above critical load, 2009.

Source: Federal, Provincial, and Territorial Governments of Canada (2010: 68). © Environment Canada, 2010

of Resource and Environment Ministers agreed on an annual target deposition or critical load of 20 kilograms per hectare as an acceptable goal, taking political and economic costs into account. This is an important qualification. The critical load represents a **policy target value (PTV)** set by politicians. At the time, scientists warned that a further 75 per cent reduction in SO_2 emissions would be needed to address the situation adequately. This is a **scientific target value (STV)**, and subsequent experience demonstrates that the scientists were correct in their assessment. Many of the environmental problems you

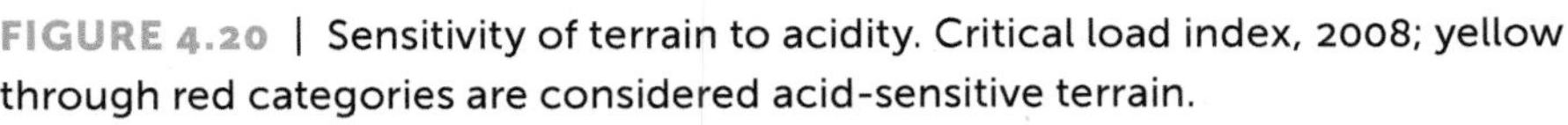

BOX 4.11 | What You Can Do: Taking Individual Action Every Day

Many of the challenges and problems discussed in this book are international in scope and require the coordinated efforts of different levels of government, industry, and individuals. Matter cycles are a relatively easy way for individuals to reduce their environmental impacts through the day-to-day decisions that we all make regarding food, water consumption, shopping, and a host of other activities. The following are some of the ways individuals can try to have a positive influence.

1. Recycle your wastes. In BC, just by recycling beverage containers, consumers contributed to the reduction of 135,000 tonnes of carbon dioxide equivalent in 2010. This is equivalent to taking 39,000 cars off the road for a year.
2. Acid deposition is profoundly influenced by the personal decisions we all make regarding our use of fossil fuels in transport and electricity consumption. Think about your decisions and how you can minimize use.
3. Many consumer items, such as TVs, cellphones, computers, and other electronic products, contain materials such as lead and nickel that contain sulphur. As you buy and dispose of these items, you are helping to increase acid deposition. Only buy items that you really need and always dispose of them correctly.
4. Use chemical fertilizers sparingly on your gardens to reduce impacts of excessive nutrients on water bodies.
5. Eat less meat. This reduces the demand for livestock, and livestock are major contributors to eutrophication.
6. Let your political representatives know that you are in favour of mandatory measures to curb sulphur emissions and treat livestock wastes, even if this costs you more money.

Source: Canadian Council of Ministers of the Environment (2008).

will read about in this text represent instances in which PTVs were established that conflicted with STVs. *Total allowable catch* in fisheries (Chapter 8) and *annual allowable cut* in forestry (Chapter 9), as well as designation of endangered species (Chapter 14), are good examples of this conflict.

In 1985, an agreement was reached among the provinces east of Saskatchewan (the area defined as "eastern" Canada within the context of acid rain) that set specific emission reductions to reach this target. Progress was rapid. The area of eastern Canada receiving 20 kilograms per hectare or more of wet sulphate per year declined by nearly 59 per cent, from 0.71 million km^2 in 1980 to about 0.29 million in 1993.

In 1998, the provinces, territories, and federal government signed the Canada-Wide Acid Rain Strategy for Post-2000, committing them to further actions to deal with acid rain. By 2004, SO_2 emissions were down to 2.3 million tonnes, a 50-per-cent reduction from the 1980 level of 4.6 million tonnes (Environment Canada, 2006a). Ontario, Quebec, New Brunswick, and Nova Scotia have announced a further halving of their provincial sulphur dioxide targets by 2015, and Nova Scotia has a cumulative reduction target of 75 per cent by 2020 (Environment Canada, 2010a).

Advances in science have allowed more comprehensive assessments of critical loads to be defined that combine sulphates and nitrogen oxides (NO_X) for both aquatic and terrestrial ecosystems. They are now expressed as ionic charge balance in terms of equivalent/hectare/year, and the old load of 20 kilograms/hectare/year is represented by 416 equivalent/hectares/year. Current critical loads for the Boreal Shield are shown in Figure 4.21, with between 21 and 75 per cent of eastern Canada still receiving deposits in excess of the critical load. The very wide range represents the uncertainty regarding long-term effects of nitrogen and the degree of future absorption in soils.

The Canada–United States Air Quality Agreement was signed in 1990 to create a mechanism for bilateral environmental cooperation in reducing transboundary air pollution. Both Canada and the US have surpassed the emission reduction requirements set out in the agreement.

The US Clean Air Act was revised to cut by half the 1980 sulphur emission levels by the turn of the century, and significant progress has been made (Figure 4.22). Total emissions of SO_2 declined by 40 per cent between 1980 and 2000 and are predicted to decline by approximately 38 per cent from 2000 levels by 2020. Overall, the amount of acid rain falling on eastern Canada originating in both countries is down an estimated 33 per cent since controls were introduced. More than half the eastern Canadian emission reductions have occurred at the smelters at Sudbury, Ontario, and Rouyn-Noranda, Quebec. However, since that time, reductions in Canada have been minimal, with western Canada showing increasing emissions, largely due to emissions from the Alberta oil industry.

Efforts to control the emissions of nitrogen oxides have not been as successful (Figure 4.23). Mobile emission reductions are being sought by introducing more stringent performance standards on exhaust emissions from new vehicles and are predicted to decline by approximately 17 per cent between 2000 and 2020. In eastern Canada, emissions of NO_X are predicted to decrease by approximately 39 per cent between 2000 and 2020. These declines are largely the result of power plant emissions reductions. In 2010, Ontario's Long-Term Energy Plan was published, setting reduction targets of 6,300 megawatts by 2025. This plan also aims to double the supply of renewable energy by 2025. Further action in the province to achieve reductions includes agreements to purchase power from 19 new renewable energy projects, including three water power projects, three landfill gas and biogas projects, and 13 wind farms.

However, in the West, NO_X emissions are predicted to increase by approximately 5 per cent between 2000 and 2020. Emissions of NO_X in western Canada surpassed emissions

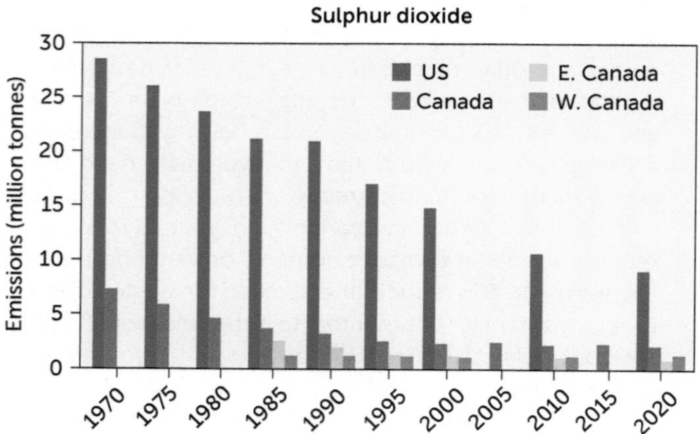

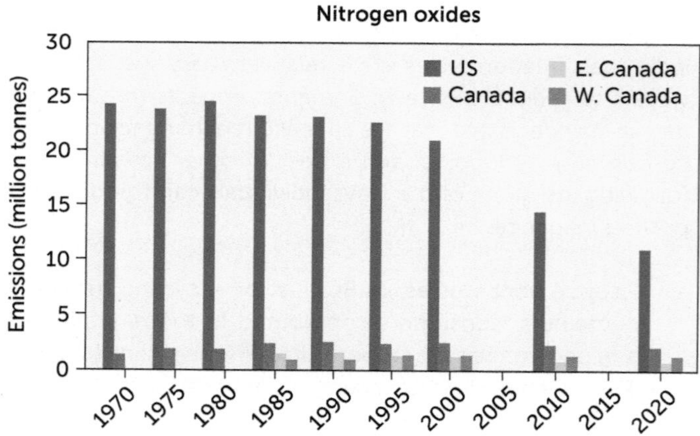

FIGURES 4.22 AND 4.23 | Estimated emissions of sulphur dioxide in the US and Canada and estimated emissions of nitrogen oxides in the US and Canada.

Source: Data from Environment Canada (2006a).

in eastern Canada by the year 2000 and will continue to increase, driven by the oil sands developments (Chapter 12). Greater reductions are predicted for the US, where NO_X emissions are predicted to decline by approximately 47 per cent from 2000 levels by 2020 (Figure 4.23).

An analysis of the US Acid Rain Program estimated annual benefits of the program to both Canada and the United States at $122 billion in 2010 and costs for that year at $3 billion (in 2000 dollars)—a 40 to 1 benefit/cost ratio. These benefits flow from such factors as improved air quality prolonging lives, reducing heart attacks and other cardiovascular and respiratory problems, and improving visibility.

Canada's sulphur oxide (SO_X) emissions declined by 46 per cent in 2011 from 2001 levels, but Canada still ranked fourth internationally in SO_X emission totals in 2011 and had the second-largest ratio of emissions to GDP among the 10 comparable countries selected by Environment Canada. In terms of total NO_X emissions, Canada ranked fourth and second when considering the ratio of emissions to GDP behind Australia (Environment Canada, 2015a).

Canada has met all its goals and commitments, some with considerable time to spare, in terms of acid deposition reductions. There has been a decreasing trend in lake sulphate levels in southeastern Canada in response to reductions in SO_2 emissions; however, many of these lakes are still acidified, and many do not meet a pH condition of 6, a key threshold for the sustenance of fish and other aquatic biota. Acid deposition remains a significant problem in Canada and will remain so for years to come. To some extent, the issue has been overshadowed by public and political interest in global climate change, but many causes for concern remain. Emission controls have focused largely on point-source control of sulphate emissions. It is more difficult to address the more diffuse nitrogen derivatives coming mainly from the transportation sector. The pattern of wet nitrate deposition has changed little over the last decade.

Concern has focused on eastern Canada, but pockets of acidity exist all across the country. The presence of acid-sensitive geology and increasing emissions of SO_2 and NO_X suggest that monitoring should expand into the western provinces to ensure that acid deposition does not damage ecosystems in that region. Large increases in emissions of SO_2 and NO_X from oil sands operations in northern Alberta are raising concerns that acid deposition could negatively affect the West. Between 2000 and 2020, emissions of SO_2 are predicted to decline by 21 per cent in eastern Canada and increase by 15 per cent in western Canada.

plherrera/iStockphoto

Automobile emissions reduce the air quality in many urban areas.

Implications

Understanding the nature of matter and the way that nutrients cycle in the ecosphere is fundamental to appreciating many of the more challenging environmental issues that society faces. Acid deposition, eutrophication, and global climate change all have their roots in disruption of biogeochemical cycles. Science is only just starting to unravel some of the secrets of these cycles, but we know enough to understand their significance. Research also clearly shows their complexity and their interconnectedness. We add nitrogen to soils to try to boost productivity and produce more food. However, this also results in eutrophication, depletion of the ozone layer (Chapter 7), and other problems. Clearly, we have to understand the basic science of this interconnectivity. However, this understanding has to be linked to our ability to manage the situation. The chapters in Part C discuss some of the main approaches in environmental planning and management.

Summary

1. Matter has mass and takes up space. It is composed of 92 natural and 17 synthesized chemical elements. The law of conservation of matter states that matter can be neither created nor destroyed but merely transformed from one form into another. Matter cannot be consumed.
2. Elements necessary for life are known as nutrients. They cycle between the different components of the ecosphere in characteristic paths known as biogeochemical cycles.
3. Humans disturb these cycles through various activities, resulting in environmental problems such as acid rain and global warming.
4. Cycles can be classified into gaseous or sedimentary, depending on the location of their major reserves.
5. Phosphorus is an example of a sedimentary cycle. The main reservoir of phosphorus is the Earth's crust.

Phosphates are made available in the soil water through erosional processes and are taken up by plant roots and passed along the food chain. There is no atmospheric component to the cycle, making it especially vulnerable to disruption. The main human use for phosphorus is as fertilizer. It is a main cause of eutrophication.

6. Sulphur is also a sedimentary cycle and like phosphorus, is an essential component for all life. Bacteria enable plants to gain access to elemental sulphur by transforming it to sulphates in the soil. Sulphur is a main component of acid deposition.

7. Nitrogen is a gaseous cycle. Almost 80 per cent of the atmosphere is composed of nitrogen gas, yet most organisms cannot use it as a source of nitrates. Instead, various bacteria help to transform nitrogen into a form that can be used by plants. As with the other cycles, these nitrates are then passed along the food chain. Nitrates are used as fertilizers and contribute to eutrophication. Various nitrous oxides also contribute to acid deposition and the catalytic destruction of ozone.

8. Carbon dioxide constitutes only 0.03 per cent of the atmosphere, but it is the main source of carbon—the basis for life—through the process of photosynthesis. Carbon becomes incorporated into the biomass and is passed along the food chain. Respiration by organisms transforms some of this carbon back into carbon dioxide, and the cellular respiration of decomposers helps to return the carbon from dead organisms into the atmosphere. Carbon dioxide emissions from burning fossil fuels are a main contributor to global climatic change.

9. Water travels between the different components of the ecosphere by means of the hydrological cycle fuelled by energy from the sun. Ninety-seven per cent of water is in the oceans. Less than 1 per cent is readily available for human use.

10. Canada has up to one-third of the world's fresh water. However, most of this is held in the solid phase as ice, and is not available for human use. Canada also has high storage capacities for liquid water, with lakes covering an estimated 8 per cent of the country. These lakes are replenished by a river flow containing approximately 7 per cent of the total river discharge in the world.

11. Major pollution problems, such as eutrophication, acid deposition, and global warming, are the result of human disruption of biogeochemical cycles.

12. Eutrophication is the nutrient enrichment of water bodies over time. Although it is a natural process, human disruption of the phosphorus and nitrogen cycles has caused a marked acceleration in the rate of eutrophication. This promotes excessive plant growth that leads to oxygen depletion when the plants die and start to decay. Over time, this leads to changes in the composition of fish species and makes water treatment more expensive. The rate of eutrophication can be slowed down by limiting the inputs of nutrients into the water body.

13. Lake Erie is a classic example of eutrophication. Although phosphorus loadings have been reduced considerably, they are still above mandated guidelines and appear to be increasing.

14. Eutrophication is becoming a significant problem in oceanic ecosystems. Some 200 "dead zones" are largely associated with terrestrial inputs of phosphates and nitrates.

15. Precipitation is naturally acidic. However, as a result of disturbances in the sulphur and nitrogen cycles, acidity has increased dramatically over much of Canada during the past few decades. The largest impacts are caused by the burning of sulphur-rich fossil fuels and the smelting of sulphur-rich metal ores. The resulting sulphur dioxide mixes with water in the atmosphere to produce sulphuric acid. Emissions of various nitrogen oxides as by-products of high-temperature combustion account for most of the remainder. The increase in acidity has a damaging effect on aquatic and terrestrial ecosystems as well as on human health.

16. Emission controls have been agreed upon to try to limit these impacts, and targets have been exceeded. However, concomitant improvements in reducing acid rain and the recovery of aquatic systems have not been seen. Many scientists believe that more stringent measures are called for.

Key Terms

acid deposition
acid shock
aerobic
anadromous
anaerobic
aquifer
benthic
biogeochemical cycles
biological oxygen demand (BOD)
buffering capacity
carbon sink
compound
condensation nuclei
critical load
denitrification
eutrophic
eutrophication
evapotranspiration
gaseous cycles
groundwater
guano

hydrological cycle
law of conservation of matter
macronutrient
matter
mesotrophic
micronutrient
mineralization
nitrogen fixation
non-point sources
nutrients
oligotrophic
oxygen sag curve
point sources
policy target value
rainshadow effect
recycling
relative humidity
rock cycle
scientific target value (STV)
sedimentary cycles
sublimation
transpiration

Questions for Review and Critical Thinking

1. Summarize some of the key differences and similarities between energy and matter.
2. Why is life dependent on biogeochemical cycles?
3. Explain why decomposer organisms are important in biogeochemical cycling.
4. What are some of the important implications of biogeochemical cycling for forestry and agricultural activities?
5. Outline the main characteristics of the hydrological cycle in Canada.
6. Which biogeochemical cycles are most responsible for eutrophication, and in what ways are they changed by human activities?
7. Are there any eutrophic lakes in your region? If so, what are the main inputs causing eutrophication, and where do they come from?
8. How can eutrophication be controlled? Discuss one example.
9. What is the pH scale, and what is it used for?
10. Which biogeochemical cycle is most responsible for acid deposition, and how do disruptions occur as a result of human activities?
11. What are the effects of eutrophication and acid deposition on aquatic ecosystems? What do you think might be the impacts of both of them together?
12. Are all areas equally sensitive to the impact of acid deposition? If not, what influences the relative vulnerability of different areas?
13. What are the main socio-economic impacts of acid deposition likely to be?

Related Websites

Canadian Council of Ministers of the Environment
www.ccme.ca

Environment Canada: Indicators
www.ec.gc.ca/indicateurs-indicators/default.asp?lang=En

Further Readings

Note: This list comprises works relevant to the subject of the chapter but not cited in the text. All cited works are listed in the References at the end of the book.

Commission for Environmental Cooperation. 2011 *Taking Stock*. Montreal: Commission for Environmental Cooperation.

Go to www.oupcanada.com/DeardenMitchell5e to access additional learning tools on your smartphone, tablet, or PC.

PART C

Planning and Management: Perspectives, Processes, and Methods

Plans are nothing; planning is everything.

—Dwight D. Eisenhower

The chapters in Part B focused mainly on the natural science pertinent to resources and the environment in Canada. In the following two chapters, Part C, attention is given to planning and management related to perspectives, processes, and methods that can be applied in resource and environmental management. A key point needs emphasis. Often, it is inappropriate to think that humans "manage" the environment or natural resources. Instead, we usually attempt to manage the *interaction* between humans and the environment. This is why resource and environmental management involves more than application of "science" or "technical expertise." It also requires sensitivity to various—and often different—values, interests, needs, and wants.

Chapter 5 focuses on perspectives regarding planning and management of natural resources and environments, while Chapter 6 considers processes and methods. Together, they provide an overview of concepts, approaches, and methods to inform the subsequent discussions in Part D on management of various resources.

Chapter 5 begins by considering the concept of *best practice*. It then examines the importance of *context* for a problem-solving situation and the need to be able to design solutions to fit specific situations. The unique characteristics of a given place and time suggest that it is best to develop approaches and solutions specific to a situation. However, when this is done, a potential problem is that some people may perceive other people or regions receiving preferential treatment, since different arrangements are being applied to them. As a result, there often is pressure to use the same or a similar approach in all places, regardless of differences among them. Thus, debate arises over the merits of using a

standard approach versus developing different approaches, depending on the circumstances in a particular place.

Best practice also stipulates that we need to understand the distinction among most probable, desirable, and feasible futures and why a ***vision*** or direction needs to be established to help in making choices. Often, those concerned with environmental problems give most of their attention to what is the most likely future and how to deal with it. Understanding what is likely to occur in the future is very important, but it is also important to recognize that the most probable future is not necessarily the most desirable future. Thus, we should have a clear sense of what kind of desirable future we aspire to so that, knowing what is likely to occur, we then can judge whether by intervening it is possible to move closer toward what is desired. A fundamental challenge, of course, is that societies are not homogeneous, and therefore at any given time there may be competing views about what kind of future is desirable. Thus, a major task is to identify, develop, and achieve a shared vision. The importance of a vision, and the role of values, is illustrated by Dan Shrubsole in his "Domestic Guest Statement."

Various possibilities for what could constitute a desired future have been identified, and we focused in Chapter 1 on two of them: ***sustainable development*** and ***resilience***. In determining what might be a desirable future, it is important to appreciate that basic values shape perspectives. In that spirit, Chapter 5 examines the difference between ***biocentric*** and ***anthropocentric*** views.

A basic concept associated with best practice is a systems perspective and how that can be applied as an ecosystem approach. In Chapter 5, discussion focuses on how the ecosystem approach can be translated from concept to practice; this is not always easy, especially since most often administrative or political boundaries do not reflect or respect ecosystem boundaries, an aspect highlighted by Taiyang Zhong in his "International Guest Statement." Another best practice element is the need for thinking simultaneously in the short, medium, and long terms. Too often, our society expects instant results or gratification, which places emphasis on the short term. In addition, elections at municipal, provincial, and federal levels usually occur every five years and sometimes as frequently as every two or three years, which further drives attention toward the immediate and short term. The point is not that we should think only in the long term but that we should be thinking simultaneously at several time scales and also have the patience and understanding to recognize that results may take some time to emerge.

Planning and management continue to be the focus in Chapter 6, but the emphasis shifts to processes and methods. For example, if a systems perspective, noted in Chapter 5, is to be used, it requires considerable ***collaboration*** and ***coordination*** among governments and Aboriginal groups, public agencies, the private sector, and non-governmental organizations. Both are needed to overcome what is often termed the ***silo effect***, or the propensity of organizations or individuals to focus only on their own interests and responsibilities and not to consider those of others. One means of achieving collaboration and coordination is through ***stakeholder*** and participatory approaches and by continuously seeking to enhance communication among participants. Chapter 6 examines alternative approaches for facilitating participation and communication. The challenge is to determine which mix of approaches to use so that the strengths of one can offset the limitations of another. And, in her "Domestic Guest Statement," Joselyn Spurgeon shares insights based on working with collaborative approaches in practice.

Best practice increasingly includes adaptive management, impact and risk assessment, and dispute resolution. These processes explicitly recognize that there are high levels of change, complexity, and uncertainty in environmental management, and that conflicts often occur. Therefore, the challenge is not to eliminate or avoid change, complexity, uncertainty, and conflict but to manage within the reality of their presence. Adaptive management involves monitoring experience in order to make systematic adjustments as a result of that experience. ***Impact and risk assessment*** encourages us to be proactive—that is, to look ahead and anticipate positive and negative results from management actions to enhance the positive and mitigate the negative. Dispute resolution methods and processes have been created to deal with the presence of different values, needs, interests, and behaviour, which need to be reconciled or at least managed.

A challenge in resource and environmental management is that strategies, programs, and plans have to gain credibility or legitimacy. This is normally realized by having a statutory or legislative base, political commitment, or administrative endorsement. The more of these factors are in place, the

Programs such as this tour along Toronto's waterfront, near the Humber Bridge, are made possible with the help of public consultations during the planning process.

more visibility and authority there will be for strategies, programs, or plans. One way to enhance their credibility is to link them explicitly to other management tools that have a statutory base, such as regional and land-use plans, considered by Bakti Setiawan in his "International Guest Statement." When connections are made with such tools or methods, the probability of initiatives being sustained and implemented usually goes up markedly.

Finally, strategies and plans need to be implemented, and there is recognition of factors or variables creating an "implementation gap." We need to understand the nature of this "gap" in order to anticipate and be proactive to minimize the effect of factors that might hinder moving from plans to action.

The discussion of perspectives, processes, and methods in Part C provides an overview of elements of best practice relating to resource and environmental management. The purpose of presenting these elements is threefold. First, being aware of them will enable you to examine ongoing initiatives to determine whether they reflect best practice. If they do not, you should consider what would have to be changed for best practice to be achieved. Second, understanding the elements of best practice will allow you to incorporate them into solutions you develop relative to emerging issues. Third, your awareness will enable you to consider how science and social sciences can be used to provide a more solid foundation for best practices in planning and management.

CHAPTER FIVE

Planning and Management Perspectives

Learning Objectives

- To appreciate the significance of different planning and management approaches
- To understand the importance of context for a problem-solving situation and the need to be able to design solutions to fit particular contexts
- To appreciate the distinctions among "government," "governance," and "management"
- To distinguish among most probable, desirable, and feasible futures and understand why it is important to identify a vision or direction to help choose the right thing to do
- To know the difference between "ecocentric" and "technocentric" perspectives
- To understand the significance of a systems perspective and how that can be applied as an ecosystem approach
- To realize the importance of thinking simultaneously in the short, medium, and long terms
- To understand the significance of "social learning" as a foundation for resource and environmental management
- To appreciate the implications of "environmental justice" when making resource and environmental decisions

Introduction

Improved resource and environmental management is likely to be achieved if two principles are taken into consideration. First, as discussed in Chapter 1, using science to inform decision-making is desirable. Second, management and decisions should reflect the best planning and management approaches in terms of concepts, processes, and methods. In this chapter, we focus on *perspectives* and consider basic concepts widely accepted for addressing resource and environmental problems. In Chapter 6, attention will turn to *processes* and *methods*, or those processes (such as public participation and community-based approaches), methods (impact and risk assessment, dispute resolution), and outcomes (effective, efficient, equitable, implementable steps) recognized as leading to more effective environmental management.

Awareness of different approaches enables us to assess what is being done in any given situation and to judge whether the approach is likely to be appropriate. The ideas reviewed in Chapters 5 and 6 serve as a lens through which you can see whether the way a problem is being addressed reflects what many professionals around the world consider the most suitable approaches.

Planning and Management Components

Context

The **context**—i.e., the specific characteristics of a time and place—needs to be systematically considered when developing a strategy, a plan, or an approach for a resource or environmental management problem. Biophysical, economic, social, legal, and political conditions differ from place to place and from time to time, indicating that it is usually inappropriate to proceed as though one model or approach were sufficient for every situation. Instead, it is often necessary to custom-design solutions to conditions. In other words, one size usually does not fit all situations. Considering context is especially important in a large country like Canada with a wide variety of ecosystems and a rich tapestry of differing cultural perspectives.

The importance of context reaffirms that it is advisable to include local people when developing a strategy or implementing initiatives, since they often have special insight into the conditions of a region or place (discussed further in Chapter 6). This is especially critical in situations involving Aboriginal populations. Understanding the significance of context also means recognizing that context can change as conditions evolve, requiring capacity and willingness to modify strategies and initiatives to ensure they remain relevant. This point is discussed further in Chapter 6 with regard to adaptive management.

While context is important, it is not unusual for public agencies to prefer a standardized approach to problem-solving. The rationale is that a standardized approach is easiest to defend or justify. If every area or region is treated the same way, none can be perceived as receiving special or preferential treatment. In contrast, if a specific approach is designed for one region or place, people elsewhere might charge that that region was favoured.

We suggest that despite possible criticism about **custom-designed solutions**, managers should recognize the real possibility of specific conditions of a place and time and design accordingly. It is better to develop an approach specially designed for the needs of a place and accept criticism about perceived favouritism than to use a standardized approach that forestalls criticism but does not really suit the specific conditions or needs. In his "Domestic Guest Statement," Dan Shrubsole points out that combinations of strategies are often appropriate to deal with problems in different places.

Perspectives on the Environment

Management Challenges

Resource management is at a crossroads. Problems are complex, values are in dispute, facts are uncertain, and predictions are possible only in a limited sense. The scientific system that underlies resource management is facing a crisis of confidence in legitimacy and power. Top-down resource management does not work for a multitude of reasons, and the era of expert-knows-best decision-making is all but over.

Some of the new directions that have been proposed include adopting learning-based approaches in place of set management prescriptions . . . , using a broader range of knowledge . . . , dealing with resilience and complexity . . . , and sharing management power and responsibility. . . .

—Berkes et al. (2007: 308)

Context in the Big Picture

Management of natural resources and the environment involves many organizations and jurisdictions that frequently have overlapping and/or conflicting legal mandates and responsibilities, numerous and often conflicting interests regarding access and rights to environmental systems, and growing skepticism about the formal mechanisms of **government**—local, state, national, regional, international—to deliver services effectively, efficiently, and equitably.

Behind such challenges is the reality that **governance** of resources and the environment takes place in situations defined by high levels of *complexity* and *uncertainty*. Furthermore, managers often deal with rapid change and at the same time may need to become agents of positive change. Finally, managers increasingly deal with *conflict* because of the many different interests related to resources and the environment.

Experience during the past three decades suggests that four other contextual aspects are also important for understanding progress related to managing resources and the environment wisely. The first is the preoccupation of many governments with debt and deficit reduction. Since the Rio de Janeiro Earth Summit in 1992, many governments have significantly reduced their allocation of funds to environmental infrastructure and services, which usually has had a serious negative impact on agencies responsible for natural resources and the environment.

For example, the federal government's Bill C-38 became law in June 2012, and had been introduced as an initiative to cut costs (Turner, 2013: 26–28; 43–44). The Bill revised the

DOMESTIC GUEST STATEMENT

Planning Challenges Related to Flood Management in Canada | *Dan Shrubsole*

Flood management is a long-standing problem in Canada. In this commentary, I briefly describe three main approaches to address the flood problem and identify its current status. In considering future flood management strategies, you will see that the changing nature of the flood problem will prompt new solutions that will likely require the involvement of new participants in the management process. Flood management in Canada illustrates the importance of vision (i.e., What is the right balance of approaches that can provide protection and disaster relief?), values (i.e., What is the role of the government and insurance sectors?), and the long-term view (i.e., What should be done by government and others to respond to climate change and a likely increase in flood damages?).

Flood plains offer many benefits to humans. When not covered by water, their relative flatness is conducive to agricultural and urban development. In Canada and many other countries, many cities and towns are located on flood-prone areas (See photographs below). As flood problems in Canada increased in the 1930s, solutions were most frequently provided through the construction of dams and reservoirs, dykes, and channel "improvements" (e.g., straightening and deepening to convey more water more quickly). These became the predominant approach, collectively referred to as "structural adjustments," to manage floods because they attempt to control or change natural processes in order to accommodate human activities. In Canada, structural adjustments were favoured for many reasons, including a funding arrangement supported by the 1953 Canada Water Conservation Assistance Act that provided a 75-per-cent grant to assist in the capital costs for diverse structural adjustments. A shortcoming with structural adjustments was not only environmental degradation but an increasing trend in flood damage losses, despite billions of dollars invested in structural adjustments. This apparent contradiction is explained by much higher flood damages that result when human development, allowed on flood-prone areas after structural works were supposed to "protect" them, is damaged by subsequent floods larger than the design capacity of the structural measures.

Canada formally shifted its reliance on structural adjustments when the national Flood Damage Reduction Program (FDRP) was introduced in 1975. It promoted non-structural adjustments, primarily though the mapping of flood plains, which could form the basis of land-use regulations as well as structural adjustments. Non-structural adjustments aim to modify human behaviour in order to live with the reality of natural processes, rather than to modify natural processes using structural adjustments. Other examples of non-structural adjustments include flood warning systems and emergency planning (e.g., sandbagging, evacuation), both long-standing initiatives in Canada. When appropriate, FDRP indicated that structural adjustments would also be used.

There is a realization that when flood damages occur, it is appropriate to provide disaster relief to people who have suffered losses. In Canada, this third approach is provided through the Disaster Financial Assistance Agreement (DFAA) of 1970. Despite all the investments in structural and non-structural flood adjustments, however, severe flooding and associated damages continue, as illustrated by payments made from DFAA for the following flood events: Saguenay River (1996, $1.7 billion), Red River (1997, $499 million), Hurricane

Calgary Stampede/Chris Bolin

THE CANADIAN PRESS/Jonathan Hayward

Calgary before and during the 2013 flood. Much of downtown Calgary is located on the flood plain of the Bow River, which overtopped its banks in June 2013. Across southern Alberta, four people died, 100,000 people were evacuated, and over $5 billion in damages are estimated. Total losses were in excess of $7.6 billion. This was the third serious flood event in southern Alberta since 2005.

Juan in Nova Scotia (2003, $200 million) Toronto (2005, $500 million), southern Alberta (2005, $400 million), and southern Alberta and Saskatchewan (2010, $956 million). Total losses for the 2013 Calgary flood were $7.6 billion and for the 2013 Toronto flood over $1.2 billion, which include among others costs payments from DFAA and insurance companies.

At least three key planning challenges need careful attention in the future. The first is climate change, which will likely make many communities in Canada more flood prone and susceptible to increased damages. Citing several reports and interviewing experts in Canada and elsewhere, the CBC reported that "flooding is linked to global warming" and the frequency and intensity of floods, and the associated risks to life and damages to property are expected to increase in the future (www.cbc.ca/news/technology/flooding-linked-to-global-warming-studies-1.975829). Regardless of where you live, what mix of structural and non-structural adjustments would you recommend for your community that are desirable, feasible, and effective in the context of climate change, and what level of increased protection, if any, should be provided?

Second, while the focus of past flood management efforts was on flooding from rivers and coasts, an emerging and significant source of flooding is from sewage back-up in buildings. This is of major concern to the insurance industry because, while most home insurance policies have not covered river and coastal flooding, they do cover sewage back-up. What is and should be the role of insurance in flood management and what will be the impact on the cost of premiums if it becomes available to homeowners? (Note Canada is the last G8 country to offer homeowners coastal and riverine coverage through private flood insurance coverage, and this is provided though very few insurers).

Third, what capacity do governments in Canada have to continue providing an average of $100 million annually since 1996–1997 in disaster relief payments, particularly in the context of climate change which will likely lead to increased flood events?

Courtesy Dan Shrubsole

Dan Shrubsole, PhD, is professor and chair, Department of Geography, and the co-director of the Centre for Environment and Sustainability, at the University of Western Ontario. His research focuses on sustainable water management, flood hazards, and environmental planning.

Canadian Fisheries Act to narrow its scope from all fish habitat to habitat of "valuable" fish only, leaving unprotected some 80 per cent of species at risk of extinction as well as more than 50 per cent of freshwater fish. It also repealed the 1992 Canadian Environmental Assessment Act and made significant amendments to the Navigable Waters Protection Act and the Species at Risk Act. Due to less funding as a result of Bill C-38, Environment Canada reduced funding to its Environmental Emergencies Program, the federal government's first-response unit for oil spills, resulting in the closure of all six regional offices and the release of 60 employees. In a different direction, new funding was provided to Revenue Canada to perform more audits on environmental NGOs, on the rationale that some of them had been overspending on "political activities," which violated their status as charitable organizations.

Second, and emerging from the concern about debt and deficit reduction, many national and state governments have been (1) downloading responsibilities for environmental services to lower levels of government, which usually do not have the human or financial resources to maintain levels of service; (2) commercializing such services; and/or (3) privatizing these services. Such decisions frequently are taken without rigorous analysis of the capacity of municipal governments or the private sector to take on such responsibilities.

Such initiatives are usually justified by referring to the principle of *subsidiarity* (allocating responsibilities to levels of government closest to where the services are used or received) or *efficiency* (providing services at least cost). However, these decisions are often ideological, reflecting a belief that market-based economies are the most effective way to allocate scarce societal resources and that less government involvement is desirable. Thus, while the rationale for the subsidiarity principle is sensible because it allows people closest to the outcome to participate directly in decisions that affect them, it also requires willingness to maintain, create, or enhance human and financial capacity at local levels to deal with resource and environmental management issues. Taiyang Zhong, in his "International Guest Statement" further explores issues

Perspectives on the Environment

Governance, Management, and Monitoring

. . . governance is the process of resolving trade-offs and providing a vision and direction for sustainability, management is the realization of this vision, and monitoring provides feedback and synthesizes the observations to a narrative of how the situation has emerged and might unfold in the future.

—Olsson (2007: 269)

Environmental governance is synonymous with interventions aimed at changes in environmental-related incentives, knowledge, institutions, decision making and behaviors. More specifically, [it refers to] the set of regulatory processes, mechanisms and organizations through which political actors influence environmental actions and outcomes.

—Lemos and Agrawal (2006: 298)

INTERNATIONAL GUEST STATEMENT

Downloading Responsibilities for Environmental Protection in China—Good or Not?

Taiyang Zhong

As mentioned in this chapter, many senior governments have been downloading responsibilities for environmental protection to lower-level governments. Downloading such responsibility helps those governments to reduce expenditures. In China, downloading of responsibilities for environmental protection has been widely observed and leads to a question whether such a practice is desirable.

The answer is, "It depends." For lower-level governments receiving the downloaded responsibilities for environmental protection, there are different characteristics related to their *ability* and *willingness* to take on the task. From the perspective of ability to protect the environment, governments can be grouped into two types: able and unable. Similarly, governments can be grouped into two types regarding willingness to fulfill the responsibilities for environmental protection: willing and unwilling. Four types of capacities emerge from combining these two dichotomies: Capacity I, governments both willing and able to protect the environment; Capacity II, governments able but unwilling; Capacity III governments willing but unable; and, Capacity IV, governments unable and unwilling. Undoubtedly, downloading responsibilities for environmental protection will be a good choice if Capacity I exists. However, downloading will be an inappropriate choice for the other three types of capacity (hereafter, termed inappropriate downloading), especially for Capacity IV. Capacity also is transformable. For instance, Capacity I could evolve to one of the other three types, and such a change would cause downloading failure. In contrast, any of the other three capacities might transform into Capacity I. If that were to occur, then downloading would be a good choice, if there were confidence such a transformation would occur.

Inappropriate downloading of responsibilities for environmental protection has resulted in or contributed to environmental deterioration in China. Despite its rapid economic growth and increasing numbers of environmental protection–related laws and regulations since its "reform and opening up" in 1978, China has experienced serious and widespread environmental deterioration of water, air, and soil in the past three decades. While poor execution of laws and regulations has been identified as a key explanation for environmental deterioration in China, inappropriate downloading also has existed behind or in parallel with their poor implementation.

China has five levels of government: central, provincial, prefectural, county, and township. Governments at and above the county level are responsible for environmental protection for their jurisdiction, and environmental protection agencies have been established accordingly. Some prefectural- and county-level environmental protection agencies are partially financed by county or prefectural government budgets and some are self-financed, meaning that they have to raise funds to cover their own expenditures (including the salaries of staff). This fundraising creates a paradox. To implement environmental

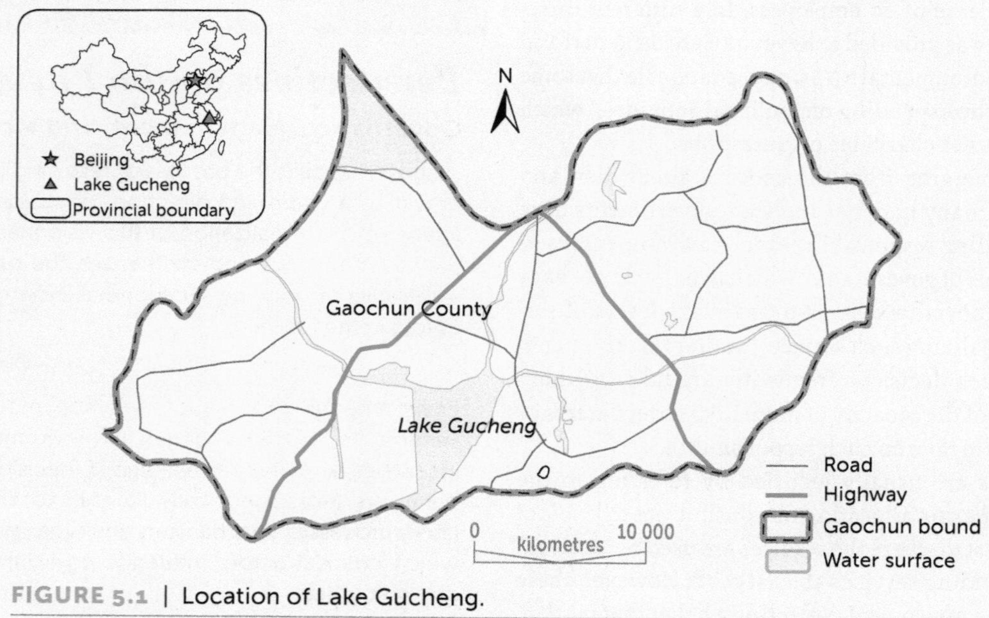

FIGURE 5.1 | Location of Lake Gucheng.

Yanbing Tong

Crab farming is one of the many industries that depend on sustainable management of Lake Gucheng.

Yanbing Tong

Dredging equipment used on Lake Gucheng. Dredging is one part of the county government's strategy for protecting the water environment.

policies, self-financed environmental agencies rely on violations of environmental laws to generate funds. Not surprisingly, inefficiency and failure are inevitable outcomes.

Nevertheless, good downloading (Capacity I) does happen in China. Environmental protection for Lake Gucheng is an example. Lake Gucheng, located in Gaochun County in Jiangsu Province, is about 32 km² in size (Figure 5.1). The county has a population of about 400,000, and Lake Gucheng provided about 70 per cent of the drinking water for the county prior to 2013. Thus, the Gaochun County government had a strong incentive to protect the lake. Because it has a relatively sufficient and dependable revenue (GDP of its non-agricultural industries has been over 90 per cent of total GDP with a growth rate of over 10 per cent since 2010), the county government has taken a series of measures demonstrating its willingness and ability to do so. For example, in 2004, a special group was established and a special plan was prepared to protect the lake. The Twelfth Five-Year Plan for Environmental Protection of Gaochun County (2011–2015) subsequently emphasized protection of Lake Gucheng. A distinctive feature is that a Water Bureau, rather than the Environmental Protection Bureau of Gaochun, became the lead agency for protecting Lake Gucheng, an arrangement different from many county jurisdictions where environmental protection agencies are primarily responsible for water protection. The Water Bureau provides more focus and commitment to ensuring the lake water is sustainably managed. Recent changes may trigger a transition in the capacity for managing Lake Gucheng. A Yangtze River drinking-water supply pipeline for the county was completed in December 2013. This pipeline makes Lake Gucheng an alternative drinking-water source rather than a unique source. As a result, the importance of Lake Gucheng for Gaochun County has lessened. It is possible that this change will weaken the Gaochun County government's willingness to protect the water of Lake Gucheng. Only over time will an answer be known.

Taiyang Zhong received his PhD from Nanjing University in 2007. He is an associate professor in the School of Geographic and Oceanographic Sciences at Nanjing University in Nanjing, China. His research focuses on China's land-use policy and related environmental issues.

of "downloading," with particular attention to the willingness and ability of lower-level governments to handle the responsibilities passed down to them.

When senior levels of government download their management responsibilities to local levels without regard for the capacity to handle those responsibilities or without consideration as to how the necessary capacity can be created, they may cite subsidiarity as the basis for decisions that in fact may have been driven more by financial cost-cutting considerations. Various ideological perspectives present quite different views of the environment and resources, and these differing views can affect planning and management dramatically.

Third, while many governments favour less government intervention, more reliance on the private sector and market forces to deliver products and services efficiently, acceptance of the value of globalization, and a "business model" that emphasizes efficiency, results-based management, and tangible products, they demonstrate less interest in using systematic and thorough consultation processes for developing and implementing policy. Indeed, in some jurisdictions, transparent, accessible consultation has almost disappeared. In such cases, while the senior levels of government embrace subsidiarity as an appropriate principle to guide decisions, in practice their actions do not reflect adequate consideration of all the preconditions required for subsidiarity to function effectively.

Fourth, since the late 1990s, many governments have been steadily backing away from concern for or commitment to environmental issues and instead have been emphasizing strategies for economic growth. An often-cited example is the decision by President George W. Bush to have the United States withdraw from the Kyoto Protocol for reducing global warming (see Chapter 7) and to refocus energy policies in the US on supply solutions with much less attention to demand-management strategies. Ironically, many polls indicate that the general public has become increasingly concerned about environmental issues. The discussion in Chapter 1 related to the "war on science" illustrates how at the federal level here in Canada there has been a steady and continuing reduction of funding for environmentally oriented departments and programs.

As Mascarenhas (2007) has explained, the above characteristics are usually associated with **neo-liberalism**, a political theory based on the belief that humans' well-being is best achieved by encouraging and facilitating individual freedom and minimizing the role of government. Defining features of neo-liberalism are strong private property rights, free markets, and free trade.

Thus, much of what is (or is not) happening in resource and environmental management around the world may be attributed to the shifting influence of differing ideologies. To be informed citizens, planners, or managers, individuals need to understand the basic values and assumptions of various ideologies so they can determine whether the arguments by governments realistically present the rationale for policies and actions. Later, in Box 5.1, the previous environmental commissioner of Ontario, Gord Miller, identifies some basic challenges and poses fundamental questions that deserve our attention. While he refers to Ontario, his comments can be applied generally across the entire country.

Vision

Ends need to be distinguished from means. In other words, before deciding how to deal with resource and environmental management problems or opportunities, managers should determine what ends or desirable future conditions are sought (Box 5.1). This consideration is often referred to as a need to have a clear vision or sense of direction.

According to Nanus (1992: 8–17), a **vision** represents a realistic, credible, and attractive future for a region, community, or group. It is ideal to have a shared vision, one to which many people are committed. Achieving a shared vision is challenging, however, since many interests exist in a society, some of which are mutually exclusive. If a shared vision about a desirable future is to be achieved, it is important to involve stakeholders in the management process, a matter discussed further in Chapter 6.

In Chapter 1, sustainable development and resilience were examined as possible visions for the future. The examples below illustrate what different organizations or groups have developed in terms of vision.

Bay of Fundy Ecosystem Partnership, Nova Scotia and New Brunswick

Promoting the ecological integrity, vitality, biodiversity, and productivity of the Bay of Fundy ecosystem, in support of the social well-being and economic sustainability of its coastal communities.

Facilitating and enhancing communication and co-operation among all citizens interested in understanding, sustainably using, and conserving the resource, habitats, and ecological resources of the Bay of Fundy.

—Bay of Fundy Ecosystem Partnership (n.d.)

Sustainable Development Strategy, Government of Quebec

A society in which the citizens' quality of life is and remains a reality. A responsible, innovative society able to excel in all of its achievements. A society based on harmony between economic vitality, environmental quality and social equity. A society inspired by a State whose spirited and enlivened leadership leads it to reach this vision.

—Quebec (2013: 10)

St. Clair Region Conservation Authority, Ontario

The St. Clair Region Conservation Authority has as its vision watersheds where human needs are met in balance with the needs of the natural environment.

— St. Clair Conservation (2013: 1)

Assiniboine Hills Conservation District, Manitoba

A future where communities, agriculture and the environment are healthy, sustainable and in balance with one another.

—Assiniboine Hills Conservation District (n.d.)

Perspectives on the Environment

Imaging a Future Yet to Be

You see things and you say "Why?" But I dream of things that never were; and I say "Why not?"

—George Bernard Shaw, Irish playwright

Perspectives on the Environment

A Vision for Your Area or Community

What would be the key features of a vision for resource and environmental management for your college or university, or community, region, or province? Does one exist now?

Fraser River Basin Charter, British Columbia

... [T]he Fraser River Basin [is] a place where "social well-being is supported by a vibrant economy and sustained by a healthy environment."

—Fraser Basin Council (n.d.)

Visions can be developed in various ways. One is to ask three questions: (1) What is likely to happen? (2) What ought to happen? (3) What can happen? In much of resource and environmental management, the focus is on the first question. Answering it helps to establish the likelihood of some future state, assuming continuation of current conditions or estimating changes in them. However, this question does not help to determine whether the most probable or likely future is also the most desirable. To deal with the issue of desirability, we also need to ask what ought to happen and therefore consider what would be desirable future conditions for a society or place. These two questions (what is most likely, what is most desirable) reflect the difference between forecasting and backcasting, as explained in the "Perspectives on the Environment" box by Tinker. Finally, the third question imposes discipline by considering what is feasible or practical. We need to address all three questions instead of relying only on the first, which is the common practice.

Perspectives on the Environment

Forecasting versus Backcasting

Forecasting takes the trends of yesterday and today and projects mechanistically forward as if humankind were not an intelligent species with the capacity for individual and societal choice. Backcasting sets itself against such predestination and insists on free will, dreaming what tomorrow might be and determining how to get there from today. Forecasting is driving down the freeway and, from one's speed and direction, working out where one will be by nightfall. Backcasting is deciding first where one wants to sleep that night and then planning a day's drive that will get one there.

—Tinker (1996: xi)

Ethics and Values

To ensure that a shared vision is endorsed by a group or society, it should be consistent with and reflect basic ethics and values. Alternatively, a vision may outline a desirable future significantly different from the present situation that, if it is to be achieved, will require a shift in fundamental values. The vision can help to clarify what different values must prevail for the desirable future to be realized.

As Matthews, Gibson, and Mitchell (2007: 337) have observed, an ethic is "a set or system of moral principles or values that guides the actions or decisions of an individual or group." Such principles or values help us to determine right from wrong and how to behave appropriately. At the same time, no set of ethics gives every needed direction, and sometimes ethical principles conflict. Furthermore, we normally do not understand or cannot predict all the consequences of our decisions or actions, and even when we can, many anticipated consequences contain "shades of grey," making it difficult to know how much of a good or bad feature will be present.

It is desirable for each of us to have a clearly articulated foundation, based on ethical principles, from which we make decisions. Ethical principles direct us regarding appropriate behaviour (e.g., always treating others as you like to be treated yourself) and also regarding process issues (e.g., striving for accountability, transparency, and equity). At a minimum, articulating such principles should help us in deciding among different options, assuming that we intend to act in accordance with them. In Chapter 11, we outline current thinking regarding a set of principles to guide decision-making for water.

We also need to be able to appreciate that the values in different societies usually reflect a mix of explicit principles and implicit and unstated principles, with the latter generally being understood as common knowledge among all or most members of the society. The presence of both explicit and implicit values and principles, of course, often raises challenges in cross-cultural situations, when someone from outside a society may not recognize or understand the significance of implicit values unless they have been exposed to that society for a significant length of time.

Two sets of values significant for resource and environmental management can be identified. At one end of a continuum are **ecocentric values**, reflecting a belief that a harmonious and balanced natural order governs relationships between living things, which humans tend to disrupt through ignorance and presumption. Other key values include reverence for, humility and responsibility toward, and stewardship of both non-human and human nature. Those with ecocentric values are not against technology per se but favour application of low-impact technology, oppose bigness and impersonality in all forms, and advocate behaviour consistent with ecological principles of diversity and change. The ecocentric viewpoint is comparable to the **biocentric perspective** identified in Chapter 1.

In contrast, a **technocentric perspective** is based on the assumption that humankind is able to understand, control, and manipulate nature to suit its purposes and that nature and other living and non-living things exist to meet human needs and wants. While ecocentrics are concerned about choosing appropriate ends and using consistent means, technocentrics focus more on means because of their confidence in human ingenuity and rights, which makes them less concerned about the moral aspects of activities or consequences. Technocentrics admire the capacity and power of technology and believe that technology and human inventiveness will overcome possible resource shortages as well as remediate or rehabilitate environmental degradation. Technocentrics are similar to anthropocentrics, introduced in Chapter 1; both believe the environment and resources exist primarily to provide direct value for humans.

While recognizing that a spectrum of values is important if we are to understand why ideas are supported or opposed, we should not assume that the values held by a group or society can be neatly allocated into these two categories. Boundaries often are blurred and indistinct, and many people will support certain aspects of values in both categories, depending on the conditions. O'Riordan (1976) shares a story about a man who asked a socially conscious friend what he would do if he had two houses. The friend replied that he would keep one and give one to the state. The man then asked what he would do if he had two cows. Again, the friend answered that he would keep one and give one to the state. The man next asked what he would do if he had two chickens. The friend responded that he would keep them both. When asked why, the friend stated, "Because I have two chickens." This story highlights that circumstances (referred to earlier as "context") can be very important in shaping outlooks about what is needed, important, and desirable. It is important for resource and environmental managers to be aware of dominant and secondary values in a society so they can determine how these values can be used or may have to be altered if a vision is to be defined and then achieved. In his "Domestic Guest Statement," Dan Shrubsole provides further insight into the shades of meaning associated with perspectives reflecting different basic values.

Systems and Ecosystem Perspective

The Saskatchewan Round Table on Environment and Economy, in its *Conservation Strategy* published almost 25 years ago in 1991, stated that ecosystems are "subdivisions of the environment consisting of communities of plants, animals, and micro-organisms, which depend on air, water, soil and other non-living elements" (72). In the same year, the final report of the Royal Commission on the Future of the Toronto Waterfront argued that an ecosystem approach emphasizes that human activities are interrelated and that decisions made in one area affect all others. The Royal Commission concluded that "dealing effectively with . . . environmental problems . . . requires a holistic or 'ecosystem' approach to managing human activities" (1992: xxi). These two statements remind us that people have been aware for some time of the value of an ecosystem approach for planning and management. Indeed, most researchers agree that the concept of ecosystem was formulated in 1935 by Arthur Tansley, who argued that organisms were affected by more than other organisms and that other key factors included soils, water, weather, and climate.

Such interpretations of ecosystems and an ecosystem approach reflect the ideas presented in Chapters 2, 3, and 4, which emphasized systems, interrelationships or linkages, energy flows, and ongoing change. In this section, we turn our attention to the characteristics, opportunities, and challenges presented by the systems or ecosystem approach for resource and environmental management.

Characteristics of the Ecosystem Approach

Slocombe (2010: 410) suggests that the ecosystem approach has a set of core characteristics, including systems concepts and analysis, ethical perspectives, stakeholder and public participation, a bioregional place-based focus, efforts to identify and develop common goals, and a systematic understanding of the ecosystem of interest. Slocombe (2010: 409–10) also argues that the ecosystem approach was developed to address a mix of problems frequently encountered in resource and environmental management. In his view, these problems include:

- People and their activities viewed as separate from nature
- Fragmentation of knowledge or disciplines, as well as of ecosystems, jurisdictions, and management responsibilities
- Single resource uses or economic sectors being emphasized, and conflicts over possible alternative uses being ignored
- The many ways in which ecological and socio-economic systems are interconnected not being recognized
- The propensity of biophysical and socio-economic systems to change, sometimes rapidly and unexpectedly, being ignored
- Rather than anticipating change and problems, being reactive and attempting to eliminate uncertainty by controlling complex, dynamic systems instead of adapting to them

Viewed in the context of the characteristics and problems identified by Slocombe, it becomes apparent why the Royal

Russ Heinl/All Canada Photos

Aerial view of Grasslands National Park, Saskatchewan.

SkyF/iStockphoto

Aerial view of the Toronto waterfront.

Commission on the Future of the Toronto Waterfront stated that an ecosystem approach:

- Includes the whole system, not just parts of it
- Focuses on the interrelationships among the elements
- Recognizes the dynamic nature of the ecosystem
- Incorporates the concepts of carrying capacity, resilience, and sustainability
- Uses a broad definition of environments—natural, physical, economic, social, and cultural
- Encompasses both urban and rural activities
- Is based on natural geographic units such as watersheds rather than on political boundaries
- Embraces all levels of activity—local, regional, national, and international
- Understands that humans are part of nature, not separate from it
- Emphasizes the importance of species other than humans and of generations other than the present
- Is based on an ethic in which progress is measured by the quality, well-being, integrity, and dignity it accords natural, social, and economic systems

Opportunities through the Ecosystem Approach

The above attributes raise some challenges for contemporary environmental and resource management. First, in a Western, industrialized society such as Canada, many people believe they have a dominant role relative to nature and that the environment and natural resources exist to satisfy human needs and wants. This is an anthropocentric or technocentric perspective, in contrast to the ecocentric or biocentric world view described earlier. By emphasizing that humans are part of nature rather than separate from it and by recognizing the inherent value of non-human species and things, the ecosystem approach questions such a belief.

Second, by taking a holistic perspective focusing on interrelationships, the ecosystem approach reminds us of the need to consider management problems and solutions in the context of linked "systems." It forces us to appreciate that decisions made about one system, such as land, can have consequences for other systems, such as water or wildlife, and vice versa. In contrast, the conventional approach to environmental or resource management has often focused on systems in isolation from one another, as reflected by having one government agency responsible for forestry, another for wildlife, another for water, another for agriculture, and another for urban development. A challenge, of course, is that as more and more interconnected systems are included in an ecosystem approach, the focus expands and at some point may become unmanageable or require an unreasonably long time to complete any analysis and develop solutions.

Third, the ecosystem approach demands that the links between natural and economic or social systems be considered. This focus is also one of the basic thrusts behind sustainable development and resilience. When such linkages are recognized, it becomes apparent that certain thresholds normally exist in natural systems and that exceeding these thresholds leads to deterioration and degradation. For example, agricultural production can be increased by adding chemical inputs (fertilizers, pesticides, herbicides). However, the cumulative effects of agrochemicals may eventually make the product grown (e.g., fruit or vegetables) unsafe for human consumption. Other concerns revolve around introducing chemicals into adjacent environments, resulting in eutrophication and pollution, as discussed in Chapters 4 and 10. This reminds us that while sustainable development accepts the need for development to meet basic human needs, some kinds of growth are not sustainable because they lead to degradation of natural, economic, or social systems. And, they sometimes can make systems more vulnerable to sudden changes or "flips" when critical thresholds are crossed, making systems much less able to withstand shocks.

Fourth, the holistic perspective reminds us that decisions made at one place or scale can have implications for other places or scales. If a community deposits untreated or minimally treated sewage into an adjacent river, people and communities downstream will bear costs related to that action. Or, if a community, province/state, or nation is unwilling to impose emission reductions on factories, some of the costs will be borne by people, provinces/states, or nations downwind, since air pollutants usually are carried well beyond the borders of the location in which they are generated, as is the case with acid deposition, discussed in Chapter 4.

Fifth, given that decisions in one place affect people and activities in other places, the ecosystem approach raises questions regarding the most appropriate spatial unit for planning and management. The conventional management unit usually has been based on political or administrative boundaries (e.g., municipal, regional, provincial, or national). In contrast, the ecosystem approach suggests that areas identified on the basis of other units, such as watersheds or airsheds, have more functional value. For example, in managing for migratory birds that travel between the Gulf of Mexico and the Canadian Arctic, national boundaries have little relevance. The management area in this situation comprises at least three nations (Canada, the United States, and Mexico).

Sixth, an ecosystem approach highlights that systems are dynamic or continuously changing. An ecosystem, whether a local wetland, prairie grassland, boreal forest, or an urbanizing area, is not static. In addition to daily, seasonal, and annual variations, ongoing longer-term changes occur, as illustrated by the transition of natural grasslands to cultivated cropland or of farmland to urban land use. Climate change, discussed in Chapter 7, exemplifies how ecosystems may change and "migrate" as result of different patterns of temperature, precipitation, and other climate variables. That is why managers and management strategies must be capable of adapting or adjusting to evolving situations. This imperative has led to growing interest in *adaptive management*, discussed further in Chapter 6.

In summary, the ecosystem approach insists that humans are part of nature rather than separate from it, that interrelationships must be emphasized, and that critical thresholds exist. When these aspects are combined, it can be appreciated why two and a half decades ago, the Royal Commission on the Future of the Toronto Waterfront (1992: 31–2) concluded that:

> the ecosystem approach is both a way of doing things and a way of thinking, a renewal of values and philosophy. It is not really a new concept: since time immemorial, aboriginal peoples around the world have understood their connectedness to the rest of the ecosystem—to the land, water, air, and other life forms. But, under many influences, and over many centuries, our society has lost its awareness of our place in ecosystems and, with it, our understanding of how they function.

The need and rationale for adopting an ecosystem approach were also spelled out some time ago by the Conservation Authorities of Ontario (1993: 2):

> The fundamental problem that exists in resource management . . . is not financial constraint. It is that the current body of legislation, agency structures, and mandates do not recognize the concept of ecosystem-based management. The overlapping of mandates between the Ministries of Natural Resources, Environment and Energy, Agriculture and Food, and Municipal Affairs, and Conservation Authorities and Municipalities is evident to everyone.

The situation has evolved as public agencies react to specific problems with specific solutions. This issue-by-issue approach results in a situation that, when viewed from an ecosystem perspective, borders on the ludicrous. Thus, many reasons can be identified as to why an ecosystem approach should be used more frequently in Canada for environmental management. However, as we have already pointed out in earlier chapters, implementing an ecosystem approach requires adjustments to arrangements for governance and management systems, aspects considered in more detail in later chapters.

Long-Term View

In resource and environmental management, it is important to have a long-term view (more than 15 years) while also being able to identify actions to be taken in the short term (less than five years) and middle term (five to 15 years). The rationale is that systems often change slowly and that a significant period of time may be required to shift values, attitudes, and behaviour. At the same time, some system changes can occur quickly and with little or no warning, so we need to be flexible and adaptable in our capacity to recognize problems and develop solutions.

Furthermore, many of our environmental problems have emerged after many decades, or even centuries, so it is unrealistic to assume that they can be reversed or "fixed" in a few years. For example, changes in the aquatic ecology of the Great Lakes (see Chapters 3, 4, and 11) reflect decades of different kinds of land use (agriculture, industry, settlement) on lands adjacent to the lakes. Unfortunately, our society usually wants "instant results" and does not often show the patience required to deal with problems created over a long period.

There are many reasons for the short-term perspective. One is the relatively short time between elections. Politicians

ENVIRONMENT IN FOCUS

BOX 5.1 | Thinking beyond the Near and Now

When did we become so focused on the present moment and our immediate situation? It seems to me there was a time not so long ago when we were focused as a society on building a better future for our children and our grandchildren. We had a broader sense of the connections between the landscape, the communities of Ontario, and the economy. . . . And we valued that. We worked for a better tomorrow, but at the same time we didn't forget about the past, about those who had made sacrifices and worked hard to create the opportunities we enjoyed.

Somehow the awareness of the past and concern about what the future might become seem to be missing from current public discourse and decision-making. . . .

It's rather like speeding down a dark northern Ontario highway on a moonless June night with only your low beams on. You have that confident, comfortable feeling because there is no one on the road and you're making good time. But if you just click on your high beams, you'll see the moose standing there only a few seconds in front of you. . . .

The analogy of a speeding car works quite well in a discussion about the "near and now," because as most drivers know, we have a tendency to focus on objects and surroundings just in front of the car. It takes training and discipline to bring your eyes up to the distant horizon where you become aware of events and objects far ahead—in both time and space. But only then can you acquire the capacity to anticipate, plan, and react to future hazards. And so it is with public decision-making that affects the environment. We all must keep our eyes on the horizon.

Source: Miller (2003: 4).

normally want to produce tangible results so they can show what has been accomplished during their term of office and why they should be re-elected. Conversely, they are reluctant to undertake projects that will require the commitment of public funds beyond their term of control. In contrast, those running for office for the first time emphasize how little has been accomplished by those previously elected and why they should be given an opportunity to demonstrate what they could do instead. This mindset drives decisions focusing on short-term, tangible results and usually results in low priority for long-term strategies involving intangible outcomes.

In many instances, changes are required in basic values, attitudes, and behaviour, such as Canadians modifying their basic patterns of activity so that the greenhouse gas emission targets can be achieved (see Chapter 7). There was much outcry from 2002 to 2011 against the targets the federal government committed to reach under the Kyoto agreement, based on fear that they would cause economic hardship or disadvantage. The former premier of Alberta, Ralph Klein, was one of the most aggressive in criticizing the targets, since they could eventually lead to less reliance on a "petro-economy," the backbone of the Alberta economy. Klein's criticism reflected the perspective that when changes occur, some gain and some lose. Those who might lose are understandably not usually enthusiastic about the changes.

The focus on tangible results also explains why one of the first casualties of budget cutbacks in the public education system usually is outdoor education and field trips, which are viewed as a luxury. And yet, if young students are to appreciate the role of natural systems and change their attitude toward them, what better way to accomplish that than by exposing the students directly to these systems through such programs? Unfortunately, the "product" or result of these programs—changed values and attitudes—is difficult to document, and it often takes many years before behaviours are sufficiently influenced and changed that they have significant positive consequences for the environment.

Thus, while a long-term perspective accompanied by patience, perseverance, determination, and commitment is necessary, most people in our society are more preoccupied with shorter-term and visible results. This creates many difficulties for those who believe that solutions require a commitment of funds and human resources over an extended and sustained period of time.

Social Learning

As Diduck (2010: 500) observes, "Social learning is an emerging framework in resource and environmental management. At its heart is the suggestion that learning is an idea that applies not only to individuals but also to social collectives, such as organizations and communities." He and others argue that it is not enough to create opportunities for stakeholders to become engaged in resource and environmental management processes. Such processes should be designed so that individuals and organizations learn from their experience and thereby become more knowledgeable and effective in the future.

Based on the "theory of action," those interested in the concept of **social learning** differentiate between "single-loop" and "double-loop" learning. The emphasis in **single-loop learning** is to ensure a match between intent and outcome. A metaphor often used is the thermostat. Reflecting single-loop learning, a thermostat is designed to monitor the temperature, and when the temperature becomes either too cold or too hot, it signals to turn the heat on or off. Thus, the thermostat receives information (about temperature in a room), takes corrective action (turns heat on or off), and in that way ensures an outcome consistent with what is intended or desired.

Double-loop learning, in contrast, addresses a different condition—a mismatch between intention and outcome. Double-loop learning happens by challenging underlying values and behaviour rather than assuming that the prevailing values and behaviour are appropriate. Returning to the thermostat metaphor, if double-loop learning were to occur, the thermostat would question the basic underlying value (Why is the temperature set for 22°C? Why not set it for 20°C and adapt to a cooler temperature?) or question the prescribed behaviour (rather than requiring more heat, put on a sweater and/or close an open window).

In resource and environmental management, we should be drawing on both single- and double-loop learning—but especially the latter, because it encourages thinking "outside the box." In other words, single-loop learning emphasizes the right way to get something done, whereas double-loop learning focuses on the right thing to do.

In the next chapter, we will examine specific approaches to facilitating public participation, and when considering choices in that regard, you should recall the distinction between single-loop and double-loop learning and why we should strive to ensure that conditions are created that encourage both.

Photo by Norman Ng/KRT/ABACAPRESS.COM/CP

Guiyu, China, has become that country's biggest e-waste destination. Such sites put health at risk through exposure to toxic pollutants as residents attempt to recover valuable metals like gold and copper from discarded electronic devices.

Environmental Justice

Environmental justice has been defined by the US Environmental Protection Agency (EPA) as "the fair treatment and meaningful involvement of all people regardless of race, colour, national origin, or income with respect to the development, implementation, and enforcement of environmental laws, regulations and policies" (see http://www.epa.gov/environmentaljustice/). "Fair treatment" means that no group of people should bear a disproportionate share of negative environmental consequences from industrial, commercial, or municipal operations, or from the implementation of federal, state, local, or tribal policies or programs (EPA, 1997).

The concept of environmental justice was triggered by a protest related to a hazardous waste landfill site in Warren County, North Carolina. The protesters opposed a decision to establish a landfill site for PCB-contaminated soil to be removed from 14 different places in the state and transported for disposal near a small, low-income community whose residents were predominantly African-American. A follow-up study by the US General Accounting Office examined eight southern states to determine if an association existed between the location of locally unwanted land uses (**LULUs**) and the racial and economic status of nearby communities. The report concluded that three of every four such landfills in the US were sited in or close to minority communities. Subsequent studies confirmed this pattern.

Environmental justice is not confined to "local matters." Due to increased restrictions on disposal of toxic wastes in developed countries, combined with increased concern about health problems associated with toxic waste sites, alternative disposal sites are often sought in other countries, often in less developed nations. The attraction for the latter is substantial financial compensation for becoming a destination for toxic wastes and opportunities to create employment in building and operating the waste sites.

The attention to environmental justice reminds us that aspirations for sustainable development always need to incorporate social considerations. In addition, the emergence of environmental justice highlights that resource and environmental policy and management decisions often have public health implications, which can and do lead to reduced resilience of local communities.

Implications

The concepts and perspectives that reflect best practice for management of natural resources and the environment are becoming more clearly identified. Important concepts include (1) recognizing the contextual factors that characterize a problem situation and being willing to design solutions

ENVIRONMENT IN FOCUS

BOX 5.2 | What You Can Do: Taking Initiative to Enhance Planning and Management of Natural Resources and the Environment

1. Ask elected officials and designated experts to explain how solutions to problems have been designed with regard to the particular conditions in the area of concern.
2. Identify a desirable future consistent with ideas presented in this chapter and book, and then ensure that your behaviour is consistent with this vision.
3. Urge your college or university to include ideas and practices consistent with ideas in this chapter in its curriculum and practices.
4. Strive to incorporate more ecocentric values into your personal outlook on living.
5. Expect public agencies to use a systems approach when dealing with resource and environmental problems, and challenge them when that does not seem to be the case.
6. Advocate both short- and long-term thinking and action related to environmental problems.
7. Actively support an NGO that reflects your own values.
8. Seek to identify double-loop rather than single-loop solutions to environmental problems.
9. Advocate for environmental justice in your own community, province, and country.

that address specific attributes of the problem; (2) establishing a vision that identifies a desirable future so that appropriate means can be identified to achieve the desired end; (3) appreciating the strengths and limitations of potential desirable futures; (4) clarifying underlying values that influence attitudes and behaviour and developing ethical principles or guidelines consistent with the desired future; (5) adapting a systems perspective to ensure that the interactions of various environmental and human subsystems are considered; (6) looking beyond the present and immediate future to consider the longer term; (7) appreciating the significance of social learning; (8) addressing issues related to environmental justice; and (9) recognizing the importance of governance issues. In the spirit of transforming these ideals into action, Box 5.2 outlines initiatives that you can undertake as an individual or as part of a group.

Summary

1. Context refers to the specific conditions related to a time and place. Since context can vary significantly by place and time, it is desirable to design solutions to fit specific environmental problems. A challenge in doing so is that some people may conclude that a region or group is receiving special consideration.

2. Attention to context reinforces the importance of incorporating the experiential knowledge of local people with scientific knowledge when seeking to understand problems and develop solutions. Because they have lived in an area for many years, local people often have insight and understanding that scientists do not.

3. Important aspects of context include rapid change, high complexity and uncertainty, and significant conflict. We should not be surprised to encounter such aspects when dealing with environmental issues.

4. Neo-liberalism has become an increasingly important ideology shaping environmental problem-solving. Characteristics include reducing the scope of government, relying on market mechanisms to allocate scarce resources, and accepting globalization. This ideology has driven many governments to a preoccupation with deficit and debt reduction and to commercialize or privatize management functions previously accepted by governments.

5. The subsidiarity principle, which stipulates that people closest to problems should participate directly in decisions affecting them, encourages involving local people in decisions. It also is used to justify decisions to download or privatize responsibilities.

6. A vision represents a realistic, credible, and attractive future for a region, community, or group. Achieving a shared vision is challenging because many interests—some of which are mutually exclusive—compete in a society. Without a vision or a well-defined end point, managers, their political masters, and society itself have difficulty in determining the most appropriate means for achieving the desired ends.

7. Explicit ethical principles should be identified in order to provide guidance when choosing among options.

8. Ecocentric and technocentric world views reflect different basic values and interests. Their existence is one explanation for the conflicts that arise when decisions must be made regarding the environment or resources.

9. Ecosystems consist of communities of biotic and abiotic elements interacting with each other. Their management requires a systems or holistic perspective.

10. A long-term view (15 years or more) needs to be maintained, but at the same time, there must be a capability to deal with immediate or short-term issues. Too often, only a short-term perspective is taken.

11. Social learning emphasizes the importance of appreciating that both individuals and organizations can and should learn from engagement in resource and environmental management decision-making.

12. Single- and double-loop learning models remind us of the difference between "doing the thing right" and "doing the right thing right."

13. Environmental justice reminds us that some communities or areas are bearing a disproportionate cost related to locally unwanted land uses and that attention must be given to matters of equity as well as of efficiency.

Key Terms

biocentric perspective
context
custom-designed solutions
double-loop learning
ecocentric values
environmental justice
governance
government
LULUs
neo-liberalism
single-loop learning
social learning
technocentric perspective
vision

Questions for Review and Critical Thinking

1. Can science be objective and provide unbiased input to inform management decisions related to natural resources and the environment? Before responding, consider what is meant by the word "objective." What are the reasons for your position on objectivity and unbiased evidence?
2. Why do many believe that it is desirable to custom-design solutions to the specific conditions of a problem rather than to design approaches applied uniformly throughout a region or nation?
3. Explain why the principle of subsidiarity generates debate.
4. What are the implications of neo-liberalism for resource and environmental management?
5. Why do many consider that establishing a vision is important for resource and environmental management?
6. What might be a vision for resource and environmental management for your community?
7. Do you believe that you are primarily ecocentric or technocentric in your values and behaviour? What are the implications of this view for the way you interact with the natural environment?
8. What are the major obstacles to effective implementation of an ecosystem-based approach? What must change if implementation is to improve?
9. If there were a model of an ideal ecosystem approach, what characteristics would it have?
10. Why is there a predisposition in governments to favour short-term rather than long-term strategies regarding resources and the environment? What is the best example of a long-term strategy in your community or province?
11. What should be done to facilitate social learning by individuals and organizations?
12. What is the distinction between "single-loop" and "double-loop" learning, and what is its significance for resource and environmental management?
13. What are the interconnections between LULUs and environmental justice? What criteria should be used to assess resource and environmental decisions to determine if environmental justice has been achieved?

Related Websites

Canada's Ecofiscal Commission
http://ecofiscal.ca

Environmental Commissioner of Ontario
www.eco.on.ca

Environmental Justice
www3.epa.gov/environmentaljustice/

Envirolink: The Online Environmental Community
www.envirolink.org

International Union for Conservation of Nature
www.iucn.org

Rio+20: United Nations Conference on Sustainable Development 2012
www.uncsd2012.org

https://sustainabledevelopment.un.org/

Further Readings

Note: This list comprises works relevant to the subject of the chapter but not cited in the text. All cited works are listed in the References at the end of the book.

Agyeman, J., P. Cole, R. Haluza-DeLay, and P. O'Riley. 2009. *Speaking for Ourselves: Environmental Justice in Canada*. Vancouver: University of British Columbia Press.

Booth, A.L., and N.W. Skelton. 2011. "'You spoil everything!' Indigenous peoples and the consequences of industrial development in British Columbia," *Environment, Development and Sustainability* 13: 685-702.

Keen, M., V.A. Brown, and R. Dyball, eds. 2005. *Social Learning in Environmental Management*. London: Earthscan.

Lenton, T.M. 2013. "Environmental tipping points," *Annual Review of Environment and Resources* 38: 1-29.

Moser, S.C., S.J. Williams and D.F. Boesch. 2012. "Wicked challenges at land's end: Managing coastal vulnerability under climate change," *Annual Review of Environment and Resources* 37: 51-78.

Muir, B.R., and A.L. Booth. 2012. "An environmental justice analysis of caribou recovery, planning protection of an Indigenous culture, and coal mining development in northeast British Columbia," *Environment, Development and Sustainability* 14: 455-476.

Go to www.oupcanada.com/DeardenMitchell5e to access additional learning tools on your smartphone, tablet, or PC.

CHAPTER SIX

Planning and Management: Processes and Methods

Learning Objectives

- To understand the strengths and limitations of key methods and processes related to resource and environmental management
- To appreciate the distinction between collaboration and coordination
- To appreciate the benefits and limitations of participatory approaches
- To understand the obstacles inhibiting communication of scientific results and conclusions to policy-makers and the public
- To appreciate the concept of adaptive co-management
- To understand the connection between risk and impact assessment
- To understand the role of strategic environmental assessment and sustainability assessment
- To identify alternative approaches to resolving conflicts
- To realize the relationship between regional and land-use planning, and resource and environmental management
- To recognize implementation barriers that must be overcome

Introduction

In Chapter 5, we argued that planning and management can reflect basic perspectives. In this chapter, attention turns to various processes and methods with regard to resource and environmental management. This chapter provides a lot of information. To make it less abstract, we suggest that after reading each section you pause and consider the implications of what you have just read for the Northern Gateway case study in Chapter 1, as well as what this reading might mean relative to an issue or problem in your own community.

Collaboration and Coordination

In Chapter 5, we noted that the systems or ecosystem approach emphasizes that different components of resource and environmental systems are interconnected and, therefore, that a holistic perspective is required. However, for practical reasons, public agencies often focus on a subset of resources or the environment. Hence, we have departments of agriculture, environment, forestry, water, and so on. If a holistic approach is to be taken, **collaboration** is needed among the various agencies and with other stakeholders.

For Himmelman (1996: 29), collaboration involves exchanging information, modifying activities in light of others' needs, sharing resources, and enhancing the capacity of others to achieve mutual benefit and to realize common goals or purposes. Selin and Chavez (1995) argue that collaboration also involves joint decision-making to resolve problems, with power being shared and stakeholders accepting collective responsibility for the outcomes.

Collaboration is needed within, between, and among organizations. Once collaboration is agreed to, then **coordination**—the effective or harmonious working together of different departments, groups, and individuals—can be sought. For example, interdepartmental committees or task forces often provide a way to coordinate the activities of different agencies. Such mechanisms provide the means through which effective collaboration can be achieved. Different public participation processes, addressed in the next section, also can be used to facilitate collaboration.

Collaboration increasingly is accepted as desirable, because the complexity and uncertainty associated with resource and environmental issues create a challenge for any individual or organization in terms of having sufficient knowledge or authority to deal with them. Indeed, this is why multi-, inter-, and transdisciplinary research teams are often used, as explained in Chapter 1. Furthermore, differing values and interests contribute to conflict, another reason for various stakeholders to come together to determine how they can meet their various needs. Done well, collaboration involves sharing information and insight to achieve multiple goals. When accomplished, collaboration can contribute to more open, participatory processes and to solutions to which different stakeholders feel committed. Thus, there is greater likelihood that acceptable solutions leading to effective implementation will be found. Joslyn Spurgeon highlights advantages of collaboration in her "Domestic Guest Statement," in which she examines the benefits of a provincial government natural resources ministry working closely with the Nature Conservancy of Canada related to protected area planning and management.

However, collaboration is not always accepted by everyone. Some may decide not to reach out to other groups because they are determined to satisfy their own interests, regardless of what others want. And when such stakeholders are powerful, they may single-mindedly pursue their own interests. Another potential disadvantage of collaboration is that all parties may compromise principles or interests to reach a "common denominator" that may not always represent a good, long-term decision. Therefore, we should remember that collaboration and coordination are means to an end, not ends in themselves. Box 6.1 outlines a notable success in using collaboration to develop a shared vision.

Perspectives on the Environment

Collaboration and Coordination

Collaboration: working together
Coordination: harmonious adjustment

Stakeholders and Participatory Approaches

Recognition of the value of stakeholder engagement and participatory processes has been evident in Canada for some time. For example, after Manitoba passed its Sustainable Development Act in 1998, it developed principles and guidelines for sustainable development. Public participation was recognized explicitly. Furthermore, it was explained that public participation means seeking consensus among citizens regarding decisions affecting them, striving to ensure due process, prior notification as well as appropriate and timely redress for any adversely affected by decisions or initiatives, and creating forums for "consultation and meaningful participation in decision-making processes by Manitobans" (Manitoba, 2014).

Similarly, the Environmental Advisory Council (2013) in Prince Edward Island prepared guiding principles for sustainable development. The principles are intended to help translate any vision into action. To that end, the council recommended that critical issues needed to be identified based on discussion with key stakeholders, and that people and communities should be at the core of planning for sustainable development. Furthermore, the council stated that any sustainable development strategy had to ensure all citizens in PEI would have access to relevant information, be able to see how decisions were made, and have opportunity

DOMESTIC GUEST STATEMENT

How Collaboration Can Support Protected Area Planning | *Joslyn Spurgeon*

The Ontario Ministry of Natural Resources and Forestry (MNRF) works to promote healthy, sustainable ecosystems and to conserve biodiversity across the province. As of 2015, Ontario's system of over 620 provincial parks and conservation reserves protected approximately 9.4 million hectares, or 9 per cent of Ontario's land base. The planning and management of provincial parks in particular is the responsibility of Ontario Parks, a branch within MNRF.

In order to support its protection objective, Ontario Parks collaborates with many non-government organizations. For over 40 years, Ontario Parks has partnered with the Nature Conservancy of Canada (NCC), one of Canada's largest national land conservation organizations. Utilizing specialized skills and resources, Ontario Parks and NCC work together to achieve this common goal of securing and protecting ecologically significant natural areas in Ontario.

> This dynamic partnership has allowed NCC to do what we do best—work directly with private landowners to build a network of protected areas that conserve unique and rare habitat across the province. (James Duncan, Nature Conservancy of Canada, quoted in MNRF, 2008)

Ontario Parks and NCC's partnership formally began in 1996 with the collaborative agreement Legacy 2000. Through this program, NCC and Ontario Parks worked together to acquire private land for new nature reserve class provincial parks. Providing the province's highest level of protection, nature reserve class parks protect specific elements of Ontario's natural heritage to support scientific research and maintain biodiversity. Development within nature reserve class parks is limited to trails, necessary signs, and temporary facilities for research and management. NCC's role for Legacy 2000 was to fundraise and conduct land negotiations, while Ontario Parks provided financial and operational support. The Legacy 2000 program was extended until 2006.

Ontario Parks and NCC entered into a new partnership in 2006, called the Greenlands agreement, to secure further ecologically sensitive land for provincial parks. As part of this agreement, Ontario Parks provided funding and assessed the natural value of potential properties. NCC matched provincial funding dollar for dollar and provided expertise to secure and steward these newly protected areas. NCC's ability to leverage funding sources and to move quickly when opportunities arose has been of invaluable assistance to Ontario Parks in protecting provincially significant natural areas. Over the span of the Legacy 2000 program and the Greenlands agreement (1996 to 2013), Ontario Parks and NCC jointly protected over 18,000 hectares of land valued at over $27 million.

The long-standing support, gained from working with partners such as NCC, remains vital as Ontario Parks strives to fulfill its mandate. This support is even more important since the establishment of the *Provincial Parks and Conservation Reserves Act, 2006* (PPCRA), which replaced the Provincial Parks Act, 1954 (PPA). The PPCRA introduced a new scientific research objective, in addition to the protection, recreation, and heritage appreciation objectives of the PPA. The PPCRA also explicitly identifies maintenance of ecological integrity as the first priority of Ontario's protected areas system. Over the lifetime of these two statutes, the Ontario Parks system grew from eight to over 330 provincial parks, as of 2015.

Much of the success of this partnership can be credited to the application of science for land selection. Ontario Parks created a prioritized list of known ecological values that, if acquired, would strengthen the province's protected areas system. NCC used this information to efficiently and effectively select land for addition to Ontario Parks.

This partnership demonstrates the value of collaboration in achieving common goals when resource challenges exist. **Partnerships** make things possible that may not otherwise happen.

In 2014, to build on the success of their long-standing relationship, MNRF and NCC signed a 15-year Memorandum of Understanding, committing to continued collaboration in implementing Ontario's biodiversity strategy through science-based habitat protection and conservation initiatives.

Ontario Parks

Clear Creek Forest Provincial Park, located in the Municipality of Chatham-Kent, is one of several protected areas secured under the Legacy 2000 program. This nature reserve class park protects nationally significant Carolinian forests.

Ontario Parks

Carden Alvar Provincial Park, located in the City of Kawartha Lakes near Orillia, protects provincially significant rare alvar (limestone plain) habitats and is home to an array of grassland bird species, such as the endangered eastern loggerhead shrike. The land was acquired by NCC, in partnership with the Couchiching Conservancy, and transferred to MNRF as part of the Legacy 2000 program.

Agreements such as Legacy 2000 and Greenlands have helped expand Ontario's protected area system through partnerships with private individuals, businesses, Aboriginal peoples, and conservation organizations. The successes achieved and lessons learned from the Ontario Parks–NCC partnership provide a platform on which to build future collaborative relationships for environmental planning and management across Ontario.

Joslyn Spurgeon, MES, is a Park Planner for the Southeast Zone of Ontario Parks, MNRF in Peterborough, Ontario. Previously she worked as a Park Planner Intern for the Southwest Zone of Ontario Parks, MNRF in London, Ontario, and for the Ontario Ministry of Agriculture, Food and Rural Affairs as a Policy and Programs Assistant in Guelph, Ontario.

to participate in decision-making processes (Prince Edward Island Environmental Advisory Council, 2013). A similar perspective was endorsed in Quebec (2013: 12), where one of 16 principles for sustainable development stipulates that participation and commitment from both citizens and citizen groups is essential to develop a vision to facilitate environmental, social, and economic sustainability. These examples show that the value of shared responsibility, public participation, and partnerships has been recognized in Canada. The challenge is to implement them effectively.

A key aspect, as explained by Simpson and de Loë (2014: 232), is to create and apply what they term "vernacular" knowledge developed through participatory processes. In their view, such knowledge "integrates scientific expertise, local knowledge, and community beliefs and values," and also encourages reasoned debate, social learning, and capacity to address value-based problems. They also suggest that developing **vernacular knowledge** helps to reduce power differentials among stakeholders, encourages discussion of value-based matters, and develops social capital.

Here we focus on public participation as a means of reallocating *power* among participants and on alternative ways of facilitating *empowerment* of people relative to the environmental management process.

Degrees of Sharing in Decision-Making

In Chapter 1, the basic characteristics of sustainable development and resilience were outlined. Several characteristics—achieving inter- and intra-generational equity, increasing self-determination—provide the rationale for sharing power in environmental management. However, redistribution of power over environmental management from government agencies and private firms to members of the public can challenge vested interests and/or undermine regulatory authority. As a result, such redistribution is not always easily or readily accepted by all stakeholders. Furthermore, power-sharing raises challenging questions about accountability and responsibility for decisions.

Arnstein (1969) provided a perspective still relevant regarding the issue of power redistribution by identifying "rungs" on the ladder of citizen participation (Table 6.1). Even though the ladder has been modified in many subsequent writings, the essential steps remain.

As long ago as the late 1960s and early 1970s in Canada, public involvement programs had moved up to Arnstein's rungs of informing, consultation, and placation. However, because of a belief by managers in public agencies that they were accountable for resource allocation decisions and expenditure of public funds, the position usually taken by public agencies was that information and advice received through public participation was only one of several sources to be considered and that the public agency would retain decision-making authority.

Resource and environmental managers believed that they had the legal mandate, responsibility, and power to decide which trade-offs best reflected societal needs and interests and to make final decisions. This viewpoint was usually reinforced because not one public interest but many different interests existed, and frequent conflicts among them were common. Giving responsibility for decision-making to citizens frequently was viewed by public agencies as dangerous, since it could too easily evolve into a form of anarchy in which there would be an absence of government and laws and no one would be responsible or accountable for decisions or behaviour.

During the 1980s, dissatisfaction with many resource and environmental management decisions arose. Growing

ENVIRONMENT IN FOCUS

BOX 6.1 | Boundary Waters Treaty, 1909

Canada and the United States share many lakes, rivers, aquifers, and wetlands along their 8,840-kilometre border. Indeed, more than half of the border passes through water bodies. Examples include the Saint John and Saint Croix rivers in New Brunswick, the Great Lakes–St Lawrence River system in Ontario and Quebec, the Red River in Manitoba, the Souris River in Saskatchewan and Manitoba, the St Mary and Milk rivers in Alberta, and the Columbia River in BC.

The two countries signed the Boundary Waters Treaty in 1909 to provide a framework for a collaborative approach and resolution of disputes over water resources shared by the two countries.

The International Joint Commission, or IJC, has six commissioners (three Canadian; three American). The IJC has power to adjudicate regarding issues associated with water development proposals in one country that could affect water levels or flows in the other country.

The six commissioners are expected to consider what would be best for both countries rather than being advocates for their own country. The record indicates that they have effectively done exactly that.

numbers of Canadians rejected the idea that "technically correct" answers could always be found. Instead, a view emerged that such decisions ultimately depended on weighing conflicting goals, aspirations, and values. In these situations, technical or scientific expertise was seen as a legitimate input, but only one of several.

From these considerations arose the idea that "stakeholders" had a right to participate in decisions. **Stakeholders** are those who should be included because of their direct interest. These stakeholders include: (1) any public agency with prescribed management responsibilities; (2) all interests significantly affected by a decision; and (3) all parties who might intervene in the decision-making process to facilitate, block, or delay it. Because more and more increasingly complex decisions had to be made, the traditional forum for public participation—the political process with elected representatives reflecting constituents' views—no longer seemed adequate. As a result, various individuals and non-governmental organizations (NGOs) began pressing for public involvement to move higher up on Arnstein's ladder. While few politicians and public servants believed that total "citizen control" was feasible or desirable, expectations were that "partnerships" and "delegated power" that gave effective power to the public were desirable and achievable.

Partnerships among governments, private companies, and the general public have become increasingly popular. The partnership concept has been implemented through **co-management** initiatives and other approaches that reflect a genuine reallocation of power to citizens and away

Perspectives on the Environment

Tensions Exist from Use of Participatory Approaches

At a conceptual level, the domains of science and of democratic politics have different goals, standards of merit, norms of participation, and procedures for resolving differences. At a practical level, desired knowledge is often unavailable, and available relevant knowledge is often not adequately used. Knowledge is often inadequate to give high confidence in the consequences of decisions, and decisions sometimes cannot be delayed until high confidence is obtained. Uncertainty is thus unavoidable and pervasive . . . .

—Parson (2000: S128)

Stakeholders from various governmental organizations (federal, territorial, and First Nations/Aboriginal) involved in Nunavut take part in a Natural Resources Canada workshop on geomatics products intended to support sustainable development in Canada's North.

TABLE 6.1 | Rungs on the Ladder of Citizen Participation

Rungs	Nature of Involvement	Degrees of Power
8. Citizen control		
7. Delegation	Citizens are given management responsibility for all or parts of programs.	Degrees of citizen power
6. Partnership	Trade-offs are negotiated.	
5. Placation	Advice is received from citizens but not acted on.	Degrees of tokenism
4. Consultation	Citizens are heard but not necessarily heeded.	
3. Information	Citizens' rights and options are identified.	
2. Therapy	Power-holders educate or "cure" citizens.	Non-participation
1. Manipulation	Committees rubber-stamp political decisions.	

Source: Adapted from Arnstein (1969).

from elected officials or technical experts. Co-management arrangements have been developed particularly with Aboriginal peoples regarding management of forests, fish, and wildlife. In these situations, power is allocated to Aboriginals or other local people. Some of the challenges associated with power-sharing with Aboriginals are highlighted in the context of marine resources in Chapter 8.

However, some Aboriginal leaders seek much more than engagement through co-management arrangements. To illustrate, Chief Perry Bellegarde of Saskatchewan, after being elected in early December 2014 as the national chief of the Assembly of First Nations, stated in his acceptance speech that:

> Canada will no longer develop pipelines, no longer develop transmission lines or any infrastructure on our lands as business as usual. That is not on. We will no longer accept poverty and hopelessness while resource companies and governments grow fat off our lands and territories and resources. If our lands and resources are to be developed, it will be done only with our fair share of the royalties. . . . It will be done on our terms and our timeline. Canada is Indian land. This is my truth and this is the truth of our peoples. (Puxley, 2014: A3)

Communication

At an international conference focused on "climate change communication," the organizers observed that communication has three main purposes: (1) to raise awareness; (2) to confer understanding; and (3) to motivate action (Scott et al., 2000: iii). Furthermore, at the same meeting, Andrey and Mortsch (2000: WP1) argued that "communication is thought to be effective only when these changes in awareness and understanding result in attitudinal adjustments and/or improve the basis upon which decisions are made."

Carpenter (1995) identified important aspects to consider regarding how scientific understanding should be communicated. They continue to be relevant, and include the following:

- Much of the public does not understand science or how scientific research is conducted.
- Other than for weather and gambling, much of the public does not understand "probability," and many people reject the idea of risk as part of life. Association and causation are often confused or assumed to be the same.
- The media do not deal well with the "ebb and flow" of scientific research, which progresses by new research disproving or challenging existing understanding. This creates confusion and doubt about the authority or credibility of scientists when different views exist.
- In the courts, expert witnesses appear for different sides in a case and present conflicting testimony. Diverging opinions should be understood as a characteristic of scientific "findings."

To overcome communication challenges, we must recognize the variety of target audiences, such as other scientists, planners and managers, elected decision-makers, and the general public. Consequently, we should be sure that messages are crafted with regard to who the recipients will be and what level of understanding they can reasonably be assumed to have, with as full as possible an appreciation for their mistaken assumptions. To guide the preparation of messages, Carpenter recommended attention to four complementary questions, regardless of audience:

1. What do we know, with what accuracy, and how confident are we about our data?
2. What do we not know, and why are we uncertain?
3. What could we know, with more time, money, and talent?
4. What should we know in order to act in the face of uncertainty?

Perspectives on the Environment

Communicating Uncertainty: Catch-22

If environmental professionals are candid about uncertainties, the client/recipient will likely be disappointed and perhaps berate the professionals for not being helpful and just simply telling them what is going to happen and what to do. If the environmental professionals ignore or obscure the uncertainties and give unambiguous predictions and advice, events may very well show them to be substantially wrong. Then their credibility will be gone, and they will not be consulted in the future.

—Carpenter (1995: 129)

The important message in this section is that while it is important to understand natural and human systems and their interactions, it also is important to determine how this knowledge and insight can be shared with others who may not have the same scientific background but are key stakeholders in terms of taking, facilitating, or thwarting action. To test yourself, consider the four questions above in relation to the Northern Gateway case study in Chapter 1. How would you answer each question, and how would you craft your answer as the target audience changes from scientists, to elected decision-makers, to the general public?

Adaptive Management

Surprise, Turbulence, and Change

Trist (1980: 114) observed over 35 years ago that there is no such thing as *the future,* but instead there are *alternative possible futures.* Which future actually emerges depends very much on choices made and on actions taken to implement those choices. He argued that "the paradox is that under conditions of uncertainty one has to make choices and then endeavour actively to make these choices happen rather than leave things alone in the hope that they will arrange themselves for the best." His conclusion continues to be relevant.

A challenge in making choices and taking initiatives is what Trist referred to as *turbulent conditions, which* have become increasingly prevalent. For example, energy plans in Canada became obsolete in the early 1970s when the Organization of the Petroleum Exporting Countries (OPEC) rapidly quadrupled oil prices. Such a price increase had not been included in the forecasts and assumptions on which energy plans had been based. It is interesting to reflect on whether we have learned much from that experience, considering the rapidly increasing but fluctuating oil prices in the last 10 years (see Chapter 12). Would anyone have been taken seriously in 2007 if they had suggested that crude oil would be selling for an all-time high of $145 a barrel in June 2008, would fall to $30 a barrel by December of the same year, and then would reach $103 in the last week of February 2011? The spike in early 2011 was triggered by unrest in Libya as citizens began the eventual overthrow of Moammar Gadhafi. Similarly, the spectacular drop in the price of oil from the summer of 2014 at about $110 a barrel to early and mid 2015 at below $50 a barrel caught many by surprise, and significantly affected national and provincial economies.

During the 1980s when decisions were being made about the east coast fishery, there was little expectation that in the early 1990s the cod fishery would be effectively closed and thousands of people in Atlantic Canada would lose their jobs (see Chapter 8). Few anticipated the terrorist attack on the World Trade Center in New York City in mid-September 2001. Today, to what extent is the possibility of terrorist attacks on basic infrastructure such as oil pipelines or water supply reservoirs incorporated into strategies and plans? These and other events, such as the economic "meltdown" in the autumn of 2008, the increasing melting of sea ice in the Arctic and Antarctic over the past decade, and the emergence of the Sunni jihadist Islamic State of Iraq and al-Sham (ISIS) during 2014 in Syria and Iraq surprised many people. Such events create bewilderment and anxiety, and raise doubts about the capability of science, planning, planners, managers, and policy-makers, because decision-makers apparently could not anticipate or adapt to rapid change.

Adaptive Environmental Management

Awareness of the need for **adaptive environmental management** was popularized by Holling (1978; 1986) and his colleagues. They concluded that policies and approaches should be able to cope with the uncertain, the unexpected, and the unknown. Holling and his co-workers observed that the customary way of handling the unknown is through trial and error. Errors or mistakes provide new information so that subsequent activity can be modified. Thus, "failures" generate new information and insight, which in turn lead to new knowledge. However, effective trial-and-error management has preconditions. The experiment should not destroy the experimenter. Or, at a minimum, someone must remain to learn and benefit from the experiment. The experiment also should not cause irreversible, negative changes. Furthermore, the experimenter should have the will and ability to learn and to begin again.

In Holling's view, a major challenge for the use of adaptive environmental management is that it can be difficult to satisfy the preconditions. For example, the concern about climate change discussed in Chapter 7 reflects the fear that we may not be able to reverse such change before serious problems have occurred. Moreover, even when errors are not irreversible, the

Perspectives on the Environment

Commentary: The Nature of Adaptive Management

Adaptive management is an approach to natural resource policy that embodies a simple imperative: policies are experiments; learn from them. In order to live we use the resources of the world, but we do not understand nature well enough to know how to live harmoniously within environmental limits. Adaptive management takes that uncertainty seriously, treating human interventions in natural systems as experimental probes. Its practitioners take special care with information. First, they are explicit about what they expect so that they can design methods and apparatus to make measurements. Second, they collect and analyze information so that expectations can be compared with actuality. Finally, they transform comparison into learning—they correct errors, improve their imperfect understanding, and change action and plans. Linking science and human purpose, adaptive management serves as a compass for us to use in searching for a sustainable future.

—Lee (1993: 9)

magnitude of the original capital investment, as well as personal and political investment in a particular decision or course of action, often makes reversing the process unlikely. Many people simply do not like to admit to or to pay for mistakes.

Adaptive Co-management

Earlier in this chapter, we introduced the concept of co-management, which we now link to adaptive management. Armitage, Berkes, and Doubleday (2007: 1) differentiate between co-management and adaptive management in the following way:

- *Co-management* is primarily concerned with user participation in decision-making and with linking communities and government managers.
- *Adaptive management* is primarily concerned with learning by doing in a scientific way to deal with uncertainty.

In their view, when the two concepts are connected, the outcome is a combination of the iterative *learning dimension* from adaptive management with the *linkage dimension* of collaborative management through which rights and responsibilities are shared jointly. Consequently, several characteristics become prominent, including: (1) learning by doing; (2) integration of different knowledge systems; (3) collaboration and power-sharing among community, regional, and national levels; and (4) management flexibility. Plummer and FitzGibbon (2007) have also argued that **adaptive co-management** and social learning (discussed in Chapter 5) complement each other and can be used to mutual benefit. Box 6.2 outlines key features of adaptive co-management.

The concept of visions and visioning was introduced in Chapter 5, and the first point in Box 6.2 refers to the role of a shared vision in adaptive co-management. Olsson (2007: 269–70) argues that visioning processes should promote two important qualities: *adaptability*, or the capacity to sustain a system on a desired trajectory or trajectories in the context of changing conditions and disturbances, and *transformability*, or the capacity to create a fundamentally new system when evolving ecological, economic, social, and political conditions make an existing system untenable or unsustainable. The feature of transformability helps achieve resilience, as explained in Chapter 1 by Ryan Plummer.

Olsson explains how these two basic ideas (adaptability; transformability) underlay the vision for a wetland area in Sweden: "to preserve and develop the natural and cultural values of the Kristianstads Vattenrike wetland area, while at the same time making careful and sustainable use of these values, and thus set a good example that can help promote the region" (2007: 272). To achieve this vision, attention had

ENVIRONMENT IN FOCUS

BOX 6.2 | Features of Adaptive Co-management

1. Shared vision, goal, and/or problem definition to provide a common focus among stakeholders and interests
2. A high degree of dialogue, interaction, and collaboration among participants
3. Distributed or joint control across multiple levels, with shared responsibility for action and decision-making
4. A degree of autonomy for different stakeholders at multiple levels
5. Commitment to the pluralistic generation and sharing of knowledge
6. A flexible and negotiated learning orientation with explicit recognition of uncertainty

Source: Armitage et al. (2007: 6).

to be given to building a sense of place and trust among stakeholders, identifying common interests, facilitating learning, encouraging both horizontal and vertical collaboration, and managing conflict.

Among various lessons learned from Kristianstads Vattenrike, Olsson (2007: 280) highlighted that creating a vision does not ensure successful adaptive co-management. There is always a risk that creating a vision may stimulate other stakeholders to articulate a different vision. Those involved in the Swedish wetland understood this challenge. They dealt with it by initially inviting a small number of people to become engaged and then gradually expanding the number as others became aware of the positive aspects of the vision.

Another lesson learned relates to the power of "transformational leadership." The Kristianstads Vattenrike initiative moved forward effectively because one creative and committed individual helped to define the desired direction, aligned people to the vision, and motivated and inspired them to become committed and engaged. All these accomplishments were important for the ultimate goal of generating movement or change in perceptions, attitudes, and values related to the wetland area. Much of the accomplishment was due to the remarkable leader's ability to recognize windows of opportunity as well as to identify and modify constraints or limitations (such as conflicts of interest, values, and opinions). Of course, the downside of reliance on a transformational leader is that the initiative becomes vulnerable if that individual retires or leaves the region.

In summarizing, Olsson provides valuable insights regarding the role of a vision in achieving adaptive co-management. He observed that it:

> helps develop values and builds motivation for ecosystem management among actors by envisioning the future together and developing, communicating, and building support for this vision. Key factors for the success of this process are dialogue, trust-building, and sense-making. The vision defines an arena for collaboration, frames the adaptive co-management processes, and fosters the development of social networks and interactions among actors, including those dealing with conflict resolution. Visioning processes can therefore be as important as implementation of rules and regulations for framing and directing adaptive co-management. (Olsson, 2007: 281–2)

Impact and Risk Assessment

Environmental impacts, intended and unintended, positive and negative, are common to all development initiatives. The use of environmental impact assessment (EIA), starting in the early 1970s, has been a response to the increasing size and complexity of projects, greater uncertainty in predicting impacts, and growing demands by the general public and special interest groups to become more involved in planning and decision-making processes (Lawrence, 2013).

Various definitions of **environmental impact assessment** have been put forward. For example, some time ago, Beanlands and Duinker (1983: 18) defined it as "a process or set of activities designed to contribute pertinent environmental information to project or programme decision-making." Thirty years later, Lawrence (2013: 5) provided a more specific interpretation when stating that impact assessment:

> in its most basic form, is the process of identifying the future consequences of a current or future action. The "impact" is the difference between what would happen with the action and what would happen without it. This definition is general enough to encompass (or not) a range of current or proposed, planned or unplanned initiating actions (e.g., projects, plans, programs, policies, legislation, activities, operational procedures).

Initially, EIA emphasized the physical and biological resources that might be affected by a project, with attention to reducing negative consequences. Partly in response to public pressure, the focus gradually broadened to incorporate social concerns, leading to the concept of social impact assessment (SIA). A major contribution regarding inclusion of social considerations into impact assessments came from Canada in the mid 1970s, when Thomas Berger completed his landmark report focused on the proposed Mackenzie Valley pipeline (Berger, 1977). In addition, more attention has been given to basic policy questions, such as establishing the appropriateness of a project's objectives, considering alternative projects that also could meet the same objectives, and examining how compensation could be provided for impacts or losses that cannot be mitigated. Elements of best practice for EIA are highlighted in Table 6.2.

Risk assessment underlies impact assessment, since it focuses on determining the probability or likelihood of an environmentally or socially negative event of some specified magnitude, such as an oil spill, and the costs of dealing with the consequences. Of course, since risks have to be estimated, our calculations may be incorrect. Thus, at the Earth Summit of 1992, the **precautionary principle** was endorsed. This principle states that in order to protect the environment when there are risks of serious or irreversible damage, lack of full scientific certainty regarding the extent or possibility of risk should not be used as an excuse for postponing cost-effective measures to prevent environmental degradation. In other words, decision-makers and managers should estimate risks on the side of caution.

TABLE 6.2 | Best Practices for Environmental Impact Assessment

1. A strong legal foundation establishes EIA as a mandatory and enforceable process, and one that provides clarity, certainty, fairness, and consistency.
2. A broad definition of the environment and related processes stipulates requirements to ensure EIA is applied to all environmentally significant undertakings.
3. The EIA process identifies the best options rather than merely acceptable proposals, and requires critical examination of purposes and comparative evaluation of alternatives to the initiative as well as of alternative means to undertake the proposal.
4. The EIA process limits ministerial discretion.
5. The EIA process is open and fair, provides a significant role for the public, and contains provisions for public notice, comment, access to information, and participant funding.
6. The EIA process has enforceable terms and conditions for approval of an initiative.
7. The EIA process explicitly addresses monitoring and other post-approval follow-up to ensure terms and conditions are met.
8. The EIA process ensures assessment work is connected to a larger context, including establishment of overall biophysical and socio-economic impacts.

Source: Sinclair and Doelle (2010: 464).

Challenges in Impact Assessment

People conducting impact assessment have to balance technical matters and value judgements. Often, there are no right or wrong answers but rather different answers, depending on the starting point for the assessment and the assumptions made.

Types of Initiatives to Be Assessed

In Canada and most other countries, impact assessments have primarily been conducted for development and waste management projects, especially major capital projects such as dams and reservoirs, nuclear or other types of power plants, oil or natural gas drilling or pipelines, waste disposal facilities, major highways, and runway expansions at major airports. The rationale has been that such development usually has the potential for significant environmental and social impact, and readily identifiable stakeholders—proponents, people, communities—would be affected.

It has been argued for some time, however, that impact assessments could and should be completed for policies and programs. The argument in favour of this approach, called **strategic environmental assessment** (SEA), is that projects often are only the means of implementing policies and programs. Waiting to conduct an impact assessment until after a policy or program evolves into a project means that the assessment may come too late. At the policy or program level, decisions may already have been taken to preclude or eliminate possible alternatives, and the project may become virtually irreversible. Partidario and Clark (2000: 4) define strategic environmental assessment as follows:

> SEA is a systematic, ongoing process for evaluating, at the earliest appropriate stage of publicly accountable decision-making, the environmental quality, and consequences of alternative visions and development intentions incorporated in policy, planning, program initiatives, ensuring full integration of relevant biophysical, economic, social, and political considerations.

In his "International Guest Statement," Bakti Setiawan examines the experience in applying SEA in Indonesia and considers general lessons from that experience.

An example of the need to consider policy issues before assessing a project occurred when BC Hydro proposed a pipeline across the Strait of Georgia to provide natural gas to Vancouver Island for generating power. The EIA was to be conducted on the specific impact of the pipeline on the environment. However, environmental groups argued for a much broader EIA that would examine the need for the power and the alternatives available rather than assessing mitigation

Courtesy: Bruce Power

Bruce Nuclear Power Plant, Ontario.

INTERNATIONAL GUEST STATEMENT

Mainstreaming Sustainable Development Principles into Development Planning and Policy-Making: The Challenges of Strategic Environmental Assessment in Indonesia | *Bakti Setiawan*

Although environmental management was initiated during the early 1970s in Indonesia, particularly with the establishment of the national Ministry of Environment and Population in 1978, followed by the Environmental Act No. 4, 1982, progressive reform continues. An example is the revision of the 1982 environmental Act with a new statute in 2009. This new Act, entitled Environmental Protection and Management (AEPM) No. 32, 2009, introduced Strategic Environmental Assessment (SEA) into environmental management and development planning. As stated in Article 15 of the AEPM, "Central and local governments shall use SEA to ensure that the principles of sustainable development are the base of and integrated into the development of a region and/or policies, plans, and/or programs (PPP)."

Some may comment that use of SEA started too late because in other countries it has been applied since the 1980s (Sadler, 2005). I argue, however, better late than never. Indonesia is a country of immense biodiversity, second only to Brazil, and therefore its sustainability is crucial not only for its 250 million people, but for the whole planet. Significant efforts have been taken in Indonesia in the past four decades to ensure that sustainable development ideas are integrated into development planning and policies. But, environmental degradation and resource depletion continue at an alarming rate.

Various scholars argue that the root cause of environmental problems is often a disconnect between the environmental agenda and real-life development planning and policy-making. The response has been to initiate various environmental assessment systems to bring more environmental rationality and dialogue into decision-making, and ensure more transparency, accountability, and responsiveness related to emerging environmental needs. Experiences from many countries have shown that, although not always easy, SEA helps to improve related decision-making processes (Taylor, 1984; Sadler, 2005; Dusic, 2010).

Based on such experiences, Indonesian scholars and policy-makers were very sure of the benefits of integrating SEA into the AEPM of 2009, with high hopes that the "rhetoric" of sustainable development would become "reality." Following the 2009 Act, the Ministry of Environment (MOE) led various initiatives to implement SEA in Indonesia. Government Regulations on SEA were prepared, and a new Ministerial Decree provided guidance on how SEAs should be conducted. Training packages were delivered across Indonesia to increase the capacity of local government planners to conduct SEAs. A Clearing House on SEA was also established at the MOE to provide information regarding SEA. In addition, SEAs were conducted for several "mega-national" plans. Today, all spatial plans prepared by provincial and regency/city governments are only approved by the central government if they were supported by an SEA.

Five years is too short to complete a definitive reflection and evaluation of SEA implementation in Indonesia. Based on my direct involvement in the introduction of SEA, however, I have gained three insights, which hopefully could benefit future practices of SEA in Indonesia and elsewhere.

First, and most crucial, the practice of SEA in Indonesia should not be trapped by an attitude in which most SEA documents become prepared only to support certain interests and to obtain plan approval. When that happens, an SEA cannot become an effective instrument in environmental management.

Second, and different to EIA, we must remember that plan and policy-making processes are political as well as technocratic processes. SEA, therefore, should not be treated only as a technocratic process. I believe that the focus of SEA should be to channel environmental evidence into decision-making and place more emphasis on dialogue about the underlying environmental values and priorities of the decision-making elite and affected parties.

Third, as Indonesia becomes more democratic, open, and transparent, every SEA planning process should provide early and sufficient opportunities for public involvement and learning in a meaningful way. Particularly as it relates to environmental issues, and still too often marginalized in policy-making in Indonesia, public engagement is an important element for any effective environmental protection system.

To reiterate, it is early to judge definitively whether SEA has significantly contributed to ensuring achievement of sustainable principles in Indonesia development. As in other countries, however, SEA provides opportunities for balancing economic development, social justice, and environmental conservation, three issues commonly seen by Indonesians as conflicting. As an "environmentalist," I tend to see everything critically and even perhaps pessimistically. Being also a planner, I have to remain optimistic and believe that a better and sustainable future is achievable. SEA, of course, cannot resolve everything, but it provides a clear and rational way for decision-making.

Courtesy Raditya Jati

Bakti Setiawan teaches urban and regional planning at Gadjah Mada University, Indonesia. He received a PhD from the University of British Columbia in 1998. From 2001 to 2005, he was Director of the Center for Environmental Studies of Gadjah Mada University. Currently, he is a Professor in the School of Architecture and Planning at Gadjah Mada University, and serves as a part-time expert on SEA for the national Ministry of Environment.

strategies for one option (i.e., a pipeline, such as the Northern Gateway project discussed in Chapter 1). Other examples of SEA applied in Canada are provided in Box 6.3, with references so you can get further details about each.

While the logic is apparent for having impact assessments completed for policies and programs as well as for projects, such assessments can be difficult. Policies can be general or specific, stated or implicit, incremental or radical, independent or linked to other policies. In that regard, strategic environmental assessment is most applicable in three types of situations: (1) sectoral policies, plans, and programs (e.g., mineral extraction, energy generation, waste management); (2) regional or area-based policies, plans, and programs (e.g., land-use plans, development plans); and (3) indirect policies, plans, and programs (e.g., fiscal, trade, or science and technology policy) (Thérival, 1993).

Other challenges arise regarding which activities should be subject to impact assessments. One issue is particularly difficult. On the one hand, society expects government regulations to be reasonable and efficient. In that regard, it is normal to have some lower limit or threshold below which assessments are not required. For example, it is unlikely one homeowner building an outdoor barbecue in her backyard would adversely affect air quality in the community. However, if every homeowner built an outdoor barbecue, air quality could be affected. The issue, then, is how to balance reasonableness and efficiency against the dilemma that many small developments *in aggregate* might have significant implications. This problem has been described as one of *cumulative effects*.

Photo by Jim Robb

Highway 407 construction, Rouge Valley, Ontario.

When Impact Assessments Should Be Done

The final report by the federal Environmental Assessment Panel (1991: 2) that reviewed the Rafferty–Alameda Dam and reservoir projects in southeastern Saskatchewan stated that "environmental impact assessment should be applied early in project planning. That is the intent of both provincial and federal processes." The panel concluded that the Rafferty–Alameda projects were "well advanced, however, when both the first and this panel became involved. This put some limits on the usefulness of the review." Unfortunately, too often in Canada, developments are well advanced before environmental impact assessments are conducted. In this regard, what is your view about the timing of the EIA for the Northern Gateway project in British Columbia? Some observers of that EIA commented that public statements from the prime minister and key ministers indicated the federal government had already made up its mind before arranging for the EIA.

EIA should be used jointly with other analyses to determine the appropriateness of development proposals and to help in the design of mitigating measures. However, as with the Rafferty–Alameda Dam, environmental assessments are often conducted after the basic decision has been taken to support a project. As a result, impact assessment often

ENVIRONMENT IN FOCUS

BOX 6.3 | Canadian Applications of Strategic Environmental Impact Assessment

Fundy Tidal Power SEA (OEER, 2008)

East Coast Offshore Hydro Carbon Exploration (Doelle, 2009; Oldreive, 2013)

Review of Manitoba Hydro's power system plan (Manitoba Public Utilities Board, 2014)

Renewable energy in Ontario (Mulvahill et al., 2013)

Great Sand Hills, Saskatchewan (Noble, 2008; Government of Saskatchewan, 2007)

Mistik 20-year forest management plan, Saskatchewan (Rushton, 2012)

becomes a tool for establishing which mitigation measures could be used to reduce or soften negative impacts.

Determining the Significance of Impacts and Effects

A difficult challenge is to determine the significance or implications of impacts. This issue is not solely scientific or technical. For example, scientific data may be able to indicate whether water is too polluted to support fish, but not whether the absence of fish is significant. Accepting that judgements about significance are not strictly technical or scientific strengthens the rationale for extending partnerships in environmental management and for ensuring that key stakeholders participate in planning and assessments.

One of the major challenges in determining "significance" is that the issues in a dispute often do not lend themselves to a monetary valuation; rather, they are characterized by intangible features. What is the value of a wetland that is to be drained to allow the building of a subdivision or to make it possible for a farmer to increase food production? What is the cost to wildlife of disturbance to their habitat resulting from a mine or a pipeline? What is the ecological value of a stand of old white pine or of Douglas fir? Questions such as these pose major challenges for scientists in designing appropriate metrics, which is why they are, or should be, raised in impact assessments. Usually, no single answer suffices to resolve impact dilemmas; people of differing views and vested interests may come to quite different conclusions about their significance and what action is appropriate. These issues are considered further in Chapter 14, which focuses on endangered species and protected areas, and we encourage you to read the related discussion in that chapter.

On 20 April 2010, an explosion on the *Deepwater Horizon*, a marine oil-drilling platform being operated by British Petroleum (BP), killed 11 workers, injured 17 others, and triggered an oil gusher on the ocean floor that released approximately 4.9 million barrels of crude oil over three months before it was contained. This event in the Gulf of Mexico near the Mississippi River Delta, is to date the largest oil spill in the petroleum industry's history. The accident had a negative impact not only on wildlife and their habitats, but also on the area's fishing and tourism industries as 6,500 to 180,000 km^2 of the Gulf were affected at various points during the oil's dispersal. Although originally slated for a full recovery by 2012, a spokesperson for the American National Oceanic and Atmospheric Agency (NOAA) indicated that the area might feel the spill's effects beyond that date (Bryant, 2011). In early September 2014, a US judge decided that BP had been "grossly negligent" and "reckless" regarding the spill. That ruling could add $18 billion in fines on top of what BP already had paid for the spill. These photos show an aerial view of the Gulf spill (left) and an employee of Plaquemines Parish, Louisiana, using a portable vacuum to collect oil from the water's surface (right).

Inadequate Understanding of Ecosystems

The scientific understanding of ecosystems may be incomplete, as discussed in Chapter 2. Furthermore, information about a specific ecosystem may not be adequate to permit estimates about what might be the effects of human intervention.

Even the most basic ecological concepts are not without problems. For example, interpretation and implications of concepts such as community, stability, succession, and climax cause disagreements among ecologists. In some instances, scientists disagree over terminology and definitions, even after more than three-quarters of a century of research. Some of these difficulties were considered in Chapters 2, 3, and 4. With uncertainty and disagreement over basic ecological concepts, it is understandable why predictions are difficult to make with confidence or why the same data result in different scientific interpretations, especially when such data are incomplete. This situation partly explains why it is not unusual for proponents and opponents at environmental hearings to have their own scientific experts who have reached opposite conclusions about impacts or risks, as noted earlier in the discussion on communicating scientific understanding.

To address in part the problem of incomplete information and understanding, Nakashima (1990) argued that more use should be made of **indigenous knowledge** or traditional ecological knowledge (TEK). He illustrated his argument by discussing the ecological understanding of seabirds by Inuit in the coastal communities of Inukjuak and Kuujjuarapik, Quebec, and Sanikiluaq, Nunavut, along southeastern Hudson Bay. He noted that Inuit hunters are positioned to contribute to the protection of the environment, since they have accumulated excellent information and insight about the range and behaviour of seabirds as a direct outcome of their hunting lifestyle. Such knowledge can be invaluable in estimating and assessing the potential impact on wildlife of an oil spill.

Incomplete understanding and inadequate data will remain a challenge for those involved in impact assessments in Canada. For this reason, the adaptive environmental management approach is attractive, given its emphasis on learning by trial and error and its acceptance of uncertainty.

The Nature of Public Involvement

Public involvement has at least three functions in impact assessment:

1. It helps to make the assessment process fair. Furthermore, decision-making that is accessible to the public enhances the credibility of the process. However, there is always a danger that the public or individuals will be "co-opted" through such processes.
2. It helps to broaden the range of issues and potential resolutions, and allows the public to share in devising mitigation measures. In this manner, citizens share in establishing the conditions under which a proposal will be approved.
3. It contributes to social change. That is, by participating in the decision-making process, the public in a particular place becomes more aware of conditions in its own environment. Such enhanced awareness can lead to new initiatives within the community to identify and to begin to address other problems. This point is often referred to as "social learning," a concept discussed in Chapter 5.

The Development of Monitoring

Chapters 2, 3, and 4 highlight that many ecological processes unfold over *decades* and that, therefore, the effects of some ecosystem changes may emerge only slowly. Because of incomplete ecological science, it is often difficult to predict which changes may occur in ecosystem structures or processes as a result of development. Baseline data are often lacking, let alone ongoing **monitoring**. There are also often too many variables to be able to collect data on them all. A common way to approach this challenge is to identify indicator variables. The different kinds of indicators and their characteristics are reviewed more thoroughly in Chapter 1. If we are to improve our knowledge of the resiliency and recuperative powers of ecosystems, monitoring is essential. Monitoring can confirm that recommended mitigating measures have actually been implemented. It can track public concerns or fears regarding a project and thereby help to ensure that they are recognized and addressed.

Too often in environmental and resource management in Canada and in other countries, such monitoring is not conducted. It is usually time consuming and expensive, and the results may not become useful until after many years of monitoring. When financial and human resources are scarce,

THE CANADIAN PRESS/Jeff McIntosh

As part of monitoring efforts in the oil sands area of Alberta, a limnologist from Alberta Environment packs water samples into a cooler before boarding a helicopter on the shore of the Athabasca River, which is downstream from many oil sands projects.

politicians or managers may be tempted to reduce or eliminate monitoring and redirect resources to new development activity, as happened with the Experimental Lakes Area (ELA) in northwestern Ontario (Box 6.4) when the federal government withdrew funding for the ELA in its omnibus Bill C-38 during the spring of 2012. In this instance, in the following year the premier of Ontario provided funding for operational support, and the International Institute for Sustainable Development in Winnipeg agreed to manage the ELA.

Sustainability Assessment

Earlier, we noted growing support for strategic environmental assessment. A different concept is known as **sustainability assessment**, an extension of sustainable development reviewed in Chapter 1.

Gibson (2007: 73–4, 80–7) reminds us that environmental assessment emerged to ensure environmental values are considered along with economic and technological matters, and that sustainability assessment is a more recent innovation. In his words, its core focus is on "efforts to apply some form of sustainability analysis, appraisal, or assessment or otherwise to adopt sustainability objectives as core guides for evaluations and decisions" (2007: 81). He further notes that the proliferation of sustainability initiatives can be surveyed through any reputable Internet search engine. We encourage you to do that and determine whether any such activities are taking place in your province, region, or community.

To stimulate your thinking about sustainability assessment, Table 6.3 presents what Gibson refers to as the basic sustainability requirements in the form of criteria for decision-making that can guide sustainability assessments. If you were to apply the sustainability requirements in Table 6.3 to present or future development proposals in your area, how well would they rate against these criteria, and what changes would you suggest for them? If the same requirements were to be applied in the Northern Gateway experience, what conclusions would you draw, and what recommendations would you offer? What is your view about the Fish Lake decision, outlined in Box 6.5?

Dispute Resolution

Conflicts and disputes occur for many reasons. They may emerge because of clashing or incompatible values, interests, needs, or actions. In an environmental context, conflicts may arise as a result of either substantive or procedural issues, or both. At a substantive level, disputes may arise about the effects of resource use or project development; about multiple uses of resources and areas; about policies, legislation, and regulations; or over jurisdiction and ownership of resources. At a procedural level, conflicts may occur regarding who should be involved, at what times, and in what ways.

Conflict is not necessarily undesirable. Conflict can help to highlight aspects of a process or system that hinder effective performance. It also can lead to clarification of differences stemming from poor information or misunderstandings. Approached in a constructive manner, conflict can result in creative and practical solutions to problems. On the other hand, conflict can be negative if it breeds mistrust or misunderstanding or reinforces biases. It can be negative if it is ignored or set aside, leading to the escalation of a problem or to the creation of stronger obstacles that must be overcome later.

ENVIRONMENT IN FOCUS

BOX 6.4 | The Experimental Lakes Research Area

Generating enough electricity to fuel society's demands while minimizing environmental impacts is one of the main challenges we face today. Hydroelectric power has generally been regarded as preferable to coal- and oil-fired generating stations, which are linked to acid deposition and climate change, and to nuclear power plants with their associated difficulties in waste disposal. So it was somewhat surprising when researchers at the Experimental Lakes Research Area (ELA) in northwestern Ontario discovered that reservoirs created for hydroelectric generation were responsible for releasing large amounts of carbon dioxide and, which is more troubling, of methane into the atmosphere. The emissions occurred as a result of bacterial decomposition of flooded peat and forest biomass.

This was not the ELA's first finding of global significance. Since its founding in 1968, ELA researchers have made significant contributions to the understanding of eutrophication and acid deposition. Fifty-eight small lakes and their watersheds are used as experimental sites to track the impact of various environmental perturbations. Research on eutrophication at the ELA was instrumental in developing the phosphorus control strategies in the Great Lakes Water Quality Agreement. In 1987, research on acidification was initiated and contributed to new estimates regarding damage to aquatic ecosystems. Again, the results were used as the basis for international accords to limit emissions. These lakes have provided further valuable information as changes in environmental conditions, such as global warming, are tracked over time.

TABLE 6.3 | Sustainability Requirements as Criteria for Sustainability Assessment

1. Socio-ecological system integrity	Build human–ecological relations to establish and maintain the long-term integrity of socio-biophysical systems and protect life-support functions on which human as well as ecological well-being depends.
2. Sufficiency and opportunity	Ensure that everyone and every community has enough resources for a decent life and that everyone has opportunities to seek improvement in ways that do not compromise future generations' possibilities for sufficiency and opportunity.
3. Intra-generational equity	Ensure that sufficiency and effective choices for all are pursued in ways that reduce dangerous gaps in sufficiency and opportunity (and health, security, social recognition, political influence, etc.) between the rich and the poor.
4. Intergenerational equity	Favour present options and actions most likely to preserve or enhance the opportunities and capabilities of future generations to live sustainably.
5. Efficiency	Provide a larger base for ensuring sustainable livelihoods for all while reducing threats to the long-term integrity of socio-ecological systems by reducing extractive damage, avoiding waste, and reducing overall material and energy use per unit of benefit.
6. Democracy and civility	Build the capacity, motivation, and inclination of individuals, communities, and other collective decision-making bodies to apply sustainability requirements through more open and better-informed deliberations, greater attention to fostering reciprocal awareness and collective responsibility, and more integrated use of administrative, market, customary, and personal decision-making practices.
7. Precaution and adaptation	Respect uncertainty, avoid even poorly understood risks of serious or irreversible damage to the foundation for sustainability, plan to learn, design for surprise, and manage for adaptation.
8. Immediate and long-term integration	Attempt to meet all requirements of sustainability together as a set of interdependent parts, seeking mutually supportive benefits.

Source: Gibson (2007: 84).

Conflicts over resource management can become high-profile news in Canada. Some of these conflicts are highlighted in subsequent chapters, such as the conflicts over the seal hunt, Native whaling, and the lobster fishery in New Brunswick, discussed in Chapter 8. One of the largest conflicts over resource management focused on the temperate rain forests of Clayoquot Sound on the west coast of Vancouver Island (Box 6.6). A more localized but still significant conflict at the national level has been the dispute between Six Nations people and developers in Caledonia, a community adjacent to the Grand River in southern Ontario. In 1784, the "Haldimand Tract" was granted to the Six Nations by the British government in appreciation for their support during the US War of Independence and as compensation for having lost their territory south of the Great Lakes to the United States. The original Haldimand Tract, just under 20 kilometres (12 miles) wide along the Grand River—from its mouth at Lake Erie for a considerable distance upriver—covered 384,450 hectares. It included the present-day cities of Kitchener, Waterloo, Cambridge, and Brantford (Figure 6.1, page 190).

Over time, much of the land in the tract was sold. For example, in 1798, the tract lands in what is now the Regional Municipality of Waterloo were sold by Joseph Brant, the Mohawk chief. However, Six Nations traditional chiefs have since argued that Brant did not have the right to sell the land and/or that some of the land was purchased from Native leaders who did not appreciate what the sale involved. As a result, the Six Nations traditional government has registered a land claim for the tract lands and maintains that it has jurisdiction over them. The Six Nations traditional chiefs have not claimed ownership over all the land but insist on being consulted before any new developments occur.

The conflict erupted on 28 February 2006 when a group of Six Nations protesters occupied the Douglas Creek Estates subdivision, a 40-hectare housing development in Caledonia, a small community southwest of Hamilton. The Native protesters moved onto the property, erected barricades, and insisted that they would not leave until the land claim was resolved. In 2007, the provincial government bought the property from the developer for $15.8 million and awarded $1 million as compensation to businesses in the Caledonia area adversely affected by the protest. The Native protesters subsequently took down their barricades but continued to occupy the area. As one observer noted, the occupied area "effectively remains a no-go area for non-natives and even the police" (Blatchford, 2014).

The provincial government and police made a conscious decision not to forcibly remove the Six Nations occupiers from the Caledonia site for fear such action would precipitate violence. Violence at Oka, Quebec, in 1990 left a police officer dead during a conflict between the Mohawks and the Quebec provincial police (during which the Canadian army was called in), and violence erupted during the Ipperwash Provincial Park dispute in 1995 when one Native protester, Dudley George, was shot and killed by an Ontario Provincial Police officer.

In terms of jurisdiction, the Ontario government's position has been that the federal government, through Aboriginal Affairs and Northern Development Canada, has the responsibility and authority to deal with land claims. However, in the summer of 2014 the federal minister for Public Safety, Steven Blaney, made no comment about the land claim dispute and instead urged the Ontario government to ensure people in Caledonia were protected by the police (Leslie, 2014). The Six Nations and the federal government have negotiated off and on since 2007, but in the interim nothing has happened on the tract of land and no apparent progress has been made in the negotiations.

In July 2014, the Six Nations Iroquois Confederacy issued a statement that the land in dispute was under the sole jurisdiction of the Haudenosaunee Confederacy Chiefs Council; they were open to have discussions related to Haudenosaunee use of the land; and they invited the premier of Ontario to initiate such discussions. In response, Brad Duguid, the Ontario minister of Economic Development, stated that the

ENVIRONMENT IN FOCUS

BOX 6.5 | Fish Lake, BC: Proposed Mine near Williams Lake, British Columbia

In early November 2010, the federal minister of Environment announced that Taseko Mines' proposed $800 million Prosperity copper–gold mine about 125 kilometres southwest of Williams Lake in the Chilcotin Region of British Columbia was not approved "as proposed," although the BC provincial government previously had approved it. The minister stated that significant adverse environmental impacts were not acceptable, and mitigation measures could not overcome the anticipated "severe damage."

The proposed mine was viewed by some in BC, and especially in Williams Lake, as a "lifeline" for the local economy, which depends on the forestry resource and was struggling due to slumping markets for lumber and the negative effects from the extensive pine beetle infestation (see Chapter 9). Several sawmills in Williams Lake had been closed, causing a significant loss of jobs. It was estimated the mine would create 750 construction jobs and then 500 permanent jobs in the mine.

Fish Lake is recognized for its 85,000 rainbow trout. Many other species, including moose, mule deer, grizzly bear, and long-billed curlew, depend on the lake. The Tsilhqot'in Aboriginal people have fished, hunted, and trapped in the area for centuries, and for them the lake is a sacred place.

Taseko Mines proposed to drain Fish Lake. Subsequently, up to 700 million tons of tailings and other waste material containing arsenic, mercury, lead, and cadmium would be placed in a new tailings pond, created by flooding an adjacent smaller lake and associated creek.

The review by the provincial government, completed in January 2010, concluded negative environmental impacts would be "offset" by a significant number of new jobs, tax revenue to local and provincial governments totalling millions of dollars, and spinoff benefits.

In contrast, the federal environmental assessment, completed in July 2010, concluded the mine would cause significant damage to fish and fish habitat in Fish Lake. In addition, concern was expressed about negative consequences for "potential or established Aboriginal rights or title."

The decision by the federal government to stop development of the copper–gold mine was noteworthy. The Prosperity Mine proposal was only the third project, in almost 20 years of environmental assessments under the Canadian Environmental Assessment Act, to be rejected by the federal government. The other two were the Kemess Mine in northern BC and the Whites Point Quarry in Nova Scotia.

Taseko Mines submitted a new environmental impact statement for the Prosperity Mine in 2012, including provisions to protect Fish Lake. During July 2013, public hearings began, with the Tsilhqot'in First Nation again stating it opposed the mine proposal because of the threat to Fish Lake. In October 2013, the Federal Review Panel indicated it had found "adverse environmental effects." The federal minister of the Environment, Leona Aglukkaq, subsequently decided the project would not be approved because of the irreversible environmental damage.

Taseko Mines initiated a judicial review in May 2014. It stated that the mine project was estimated to be worth $1.5 billion and was the tenth-largest undeveloped copper–gold deposit in the world. It claimed Natural Resources Canada had given the federal panel incorrect information related to the design of a tailings pond. Taseko also argued that the federal review process had not been fair because parts of the revised Canada Environmental Assessment Act which came into effect in 2012 were unconstitutional. The appeal also claimed that the federal minister of Environment had met with Chief Roger William of the Xeni Gwet'in First Nation, after the panel hearings had finished but Taseko had not been advised about the meetings and had had no opportunity to comment on submissions or information presented by the First Nation to the minister.

ENVIRONMENT IN FOCUS

BOX 6.6 | Clayoquot Sound, Vancouver Island

On 13 January 1993, a full-page advertisement appeared in the *New York Times* with the question: "Will Canada do nothing to save Clayoquot Sound, one of the last great temperate rainforests in the world?" It was paid for by eight major international conservation groups. Six months later, Greenpeace International in London produced a 17-page colour booklet, *British Columbia's Catalogue of Shame*, outlining the background to the Clayoquot decision and demanding "an end to all clear-cut logging in Clayoquot Sound, full inventory of all plants and animals to be carried out, and outstanding Native land claim issues to be settled." Robert Kennedy Jr flew in as a lawyer representing the Natural Resources Defense Council of the US and promised the support of his organization. A resource and environmental management issue that had made nightly headline news in Canada also resulted in the arrest of more than 800 protesters and captured worldwide attention.

At stake was the future of one of the greatest remaining temperate rain forests of the world and the largest remaining tract of old-growth forest on Vancouver Island, which was slated to undergo forest harvesting. The area was also under Aboriginal land claim negotiations, coveted by the mining industry, and an arena for conflict between the rapidly expanding aquaculture industry and fishers and recreationists, and it included part of a national park.

The attention drawn to Clayoquot Sound as a result of the protests peaking in the summer of 1993 resulted in several innovations. The area planned for complete protection was expanded. Part of the sound is now included in an international biosphere reserve created in 2000 and recognized by UNESCO. Five First Nations purchased the tree farm licences from the main forestry company, and created a new company called Iisaak Forest Resources Ltd. During 1999, Iisaak signed an agreement with environmental NGOs to not log in ecologically intact catchment basins, even though there is pressure on it to expand logging operations. Tourism has continued to increase in the area, again helping to combat poverty and attracting more support for further preservation.

provincial government still owned the Douglas Creek Estate lands after its purchase from the developer. As Blatchford (2014) observed, "As it was in 2006, so it is in 2014: Caledonia remains simply too hot to touch."

The Caledonia conflict is not unique. In August 2007, a $275 million wind farm project started in 2006 near Shelburne, Ontario, in the northern part of the Grand River basin was stalled because an Aboriginal group claimed that it owned both the land and the wind above the land (Burt, 2007a; 2007b). In this instance, the Six Nations served notice of its land claim rather than occupying the site. The developer of the wind farm, Calgary-based Canadian Hydro, planned a two-phased development, with 45 turbines in the first phase. The second phase, with an additional 88 turbines, was challenged.

One of the spokespersons for the Six Nations, Kahentinetha Horn, was quoted as saying that "We've been robbed of our land and now we want it back. It is our land and it is our wind. They need our permission to use it. We are very concerned about the use of the air, land, and water" (Burt, 2007a: B1). The wind farm project is also located on Haldimand Tract land and hence was subject to the same challenge by the Six Nations as the development at Caledonia.

Canadian Hydro commented that a delay of one year would increase costs by up to $10 million because of the incremental expenses for storing, handling, and transporting the turbines, along with expected higher prices for materials and services in the future. The project, called the Melancthon wind facility and which was the first utility-scale wind farm in Ontario, continued, and the second phase was completed in late 2008. The project contains 133 wind turbines that generate 200 megawatts of power, sufficient to meet the energy needs of about 70,000 average households. In Chapter 12, claims and counterclaims related to health problems resulting from wind farms are presented.

Whether conflict is positive or negative, it is often present because people see things differently, want different things, have different beliefs, and live their lives in different ways.

CP Photo/Hamilton Spectator–Sheryl Nadler

Caledonia protesters at blockade.

Such differences can be exacerbated by other factors. These factors include lack of understanding of other people or groups; using different kinds and sources of information; differences in culture, experience, or education; and differing values, traditions, principles, assumptions, experiences, perceptions, and biases. Conflicts are a normal part of life, and we need to devise ways to deal with them.

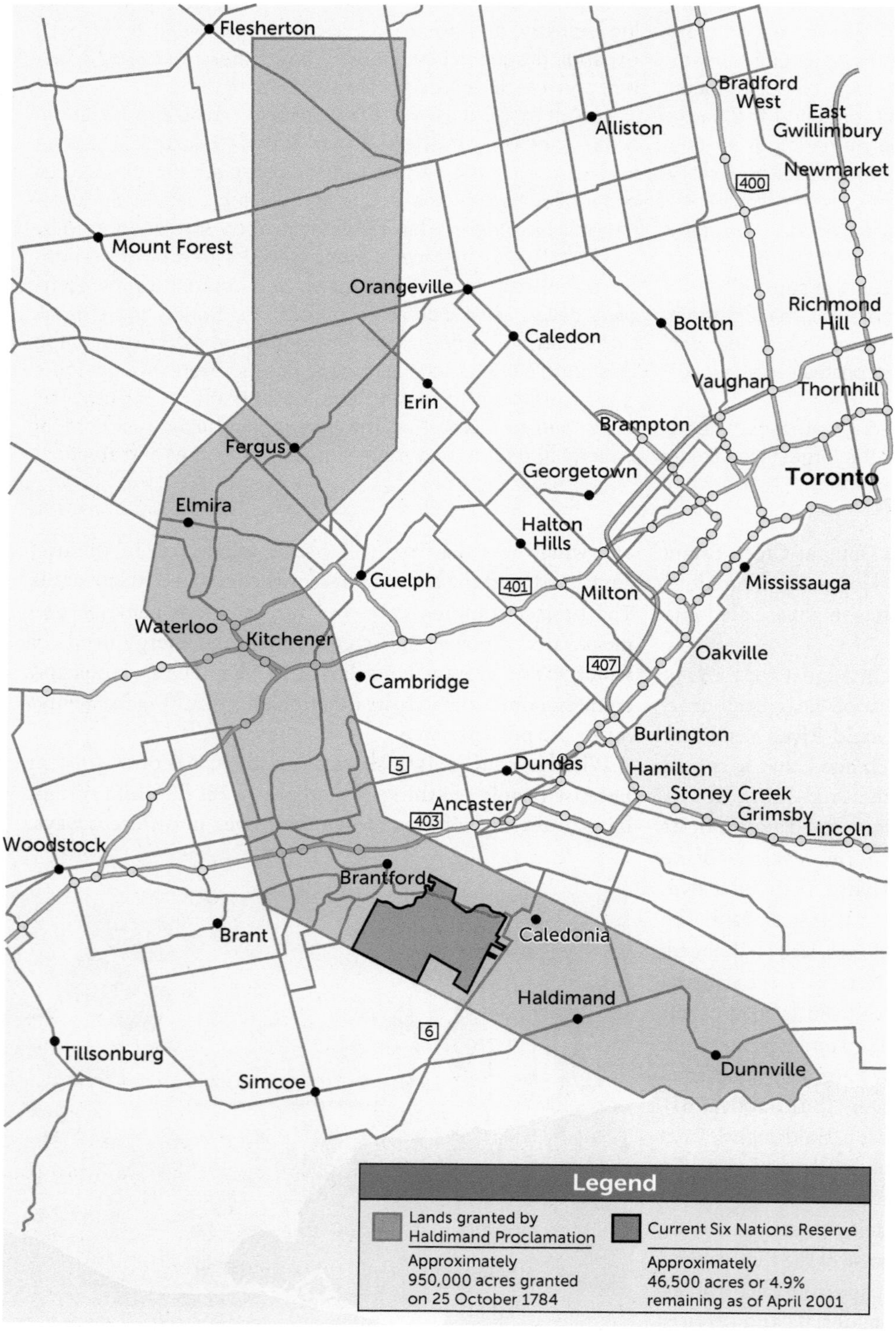

FIGURE 6.1 | Haldimand Tract.

Approaches to Handling Disputes

Disputes usually centre on three main issues: *rights*, *interests*, and *power*. The traditional means of dealing with societal disputes are political, administrative, and judicial. The latter is the most familiar and involves court action. In litigation, the main issues of concern are *fact*, *precedent*, and *procedure*. Attention focuses on establishing a winner or on punishing an offender.

The judicial or litigation approach uses a process that has evolved over centuries. Standards for procedure and evidence are well established. Accountability is ensured through appeal mechanisms and the professional certification of lawyers. However, the judicial process is often viewed as unduly adversarial, time consuming, and expensive. An adversarial and adjudicative process may also encourage participants to exaggerate their private interests, conceal their "bottom lines," withhold information, and try to discredit their opponents. In addition, the courts do not always provide a level playing field when, for example, a small group of private citizens or a First Nation opposes a resource project proposed by a large multinational corporation or government agency. Because of greater financial resources, the latter can afford expensive legal expertise and invest in gaining access to and influence within the corridors of political power.

One alternative to the judicial approach is alternative dispute or conflict resolution. **Alternative dispute resolution (ADR)** emphasizes the interests and needs of the parties involved. And while the judicial approach ends by declaring a winner and loser or identifying a party to be punished, the focus of ADR is on reparation for harm done and on improving future conduct. Another key distinction between the two is that the judicial approach emphasizes *argument*, while the ADR approach stresses *persuasion*.

Attributes of Alternative Dispute Resolution

At least six strengths or advantages of ADR can be identified (Shaftoe, 1993):

1. Emphasis on issues and interests rather than on procedures
2. An outcome normally resulting in a greater commitment to the agreement
3. Attainment of a long-lasting settlement
4. Constructive communication and improved understanding
5. Effective use of information and experts
6. Increased flexibility

These strengths highlight some limitations of the judicial or court-based approach. However, we should not conclude that legally based approaches are never appropriate for dealing with environmental issues. No approach is perfect, and ADR is no exception. Thus, while in some circumstances ADR may be more effective than litigation, the key is to recognize the strengths and weaknesses of each approach and to determine which one would be most effective.

Types of Alternative Dispute Resolution

ADR approaches include public consultation, negotiation, mediation, and arbitration. Various aspects of *public consultation* were reviewed earlier in the context of the ideas of partnerships and stakeholders. Public participation has been used explicitly since the late 1960s for resource and environmental management in Canada. Initially, such consultation focused on having the public help in identifying key issues and in reviewing possible solutions. This public input was one of many considered by the managers who ultimately determined which trade-offs were appropriate and then made the final decisions. Members of the public had no real power or authority in the management process.

By the mid 1980s, this approach had been modified as public participation moved toward the concepts of partnership and delegated power. Some co-management initiatives illustrated the shift toward giving real power to the public. However, public consultation is not normally considered one of the emerging types of alternative dispute resolution, because all decisions related to the dispute are the exclusive domain of stakeholders in any case.

Negotiation is one of the two main types of ADR. Parties involved in a dispute come together in a voluntary, joint exploration of issues with the goal of reaching a mutually acceptable agreement, and participants can withdraw at any time. Through joint exploration, the parties strive to identify and define issues of mutual concern and to develop mutually acceptable solutions. The normal procedure is to reach an agreement by consensus.

Baxternator/iStockphoto

Turbine construction.

© Bruce Mitchell

The Melancthon wind facility in Shelburne, Ontario.

Mediation is the second main type of ADR. Its distinguishing feature is a neutral third party (called a mediator) who helps the disputants overcome their differences and reach a settlement. The third party has no power to impose any outcome. The responsibility to accept or reject any solution remains with the stakeholders in the dispute. In addition, the choice of mediator has to be acceptable to all parties in the conflict.

Mediators play various roles. They assist the parties to come together and in this role act as facilitators. They can also help the parties with fact-finding. The mediators do not necessarily have the expertise to provide the needed information, but they can help to identify essential information and then

Perspectives on the Environment

Consensus

Traditional [indigenous] society was based upon the principle of consensus for government. . . . Consensus must be the most perfect form of democracy known because it means that there is no imposition of the rule of the majority. Everyone has input and no one is excluded.

—Ovide Mercredi, in Mercredi and Turpel (1993: 115)

assist in finding it. Mediators help each stakeholder understand the interests and objectives of the other stakeholders, find points in common, and settle differences through negotiation and compromise. Key roles for the mediator include maintaining momentum in the negotiations, keeping the parties communicating with each other, and ensuring that proposals are realistic.

Arbitration differs from negotiation and mediation because it normally involves stakeholders accepting a third party who will make a decision on the issue(s) in conflict. In mediation, the third party has no power to impose a settlement. In arbitration, the arbitrator's decision is usually binding on the parties. However, in instances known as "non-binding arbitration," the arbitrator makes a decision on the conflict, but the stakeholders may accept or reject it. In some ways, the judicial or court-based approach is similar to binding arbitration, since a judge reaches a decision that is imposed on those involved in the dispute. The main difference is that in arbitration, the stakeholders usually have a voice in selecting the arbitrator. In the judicial procedure, the participants play no role in determining which judge will hear their case.

As already noted, public consultation or public participation has long been used for environmental management in Canada, so there has been considerable experience with it. Judicial or court-based approaches have been used ever since the country was settled by Europeans. Negotiation and mediation are newer approaches, although aspects of negotiation have been used as part of public consultation and judicial approaches. Some of the case studies in Part D provide further details as to how negotiation and mediation are used to address conflicts over the environment. At this point, you might consider how ADR methods could be used to deal with the different interests represented in the Northern Gateway situation or in the dispute involving the Six Nations, developers, the community of Caledonia, the Ontario Provincial Police, and the provincial and federal governments.

Regional and Land-Use Planning

Regional and land-use planning represents a process and a method, and ideally the product (or plan) reflects a vision of desirable development in a region. Resource and environmental managers should be aware of regional and land-use planning for several reasons. First, work undertaken to create or update a plan is often directly relevant to resource and environmental management because it can provide valuable information and insight. Second, regional and land-use plans frequently are based in law and thus govern activity in an area. In contrast, many resource and environmental management plans, such as a watershed or biodiversity plan, usually do not have a legal basis, and this often creates difficulty for effective implementation. Once a resource management plan has been created, it is common for various agencies to have responsibility for implementing specific recommendations. However, such agencies usually have other responsibilities as well, and they must determine what priority recommendations from resource management plans should have. As a result, if resource managers can link their plans to official regional land-use plans, their recommendations are more likely to be acted upon.

The same argument can be made with regard to environmental impact assessment. As with regional and land-use plans, environmental impact assessment has a legal basis at both the federal and provincial levels. Thus, recommendations in a resource management plan are more likely to lead to action if they are related to associated impact assessment statements and to regional and land-use plans. Put another way, if such links are not created, it becomes too easy for decision-makers to overlook or ignore resource management plans because they usually do not have any legal underpinning.

In the section on system and ecosystem perspectives in Chapter 5, we noted that ecosystems are dynamic and therefore continuously changing. One implication is that resource management plans need to be updated to ensure their relevance. The notion of monitoring and modifying plans in light of changing circumstances, new knowledge, and lessons learned is also embodied in adaptive environmental management, as already discussed. In most jurisdictions, provision is made for reviewing, updating, and modifying regional and land-use plans. This is another reason why it is important to link resource management plans to them, since both sets of plans can be reviewed and updated at the same time.

Implementation Barriers

Many challenges accompany moving from plans to implementation. While attention has been allocated to determining how to overcome what is called the **"implementation gap"**

(Joseph et al., 2006), simple solutions rarely exist. In this section, we identify key matters requiring attention to achieve effective implementation (Mitchell, 2009; 2014). Specifically, attention needs to be given to:

1. Recognizing the *context* and developing a custom-designed solution
2. Maintaining a *long-term perspective*, usually including initiatives phased over time
3. Identifying a *vision* of the desired future condition to be achieved
4. Establishing *legitimacy* and *credibility* for the proposed direction and the means to achieve it. This is normally achieved through a mix of legislation, policy, administrative arrangements, and sufficient funding.
5. Ensuring an initiative has one or more *leaders* or *champions*, especially to keep moving forward when obstacles, setbacks, and disappointments emerge
6. Facilitating willingness to *share* or *redistribute* power
7. Establishing a *multi-stakeholder* approach to obtain commitment and buy-in by diverse stakeholders
8. Building capacity for *adaptability*, *learning*, and *flexibility*
9. *Monitoring* and *assessing* outputs and outcomes so adjustments can be made
10. Emphasizing effective *communication* to stakeholders regarding ends, means, and achievements
11. Using *demonstration projects* to highlight tangible evidence of progress
12. Profiling and celebrating *accomplishments*, and openly acknowledging those who facilitated the accomplishments

Addressing these 12 points does not guarantee effective implementation. Other points could be added, and you are encouraged to consider such possibilities. However, experience indicates that attention to these points often does lead to improved implementation.

Implications

The approaches discussed in this chapter represent what many would view as ideals for resource and environmental management regarding processes and methods. Some pose fundamental challenges to us as individuals and society. For example, basic values in Western industrialized societies (and many others) include self-interest and competition. It is often assumed or believed that scarce resources—natural and/or human—are allocated most efficiently and equitably through competition. It is thought that as each agent—individual citizens, interest groups, corporations, resource managers—pursues its own best interests, social balance will be ensured as governments mediate the process in the greater public interest. However, the concepts of *collaboration*, *coordination*, *partnerships*, and *stakeholders* suggest a different paradigm, one based on a willingness to recognize the legitimacy of many interests and needs and to try to accommodate them. In a similar manner, *alternative dispute resolution* is predicated on the idea of groups working together for mutual gain. In a different way, *adaptive management* rejects a belief that humans can completely understand and control natural systems. Instead, this approach accepts that our understanding will always be incomplete and limited, resulting in ongoing surprises that will require us to adapt and modify our policies and practices.

Impact and *risk assessments* further reflect acceptance of uncertainty with regard to resource and environmental systems and encourage us to strive to anticipate and monitor

ENVIRONMENT IN FOCUS

BOX 6.7 | What You Can Do: Taking Initiative to Enhance Procedures and Methods for Natural Resource and Environmental Management

1. Critically examine any initiative related to resource or environmental problems and determine whether these approaches and their inherent values have been included. If any elements are absent, draw attention to the need to incorporate them.
2. Reflect on whether the values you have been acculturated to believe—such as self-interest and competition—are appropriate. Alternative perspectives exist, and we should always address problems by questioning why and how we tend to deal with them in particular ways.
3. Pay attention to related approaches, such as regional and land-use planning and risk and impact assessment, to see how they can support or advance resource and environmental management.
4. Do your best to share with others your information and understanding, not only to improve our understanding of structures and processes related to natural and human systems but also to enhance appreciation of the almost inevitable range of underlying values, assumptions, and attitudes that shape behaviour.

outcomes—intended and unintended, desirable and undesirable—so that we can determine where and when adjustments are needed. It is important to remember that all these procedures can be vulnerable to political interference, regardless of how well designed they are. Such potential vulnerability emphasizes the importance of open processes so that at least a range of stakeholders can be aware of what should be happening and what is happening, and thus be able to speak out if there is a gap between what should be and what is happening.

In Chapter 5, we stressed the importance of a systems approach, and the discussion in this chapter about *regional and land-use planning* highlights that resource and environmental management does not occur in a vacuum. Other management processes occur in parallel, which means that it is important to watch for how connections can be made with these processes, particularly when they have a legal basis. Furthermore, if we want to facilitate positive change it is necessary to pay attention to factors that contribute to *implementation gaps* or *failure*.

Finally, *communication* reminds us that it is critically important that stakeholders share information, insights, needs, and priorities with each other in problem-solving situations. Indeed, inadequate communication often is the variable that undermines otherwise well-conceived management initiatives.

What can you do as an individual? Opportunities are identified for your consideration in Box 6.7.

Summary

1. If a systems approach is to be used, collaboration and coordination are required.
2. Collaboration involves exchanging information, modifying activities in light of others' needs, sharing resources, enhancing the capacity of others in order to achieve mutual benefit and to realize common goals or purposes, and joint decision-making to resolve problems during which power is shared and stakeholders accept collective responsibility for their actions and the outcomes.
3. Participatory approaches aim to incorporate insight from individuals and groups affected by decisions or with responsibility for issues, and also aim for a sharing of power and authority. Not all groups welcome power-sharing, since relinquishing power may undermine their role in environmental management.
4. Stakeholders should be involved in decision-making because of their direct interest and should include (a) any public agency with prescribed management responsibilities; (b) all interests significantly affected by a decision; and (c) all parties who might intervene in the decision-making process or who might block or delay the process.
5. Co-management involves sharing power through giving responsibility and authority to local people for certain aspects of resource and environmental management.
6. Effective communication of science and vernacular knowledge is essential, and communications should be prepared for the target audience and its level of understanding.
7. Effective communication should address four complementary questions: (a) What do we know with what accuracy, and how confident are we about our data? (b) What do we not know, and why are we uncertain? (c) What could we know, with more time, money, and talent? (d) What should we know in order to act in the face of uncertainty?
8. The concept of adaptive environmental management accepts that (a) surprise, uncertainty, and the unexpected are normal; (b) it is not possible to eliminate them through management initiatives; and (c) management should allow for them. Thus, management is viewed as an experiment, requiring systematic monitoring so we can learn from experience.
9. Adaptive co-management includes (a) learning by doing; (b) integration of different knowledge systems; (c) collaboration and power-sharing among community, regional, and national levels; and (d) management flexibility.
10. Environmental impact assessment identifies and predicts the impact of legislative proposals, policies, programs, projects, and operational procedures on the biophysical environment and on human health and well-being. It also investigates and proposes means for their management.
11. Risk assessment focuses on determining the probability of an event of some specified magnitude, as well as the likelihood of the associated consequences. Since risks have to be estimated, our calculations may be incorrect. For this reason, the precautionary principle is used, which states that in order to protect the environment when there are risks of serious or irreversible damage, lack of full scientific certainty should not be used as an excuse for postponing cost-effective measures to prevent environmental degradation.

12. Sustainability assessment focuses on applying some form of sustainability analysis, appraisal, or assessment or otherwise adopting sustainability objectives as core guides for evaluations and decisions.

13. Disputes usually centre on three main issues: rights, interests, and power. The traditional means of dealing with societal disputes are political, administrative, and judicial. Increasingly, attention is being drawn to alternative dispute resolution in which information and understanding are shared and efforts are made to find solutions that address the needs of all stakeholders.

14. Regional and land-use plans often are based in law and govern activity in an area. In contrast, many resource and environmental management plans do not have a legal basis, and this often creates difficulty for implementation. By connecting resource and environmental management plans to regional and land-use plans, statutory authority can be obtained.

15. Implementation failure is a non-trivial issue when moving from a plan to action, and must receive ongoing attention.

Key Terms

adaptive co-management
adaptive environmental management
alternative dispute resolution (ADR)
arbitration
collaboration
co-management
coordination
environmental impact assessment
"implementation gap"
indigenous knowledge
mediation
monitoring
negotiation
partnerships
precautionary principle
risk assessment
stakeholders
strategic environmental assessment
sustainability assessment
vernacular knowledge

Questions for Review and Critical Thinking

1. Explain the difference between collaboration and coordination. Why are both needed in resource and environmental management?
2. What does the word "stakeholder" imply for resource and environmental management? How would you go about identifying stakeholders in a specific problem-solving situation?
3. What are the implications of "vernacular knowledge"?
4. What are the underlying principles of co-management?
5. Why is it often difficult to communicate results from scientific research to the public? What can be done to improve such communication?
6. Do you believe that scientists are objective when they conduct research?
7. What motivated people to develop the concept of adaptive management? What are its strengths and weaknesses? How might it be applied to an environmental problem in your community or province?
8. What are the main characteristics of adaptive co-management?
9. Why is the precautionary principle considered important? Has it been effective in practical terms?
10. What is the difference between strategic environmental assessment and sustainability assessment?
11. What are the distinctive features of alternative dispute resolution? In what kinds of situations might it be a better way to deal with conflicts than the judicial approach?
12. What is the benefit of connecting or relating resource and environmental management to regional and land-use plans and to environmental impact assessments? Is that being done in your community or province?
13. To make the transition from a plan to action, which variables do you believe are most important to consider to ensure effective implementation? Will the importance of the variables change in different cultures?
14. To what extent did collaboration and coordination occur during the process used to deal with the Northern Gateway project discussed in Chapter 1? What initiatives should be taken to achieve a more collaborative and coordinated approach in the future?

Related Websites

Resilience Alliance: Adaptive Co-management
www.resalliance.org/key-concepts

Clayoquot Sound

Clayoquot Biosphere Trust
www.clayoquotbiosphere.org

Friends of Clayoquot Sound
www.focs.ca

Rainforest Portal
www.forests.org

Co-management

Pacific Coast Federation of Fishermen's Associations
www.pcffa.org

International Association for the Study of the Commons
www.iasc-commons.org/about

Conflict Management

The Conflict Resolution Information Source
www.crinfo.org

Public Dispute Resolution
www.sog.unc.edu/programs/dispute

Environmental Impact Assessment

Canadian Environmental Assessment Agency
www.ceaa.gc.ca

Environment Canada, Priority Substances Assessment Program
www.ec.gc.ca/ese-ees/default.asp?lang=En&n=BA0E21A9-1

Experimental Lakes Research Area
www.umanitoba.ca/institutes/fisheries

Parks Canada, Environmental Assessment Overview
www.pc.gc.ca/nature/eie-eia/index_e.asp

Fraser River Estuary Management Program
www.bieapfremp.org/main_fremp.html

International Joint Commission
www.ijc.org

Kristianstads Vattenriket Biosphere Reserve
www.vattenriket.kristianstad.se/eng/biosphere.php

Manitoba Round Table for Sustainable Development
www.gov.mb.ca/conservation/susresmb/mrtsd/index.html

Monitoring

Community Based Environmental Monitoring Network, Atlantic Canada
cbemn.ca

Ecological Monitoring
www.ec.gc.ca/faunescience-wildlifescience/default.asp?lang=En&n=B0D89DF1-1

Land Stewardship Centre
www.landstewardship.org/stewardship-canada/

Monitoring and Reporting on Ontario's Forests
www.ontario.ca/page/forest-monitoring

NatureWatch
www.naturewatch.ca

Further Readings

Note: This list comprises works relevant to the subject of the chapter but not cited in the text. All cited works are listed in the References at the end of the book.

Acharibasam, J.B., and B.F. Noble. 2014. "Assessing the impact of strategic environmental assessment," *Impact Assessment and Project Appraisal* 32: 177–87.

Armitage, D., and R. Plummer. 2010. *Adaptive Capacity: Building Environmental Governance in an Age of Uncertainty*. Heidelberg: Springer.

Bice, S., and K. Moffat. 2014. "Social license to operate and impact assessment," *Impact Assessment and Project Appraisal* 32: 257–62.

Blatchford, C. 2010. *Helpless: Caledonia's Nightmare of Fear and Anarchy, and How the Law Failed All of Us*. Toronto: Random House/Doubleday Canada.

Curry, J., H. Donker, and R. Krehbiel. 2014. "Land claim and treaty negotiations in British Columbia, Canada: Implications for First Nations land and self-governance," *Canadian Geographer* 58: 291–304.

Dalal-Clayton, B., and B. Sadler. 2011. *Sustainability Appraisal: A Sourcebook and Reference Guide to International Experience*. London: Earthscan.

Devries, L., and A. Green. 2011. *Conflict in Caledonia: Aboriginal Land Rights and the Rule of Law*. Vancouver: University of British Columbia Press.

Gibson, R.B. 2012. "In full retreat: The Canadian government's new environmental assessment law undoes decades of progress," *Impact Assessment and Project Appraisal* 30, 3:179–88.

Goldstein, B.V. 2012. *Collaborative Resilience: Moving through Crisis to Opportunity*. Cambridge, Mass: MIT Press.

Hanna, K.S., ed. 2009. *Environmental Impact Assessment: Practice and Participation*, 2nd edn. Toronto: Oxford University Press.

Miller, J. 2009. *Compact, Contract, Covenant: Aboriginal Treaty-making in Canada*. Toronto: University of Toronto Press.

Noble, B.F. 2015. *Introduction to Environmental Impact Assessment: A Guide to Principles and Practice*, 3rd edn. Toronto: Oxford University Press.

Ohsawa, T., and P. Duinker. 2014. "Climate-change mitigation in Canadian environmental impact assessments," *Impact Assessment and Project Appraisal* 32: 222–33.

Sadler, B., R. Aschemann, J. Dusik, T.B. Fischer, M. Partidario, and R. Verheem. 2011. *Handbook of Strategic Environmental Assessment*. London: Earthscan.

Squires, A., and M.G. Dubé. 2013. "Development of an effects-based approach for watershed scale aquatic cumulative effects assessment," *Integrated Environmental Assessment and Management*. 9: 380–91.

Therivel, R. 2011. *Strategic Environmental Assessment in Action*, 2nd edn. London: Earthscan.

Trist, E. 1980. "The environment and system-response capability," *Futures* 12, 2: 113–27.

Williams, B., and E. Brown. 2014. "Adaptive management: From more talk to real action," *Environmental Management* 53, 2: 465–79.

Wyborn, C., and R.P. Bixler. 2013. "Collaboration and nested environmental governance: Scale dependency, scale framing, and cross-scale interactions in collaborative conservation," *Journal of Environmental Management* 123, 3: 58–67.

Go to www.oupcanada.com/DeardenMitchell5e to access additional learning tools on your smartphone, tablet, or PC.

PART D

Resource and Environmental Management in Canada

Parts B and C focused on science and management related to resources and the environment. In Part D, we discover how ideas and methods from science and management can be applied in practical problem-solving situations.

Several comments about the structure of this section should be helpful. It may appear contradictory to argue for a systems or ecosystem approach in Parts B and C and then organize Part D on the basis of specific "resources" or attributes of the environment, such as agriculture, forestry, or wildlife. Indeed, it would be inappropriate to isolate components of resource or environmental systems and examine them on a sector-by-sector basis, as the chapter headings in Part D might suggest. However, it is appropriate to use one resource or environmental aspect as the starting point for a discussion, as long as we give attention to other elements of the ecosystem and their linkages. This is the approach used in this section.

Four types of resources or environments are considered in the following eight chapters. The first, addressed in Chapter 7, is the atmospheric system, with emphasis on climate change. The second, the focus of Chapters 8 to 11, comprises various renewable resources—oceans, forestry, agriculture, and water systems. The third type, considered in Chapter 12, deals with non-renewable resources—minerals and fossil fuels that are created (or renewed) over the course of a geological time span rather than human lifespans. The fourth type, place-based, focuses on the environmental opportunities and challenges in urban areas (Chapter 13), in which four of five Canadians now live, and on endangered species and protected areas (Chapter 14).

Interest centres on examining how science can be used to inform analysis and management and how elements of best practice in management have been or could be applied. For example, after examining the nature of weather and climate, Chapter 7 turns to assessing the scientific evidence related to climate change and to the role of climate models in aiding our understanding of changes. While solid scientific understanding of environmental systems and how they may be changing is of critical importance, it is equally important to

communicate that understanding to non-technical specialists. Consequently, this chapter addresses the challenges encountered by researchers when they seek to communicate scientific insight about climate change to policy-makers and the general public. These challenges too often are not systematically addressed by scientists, who are frequently more interested in the "purity" of their scientific work and in communicating their findings to peers. As in other chapters, we attempt to relate scientific understanding to "real-world" situations.

Case studies give you opportunities to learn about how science and management can be connected. For example, Chapter 8 on oceans looks at the challenges involved in the depletion of the Pacific salmon fishery, the debate over the seal hunt off the east coast, and the closure of the northern cod fishery in Atlantic Canada. In later chapters, case studies cover the environmental impact of the James Bay hydroelectric project in northern Quebec, the development of diamond mines in the Northwest Territories and Nunavut, the rapid growth of the Alberta oil sands, the implications of the Walkerton, Ontario experience for water security, the lessons learned about managing natural hazards from the flooding of Calgary in June 2013, and the opportunities and challenges in the development of wind and other renewable sources of energy production. In addition, some examples deliberately examine how a mix of ecosystems interact, such as in the case of the tar ponds on Cape Breton Island, examined in Chapter 11.

The issues and examples considered here raise fundamental questions about humans' relationships with the environment and resources. We see a range of attitudes toward the environment and other living things, covering the spectrum from humans dominating nature to humans striving to live in harmony with nature. The extinction of species, such as those reported in Chapter 14, reminds us that we have been (and can still be) incredibly arrogant in believing that it is acceptable for us to eliminate some species forever. In contrast, as also shown in Chapter 14, conscious decisions are being taken to protect valued areas, in some instances because we believe it is important to protect examples of different biomes. Notwithstanding significant and positive accomplishments, current lifestyles in Canada continue to contribute to global climate change in a major way, as discussed in Chapters 7 and 15. The changes associated with climatic warming may confound attempts to identify and protect examples of biospheres that may change in the future because of different climatic conditions.

Finally, the case studies and examples illustrate how pervasive conflict can be in resource and environmental management. This reinforces our belief that resource and environmental management must recognize, identify, and incorporate different values and interests. For this reason, managers often spend significant time trying to resolve conflicts. Given this reality, scientists must also develop a greater appreciation that their work will usually be used in situations in which values and emotions can be as important as, or of greater importance than, theories, models, and quantitative evidence.

The mix of case studies and examples in Part D and throughout this book will help you to appreciate that change, complexity, uncertainty, and conflict are integral parts of resource and environmental management.

CHAPTER SEVEN
Climate Change

Learning Objectives

- To understand the difference between weather and climate
- To know the difference between climate change and global warming
- To appreciate why the science of climate change is characterized by complexity and uncertainty
- To understand the nature of scientific evidence regarding climate change
- To understand the scientific explanation for climate change
- To realize the implications of climate change for natural and human systems
- To appreciate the challenges of sharing information and insight related to climate change
- To comprehend the Kyoto Protocol, as well as subsequent international summits seeking to renew or replace it
- To understand the role of the Intergovernmental Panel on Climate Change
- To understand the strategies and tactics of "climate change deniers"
- To appreciate Canada's role in the global context as a contributor to both climate change challenges and solutions
- To appreciate the importance of including both mitigation and adaptation in a strategy for reducing vulnerability to climate change
- To understand the implications of "geo-engineering" initiatives related to climate change
- To discover what you can do as an individual to minimize the impact of climate change

Introduction

Climate is naturally variable. It is never exactly the same from one period to another. Sometimes it can shift dramatically within a few hundred or thousand years, as it does when ice ages begin and end. Usually it varies within much narrower limits. For most of the past 1,000 years, for example, the world's average temperature has remained within about half a degree of 14°C.

Perspectives on the Environment

Wired to Ignore Climate Change

Through our long evolution, we have inherited fundamental and universal cognitive wiring that shapes the way we see the world and interpret threats that motivates us to act on them. Without doubt, climate change has qualities that play poorly to these innate tendencies. It is complex, unfamiliar, slow moving, invisible, and intergenerational. Of all the possible combinations of loss and gain, climate change contains the most challenging: requiring certain short-term loss in order to mitigate an uncertain longer-term gain.

—Marshall (2014: 226)

JohnnyH5/Thinkstock

Most of California has been experiencing severe drought since 2011.

Over the past 100 years or so, however, the world's climate has changed noticeably. The world's average temperature was approximately 0.6°C warmer at the end of the twentieth century than it was at the beginning. In 2013, the annual combined land and ocean surface temperature was 0.62°C above the average of 13.9°C for the twentieth century. The year 2010 is currently the warmest, being 0.66°C above average. Furthermore, 9 of the 10 warmest years in the 134 years that the US *National Oceanic and Atmospheric Administration* (NOAA) has kept records occurred in the twenty-first century, with 1998 being the other in the top ten. The US National Aeronautics and Space Administration (NASA) (2014) records show slightly different temperatures, but the patterns are the same. For Canada, both 2013 and 2014 were warmer than average. Such changes may seem trifling, but the difference between global temperatures now and at the peak of the last ice age is a mere 5°C. However, much uncertainty and complexity are encountered in seeking to understand the significance of such changes, requiring knowledge about both science and societies.

Nature of Climate Change

The condition of the **atmosphere** at any time or place—that is, the **weather**—is expressed by a combination of several elements, primarily (1) *temperature* and (2) *precipitation* and *humidity*, and, to a lesser degree, (3) *winds* and (4) *air pressure*. These are called the elements of weather and climate because they are the ingredients out of which various weather and climatic types are compounded. The weather of any place is the sum total of its atmospheric conditions (temperature, pressure, winds, moisture, and precipitation) for a *short* period of

GEFHunter/iStockphoto

The 2013 Alberta floods forced approximately 100,000 people from their homes.

Perspectives on the Environment

Weather and Climate

Canada is perceived to be a cold, northern country. . . . However, as usual, averages mask a lot of variation, especially in a country as big as Canada. Vancouver, for example, has an average temperature of 10°C, Toronto 8°C, and Halifax 6°C, compared with Alert in the Arctic at −18°C. Precipitation also varies widely, with more than 3,200 millimetres along parts of the west coast and less than 200 millimetres in the Arctic. This variation, spanning more than 40 degrees of latitude between the northern and southern extremities, is reflected in the ecozones described in more detail in Chapter 3.

—After Trewartha (1954: 4)

time. It is the momentary state of the atmosphere. Thus, we speak of the weather, not the climate, for today or of last week.

Climate, on the other hand, is a composite or generalization of the variety of day-to-day weather conditions. It is not just "average weather," because the variations from the mean, or average, are as important as the mean itself.

A distinction should also be made between climate change and global warming. Climate represents average day-to-day weather conditions as well as seasonal variations for a particular place or region. In that context, **climate change** is defined as "a long-term shift or alteration in the climate of a specific location, a region, or the entire planet" (Hengeveld et al., 2002: 1). A shift is measured for variables associated with average weather conditions, such as temperature, precipitation, and wind patterns (velocity, direction). A change in variability of climate is also considered climate change. In contrast, **global warming**, often mentioned by the media, addresses changes only in average surface *temperatures*. It does not address whether conditions are becoming wetter or drier, for example. A frequent misunderstanding is that global warming means uniform warming throughout the world. An increase in average global temperatures drives alterations in atmospheric circulation patterns, which can contribute to some areas warming quickly, others more slowly, and others even to become cooler.

What are the "causes" of climate? The Earth's surface and atmosphere are heated differentially by short-wave radiation from the sun. The differences in heat and pressure between the poles and the tropics fuel the global circulation system as heat and moisture are redistributed around the world. The temperature balance of the Earth is maintained through the return of the continually absorbed solar radiation back to space as infrared radiation, consistent with the first law of thermodynamics (Chapter 2). Long-term temperature changes result from shifts in the amount of energy received or absorbed. These shifts may be caused over long cycles (100,000 years) by factors such as the shape of the Earth's orbit around the sun, wobbles of the Earth's axis, and the angle of tilt.

Natural events, such as the eruption of large volcanoes and changes in ocean currents, such as **El Niño**, have an influence on climate. Volcanoes, when erupting, eject large quantities of dust and sulphur particles into the atmosphere, which reduce the amount of solar radiation reaching the surface of the Earth. Changes in ocean currents can also be influential (Chapter 8). El Niño represents a marked warming of the waters in the eastern and central portions of the tropical Pacific as westerly winds weaken or stop blowing, usually two to three times every decade. In normal years, the trade winds amass warm water in the western Pacific. As the winds slacken, this water spreads back eastward and toward the poles into the

Perspectives on the Environment

Greenhouse Effect

The **greenhouse effect** describes the role of the atmosphere in insulating the planet from heat loss, much like a blanket on our bed insulates our bodies from heat loss. The small concentrations of greenhouse gases within the atmosphere that cause this effect allow most of the sunlight to pass through the atmosphere to heat the planet. However, these gases absorb much of the outgoing heat energy radiated by the Earth itself and return much of this energy back towards the surface. This keeps the surface much warmer than if they were absent. This process is referred to as the "greenhouse effect" because, in some respects, it resembles the role of glass in a greenhouse.

—Hengeveld et al. (2002: 2)

These coral fossils, from the Canning River in the Arctic National Wildlife Refuge, Alaska, illustrate how climates have changed in the past.

rest of the Pacific. This triggers weather changes in at least two-thirds of the globe, causing both droughts and extreme rainfall in areas along the Pacific and Indian Oceans, including Africa, eastern Asia, and North America.

However, it is increasingly apparent that climatic change may occur more rapidly than ever before as a result of human activities. We examine these factors below.

Scientific Evidence Related to Climate Change

In the context of the distinctions among weather, climate, global warming, and climate change, the following statements are supported by solid scientific evidence:

1. The world has been warming. The Intergovernmental Panel on Climate Change (IPCC) (2014b: 1) reports that each of the previous three decades was warmer at the surface of the Earth than for the decades extending back to 1850, and that from 1983 to 2012, in the northern hemisphere, the Earth most likely experienced the warmest 30 years during the past 1400 years. Starting in 1850, the global average of the combined land and ocean surface water temperature increased by 0.85°C (0.65 to 1.06°C) (Figure 7.1a).
2. **Greenhouse gas** emissions have been rising for several decades (Figures 7.1c and 7.1d). The concentrations of carbon dioxide, methane, and nitrous oxide are at higher concentrations now than at any time over the past 800,000 years, driven largely by economic and population growth (IPCC, 2014a: 4).
3. In most parts of the world since 1980, glaciers have lost more mass than they have gained. The Canadian Cryospheric Information Network (2014) reports that cumulative losses have increased from 226 gigatonnes per year (Gt/year) in 1979–2005 to 301 Gt/year in 2005–2009. Reduction in glaciers has been the most substantial in western Canada, Alaska, and Patagonia.
4. In many areas of the world, reduced snow cover has been documented, as well as earlier spring melting of ice on rivers and lakes. For example, snow cover in the northern hemisphere has decreased by approximately 10 per cent since 1996. The cold temperatures and large amounts of snow in the winters of 2004, 2008, and 2014 across most of Canada were exceptions to this general pattern.
5. Regarding Arctic sea-ice cover, the Canadian Cryospheric Information Network (2014) reports that since satellite monitoring of sea ice began in the late 1970s, total sea ice in Canada has been declining each decade, the losses being greatest in the fall (September–November, -7.0 ± 1.5 per cent). Multi-year ice coverage has decreased (by -12.5 ± 2.1 per cent) annually since 1981. Changes are not homogenous, with ice having increased in the Bering Sea by 7.3 per cent and decreased in the Gulf of St. Lawrence by 13.8 per cent.
6. Over one-half of Canada is underlain by permafrost. Bore holes were drilled for monitoring during the latest International Polar Year (2007–2009), and data show that permafrost is warming in many regions, especially in the Western and High Arctic.

Perspectives on the Environment

Implications of Sea-Level Rise

Rising sea levels threaten familiar shoreline environments. Coastal wetlands, which are important ecosystems and barriers against shoreline erosion, gradually disappear. Bluffs and beaches are more exposed to erosion by waves, groundwater is more likely to become contaminated by salt water, and low-lying coastal areas may be permanently lost. In addition, wharves, buildings, roads, and other valuable seaside property face a greater risk of damage as a result of flooding from storms.

—Canadian Council of Ministers of the Environment (2003: 13)

vicnt/iStockphoto

Following a volcanic eruption, large amounts of sulphur dioxide (SO_2), hydrochloric acid (HCl), and ash spew into the Earth's stratosphere. In most cases, HCl condenses with water vapour and is rained out of the volcanic cloud. SO_2 from the cloud is transformed into sulphuric acid (see Chapter 4). The sulphuric acid quickly condenses, producing aerosol particles, which linger in the atmosphere for long periods of time.

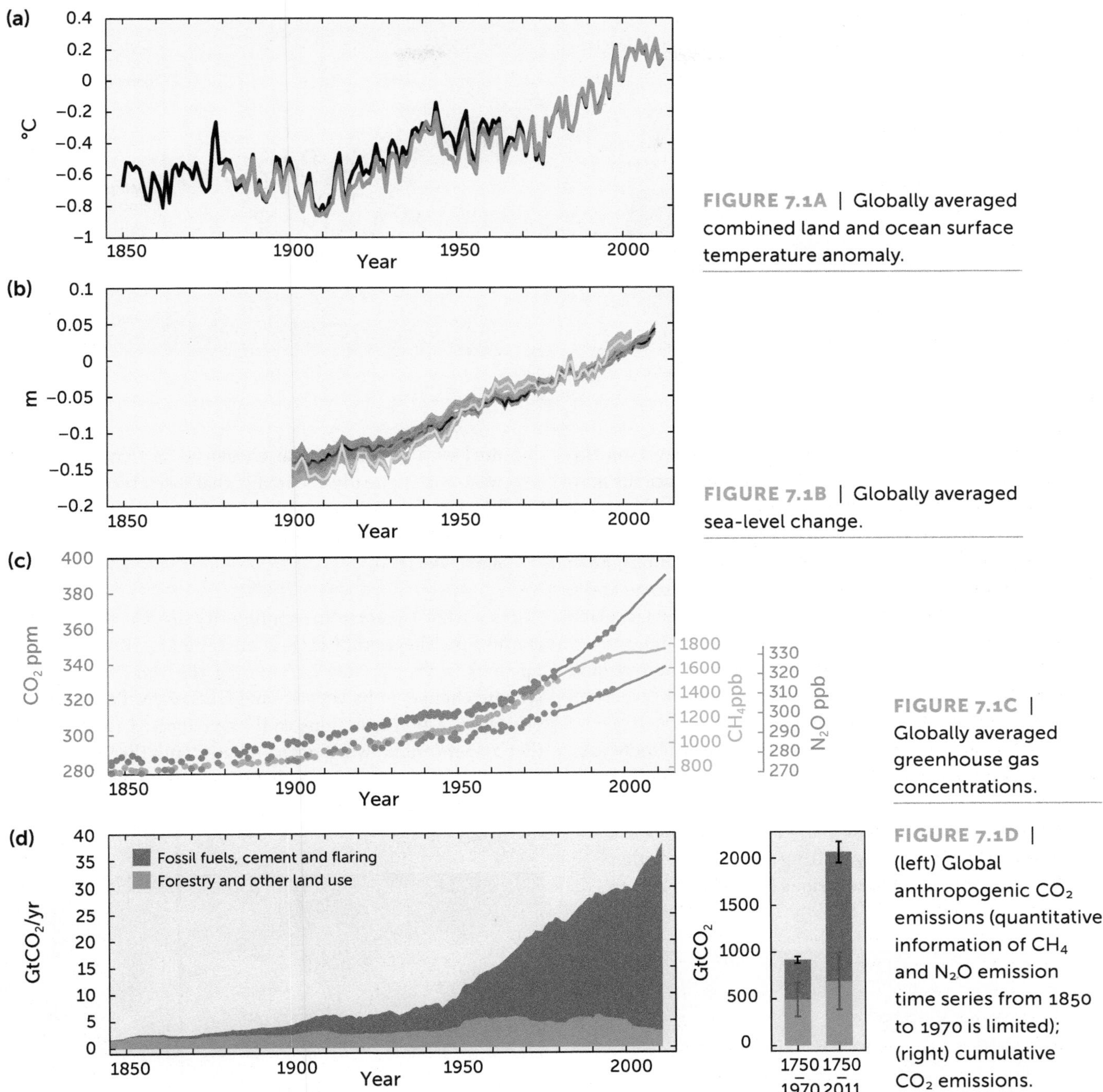

FIGURE 7.1A | Globally averaged combined land and ocean surface temperature anomaly.

FIGURE 7.1B | Globally averaged sea-level change.

FIGURE 7.1C | Globally averaged greenhouse gas concentrations.

FIGURE 7.1D | (left) Global anthropogenic CO_2 emissions (quantitative information of CH_4 and N_2O emission time series from 1850 to 1970 is limited); (right) cumulative CO_2 emissions.

FIGURE 7.1 | Observations and other indicators of a changing global climate system. Observations: (a) Annually and globally averaged combined land and ocean surface temperature anomalies relative to the average over the period 1986 to 2005. Colours indicate different data sets. (b) Annually and globally averaged sea-level change relative to the average over the period 1986 to 2005 in the longest-running data set. Colours indicate different data sets. All data sets are aligned to have the same value in 1993, the first year of satellite altimetry data (red). Where assessed, uncertainties are indicated by coloured shading. (c) Atmospheric concentrations of the greenhouse gases carbon dioxide (CO_2, green), methane (CH_4, orange) and nitrous oxide (N_2O, red) determined from ice core data (dots) and from direct atmospheric measurements (lines). Indicators: (d) Global anthropogenic CO_2 emissions from forestry and other land use as well as from burning of fossil fuel, cement production, and flaring. Cumulative emissions of CO_2 from these sources and their uncertainties are shown as bars and whiskers, respectively, on the right-hand side. The global effects of the accumulation of CH_4 and N_2O emissions are shown in panel c.

Source: IPCC (2014a: 3).

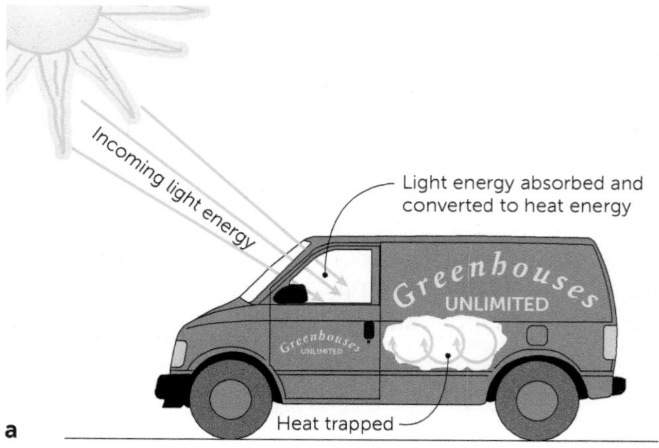

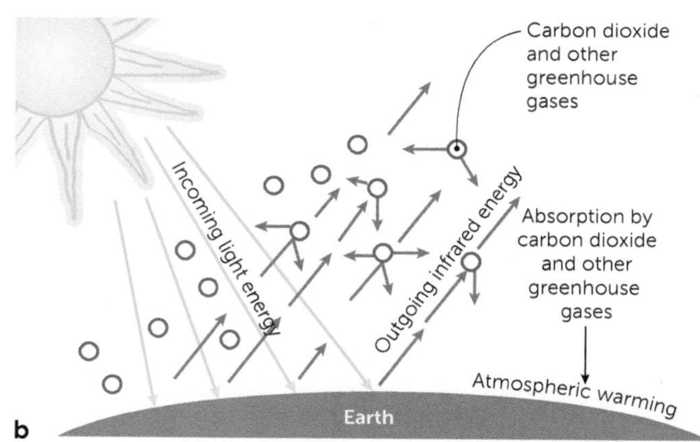

FIGURE 7.2 | The greenhouse effect.

7. Between 1901 and 2010, the global sea mean level went up by 0.19 ± 0.02 metres (IPCC, 2014a: 3). And, since the middle of the nineteenth century, the rate of sea level increase has been greater than the mean rate over the preceding two millennia (Figure 7.1b). We must be cautious, however, in interpreting such findings since, in some areas, land is still rebounding from the weight of the last glaciation. Thus, data from tidal gauges must be interpreted in light of the combination of sea-level rise and land rebound, which could mask the increase in sea-level rise.

The following comments from Hengeveld (2006: 28), expressed a decade before, still reflect the above findings:

> The debate about climate change within the science community is gradually shifting away from whether it is happening and how serious it will be to how to deal with it. The general consensus is that global warming is already occurring, that fossil fuels combustion is the primary cause, and that the negative impacts of weather and climate events will get much worse.

It is not just the scientific community that has reached this consensus. The world's largest oil company, Exxon, which up to 15 years ago was questioning the veracity of global climate change, in its 2015 annual *Outlook for Energy* report observed carbon emissions could be expected to rise a further 25 per cent between 2010 and 2030 and then decline by 5 per cent by 2040 as demands for power rise by 35 per cent by 2040. Further, it indicates that global CO_2 emissions will

AVTG/iStockphoto

The forest industry is a major contributor to the rising levels of carbon dioxide in the atmosphere, not only through deforestation, but also through emissions from processing plants.

MartinKovalenkov/iStockphoto

Some countries, such as the Maldives in the Indian Ocean, are so low-lying that they could be mostly flooded as early as 2050 if global sea levels rise as predicted. Indeed, in late 2008 the president of the Maldives announced an emergency plan whereby revenue from tourism is to be set aside in a special fund for the purchase of land in Sri Lanka, India, or Australia so the nation of over 300,000 people, in a worst-case scenario, can continue to exist in another location.

A view of the Moose River from Moose Factory Island. Traditional environmental knowledge is vital to understanding the complex changes that occur in regions such as Moose Factory and Moosonee. Climate change has affected not only average temperatures but also animal and bird migration, weather patterns, and the freeze–thaw cycles of the Moose River.

be higher by 6 billion tonnes in 2040. These figures far surpass any predictions from the scientific models, discussed in more detail in the next section. Unfortunately, so also do the empirical data now being collected on climate change, suggesting that Exxon may well be right.

Perspectives on the Environment

Columbia Icefields, Alberta: Glaciers and Climate Change in Canada

What may be the most visited glaciers in North America—the Columbia Icefields in Alberta—are being reduced by over 5 metres of ice annually, and Parks Canada has reported they might disappear within a generation.

The Columbia Icefields comprise six glaciers, with the biggest being the Athabasca glacier located in Jasper National Park. The average annual snowfall on the Athabasca glacier is 7 metres, but the glacier has been gradually receding over 150 years. Monitoring by Parks Canada indicates that the toe of Athabasca glacier has receded 1.5 kilometres since 1890 and is also becoming thinner.

While the reduction in the Athabasca glacier has implications for tourism, more general negative implications of receding glaciers in Alberta and British Columbia include reduced capacity for hydro power production and lower water supplies for irrigation districts and municipalities. Quite rightly, this melting is changing the perception of the glacier from a distant and somewhat abstract phenomenon to the natural "water towers" of the West that provide irreplaceable services to many sectors of the economy.

One attribute of "good science" is the use of cross-checking data sources to ensure that findings are not unduly influenced by measurement error or limitations of any single data source. The findings above related to temperature, greenhouse gas concentrations, glaciers, snow cover, river and lake ice breakup, permafrost, and sea-level rise all indicate that climate change is occurring. In the next section, we turn our attention to the reasons for this change. Once the pattern and causes of climate change are understood, we have a foundation for considering the implications for designing possible policies and actions.

Modelling Climate Change

The uncertainty associated with global climate change has led scientists to explore different ways of assessing past and future climates (Box 7.1). One approach is **climate modelling**. While concern about climate change due to greenhouse gas (GHG) emissions is relatively recent, climate modelling is not. The earliest global climate models date back to the 1950s, far ahead of when scientists became concerned about carbon dioxide emissions and their effect on the atmosphere. However, more recent concerns about global warming have propelled the science of climate modelling to the forefront.

Climate Models

All climate models consider some or all of five components in order to predict future climates:

- radiation—incoming (solar) and outgoing (absorbed, reflected) energy
- dynamics—the horizontal and vertical movement of energy around the globe
- surface processes—the effects of the Earth's surface (snow cover, vegetation) on climate (i.e., albedo, emissivity)

Scientists core a coral reef in the Myeik Archipelago, Myanmar.

ENVIRONMENT IN FOCUS

BOX 7.1 | Measuring Climate Change

An essential step in attempting to assess climatic change is to see how present variations in climate compare with those of the past. Current data are largely instrument-based weather observations—the instrumental record. Even here there are difficulties. More modern and accurate data—for example, data on the upper atmosphere gathered by satellite—are available only for the past four decades or so. This period also coincides with the greatest human impact on climate and does not provide any type of control for climate change in the absence of industrialization.

Former climates are reconstructed by scientists using proxy information from many different sources. For example, historical records of climate-influenced factors such as the price of wheat in Europe over the past 800 years, the blooming dates of cherry trees in Kyoto, Japan, since 812CE, the height of the Nile River at Cairo since 622CE, and the number of severe winters in China since the sixth century; sailors' and explorers' logs; and other such sources all contribute to a picture of past climates.

Scientists also use climate-sensitive natural indicators such as tree rings and glacial ice. Cores obtained from ice in Greenland and Antarctica that go back tens of thousands of years have been analyzed using the ratio of two oxygen isotopes that indicate the air temperature when the original snow accumulated on the glacier surface. Tree rings are also very useful as the width and density of tree rings reflect growth conditions, including climate. Some species—red cedar in coastal BC, for example—may live for well over 1,000 years and can provide valuable indicators as to past climates. In some areas, and most notably in tropical rain forests where growth conditions may not differ appreciably between seasons, the utility of tree rings as climate analogues is limited. However, the same kinds of rings also characterize the growth of many long-living corals in the tropics, which may be more than 800 years old, and provide valuable evidence about previous El Niño events.

- chemistry—the chemical composition of the atmosphere and its interactions with other Earth processes (i.e., carbon cycling)
- time step and resolution—the time scale of the model (minutes or decades) and the spatial scale of the model (your backyard or the entire globe)

The nature of the Earth's climate and its complexity make comprehensive climate modelling difficult. The many components, interactions, and feedback loops in the global climate cannot be entirely represented by any mathematical model, and therefore all models simplify certain aspects of climate. There are four main types of climate models, each increasing in complexity. They are outlined in Box 7.2.

Unlike energy balance models (EBMs), **general circulation models (GCMs)** attempt to examine all of the climatic elements and processes, making these models very complex. GCMs model the Earth's atmosphere and oceans under certain

ENVIRONMENT IN FOCUS

BOX 7.2 | Four Types of Climate Models

1. Energy Balance Models (EBMs)
   EBMs can be either non- or one-dimensional. In the first case, the Earth (or any point on the Earth) is treated as a single entity, and only incoming and outgoing radiation are modelled. In one-dimensional EBMs, temperature is modelled as a function of latitude and radiation balance.
2. One-Dimensional Radiative-Convective (RC) Climate Models
   In this model, the one dimension is altitude. One-dimensional RC models take into account incoming and outgoing solar radiation, as well as convective processes that affect the vertical distribution of temperature. These models are useful for examining the vertical distribution of solar radiation and cloud cover and are very useful for examining the effects of volcanic emissions on temperature.
3. Two-Dimensional Statistical-Dynamic (SD) Climate Models
   This model takes into account either the two horizontal dimensions or one horizontal dimension and the vertical dimension. The latter are most frequently modelled, thus combining the latitudinal EBMs with the vertical RC models. These models can examine wind speed, direction, and other horizontal energy transfers.
4. General Circulation Models (GCMs)
   While the first three types of climate models are still used for various purposes in climate research, since the 1980s general circulation models (GCMs) have largely taken over the field of climate modelling, and most model development is devoted to them. It is by far the most complex type of model, since the GCM takes into account the three-dimensional nature of the Earth's atmosphere, oceans, or both.

Perspectives on the Environment

Intergovernmental Panel on Climate Change

The Intergovernmental Panel on Climate Change (IPCC) was established in 1988 by the World Meteorological Organization and the United Nations Environment Programme. Its main website is at http://www.ipcc.ch/.

The IPCC was created to assess scientific, technical, and socio-economic information related to understanding the risks from human-induced change to climate. The IPCC does not conduct original research, nor does it monitor climate data. Its assessments are based on peer-reviewed and published scientific literature.

The IPCC has three working groups and a task force. Its *First Assessment Report*, published in 1991, had an important role related to the UN Framework Convention on Climate Change, adopted at the Earth Summit at Rio de Janeiro in 1992.

Its *Second Assessment Report*, published in 1995, became a significant input into negotiations that resulted in the Kyoto Protocol in 1997. The Kyoto Protocol is discussed later in the chapter.

The *Third Assessment Report*, produced in 2001, was the product of the work of more than 2,000 scientists from many disciplines from all around the world.

A *Fourth Assessment Report* was published in 2007, and the 2007 Nobel Peace Prize was awarded jointly to the IPCC and former US Vice-President Arnold (Al) Gore "for their efforts to build up and disseminate greater knowledge about man-made climate change, and to lay the foundations for the measures that are needed to counteract such change." (Nobelprize.org, 2007).

A *Fifth Assessment Report* was published in 2014, and is discussed later in this chapter.

climate change scenarios, the most popular being "2 × CO_2." In this situation, the Earth's climate is modelled to indicate the changes that would occur if atmospheric concentrations of carbon dioxide were doubled from pre–Industrial Revolution levels, which many scientists believe will occur by 2050.

In a GCM, the Earth's surface is divided into a grid; a larger grid results in a simpler model and a smaller grid requires more calculations. For each grid, a series of equations are solved at the surface of the grid (sea level) and for several layers of the atmosphere and subsurface layers (the vertical dimension). The equations deal with:

- conservation of momentum
- conservation of mass
- conservation of energy
- ideal gas law

Beginning with present-day or known values, the solutions for these equations are solved and repeated at each time step of the simulation, and then the results are interpolated between the grid points to cover the Earth's entire surface. Most models operate at spatial resolutions of a few degrees latitude and longitude and at time steps of less than one hour. The vertical dimension is often divided into 10 layers, with two subsurface layers. Because of these simplifications, GCMs are best used for global or overall climate modelling, not for regional representations of climate change.

Other aspects of the global climate are simplified as well, thus limiting the predictive capabilities of many GCMs. For example, known or present-day values are required to run many models, but in some areas of the world, these values are unavailable or scarce for some variables (temperature, sea-ice cover, cloud cover). Therefore, assumptions are made to fill in the missing values, which may not be accurate. In addition, many complicated feedbacks cannot all be accounted for in GCMs, partly because of their complexity and uncertainty about how they react under given circumstances. While the relationship between greenhouse gas emissions and temperature is a relatively straightforward positive feedback loop (where a positive change in one variable results in a positive change in the other), the relationship between increased temperature and cloud cover relies on many other variables. Finally, many of the climatic interactions at the Earth's surface are difficult to model and are under-represented in many GCMs. For example, ocean layers and interactions are difficult to model, but their effect on regional and global climate can be significant (Chapter 8).

In summary, while GCMs are becoming increasingly sophisticated, many complex aspects and interactions of the global climate need to be understood more fully, and computational facilities need to be better developed.

Limitations of GCMs

While GCMs provide overall indications of future climates, their limitations for policy and planning need to be appreciated. Scientists recognize that the coarse spatial resolution, poor predictive capacity for precipitation, relatively weak simulation of oceans, lack of baseline data, and many other limitations cause GCM outputs to be highly variable. Others caution against the misinterpretation that GCMs are accurate and realistic models of global climate and stress that much more improvement is needed so that GCMs may best represent the complex nature of the Earth's climate.

Scientific Explanations

The IPCC (2014c: 6–8) reported that between 1970 and 2010 total anthropogenic GHG emissions continued to grow, with increases being the highest toward the end of the period. Despite various mitigation policies, annual GHG emissions went up 2.2 per cent annually between 2000 and 2010, in contrast to an annual average increase of 1.3 per cent between

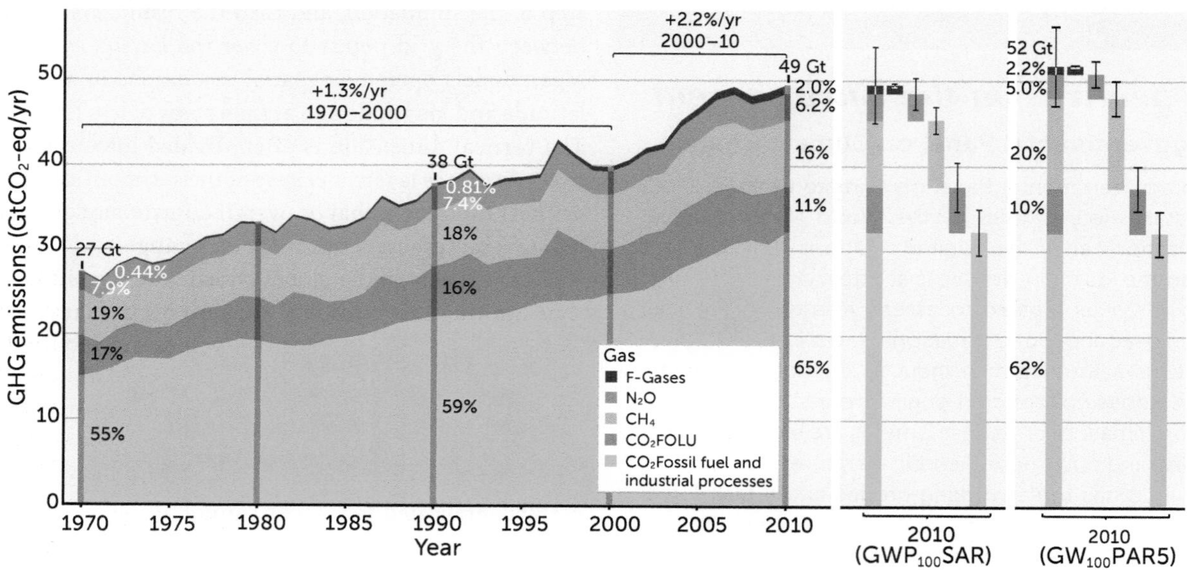

FIGURE 7.3 | Total annual anthropogenic GHG emissions ($GtCO_2eq/yr$) by groups of gases, 1970–2010: CO_2 from fossil fuel combustion and industrial processes; CO_2 from Forestry and Other Land Use (FOLU); methane (CH_4); nitrous oxide (N_2O); fluorinated gases covered under the Kyoto Protocol (F-gases). At the right side of the figure, GHG emissions in 2010 are shown again broken down into these components with the associated uncertainties (90% confidence interval) indicated by the error bars. Total anthropogenic GHG emissions uncertainties are derived from the individual gas estimates. Global CO_2 emissions from fossil-fuel combustion are known within 8% uncertainty (90% confidence interval). CO_2 emissions from FOLU have very large uncertainties attached in the order of 50%. Uncertainty for global emissions of CH_4, N_2O, and the F-gases has been estimated as 20%, 60%, and 20%, respectively. Emissions are converted into CO_2-equivalents based on GWP100 6 from the *IPCC Second Assessment Report*. The emission data from FOLU represents land-based CO_2 emissions from forest fires, peat fires, and peat decay that approximate to net CO_2 flux from FOLU.

Source: IPCC (2014b: 5).

1970 and 2000. The highest increases of emissions in human history occurred between 2000 and 2010, with the global recession in 2007–2008 only slowing them temporarily.

The IPCC (2014c) also stated that, during the period 1970–2010, 78 per cent of total GHG emissions were from combustion of fossil fuels and industrial processes. During this period, CO_2 was the main greenhouse gas, at 76 per cent of the total human-generated GHG gases in 2010. In contrast, methane accounted for 16 per cent; nitrous oxide, 6.2 per cent; and fluorinated gases, 2 per cent (Figure 7.3). The IPCC also noted that approximately half of cumulative CO_2 emissions between 1750 and 2010 happened since 1970.

In terms of drivers, the IPCC (2014b) noted that both population and economic growth have been the most significant contributors of increases in CO_2 emissions due to combustion of fossil fuels. And, it noted that, despite emission reduction measures related to energy intensity, the overall release of CO_2 emissions grew between 2000 and 2010, especially due to increased use of coal relative to other energy resources.

Without new and more effective measures to reduce GHG emissions, the IPCC concluded that emissions will continue to grow. Specifically, baseline scenarios indicate that, absent further mitigation measures, global mean surface temperature will increase between 3.7°C and 4.8°C by 2100. In terms of GHG, baseline scenarios (which reflect no further incremental initiatives to reduce emissions) go beyond 450 parts per million (ppm) CO_2 by 2030 and reach levels between 750 and 1,300 ppm CO_2 by 2100.

Implications of Climate Change

The implications of climate change are potentially widespread and significant. In this section, we briefly outline some of the impacts on different resource-based systems, and you will find complementary discussions in most chapters.

Terrestrial Systems

It is conceivable that within your lifetime, many terrestrial systems, along with the associated fauna and flora, will change dramatically. For example, on the Canadian Prairies, boreal forests may shift anywhere from 100 to 700 kilometres to the

Perspectives on the Environment

Global Reach of Climate Change

In Canada and across the globe, we are already seeing the effects of warming temperatures and changing climate conditions. As climate change persists, we can expect, for example, further melting of glaciers and sea ice, rising sea levels, earlier springs, shifts in the distribution of animals and plants, and increasingly volatile weather. No region and no aspect of our geography will be immune; but impacts will vary in time and intensity.

—NRTEE (2010: O13)

north, to be replaced by grasslands and more southern forest species. In the Arctic, the southern permafrost border could move 500 kilometres northward, and the treeline could move from 200 to 300 kilometres to the north. These shifts are illustrated in Figure 7.4. Boreal forests in particular would also be affected by increases in insect infestation, disease, and fires.

The consequences of change to terrestrial systems could be dramatic. For example, polar bears may no longer remain to breed in Wapusk National Park in Manitoba, yet the park was created in 1996 to protect polar bear habitats. At the other extreme, the hoary marmot in the Rockies and other areas in the Western Cordillera is likely to thrive, since changing climate leads to more avalanches, which will expand its preferred habitat of open meadow. These examples indicate that the rationale for national and provincial parks, created to protect representative ecosystems (Chapter 14), may dramatically change as the distinctive ecosystems currently protected by such parks evolve into something totally different.

Perspectives on the Environment

Implications for Terrestrial Ecosystems

Climate-related shifts in species distributions have already been documented for plants and animals in Canada. In many locations, differential range shifts among species are likely to result in novel ecosystems that have different species assemblages, structural attributes, and ecological functions than existing ones.

For some species, the current and projected rates of environmental change exceed their natural ability to adapt, increasing stress and threatening biodiversity. As a result, climate change is magnifying the importance of managing ecosystems in a manner that enhances resilience and preserves biodiversity.

—Warren and Lemmen (2014b: 4)

Perspectives on the Environment

Implications of Climate Change for Food Production

The net medium-term outlook is for a likely modest increase in agricultural food production. Longer and warmer growing seasons would allow higher-value warmer-weather crops to be grown further north (where soil conditions permit), lengthen outdoor feeding seasons for livestock, and allow the maple syrup industry to expand northward. However, there will likely be new pests and diseases, as well as more severe outbreaks of current ones, and challenges associated with extreme weather events and the reduced predictability of inter-annual weather variability that could negatively affect production.

—Warren and Lemmen (2014b: 3)

Agriculture

One of the major limitations on agricultural activity in most areas of Canada is our cold climate. In southern Canada, the frost-free growing season is about 200 days, and in the Far North the growing season is normally just a few weeks. Furthermore, early frosts or severe winters can damage even dormant vegetation (Chapter 10).

There is not scientific consensus as to whether, on balance, Canada would be one of the countries to benefit from global warming. A positive gain could occur in some regions, since it would extend the growing season and reduce the damage from severe cold or frosts. For example, some scenarios

morrbyte/iStockphoto

Although this rural scene may look bucolic, the rising numbers of cattle worldwide contribute significantly to two of the problems discussed in this book: eutrophication and increased methane levels leading to global climatic change.

Perspectives on the Environment

Climate Change and Environmental Refugees

Future climate change is expected to have considerable impacts on natural resource systems, and it is well established that changes in the natural environment can affect human sustenance and livelihoods. This in turn can lead to instability and conflict, often followed by displacements of people and changes in occupancy and migration patterns. Therefore, as hazards and disruptions associated with climate change grow in this century, so, too, may the likelihood of related population displacements.

—McLeman and Smit (2003: 6)

indicate that by 2050, growing conditions in Whitehorse and Yellowknife would approximate those now found in Edmonton, and that conditions in New Brunswick would become similar to those now experienced in the Niagara Peninsula in Ontario (Hengeveld et al., 2005: 37). On the negative side, however, challenges also may arise. Many plants are vulnerable to heat stress and drought, and if temperatures increased appreciably or water became limited, crops could be adversely affected. Thus, it is difficult to generalize, because, as discussed in Chapter 10, Canada is expected to experience more agricultural losses than gains; but then, as noted in Chapter 8, the opposite will take place in the marine environment. In the next subsection, we look at the effect of climate change on aquatic systems.

Moreover, climate change may have significant effects on food production in other regions of the world, and the first people to be hurt would be the poorest farmers. Such conditions and consequences could lead to significant increases in migration, which could cause regional instability, as well as in international migration. The latter would contribute to growing numbers of "environmental" refugees for whom Canada could be a destination of choice.

Freshwater Systems

Every part of Canada except the southern Prairies has become wetter, with precipitation increasing between 5 per cent and 35 per cent since 1950. At the same time, generally higher temperatures cause higher rates of evapotranspiration. What might be the outcomes? On the west coast of British Columbia, increased cloud cover and more rain can

ENVIRONMENT IN FOCUS

BOX 7.3 | Ozone Depletion

Ultraviolet radiation from the sun causes some oxygen molecules to split apart into free oxygen atoms. These may recombine with other oxygen molecules to form **ozone** (O_3) in the outer layer of the atmosphere, known as the stratosphere. This **ozone layer** helps to filter out ultraviolet (UV) radiation from penetrating to the Earth's surface where it destroys protein and DNA molecules. Without this protective layer, it is doubtful whether life could have evolved on Earth at all.

Although there are natural causes of variation in ozone levels, observations suggest that this layer is being broken down by the emission of various chemicals from the Earth. Since 1979, the amount of stratospheric ozone over the entire globe has fallen by about 4 to 6 per cent per decade in the mid latitudes and by 10 to 12 per cent in higher latitudes. These decreases have led to average increases in exposure to ultraviolet-b (UV-b) of 6.8 per cent per decade at 55°N and 9.9 per cent in the same latitude in the southern hemisphere. In general, penetration of UV-b radiation increases by 2 per cent for every 1 per cent decrease in the ozone layer. UV-b radiation is responsible for various health problems in humans and animals, mainly related to eyes, skin, and immune systems. Human vulnerability to UV-b depends on a person's location (latitude, altitude), duration and timing of outdoor activities, and precautionary behaviour (use of sunscreen, sunglasses, or protective clothing).

Canada hosted an international meeting in 1987 to design a program to eliminate ozone-depleting substances. Despite the targets set by the **Montreal Protocol**, ozone depletion continued to increase. In a follow-up meeting in 2007, also hosted by Canada, more ambitious targets were set, more in accord with the scientific target values (STVs). The new agreement saw developed countries capping production of ozone-depleting hydrochlorofluorocarbons (HCFCs) at 2009–10 levels by 2013, replacing the earlier date of 2016. Agreement was also reached to reduce production by 75 per cent by 2010 and by 90 per cent by 2015. Significantly, developing countries, including India and China, agreed to end production by 2020 rather than by 2030.

In a historic announcement in the autumn of 2014, scientists announced for the first time that the ozone layer was slowly recovering as a result of these steps. The progress is important, not only because of the serious nature of ozone depletion, but also because it illustrates that real progress can be made on complex international issues when the world works together.

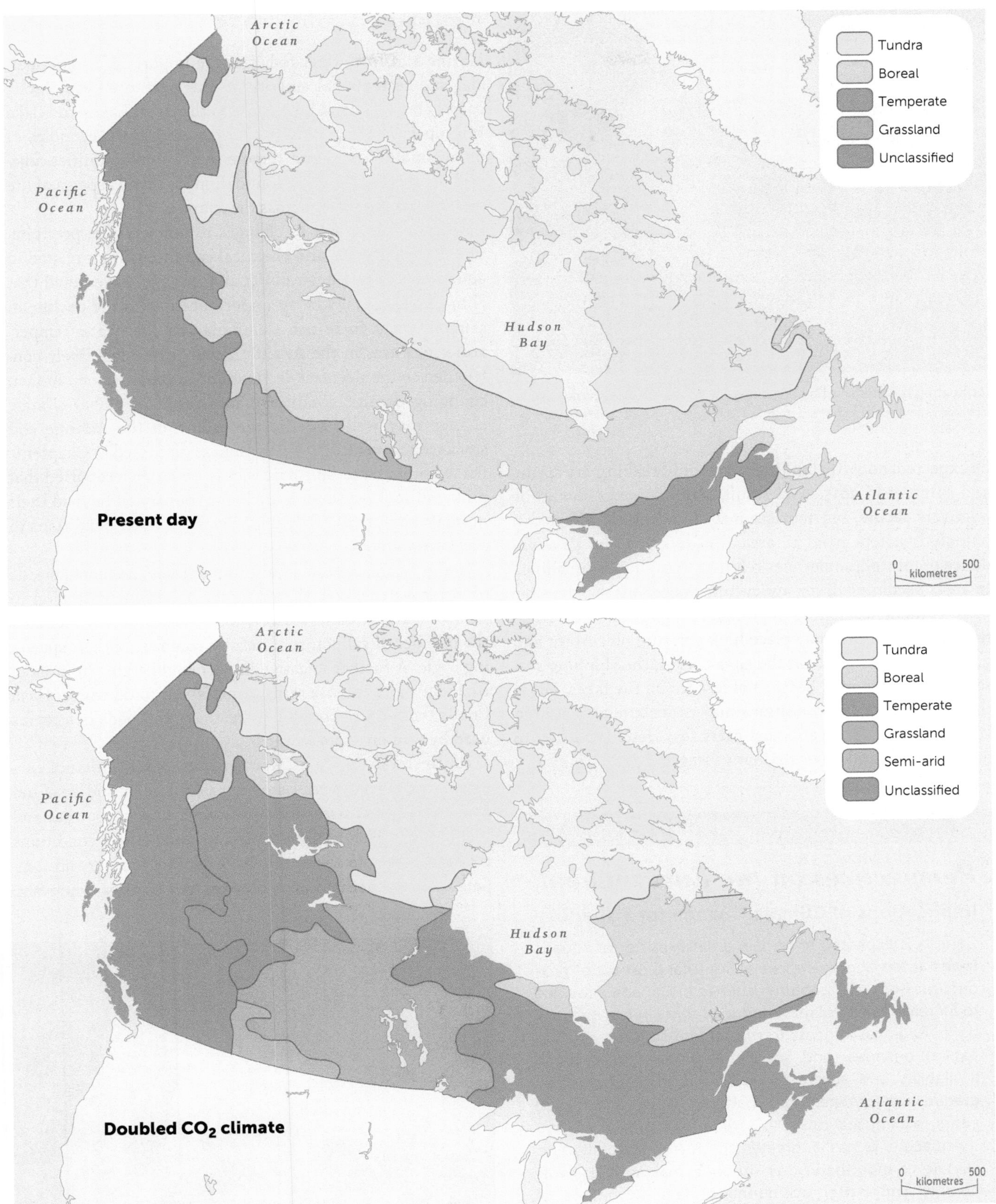

FIGURE 7.4 | Changes in forest and grassland boundaries resulting from a typical doubled CO_2 climate. The montane region of western Canada is "unclassified" because altitude changes result in various terrestrial systems.

Source: Adapted from Hengeveld (1991: 44) and Curran (1991).

Polar bear on the Hudson Bay coast near Wapusk National Park.

be expected, notwithstanding the record-breaking dry spring and summer of 2015. As a result, water supplies should be relatively secure, but tourism may be adversely affected if potential visitors avoid an area already known for its abundance of rainfall, sometimes referred to as "liquid sunshine." In areas becoming dryer, agriculture operations may become more vulnerable, leading to pressure for expansion of irrigation systems, which may place high pressure on surface and groundwater systems. On the Great Lakes, the shipping season may be extended because of less ice on the lakes, but at the same time, drier conditions may contribute to a drop in lake levels so that lakers must carry less freight in order to navigate locks and other shallow passages.

Perspectives on the Environment

Implications of Climate Change for Fisheries

Canada is expected to remain a net exporter of aquatic foods at the aggregate level, with total biomass of production from wild capture fisheries in Canada expected to increase due to climate-induced shifts in fish distributions. Regional impacts from invading species, physical habitat changes, and societal responses to shifts in availability and access to aquatic food resources will gradually determine future patterns of use and overall economic implications.

Aquaculture has a greater scope for adaptation to climate change than other fisheries, making it less vulnerable and better positioned to take advantage of opportunities than capture fisheries, and subsistence fisheries in particular.

—Warren and Lemmen (2014b: 3)

Fisheries

Marine and freshwater fisheries are important for commercial and recreational activity on the west, east, and Arctic coasts and on inland lakes such as the Great Lakes and Lake Winnipeg. The fishery is a key component of the economy of many small coastal and remote interior communities adjacent to lakes and is also a foundation for many aspects of life of indigenous peoples across the country.

Fish are vulnerable to changes in temperature, precipitation, wind patterns, and chemical conditions in or related to aquatic systems. Hengeveld et al. (2005: 39) have noted that climate change may be an important cause of the decline in salmon stocks in British Columbia and that water temperature increases in the Atlantic Ocean have most likely contributed to the decrease in flounder in those waters. In fact, changing oceanic conditions as a result of global climate change may well underlie the failure of the Atlantic cod stocks to recover from overfishing, as discussed in Chapter 8. On the other hand, in Arctic waters it has been reported that pink and sockeye salmon are being found well beyond their normal range, most likely due to warmer water conditions in northern waters.

In the future, if water levels drop or there are more periods of lower water levels, the mortality of spawning salmon in BC rivers and streams is likely to increase, thereby reducing the number of salmon successfully completing their spawning cycle. A further negative impact could result from more frequent short, intense rainstorms, which could trigger flash floods that in turn could damage the gravel beds in streams used by salmon as spawning beds.

For freshwater systems, warmer water would enhance conditions for warm-water fish such as sturgeon and bass but create additional stress for cold-water fish such as trout and lake salmon. Fish better adapted to warm-water conditions could migrate into waters that have become warmer and compete with and perhaps even prey on species already present.

An ice breaker clears ice in the Arctic.

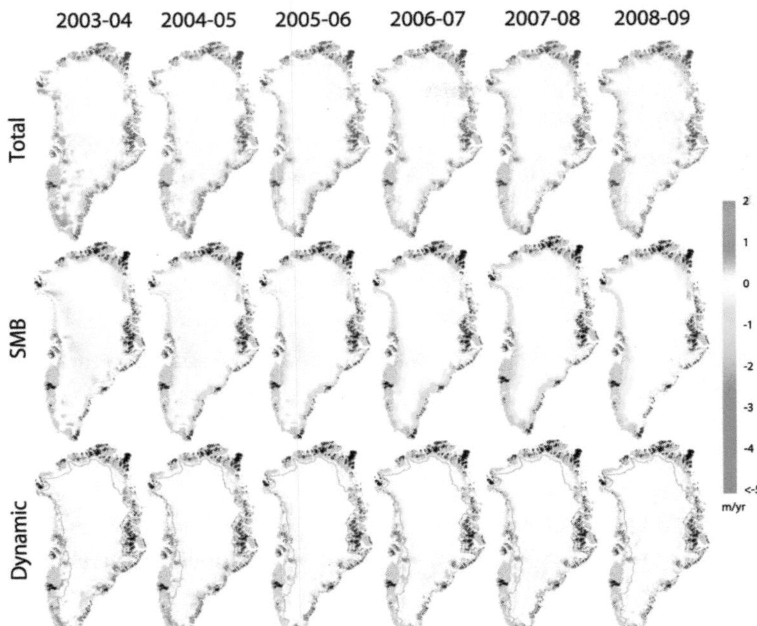

FIGURE 7.5 | Ice loss in the Greenland ice sheet. Annual total, SMB-related, and ice dynamics-related thickness change rates of the GrIS for 2003–2009 balance years from ICESat, ATM, and LVIS laser altimetry observations. Dotted lines on the dynamic thickness change maps mark the ELA (average 2003–2009 SMB = 0). Black regions show weakly or not connected glaciers and ice caps. Balance years start on September 1 and end on August 31 of the following year.
Source: Csatho et al. (2014).

Higher temperatures and increased evapotranspiration could also lower water levels in lakes, and one result would be degradation of shoreline wetlands that provide key habitat for some species of fish. On the positive side, ice cover may be reduced during warmer winters and result in reduced winter mortality of some fish species.

Cryosphere

Warmer temperatures in higher latitudes are expected to cause melting of ice, such as the Greenland ice sheet (Figure 7.5). Csatho et al. (2014) have calculated that between 2003 and 2009, the Greenland ice sheet lost about 243 million tonnes of ice annually.

© Hugh Saxby

Glacial retreat of the Athabasca Glacier, 1992 to 2005.

As ice cover in Arctic latitudes is reduced, various consequences will follow. One of the most obvious is rising sea levels because of the incremental water added to the oceans from melting ice sheets, as well as from glaciers that drain to the ocean via rivers and lakes. Csatho et al. (2014) estimate that the Greenland ice sheet melting between 2003 and 2009 contributed to a 0.68 millimetre annual sea-level rise.

One "positive" outcome of the reduction in Arctic ice cover is that the Northwest Passage has become nearly ice free and therefore readily navigable for about five weeks in the late summer. For some Canadians, however, easier passage raises concerns about Canadian sovereignty in this area, since non-Canadian ships without special ice-breaking capacity can now navigate the passage.

Melting of ice has not been confined to the polar regions. In the Rockies, glaciers less than 100 metres thick could

Perspectives on the Environment

Glaciers Melting

Since the early twentieth century, with few exceptions, glaciers around the world have been retreating at unprecedented rates. Some scientists attribute this massive glacial retreat to the Industrial Revolution, which began around 1760. In fact, several **ice caps**, glaciers, and **ice shelves** have disappeared altogether in this century. Many more are retreating so rapidly that they may vanish within a matter of decades.

—National Snow and Ice Data Center (2014)

disappear by 2030. Such glaciers are relied upon to provide water to the rivers that drain from the eastern slope of the Rockies across the Prairie provinces, causing concern about water security in the mid and long term. However, it is also important to recognize that not everyone agrees that glaciers are receding and that, in some places, glaciers are growing.

Another consequence will be degradation of permafrost in both alpine and high-latitude regions. One result will be changes in the hydrology of aquatic systems in northern regions as well as stability of adjacent land. As Hengeveld et al. (2005: 41) have observed, "decaying permafrost would also destabilize coastal land areas, increasing the risks of landslides and compounding the coastal erosion caused by rising sea levels and reduced ice cover."

As well, reduced ice cover and degradation of permafrost would reduce the expansive and stable frozen surface that northerners count on for winter travelling as well as for hunting and other traditional activities. There also would be a shorter season and lower load capacity for "winter roads" constructed over snow and ice and relied on for the delivery of goods to and from remote communities in Canada's Arctic and Subarctic. Winter roads also are important for transporting equipment, fuel, and other goods to the various mines across northern Canada and in helping to move the resources from these projects to southern markets.

Shrinking sea ice contributes to a decline in polar bear populations (Chapter 3). Furthermore, some communities, such as Arviat in Nunavut, have developed measures to reduce the danger from polar bears coming into the community looking for food while they wait for the delayed freeze-up of sea ice. The Nunavut government and the World Wildlife Fund have provided two large metal shipping containers in which Arviat residents, on western Hudson Bay, can store seal and caribou meat, while smaller metal bins are used to store food for dog teams. And dog teams are encircled by electric fencing.

Ocean and Coastal Systems

Both sea temperatures and sea levels will increase. The IPCC (2014a: 4) concluded that between 1901 and 2010 the global mean sea level increased by 0.19 metres. Furthermore, data indicate that the rate of sea-level rise from the mid nineteenth century onward has been greater than the mean rate of increase over the preceding 2,000 years. The rise in sea levels will affect coastal communities, the severity depending on the nature of the coastline and the amount of increase. However, it is also clear that wave action may change, becoming more severe in areas previously covered by ice for part or most of the year. Wave action on shorelines will contribute to erosion and to changes in wetland complexes, both enhancing and damaging them.

Infectious Diseases

Given the predictions about climate change in North America—warmer temperatures, more rainfall—Health Canada (2007) has indicated that Canadians can expect to experience a greater incidence of disease.

Greer et al. (2008: 716) noted that most people recognize the close association among climate, environment, and infectious disease in developing countries, but this association is not so obvious in nations like Canada where people normally enjoy clean drinking water, lower exposure to insect vectors, and higher-quality housing. All these advantages

ENVIRONMENT IN FOCUS

BOX 7.4 | Sea Ice in the Arctic and Implications for Cruise Tourism

Records show that surface air temperatures are increasing in the Canadian Arctic. The extent of northern hemisphere sea ice has also been decreasing since 1979. One conclusion is that these two patterns should lead to an increase in cruises in Arctic waters, which currently extend from about the end of July until mid-September.

Stewart et al. (2007: 377) observed, however, that the record of sea ice provides "little to no evidence" in support of claims that climate change has affected sea-ice conditions in the Canadian Arctic to the extent that it would allow easier movement of ships through the Northwest Passage. In their words:

> While some increases in open water have been recognized, the navigable areas through the Northwest Passage actually have exhibited increases in hazardous ice conditions; navigation choke points remain and are due primarily to the influx of multi-year ice into the channels of the Northwest Passage. Thus, cruise operators working in the Northwest Passage face considerable uncertainty. In the future, rather than widespread accessibility, as some have claimed, there is likely to be much more variability of ice conditions across this region.

Whether such analysis is optimistic or pessimistic depends on one's point of view, but the fact is that cruise lines have dramatically increased their Arctic business over the past 15 years, including transiting the Northwest Passage—not always successfully. In 2010, one ship ran aground and had to be towed by a Canadian icebreaker to Kugluktuk, Nunavut, from where the adventure tourists were flown south.

reduce the vulnerability of residents. Nevertheless, Greer et al. concluded that predicted climate changes will increase both the incidence and burden of infectious diseases. Examples include:

1. Lyme disease (a tick-borne borreliosis), currently uncommon in Canada, is found mainly in southern Ontario and British Columbia. Temperature is the key factor limiting the northern extent of Lyme disease, and anticipated warmer temperatures may lead to expansion of the tick's range 200 kilometres north by 2020. If this were to occur, Lyme disease could appear in Alberta and Saskatchewan.
2. Other diseases, such as dengue fever, could spread northward as the habitat for mosquitoes expands.
3. Earlier springs will also facilitate expansion of West Nile virus, carried by mosquitoes. The first recorded West Nile virus appeared in Canada in 2002.

Adaptation to Climate Change

Five types of **adaptation** are usually recognized: (1) prevent the loss by adopting protective measures that reduce vulnerability; (2) tolerate the loss by doing nothing and absorbing the cost of losses when they happen; (3) spread or share the loss by distributing the costs over a larger population, such as through insurance; (4) change the affected activity by ceasing to do certain things or by shifting to other activities; and (5) change the location of the activity by moving to a less vulnerable location. These adaptations, except for the option of doing nothing, are discussed in three groups below: protection, accommodation, and retreat.

Protection usually involves structural measures to protect property, buildings, and infrastructure. These measures can involve individual initiatives or major public works projects, such as sea walls, revetments, and groynes designed to trap sediment and to protect coastal areas.

Accommodation usually involves a mix of approaches—redesign of structures to reduce their vulnerability, zoning to guide appropriate land use involving low capital investment in vulnerable areas, and other measures such as rehabilitating coastal dune systems, renewing wetlands, nourishing beaches, and replacing causeways with bridges. However, "stabilizing" natural systems can undermine the natural functioning of ecosystems and can be counterproductive.

Retreat, the third general approach, seeks to avoid vulnerability. It usually involves recognizing the high risk or vulnerability of a place and consciously deciding to relocate buildings, other capital works, or infrastructure away from hazardous places. The initial cost of relocating is normally very high, but in the long term the costs are usually much lower than what would have been spent on rebuilding or repairing properties after each damaging natural event.

A pair of trucks drive the Ice Road in the Northwest Territories. Truckers drive the frozen ice highway on the Mackenzie River in the few months it is safe for use.

Communicating Global Change

In Chapter 6, we identified communication as one of the chief attributes of best practice related to resource and environmental management. Andrey and Mortsch (2000) have highlighted several challenges for communicating information or understanding about global change.

1. *Global change is a complex issue.* The global climate system is enormously complex, mainly because of the many linkages and feedback mechanisms in the atmospheric system. Furthermore, the associated socio-economic system is complex and continuously changing.

   A related complication is that while many people have heard about "global warming" or "global change," the level of in-depth understanding is usually poor. Polls consistently show that many Canadians have a poor understanding of the meaning, causes, or effects of global change. In addition, few see the connections between energy use and deforestation and climate change. Another complication is that the media often provide misleading or incorrect information. In that regard, Hengeveld (2006: 29) identified a particular problem for scientists related to media reporting:

   > Scientists need to challenge journalists on their tendency to seek "balanced reporting" by presenting opposing views of a topic with equal weight, without considering or reporting the credibility or marginality of these views. Such reporting can create a significant bias in communication—a bias that some argue is particularly apparent in high-profile North American media.

   A further complication is that scientists and the general public often do not speak the same language when they talk of global change. As Chalecki (2000: A2, 15) observed, "Scientists often examine small pieces of larger

© AP Photo/Dave Martin/CP

Erosion caused by high surf destroyed this home.

environmental problems in great detail within the limits of their discipline, while most non-scientists have a somewhat fuzzy understanding of the larger issues, often fed by outdated knowledge and half-formed opinions."

2. *Uncertainties exist regarding almost every aspect of the global change issue, and these uncertainties increase when moving from natural to human systems.* There are four main sources of **uncertainty**: (1) statistical randomness, or the variability in nature; (2) lack of scientific understanding of the processes involved; (3) lack of or inadequate data; and (4) imprecision in risk assessment methods because of varying protocols for conducting research. All of these are relevant in global change research. They collectively contribute to uncertainty, which encourages a "wait-and-see" attitude on the part of some policy-makers because they are skeptical about the information and understanding provided by scientists (Fraser Institute, 1999). Ehrlich and Ehrlich (1996) refer to such a view as "brownlash" because the intent is to "minimize the seriousness of environmental problems" and "help to fuel a backlash against 'green' policies."
3. *The impacts of global change will be disproportionately heavier on people in less developed countries and on future generations.* Human-induced climate change impacts will fall mainly on future generations. Furthermore, areas at greatest risk are those with limited fresh water, prone to drought, along coasts, and generally in less developed nations. One consequence is that many people in developed nations, confronted by the various issues and problems in their lifetimes, will give less attention to global change challenges. Most give priority to issues with some immediacy or urgency, and global change does not fall into that category. As Andrey and Mortsch (2000) observe, the consequences of climate change are diffuse rather than concentrated, indirect rather than direct, unintended rather than intended, and affect statistical or anonymous people rather than identifiable individuals.
4. *The basic causes of global change are embedded in current values and lifestyles.* In the developed world, including Canada, relatively high standards of living and materialistic lifestyles depend on extensive use of energy based on **fossil fuels**. Much of this use is devoted to residential heating and cooling and personal transportation by car. It is the cumulative effect of billions of people going about their normal lives that contributes to global warming. Thus, it is easy for any one individual to conclude that a change in his or her lifestyle will make virtually no difference, and the "tragedy of the commons" is played out at a global scale. This creates a dilemma for any individual, city, province, or country, because the scale of the challenge requires unprecedented collaboration (see Chapter 6). In short, individuals believe that they are helpless to make a difference on their own, while for many people, more immediate issues compete for attention and resources.

In his "International Guest Statement," Yong Geng helps us to understand the complexities, uncertainties, and conflicts associated with climate change by explaining some key issues and perspectives from China, an increasingly important player at a global scale related to climate change.

INTERNATIONAL GUEST STATEMENT

Responding to Climate Change: Perspectives from China | *Yong Geng*

Climate change is receiving increasing attention worldwide. Thus, it is critical for you to better understand current progress and challenges regarding climate change. This chapter provides a lot of useful information and insights, mainly from Canadian perspectives. However, different countries are facing different challenges and therefore need custom-designed mitigation measures that reflect their own realities, although sometimes they share similar challenges. Here I would like to present a Chinese perspective so that you can broaden and enhance your knowledge on climate change.

While the largest developing country (both from population and GDP points of view), China has an immature statistics system. For example, the cumulative aggregated Gross Domestic Product (GDP) statistics from all the provinces are always higher than the national GDP statistics released by the National Statistics Bureau, leading to uncertainty about greenhouse gas (GHG) emissions in China since GHG emission intensity does not change dramatically with the current coal-dominated energy system. Thus, even when using the same accounting method, GHG emissions calculated on the basis of the two publicly available official energy data sets differed by 1.4 Gt for 2010—equivalent to the annual GHG emissions of Japan, the world's fourth-largest emitter, with 5 per cent of the global total (Guan et al., 2012). Therefore, more efforts are needed to provide accurate and reliable statistical data about GHG emissions.

Also, China's economic development is unbalanced. While eastern China has achieved significant progress, western China is still struggling with poverty reduction and meeting basic needs. This situation results in different provincial governments giving different priorities to action on climate change. Figure 7.6 presents the evolution of GHG emissions in different Chinese provinces from 1995 to 2008. Regional disparities mean that GHG emission reduction targets must be addressed at the provincial level. However, the provinces' current GHG emission reduction targets are based upon their respective GDP values, and thus wealthier provinces should establish much higher reduction targets, and poorer provinces more modest ones, even if they have larger reduction potentials.

From a sectoral point of view, the issue of China's GHG emissions is also intriguing. Figure 7.7 compares energy consumption embodied in the supply chain for goods and services in 29 sectors with the energy used in the actual production process in each sector (Liu et al., 2012b). Figure 7.7 indicates

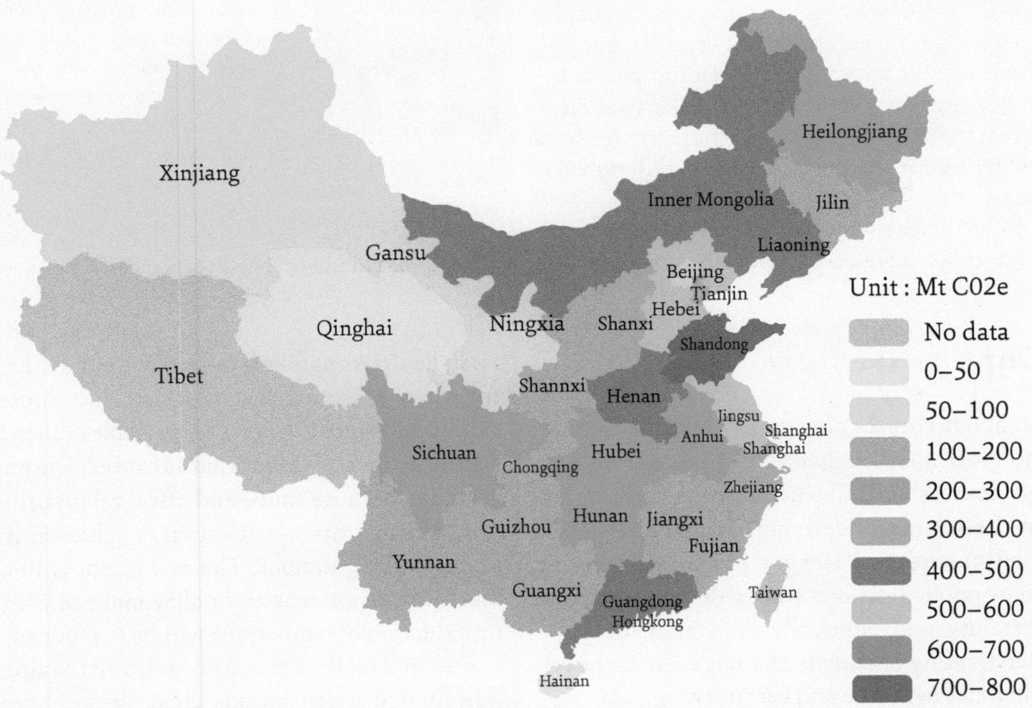

FIGURE 7.6 | Regional disparity of China's GHG emissions.

Source: Liu et al. (2012a).

Continued

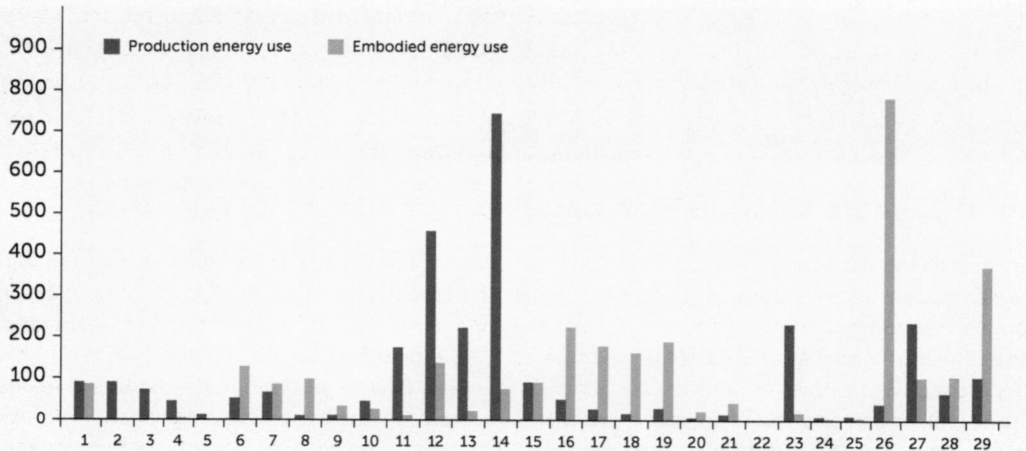

FIGURE 7.7 | Production energy use versus embodied energy consumption for 29 economic sectors, in million tonnes of standard coal equivalent.

Source: Liu et al. (2012b).

that considerable energy use is embodied in the supply chain, especially for "Construction" (sector 26) and "Other Service Activities" (sector 29), which is not apparent if energy use is shown only on a production basis. Therefore, when allocating GHG emission reduction targets to various sectors, both production and consumption perspectives must be considered. Otherwise, energy-intensive sectors (such as iron/steel [sector 14] and cement [sector 12]) will never reach their targets, if the final consumption demand is still soaring (such as in the construction sector). In addition, the above highlights the importance of cooperation among different sectors through various green supply chain initiatives so that the reduction of overall GHG emissions can be achieved, such as through eco-design, green purchasing, customer cooperation with environmental concerns, industrial symbiosis (by-product exchanges among different companies located in the same industrial park), and reverse logistics (the reuse of products and materials for the purpose of recapturing value or proper disposal).

In general, the Chinese experiences provide valuable policy insights for other developing countries and can also enrich the understandings of readers in developed countries. Specifically, climate change is a complex challenge faced by all nations. Although countries may face different difficulties, such as different climatic zones, economic development levels, and culture, as well as imbalanced development, it is crucial for all countries to collaborate to respond to climate change. No country can survive if the whole global ecosystem collapses.

Professor Yong Geng received his doctorate from Dalhousie University and is the Dean of, and Distinguished Professor in, the School of Environmental Science and Engineering at Shanghai Jiao Tong University, China. He was one of the lead authors for the fifth *Assessment Report of the Intergovernmental Panel on Climate Change* (IPCC-AR5), for Chapter 10 (industry) of the third working group. He is also leading several national key research projects on low-carbon development in China, and served as a reviewer for China's white paper "China's Policies and Actions on Climate Change," published in 2011 and for a second white paper "China's Policies and Actions on Extreme Climate," published in 2014.

Climate Change Deniers

Communication about climate change has become increasingly important, given that Hoggan (2009) has shown how **climate change deniers** skilfully use communication tactics to question the science underlying climate change. As Anderegg (2010: 655) observes, "Hoggan provides a sobering perspective of how public relations strategies can be used to propagate uncertainty and politically motivated messages into public understanding of climate change, even as the science itself accumulates evidence and certainty."

Hoggan identifies various approaches or tactics used by climate deniers to highlight serious uncertainty associated with the findings and conclusions of climate change science. First, he draws parallels to tactics used by the tobacco industry when it argued that there was no direct link between cancer and smoking. Various variables other than anthropocentric actions are identified as causes. The purpose is to suggest that, because cause-and-effect relationships are difficult to establish, until clarification is achieved it is inadvisable to develop regulations. The real intent is to create doubt in the minds of citizens and policy-makers, with the result that introduction of regulations will be postponed.

A second tactic is based on "Astroturf campaigns," in which well-funded organizations create what appear to be grassroots criticism of climate change science. The reality is that the campaigns are facilitated by organizations with a vested interest, such as the fossil-fuel industry. The intent is to raise uncertainty about whether climate change is occurring. A key element in this tactic is use of "experts" who state that they disagree with or challenge the science supporting climate change. The intent is to create doubt in the minds of the public. The media are often complicit in disseminating such views, given their commitment to "balanced" reporting. As a result, the media usually provide comments from supportive and dissenting scientists, but rarely provide independent assessment about the proportion of researchers supporting or opposing the science underlying climate change. Nor do they often assess the qualifications of the spokespeople.

Third, a close cousin of the Astroturf campaigns is the tactic of assembling results of surveys of researchers critical of climate change science. Again, the dissenting commentators often are not scientists actively involved in climate change research, and the target audience of the survey results is not other scientists. Instead, the target is the general public and policy-makers, and the latter are often not scientists. As Hoggan observed, the ultimate goal is to convince both the general public and policy-makers that because there is much uncertainty and confusion associated with climate change science, the best course would be to wait. Thus, the climate "deniers" become climate "delayers."

Given the arguments presented above, what should you do when you hear someone arguing that the science underlying climate change does not provide a solid basis to develop actions? We suggest you ask yourself the following questions posed by Hoggan (2009: 231):

- Does the "expert" have relevant credentials? That is, does he or she have a credible academic background?
- Is the "expert" actively engaged in scientific research related to climate change? And, if so, is he or she publishing regularly in peer-reviewed journals? Or, are their written statements found only in "op-ed" commentaries or letters to the editor in newspapers or magazines?
- Is the "expert" being paid by groups with a direct interest in climate change research and policies, such as petroleum companies or associations, or is the person affiliated with a think-tank with an ideology opposing government being involved in solutions to challenges created by climate change?

Notable Climate Denier Events

Two examples highlight how deniers or skeptics create doubt and uncertainty about the science associated with climate change.

One example relates to the reports from the IPCC in 2007, already referenced in this chapter. The thousands of pages in the multi-volume report made it likely, notwithstanding a peer-review process, that some errors would be included. And, indeed, that happened. Particular attention was drawn to a statement that glaciers in the Himalayas were likely to disappear by 2035. It was acknowledged later by those responsible for the report that the statement about the Himalayan glaciers was an error. However, that acknowledgement did not stop citation of this error time and time again across the Internet and in many other media, with no comparable acknowledgement that in nearly all parts of the world there were significant reductions in the extent and magnitude of glaciers. The main message from the deniers was simple: given such an error, why should other conclusions in the IPCC reports be trusted? On the other hand, other statements in the IPCC reports, which could be claimed to be underestimates or understatements of the rate of change of climatic conditions, never received commentary.

Another example was the leaking of e-mail messages and other documents from scientists at the University of East Anglia Climatic Research Unit during November 2009. Comments in those messages that appeared to indicate the scientists were actively trying to suppress evidence contradicting results of their research were emphasized. The release of this information, a few weeks before the United Nations–sponsored climate change summit in Copenhagen during December 2009 (discussed later in this chapter), was viewed by some as a deliberate act to undermine the Copenhagen meetings. Indeed, some commentators remarked that the release of the e-mails from the research institute helped to energize the climate change skeptics and also contributed to destabilizing the summit.

The ensuing controversy became known as "**Climategate.**" It led to the head of the research institute being placed on temporary leave and four reviews being conducted. The final review report, published in July 2010 and authored by Sir Muir Russell, a former civil servant, concluded there was no evidence of dishonesty or corruption by the scientists. However, he commented that the scientists in the institute should have done a better job in sharing their data with critics of their work.

What is your view about the position and tactics of the climate deniers and skeptics? What are your conclusions about how communication can and should be used to help people understand that uncertainty is a core element of science? How can we move forward, when we will rarely have complete understanding of the natural and human environments and the ways in which they interact?

Kyoto Protocol

During December 1997, representatives from more than 160 countries met in Kyoto, Japan. The outcome was an agreement, referred to as the **Kyoto Protocol**, with targets for 38 developed nations as well as the European Community to ensure that

> their aggregate anthropocentric carbon dioxide equivalent emissions of the greenhouse gases [e.g.,

> carbon dioxide (CO_2), methane (CH_4), nitrous oxide (N_2O), hydrofluorocarbons (HFCs), perfluorocarbons (PFCs), sulphur hexafluoride (SF_6)] . . . do not exceed their assigned amounts . . . with a view to reducing their overall emissions of such gases by at least 5 per cent below 1990 levels in the commitment period 2008 to 2012. (Kyoto Protocol, 1997: Article 3)

The Protocol would become legally binding when ratified by at least 55 countries accounting for at least 55 per cent of the developed world's 1990 emissions of carbon dioxide. Table 7.1 shows the targets for selected countries. Developing countries, including China and India, were not included in the targets because their per capita emissions were much lower than those of developed countries. Another reason was that their economies were judged to be much less able to absorb the costs of changing to cleaner fuels, since the main source of greenhouse gas emissions is carbon dioxide from use of fossil fuels.

Canada was to reduce greenhouse emissions to 6 per cent below 1990 levels by between 2008 and 2012. Canada ratified the Protocol in December 2002. However, at the end of March 2001, shortly after taking office, US President George W. Bush stated that he opposed the Kyoto agreement, the US would not agree to it, and the US would develop its own approach. He argued that it was inappropriate for China and India, countries with the largest populations, not to be included in the Kyoto targets. Bush was correct that these two countries have the largest populations, but he ignored the fact that their per capita emissions of greenhouse gases are much lower than those of the United States, which has the worst record. With only 4 to 5 per cent of the world's population, the US accounted for about 25 per cent of the global emissions of greenhouse gases.

TORU YAMANAKA/AFP/Getty Images

Delegates from more than 160 countries at the conference in Kyoto, Japan, which led to the Kyoto Protocol, December 1997.

TABLE 7.1 | Greenhouse Gas Emission Reduction Targets by 2012 under the Kyoto Protocol for Selected Countries

Country	Reduction Commitment as Percentage of Base Year (1990)
Australia	108
Canada	94
France	92
Germany	92
Japan	94
Netherlands	92
New Zealand	100
Norway	101
Russian Federation	100
Sweden	92
United Kingdom	92
United States	93

Source: Kyoto Protocol (1997: Annex B).

Bush explained in February 2002 that the US would use a "voluntary approach" related to greenhouse gas emissions, with the purpose of reducing "greenhouse gas intensity" by 18 per cent over 10 years, a general approach later endorsed by Canadian Prime Minister Stephen Harper. Greenhouse gas intensity is the ratio of greenhouse gas emissions to economic output. Unlike the Kyoto Protocol, which requires an absolute reduction in greenhouse gas emissions, the American approach would result in emissions continuing to increase as its economy grows but at a slower rate than without this arrangement.

The Bush approach was based on determination to protect the US economy in the short term, ensure that jobs were not lost because of the costs associated with reducing emissions, and maintain its international economic competitiveness. Because the US is such a dominant player in the global economy, its position has been cited by people in other countries, including Prime Minister Harper in Canada, who believe it would be economically foolish to accept the Kyoto Protocol targets when the nation with the largest economy had decided not to do so.

Against this background, we now turn to some of the specific aspects of the Protocol and then to Canada's approach.

Specific Features of the Kyoto Protocol

Legal Basis

Unlike the Framework Convention on Climate Change signed at the Earth Summit in Rio de Janeiro in 1992, which committed countries only to "aim" to stabilize emissions at 1990 levels by 2000, the Kyoto Protocol commitments are legally binding on nations under international law.

Assigned Amounts

For the period 2008–12, the Protocol states that overall average emissions were to be 94.8 per cent relative to 1990 levels. "Assigned amounts" were identified for each developed nation (Table 7.1). While the targets were set for allowed emissions with reference to population, gross national product, and carbon intensity of economies, the final targets were determined politically.

Greenhouse Gases

The Protocol identified six greenhouse gases. Three were viewed as the main greenhouse gases produced by human activity: carbon dioxide, nitrous oxide, and methane. The other three—hydrofluorocarbons, perfluorocarbons, and sulphur hexafluoride—are released in small quantities but are long-lasting and significant contributors to climatic change.

Exclusion of Most Forest and Soil Sinks

The assigned emission amounts for most nations were a percentage of gross emissions in 1990. Gross emissions are the anthropocentric (human-caused) greenhouse gas emissions from energy, industrial processes, agriculture, and waste. However, they do not include carbon fluxes from forests, soil, and other carbon reservoirs.

When a nation calculated whether it was complying with its target emissions, it had to count emissions and carbon flux changes due to afforestation, reforestation, and deforestation since 1990. In Canada, the view of the federal government after signing the Protocol was that it could interpret the Protocol to include loss of carbon from agricultural soil in calculating the balance between emissions and carbon flux removal. Indeed, the target for Australia of 108 per cent of 1990 emissions was partly based on arguments that it had positive net emissions related to land-use change and forestry in 1990.

Because of methodological challenges in measuring emissions from land-use change and forestry, some observers were concerned that countries would use forest and soil sinks to claim credits that are difficult to verify. There were also problems in reaching agreement about the meaning of key terms such as reforestation, afforestation, and deforestation.

At a conference in Milan during December 2003, the signatories to the Kyoto Protocol agreed on how industrialized countries could earn credit toward their emission targets by preserving or establishing forests.

Clean Development Mechanism

Emission reduction commitments could be fulfilled through a clean development mechanism, allowing **emission credits** in countries not given targets through the Protocol to be used by countries included in the Protocol targets. Initiatives are certified as satisfying the clean development mechanism when they involve voluntary participation by each party; real, measurable, and long-term benefits for **mitigation** of climate change; and emission reductions in addition to those that would have occurred without the initiative.

The major concern about the clean development mechanism is that emission credit may be given for projects that would have occurred without such a mechanism in place.

Emissions Trading

Under the Protocol, a country could meet its emission commitments by acquiring from other countries "emission reduction units" when the selling country creates initiatives that allow it to reduce emissions or enhance sinks beyond its own targets. When a nation buys some emission reduction units, they are added to its allowable emissions and subtracted from the allowable emissions of the selling country.

However, because developing countries were not given emission targets under the Protocol, in order to allow them to develop their economies, they cannot sell emission credits to developed countries, even when such sales could benefit them economically. Developing countries also cannot agree to voluntary emission targets, which could benefit some if they could introduce low-cost emission reductions and then sell emission credits.

The theory of **emissions trading** is based on the belief that it is more efficient for one country to purchase emission credits from another country that can generate credits in a less costly manner.

Canada's Initial Approach to Implementing the Kyoto Protocol

On 10 December 2002, the House of Commons voted 195 to 77 to ratify the Kyoto Protocol. The Liberal majority led those supporting the motion, while the Canadian Alliance and Progressive Conservative parties opposed it. Through this vote, Canada committed itself to cut average greenhouse gas emission levels to 6 per cent below 1990 levels by 2008–12. Prime Minister Jean Chrétien signed Canada onto the Kyoto Protocol on 16 December 2002.

Canada ratified the Kyoto Protocol without a clear plan on how it would be implemented. The prime minister argued that details would be worked out. In contrast, Stephen Harper, leader of the Canadian Alliance, argued that it was inappropriate to ratify the Protocol without providing a clear plan as to how it would be achieved. His view was that its implementation would turn into a great disaster for Canada and Canadians.

The federal government allocated $2 billion in its 2003 budget for Kyoto Protocol initiatives over a five-year period. One specific initiative, the creation of Sustainable

Development Technology Canada, was identified. This arm's-length foundation was to receive $250 million to support new technologies not yet commercially viable. The remaining $1.75 billion was to be allocated to other initiatives once the details were worked out, with the money "to support climate change science, environmental technology, and cost-effective climate change measures and partnerships in areas such as renewable energy, energy efficiency, sustainable transportation, and new alternative fuels."

The components of a plan for implementing the Kyoto Protocol included requiring major industrial emitters to reduce their greenhouse gas emissions, levying taxes on private vehicles such as sport-utility vehicles, setting minimum requirements for fuel alcohol, providing subsidies to install energy-efficient windows, and establishing an emissions trading framework.

The federal government compiled a list of large industrial emitters of greenhouse gases, such as oil and gas, mining, and pulp and paper companies, each of which generates large amounts of carbon dioxide per unit of product. Each industry was to be required to reduce emissions extensively.

"Accomplishments" in Reducing GHG Emissions in Canada

In the early fall of 2004, the federal deputy minister of Natural Resources, speaking at a conference in Australia, stated for the first time that Canada would not meet its commitments under Kyoto and would be unlikely to realize even two-thirds of the reductions of GHGs that Canada had committed to achieve under Kyoto. Indeed, by December 2004, data indicated that emissions of GHGs in Canada had increased by 20 per cent relative to the base year of 1990.

CT757fan/iStockphoto

The role of the oceans in helping to mitigate the impacts of global warming through absorption of carbon dioxide is still uncertain, as is the oceanic response to warmer temperatures. Scientists are already detecting larger wave swells in many parts of the world that may be linked to these changes.

A Change of Federal Government and a Change of Course

In January 2006, a federal election led to a minority Conservative government (after the merger of the Progressive Conservatives and the Canadian Alliance). As leader of the opposition, Stephen Harper, the new prime minister, had consistently opposed the Kyoto Protocol, arguing that it would hurt economic growth in Canada. In addition, Harper had frequently expressed doubt about the credibility of climate change science.

Once in office, Harper indicated that Canada's Kyoto commitment was unrealistic and unachievable. He also noted that if Canada were to remain economically competitive with its largest trading partner, the United States, it would be unwise to reduce GHG emissions unless and until the US had also accepted a binding target to reduce GHGs. Furthermore, he argued that it was not reasonable that countries such as China and India were not included in the agreement with binding targets.

In 2007, Prime Minister Harper attended an APEC (Asia Pacific Economic Cooperation) summit of 21 Pacific Rim countries in Australia. The main outcome was a joint statement endorsing a long-term but unspecific target to cut GHG emissions by all participants, including the US and China. This unspecified non-binding target was characterized as an **aspirational approach**. In other words, there was no legal obligation to meet the target. This was the first time that the United States and China had reached a climate change agreement. In addition, other developing countries had agreed to participate, something not required under the Kyoto Agreement. Harper was reported as having said at the summit, "Kyoto divided the world into two groups, those that would have no targets and those that would reach no targets. The reality is that the world is now making efforts toward a new protocol post-2012." He acknowledged that much more work needed to be done but that having China and the United States "on board" was a noteworthy accomplishment.

UN-Sponsored Climate Change Conferences

UN-sponsored climate change conferences have been an annual event, starting with the first one during 1995 in Berlin, and the third in 1997 at Kyoto when the Kyoto Protocol was developed. In this section, we review selected conferences, starting with the one in Bali during December 2007, with particular attention to the positions taken by Canada.

Bali

In Bali, Indonesia, 192 countries were represented at the fourteenth annual climate change conference, which extended over two weeks. The purpose was to start a process for creating a new framework to replace the Kyoto Protocol when it expired in 2012. At the conference, UN Secretary-General Ban Ki-moon remarked that "The situation is so desperately serious that any delay could push us past the tipping point, beyond which the ecological, financial, and human costs would increase dramatically." And, as noted earlier in this chapter, global attention to climate change had increased after the 2007 Nobel Peace Prize had been jointly awarded in October to former US Vice-President Al Gore for his climate change activism, and to the UN IPCC in recognition of the significance of their work and the seriousness of climate change for worldwide stability and peace.

Throughout the Bali Conference, federal government representatives from Canada and the United States argued that GHG reduction commitments should be required for all countries but that numerical targets should not be specified. At the last moment during negotiations, the US government shifted its position regarding explicit targets after a delegate from Papua New Guinea directed the following remark at the US representatives: "We seek your leadership. But if for some reason you are not willing to lead, leave it to the rest of us. Please get out of the way."

At the conference, Canada was labelled as a "climate hypocrite" by Yvo de Boer, the head of the UN climate change agency, because Canada called for binding targets on developing countries but had refused to accept them for itself under Kyoto. Rajendra Pachauri, the head of the IPCC, suggested that Canada's position made it clear that the Canadian government was not prepared to take significant action on climate change. During the conference, Canada received numerous "Fossil of the Day" awards created by non-government organizations.

Canada also lobbied to change the base year of 1990 established for the Kyoto Protocol. The base year of 1990 had been the international benchmark since the Kyoto Protocol was created in 1997, and any decision to move that date forward would reward nations that had been slow in curbing GHG emissions. In that regard, the Conservative government's approach to the baseline year had been to refer not to 1990 but to 2006, the year when the Conservatives were elected to power.

The outcome at Bali was mixed. The participating nations agreed to continue meeting to determine what to do about climate change and in particular how to reduce GHG emissions.

Post-Bali

The sixteenth annual climate change conference, in Denmark, occurred over two weeks in 2009, and what became known as the **Copenhagen Summit** has been viewed as either a total failure or a modest success. Those viewing it as a failure believed giant strides forward had been essential and noted that (1) the 192 countries represented at the conference were unable to develop a new legally binding agreement to replace the Kyoto Protocol; (2) no firm national targets for GHG emissions were included in the declaration (the Copenhagen Accord), and instead nations agreed to set their own emission reduction targets; (3) no deadlines were specified for future action; and (4) there was a deep divide between developed and developing countries, with developed nations not prepared to take actions to reduce GHGs unless developing countries did the same, and developing countries unwilling to curtail GHG emissions if that would dampen economic growth needed to overcome huge poverty problems.

Those who concluded the conference was a success stressed that expectations for a legally binding treaty were unrealistic, and that "baby steps" forward represented a positive outcome. Specific achievements included: (1) an agreement between both developed and developing nations that GHGs need to be limited and that global temperatures need to be stopped from rising by more than 2°C; (2) the first time major developing countries such as China, India, and Brazil agreed

Greg Perry

One view of the interaction between government and science.

© AP Photo/Binsar Bakkara/CP

Environmentalists dressed as polar bears demonstrate in front of the conference centre where the negotiations for a post-Kyoto agreement took place during the UN Climate Conference in Nusa Dua, Bali, Indonesia, in December 2007.

Perspectives on the Environment

An Asymmetrical Climate Deal at Copenhagen

The reason no deal was possible is that public opinion in the developed countries is still in denial about the fact the final climate deal must be asymmetrical. Until the general public grasps that, especially in the United States, there will be no real progress.

. . . The developed countries must cut their emissions deeply and fast, and give the developing countries enough money to cover the extra cost of growing their economies with the clear sources of energy that they must use instead of fossil fuels. That's the deal, but most voters in the United States don't understand it yet.

—Dyer (2009: A11)

their GHGs needed to be curtailed; and (3) establishment of a Copenhagen Green Climate Fund, with the intent to have primarily developed nations contribute $100 billion (US) by 2020 to help developing nations cut carbon emissions, and developing countries agreeing to make their records open for international scrutiny regarding emissions plans.

At the conclusion of the Copenhagen Summit, Prime Minister Harper stated that the agreement reached was "comprehensive and realistic" and thus was supported by Canada. In contrast, media commentators suggested that the Copenhagen Summit had been a "public relations nightmare" for Canada. At the very popular and public Fossil of the Day award ceremonies each day at the summit, Canada was invited to accept the award, on its own or as part of a group of countries, 10 times, more than any other nation. In conferring the award on Canada, its presenters stated that Canada's target for reducing GHG emissions was among the worst in the industrialized world, and its plan was so weak that even its modest targets were unlikely to be achieved. Canada also was criticized by developing nations and environmentalists for refusing to make concessions to help reach an agreement and thereby lost its traditional role as a progressive player on the global stage. It should be observed that some believe Canada's loss of a leadership role began well before Copenhagen. The level of commitment, or not, to the summit of the Canadian government was suggested by some to have been demonstrated when the prime minister attended a dinner hosted by the Queen of Denmark on the evening when Canada made its official presentation.

The minister of Environment, Jim Prentice, argued in a three-and-a-half minute speech that the Kyoto Protocol needed to be replaced, that all major emitters had to be signatories to any agreement, and that Canada's climate change strategy reflected the reality that Canada had a large and diverse land mass and its energy sector was important for meeting global demand. Prentice also noted that Canada's approach reflected its strong economic ties with the United States, requiring Canada to align its approach to that of the US, and that Canada would contribute to the proposed climate-aid fund, but he would not speculate on what amount Canada would provide.

In December 2010, the **Cancún Summit** followed one year after the Copenhagen Summit, with 193 nations represented. As at Copenhagen, some modest gains were achieved, but major issues were left unresolved. In terms of positive outcomes, the Cancún agreements included: (1) a general framework to assist developing nations in reducing their carbon output and dealing with negative effects of climate change; (2) commitment by developed countries to provide US$30 billion to support climate action in the developing world up to 2012, with the intent to raise $100 billion by 2020; (3) technology transfer from developed countries to developing countries to enhance adaptation and mitigation; and (4) endorsement of a system to compensate developing nations for not cutting down trees in rain forests. Furthermore, there appeared to be willingness to examine **geo-engineering** initiatives as one option to complement other mitigation strategies.

However, various major issues were not resolved. Specifically, delegates at the conference postponed determining how developed and developing nations would work collaboratively to significantly reduce GHG emissions over the next 10 to 15 years. Thus, no progress was made at either Copenhagen or Cancún on this issue. In addition, the specific contributions developed nations would make to the Green Climate Fund were never clarified, nor was it determined whether the Kyoto Protocol would be extended after 2012 if a new agreement was not reached.

© AP Photo/Anja Niedringhaus/CP

A journalist reads a draft of the Copenhagen Accord at the December 2009 climate conference in Copenhagen, Denmark. Some feel the conference was a total failure while others argue that the talks inched participating countries closer to action.

At Cancún, the Canadian government maintained its positions from Copenhagen. During the conference, the NGO Germanwatch released survey results based on views of 190 climate experts regarding efforts by nations to address climate change. The survey considered actual measurements of each country's GHG emissions, whether they had been increasing or decreasing, and their national policies. Of the 57 countries identified in the survey, Canada was ranked fifty-fourth, ahead of only Australia, Kazakhstan, and Saudi Arabia. Canada placed last among the top 10 carbon dioxide emitters and second-last among developed nations. The United States was ranked fifty-first, while the countries ranked best overall were Brazil, Sweden, and Norway, in that order.

Subsequent conferences sponsored through the United Nations Framework Convention on Climate Change were held in Durban, South Africa (2011), Doha, Qatar (2012), Warsaw, Poland (2013), and Lima, Peru (2014). Here, we focus on the meeting at Lima in December 2014, as well as another significant initiative just before it.

In mid November 2014, a few weeks before the twentieth UN climate change conference in Peru, the United States and China signed what was characterized as a groundbreaking agreement. Announced by US President Barack Obama and Chinese President Xi Jinping, in Beijing, China, the agreement stipulates that the US will reduce its CO_2 emissions by between 26 and 28 per cent by 2025 relative to 2005 levels. The previous target for the US, which it is on track to achieve, was to reduce emissions by 17 per cent by 2020. For China, the commitment is to have its CO_2 emissions peak by 2030 and then decline. While the Chinese would therefore continue increasing GHG emissions for 16 more years, this was the first time it had agreed to a schedule to begin reducing GHG emissions. These two major nations hoped their agreement would help to bridge the wide gulf between developed and developing countries at future climate change conferences.

At the same time, some aspects of the agreement are not clear. For example, neither nation indicated how it would meet the new goals. Furthermore, it was not explained if China's continued growth in emissions might negate reductions achieved by the US. And, not surprisingly, Republicans in the US Congress expressed concern and opposition to the agreement, claiming it would reduce jobs and damage the US economy.

For Canada, the agreement between the US and China created pressure, given the prime minister's ongoing insistence that Canada needs to work in concert with the US, due to the tight interconnections between the two economies. This argument served the Conservative government well when President Bush argued that the US would not subscribe to the Kyoto Protocol, because it could undermine the American economy. That argument aligned with the values of the federal Conservative government, but the new agreement between the US and China altered the context.

Two weeks after the agreement was announced by China and the US, the twentieth annual climate conference began in Lima, Peru, attended by representatives of 192 nations. It was anticipated this conference would create the necessary conditions and agreements to achieve a new accord to replace the 1997 Kyoto Protocol at the twenty-first annual climate conference to occur during December 2015 in Paris, France.

In mid December 2014, after extended negotiations, a climate change agreement, labelled as the Lima Accord, was announced (UN, 2014a). It was described as the first international agreement that committed every nation to reduce its rate of GHG emissions. Specifically, under the agreement, every nation was required to prepare and forward, by 31 March 2015, details regarding its domestic policy to limit GHG emissions as a result of burning coal, gas, and oil. Such plans, referred to as "Intended Nationally Determined Contributions," or INDCs and to be publicly available on a UN website, would become the basis for the anticipated accord or protocol to be developed in Paris in December 2015, and implemented no later than 2020.

However, the Lima Accord contains few obligations for nations to put forward details of their plans. In addition, there is no requirement for each plan to be reviewed and compared. The accord states that nations "may include" information regarding choice of base year and annual targets for GHG reductions, time frames and/or periods for implementation, scope and coverage, and planning processes (UN, 2014a: 3, point 14). An earlier draft had specified that each nation "shall provide" such specifics.

This agreement was considered historic because agreements at previous climate change conferences always were stymied by the terms of the Kyoto Protocol that required developed nations to reduce GHG emissions, but with no comparable action from developing nations, including China and India, two of the largest generators of GHGs. At Lima, delegates from India continued to argue that developing countries should be treated differently, but that view did not prevail. The relevant wording in the Lima Accord is "common but differentiated responsibilities and respective capabilities, in light of different national circumstances" (UN, 2014a: 2, no. 3). Thus, the US and China agreement two weeks earlier is viewed as highly significant. However, the value of the Lima Accord will ultimately depend on how rigorously national governments work to develop their domestic policies and related regulations.

Also, the Lima Accord included agreement for donations from developed countries to a $10 billion Green Climate Fund, to help developing nations both reduce their GHG emissions and adapt to climate change. In addition, the accord recognized developing countries' vulnerability to "loss and damage" in extreme weather events, and included the opportunity to access funds for post-disaster recovery.

At the Lima conference, Canada was represented by Leona Aglukkaq, minister of Environment. In her statement to the conference, she stated that Canada accounts for less than 2 per cent of GHG emissions and has one of the cleanest electricity systems in the world, with 80 per cent of its electricity coming from sources with zero GHG emissions (Government of Canada, 2014a). She called Canada a "clean energy leader," and stated that Canada was continuing to move ahead with a "balanced sector-by-sector regulatory approach to reduce greenhouse gas emissions." She noted that Canada already had taken "decisive action" to regulate both the transportation and electricity sectors, and its actions to reduce emissions from coal had "positioned Canada as a world leader in this regard." She also said that Canada had aligned its transport regulations with those in the US, and supports "a North American approach to the oil-and-gas sector." Finally, she commented that Canada's record spoke for itself, and that Canada had demonstrated that "it is possible to protect the environment while supporting economic growth." As evidence, she observed that in 2012 the per capita emissions in 2012 were 5.1 per cent lower than levels in 2005, even though the economy had grown by 10.6 per cent in the same time period.

Not everyone was as positive about Canada's role related to climate change. In the *Montreal Gazette*, Leehi Yona (2014) wrote, "Our government is backing out of commitments, blocking binding agreements and promoting tarsands expansion as if its extraction and burning didn't have potentially horrible human-rights implications, in addition to environmental ones"; and, furthermore, "When we once were leaders in multilateral diplomacy, Canada currently is referred to as a rogue country at the climate change negotiations, likened to a poor team player who refuses to play by the rules." She continued, "In fact, we are only surpassed by Australia at this point for the worst climate record worldwide." Yona was a youth delegate at the Lima conference, and had been named Canada's Top Environmentalist Under 25 in 2013.

Others would support the above assessment, noting that at the Bali Conference in 2007 Canada received the Colossal Fossil Award as the country making the least constructive contribution to negotiations, and at the 2010 Cancún conference received three Fossil of the Day awards on the opening day (first, second, and third place), thus "sweeping" the awards. Those awards were determined by over 400 leading international organizations voting for countries viewed to be doing the most to disrupt or undermine UN climate change discussions. And, at the Warsaw conference in 2013, Canada won a Lifetime Unachievement Fossil Award on the last day of the meeting, with the explanation it had been earned through a long-standing failure to make meaningful contributions at these meetings; rather, Canada consistently was viewed to have blocked and stalled progress. At the Warsaw meetings, Christian Holz, Executive Director of Climate Action Network Canada, observed that "Canada's record is indeed one of continued failure on climate. Having abandoned its Kyoto target a long time ago, it holds the questionable distinction to be the only country in the world to withdraw from the Protocol" (Climate Action Network Canada, 2013).

Subsequently, in 2014, Germanwatch and the Climate Action Network Europe listed Canada among the world's worst countries regarding CO_2 emissions in its "Climate Change Performance Index" (Burck, Marten, and Bals, 2014). Of 61 countries ranked, Canada was fifty-eighth, immediately below Russia and Australia and above only Iran, Kazakhstan, and Saudi Arabia.

Finally, other international leaders have urged Canada to be more proactive on climate change. For instance, when French President François Hollande visited Ottawa in early November 2014, he urged Canada to do more to help the global community achieve a major international agreement well before the climate change conference scheduled for Paris in December 2015. He pointed out that the European Union had committed to reduce GHG emissions by 40 per cent by 2030 relative to levels in 1990. And in early December 2014, Ban Ki-moon, Secretary-General of the United Nations, called on Canada to become more "ambitious and visionary" in dealing with climate change. Ban observed that various oil-producing countries, such as Saudi Arabia, were moving away from reliance on fossil fuels and called on Canada to move in the same direction in making some "transformative changes." The month before those remarks, Ban had called on G20 nations at their annual summit meeting in Australia to make climate change a priority in their discussions.

Perspectives on the Environment

Assessment of Canada's Record for GHG Emissions

Canada ranks 15th out of 17 peer countries and scores a "C" grade on its environmental performance report card. Canada's poor record in several areas—including climate change, energy intensity, smog, and waste generation—drags down its comparative performance. Only Australia and the U.S. rank below Canada. [The top three ranked countries are France, Norway, and Sweden].

Canada, one of the world's largest GHG emitters, earns a "D" for its GHG emissions per capita. In 2010, Canada's GHG emissions were 20.3 tonnes per capita—significantly higher than the 17-country average of 12.5 tonnes per capita. Between 1990 and 2010, Canada's per capita GHG emissions decreased by nearly 5 per cent, while total GHG emissions in Canada grew by 17 per cent.

—Conference Board of Canada (2014a)

A final observation is from Julie Gelfand, the commissioner of the Environment and Sustainable Development for Canada. When introducing her office's Fall 2014 report, Gelfand stated that examination of Canada's climate change commitments in 2012 led to the conclusion that "the government's approach to introducing regulations sector by sector was unlikely to reduce emissions enough to meet the Copenhagen target" (Auditor General of Canada, 2014: 1). (Canada had committed to reduce its GHG emissions to 17 per cent below 2005 levels by 2020.) Continuing, she wrote, "Our most recent audit of climate change showed little has changed over the last two years. We found that federal measures in place will have little effect on emissions by 2020. The government has introduced regulations in the transportation and electricity generation sectors. However, regulations in the oil and gas sector—where emissions are growing the fastest—are still not in place 8 years after the government first indicated it would regulate this area"(1). In that context, she stated that the evidence indicated Canada would therefore not meet its 2020 GHG emission reduction target. Furthermore, she observed, "The federal government does not have an overall plan that maps how Canada will achieve this target. Canadians have not been given the details about which regulations will be developed, when, nor what greenhouse gas reductions will be expected. Finally, the federal government has not provided the necessary coordination so that all levels of government, working together, can achieve the national target by 2020" (1).

Domestic Approach to Climate Change

As shown from the discussions at the international climate change conferences, the federal Conservative government's position had been consistent: (1) the Canadian approach to climate change has to be harmonized with the United States, given the importance of trade with the US; (2) Canada will not unilaterally take a leadership role at a global scale because that would hurt Canada's economic competitiveness and thereby negatively affect the standard of living for Canadians; (3) all countries, especially China and India, must be part of any international agreement, targets, and timelines; (4) the Kyoto targets are unrealistic, and "intensity-based" emission regulations should be used instead; (5) 2006 rather than 1990 should be used as a baseline against which to measure GHG emissions; and (6) a sector-by-sector approach will be used to recognize the needs of different industrial groups.

Reflecting the above views, the Conservative majority in the Senate defeated the Climate Change Accountability Act by a vote of 43–42 in mid-November 2010. Marjorie LeBreton, the government leader in the Senate, stated that Conservative-appointed senators voted against the bill because it would have hurt Canada's economy—also the view of the government when the House of Commons passed the bill in May 2010. The proposed legislation called for cuts to GHGs of 25 per cent below 1990 levels by 2020. In contrast, the Conservative government argued that a cut of 17 per cent relative to emission levels in 2005 to be achieved by 2020 was appropriate, and was the same target identified by the Obama administration for the United States. By recalibrating its GHG reduction target, Canada became the only country to reduce its aspiration level after the Copenhagen conference.

Provincial governments did not necessarily share the view of the federal government. In July 2008, British Columbia, Manitoba, Ontario, and Quebec joined as partners in the Western Climate Initiative (WCI), begun in February 2007 by five western US states (Arizona, California, New Mexico, Oregon, Washington) to work collaboratively in establishing and implementing mechanisms to reduce GHG emissions. Those states also committed to reducing GHG emissions by 15 per cent below 2005 levels by 2020, as well as adopting clean tailpipe standards for passenger vehicles. Saskatchewan, Nova Scotia, New Brunswick, and Yukon joined the WCI as observers, while Alberta and Newfoundland and Labrador were neither partners nor observers. In 2011, all the states except California withdrew from the WCI, leaving California and the four Canadian provinces as partners.

A key goal of the WCI was to create a multiple-sector market-based program to reduce GHG emissions, and a regional cap-and-trade program was subsequently designed. In September 2013, California and Quebec jointly agreed to link their carbon emission regulations, beginning on 1 January 2014 (Vaiciulis and Fluker, 2013). This formal agreement was the first under the WCI. Vaiciulis and Fluker (2013) observed that it was "both remarkable and unfortunate that Alberta—a jurisdiction which promotes market-based tools to address environmental problems—has chosen not to participate in the WCI." They recognized that if Alberta were to become a partner in the WCI then that province would "have to replace its intensity-based carbon emission reduction obligation with a real and absolute cap on carbon emissions that is lowered over time."

In mid April 2015, Premier Kathleen Wynne of Ontario announced that her province would join Quebec and California in a cap-and-trade approach to reducing GHGs. She stated that specific details of the program would be worked out over the next six months, but that experience from California and Quebec indicated that to fund this initiative the price of gasoline would increase between 2.0 and 3.5 cents per litre, an amount she viewed as "small" given the climate change–related costs already being incurred due to flooding, crop damage, and rapidly increasing insurance claims. She also noted that this initiative by the Ontario government would result in 75 per cent of all Canadians living in a province with some type of carbon pricing.

Wynne explained that the approach would establish a hard ceiling on pollution for each sector in the provincial economy. Thus, a limit would be established for GHG emissions, with rewards for companies that innovate and reduce emissions, while requiring payments by firms that exceed their caps. In practical terms, each business would be assigned its own GHG quota, and could sell any part of its quota not needed due to reducing its emissions.

Furthermore, Wynne stated that money raised through the cap-and-trade system would be invested into projects or initiatives to reduce GHG emissions and support businesses to maintain their competitive position. Examples include developing more energy-efficient domestic appliances to reduce household energy consumption, installing more public transit to reduce use of private vehicles, and assisting in technology development to reduce GHG emissions from factories and businesses.

However, not all governments support a cap-and-trade system. (Details of British Columbia's carbon tax program and Alberta's program focused on large industrial emitters are outlined below.) The federal Conservative government had rejected carbon pricing on the argument that it hinders economic development. Then-premier of Alberta Jim Prentice remarked that if a cap-and-trade system would work for Quebec and Ontario he had no issue with their choosing that approach but had never believed that such a system was appropriate for Alberta.

Brad Wall, Premier of Saskatchewan, has another perspective, which is that neither setting a price on carbon nor establishing a target for GHG should be a priority. Instead, he has argued that the best approach is to invest in innovative projects to make burning of coal more efficient. His rationale is that Canada accounts for less than 2 per cent of global GHG gases, and one-third of worldwide GHG emissions are produced by burning coal. Given that use of coal is expanding at a global scale, he believes the highest priority should be to create technology that will burn coal cleanly. If that is not done, in his view Canada will be on the margin of helping to reduce GHG emissions. In response, Premier Wynne said she agrees Canada's population is small at a global scale, as are our GHG emissions. However, she argues that, given Canadians are very high per capita GHG emitters, we have a responsibility to reduce our own GHG emissions. The above remarks highlight that different views exist about the best approach to address climate change, and that they often reflect local circumstances, such as Saskatchewan being a major user of coal.

In the light of these perspectives, we now turn to consider approaches by Canadian provinces that are not based on a cap-and-trade system. First, the approach of Alberta is presented, followed by that of British Columbia. Alberta has developed a Greenhouse Gas Reduction Program, which mandates all facilities emitting more than 100,000 tonnes of GHGs annually to reduce their emissions intensity by 12 per cent each year. The reductions can be achieved in any combination of (1) improving operations, (2) purchasing Alberta offset credits, (3) contributing to the provincial Climate Change and Emissions Management Fund, and (4) purchasing or using Emission Performance Credits (Alberta, Environment and Sustainable Resource Development, 2014).

- Offset Credits: An emitter can purchase offset credits from other facilities, municipalities, agricultural producers, and others that emit less than 100,000 tonnes of GHGs. Facilities that successfully reduce their emissions and report them to the Alberta Offset Registry receive one offset credit for each tonne of reduced emissions. The firm owning the offset credits can then sell them to other Alberta emitters that have not met required reduction targets. The value of the offset credits is established by the market, so it varies. The government states that the offset system provides an incentive for all participants in the economy to innovate to reduce GHGs.
- Climate Change and Emissions Management Fund: Companies can choose to pay $15/tonne into the fund for emissions above their target. The provincial government then uses the funds to support emission reduction technologies.
- Emission Performance Credits: Unlike the offset credits, if a facility covered by the Greenhouse Gas Reduction Program reduces its emissions intensity below its specified reduction target, it becomes eligible for an Emission Performance Credit. Such credits can be reserved for future use or traded with facilities owned by the same firm. They also can be registered with the Alberta Emission Performance Credit Registry and then be purchased by other firms that have not achieved their reduction targets.

The Alberta government reported that between 2007 and October 2014, 51 million tonnes of GHGs had been reduced from business activities, and that $503 million had been paid into the fund. More than $222 million of that amount had been invested into what were termed "clean energy projects." The main critique of this approach is that a business could

Perspectives on the Environment

Greenhouse Gas Intensity

The national greenhouse gas intensity measures the quantity of GHG emissions in relation to the economic output of a country and is independent of the absolute quantity of GHG emitted.

—GRID (2012)

cut its emission intensity or rate to conform to the regulated annual reduction of 12 per cent, but if its operations are steadily expanding, the actual emission of GHGs will continue to grow each year.

Another option is a **carbon tax**. The purpose of such a tax, introduced by the BC government in 2008, is to modify human behaviour to favour activities that generate lower GHG emissions. When the then federal Liberal leader, Stéphane Dion, proposed a carbon tax in 2008, Prime Minister Harper stated that it was "crazy economics" and "crazy environmental policy" and that it would "shaft" all Canadians. In the federal election of October 2008, the Conservatives were returned as a minority government, and many commentators suggested that one of the problems for the Liberals during the campaign was difficulty explaining the carbon tax in easily understood terms. The Conservatives had included a cap-and-trade approach to climate change as part of their 2008 election platform, which made their later opposition to the same approach by Quebec and Ontario puzzling.

Initiatives at the provincial level have precedents in the United States. While the US federal government has not been a leader, some states have taken leadership roles in moving away from reliance on fossil fuels. For example, in January 2010 California approved a plan for Low Carbon Fuel Standards, which impose a stringent new pollution standard on imported fuel used for transportation. Effective in 2011, the standard set a threshold of 96.88 grams of carbon dioxide equivalent per megajoule of fuel, a challenging standard for even corn-derived ethanol to meet. Other states subsequently agreed to work toward a regional fuel standard, prompted by the California initiative.

The differing positions taken by the federal government, the opposition parties, and the provincial governments highlight that policy-makers have a range of choices, each with strengths and weaknesses.

Policy and Action Options

Regarding climate change, strong agreement exists on several matters related to policy and action. (1) International collaborative action is required, since climate change is a shared problem. No one country can take unilateral action to resolve it. The challenge, of course, is that each national government may be reluctant to take the "first step" for fear that it might become less economically competitive with other nations. (2) A mix of strategies is required, including both mitigation and adaptation.

In the discussion of the Kyoto Protocol and the process to create a successor framework, we noted the importance of nations working collaboratively to reduce GHG emissions. We also saw that some of the most developed countries, including the United States and Canada, have often argued that they will not take a leadership role because of a concern about hindering economic growth and impairing short-term livelihoods. One consequence is that it has been very difficult to develop any meaningful international strategy to address the fundamental causes of climate change. Work will have to

Perspectives on the Environment

Carbon Tax or Cap-and-Trade?

What is a carbon tax?

Pricing carbon emissions through a carbon tax is one of the most powerful incentives that governments have to encourage companies and households to pollute less by investing in cleaner technologies and adopting greener practices. A carbon tax is a fee placed on greenhouse gas pollution mainly from burning fossil fuels. This can be done by placing a surcharge on carbon-based fuels and other sources of pollution such as industrial processes.

A carbon tax puts a monetary price on the real costs imposed on our economy, our communities and our planet by greenhouse gas emissions and the global warming they cause. A shift by households, businesses and industry to cleaner technologies increases the demand for energy-efficient products and helps spur innovation and investment in green solutions.

Under this system, the price to pollute sets the strength of the economic signal and determines the extent to which green choices are encouraged. For example, a stronger price on emissions will lead to more investment in cleaner energy sources such as solar and wind power. And although a carbon fee or tax makes polluting activities more expensive, it makes green technologies more affordable as the price signal increases over time. Most importantly, a carbon tax gets green solutions into use. See the accompanying table about BC's carbon tax.

What is a cap-and-trade system?

In a cap-and-trade system, government puts a firm limit, or cap, on the overall level of carbon pollution from industry and reduces that cap year after year to reach a set pollution target. As the cap decreases each year, it cuts industry's total greenhouse gas emissions to the limit set by regulation, and then forces polluters that exceed their emissions quota to buy unused quota from other companies.

The government creates and distributes pollution quotas, most fairly through an auction. This creates an incentive for firms to reduce their emissions and be able to sell rather than purchase pollution quotas. Under this system the market determines the price of quotas.

In this way, the emission cap ensures that total pollution goes down and companies are given an economic incentive to find better ways to reduce harmful greenhouse gas emissions and support clean energy.

—David Suzuki Foundation (2014)

Perspectives on the Environment

Carbon Tax in British Columbia

As of July 1, 2008, the government of British Columbia introduced a carbon tax on nearly all fossil fuels—gasoline, diesel, coal, propane, natural gas, and home heating oil. The rationale was a conviction that consumers respond to price signals and would reduce their use of fuels and thereby overall emissions. The intent is to reduce GHG emissions by 33 per cent below the levels of 2007 by 2020.

To allow time to adjust, the carbon tax started at a relatively low rate of $10 per tonne of associated carbon, or carbon-equivalent, emissions. This represents about 2.4 cents per litre at the gas pump and 2.8 cents per litre for diesel and home heating oil. The rate per tonne increased by $5 a year for each of four years, and reached $30 a tonne (or about 7 cents per litre of gasoline) in 2012. The tax is levied on a per volume basis, and therefore is not related to the actual selling price of the fuel.

The tax is intended to be revenue neutral, with the collected revenue returned to residents of the province through lower personal and business income taxes. A Low Income Climate Action tax credit is paid quarterly so that the tax would not unfairly affect low-income British Columbians.

Elgie and McClay (2013) evaluated the BC carbon tax system for the period 2008 to 2012. Their analysis showed that over that period the per capita consumption of fuels in BC declined by 19 per cent compared to the rest of Canada, GHG emissions similarly falling, the provincial economy maintained its relative position, and BC came to have the lowest income tax rate in the country. In addition, they report that the carbon tax now has bipartisan support in the provincial legislature and a 64-per-cent public approval rating. Thus, in their view, the carbon tax is a success.

—Adapted from British Columbia Ministry of Finance (2011a; 2011b), and Elgie and McClay (2013)

continue on creating an international approach. Central elements to any approach will be mitigation and adaptation.

Mitigation

Mitigation involves reducing emissions of GHGs, which in turn will limit future temperature changes. Many scientists had agreed that a critical threshold would be an increase of 2°C in temperature, but by 2013 at the Warsaw climate change conference delegates were told that a 4°C change should be planned for—highly likely as early as the 2060s. Ensuring that global warming does not pass 2°C would require emissions of GHGs not exceeding twice the current CO_2 levels, or about 560 ppm. Attaining such an emissions target is not a perfect solution, but would allow time for other adaptations to be introduced. To achieve this goal, emissions would have to be reduced significantly below current levels, and about 75 per cent of energy production would have to be based on "carbon-free" sources. To reach 75 per cent carbon-free energy production requires development and implementation of new technologies.

In contrast, if CO_2 emissions continue at present levels, then incremental warming of between 2°C and 6°C is likely before the end of the twenty-first century. If production of all GHGs were stopped immediately, it is most likely that, because of past emissions, the Earth would still warm by at least 1°C.

In terms of mitigation strategies, a mix of options exists (after Hengeveld, 2006: 30–2). They include carbon taxes, cap-and-trade systems, new technologies, carbon sequestration, and geo-engineering.

New technologies include alternatives to fossil-fuel combustion for heating buildings, running manufacturing and industrial equipment, and powering vehicles, aircraft, and ships. A specific example is fuel switching, through which fossil-based fuels are replaced by other fuels, ranging from hydro-generated electricity to ethanol fuels. Wind-based energy is another alternative, discussed in more detail in Chapter 12. Other options include energy from renewable biomass and developing a "hydrogen economy."

Carbon can be sequestered in biological sinks. Land-use practices that encourage agricultural crops and forest systems with the capacity to sequester carbon have been endorsed as a legitimate way for nations to achieve GHG targets under the Kyoto Protocol. A challenge here is that biological sinks are not permanent, and hence ways must be found to prevent the sequestered carbon from entering the atmosphere.

Geo-engineering is sometimes considered to be a third tool, in addition to mitigation and adaptation, but here we include it under mitigation since the intent is to reduce GHG emissions and thereby reduce global warming through systematic large-scale manipulation of the Earth's climate. Examples of geo-engineering can involve **carbon sequestration** by *direct* (capture of carbon dioxide from the air) or *indirect* (iron fertilization of oceans) approaches. Another approach is management of solar radiation, such as by producing stratospheric sulphur aerosols, or using space mirrors and enhancement of cloud reflectivity. So far, few large-scale geo-engineering approaches have been initiated outside of laboratory experiments. A good example is provided in Chapter 2 (Box 2.5) regarding the iron dumping case of Haida Gwaii. Smaller-scale geo-engineering approaches include "cool roof" projects and tree planting.

Advocates of geo-engineering approaches argue that climate change has already passed key "tipping points," and as a result future reductions in GHGs will not be sufficient to reverse climate change. They claim that geo-engineering could reverse, even if temporarily, some negative aspects of

DOMESTIC GUEST STATEMENT

Global Policy Challenges | *Barry Smit*

Climate change is a classic "tragedy of the commons" at a global scale. The atmosphere is a "common resource," open to all. Some countries argue that if they were to cut back emitting greenhouse gases (GHGs) others would continue or increase their emissions. Yet all countries suffer from the impacts of climate change, and more and more people are experiencing changes in floods, droughts, storms, heat waves, sea levels, and diseases, all affecting their food security, their health, their livelihoods, and their lives. Many of the most vulnerable have contributed little to global emissions.

As with any common resource, the issue requires some kind of shared global action. Some countries, notably rich countries including Canada, have not supported or not lived up to international agreements to curtail GHG emissions. One argument for inaction is that a country should not be required to reduce its emissions unless all countries are required to do likewise. The UN Framework Convention on Climate Change (UNFCCC), to which Canada is still a party, provides the principles that guide international action. It recognizes that the rich countries cumulatively have contributed by far the greatest amounts of GHGs, and they still have vastly higher per capita emissions than the developing world. Hence, the agreed first step was for the rich countries (Annex 1) to take the first steps in reducing GHG emissions (Kyoto), on the understanding that once these responsibilities had been addressed and technologies developed, the rest of the world would follow suit. Some countries have honoured their Kyoto commitments, others have not, and Canada withdrew from Kyoto.

The other main argument for stalling on mitigating climate change is that taking action to reduce GHG emissions would hurt a country's economy. Of course, there would be some adjustments, some "losers" and some "winners." But not taking action will certainly hurt a country's economy, as well as its ecosystems, its resources, its communities, and the lives of its people. From a solely economic point of view, eminent economist Sir Nicholas Stern calculated the cost of mitigating climate change to be in the order of 2 per cent global GDP, and the cost of not mitigating to be 5–20 per cent global GDP. Several countries, including Norway (which, like Canada, has cold winters and an important oil and gas sector), have shown that it is possible to reduce or stabilize GHG emissions without damaging their economies. On the contrary, their economies are benefiting from being at the cutting edge of developments in alternative energy and efficiency.

The climate change issue is highly politicized, reflected in campaigns to discredit climate change science, muzzle scientists, and limit public policies that might constrain short-term interests in the fossil-fuel sector. These public relations campaigns employ the same strategies (and some of the same people) as the tobacco companies have done in their challenge to the science linking smoking to lung cancer.

In Canada there has been little effective action by successive federal governments to reduce GHGs, and Canada is nowhere near meeting its weak GHG reduction targets for 2020. However, several provinces have made progress in reducing their carbon footprints. British Columbia has a successful carbon tax and a clean energy vehicle initiative. Ontario has almost completed its shutdown of all coal-fired power plants, and Quebec has launched its cap-and-trade system, linked to California's successful trading permit system. Also, there is evidence that many municipalities are acting within their jurisdictions to reduce GHG emissions. In the absence of a unified climate policy, Canada is seeing the evolution of a patchwork of provincial and municipal initiatives, including regulations, taxes, and incentives. Of course, many individuals and businesses are also acting on their own volition.

Notwithstanding efforts to reduce GHG emissions, we are guaranteed to experience climate change in future decades. Hence, there is a need to adjust to its effects (known as adaptation). Unlike mitigation, the immediate beneficiaries of adaptation are the adaptors. Adapting farming practices to better suit a changing climate is clearly in the interest of the farmer. Internationally, there are questions of who pays, how

Courtesy Tristian Pearce

Inuit in the Canadian Arctic are having to use boats as well as snow machines to hunt for food as the ice regime changes.

Continued

Courtesy Barry Smit

Families in coastal Nigeria are having to adapt to loss of food sources and livelihoods as fish stocks have moved with changing ocean temperatures.

much, who receives, for what activities, and so on. In Canada, no national adaptation program exists, but several provinces, including BC and Ontario, have climate change adaptation initiatives. In practice, adaptation is most commonly undertaken by incorporating climate change risks into resource management programs, infrastructure planning, disaster management, water resource planning, and other sectoral programs—sometimes called "mainstreaming" or "climate-proofing." It is already evident that there are limits to adaptation, reinforcing the need for effective action on reducing global GHG emissions.

Courtesy Barry Smit

Barry Smit, PhD, O. Ont., is a geographer and professor emeritus at the University of Guelph. He has been active in the science and policy of climate change in Canada and internationally for 30 years, and was a co-recipient of the 2007 Nobel Peace Prize as a member of the IPCC.

climate change and thereby provide more time and opportunity to reduce GHG emissions through various mitigation measures. Critics express concern about the safety and appropriateness of geo-engineering methods, and worry about unintended side effects at a global scale.

Adaptation

As noted above, even if all GHG emissions were stopped tomorrow, there are enough GHGs already in the atmosphere to generate significant climate change. The change will have impacts, some positive and some negative. Given that there will be negative impacts, we need to develop adaptation strategies so that adversely affected activities and regions can create capacity for resilience.

In developing countries in particular, the tendency has been to prepare strategies that emphasize recovery following a disaster, such as preventing starvation as a result of a loss of crops because of flooding, hail, drought, disease, or pests. Today, social scientists argue that more attention should be directed toward creating proactive capacity to deal with disasters.

For example, climate change is likely to have an impact on agricultural production. And as Hengeveld (2006: 32) observed, some choices—such as increasing production through greater crop specialization, more water-intensive crops, more tile drainage and water competition, and less grazing—will make agriculture more vulnerable to climate extremes.

In the resource-based recreational sector, warmer winters are likely to adversely affect downhill skiing operations, so an investment in snow-making equipment now would be prudent as an alternative to waiting for government support after a series of lower-than-average snowfall years. Scott et al. (2014) completed a study of the effect of climate change on the future of Winter Olympic Games, and concluded that while the 19 previous cities or regions that hosted the Winter Olympics had suitable climates up to and including 2010, no more than 11 of them would have suitable conditions by the 2050s and no more than six of them by the 2080s, if global warming continues as predicted.

Choices are always available, and both policy-makers and individuals in a resource-based sector can opt for choices that allow greater scope for adaptation in the future when climate conditions are quite likely to be different from what they are today. However, to promote more adaptive choices, governments will have to review current systems of incentives, such as crop insurance and agriculture support programs. Any proposed changes would probably meet vocal resistance, since some people profit from such programs and can be expected to oppose any changes to them. Currently, more attention is being given to adaptation.

It is unlikely, however, that either mitigation or adaptation strategies on their own will suffice, as highlighted by Barry Smit in his "Domestic Guest Statement." Both are needed, and each one creates many opportunities for those able and willing to look beyond "business as usual" practices.

What Else?

Clearly, considerable uncertainty remains about the precise effects of anticipated climate change. Furthermore, concerted and coordinated initiatives by provinces, states, and nations will be necessary to reduce the projected negative impacts. Some of the multilateral initiatives underway have been identified in this chapter, but it is obvious that some nations have

Perspectives on the Environment

Views about Climate Engineering

Cusack and colleagues (2014) assessed what they refer to as "climate engineering," another term for "geo-engineering," in terms of its capacity to remove carbon dioxide from the atmosphere and/or reduce solar input. They assessed strategies related to six criteria: (1) technical potential, (2) cost effectiveness, (3) ecological risk, (4) public acceptance, (5) institutional capacity, and (6) scope of ethical concerns. The strategies included: (1) forest management (reforestation, stopping/reducing deforestation); (2) soil management (reducing erosion, improving agricultural practices, adding **biochar**/charcoal: (3) geological burial of liquid CO_2 (injecting it into deep rock and/or ocean sediment); (4) solar radiation management (cloud seeding, aerosols, reflection) and (5) ocean fertilization (algal blooms, biomass deposition into the deep ocean).

They concluded that abatement is the most desirable strategy, but also that some geo-engineering strategies, and especially forest and soil management for carbon sequestration, merit wide-scale application because they pose relatively low risk and create the fewest ethical concerns. Other geo-engineering strategies, such as biochar production and geological carbon capture and storage, were assessed not as positively but were viewed as deserving more study and consideration. The strategies ranked the lowest on most criteria were iron fertilization of the oceans and solar radiation management, even though both were assessed to be cost effective.

Overall, their conclusion is that abatement (i.e., reduction) of GHG emissions should be the main strategy to reduce the impact of climate change, complemented by some low-risk, cost-effective climate engineering approaches.

Shortly after the research findings were published, Dr. Jon Axsen, an assistant professor in the School of Resource and Environmental Management at Simon Fraser University in Burnaby and one of the co-authors, was quoted as commenting, "There is no silver bullet. There is no technology fix. There's no button that we're going to press some day to reduce the warming that we're going to experience. What we need to do is have climate policy now and start creating real action now" (Moore, 2014).

been unwilling to participate in coordinated global activities that could create short-term economic disadvantage for them. But what can individuals do?

Hengeveld et al. (2005: 51) provide thoughtful guidance:

> How can the individual Canadian citizen influence the outcome of a global environmental issue that is already challenging the wisdom and resources of the world's governments and international agencies? The answer, simply put, is that it is the individual citizens who must create the environment of opinion which will encourage governments to act.
>
> And it is the individual citizens who can take actions themselves to reduce their personal emissions and who can support the policies that an effective response to the risks of climate change will demand.
>
> . . . Each time we turn on a hot water tap, or open a refrigerator door, we add to the problem. By changing our attitudes and lifestyles, by becoming more knowledgeable about the issue and rethinking our attitude to the environment, we can make a difference.

Box 7.6 presents some options. A change in one person's behaviour will not have a major impact. However, cumulatively, many individual actions can be significant, as emphasized in Chapter 15. The challenge will be to decide whether we are prepared to make such modifications to our behaviour, since in many instances we will not be the direct beneficiaries—more likely, people one or two generations in the future, such as your grandchildren, will reap the benefits.

As you reflect on what you could do relative to climate change, we encourage you to think about the extent to which it is an ethical issue. In that regard, you may wish to read more about the concept of **climate justice**, which approaches climate change by examining its causes and effects associated with both environmental and social justice. In other words, to what extent should we consider the implications of climate change with reference to matters such as human rights, collective responsibility, historical and legal obligations, and equity? In particular, how should you react to the fact that often those who contribute the least to climate change are most vulnerable and incur the greatest negative consequences from it?

Perspectives on the Environment

The Power of One

What makes climate change stand out from *all* other global problems is that our individual contributions can be measured down to the last gram. We cannot identify our contributions to any other wicked problem, such as poverty, terrorism or drug abuse—let alone quantify it. But with climate change, we can say with confidence whether our contribution is going up or down, how it compares with that of other people, and what changes would be needed to reduce it.

—Marshall (2014: 192)

ENVIRONMENT IN FOCUS

BOX 7.6 | What You Can Do: Taking Action on Climate Change

1. Much of global climate change is influenced by our society's love affair with the automobile. Find something else to love, such as a bicycle or a bus. Simply aim to reduce your consumption of fossil fuels.
2. Use energy more efficiently in your home and in all other aspects of life. Make sure your appliances, lighting, and heating are energy efficient.
3. Encourage power utilities to invest more effort in renewable energy resources, as discussed in Chapter 12.
4. Consider getting by without air conditioning in your car and at home, or if and when you use it, do so sparingly. Plant shade trees to reduce the summer temperature in your house.
5. Plant trees to help absorb atmospheric carbon dioxide.
6. Let your political representatives know that you favour mandatory measures to curb emissions, even if it costs more money in the short term.

Summary

1. The *weather* of any place is the sum total of its atmospheric conditions (temperature, pressure, winds, moisture, and precipitation) for a *short* period of time. It is the momentary state of the atmosphere. *Climate* is a composite or generalization of the variety of day-to-day weather conditions. It is not just "average weather," since the variations from the mean, or average, are as important as the mean itself.
2. Scientific evidence confirms that the world has been warming, with the average global temperature at the Earth's surface having increased by about 0.6°C, with an error range of plus or minus 0.2°C, since the late nineteenth century.
3. The increase in the average temperature for the northern hemisphere during the twentieth century was the largest of any century in the past 1,000 years.
4. Evidence showing increases in greenhouse gases in the atmosphere, loss of mass in glaciers, reduction in permafrost and snow cover, and rises in sea level is consistent with global temperature increases.
5. There are four basic climate models; the most commonly used is the general circulation model. GCMs are best used for global or overall climate modelling rather than for regional representations of climate change.
6. Coarse spatial resolution, poor predictive capacity for precipitation, relatively weak simulation of oceans, lack of baseline data, and many other limitations make GCM outputs variable.
7. The Intergovernmental Panel on Climate Change states clearly that most warming since the mid twentieth century is associated with human activities.
8. At a global scale, records document that mean sea level has been rising at a rate of 0.1 to 0.2 metres per century during the past 100 to 200 years.
9. There are five ways to adapt to the hazards caused by climate change: prevent the loss, accept the loss, spread the loss, change behaviour, and change the location for activity.
10. Climate change has implications for terrestrial systems, agriculture, freshwater systems, fisheries, the cryosphere, ocean and coastal systems, and infectious diseases.
11. Climate change negatively affects the poorest people the most and can trigger out-migration, which can lead to "environmental refugees" for whom Canada will be one destination.
12. The challenges of communicating information or understanding about global change include: (1) global change is a complex issue; (2) uncertainties exist regarding almost every aspect of the global change issue, and they increase when moving from natural to human systems; (3) the impact of global change will be disproportionately heavier on people in less developed countries and on future generations; (4) the basic causes of global change are embedded in current values and lifestyles.
13. Climate change deniers aim to raise doubt in the minds of the public and decision-makers about the science of climate change, with the intent to delay decisions about changes needed to reduce greenhouse gas emissions.
14. During December 1997, representatives met in Kyoto and reached an agreement, popularly referred to as the Kyoto Protocol, with targets for 38 developed nations as well as the European Union to reduce their overall emissions of GHGs by at least 5 per cent below 1990 levels by the period 2008–12.

15. Canada, which ratified the Protocol in December 2002, committed to reduce GHG emissions to 6 per cent below 1990 levels by between 2008 and 2012. In contrast, US President George W. Bush stated that the US would not agree to the Protocol and would develop its own approach.
16. After the federal election in mid October 2015, Prime Minister Trudeau stated that Canada would become much more engaged domestically and internationally in addressing climate change. What key initiatives do you believe the federal government should take on its own and in collaboration with provincial governments to address domestic aspects of climate change, and with other nations to address international dimensions of climate change?
17. Despite its commitment to the Kyoto Protocol, Canada has been unsuccessful in reducing GHG emissions.
18. Canada has received the "Fossil of the Day" award from NGOs at various international climate change conferences because of its poor performance in reducing GHG emissions.
19. At the Bali Conference in December 2007, an effort was made to develop a new climate change agreement to replace the Kyoto Protocol. At that event, Canada argued against specific targets and wanted the timeline extended from 2020 to 2050.
20. Canada was labelled a "climate hypocrite" at the Bali Conference.
21. Annual climate summits from 2009 in Copenhagen to 2014 in Lima made only incremental progress to develop an international accord to replace the Kyoto Protocol.
22. Both mitigation and adaptation must be used in policies and strategies to deal with climate change.
23. Options to reduce GHG emissions include carbon taxes, cap-and-trade systems, new technologies, carbon sequestration, and geo-engineering.
24. The concept of climate justice has emerged to encourage us to consider both environmental and social implications of climate change.
25. Geo-engineering involves deliberate and systematic large-scale manipulation of the global climate system to reduce the impact of GHG emissions on temperature increases and to facilitate recovery of the ozone layer in the atmosphere.

Key Terms

adaptation
aspirational approach
atmosphere
biochar
Cancún Summit
carbon sequestration
carbon tax
climate
climate change
climate change deniers
"Climategate"
climate justice
climate modelling
Copenhagen Summit
El Niño
emission credits
emissions trading
fossil fuels
general circulation models (GCMs)
geo-engineering
global warming
greenhouse effect
greenhouse gas
ice caps
ice shelves
Kyoto Protocol
mitigation
Montreal Protocol
ozone
ozone layer
uncertainty
weather

Questions for Review and Critical Thinking

1. Explain the difference between weather and climate.
2. What are some of the key natural and human causes of climate change?
3. How credible is the evidence for climate change or global warming? For which aspects is there the most uncertainty?
4. Have you noticed any indication of climate change in the area in which you live? If so, what are they, and how confident are you that they are valid and reliable indicators of climate change?
5. What would be the best sources of traditional ecological knowledge about climate change in your area?
6. Why have general circulation models (GCMs) become dominant in the modelling research focused on climate change? What are their limitations?

7. What is viewed as the main cause of increased carbon dioxide emissions to the atmosphere in the twentieth and twenty-first centuries?
8. Which of the negative impacts of climate change should be of greatest concern to Canadians? Will the priority shift depending on which Canadian region is considered?
9. What role should Canadians have with regard to the challenge of environmental refugees?
10. What are the main strategies normally used to adapt to natural hazards caused by climate change?
11. What are the basic communication challenges related to climate change, and what, in your view, should the first steps to overcome them be?
12. Do you agree or disagree with the views of climate change deniers?
13. What was the significance of "Climategate"?
14. What are the strengths and limitations of the Kyoto Protocol? If it did not exist and you were to start with a "blank sheet," what type of protocol would you propose?
15. Why had the Canadian Conservative government consistently opposed the Kyoto Protocol? What had it proposed as an alternative? What are the positions of provincial and territorial governments?
16. After the federal election in mid October 2015, Prime Minister Trudeau stated that Canada would become much more engaged domestically and internationally in addressing climate change. What key initiatives do you believe the federal government should take on its own and in collaboration with provincial governments to address domestic aspects of climate change, and with other nations to address international dimensions of climate change?
17. Why do people argue that climate change will only be addressed successfully if there is international collaborative effort? In that context, do you agree or disagree that developing nations such as China and India have to be signatories to any international agreement?
18. What has been the significance of the annual international climate change conferences?
19. How should mitigation measures—carbon tax, cap-and-trade, technology, carbon sequestration, geo-engineering—be used together to reduce GHG emissions?
20. There have been different perspectives in Canada regarding the best way to reduce greenhouse gases. What do you think is the best strategy to resolve differences about climate change among federal, territorial, and provincial governments, among the provincial governments as a group, and among municipalities?

Related Websites

Centre for International Climate and Environmental Research, Oslo (CICERO)
www.cicero.uio.no/home/index_e.aspx

Climate Action Network Canada
www.climateactionnetwork.ca

The Climate Group
www.theclimategroup.org

David Suzuki Foundation, Climate Change: Impacts and Solutions
www.davidsuzuki.org/issues/climate-change

Environment Canada: Climate Change
www.ec.gc.ca/cc/

Environment Canada: Climate Trends and Variations Bulletins
www.ec.gc.ca/adsc-cmda/default.asp?lang=En&n=4A21B114-1

Environment Canada: Environmental Indicators
www.ec.gc.ca/indicateurs-indicators

Environment Canada: Weather and Meteorology
www.ec.gc.ca/meteo-weather/default.asp?lang=En&n=FDF98F96-1

European Commission: Climate Change
http://ec.europa.eu/environment/nature/climatechange/index_en.htm

Federation of Canadian Municipalities: Partners for Climate Protection
www.fcm.ca/home/programs/partners-for-climate-protection.htm

Government of Canada: ecoACTION/ecoENERGY
www.ecoaction.gc.ca

Intergovernmental Panel on Climate Change: Fifth Assessment Report
www.ipcc.ch

Natural Resources Canada: Impacts and Adaptation
https://www.nrcan.gc.ca/environment/impacts-adaptation

Union of Concerned Scientists: Global Warming
www.ucsusa.org/global_warming

United Nations: Framework Convention on Climate Change
http://unfccc.int/2860.php

United States Environmental Protection Agency: Climate Change
www.epa.gov/climatechange

World Meteorological Organization
www.wmo.ch/pages/index_en.html

Further Readings

Note: This list comprises works relevant to the subject of the chapter but not cited in the text. All cited works are listed in the References at the end of the book.

Burch, S.L., and S.E. Harris. 2014. *Understanding Climate Change: Science, Policy, and Practice*. Toronto: University of Toronto Press.

Dunlap, J. P., R. Dunlap, and M. Freeman. 2008. "The organization of denial: Conservative think tanks and environmental skepticism," *Environmental Politics* 17: 349–85.

Gleick, P., et al. 2010. "Climate change and the integrity of science," *Science* (7 May): 689–90.

Government of Canada. 2013. *Canada's Sixth National Report on Climate Change, 2014*. Ottawa: Minister of Environment.

Grunster, S. 2010. "Self-interest, sacrifice and climate change: (Re-)framing the British Columbia carbon tax," in M. Maniates and J.M. Metyer, eds, *The Environmental Politics of Sacrifice*. Cambridge, Mass.: MIT Press, 187–215.

Guterl, F. 2013. *The Fate of Species*. New York: Bloomsbury.

Hamilton, C. 2010. *Requiem for a Species: Why We Resist the Truth about Climate Change*. London: Earthscan.

Hansen, J. 2009. *Storms of My Grandchildren*. New York: Bloomsbury.

Hayden, A. 2014. *When Green Growth Is Not Enough: Climate Change, Ecological Modernization and Sufficiency*. Montreal: McGill-Queen's University Press.

Hoggan, J. 2009. *Climate Cover-Up: The Crusade to Deny Global Warming*. Vancouver: Greystone Books.

Howe, H.P. 2014. *Behind the Curve: Science and Politics of Global Warming*. Seattle: University of Washington Press.

Klein, N. 2014. *This Changes Everything: Capitalism vs. the Climate*. Toronto: Alfred Knopf Canada.

Lynas, M. 2008. *Six Degrees: Our Future on a Hotter Planet*. Washington, DC: National Geographic.

McBean, G. 2015. "Climate change: Adapting to the risks in a changing climate," in B. Mitchell, ed., *Resource and Environmental Management in Canada: Addressing Conflict and Uncertainty*, 5th edn. Toronto: Oxford University Press, 194–220.

Mann, M.E. 2013. *The Hockey Stick and the Climate Wars: Dispatches from the Front Lines*. New York: Columbia University Press.

Marshall, G. 2014. *Don't Even Think about It: Why Our Brains Are Wired to Ignore Climate Change*. New York: Bloomsbury.

Moser, S.C. and L. Dilling. Eds. 2007. *Creating a Climate for Change: Communicating Climate Change and Facilitating Social Change*. Cambridge: Cambridge University Press.

National Round Table on the Environment and the Economy. 2009. *True North: Adapting Infrastructure to Climate Change in Northern Canada*. Ottawa: NRTEE.

Oreskes, N., and E. Conway. 2010. *Merchants of Doubt*. London and New York: Bloomsbury Press.

Orr, D.W. 2009. *Down to the Wire: Confronting Climate Collapse*. Oxford: Oxford University Press.

Pizzolato, L., S. Howell, C. Derksen, J. Dawson, and L. Copeland. 2014. "Changing sea ice conditions and marine transportation activity in Canadian Arctic waters between 1990 and 2012," *Climatic Change* 123, 2: 161–73.

Purdin, M., D. Houle, and E. Lachapelle. 2014. *The Political Economy of California and Québec's Cap and Trade Systems*. Ottawa: Sustainable Prosperity.

Scheer, D., and O. Renn. 2014. "Public perception of geoengineering and its consequences for public debate," *Climatic Change* 125, 3–4: 305–18.

Scott, D.N., et al. 2000. *Climate Change Communication: Proceedings of an International Conference*. Waterloo, Ont.: University of Waterloo; Hull, Que.: Environment Canada, Adaptation and Impacts Research Group.

Stern, N.H. 2007. *The Stern Review of the Economics of Climate Change*. Cambridge: Cambridge University Press.

Tam, B.Y., W.A. Gough, V. Edwards, and L.S. Tsuji. 2013. "The impact of climate change on the well-being and lifestyle of a First Nations community in the western James Bay region," *Canadian Geographer*, 57, 4: 441–56.

Toronto and Region Conservation and ESSA Technologies. 2012. *Mainstreaming Climate Change Adaptation in Canadian Water Resource Management: The State of Practice and Strategic Directions for Action*. Toronto: Toronto and Regional Conservation Authority.

Go to www.oupcanada.com/DeardenMitchell5e to access additional learning tools on your smartphone, tablet, or PC.

CHAPTER EIGHT

Oceans and Fisheries

Learning Objectives

- To understand the nature of oceanic ecosystems and their similarities to and differences from terrestrial ecosystems
- To know the main challenges facing the oceans
- To learn about some of the global management responses to these challenges
- To understand the reasons behind the collapse of Canada's east coast groundfish fishery
- To appreciate the background to Aboriginal use of marine resources and to examine some current conflicts
- To gain an understanding of Canada's main strategies for ocean management
- To be aware of some of the challenges regarding aquaculture

Introduction

The major challenges faced by society today are global and transnational. They are very difficult to solve not just because of their scale—the changing composition of the atmosphere or pollution of the world's oceans—but because they need nations to act in ways that, over the short term, may yield little direct advantage to them. Can governments act for the long-term good of the majority when they may incur the wrath of voters at home?

Canada does not have a good record in this regard, especially recently and related to ocean resources. Canada would not join the worldwide moratorium on bottom trawling suggested by then US President George Bush, is a noted laggard in its international commitments to establish marine protected areas in which fishing is not allowed, and refused to support an international treaty to protect the bluefin tuna.

The Atlantic bluefin tuna is the most valuable fish in the sea, fetching over $100,000 each at market in Tokyo, with the record close to five times that amount. Obviously, the fish is highly sought after, and that demand has resulted in an 80 per cent reduction in stocks over the last 100 years. As a result, in 2010 Monaco proposed a temporary fishing ban, supported by the US and many other governments signatory to the UN Convention on International Trade In Endangered Species (CITES). The ban was opposed by Japan and Canada, among others.

The management body for the tuna, the International Commission for the Conservation of Atlantic Tunas (ICCAT), has consistently set quotas well above the catches suggested by its own scientists. In 2008, for example, the suggested quota was 8,500 to 15,000 tonnes, but members agreed on a 22,000-tonne limit. There is also virtually no recourse for catching over the limit. In 2007, France was allocated 5,500 tonnes but reported catching double that amount. Unfortunately, given the value of the fish, these legal quotas are normally far exceeded by the illegal and unreported catch.

Canada only has a small allocation of the fishery, the rod-and-reel fishery based in PEI, and this fishery is well managed. However, in voting to keep this fishery going, Canada is contributing to the overall demise of the species. If all nations continue to act solely in their own best interests in the short term, as Canada has done in this case, then the very severe global challenges faced by the oceans will never be solved. In 2014 the Pacific bluefin tuna was also added to the list of endangered species, with populations having declined between 19 and 33 per cent over the last 20 years. Most fish now caught are juveniles that have not yet had chance to spawn.

Perspectives on the Environment

High-Intensity Stressors and Extinction

Not only are we already experiencing severe declines in many species to the point of commercial extinction in some cases, and an unparalleled rate of regional extinctions of habitat types (e.g., mangroves and seagrass meadows), but we now face losing marine species and entire marine ecosystems, such as coral reefs, within a single generation. Unless action is taken now, the consequences of our activities are at a high risk of causing, through the combined effects of climate change, overexploitation, pollution and habitat loss, the next globally significant extinction event in the ocean.

It is notable that the occurrence of multiple high-intensity stressors has been a prerequisite for all the five global extinction events of the past 600 million years

—Barnosky et al. (2011)

Oceanic Ecosystems

The oceans and their well-being are integral to sustaining life on this planet. They are key components in global cycles and energy flows (Chapter 2). Marine ecosystems are home to a vast array of organisms displaying greater diversity of taxonomic groups than their terrestrial counterparts. Marine organisms help feed us, and they are also the source of many valuable medicinal products. We use the seas to dump our waste products and to transport most of our goods around the world. The oceans enrich our cultures, and nations draw strength and inspiration from their links to the vital life-giving nature and awesome power of the seas.

One of the major difficulties working against sustainable human use of the oceans is our lack of understanding of oceanic ecosystems. In 2003, a $1 billion, 10-year expedition announced that it had described 150 new species of fish and another 1,700 plants and animals in just the first three years of its travels and anticipated that as many as 5,000 species of fish were waiting to be discovered. By 2010, the expedition had described more than 250,000 marine species with approximately 750,000 remaining to be described (Census of Marine Life, 2010). Not all new discoveries are small and in remote locales. For example, one discovery was a new species of squid more than 9 metres long in the Gulf of Mexico; another was a giant jellyfish in the heavily studied waters off Monterey, California. If we know so little about oceanic ecosystem components, it is even more difficult to understand the functional relationships among them.

Yet the general principles that govern life and energy flows and matter cycles, discussed in Chapters 2 and 4, also hold true for oceanic ecosystems (see Box 2.4). But there are important differences. On land, water is the most common limiting factor for life. In the oceans, this is obviously not the case; here it is nutrients. While the oceans cover more than 70 per cent of the Earth's surface, they account for only 50 per cent of global primary productivity. Much of the ocean's surface is the marine equivalent of a desert, with productivity limited to the areas where nutrients are abundant. Generally, nutrient concentrations increase with depth because of the decomposition of organisms falling from the surface layer.

A vast quantity of tuna awaiting inspection and auction at Tokyo's Tsukiji fish market, the world's largest daily fish market.

The oceans sustain an amazing variety of life. Here are two fish with very different life strategies. The whale shark, here in Oslob in the Philippines, the world's largest fish, cruises the world's oceans feeding on plankton. On the other hand the frogfish, here in Thailand, rarely moves and sits disguised on coral reefs, until it spots prey such as crustaceans or other fish to ambush and gulps them down in one of the fastest predatory moves on the planet.

The most productive areas are coastal zones and in parts of the ocean where upwellings from the deep ocean return nutrients to the surface layers and where photosynthetic activity occurs. In terrestrial ecosystems, productivity generally increases from the poles to the tropics. In the ocean, this is not true. Although there are productive areas in the tropics (Box 8.1), some of the most highly productive marine areas in the world are situated off the coast of Canada, such as the Grand Banks and in the Arctic Ocean, where nutrient upwellings occur. These upwellings promote large phytoplankton populations, especially in the Arctic where there is virtually unlimited light in the summer. Many species of whales and birds migrate to these waters to take advantage of this abundance. The largest whale, the blue whale, and the bird with the largest wing span in the world, the albatross, are two good examples.

Besides nutrient availability, the other major ecological influences on marine life are temperature and light. Both temperature and light decrease with depth. This means that surface waters in the euphotic zone (Box 2.4) are warmer and have higher light levels, resulting in higher productivity. There is usually a sharp transition in temperature between the warmer surface waters and the cooler waters underneath. This is known as the **thermocline** and generally occurs at a depth of 120 to 240 metres, depending on latitude and ocean currents.

The deepest part of the ocean is more than 9,000 metres deep, but more than three-quarters is between 4,000 and 6,000 metres in depth. Most productivity is on the continental shelves at a depth of less than 200 metres, and especially within the top 100 metres. Most fisheries are concentrated in these areas. However, that pattern may change in the not-too-distant future. Scientists have discovered that the biomass of mesopelagic fish, which live between 200 and 1,000 metres deep, may be as high as 10 billion tons. This large biomass also has significant implications for the global carbon flux. Mesopelagic fish rise to the surface at night to feed but retreat to depth during the day, effectively conveying larger amounts of carbon deeper in the ocean than previously thought.

There are also deeper communities, mainly made up of bacteria that derive their energy from sulphide emissions, centred around hydrothermal vents on the sea floor. Rich communities of tube worms, clams, and mussels have been documented at depths exceeding 2,000 metres at more than 100 sites worldwide, including off the west coast of Canada. Scientists speculate that life on Earth originated in such hydrothermal vent systems, based on chemosynthesis. Similar kinds of chemoautotrophic-based communities are found on whale skeletons at depth, nourished by sulphides produced as the carcasses decay, as discussed in Box 2.2.

Another difference between terrestrial and marine ecosystems is in the shape of the biomass pyramids, previously discussed in Chapter 2. In terrestrial ecosystems, you will recall, the pyramids stand upright. There is a broad base of primary producers and a reduced biomass at each subsequent trophic level. This arrangement is reversed in oceanic pyramids because the biomass of the primary producers, the phytoplankton, alive at any one time is quite small compared to that of their predators. The food chains still depend on a broad energy base, but the turnover of biomass at the first trophic level is rapid. This continuously replenished, short-lived base supports long-living predators, such as the blue whale, that store energy over a much longer period.

The **carbon balance** in oceanic ecosystems is the subject of much scientific research because of the crucial importance of the oceans in absorbing carbon dioxide, a greenhouse gas, and the role it may play in mitigating the impact of global climate change (Chapter 7). The ocean surface takes up about 2 billion tonnes of carbon per year by gas exchange, equivalent to one-third of annual anthropocentric emissions. This uptake is driven by wind exchange and the imbalances between the amount of carbon in the atmosphere and the oceans. Marine primary producers get their carbon from the dissolved CO_2 in the water as bicarbonate. There is a balance between the amount of CO_2 in the atmosphere and bicarbonate in the water. If there is too much in either compartment, a gradient is created, and the carbon migrates along the gradient between the ocean's surface and the atmosphere. However, carbon is also continuously being moved out of the surface layers of the ocean into deeper water, where it is stored in dead organisms, ocean sediments, and coral reefs (Figure 8.1). The more that is stored at depth, the greater will be the gradient pulling carbon out of the atmosphere and into the surface waters to compensate for these losses. Scientists estimate that the oceans have absorbed around 30 per cent of the anthropocentric CO_2 emissions occurring since 1750. However, about half of these CO_2 emissions released between 1750 and 2011 have occurred in the past 40 years. The lag time in these movements is considerable and too slow for us to hope that the process can compensate for the exponential amounts of CO_2 released into the atmosphere by human activities. The Intergovernmental Panel on Climate Change (IPCC, 2014a) predicts that ocean acidity will increase by 150 per cent by 2100 (Box 8.1).

Acidification is already having severe impacts on some fisheries in Canada. In the Strait of Georgia in BC, for example, the aquaculture firm Island Scallops found 95 per cent of its stock, about 10 million scallops, dead in mid 2013. Ocean acidity had eaten holes through the shells of the hybrid Pacific scallops, specifically bred for aquaculture, and killed the larvae. The company then introduced the native rock scallop into the same cages and they survived, apparently hardier than their non-native cousins. However, they are also slower growing and take an extra year to mature. The company laid off half its workers and is now working with scientists from

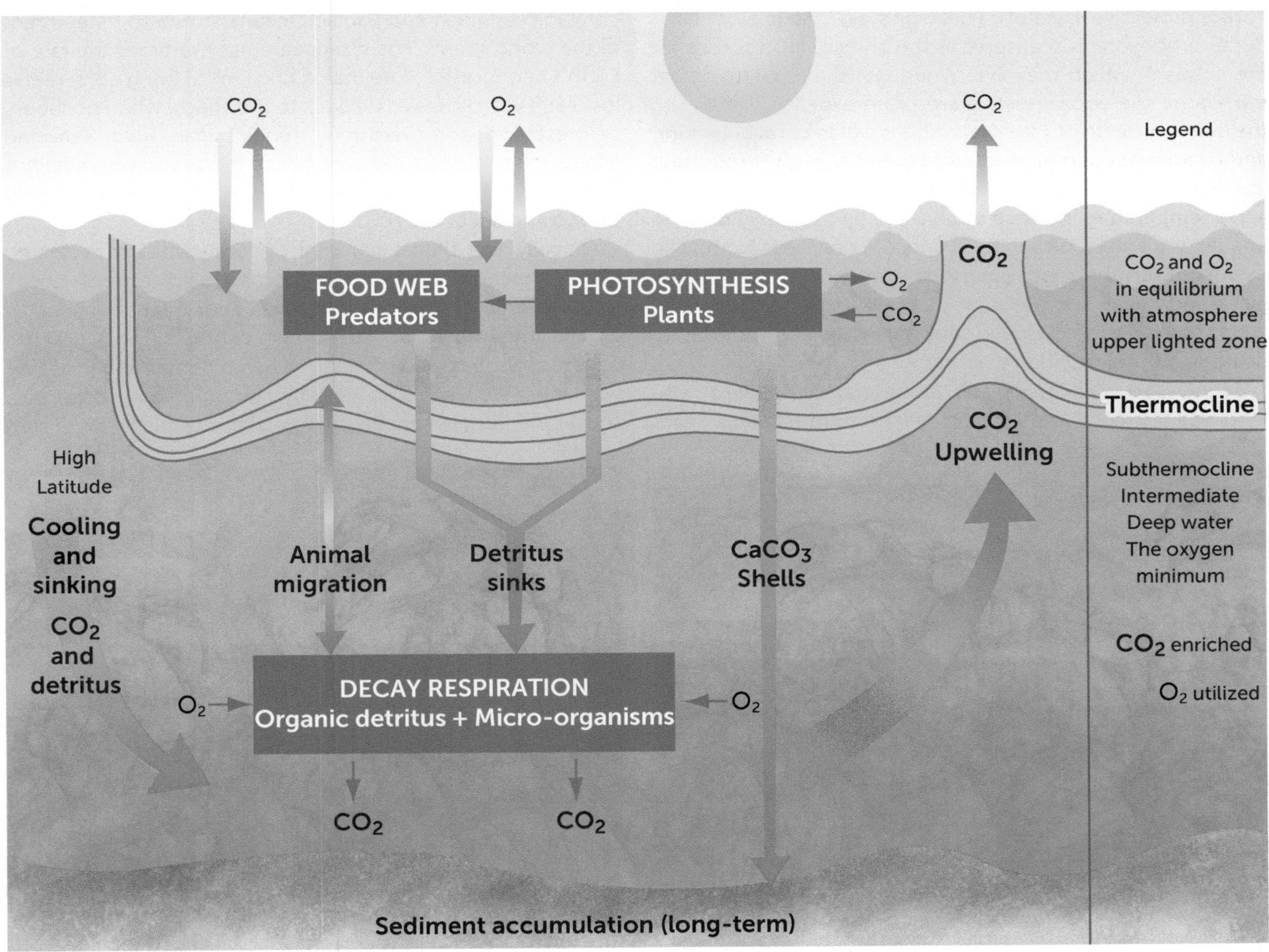

FIGURE 8.1 | The ocean–atmosphere carbon cycle.

Source: Field et al. (2002: 13).

ENVIRONMENT IN FOCUS

BOX 8.1 | Coral Reefs—The Rain Forests of the Sea

Coral reefs are in many ways oceanic analogues of the tropical rain forests. Found throughout tropical and subtropical seas, they are among the most diverse and productive ecosystems on Earth. Like the rain forests, they have an ancient evolutionary history, having first appeared more than 225 million years ago, with some living reefs perhaps as old as 2.5 million years. With solar radiation their primary source of energy, these habitats are found predominantly within 30° north and south of the equator at depths of fewer than 50 to 70 metres.

Coral reefs consist of individual **coral polyps** and the calcium carbonate skeletons deposited by prior generations of corals and other reef-associated organisms (e.g., coralline red algae and molluscs). These limestone secretions serve as a substrate for live coral polyps to grow and flourish.

Many coral species are involved in symbiotic relationships with unicellular algae, or **zooxanthellae**, that live inside the coral's protective skeleton. These photosynthetic algae produce carbohydrates that serve as the primary food source for the corals in which they live. When water temperatures get too warm, the zooxanthellae are often expelled, leading to the eventual death of the corals. This is called **coral bleaching** and has been recorded over large areas of reefs throughout the world over the past two decades. In tropical shallow waters, a temperature increase of only 3°C by 2100 may result in annual or biannual bleaching events of coral reefs from 2030 to 2050. Even the most optimistic scenarios project annual bleaching in 80–100 per cent of the world's coral reefs by 2080. This is likely to result in severe damage and widespread death of corals around the world.

Acting as sources of food and refuge to an incredible diversity of sea life, coral reefs are vitally important habitats. Shark populations, for example, have been found to be healthier on healthy coral reefs, and overfishing of sharks leads to a decline in reef health. There is an obvious connection between these vastly different oceanic trophic levels. These complex ecosystems also provide a number of critical ecosystem services, including the regulation of environmental disturbances, the treatment of organic wastes, the production of food, and the creation of recreational opportunities—for example, for scuba diving.

Despite their value, coral reefs are highly threatened worldwide, having been plagued by the effects of destructive fishing practices, coastal erosion, marine pollution, and irresponsible tourism activities. Southeast Asia is the world's epicentre for coral reef diversity, and more than 80 per cent of its reefs are considered threatened, with 50 per cent in the high-risk category. Over the past two and a half decades, coral in the Indian and Pacific Oceans, home to 75 per cent of the world's reefs, has disappeared at five times the rate of Earth's rain forests. More than 3,000 km^2 of living coral reef is lost each year. Losses date back to the 1960s, when pollution, deforestation, and overfishing trends began. Reefs vanished at an annual rate of 1 per cent during the 1980s, with declines climbing through the 1990s to the current rate of 2 per cent (Bruno and Selig, 2007).

Globally, less than 2 per cent of coral reefs are protected from extraction, poaching, and other major threats. Local, national, and international initiatives have been launched to counter the effects, but consumers can help, too. Coral has become a fashionable accessory; avoid purchasing jewellery with coral. You can also help by not purchasing coral as a souvenir or for your aquarium. If you keep tropical fish, ensure

© Philip Dearden

Healthy coral reefs are very complex structures full of colour and movement that take centuries to develop and may last for thousands of years.

© Philip Dearden

An example of a reef that has experienced coral bleaching.

that they have been sustainably bred in captivity. As fish species are removed from the reefs, the whole community becomes less stable and more likely to collapse (see Box 8.3).

The Banggai cardinal fish, a reef species, is an example of what can happen to fish populations if they are over-exploited for the aquarium trade. The fish is found only in the Banggai Archipelago near Sulawesi in Indonesia, and its iridescent beauty and rarity have made it a favourite of aquariumists. The fish has experienced an 89-per-cent drop in population since the aquarium trade began in 1995, and in 2007 it was declared an endangered species by IUCN. The fish has no dispersal capability, low fecundity, long gestation periods, high early mortality, and a very restricted habitat. These are conditions that make some species more vulnerable to extinction than others, as discussed in Chapter 14. Breeding programs have been undertaken, but unless unsustainable exploitation can be controlled, ultimately they will not work.

Excess carbon dioxide in the atmosphere, a main source of global warming (Chapter 7), is also predicted to lead to the extinction of coral reefs. The CO_2 is absorbed by the oceans and produces carbonic acid, making the oceans more acidic. The hydrogen ions released from this acid lower the pH (like acid rain; see Chapter 4). The oceans have absorbed over a third of the fossil-fuel CO_2 emitted into the atmosphere since pre-industrial times, causing a measurable reduction in seawater pH and carbonate saturation. If CO_2 emissions continue to rise at current rates, upper-ocean pH will decrease to levels lower than have been experienced for tens of millions of years and, critically, at a rate of change 100 times greater than at any time over this period. Scientists predict that by the end of the century, nowhere on Earth will water chemistry still permit the growth of coral reefs. Their calcium skeleton will simply be melted away by the increased acidity, and the concentration of available carbonate ions will be too low for marine calcifiers, such as coral reefs, molluscs, crustaceans, and some algae, to build their shells and skeletons. Ocean acidification will have a very visible impact on coral reefs, but its impact will be felt not only throughout the oceans but throughout planetary life-support systems. It is one of the greatest challenges we now face.

Cold-water corals are expected to be particularly vulnerable to acidification due to their very slow growth. Such corals were only recently discovered off Canada's coasts. Scientists on a research ship in 2003 discovered a reef between Cape Breton Island and Newfoundland. Unfortunately, the reef, made up mainly of *Lophelia pertusa*, had already been badly damaged by bottom trawling. Cold-water corals are found in waters ranging from 3–14°C and occur mainly where cold, clear, nutrient-rich waters are present. However, a recent expedition to Baffin Bay found bamboo coral growing in muddy waters at 900 metres deep. Living mostly in perpetual darkness, cold-water corals do not possess symbiotic, single-celled algae like warm-water corals and rely solely on zooplankton and detritus for sustenance. Some species, such as *Lophelia*, can form large, complex, three-dimensional reef structures several metres high. Other soft corals living in colder waters, such as *Gorgonia*, form not reefs but large "gardens" covering vast areas—for example, around the Aleutian island chain in the North Pacific. The ecological functions of such reefs and gardens in the deeper waters are similar to those of tropical reefs: they are biodiversity hotspots and home, feeding, and nursery grounds for a vast number of other organisms, including commercial fish and shellfish species.

© Philip Dearden

Philip Dearden

Philip Dearden

Coral reefs are home to some of the most complex and colourful organisms on Earth. Here are the Banggai cardinal fish from Indonesia, an endemic nudibranch from the Andaman Sea, and a clam and coral from the Maldives.

several universities to try to breed a faster-maturing, more acid-resistant scallop for aquaculture.

The carbon-saturated water does not stay where it is but moves around the globe, mainly as a result of differing water densities. This is known as **thermohaline circulation** and involves warm surface water that is cooled at high latitudes sinking into deeper basins with water close to 0°C. The key to this circulation is the high salt content of the sea water that allows the water density to increase before it freezes and sinks at certain sites. The main sites for conversion are in the North Atlantic, the Arctic Ocean, and the Weddell Sea in the Antarctic. When the water sinks, it carries with it large quantities of carbon. This sinking is the main mechanism for the removal of atmospheric carbon by the oceans. The cold water is then carried along the ocean floor until it mixes with surface waters and is transported back by wind-driven currents to the conversion areas (Figure 8.2)

The system is in fact a series of interlinked and variable currents that serve to mediate the Earth's climate through the transport of heat and water around the globe (Figure 8.2). Its scale is vast, with the flow estimated at more than 100 Amazon Rivers and the heat delivered to the North Atlantic being about one-quarter of that received directly from the sun. One of the main concerns with global warming (Chapter 7) is the impact it may have on thermohaline circulation. For example, with increased temperatures, there will be increased freshwater melting from the polar ice caps. Fresh water is less dense and will not sink to the same depth as super-cooled salty water, and therefore less carbon will be sequestered for shorter periods of time.

This is a classic example of a positive feedback loop (Chapter 3): the warmer the atmosphere gets as a result of increased CO_2 emissions, the more ice will melt, resulting in less CO_2 being absorbed by the ocean, which will result in increased atmospheric warming—and more melting. The cycle will perpetuate itself unless equally strong negative feedback loops come into play. One example of a potential negative feedback loop in this context is the plankton that produce dimethyl sulphide gas. Given enough nutrient supply, a warmer climate should produce a greater abundance of plankton. The gas is important in enhancing the formation of atmospheric sulphate aerosol particles and cloud condensation nuclei that would tend to screen out sunlight and hence produce a negative feedback loop for the effects of global warming. Unfortunately, scientists do not feel that the effects of this negative feedback loop will be enough to counteract the effects of the numerous positive feedback loops likely being triggered by global warming.

There is much scientific uncertainty about these global systems. Scientists know they exist and that they are of crucial importance in determining global climatic conditions. They also know that these are dynamic systems that change over time. However, because of a lack of good baseline data, it is often difficult to assess the dimensions of natural change and the underlying mechanisms. Large spatial changes happen only rarely and slowly, requiring the collection of very long data sets of frequent measurements in order to understand them. Ocean scientists are trying to establish these kinds of monitoring systems so that we can understand observed changes and reduce uncertainty (Box 8.2). Meanwhile, the physical evidence to support global climatic change continues to grow. For example, 2012 saw the lowest coverage of Arctic sea-ice cover since satellite imagery began tracking the sea-ice cover in the late 1970s. There has been some recovery since then but the total area is still much less than it was a decade ago.

Ocean Management Challenges

Oceanic ecosystems have been providing humans with sustenance since time immemorial. Coastal zones, including the continental shelf, occupy about 18 per cent of the Earth's surface, supply about 90 per cent of the global fish catch, and account for roughly 25 per cent of global primary productivity. Approximately 50 per cent of the world's population now lives in the coastal zone, i.e., within 100 kilometres of a coast. By 2100, nearly 75 per cent of the world's population will live within the coastal zone, mostly clustered into "mega-cities."

The oceans are crucial to the way in which planetary ecosystems work and to the functioning of human society. Global research indicates that virtually no region of the ocean is untouched by humanity, and more than 40 per cent is heavily affected. In 1883, Thomas Huxley, the great nineteenth-century biologist, voiced the common opinion that "probably all the great sea fisheries are inexhaustible." This statement has proven to be far from the truth. This section reviews some

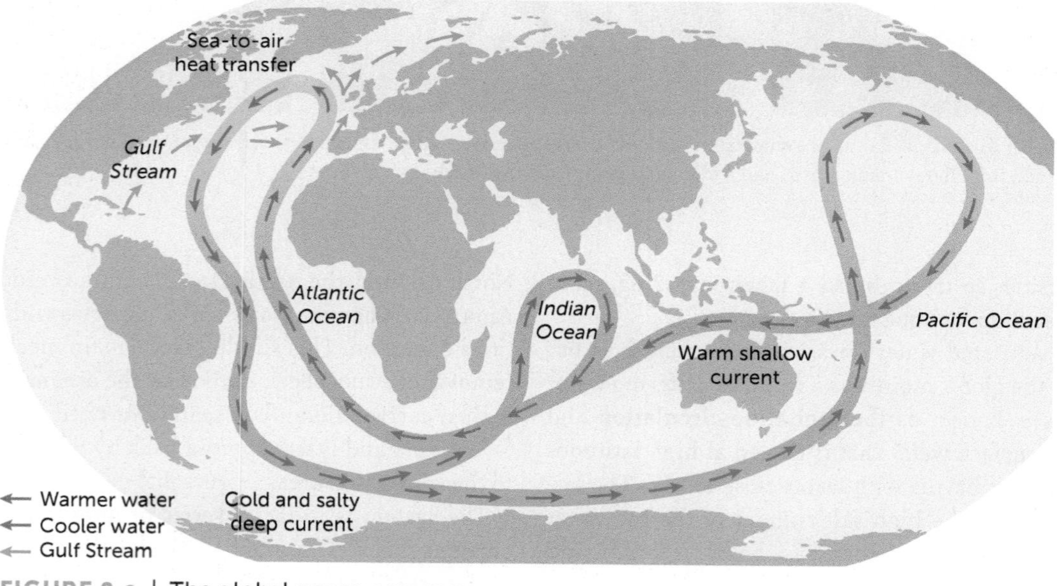

FIGURE 8.2 | The global ocean conveyor.

ENVIRONMENT IN FOCUS

BOX 8.2 | Regional-Scale Nodes and the Canadian NEPTUNE Project

Ocean Networks Canada operates the NEPTUNE and VENUS cabled ocean observatories that collect data on physical, chemical, biological, and geological aspects of the ocean over long time periods. Such Internet-linked, sensor-robotic networks offer novel approaches to human interaction with many remote or dangerous oceanic processes intrinsic to the habitability of our planet. Continuous, real-time information flow from the ocean via electro-optical cables allows rapid growth in our understanding of (1) the habitats and behaviour of known and novel life forms, (2) many climate-changing processes, (3) erupting underwater volcanoes, (4) the migration of charismatic marine mammals, (5) the assessment and management of living and non-living marine resources, (6) the timing and intensity of major undersea earthquakes, (7) the mitigation of natural disasters, and (8) a host of new discoveries continuously unfolding within the "inner space" of the global ocean. Researchers, educators, and members of the public have open web access to all imagery and information in their own laboratories, classrooms, and living rooms as the technologies and visualization software required to operate these in situ, submarine sensing networks become more sophisticated.

In 2009, NEPTUNE Canada (www.oceannetworks.ca) completed installation of its regional-scale observatory with an 800-kilometre cable loop from the shore station at Port Alberni, Vancouver Island, connecting five observatory nodes in coastal, continental slope, abyssal plain, and spreading ridge environments. Ironically, in 2011 one of the main instrument nodes on the floor of the ocean was badly damaged by a deepwater trawler. The area is supposed to be off limits to trawling and the incident illustrates the difficulties in enforcing such regulations in the oceans. This illegal trawler was caught because it was detected by the cameras of the instrument platform. However, in the vast majority of such cases, no cameras exist and illegal trawling continues.

VENUS (www.oceannetworks.ca) is a coastal observatory in waters near Victoria and Vancouver. The first 4-kilometre line was installed in Saanich Inlet, with the node 100 metres deep near the oxic/anoxic transition zone within the fjord. The second 40-kilometre line with two nodes extends from the Fraser River Delta across much of the Strait of Georgia. The observatories investigate ocean and biological processes and delta dynamics in waters up to 300 metres deep. Real-time data and imagery are relayed from Saanich Inlet through the VENUS website. VENUS is used in an interactive mode for researchers to trigger experiments remotely and for educators to involve students in online studies. ONC now also operates a community observatory in the Arctic Ocean off Cambridge Bay, Nunavut.

FIGURE 8.3 | The Oceans Network Canada undersea observatory network.

Source: http://www.oceannetworks.ca/about-us. Image courtesy of Ocean Networks Canada.

of the main management challenges facing ocean ecosystems as a result of fisheries and other human activities (Figure 8.5).

Fisheries

The most important fishing grounds in the world are on and along continental shelves within fewer than 200 nautical miles (370 kilometres) of the shore. The distribution of these fishing grounds is patchy and localized. More than half of the marine landings are caught within 100 kilometres of the coast in depths generally less than 200 metres covering an area of less than 7.5 per cent of the world's oceans, and 92 per cent of marine landings are caught in less than half of the total ocean area. These areas of the ocean play a major role in sustaining global populations.

Global annual per capita fish consumption had risen from 9.9 kilograms in the 1960s to over 27 kilograms by 2014, supplying 3 billion people with over 20 per cent of their protein

INTERNATIONAL GUEST STATEMENT

The Rise and Fall of Industrial Fisheries | *Daniel Pauly*

Industrial fishing started in 1880, when the first steam trawlers were deployed along the English coast. This form of fishing spread rapidly in the North Atlantic, as it did in the North Pacific when Japan developed similar fishing methods. However, only after World War II did industrial fisheries begin their conquest of the world ocean. The growth of these fisheries was particularly rapid in the 1950s and 1960s, in terms of both input into the fisheries (invested capital, vessel tonnage, etc.) and output (tonnage or ex-vessel values of the landings). This period was also a time when fisheries appeared to behave like any other sector of the economy, with increased inputs leading to increasing outputs.

The 1950s and 1960s also saw the first massive fisheries collapses, as stocks that sustained entire fishing fleets, processing plants, and thousands of workers and their families, such as the California sardine fishery, disappeared practically overnight. Other fisheries were rebuilt after a few years, such as the Peruvian anchoveta fishery, which first experienced a massive collapse in 1972. The Peruvian example illustrates an approach prevalent in the heyday of the California sardine fishery: blame the environment. In Peru it was said El Niño did it—never mind the fact that the catch in the year prior to the collapse was about 16 million tonnes, rather than the 12 million tonnes officially reported, which itself hugely exceeded what the best experts of the time had recommended as sustainable.

Various concepts have been deployed to apprehend these events. One of these is Garrett Hardin's "Tragedy of the Commons," which can be used to explain why the pathologies mentioned above were likely to occur in the largely unregulated fisheries then prevalent. These pathologies—which are still with us—have other aspects, notably: (1) not effectively monitoring the fisheries, which results in, among other things, catches that are generally under-reported, (2) ignoring scientific advice aimed at restricting the catch and buildup of fishing effort, and (3) blaming "the environment" for the fisheries collapse that inevitably follows. These and related pathologies existed long before the overfishing became widespread. However, when generalized overfishing became undeniable, a battery of new terms had to be coined to deal, at least conceptually, with the new developments. Hence the words "**bycatch**" (fish caught but not targeted by fishing operations) and "discards" (bycatch that is thrown overboard, mostly dead), and the emergence of the concept of **illegal, unreported, and unregulated (IUU) fisheries**.

In 1975, catches peaked in the North Atlantic, before going into a slow decline continuing to the present. This pattern was accentuated when the giant stock of northern cod off Newfoundland and Labrador collapsed, plummeting

Philip Dearden

Philip Dearden

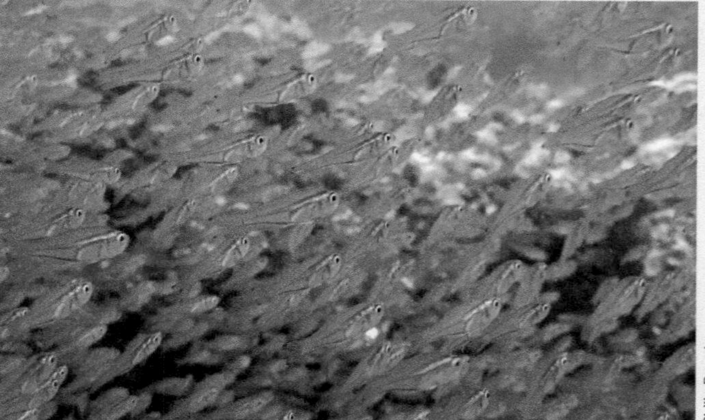

Philip Dearden

Industrial fisheries at work in Myanmar. Myanmar has only relatively recently opened up to fishers from elsewhere, a geographical expansion as a result of political change. However, fisheries have quickly been over-exploited. Here fishers from Thailand unload barrels full of what has been termed "trash" fish (fish with no market value) from their trawler. The very small fish that provide the base to the marine food web (bottom) are now caught to be turned into fish meal largely for aquaculture. From Chapters 2 and 3 you will realize why this is a very short-sighted strategy.

thousands of families and an entire Canadian province into dislocation and economic hardship, and setting off a frantic search for something to blame (hungry seals, cold water, etc.) other than the out-of-control fishing industry.

The relatively well-documented freshwater and coastal fisheries of ancient times had the capacity to induce severe decline in and even extirpation of vulnerable species of marine mammals, fish, and invertebrates, as documented by a variety of sources. However, only since the onset of industrial fishing has the successive depletion of inshore stocks, followed by that of more offshore stocks, become routine. Thus, in the North Sea, it took only a few years for the accumulated coastal stocks of flatfish and other groups to be depleted and for the newly deployed English steam trawlers to be forced to move on to the central North Sea, then further, all the way to Iceland. A southward expansion soon followed, toward the tropics and through the development of industrial fishing in the nascent Third World, often through joint ventures with European (e.g., Spanish) or Japanese firms. Obviously, this expansion created new resource access conflicts and/or intensified earlier ones: hence the protracted "cod war" between Iceland and Britain, or the brief "turbot war" of March 1995 between Canada and Spain. At the close of the twentieth century, the bottom-fish resources of all large shelves of the world, all the way south to Patagonia and Antarctica, had been depleted, mainly by trawling, along with those of seamounts and oceanic plateaus. Indeed, from 1950 to 1980, industrial fisheries expanded their reach by about 1 million km^2 per year; it increased by 3–4 million km^2 per year in the 1980s, then declined. By 2000, the geographic expansion was essentially over, and the emphasis turned to two other forms of expansion.

The second dimension of the expansion of fishing was bathymetric (i.e., offshore), which affected both the open (pelagic) waters and the sea floor. In the pelagic realm, the exploitation of tuna, billfishes, and sharks by longlines and similar gear has strongly modified oceanic ecosystems, which now have much reduced biomass of large predators. This is intensified by the use of fish aggregating devices (FADs, some form of floating object, usually tethered to the sea bottom, that provides shade under which fish congregate), which, starting around the Philippines, have spread throughout the inter-tropical belt and have made accessible to fisheries small tuna and other fish that could not be captured before, thus representing an additional expansion of sorts. In the demersal or seafloor realm, trawlers were deployed that can reach down to depths of several kilometres. They yield a catch increasingly dominated by slow-growing, deepwater species with low productivity, which cannot be exploited sustainably. Therefore, given that the high seas (the waters outside countries' 200-mile exclusive economic zones) are legally unprotected against such depredations, their oceanic plateaus and seamounts are subjected to intense localized fishing pressure, with subsequent collapse of the resources; the same is then repeated on the adjacent plateau or seamount. This fishing mode is no more sustainable than tropical deforestation, discussed in Chapter 9.

Finally, the geographic and bathymetric expansions, which deplete traditional species, also cause previously spurned fish species to be caught and processed, thus generating a "taxonomic" expansion. This is the reason why North American and European fish markets increasingly display unfamiliar seafood.

Overall, these three expansions—geographic, bathymetric, and demersal—and the massive import of seafood products by the global North from the global South are the reasons why global fisheries appear sustainable. These are also the reasons why they are not.

Philip Dearden

Daniel Pauly received his doctorate from the University of Kiel in Germany and for many years taught and did research at the International Center for Living Aquatic Resources Management in the Philippines. He is a professor of fisheries at the University of British Columbia and is the principal investigator of the Sea Around Us project, which documents and communicates the impact of global fisheries on marine ecosystems (see www.seaaroundus.org).

requirements and 17 per cent of the world's annual animal protein supply (FAO, 2014b). More than 1 billion people rely on fish as their primary source of protein. This supply is tapped by fishers ranging from villagers using homemade canoes trying to feed their families (Box 8.3) through to multi-million dollar offshore factory ships owned by multinational corporations. Given this great scale and variation, it is only recently that fisheries scientists have begun to understand more about what is happening in global fisheries as discussed by Daniel Pauly in the above "International Guest Statement."

Clear evidence, obtained from bottom sediment cores going back hundreds of years, shows that fish populations fluctuated widely as a result of changing environmental conditions, even before the advent of modern fishing. However, the scale and speed of current changes are unprecedented. More than 80 per cent of global fisheries are now fully utilized or overexploited (Figure 8.6). Because of advances in technology and subsidies, fishing capacity is now estimated to be as much as 2.5 times what is needed to harvest a sustainable yield from the world's fisheries. Figure 8.7 shows a gradual levelling off in recent years, but many scientists argue that this masks a major unprecedented collapse of ocean fisheries. Scientists at the Fisheries Research Centre at the University of British Columbia, for example, revealed that the catch data shown in the graph may be up to 25 per cent above actual catch data. This may be the result of the routine reporting of inflated catches by China (Watson and Pauly, 2001). The problem is that permitted catch levels are based largely on historical catch information. If the latter is inflated, it leads to unsustainable catch levels in the future. Some fisheries scientists have

ENVIRONMENT IN FOCUS

BOX 8.3 | Fishing and Poverty

Many of the poorest people in the world are fishers who rely on the sea to provide them and their families with their livelihoods. Sustainable for centuries, many of these fisheries are now in a state of collapse through the pressures of increasing demands and the reduced ability of the ocean to provide. The Moken, or so-called "Sea Gypsies" of the Andaman coast of Malaysia, Thailand, and Myanmar, are a case in point. They are traditionally people of the sea to the point that their boats are their houses and they move around for most of the year collecting seafood, only settling on land for the monsoon season. However, as both the abundance of seafood and their access to it has declined, as islands either are developed or are protected as national parks, so has the base of their livelihoods. Many of them have now settled on land permanently and maintain boats only to participate in declining fisheries along with other coastal communities. Originally seafood gatherers in a pre-hunting stage of society, many are now switching to hunting activities such as fishing. As the fisheries continue to decline, new livelihoods will need to be devised and are even now appearing with the growth of low-input aquaculture.

Living alongside the Moken in the Myeik Archipelago in Myanmar are some Karen people. The Karen are an ethnic minority who usually dwell in highland areas of Myanmar and Thailand, where they are known for their approach to slash-and-burn agriculture, which is more conservation oriented than that of other peoples in the region. However, since 1949 they have been engaged in an armed struggle with the Myanmar government. Tiring of the fighting, a few settlements have moved to the isolated islands of the Myeik Archipelago, where some Karen have intermarried with the Moken. However, it appears that the Karen have also learned from the Moken how to access the riches underwater and are

Karen fishers with part of their two-day catch of parrotfish speared on the reefs.

Moken women cooking shellfish.

FIGURE 8.4 | The main homeland area of the Moken and Karen people.

Moken village.

doing so very efficiently. Using boats with an air compressor and hoses, four divers at a time go down onto the reefs to spearfish at night. Many of the fish are sleeping, especially the parrotfish, and are easy prey for the fishers. The parrotfish, in one of the many marvels of evolution found on coral reefs, make a mucus bubble to sleep in at night. The bubble provides protection from nocturnal olfactory hunters. However, the bubble provides no protection against spears. In a 2015 dive expedition, we were amazed to see the numbers of fish that can be speared in this fashion, as shown in the photograph, the result of two nights' fishing by eight men.

It is not just the sheer number of fish that are being speared that is important; it is also the species of fish. Most of them, maybe three-quarters, are parrotfish. Parrotfish are keystone species (Chapter 2) on reefs. They keep algae growth in check by nibbling the coral. When they are removed, algae move in and smother the coral. This outcome is precisely what has happened in the Caribbean over the last 30 years, where live coral cover is now down to 20 per cent (Jackson et al., 2014). Coral scientists identified maintaining parrotfish populations as the single-most important goal in reef conservation. What we found in the Myeik was the converse of this, with an economy that has developed to rid the reefs of the fish.

What would you do?

predicted the global collapse of all taxa currently fished by 2048, if current levels of exploitation continue (Worm et al., 2006), although others (e.g., Branch, 2008) dispute this finding. What do you think should be done, given the conflicting scientific evidence and opinion?

The fish being caught are also substantially smaller than the ones caught in the past (Figure 8.8). Research suggests that for top predators, current sizes are one-fifth to one-half what they used to be. Modern fisheries management often encourages fishers to select the large individuals of targeted stocks, either by using size-selective gear or by releasing small individuals back to the water. The reasoning has been that this allows smaller, younger individuals to grow up to reproductive age, thereby sustaining the stock. Recent research, however, shows that removing the larger, older individuals of a population may actually undermine stock replenishment. Some researchers have proposed that maintaining old-growth age structure can be important for replenishing fished populations. It is termed the Big Old Fat Fecund Female Fish (BOFFFF) hypothesis. Research shows that removing BOFFFF and other large adults can result in evolutionary changes in populations.

Changes in fish populations are not immediately obvious, since scientists tend to look only at the most recent data rather than comparing them with historical catches. This problem is known as a **shifting baseline** in which scientists have no other option than to take the current degraded state as the baseline rather than the historical ecological abundance. Removal of virtually all the large predatory fish from oceanic ecosystems will have significant implications for the structure and functioning of these ecosystems.

Some authors now suggest that the impact of commercial fishing is so great that "evolutionary impact assessments" should be undertaken, since fishing causes changes to occur in decades rather than millennia, as would happen under normal conditions. The scientists note that fisheries-induced mortality is now reckoned to exceed natural mortality by 400 per cent and that increased mortality generally means that fish will reach sexual maturity at a younger age and increase levels of reproduction, but these younger fish produce smaller fish, as explained in the BOFFFF hypothesis. These trends are further exacerbated when fisheries selectively target larger or more mature individuals.

Many fish species show changes in their size and age at maturation, reduced annual growth, and loss of genetic diversity (Hutchings et al., 2012). Such fisheries-induced evolution may be slow to reverse, or even could be irreversible, and will affect many other species through trophic and

"Then" - - - - - - - - - - ► "Now"

Human expansion

5. Climate change

4. Introductions

3. Mechanical habitat destruction

2. Pollution

1. Fishing

Altered ecosystems

FIGURE 8.5 | Historical sequence of human impacts on marine ecosystems.

Source: Jackson et al., (2011)

Philip Dearden

Many of the fishers of the world operate from small, unpowered dugouts, such as this one off the coast of Zanzibar, with his hand-sewn, rice bag sail. Although individually each boat may have little impact on fisheries stocks, in some areas the sheer number of boats mean that catches are declining.

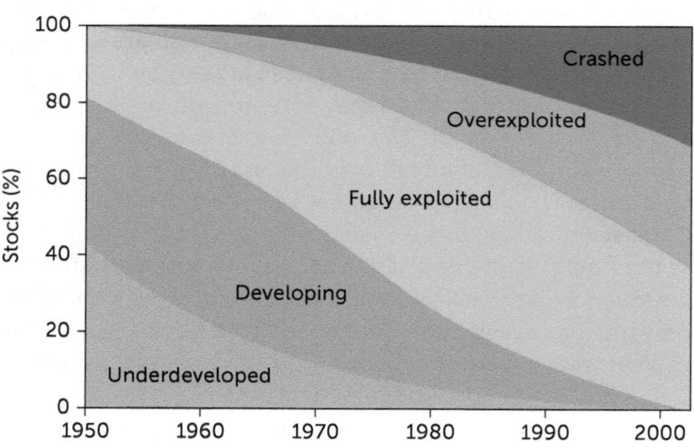

FIGURE 8.6 | State of the world's fishery stocks.

Source: Nellemann et al. (2008: 17).

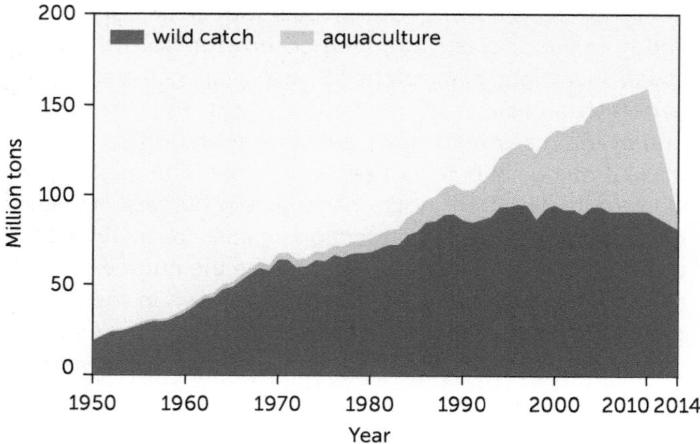

FIGURE 8.7 | World seafood production, 1950–2014.

Source: Adapted from Theobold, M., "Fish Production Reaches a Record," Vital Signs, *03 December 2009: <http://vitalsigns.worldwatch.org/vs-trend/fish-production-reaches-record>. Data source:* FAO *(2014b).*

ecological interactions. Managing fisheries from an evolutionary perspective will almost certainly require a variety of strategies. For some fisheries, we may need no-take zones such as **marine protected areas (MPAs)**, as discussed later in the chapter, where the full range of sizes and ages of a given species can thrive. For those that target migratory species, setting both maximum and minimum size restrictions might work better.

The total catch consists of many different species, which creates several problems. Ideally, fishing should be self-regulating. As the catch of the target species declines, this should result in a reduced fishing effort as it becomes unprofitable. Unfortunately, this is not what happens. Instead, fishing fleets increase their efforts toward the target species and then turn to the next most profitable species until that, too, is depleted. Then they pursue the next most profitable species and so on. This is a familiar foraging behaviour in ecology, known as **prey switching**. In the fishery, it leads to **serial depletion** in which one stock after another becomes progressively depleted even if the total catch remains the same. This phenomenon has been well documented in whales (Box 8.4). Unfortunately, after switching the target species, many fisheries take some of the depleted species as bycatch, making it even more difficult for the stocks to recover.

The shift in target species is not the only change in the world's fishing activities. We are progressively exploiting lower and lower trophic levels to derive our catch. Fisheries in many areas have now focused on invertebrates, like the Atlantic crab. Large-sized fish no longer exist. This is known as **fishing down the food chain**. The gains in fish catch shown in

Perspectives on the Environment

Fish Stocks in Decline

. . . persistent changes in size-at-age may be a harbinger of declining condition, reproductive capacity, or the ability to withstand additional anthropogenic or environmental stressors. Declines in size-at-age have often been precursor indicators of impending population collapse. In several Pacific and Atlantic biogeographic units, this review noted long-term declines in size-at-age that may be indicators of significant changes in population productivity and resilience which should be a cause for concern and investigation.

—Fisheries and Oceans Canada (2010)

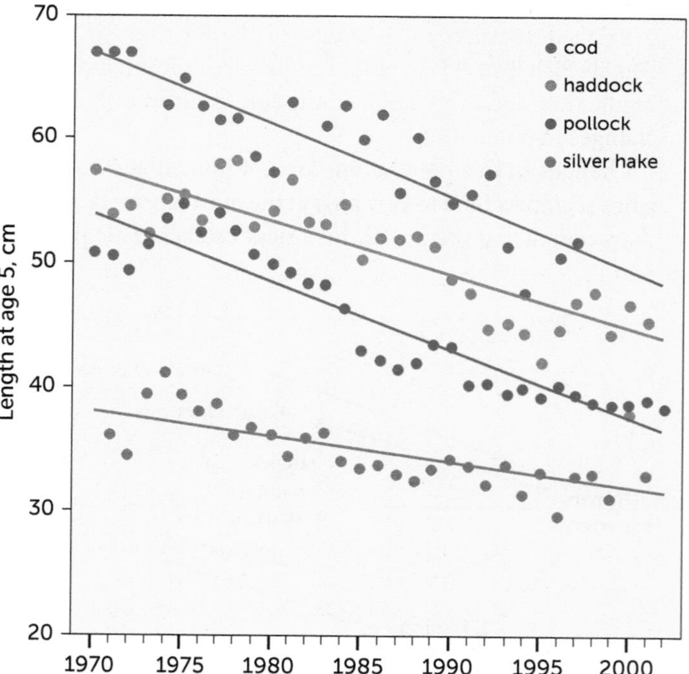

FIGURE 8.8 | Fish size decline, 1970–2000.

Sources: Fisheries and Oceans Canada (2003); DFO *(2010: 25).*

Philip Dearden

This shark was caught by a "ghost net" snagged on the bottom but still doing the deadly function it was designed for.

Figure 8.7 were mainly the result of reaching further down the food chain to previously underexploited trophic levels, as well as accessing fish from greater and greater depths (Figure 8.9).

Eating lower on the food chain is not a bad idea. Few of us habitually eat wolves, tigers, and other top terrestrial predators, but in the oceans we target the top predators. It takes close to 60 million tonnes of potentially edible fish per year to feed the 3 million tonnes of the three major tropical tuna species we harvest annually; this is due to the second law of thermodynamics, discussed in Chapter 2. If we were to replace some of the tuna in our sandwiches with the anchovies, sardines, squid, and other species the tuna eat, we would open up a substantial supply of protein that could feed millions more.

Besides the impact on target species, fishing activities have many other ecological repercussions. Of particular concern is the impact on non-target organisms, or bycatch. Estimates

ENVIRONMENT IN FOCUS

BOX 8.4 | Leviathan

> The mammoth bones of the California Gray lie bleaching on the shores of those silvery waters, and are scattered along the broken coasts, from Siberia to the Gulf of California; and ere long it may be questioned whether this mammal will not be numbered among the extinct species of the Pacific.
>
> —Captain Charles Scammon, 1874

Canada has the longest coastline in the world, as well as some of the richest waters. Cold oceanic waters from the north and deep upwelling currents mix with warmer waters from the tropics to create an abundance of life. Rich nutrient supplies, accompanied by shallow seas and long daylight hours in the summer, have created some of the richest waters off the east coast. Plankton flourish and provide the base for a diverse food web that supports three main groups of marine mammals—the Odontoceti or toothed whales, the Mysticeti or baleen whales, and the Pinnipedia or seals and walruses. The baleen whales all feed on plankton, small fish, and marine algae by means of plates of baleen in their mouths that filter these organisms from the water. From these small food items, the baleen whales have evolved as the largest creatures on this planet. The blue whale is the largest of the baleen whales; the largest recorded was a female more than 30 metres long and weighing 140 tonnes. The blue whale, as well as other baleen whales such as the fin and sei whales, was once found in abundance off the east coast, as was the largest toothed whale, the sperm whale. These whale populations were all decimated by hunting and are only now starting to recover.

In the late fifteenth century, Europe found itself increasingly short of the oil needed to light its lanterns. Marine mammals, with a thick layer of blubber, were the solution. Exposed to high heat, the blubber can be rendered down to oil. The Basques—a seafaring people from northern Spain—discovered the rich whaling grounds off the east coast of Canada. The abundance of whales in these waters at that time is difficult to imagine. Whales could be harpooned from shore. Early mariners complained of whales as a navigational hazard because they were so numerous; one missionary in the Gulf of St Lawrence reported that the whales were so numerous and loud that they kept him awake all night! The limiting factor was not the number of whales but the ability to process them, and as increasing numbers of shore stations were established, another toehold of colonization began.

As human numbers increased, whale numbers declined. First to go was the one hunted the most, the right whale. The right whale was targeted because it was slow, it floated when it was killed, and one whale could be rendered into more than 16,000 litres of oil. As well, the baleen was used for other indispensable purposes such as clothing supports, brush bristles, sieves, and plumes for military helmets. A Basque shipowner could pay off his ship and all his expenses and still make a good profit in one year from such whales. Although the whales gained some respite when England destroyed the Spanish Armada in 1588, other nations finished off the job.

Other whales—sperm, humpback, blue, fin, sei, and minke—soon joined the right whale as commercially, if not biologically, extinct. This is a classic example of serial depletion. By the early 1970s, there were no commercially viable populations of large whales remaining. A global moratorium on whaling was announced in 1987 that still stands today, despite pressure from Japan and Norway, both of which continue to kill whales

Continued

Humpback whales were once common off both the Pacific and Atlantic coasts of Canada.

Whale harpoon in the Fisheries Museum of the Atlantic, Lunenburg, Nova Scotia.

for "research purposes." "Scientific whaling" not only bypasses any internationally agreed catch limits but also circumvents all other rules regarding protected species, closed areas, killing of juveniles, killing methods, and so on.

Iceland became the third country left whaling when it resumed commercial whaling practices in 2006 and by the end of 2013 had killed 414 endangered fin whales and 331 minke whales. In 2011 Japan suspended its annual whale hunt in Antarctica due to harassment by anti-whaling vessels. However, plans were underway to restart the hunt in 2015 with a greatly reduced quota. Iceland has also felt the lack of demand and in 2011 postponed the start of its fin whaling season, although there remains a self-imposed quota of 154 whales per year. The International Whaling Commission estimates the global population of fin whale to be between 1,400 and 7,200 animals, and the IUCN lists the species as endangered. Norway continues whaling, despite shrinking markets.

The removal of such a large biomass from the top of the food chain obviously has ecological repercussions for other organisms. One possible implication is an increase in other krill eaters that would benefit from removal of these large and efficient competitors. For example, it has been suggested that increases in the populations of krill-eating seals (e.g., fur and crab-eating seals) in the Antarctic were caused by whaling. More breeding sites are required to support the higher populations of seals, so seals colonize areas previously used for nesting by birds such as the albatross. Did declining whale numbers also lead to a decline in the albatross? We cannot say for sure, but the example does illustrate the complexities of changes in food webs.

Populations for most species have been slow to recover because of the slow reproductive rates of these K-strategists (Chapter 3). Whaling is now controlled throughout most of the world, and on all of Canada's coasts, a population resurgence is occurring, albeit very slowly for some species such as the right whale. The largest whale, the blue, is also in trouble. Although numbers still exist, finding a mate is difficult for this wide-ranging species. Scientists have found evidence that the blue is interbreeding with the more common fin whale, the second-largest whale in the world, and fear that this hybridization will result in a loss of genetic identity for the blue, which could then disappear as a species. Unfortunately, the rapacious killing by our ancestors denied all future generations the spectacle of our seas full of these mighty creatures. Are our actions today denying future generations similar opportunities?

suggest that 25 per cent of the world's catch is dumped because it is not the right species or size. Virtually all organisms dumped overboard die. The world's largest turtle, the leatherback turtle, is rated as critically endangered on the IUCN Red List (see Chapter 14). In 1980, some 91,000 leatherbacks remained in the Pacific; there are now fewer than 5,000. The Atlantic population is stronger, and the turtles spend a significant amount of time foraging off the Scotian Shelf. They are mainly the victims of the **longline** and gill-net fisheries. Longline fishing in all the world's deep oceans kills some 40,000 sea turtles each year, along with 300,000 seabirds and millions of sharks. Bycatch of albatross, petrels, and shearwaters in longline fisheries is one of the greatest threats to these seabirds. All 21 of the world's species of albatross are now considered at risk of extinction, along with 57 species of sharks and rays.

Some innovative ways to address bycatch are starting to be developed, in some cases helped along by cash prizes offered by NGOs. The World Wildlife Fund, for example, launched the International Smart Gear Competition to encourage innovative, practical, and cost-effective gear designs that safeguard marine life while enabling fishers to better target their intended catch. One winner, knowing that most turtles are hooked at shallow depths, proposed a system for setting baited hooks deeper than 100 metres, thereby minimizing encounters with sea turtles while maintaining the catch of target fish. Turtle mortality can be further reduced by changing the types of hooks used and using fish rather than squid as

As large, long-lived fish high on the food chain are depleted, we seek smaller species. Reprinted by permission of Adrian Raeside.

bait. Another winner proposed placing magnets on fishing lines to scare away sharks, which are particularly sensitive to magnetic fields.

One of the most destructive means of fishing is **bottom trawling**, in which heavy nets are dragged along the sea floor, scooping up everything in their path. This is a common method for catching shrimp, and the ratio of shrimp to other organisms caught is generally around 10 per cent (i.e., one shrimp caught for every 10 organisms caught unintentionally). Trawling has been estimated to be as damaging to

FIGURE 8.9 | Fishing down the food chain.

© Splashdown Direct/Michael Nolan/Rex Features/CP

Rich ocean waters attract many pelagic (open ocean) bird species, such as this adult waved albatross.

the seabed as all other fishing gear combined. The damage extends to more than half of the seabed area of many fishing grounds and is worse in the inner and middle parts of the continental shelves, with particular damage to small-scale coastal fishing communities.

One noted victim of bottom trawling is the ancient sponge reefs off the coast of BC. The sponge reefs, at depths between 165 and 240 metres, are more than 9,000 years old and may reach as high as a six-storey building. Previously, they were known only from fossils in Europe dating from 146 to 245 million years ago, and they were thought to be extinct before their discovery in 1988. Sponge reefs are widely believed to be the first multi-cellular animals on Earth, appearing almost 570 million years ago. The reefs thrive in silica-rich water and are the only siliceous sponge reefs on the planet. Some sponges live in shallower water but as individuals rather than in reefs. The federal government called for *voluntary* trawl

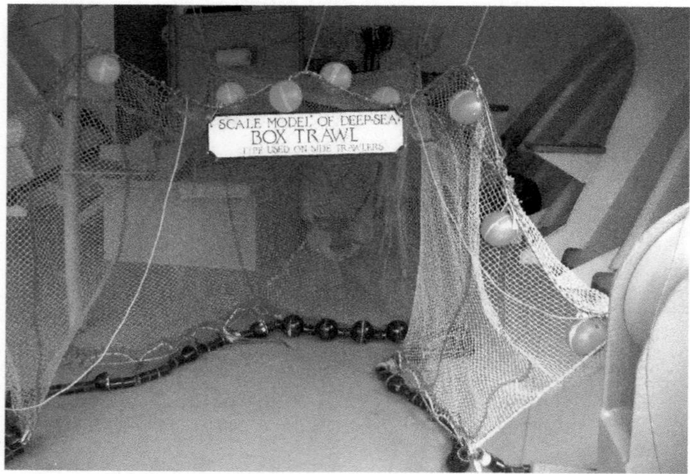

Philip Dearden

Model of a box trawl in the Fisheries Museum of the Atlantic, Lunenburg, Nova Scotia. The large weights are dragged along the sea floor, destroying everything in their path.

restrictions, but in 2002, after documentation of extensive damage to the most pristine reefs by trawling, mandatory closures for groundfish trawling were finally implemented to protect the northern reefs. In 2006 the original boundaries were expanded and closures included shrimp trawling. In 2015 permanent protection was extended to nine small reefs in the Strait of Georgia.

In addition to the direct destructive effects of fishing on non-target organisms, indirect effects occur through food chain relationships (see Hutchings et al., 2012, for an excellent overview). Steller's sea lion, for example, was once abundant in the North Pacific, with more than 300,000 animals recorded in 1960. By 1990, this number had fallen to 66,000, and the US declared the sea lion endangered. The main reason for the decline is thought to be the decline in pollock, their chief food source. As the harvests of cod diminished elsewhere, the demand for pollock increased, leading to unprecedented catches and a subsequent decline in sea lion numbers.

Scientists have recently suggested that another factor may have contributed to this decline. Earlier industrial whaling activities removed the bulk of the killer whale's main prey. In response, the killer whale started "fishing down the food chain," eating sea lions in much greater numbers. Reaching even further down the food chain, the killer whale are now implicated in the decline of sea otters in the North Pacific (Chapter 3). Other scientists (e.g., Trites et al., 2007) have questioned this relationship. But sea lions and sea otters are not the only marine mammals to experience declining numbers; two-thirds of all marine mammals are now classified as endangered on the IUCN Red List (Chapter 14).

Another challenge related to ecosystem dynamics is the rapid growth in jellyfish populations in many parts of the world. Over 2,000 species of jellyfish have been found to be increasing in number and also appearing earlier every year as a result of warming ocean temperatures. Warmer ocean temperatures favour flagellate-dominated food chains (zooplankton) preferred by jellyfish rather than diatom-based food chains (phytoplankton) favoured by fish. In effect, evolution is running backward to the Precambrian period when jellyfish were more dominant than fish in the world's oceans. The current growth in jellyfish populations is related to several factors, including increased nutrient supplies from agricultural runoff and warmer waters, but a main factor is thought to be fisheries depleting the larger fish and turtles that prey on jellyfish.

This increase in jellyfish has many implications. Jellyfish, for example, eat vast quantities of plankton, which thus reduces the base of the food chain for many fish species. Ocean bacteria are critical in absorbing and recycling nutrients such as phosphorus, carbon, and nitrogen. Unlike the dead bodies of fish, jellyfish biomass contains high levels of carbon that bacteria cannot effectively recycle; instead, the

Steller's sea lion, the world's largest sea lion, is now highly endangered in the North Pacific. These are at Cape St James, off the southern tip of the Haida Gwaii (formerly the Queen Charlotte Islands), also the windiest spot in Canada.

jellyfish exhale increasing amounts of carbon dioxide, which in turn adds to global warming. Scientists have detected a 40 per cent decline in global phytoplankton levels since 1950. Since phytoplankton are responsible for half of the annual oxygen production, this decline is obviously of concern.

Pollution

As the recipient of all the polluted water that flows off the land as well as airborne contaminants, the world ocean is the ultimate sink for many pollutants. The scale of global pollution is now astounding—even the oceans are being rendered eutrophic (Chapter 4), in some cases from farming practices thousands of kilometres away.

About 80 per cent of ocean pollution comes from activities on land. The remaining 20 per cent comes from activities at sea, such as waste disposal, oil spills, vessel traffic, oil and gas exploration, and mining. Although we are all familiar with major oil spills, such as that of the *Deepwater Horizon* explosion and wellhead blowout in the Gulf of Mexico, we think little of the many diffuse sources of oil, such as leaking car engines, that eventually seep into the oceans. In fact, the total amount from non-point sources of pollution is considerably greater than from point-source pollution. During the past 25 years, many governments have made considerable progress in monitoring and regulating point-source pollution, such as effluent discharge from factories. However, addressing non-point-source pollution is a much more challenging task, since it requires a change in behaviour by billions of people.

Chemical pollutants take two main forms: toxic materials and nutrients. We live in a chemical society, with more than 100,000 chemicals used in manufacturing and released into the environment every year. Many of these chemicals are harmful to life; when they end up in the ocean, they may cause instant death if released in sufficient quantity, or they may have sub-lethal effects such as inhibition of reproduction. The chemicals are also subject to *bioconcentration*, discussed in more detail in Chapter 10. Synthetic organic chemicals and toxic metals tend to concentrate along two main interfaces in the ocean: the boundary between the seabed and water and the boundary between the water and the atmosphere.

One rapidly emerging impact relating to pollution is **endocrine disruption**. The endocrine system consists of glands and hormones that control many bodily processes such as sex, metabolism, and growth. Many chemicals in everyday use have been found to mimic these processes and may stimulate, replace, or repress the natural processes. More than 50 such endocrine disrupters have been positively identified, and scientists suspect that there are hundreds more. Many of them are in commonly used products such as soaps and detergents. The major effect of these chemicals on marine life detected so far is the feminization of various aquatic species. Hermaphroditic fish are appearing all over Europe and also in the Great Lakes. Increasing numbers of reports from the Arctic are noting hermaphroditic polar bears. Many endocrine disrupters, such as the pesticide DDT and other organochlorines, are vulnerable to both the *grasshopper effect* and *biomagnification* (as described in Chapter 10) and would logically find their way to the top Arctic predator. More research is now underway on this issue, since it is feared that these so-called "gender-benders" may be at least partly behind the documented fall in human male sperm counts in industrialized societies over the past 50 years.

Oxygen depletion occurs as a result of nutrient enrichment, as described in Chapter 4, and leads to large dead areas within the oceans. These areas (**hypoxic** or oxygen-deficient areas) have doubled in abundance every 10 years since the

This dovekie was killed by an oil spill. Oil penetrates through the feathers to the layer of down beneath and decreases the effectiveness of the feathers' insulating properties.

1960s, most recently increasing from 149 in 2003 to more than 400 in 2011. Shang, Yu, and Wu (2006) found that low levels of dissolved oxygen decreased the activity of certain genes that control the production of sex hormones and sexual differentiation in embryonic zebra fish. As a result, 75 per cent of the fish developed male characteristics versus 61 per cent of those raised under normal oxygen conditions. This gender shift decreases the likelihood that they will be able to reproduce in sufficient numbers to maintain sustainable populations. The study raises new concerns about dead zones. Fish and other creatures trapped in these zones often die. Those that escape may be more vulnerable to predators and other stresses. This study suggests that dead zones potentially pose a third threat—the inability of offspring to find mates and reproduce.

Global warming will further promote the growth of dead zones. As water warms, it can hold less oxygen. Furthermore, the ocean receives its oxygen from the atmosphere and from photosynthesizing algae floating at the top. The oxygen is distributed to the deeper ocean as the water sinks. However, global warming will lead to lighter surface water since it will contain more fresh water from melting ice. It will also become lighter as thermal expansion occurs. The net effect will be less mixing of surface waters and further reductions in oxygen content in the ocean, especially in deeper waters. The drop in oxygen levels will further promote the growth of jellyfish, which can store oxygen in their jelly, over oxygen-demanding fish. Danish researchers have calculated that, even if we reduce carbon emissions to zero by 2100, the effects of global warming will cause oxygen levels to fall by 30 per cent over the next 1,000 years. It seems that a low oxygen-level ocean is going to be the reality of the future.

Plastics are also an increasing source of concern, even in more isolated areas such as the Canadian Arctic, where 84 per cent of fulmars have plastic in their stomachs. Fulmars are particularly vulnerable since they skim the top of the water searching for food, but other species are also starting to show significant accumulations: 11 per cent of thick-billed murres from five Arctic colonies, for example, were found to contain plastics in their stomachs. Unlike fulmars, murres dive deep to find food. Ingestion can lead not only directly to death but also to more subtle effects such as loss of appetite, stunted growth, and exposure to pollutants that can leach out of the plastics.

Philip Dearden

A manta ray meets a plastic bag off the coast of Komodo Island in Indonesia. Mid-water plastic bags are often ingested by species that either think they resemble food or simply cannot avoid them.

In the North Sea, seven European countries have jointly implemented an aggressive program to reduce the amount of plastic in the oceans and, consequently, in bird populations. Canada as yet has no such program, even though the levels evident now in the Arctic exceed those set as acceptable by the European partners. The United Nations Environment Programme estimated that the average North American uses around 100 kilograms of plastic a year and predicted that this figure would rise to 140 kilograms by 2015. Furthermore, with an increasingly ice-free Arctic Ocean greater boat traffic means increasing potential for more plastic disposal unless measures are put in place.

Energy

World demand for energy, particularly oil and gas, continues to rise (Chapter 12). Every time you jump into your car or go on an airplane, you are sending a financial message to industry and the government that you support further development of fossil-fuel sources. Many of the world's main oil fields, such as the North Sea in Europe and Hibernia off the coast of Newfoundland, are situated in sedimentary basins under the oceans. More than 60 per cent of current global production comes from these sources. Offshore oil rigs are a source of chronic, low-level pollution caused by the disposal of drilling mud and drill cuttings, which smother the local environment and are often contaminated with oil or chemicals. Oil is pumped to the surface and loaded on tankers or piped ashore, where it is often stored close to the ocean before being refined and further distributed. There is potential for spillage at every stage. Many seabirds and marine organisms are highly vulnerable to oil pollution. Following the wreck of the *Exxon Valdez* off Alaska, for example, more than 750 sea otters died; however, the long-term effects of the spill, including mortality of species such as sea otters, were much greater because of ongoing impacts such as contaminated food chains. Oil is lethal to marine life in its physical effects and its chemical composition. Cleanup attempts following oil spills can also damage many species.

Most accessible ocean oil basins have already been developed. Exploration and development are pushing into increasingly challenging and fragile environments, such as the Arctic Ocean and North Pacific, and are seeking oil

cabman237/iStockphoto

Coastal mega-cities, like Mumbai, India, place marine ecosystems under increasing pressures, resulting in issues such as coastal erosion, intrusion of sea water into fresh water supplies, loss of habitat for birds, fish, and other marine wildlife, depletion of fishery resources, and marine pollution.

at ever-greater depths, as was the case with the *Deepwater Horizon* disaster. The most effective way to reduce the effects of oil exploration and development in these regions is by reducing demand for oil products.

Recent research has highlighted the potential for seabed-based methane hydrates to meet some energy demands. Methane hydrates are ice-like deposits found in the top few hundred metres of sediment in certain deep ocean areas of the continental margins. The methane gas is actually trapped in ice cages and can be easily extracted from it, but removing the hydrates from the seabed has proved problematic. Energy experts have tried using antifreeze to remove the methane from hydrates, and research has focused on trying to pipe warm surface water down to melt the hydrates and then piping the gas to the surface. However, melting the hydrates to release methane may cause the seafloor to become unstable and could have untold ecological impacts. In addition, methane lost to the atmosphere during the process would exacerbate global warming.

Coastal Development

Twenty-one of the world's 33 mega-cities (over 10 million people) are coastal. With half of the world's population living in coastal regions, and that proportion expected to grow significantly during the twenty-first century, these regions also contain the highest concentrations of supporting infrastructure, industrial plants, energy use, and food production in the world, and they are the focal points of global tourism. Half of the world's coastal wetlands have been filled in to support these developments. Meanwhile, as in Canada, environmental decision-making and management within the coastal zone are often highly fragmented among many different agencies, highlighting the importance of governance, discussed in Chapter 5. These extreme pressures on fragile ecosystems with ineffective management control have often led to highly degraded coastal environments in many countries.

Climate Change

As a result of global warming (Chapter 7), sea levels rose an average of 1.5 millimetres per year between 1901 and 1990, and have doubled the rate since that time (Stocker et al., 2013). The IPCC estimates that this will raise the global average sea level by 15 to 95 centimetres by the end of this century. The main causes of sea-level rise include thermal expansion of sea water and the melting of ice in land-based glaciers. Over-pumping of groundwater supplies that eventually run off into the ocean is another cause. Sea-level rise is not, however, uniform. For example, the Bering Sea between Alaska and Russia rose 0.5 millimetres per year since 1993, whereas the Indonesian Seas rose 6.4 millimetres. Higher sea levels increase the impact of storm surges, accelerate habitat degradation, alter tidal ranges, exacerbate flooding, and change sediment and nutrient circulation patterns. Rising levels will displace approximately 1 billion people, many of them among the poorest in the world.

Estimates suggest that an increase in mean sea-surface temperature of only 1°C could cause the global destruction of coral reef ecosystems. The waters off British Columbia have already experienced a rise in sea-surface temperature of 0.3–0.9°C over the past 55 years. Increases in temperature may slow or shut down the thermohaline circulation (Figure 8.2), causing widespread climatic change, changes in the geographic distributions of fisheries, and increased risk of hypoxia in the deep ocean. Scientists have already detected changes in the distribution patterns of many marine species as a result of changes in ocean temperatures attributed to

Philip Dearden

This Humboldt squid was washed ashore, along with many others, on the west coast of Vancouver Island, far north of its normal range in Central America. They are voracious predators and have even been known to attack divers.

global warming (Cheung et al., 2010). The North Pacific in particular has warmed significantly, 3–4°C above the long-term average in 2014. Even without the contribution of the El Niño current, this increase was several degrees higher than normal. This change brings in many new species such as sunfish and thresher sharks. It also brings in new predators such as mackerel and Humboldt squid, voracious predators on juvenile salmon. Estimates suggest that per decade species will move poleward at a rate of about 135 kilometres or move 3.5 metres deeper. In Canada, the greatest species losses will occur in southern waters, but overall, Canada is predicted to gain more species than it will lose (Cheung et al., 2011).

The Arctic Ocean is one of the most sensitive indicators of global climate change. In addition to the loss of perennial ice cover, the amount of the oldest and thickest ice within the remaining multi-year icepack has declined significantly. The oldest ice types have essentially disappeared, and 58 per cent of the multi-year ice now consists of relatively young two- and three-year-old ice, compared to 35 per cent in the mid 1980s. Scientists are predicting an ice-free Arctic in another 40 years. Changes in ice conditions are critical for some species, especially those that rely upon ice coverage for foraging and breeding. Changes in populations have already been noted in hooded, ring, and harp seals, and Pacific walrus also showed greater stress in 2014. Early breakup of sea ice is thought to be one of the main contributing factors in the increased stress experienced by polar bear populations (Rode et al., 2010; Durner et al., 2011).

Global Responses

International Agreements

Strong international action can help to address these problems, and there are many examples of international treaties concerning the oceans. The overall international legal framework is provided by the United Nations Convention on the Law of the Sea (UNCLOS), which entered into force in 1994. Activities under its jurisdiction include protection and preservation, navigation, pollution, access to marine resources, exploitation of marine resources, conservation, monitoring, and research. One of the most important provisions was the agreement for coastal nations to establish **exclusive economic zones (EEZs)**. The Convention also established 45 per cent of the seabed as common property. Canada ratified the Convention in November 2003.

Other agreements include the 1972 London Convention on dumping waste, which has led to a gradual decline in the amount of sewage sludge and industrial waste dumped into the oceans. In terms of fisheries, the UN moratorium on high seas driftnets effective in 1992 was quite successful. The same kind of approach now needs to be applied to reduce the impact of other highly damaging types of fishing gear, especially longlines and industrial trawlers with high rates of bycatch.

However, Daniel Pauly, of the Fisheries Centre at the University of British Columbia, suggests that to achieve real sustainability, we need to rethink how fishing is undertaken. Policy-makers have concentrated on promoting industrial fisheries under the mistaken belief that they catch the vast majority of fish. Pauly (2006) argues, however, that not only are small-scale inshore fisheries (artisanal fisheries) as productive as industrial fisheries but they are much more efficient and less damaging, and provide more support for local communities. A wealth of knowledge has built up around the world that reflects the intimate relationship that artisanal fishers have with the resource and the more geographically based management schemes that have evolved to reflect this relationship.

Pauly and others say that the quickest way to effect a change in fishing methods is to end the subsidies that support commercial fisheries, estimated at over $15 billion per year. Subsidies make up about 25 per cent of the total landed values from the catch of these fleets, whereas the reported profit per landed value is no more than 10 per cent. Were the subsidies removed, the fisheries would die as uneconomical (Sumaila and Pauly, 2007). Since more than half the subsidies are for fuel, eliminating fuel subsidies would be simple and effective, while contributing to a reduction in fossil-fuel consumption.

Although not an agreement, another international movement that may show some promise for improving fishery management is certification, just as forestry certification programs have begun to influence that industry (Chapter 9). The Marine Stewardship Council, based in London, is an independent global assessment body that sets standards and coordinates efforts in this area. The formation of the council was spurred by the spectacular collapse of the east coast cod fishery, discussed in more detail below. The council has certified BC's spiny dogfish fishery as the world's first sustainable shark fishery, which means it had to meet requirements for healthy fish stocks, minimal ecosystem impacts, and an effective management system. The certification lasts for five years and there is an annual audit. If monitored and implemented rigorously, and with public awareness about the importance of eating only certified products, certification schemes may help improve fisheries management. More than 250 fisheries are now certified worldwide as sustainable.

Marine Protected Areas

Compared to the terrestrial environment, where ecological communities are often associated with areas defined by geographical features (such as mountains and rivers), precise boundaries of distinct communities or processes in oceans are rare. Geographic scales are large, and biological processes are not self-contained within a given area. The water overlying the seabed is a mobile third dimension that provides nourishment for much of ocean life. These characteristics of the ocean environment mean that surveys take time and are costly, and because of the high variability in sizes of marine populations, survey results are typically uncertain. Until recently, these difficulties prevented scientists from assessing the effectiveness of marine protected areas (MPAs). However, many studies from around the world (e.g., Edgar et al., 2014) now confirm that marine reserves:

- Conserve both fisheries and biodiversity
- Are the best way to protect resident species
- Provide a critical benchmark for the evaluation of threats to ocean communities
- Are required in networks for long-term fishery and conservation benefits
- Are a central management tool supported by existing scientific information

The establishment of MPAs has lagged substantially behind their terrestrial counterparts—just over 1 per cent of the ocean has been designated as "protected." However, with increasing political awareness of the importance of the oceans and their highly degraded state, MPAs are starting to receive some attention. The 2002 World Summit on Sustainable Development set 2012 as the target date for completion of an effectively managed, ecologically representative network of marine and coastal protected areas within and beyond areas of national jurisdiction covering 10 per cent of the oceans. This target was not met, and the timeline was extended to 2020. One of the main challenges in meeting this target is that almost all the ocean is under some form of use (e.g., see Ban and Alder, 2008, for an analysis of ocean use in BC). For MPAs to be established and made effective, some of this use must be displaced and most users either will not, or cannot, give up their use.

Canada's Oceans and Fisheries

Canada has some of the most productive marine environments in the world, and these environments were critical in sustaining populations of Aboriginal peoples and attracting European attention on both coasts. Unfortunately, the squandering of this rich biological heritage stands as one of the sharpest reminders of our inability to manage ourselves in a way that sustains resources over a long period of time. Major fisheries have collapsed on both coasts, but the value of the industry is still substantial, with the marine fishery worth over $2.2 billion in 2012. Overall, the catch has doubled in value over the past 15 years. This increase is mainly due to the growth in shellfish catches spurred by the closure of the Atlantic cod fishery. Similarly, in freshwater fisheries, although catch levels continue to decline, the value of the catch has increased because of higher prices. The freshwater fishery accounts for about 3 per cent of the total value of commercial fishing in Canada, with 88 per cent of this coming from Ontario and Manitoba.

The management of Canada's fisheries has improved following some very obvious failures, strong criticisms, and constructive suggestions. The commissioner of the Environment and Sustainable Development, for example, devoted a Chapter of the 2011 report to how to improve fisheries management (OAG, 2011). New policies and procedures have been outlined under the Sustainable Fisheries Framework that emphasize a precautionary, ecosystem-based approach that

Perspectives on the Environment

Canada's Motto

A Mari Usque Ad Mare
"From Sea to Sea"

Canada has the longest coastline of any country and the second-largest continental shelf, equal to 30 per cent of Canada's land mass (Figure 8.10). There are some 1,200 species of fish and many globally important populations of marine mammals. Recent estimates suggest there is a minimum of 16,500 species in total in Canadian marine waters (Hutchings et al., 2012). Unfortunately, several of these species are also on Canada's list of species at risk (see Chapter 14), including the beluga, bowhead, northern right, and Georgia Strait killer whales. More than 7 million Canadians live in coastal communities.

The federal government largely holds jurisdiction for the marine environment below the high-water mark, involving 27 different federal agencies and departments. The lead agency is the Department of Fisheries and Oceans (DFO; since 2008, formally titled Fisheries and Oceans Canada), which has traditionally focused its efforts on commercial fishery management but is also responsible for all marine species (except seabirds, which come under Environment Canada). DFO is also the lead agency for Canada's Oceans Strategy, discussed later. Provincial governments are responsible for shorelines, some areas of seabed, and some specific activities, such as **aquaculture**. However, in BC the responsibility for aquaculture has been transferred to the federal government. Municipal governments also influence the coastal zone, since they have responsibility for many land-based activities affecting the oceans. There are quite a few areas of overlap between these different levels of jurisdiction, and, inevitably, conflicts arise. As a result, coastal and marine resource management is typically fragmented and often ineffective. In addition, Canada's very large coastal zone, ranging from the Mediterranean climate of BC's Gulf Islands to the High Arctic, encompasses a wide range of conditions and activities. The surface area of Canada's ocean estate is 7.1 million km^2.

ENVIRONMENT IN FOCUS

BOX 8.5 | Marine Protected Areas: What are the Challenges?

The oceans constitute one of the major conservation challenges of our time. This is particularly so in the tropical oceans where over 1 billion people directly depend on the oceans for their sustenance. Coral reefs are the most important drivers of productivity and biodiversity in the tropical oceans, yet are declining faster than any other species group on Earth (see Figure 3.13). Establishing marine protected areas (MPAs) is a major tool for trying to conserve reefs, but implementation is challenging. This challenge is one focus of the MPA Research Group (MPARG) at the University of Victoria (http://mparg.wordpress.com). So what have we learned?

1. *Work with the people.* Many terrestrial parks were created when there was relatively little human use. However, coral reefs are intensely used by millions of people daily. It is simply not possible or practical to draw a line around a reef and order people not to cross the line. Thus it is essential to work with and through the people to try to develop conservation goals. For example, National Marine Parks in Thailand are, in theory, no-take zones, where fishing is not allowed. In practice, this is seldom the case. In Mu Koh Chang National Marine Park Kristin Lunn worked with the fishers and found that not one of them knew that they were fishing in a no-take zone. Working with the fishers, Lunn mapped where they fished and identified areas where there was still biodiversity but not high-intensity fishing, and recommended these areas be established as no-take zones. They also developed baseline data on fishing effort to be able to measure changes in catches in the future (Lunn and Dearden, 2006). However, working with villagers is not always so easy, as Bennett and Dearden (2013) reported on their work on the Andaman coast of Thailand, where government agencies had not consulted with communities before establishing no-take zones and other conservation measures.
2. *Develop alternative livelihoods.* People cannot stop feeding their families. If we are to reduce the pressure on reefs, then it is necessary to provide alternative means of incomes for family support. One effective approach is to develop **ecotourism** activities on and around the reefs. Ecotourism can provide an **incentive-based** mechanism for conservation because there is a direct feedback loop from the conservation activity to improving livelihoods. However, challenges arise with this approach as well. "Ecotourism" has become a marketing mantra to attract more customers, and, unless managed effectively, may end up having an even greater negative impact than the original activity. Ecotourism should have at least the following characteristics: be nature based, be educational, and have a positive impact on conservation. Being "sustainable" is inadequate. All tourism should be sustainable. Ecotourism goes one step further than regular tourism by benefiting conservation. It is also necessary to monitor the impacts of reef tourism (e.g., Roman et al., 2007; Dearden et al., 2010) to ensure that adverse impacts are not occurring. For example, in Thailand, Augustine and Dearden (in press) found that changes in the nature of scuba diving over time were reducing the effectiveness of the activity as a conservation mechanism.
3. *Establishing MPAs is not the goal.* Establishing MPAs has become a very visible sign of the need for greater ocean conservation. However, it should be remembered that protected areas are but one mechanism to achieve conservation (Chapter 14) and other effective means are available to achieve conservation goals in some situations (e.g., see Eli Enns's "Domestic Guest Statement" in Chapter 14). For example, in her work in the Comoros in Africa, Melissa

Courtesy Petch Manopawitr

Courtesy Melissa Hauzer

The best science, both natural and social, is needed to fully understand many situations. Here MPARG researchers monitor coral health in Thailand (left) and interview local fishers in Comoros, Africa (right).

Hauzer found that the communities already had management mechanisms to control overfishing without the need for central government control (Hauzer et al., 2013).

4. *Use the best science, both natural and social, preferably together.* In 2010, the Andaman coast of Thailand experienced widespread strong coral bleaching (see Box 8.1) that killed virtually all corals in some locations. Such an event, the result of higher water temperatures as a result of global warming (Chapter 7), is obviously also of great concern to the human communities dependent on reefs for their livelihoods. This event spurred the initiation of a research effort (Project IMPAACT: http://projectimpaact.asia/) to examine both the ecological and socio-economic dimensions of bleaching. For example, Petch Manopawitr is looking at the design of the MPA network on the Andaman coast to determine how the parks can be made more resilient (Chapter 1) to future events. This approach involves mapping areas of bleaching intensity, adjusting park boundaries, establishing new areas for protection, and studying the needs of the recovery process. How can the reefs recolonize, a secondary succession as discussed in Chapter 3? Studying dispersal tracks for coral larvae pointed out the critical need to protect reefs further north in Myanmar, as a larvae source for the Thai reefs (see Box 8.1). At the same time, Nathan Bennett was studying the dependency of various coastal communities on reefs for livelihoods and their vulnerability to future reef bleaching events (Bennett et al., 2015).

The discussion in this box illustrates some of the challenges and solutions to developing MPAs in the tropics, but similar challenges and solutions also exist within Canada (e.g., see Ayers et al., 2012; Heck et al., 2012; Augustine and Dearden, 2014). This box also highlights the key role that students can play in helping understand and address important global conservation challenges. All the lead authors of these studies were graduate students with MPARG who completed the research as part of their degree programs.

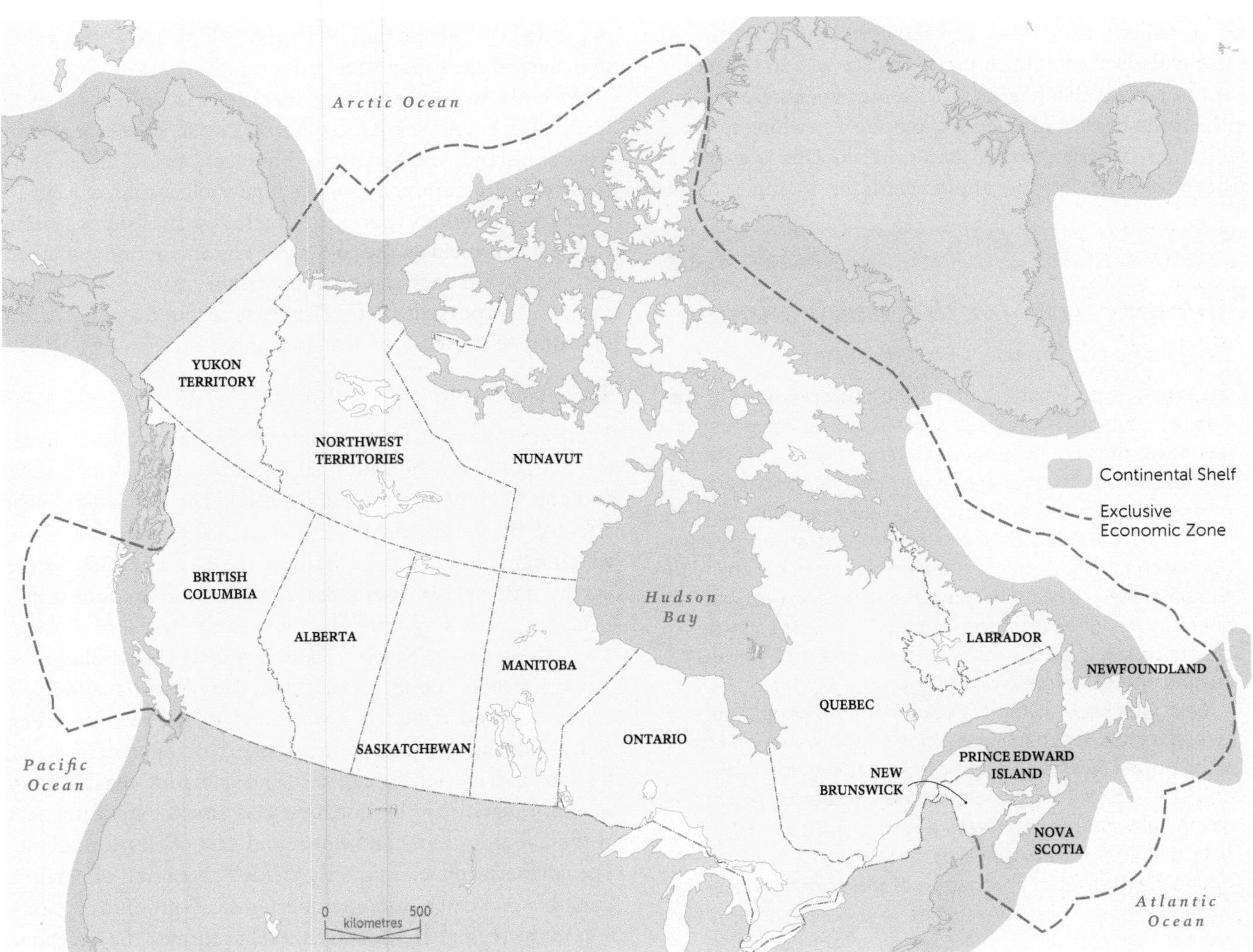

FIGURE 8.10 | Canada's coastline and continental shelf.

avoids overfishing, takes into account impacts on endangered species, and ensures that fisheries impacts are within safe ecological limits. These policies are applied through an Integrated Fisheries Management Plans. Nonetheless, in 2012 an assessment of 155 main fisheries stocks revealed that under half could be classified as healthy and 10 per cent were "critical." The number of fisheries stocks being exploited over approved levels fell in Canada from 11 stocks in 2011 to 7 stocks in 2012. Although this is a good trend, the question remains as to why any stocks should be allowed to be exploited at excessive levels in Canada today. In 2014, the government did, however, ban issuing of further commercial fishing licences in the Beaufort Sea until it is shown that there are surplus and sustainable stocks. This is good news, but again, the question has to be asked, how could any licences at all have been issued until this basic information is known?

The Fisheries Act is federal legislation dating back to Confederation and was established to manage and protect Canada's fisheries resources. It applies to all fishing zones, territorial seas, and inland waters of Canada and is binding on federal, provincial, and territorial governments. The Act was revised in 2012. A major change was in the requirement to protect fish habitat. This requirement was replaced, without the benefit of science input, by a new one to protect habitat for fisheries, rather than for fish. This is a very significant change, leaving unprotected, for example, most of the freshwater fish in Canada, even if they are classified as threatened. It confers protection on non-native species, even hatchery fish, as long as they have value in a fishery. These changes have dismayed prominent Canadian fisheries scientists (see Hutchings and Post, 2013) who have pointed out the extremely anthropocentric position (see Chapter 5) that this represents. If there are no humans in the area, there is no fishery and therefore no habitat protection. There are many places in Canada's vast territory where there are no humans. However, the same species may have habitat protection elsewhere, if there is someone there to catch the fish.

Perspectives on the Environment

Revisions to Canada's Fisheries Act

In closing, it is our opinion that the 2012 revisions to the habitat protection provisions of Canada's Fisheries Act will have negative consequences for: (1) the persistence and viability of fish that are neither part of nor supportive of a fishery; (2) the protection of native aquatic species at risk; (3) Canada's ability to implement an ecosystem approach to sustainable management; (4) DFO's ability to evaluate the scientific validity of applications for habitat alteration and destruction; and (5) Canada's commitments to fulfill national and international obligations to sustain and conserve biodiversity.

Being the second-largest country in the world, Canada is responsible for 20% of the globe's fresh water, one third of its boreal forests and associated aquatic environment, and the world's longest coastline. However, this geographical wealth comes with a responsibility to be internationally respected stewards of this vast environment. Politically motivated abrogation of the country's national and international responsibilities to protect fish and fish habitat suggests to us that Canada might no longer be up to the task.

—Hutchings and Post (2013: 500–1)

Case Study: East Coast Fisheries

The marine fishery has been an essential component of the economy and culture of Atlantic Canada for centuries. After 1977, when Canada declared a 200-nautical-mile fishing limit off its coasts, cod were the mainstay for more than 50,000 fishers and 60,000 fish-plant workers in Atlantic Canada. In Newfoundland and Labrador alone, about 700 communities depended entirely on the cod fishery, which had a 1991 value to fishers of more than $226 million.

However, in 1992 and 1993, decisions to reduce harvests resulted in employment losses for 40,000 to 50,000 people in Newfoundland, the Maritime provinces, and Quebec. How could this dramatic collapse of a renewable resource occur in such a relatively short period of time? Why did fisheries scientists fail to anticipate the collapse? Why was action not taken earlier to avoid degradation of the fishery and economic disruption? Is it possible for the fishery to rebound and become a mainstay of the regional economy once again?

The Nature of the Collapse

There are four main areas for this fishery in Atlantic Canada: the Scotian Shelf, the Gulf of St Lawrence, the Grand Banks, and the Labrador coast (Figure 8.11). The two areas most affected by the harvesting cutbacks are the Scotian Shelf, which extends from the mouth of the Bay of Fundy to the northern tip of Cape Breton Island, and the Labrador coast.

These areas supported two different kinds of fishery. The fishery on the Scotian Shelf is readily accessible to the inshore fishers along the coast of Nova Scotia and New Brunswick and included a wide mix of species, including cod, haddock, flounder, pollock, hake, herring, redfish, crab, scallop, and lobster. In contrast, the Labrador coast fishery was dominated by the northern cod stock, extending east of the Labrador coast and north and east of Newfoundland. The northern cod traditionally yielded about half of Atlantic Canada's cod catch and one-quarter of all groundfish landings in the region. The northern cod has formed the backbone of the Atlantic fishery. This explains why stock depletion has been such a blow to regional economies, where fishing has provided a significant percentage of the jobs—and almost all jobs in small outport communities. These communities were further affected by the international attention and subsequent harvesting cuts to the seal fishery (Box 8.6).

The northern cod were caught by larger inshore vessels and especially by offshore draggers or factory trawlers, multi-million dollar boats that drag huge nets across the bottom

ENVIRONMENT IN FOCUS

BOX 8.6 | The Seal Hunt

Since the mid eighteenth century, the harp seal had been the target of hunting, mainly for pelts. Between 1820 and 1860, for example, about half a million harp seals were killed every year. In 1831, more than 300 ships and 10,000 sealers pursued the hunt; 687,000 pelts were taken. However, publicity over the hunt in the early 1980s led to bans on the importation of sealskins into Europe. Celebrities such as French actress Brigitte Bardot appeared on television across the world as they tried to protect helpless white-coated seal pups from being clubbed to death. Eventually, following bans on the import of sealskins by the US and the European Community, the Canadian government banned the hunt in 1987, and the number of seals is estimated to have tripled. Now, however, a new hunt has begun, ostensibly to help in the recovery of the endangered cod stocks.

Today, most scientists agree that seals do not substantially alter the cod recovery and politicians are now stating that the seal hunt must continue to provide economic revenue for Inuit communities. International environmental groups have suggested that the real motive for reinstituting the seal hunt is not related to seal predation on cod but rather to the need for a political scapegoat in economically depressed areas and the demand for seal penises on the Asian market.

By 2009 the European Union had implemented a complete ban on the imports of seal pelts, dramatically reducing Canada's market. In response, Canada challenged the ban and continued to develop relationships with Asian markets.

© IFAW/L. Stevenson

A beater, like this harp seal pup, is one that has moulted its white fur.

In 2011 the Canadian government developed an arrangement with China to open up the seal market. China is the world's leading consumer of seafood and offers an alternative to the now non-existent European market. In 2013, Taiwan, a previous leading consumer of Canadian seal products, banned trade in marine mammals and their products.

Following up its previous five-year management plan, DFO introduced a 2011–2015 seal management plan. The total allowable catch (TAC) of seals was set annually to allow for adjustments to changing environmental conditions and changes in harvest levels in Arctic Canada and Greenland. This plan set TACs much higher than the 2006–2010 period, yet no harvest has filled even a quarter of the quota. In 2011, 38,000 seals were taken, and numbers steadily increased to 69,000 in 2012 and 91,000 in 2013. The one-year TAC for 2013 and 2014 was set generously at 400,000 harp seals. 2014 was also the first year that it became mandatory for sealers to complete a training program before embarking on their first sealing hunt. However, poor ice and weather conditions in 2014 left the hunt with 55,000 seals.

Markets for seal pelts vary significantly from one year to the next. For example, the landed value of the harp seal hunt in 2006 was $33 million. The average price per pelt received by sealers was $97, an increase of 77 per cent over the 2005 average value of $55. In 2009, the price was down to $15 per pelt, partly due to the EU ban. By 2010, the value had begun to recover with an average pelt price of $20–25. In 2013, the average seal pelt was $38, the best year since 2008. Income from sealing may account for 35 per cent of total annual income for some coastal families, and many of their communities have unemployment rates more than 30 per cent higher than the national average.

In 2011 a new seal hunt was proposed, this time in the southern Gulf of St Lawrence, but for a different quarry, the grey seal. Seal numbers have been increasing in the area, and catches of the southern cod falling, so the Fisheries Resource Conservation Council, made up of scientists and fishing industry representatives appointed by the minister, proposed killing 140,000 seals in the area as part of an experiment. Independent scientists criticized the proposal, both as an experimental design and because of the overall impacts on the ecosystem. However, in 2012 only eight seals were taken from the Gulf of St Lawrence, as opposed to over 1,500 in 2011. Due to lack of interest by buying nations, the seal hunt in the southern Gulf was suspended in both 2012 and 2013, with no signs of continuation in the future.

of the ocean and stay on the fishing grounds for extended periods. However, the northern cod migrate to the shores of Newfoundland in the summer and thus also supported an inshore fishery that relied on much smaller boats using traps, hooks, and nets. The inshore fishery has been an important one. Until the late 1950s, the inshore catch was typically over 150,000 tonnes. By 1974, as a result of overfishing, the inshore catch had fallen to 35,000 tonnes. After Canada declared its exclusive fishing zone in 1977 and banned fishing by foreign draggers in that area, the inshore catch increased. It peaked at 115,000 tonnes in 1982, but by 1986 the catch had fallen to 68,000 tonnes, and the fish caught were very small. Local fishers had identified the first signs of serious problems.

Unfortunately, the models used by the fishery scientists indicated that stocks were still abundant, so these early warnings were not heeded. Total catches of northern cod increased, reaching 252,000 tonnes in 1986, almost twice what they were in 1978. However, by 1989, on the basis of new scientific advice, the minister reduced the **total allowable catch** (TAC) for northern cod to 235,000 tonnes. By 1991, it was clear that the stock was in trouble and the TAC was reduced to 120,000 tonnes, and in July 1992 a moratorium on northern cod until May 1994 was announced. Ottawa agreed to provide $500 million (later rising to $912 million) to compensate the 20,000 fishers and plant workers expected to lose their jobs (Figure 8.12).

In 1993, the government banned cod fishing in five more areas and sharply reduced quotas for other valuable species. The result was a total loss of 35,000–40,000 fisheries jobs in Atlantic Canada since the closures began in 1992. In Atlantic Canada, there were 17,200 groundfish licence holders in 1992 and 10,783 in 2000, representing a decline of roughly 35 per cent. In total, the government spent $3.9 billion for income support, industry adjustment measures, and economic development assistance programs for the Atlantic fishing industry between 1992 and 2001.

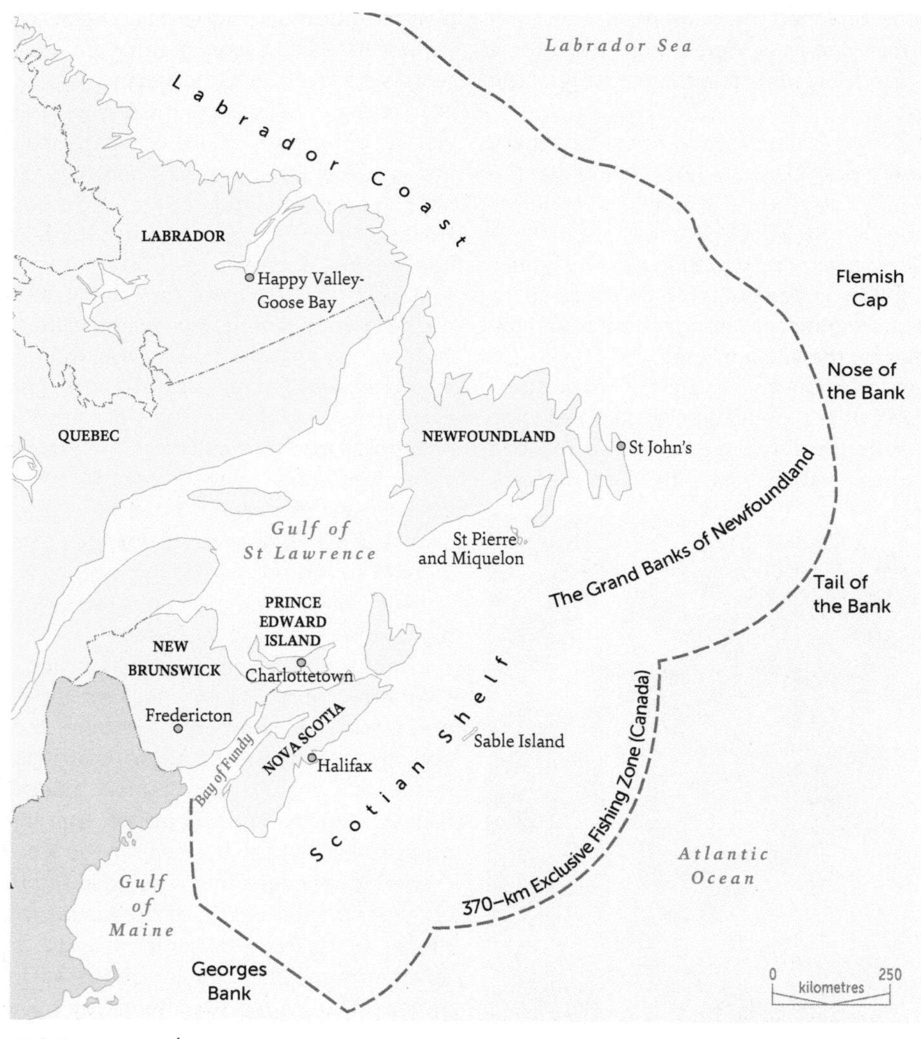

FIGURE 8.11 | Major fishing areas in Atlantic Canada.
Source: Adapted from Cameron (1990: 30).

Small outport communities in Newfoundland have always relied heavily on harvesting marine products, from seals to fish.

In 2003 what remained of the cod fishery was closed. The Atlantic cod was officially listed as endangered, as the Committee on the Status of Endangered Wildlife in Canada (COSEWIC; see Chapter 14) estimated a 97-per-cent decline in cod off the northeast coast of Newfoundland and Labrador over the previous 30 years.

Some Reasons for the Collapse

At the time of the collapse, possible reasons suggested that changing environmental conditions, creating colder, less hospitable water temperatures for a period during the 1990s, had driven the cod away, while growing seal populations had devoured entire stocks of both cod and capelin, the favourite food source for cod. However, research shows that environmental factors played only minor roles in the disappearance of the fish and that they had been fished to commercial and ecological extinction. The politicians and bureaucrats running Canada's Atlantic fisheries created opportunities for overfishing through providing inappropriate incentives for processing plants and lucrative subsidies (unemployment insurance) to all fishers and plant workers involved in the fishery. Similar perverse subsidies are still a significant contributor to overfishing around the world.

Foreign Overfishing

Once Canada established the 200-nautical-mile fishing limit, foreign fleets were required to fish outside that boundary or to fish inside the boundary only for that portion of the domestic quota not taken by Canadian vessels. Foreign fishing fleets were monitored by the Northwest Atlantic Fisheries Organization (NAFO). However, in 1986, Spain and Portugal entered the European Community (EC), and that year the EC unilaterally established quotas considerably higher than those set by NAFO. Furthermore, the EC boats harvested fish well beyond the EC limits. The EC then raised the quota the following year, and again the NAFO quota was exceeded by the actual catch. In 1988, just half of the EC target was achieved, even though it was 4.5 times higher than the target recommended by NAFO. The EC, now known as the European Union (EU), later rejected a NAFO northern cod moratorium. In 1993, however, the EU finally accepted all NAFO quotas, after having set its own quotas at a much higher level since the mid 1980s.

Thus, strong evidence exists that foreign vessels, especially those from Spain and Portugal, were overfishing at least

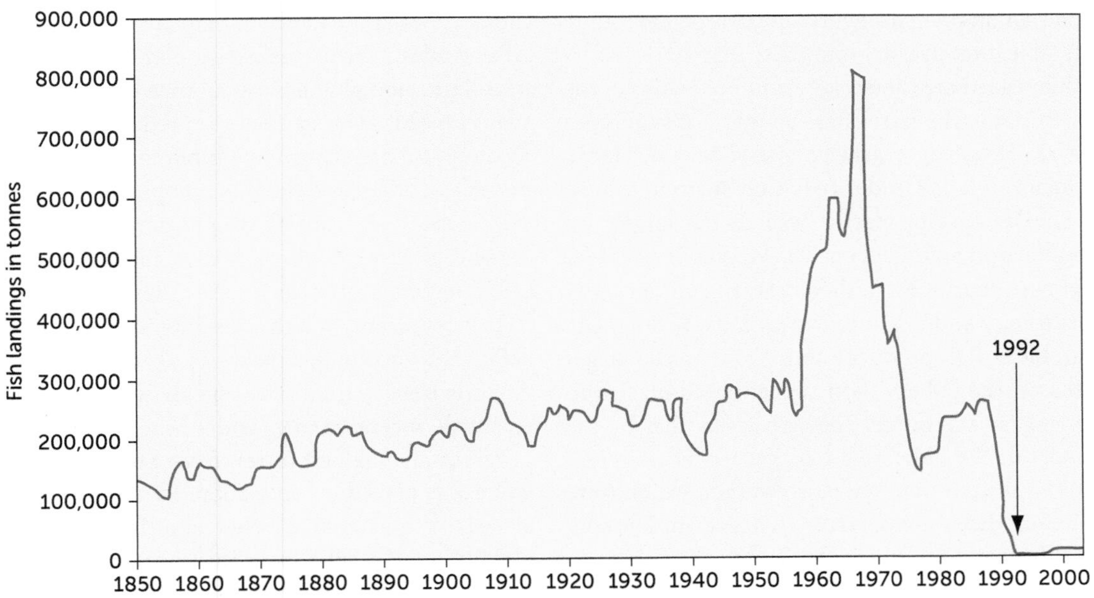

FIGURE 8.12 | Collapse of Atlantic cod stocks off the east coast of Newfoundland, 1992.

Source: *Millennium Ecosystem Assessment (2005).*

during the mid and late 1980s. Since cod migrate toward the coast in summer and then move offshore in winter to spawn in deeper waters, the fish are vulnerable to foreign fishing.

Domestic Overfishing

Despite the pressure placed on the stocks by foreign fishing vessels, most of the principal fishing grounds have been under Canadian control since the 200-mile limit was set. Two fisheries—both inshore and offshore—must be managed, which has been and continues to be a challenge.

For hundreds of years, the inshore fishery consisted of many fishers (particularly from Newfoundland) relying on small wooden boats, lines, traps, and nets to catch cod during the spring and summer months when the cod move close to shore. Until the mid 1950s, the inshore fishery, combined with limited offshore fishing by Canadian boats, resulted in annual landings of 200,000 tonnes or more. Foreign fishers were harvesting another 30,000–50,000 tonnes each year. Such harvesting did not appear to adversely affect the then estimated breeding stock of 1.6 million tonnes in the North Atlantic.

In the mid 1950s, the introduction of large offshore trawlers that operated year round in the North Atlantic significantly changed this pattern. Initially, catches were very high, but the spawning stocks were placed under great pressure. In the 1970s, yields reached a high of 800,000 tonnes per year before they started to drop. Until 1977, foreign trawlers did most of the offshore fishing. Following the establishment of the 200-mile limit, the Canadian offshore fleet expanded, and Canadian-based offshore trawlers became the main harvesters of northern cod. By the time the moratorium was placed on the fishery in the summer of 1992, Newfoundland was the base for some 55 large and 30 medium-sized offshore trawlers. Thus, Canadian offshore draggers, operating year round, placed considerable pressure on groundfish stocks.

Critical in this regard are the ecology and behaviour of the northern cod. Initially, the harvesters caught a mix of ages and sizes of fish. However, market demand and net mesh sizes led to a focus on larger, older fish. Cod swim in groups or schools of similar ages primarily because the larger cod will eat the smaller and younger cod. The emphasis on larger fish had two consequences. First, the northern cod normally do not reach maturity and begin to spawn until seven years of age. Second, older fish produce more eggs. As the larger fish became scarce, the fishery then concentrated on fish in the five-to-seven-year age range. The result was that by the early 1990s, most of the older fish had been overharvested and attention had shifted to pre-adolescent fish, which were being caught before they were old enough to spawn. The consequence was a dramatic decline in the fish stock.

A further complication was that many domestic fishers overharvested. Estimates suggest that up to 50 per cent more fish were being landed than were being reported.

Imperfect Science and Management

Fishery scientists did not anticipate the collapse of the Atlantic fishery, especially the northern cod stocks. One reason was that sampling procedures do not provide sufficient ecological information about fish stocks. Until 1991, the total allowable catch was based on the assumption of a biomass of 1.1 million tonnes of cod. However, in 1991, the sampling from DFO research ships indicated only 600,000 tonnes. Sampling in distant areas did not reveal that the cod had migrated to other areas. Significant numbers of diseased or dead fish had not been found. The scientists simply did not know what had happened. They had been receiving warnings for a number of years from the inshore fishers that the fish being caught were fewer, smaller, and lower in weight. However, the scientists, who put much greater credence in the quantitative data gathered by DFO research vessels and from what were likely under-reported offshore landings, considered the observations of inshore fishers as anecdotal and less credible.

Inappropriate Incentives for Processing Plants and Fish Workers

By the early 1990s, Newfoundland had about 100 large and small fish-processing plants, some two-thirds of which processed northern cod. In Atlantic Canada as a whole, the number of plants increased from about 500 in 1977 to nearly 900 in 1988, and employment grew from approximately 25,000 full-time jobs to about 33,000. The provincial governments, which license on-shore fish-processing plants, provided incentives for the development of new processing plants as a way of creating new jobs in small communities. This placed political pressure on DFO to keep increasing the total allowable catch.

Another incentive for people to enter or stay in the fishing industry was the federal unemployment insurance program. After working for 10 weeks, fish-plant workers were permitted to collect unemployment insurance for the other 42 weeks of the year. This arrangement resulted in several individuals in a community sharing one job but all qualifying for separate benefits. For fishers, the unemployment benefits were based on the sale value of fish caught during the May–November season (26 weeks), which created the potential for receiving unemployment benefits for the other 26 weeks of the year.

This program, which was intended to provide a social safety net, encouraged more people to become involved in the Atlantic fishery than could be justified economically. There was little incentive to consider other types of work, and the program also helped to reinforce an outlook in which little value was placed on education. By the time the fishery was closed, 50 per cent of Newfoundland's 19-year-olds were already on unemployment insurance, and 80 per cent of the fishery workers did not have a high school diploma. Thus, the fishery involved more people than realistically could be supported over the long term, yet unemployment insurance programs provided little incentive for individuals to consider alternatives. This made the trauma of the 1992 moratorium even greater than it might otherwise have been.

Changing Environmental Conditions

One theory for the depletion of groundfish in the North Atlantic fishery is based on the idea of environmental change. Records show that in 1991 the ocean temperatures off Newfoundland were the coldest ever measured. The water warmed slightly in 1992, then cooled again in 1993. It is possible that colder waters, combined with overfishing in the previous two decades, prevented or inhibited the shrunken stocks from regenerating. However, since relatively little is known about the migratory patterns of the northern cod, it is difficult to determine what the specific implications of changing water temperatures might have been. Furthermore, water temperatures began to rise and stabilize around 1998, restoring a theoretically favourable habitat for groundfish. Despite this warming trend, no significant recovery has been observed within the affected groundfish stocks.

Predators

At the time of the fisheries collapse, it was also popular to blame predation. Seals in particular were identified because of their "voracious appetites" and their growing numbers because of the closure of the seal hunt in the early 1980s (Box 8.6). There is no scientific evidence to support this view.

However, there is some evidence to suggest that seal predation may be a factor in the slow recovery of the east coast groundfish stocks. The seal population has more than doubled in the past three decades, and although cod represents only a small percentage of seals' diets, they are consuming more northern cod than fishers are catching. In fact, the total allowable catch for northern cod in 1999 was only 9,000 tonnes, or less than 20 per cent of corresponding predation by harp seals in that year.

The science of seals and cod is inconclusive and will remain inconclusive for the foreseeable future. Seals are a significant source of mortality for northern cod in the Northwest Atlantic and the Gulf of St Lawrence. Nevertheless, reducing the abundance of harp seals may or may not lead to recovery of depleted cod stocks. Even if a reduced seal population resulted in an increased number of fish in the ocean, there are other predators in marine ecosystems. Any increase in the size of a commercially important fish stock could well be eaten by these other predators before being caught by fishers. Furthermore, seals eat predators of commercially important fish, and so fewer seals could actually mean fewer fish for fishers.

Fishing down the food chain has been discussed earlier and is exemplified in Atlantic Canada with the replacement of cod fisheries by shrimp and crab fisheries. Recent observations of the poor physiological condition of many predator fish in the area also suggest an overall lack of prey, forcing predator species such as the Atlantic cod to the same alternative as human fishers: "fishing down the web." After the cod were fished down, fishing pressure increased on shrimp. "Cod feed on shrimp. If you remove the shrimp, how will the cod ever recover?" asks Daniel Pauly.

It is difficult for urban dwellers to imagine the close relationship that built up over the centuries between the people in the outports of Newfoundland and the sea. Virtually every family would be involved in some way with fishing. When the fish were exposed to such fishing pressure that they could no longer be caught in any numbers, it was not just the economy that suffered but a whole way of life.

Lessons

The collapse of the Atlantic groundfish fishery highlights how some contemporary resource management practices may encourage resource liquidation. In theory, fisheries managers around the world and in Canada seek to manage the fishery according to three priority areas: ecological sustainability, economic goals, and social outcomes. In reality, these goals are often in conflict, at least in the short term, and the second goal often becomes paramount because of political interference. The case study illustrates that fisheries

Perspectives on the Environment

Fishery Collapse: A Bureaucratic Tragedy

The disaster in the cod fishery is now worse than anyone expected. . . . It may be a generation before we see a recovery of the cod. That a five-hundred-year-old industry could be destroyed in fifteen years by a bureaucracy is a tragedy of epic proportions.

—Ransom Myers, quoted in Harris (1998: 332–3)

management requires scientific understanding of the biophysical resource system, a greater appreciation of traditional or local ecological knowledge, and parallel understandings of the history, culture, economy, and politics of the region, as well as federal and provincial fisheries and regional development policies. The Atlantic fishery also provides an excellent example of how inexact science often is and the extent to which complexity and uncertainty dominate. It demonstrates conflict among different values and interests (Chapter 5) and the manner in which conditions can change dramatically over a relatively short time period.

The situation is readily comparable with the framework introduced in Chapter 1. Not only were our simplified models of the complex biophysical system inadequate for a proper understanding of the east coast fisheries, but our resulting attempts to assess the status of the system were inadequate and societal expectations and management directions were unclear. Some of the approaches suggested in Chapter 6, relating to identifying stakeholders, resolving conflict, and taking more ecosystem-based and adaptive approaches, could usefully be applied to resolving these problems.

Aboriginal Use of Marine Resources

One of the most challenging aspects of fisheries management is allocation of catch, especially when catches are declining. This is particularly difficult when allocation involves Aboriginal communities. There is a patchwork of treaties with Aboriginal peoples in different regions of Canada, and the rights to sustenance from fishing were often written into these treaties. However, it has never been clear which regulations Aboriginals should follow and how broad a range of activities the concept of sustenance might cover. Over the past decade, many important court cases have helped to clarify some of these issues. Nonetheless, high-profile conflicts still occur on both coasts, as detailed in the examples below.

In the fall of 1999, a violent and complex dispute erupted between Aboriginal and non-Aboriginal fishers in Miramichi Bay in northeastern New Brunswick. Lobster traps were cut and damaged, threats were exchanged, boats were rammed, and multiple shots were fired.

The crux of the dispute lay in the Supreme Court of Canada's 1999 decision in the case of a Nova Scotia Mi'kmaq, Donald Marshall Jr, who had caught and sold eels out of season and claimed protection under a 1760 treaty. The Court's ruling upheld the treaty, which effectively gave Mi'kmaq, Maliseet, and Passamaquoddy bands the right to earn a "moderate livelihood" from year-round fishing, hunting, and gathering. The decision spurred an immediate reaction among the Natives of the Burnt Church band of Miramichi Bay to resume catching and selling species like lobster, even though the season was formally over. Within days, the Native bands had more than 4,000 traps in the water. This infuriated the non-Native fishers who believed that this continued harvest would lead to the destruction of the lobster fishery.

Despite the rising tension between the two groups, DFO was hesitant to intervene, stating that Natives now had a right to fish that had been denied for more than two centuries. The *Marshall* case specifically indicated that the federal government still retained the right to regulate the fishery but that Ottawa's authority to regulate treaty rights was limited to those actions that could be "justified." This view led to an examination of the term "justification" and, more specifically, of whether or not the DFO's limit on the number of lobster traps and length of fishing season was reasonable and

A First Nations fisher uses a dip net to intercept a chinook salmon at Moricetown Falls, Bulkley Valley, British Columbia.

"justifiable" according to the rights of the Mi'kmaq in their 1760 treaty.

After several years of research into the affected lobster stocks, DFO announced an agreement with the Burnt Church band. The $20-million agreement included enhanced commercial fishery access for Native fishers, including additional lobster licences and extra boats and gear. However, a quota was set for the Native fall fishery of 25,000 pounds of lobster for food and 5,000 pounds of lobster for ceremonial use. Furthermore, the fishery would be limited to six weeks or until the quota was filled, and the sale of lobster would be strictly prohibited at all times. Since the federal decision, violent conflicts have significantly decreased and an improved relationship has emerged among all parties.

On the west coast, Native communities have very high unemployment rates, and the fishery plays a critical role in livelihoods. There is an Aboriginal right, established by the courts, to fish 24 hours a day, seven days a week, wherever Aboriginal people wish, for food and ceremonial purposes. In the past, this right was sometimes abused, with fish being caught for commercial use. This prompted DFO to establish a special Natives-only commercial salmon fishery for some areas. In 2003, the BC Appeal Court, following complaints by non-Native fishers, struck down the Natives-only commercial salmon fishery. The judge said that it amounted to "legislated racial discrimination" and was against the Charter of Rights. DFO then cancelled the program, but Native fishers vowed to continue catching and selling the salmon as they always had. Many critics point out that Natives are being allocated fishing rights not because of their ethnicity per se but because their fisheries were wrongfully appropriated in the first place. In 2008, a Supreme Court of Canada decision ruled that such redistributive justice was necessary and there are continuing steps to negotiated fishing rights. Others have argued that non-Native fishers should not bear the costs for wrongs perpetrated in the past by society as a whole. What do you think?

In many ways, the story of the BC coastal Aboriginal cultures is a story of the sea in general and of salmon in particular (Box 8.7). The bounty of the sea allowed these peoples to establish a more sedentary lifestyle than that of other Aboriginal peoples in North America. Consequently, nowhere else did hunter-gatherer societies develop such complex social structures, rigid hierarchies, and dense populations in permanent winter villages. From these villages, the people developed complex and effective hunting practices for whales, sea lions, seals, sharks, tuna, wolf eels, sole, oolichan, greenlings, herring, halibut, crabs, clams, mussels, skate, sturgeon, and, above all, salmon. The salmon fishery was managed effectively; no stocks crashed. And the salmon was venerated through myth and legend among the coastal peoples.

Conflict and sometimes tenuous resolution will continue to arise as Canada strives to achieve equitable solutions to fish resource allocation problems involving Aboriginal peoples. The clock cannot be rolled back to pre-treaty times, yet there must be some recognition of the central role that fish and fishing have played in the societies of many Aboriginal peoples in Canada and of their intimate knowledge of coastal ecosystems (Box 8.8).

ENVIRONMENT IN FOCUS

BOX 8.7 | Salmon: The Stories They Tell

From the shores of Japan to almost 2,500 kilometres up the Yukon River, a tangible thread exists—the Pacific salmon. Every year, millions of salmon make their way back from the other side of the Pacific Ocean to the streams of their birth. The five species of Pacific salmon—chum, coho, chinook, pink, and sockeye—are anadromous—that is, they spend part of their lives in fresh water and part in salt water. They depend on a wide range of conditions that link the mountains to the seas: the amount of snowpack to feed the streams, the lack of floods to wash away spawning gravel, unpolluted rivers and estuaries, the right temperature for entry into the marine environment, avoidance of predators, and avoidance of fishing nets. If any of these myriad factors go awry, then higher mortality rates can drastically reduce the numbers of fish returning to spawn in subsequent years. These factors are the links in a chain reflecting the limiting factor discussed in Chapter 2. It also means that salmon are good indicators of the overall health of our environment and our resource management practices.

What have these indicator species been telling us? The story is not a good one. Salmon in their millions sustained populations of coastal Aboriginal peoples. Early descriptions of the Fraser River by explorers talk about a river that could be crossed on the backs of the salmon. But early logging and mining practices, along with wasteful fishing practices, soon made a considerable dent in these numbers. Habitat destruction and overfishing led to the virtual closing of the fishery in many areas by the 1990s. Scientists estimate that the salmon biomass has been diminished by half from pre-commercial fishing levels. Some stocks have been declared extinct, while

Continued

Grizzly bear tracks alongside a coastal river in the Great Bear Rainforest, British Columbia. Research now shows that the nutrients bears carry back from the oceans and rivers are central to promoting rich forest growth along many coastal streams.

others are now on the official endangered species list in both Canada and the US.

The salmon have also been trying to tell us something that scientists are only now starting to realize. Salmon spend anywhere from two to seven years in the ocean environment before returning to spawn and die. When they die, the nutrients they have collected over this sojourn do not disappear (law of conservation of matter) but are released into the surrounding environment. The salmon provide food and nourishment not only for the plankton and insects that feed the next generation of fish and propel their journey to the sea but also for the terrestrial riverine environment. When the fish die, they provide a feast for many other species, including eagles, raccoons, and bears. As the fish are digested, their nutrients are distributed throughout the forest as feces, providing the rich fertilizer on which some of the tallest trees in the world depend. Tom Reimchen of the University of Victoria estimates that BC's bears could be transferring 60 million kilograms of salmon tissue into coastal forests each year. When we take away the fish, we take away this fertilizer, and forest growth suffers. Scientists have found that up to 40 per cent of the nitrates in the old-growth forests in coastal BC originate from marine environments. Rivers with barriers to salmon, such as waterfalls, have noticeably poorer nearby forest growth. If we want to protect at least some of these so-called salmon forests in their natural state, shouldn't we be trying to protect the processes that created them and continue to sustain them, the Pacific salmon?

Scientists have now discovered another aspect of this linkage. Not only do salmon collect nutrients from the ocean, they also collect pollutants and concentrate them within their bodies (Chapter 10). Scientists in Alaska have found that when the fish die in their millions after spawning, there is a sevenfold increase in the concentration of PCBs in remote, pristine, freshwater lakes. Lakes with the highest numbers of spawning salmon also have the highest concentrations of PCBs.

The biggest challenge, however, may be global warming and the changes this will bring to all aspects of the salmon habitat. From the amount of snowpack in the mountains that controls the water in the rivers, through river temperatures, to changes in oceanic currents and predator–prey relationships, the salmon will be very vulnerable. Already, some species are at the edge of their temperature tolerance range (Chapter 2) for fresh water, and the most productive salmon river in the world, the Fraser, may soon be too warm: the water temperature of the Fraser has risen over 2°C during the past 55 years. Over the same period, sea-surface temperatures have risen between 0.3°C and 0.9°C on the BC coast. In response, the annual cycles of phytoplankton bloom that nourish the entire food chain are occurring earlier, raising the possibility of a growing mismatch between food supplies and emergence of salmon smolts into the ocean.

The salmon have an eloquent and tragic story to tell about how we are treating their environment, and they will be one of the best indicators of the impact of global change on coastal and marine environments. The story is not an easy one to interpret. In 2010, some 31 million sockeye returned to the Fraser, a run not equalled in size in the last century. Theories abound as to the cause, ranging from the fertilization of the northern ocean by an Alaskan volcano that produced increased nutrients and an exceptional plankton bloom when the salmon were feeding, through to enhanced survivorship of smolts because of favourable ocean conditions when the salmon first entered salt water. This is a mystery story that will continue to puzzle scientists for decades to come.

ENVIRONMENT IN FOCUS

BOX 8.8 | So How Many Whales Was That? Traditional Ecological Knowledge (TEK) and Science in Canada's Arctic

DFO scientists believed that bowhead whales numbered only in the hundreds and were divided into two separate populations. Since 1996, their figure of 345 bowhead whales was used to determine an Inuit bowhead whale quota in Nunavut of about one every two years. But the scientists' new, much higher bowhead whale estimate—showing a population that could run as high as 43,105—supports an annual hunt of between 18 and 90.

Inuit have said for years that the eastern Arctic's stock of bowhead whales is part of one large and healthy population. The first sign that bowhead whales were more numerous than scientists first thought came from a study of Inuit bowhead knowledge completed in 2000. That study was based on interviews with 252 Inuit hunters and elders in 18 communities. In those interviews, most Inuit informants said they see far more bowhead whales now than in the 1950s. It took more than seven years for DFO's science to catch up. DFO estimates of the bowhead population jumped from 345 in 2000 to about 3,000 in 2003, then to 7,309 in 2007, and to 14,400 in 2008. There is still a large range of uncertainty, though, with current figures, varying between 4,800 and 43,105 bowhead whales in the eastern Arctic.

However, the message to take from the reassessment is not that one side was right and the other wrong. It is that population estimates in remote locations are very difficult to make, and all sources of information should be considered. It is also appropriate to take a precautionary approach, especially when endangered species are being considered.

Pollution

The main sources of marine toxic pollution in Canada originate with the deposition of airborne pollutants from fossil-fuel combustion, agricultural runoff, inadequately treated sewage, and by-products or waste materials from refining processes (e.g., effluent from pulp and paper mills). Some chemicals, known as POPs (persistent organic pollutants), including PCBs (polychlorinated biphenyls) and DDE (the breakdown product of the now-banned pesticide DDT, discussed in Chapter 10), can take decades or even centuries to degrade and tend to bioaccumulate in the fatty tissues of organisms over time. The concentrated contaminants are then passed along through the food chain (biomagnification—see Chapter 10) and can reach very high concentrations in the tissues of animals in the top trophic levels (such as polar bears, whales, and humans).

The killer whales of the Strait of Georgia are among the most contaminated mammals on the planet (Ross et al., 2000). Although PCBs have been the main concern, levels of a toxic flame retardant (PBDE) are expected to surpass PCBs as the leading contaminant in endangered southern resident killer whales by 2020. Unlike PCBs, largely used as coolants in industrial transformers before being banned 35 years ago, PBDEs are widely used as flame retardants in polymer resins and plastics and are found in consumer products such as furniture, TVs, stereos, computers, carpets, and curtains. PBDEs find their way into the marine environment through the air or through runoff and effluent and pose a risk to the endocrine system, reproductive health, and the immune system. PBDE levels in harbour seals in Puget Sound in the state of Washington increased steadily from 14 parts per billion in 1984 to 1,057 in 2003. Killer whales carry 10 times the contaminants of harbour seals, which means an increase in PBDEs in seals is an immediate cause for concern about the whales.

The dangers of pollutants are further exacerbated by the long-range transport of toxins in the atmosphere, and many Aboriginal people in Canada's North have bioaccumulated high levels of toxins in their bodies because of their reliance on marine mammals. Some of these toxins are also endocrine disrupters, which have been linked to severe growth, development, and reproductive problems in wildlife populations, as discussed earlier in this chapter. However, even toxic substances that are not persistent or bioaccumulative (such as benzene) can have significant harmful effects on the health of the marine environment.

In recent years, Canada has made progress in reducing emissions from a number of marine toxic pollution sources. Agricultural industries now use more environment-friendly pesticides and fertilizers and have increased conservation tillage to reduce runoff pollution. There has also been a significant decrease in the amount of toxic pollutants coming from other industries such as pulp and paper, petroleum refining, and aluminum.

Already, some of these reductions are apparent in ocean life. Temporal trends of persistent, bioaccumulative, and toxic (PBT) chemicals were examined in beluga whales in the St Lawrence estuary. Blubber samples of 86 stranded adult belugas were collected between 1987 and 2002 and analyzed for several regulated PBTs, including PCBs, DDT and its metabolites, chlordane (CHL) and related compounds, HCH, HCB, and Mirex. Concentrations of most of the PBTs examined had exponentially decreased by at least a factor of two in belugas between 1987 and 2002, while no increasing trends were observed for any of the PBTs measured (Lebeuf et al., 2007).

Although the concentration of toxins in the Canadian environment has declined, they have not disappeared. Existing toxic residues will be recycled and dispersed throughout ecosystems for some time. In addition, toxic substances from sources outside Canada continue to enter our ecosystems through oceanic and atmospheric transport. One study of contaminant concentrations in the eggs of double-crested cormorants shows a significant decrease in the past 35 years (Canadian Wildlife Service, 2003). However, the lack of further declines, despite the banning of these chemicals in Canada, leads scientists to believe that it may be the result of long-range transport of POPs used outside of Canada, as well as the slow release of contaminant residues from bottom sediments and dump facilities.

In Canada, federal law and policy have declared the management and reduction of toxic substances in the environment "a matter of national priority." Under the Canadian Environmental Protection Act, the minister of Environment is mandated to virtually eliminate the production of POPs and manage the discharge of other pollutants and wastes into the environment. Canada was also active internationally and was the first nation to ratify an international treaty, the Stockholm Convention on Persistent Organic Pollutants, which aims to identify problematic substances for which comprehensive global action is required.

Organic pollution is also of concern in some areas (see Chapter 4). Given the volume of water in the ocean, it might be thought that an infinite adsorption capacity exists for receiving and breaking down organic wastes. However, where there are dense populations and waste is deposited in a site with low adsorptive capacity, even the ocean can become polluted. On the east coast of Canada, for example, 52 per cent of all towns and cities lack any sewage treatment. The problem became quite obvious in Halifax, where sewage had been deposited directly into the harbour since 1749 and toilet paper, tampon applicators, and condoms were a familiar sight. However, Halifax now has treatment plants for the 181 million litres of raw sewage pumped out every day.

At the other end of the country, Victoria has taken a different approach. The city pumps out 100 million litres of raw sewage into Juan de Fuca Strait every day through two deep-sea pipes that extend more than a kilometre offshore and are more than 60 metres deep. Victoria's situation is different from that of Halifax in that the large volume of fast-moving, cold water in the Strait breaks down and disperses the sewage very quickly. The plume from the discharge never reaches the surface in summer and only 1 per cent of the time in winter. Marine biologists have monitored the situation for years

© All Canada Photos/Ian McAllister

The population of the southern pods of the killer whale has fallen 20 per cent over the last 15 years and is now considered endangered.

Courtesy the Capital District, Regional Source Control Program

Ad from CRD (Capital Regional District, BC) campaign to control source pollution.

and detected virtually no negative impacts. Most biologists are satisfied that the dilution of organic waste is acceptable. However, there is much greater concern over the non-organic wastes that are disposed of illegally through the sewage system. Over a two-year period, estimates suggest that these wastes in Victoria include 2,920 kilograms of oil and grease, 17,400 kilograms of zinc, 9,000 kilograms of copper, 2,560 kilograms of cyanide, and 1,360 kilograms of lead. The regional government has introduced educational programs on waste disposal, since the most effective way to deal with these substances is to halt their entry into the sewage system rather than trying to treat them once they are there (see the CRD ad on previous page).

In 2005, Victoria commissioned an independent study to review liquid waste practices, which suggested that an increasing population would soon require increased sewage treatment. Both senior levels of government agreed and promised to help with some of the costs. A plan was devised at an original cost of more than $782 million, which has now doubled. However, local governments have refused to rezone lands to allow treatment facilities to be built. Many scientists and health professionals also question whether this is the wisest investment for that amount of money. There is a strong consensus among health professionals that current disposal practices pose no medical risk, and marine biologists have failed to find any significant biological changes over time. One of their main points of contention is that no study has been undertaken on the impact of the land-based treatment and disposal that is now being planned. As of 2015, the impasse had still not been resolved.

Some Canadian Responses

Canada's Oceans Strategy

The Oceans Act was passed in 1998 to provide a comprehensive and coordinated approach to marine resource management in Canada. One of the main requirements of the Act was for the minister of Fisheries and Oceans to develop a national Oceans Strategy. This strategy established three principles to guide *all* ocean management decision-making:

1. *Sustainable development* "recognizes the need for integration of social, economic, and environmental aspects of decision-making and that any current and future ocean resource development must be carefully undertaken without compromising the ability of future generations of Canadians to meet their needs."
2. *Integrated management* "is a commitment to planning and managing human activities in a comprehensive manner while considering all factors necessary for the conservation and sustainable use of marine resources and shared use of ocean spaces."
3. The *precautionary approach* is defined in the Oceans Act as "erring on the side of caution."

These underlying principles provide the essential litmus test against which all ocean management decisions should be judged and to which the federal government is accountable. Unfortunately, this has not proved to be the case. Globally important glass-sponge reefs off the coast of BC have been heavily damaged as a result of a lack of protection from fishing—a failure to apply the precautionary principle and poor consideration of values other than economic ones.

Marine Protected Areas in Canada

Canada, like the rest of the world, has paid little attention to protecting the marine environment through marine protected areas (MPAs), especially when compared to the attention and protection given the terrestrial environment (Chapter 14). Depending on the definition applied, estimates suggest that Canada has more than 790 protected areas, with a marine component covering approximately 4.6 million hectares, or 0.66 per cent of Canada's ocean area (Environment Canada, 2011a). However, almost all of this area is in terrestrial protected areas that happen to be coastal. This figure compares with more than 9.8 per cent of the terrestrial environment under protection.

In response to this situation, three programs have been created at the federal level to establish MPAs (Table 8.1). The first is an MPA program established under the Oceans Act within the Department of Fisheries and Oceans. The purpose of these MPAs is to conserve commercial and non-commercial fisheries, protect species at risk, and conserve unique habitats—i.e., areas of high biodiversity or biological productivity. Five Atlantic MPAs have been designated: The Gully near Sable Island, Basin Head in the Gulf of St Lawrence, Eastport in Bonavista Bay, Gilbert Bay in the Labrador Sea, and Musquash Estuary in the Bay of Fundy. In addition, the Endeavour Hydrothermal Vents and Bowie Seamount MPAs have been created in the Pacific as well as Tarium Niryutait in the Arctic. DFO committed to establishing nine MPAs between 2005 and 2010. Besides the five Atlantic MPAs designated within this period, another eight areas of interest are under consideration: Anguniaqvia Niqiqyuam (NWT), St Lawrence Estuary (Quebec), Race Rocks (BC), Hecate Strait/Queen Charlotte Sound (BC), Laurentian Channel (Quebec–Atlantic Canada), St Anns Bank (Cape Breton, NS), Shediac Valley (NB), and American Bank (Quebec).

Second, through the Canadian Wildlife Service (CWS), Environment Canada has several programs that may include designation of marine sanctuaries such as national wildlife areas and migratory bird sanctuaries. Although some of the CWS sanctuaries are large, especially in the Arctic, they are designed primarily to protect specific species (particularly

TABLE 8.1 | Federal Statutory Powers for Protecting Marine Areas

Agency	Legislative Tools	Designations	Mandate
Fisheries and Oceans Canada	Oceans Act	Marine protected areas (MPAs)	To protect and conserve: • fisheries resources, including marine mammals and their habitats • endangered or threatened species and their habitats • unique habitats • areas of high biodiversity or biological productivity • areas for scientific and research purposes.
	Fisheries Act	Fisheries closures	Conservation mandate to manage and regulate fisheries, conserve and protect fish, protect fish habitat, and prevent pollution of waters frequented by fish
Environment Canada	Canada Wildlife Act	National wildlife areas	To protect and conserve marine areas that are nationally or internationally significant for all wildlife but focusing on migratory birds
		Marine wildlife areas	To protect coastal and marine habitats that are heavily used by birds for breeding, feeding, migration, and overwintering
Parks Canada	National Parks Act; National Marine Conservation Areas Act	National parks; national marine conservation areas (NMCAs)	To protect and conserve for all time marine conservation areas of Canadian significance that are representative of the 29 natural marine regions identified on Canada's coasts, and to encourage public understanding, appreciation, and enjoyment

seabirds) rather than ecosystems, and they have no minimum standards to control extractive activities.

The third program involves national marine conservation areas (NMCAs), developed by Parks Canada. These areas differ from terrestrial national parks in that they are managed for sustainable use. NMCAs are larger than the MPAs established by DFO, selected to represent Canada's ocean heritage, and contain an explicit mandate for recreation and education. NMCAs contain zones with special protection measures, such as no fishing. The location and size of these zones is decided through consultation among fishers, scientists, conservationists, government agencies, and other stakeholders. These decisions are crucial. Setting aside small fragments in unproductive areas will produce few benefits.

Philip Dearden

The federal and Ontario governments have agreed to create an NMCA on the north shore of Lake Superior. It would be the largest freshwater protected area in the world.

Outside of no-take zones, commercial and recreational fishing will continue in NMCAs, although additional conservation measures may be stipulated. Some activities, such as exploration or exploitation of hydrocarbons, minerals, aggregates, or any other inorganic material, are prohibited. Dumping is not allowed. Conservation interests sought to have bottom trawling, dragging, and fin-fish aquaculture prohibited as well because of their destructive impact on ocean ecosystems, but such prohibitions were not included in the National Marine Conservation Areas Act.

The goals of NMCAs are to conserve areas representative of the ocean environment and the Great Lakes and to foster public awareness, appreciation, and understanding of our marine heritage. The interpretation aspect of these areas may be their greatest contribution and a unique Parks Canada mission. Canadians are poorly informed about the marine environment. Creating ocean literacy among Canadians, who must support public policies for the sustainable use and protection of Canada's marine environment, will pose unique challenges to interpreters.

One of the main challenges with all these programs is to actually designate areas. It is essential that local communities support these conservation measures, and gaining support can be time consuming. Prime Minister Jean Chrétien made a commitment at the World Summit in Johannesburg in 2002 to create five NMCAs by 2007. By 2011 only one site, Haida Gwaii in BC, had been protected under the Act. Some progress has been made at sites in Lake Superior, the southern

DOMESTIC GUEST STATEMENT

Public and Political Will Needed to Protect Our Oceans | *Sabine Jessen*

Overfishing, removal of top predators, and fishing down marine food webs are having huge impacts on ocean ecosystems. Scientists point out that there are a variety of solutions to reducing fish mortality and ensuring the health of ocean ecosystems: reducing quotas, reducing overall effort, cutting subsidies, reducing bycatch, and creating networks of marine reserves where no fishing is allowed.

With all the scientific evidence available to show the decline in ecosystem health and the various tools to address this problem, why has it been so difficult for most countries to make these needed changes?

Part of the answer lies in the serious disconnect between what scientists are telling us and what the public believes is happening in the oceans. When the public is asked to name the greatest threat to ocean ecosystems, their answer is usually pollution. But scientific studies clearly show that the greatest threat is overfishing—the most serious problem is in what we are taking out of the oceans, not what we are putting in. Couple this with the results of another poll of Americans, asking them what the most important decision was that they make every day. You might be shocked to hear that deciding what to wear was considered the day's most difficult decision for one in every 10 people.

Why have I highlighted these points in talking about ocean management? Simply, without public understanding of the issue, and public demand for change, it is difficult to persuade politicians to make the difficult decisions that will lead to the fundamental changes required to better manage our oceans. Political support determines the priorities and the resources allocated to address these issues. Ocean management programs and marine protected areas are receiving very few resources in Canada, and the government has just announced plans to cut these resources.

While Canada has made many commitments to better oceans management, including marine protected areas, we still have reached only about 1 per cent protection of Canadian waters. And the MPAs that have been established rarely exclude fishing. While California has almost completed a network of fully protected marine reserves and Australia is moving ahead with a national network of marine protected areas, Canada lags behind these efforts.

A group of 14 scientists in Canada recently developed guidelines for MPAs and MPA networks in Canada to help the government and the public do it right. MPA networks in Canada must include areas that are fully protected from human uses, especially fishing, if ocean ecosystems are to recover and be more resilient in the face of climate change.

Until concrete steps are taken, we will continue to witness the ongoing destruction of the blue frontier. And by the time the public really understands and demands change, it could be too late.

Courtesy Sabine Jessen

Sabine Jessen is the National Manager for Oceans and Great Freshwater Lakes at the Canadian Parks and Wilderness Society, and one of the foremost activists pushing for increased conservation of Canada's ocean environment.

Strait of Georgia in BC, Lancaster Sound in the Arctic, and the Magdalen Islands in the Gulf of St Lawrence. Parks Canada has a marine system plan analogous to its terrestrial system plan (Chapter 14), with 29 marine regions. The goal is to have representation within each of these regions. Canada has international treaty commitments under the Convention on Biological Diversity to protect 10 per cent of its marine territory by 2020. Clearly this commitment will not be met.

Aquaculture

One response to the declining catch in wild fisheries is to produce more seafood through farming or aquaculture. Aquaculture is the fastest-growing food production sector in the world and accounts for nearly half of the fish produced worldwide. It is expected that by 2030 it will be the dominant source of fish and seafood. However, the global market is dominated by the production of salmon and shrimp, energy-intensive species for expensive markets rather than species designed to feed the poor.

Canada has been part of this growth and in 2014 ranked twentieth in the world in aquaculture production, although DFO predicts that Canada has the potential to be among the top three. Farmed fish and seafood production was valued at over $800 million in 2012, constituting approximately 34 per cent of all Canadian fisheries value. Salmon is the predominant farmed species in Canada, producing 116,101 tonnes in 2012 and generating more than $690 million. Ninety-seven per cent of Canada's farmed fish and seafood is exported to the United States. Over 3,000 people are employed in aquaculture, and it is predicted that employment levels will quadruple over the next 15 years.

BC has Canada's largest output, worth $667 million in 2011 (Figure 8.13), followed by New Brunswick, PEI, and Newfoundland and Labrador. Most of BC's production comes from salmon. Salmon production contributes 88 per cent of all cultured seafood in BC. The 2010 cultured salmon harvest of 78,700 tonnes was the largest harvest since 2006. The increasing importance of cultured salmon to BC fisheries production can be seen in Figures 8.13 and 8.14. British Columbia is the fourth-largest producer of farmed salmon in the world after Norway, Chile, and the United Kingdom.

A typical salmon farm consists of 10 to 30 cages, each 12 or 15 metres square, and contains on average 20,000 fish. The cages are made of open nets that allow water to flow through and antibiotics, uneaten food, feces, and chemicals used to prevent excessive marine growth on the cages to flow out.

There are more than 140 fish farms on the BC coast, mainly concentrated in three small areas. In addition, many applications await approval to expand operations to other areas along the coast. BC's salmon farming industry employs almost 3,000 people in full-time, year-round jobs either directly (on farms) or indirectly (in processing). More than 92 per cent of the direct jobs are located in coastal communities outside of Greater Victoria and Vancouver. These economic opportunities can be lifesavers for some remote communities, especially Aboriginal communities. Nonetheless, there are several concerns about aquaculture.

Escapement. Salmon farms in BC mainly raise Atlantic salmon, primarily because the Norwegian-dominated industry had more experience with, and well-developed markets for, Atlantic salmon. The Atlantic salmon are also more efficient in converting feed into flesh, are less aggressive, and tolerate crowded conditions. The farming of Atlantic salmon is an environmental concern because escapement from farm fish cages, often in high numbers, occurs regularly. It has been estimated that up to 2015, more than 1 million Atlantic salmon had escaped from BC aquafarms. In 2010, 15,700 Atlantics escaped from a farm which was using the latest net-pen technology. There is irrefutable proof that Atlantic salmon

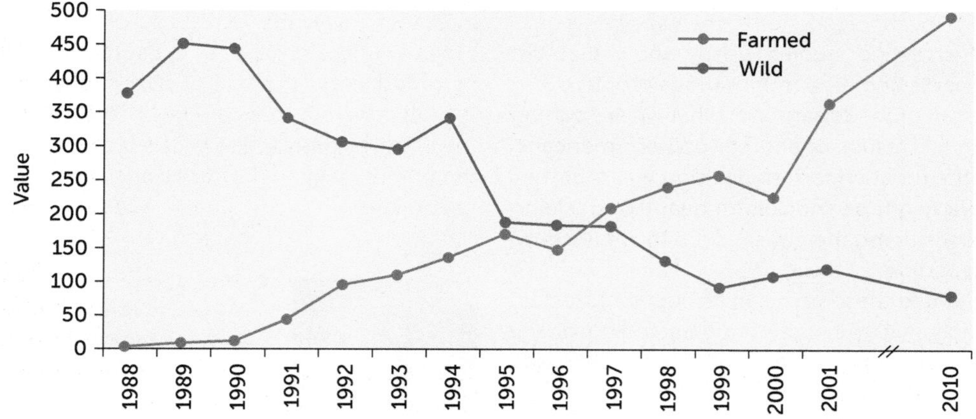

FIGURE 8.13 | Value of BC salmon exports in millions of dollars.

Source: Adapted from BC Salmon Market Database, at: www.bcsalmon.ca/database/export/summary/sumvlpd.htm.

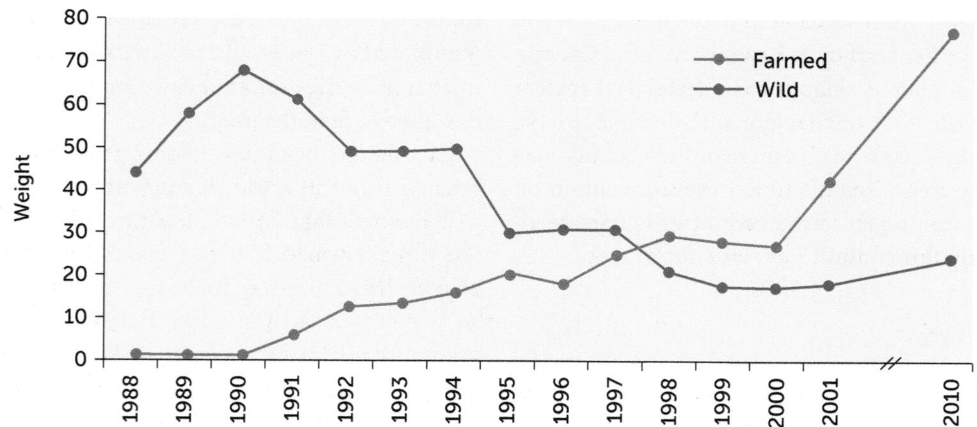

FIGURE 8.14 | Weight of BC salmon exports in millions of kilograms.

Source: Adapted from BC Salmon Market Database, at: www.bcsalmon.ca/database/export/summary/sumvlpd.htm.

are now spawning wild in Pacific rivers. DFO maintained for many years that this was impossible, until scientists proved otherwise. There are concerns that these escapers, an invasive species (Chapter 3), may displace the native salmon. A recent model estimated that farmed Atlantic salmon were present in over half of surveyed rivers and streams in British Columbia (Fisher et al., 2014).

If salmon farming were confined in British Columbia to native Pacific species alone, it might not help. At the moment, there is no evidence that Atlantic and Pacific salmon interbreed. However, if Pacific salmon were to be found both wild and in farms, there would undoubtedly be interbreeding. This genetic introgression could have a devastating effect on wild stocks, as determined by McGinnity et al. (2003) on the east coast. There is considerable scientific uncertainty entailed in all these issues. And although DFO's stated policy is to "err on the side of caution," the department has failed to do so with respect to the dangers associated with escapement.

Disease. The high stocking levels of fish in netted areas promote rapid spread of infectious diseases and parasites. Since fish farms are along migration routes for wild salmon, diseases and/or parasites can be passed along easily, with a detrimental impact on wild populations. In Clayoquot Sound on the west coast of Vancouver Island, a viral disease, infectious hematopoietic necrosis (IHN), caused the parent company to destroy over half of its fish. Unfortunately, this response was not enough to contain the disease, and several other farms in Sechelt and along the BC coast also became infected. The total cost of depopulating and cleaning these farms was estimated at $27 million. However, taxpayers paid over $4 million to the companies in compensation.

Lice. Strong scientific evidence indicates that pink salmon smolts (salmon that are changing from a freshwater to a saltwater environment) in certain areas of the coast are being weakened by excessive sea lice coming from farms near their migration routes. One study found 90 per cent mortality among populations of juvenile pink salmon due to lice and predicted that stocks in some rivers will be extinct within 10 years if no mitigating actions are taken (Krkošek et al., 2007).

Pollution. To combat the diseases mentioned above, farmed salmon are treated with antibiotics. More antibiotic per weight of livestock is used by salmon aquaculture than by any other form of farming. Antibiotics can harm other marine organisms, since they are released directly into the ocean. As well, excess food and feces create a large amount of organic pollution. The substances build up on the ocean floor, depleting oxygen levels, releasing noxious gases (as a by-product of decomposition), and smothering benthic organisms. On a daily basis, the aquaculture industry in BC dumps the same amount of sewage in the ocean as a city of half a million people. Because this occurs in relatively protected coves and inlets, the waste is not readily dispersed as is, for example, that of the city of Victoria.

Predator control. Predators such as seals and sea lions are one of the main problems for the farmers, since they literally eat profits. Farmers are permitted to shoot animals that rip nets open. In 2010, farmers reported killing 56 harbour seals and 170 California sea lions. Many observers think that these killings are grossly under-reported.

Energetics. Unlike the herbivorous fish produced in the vast majority of fish farms around the world, salmon are carnivorous. As a result, farmed salmon are mainly fed other fish, in pellet form, such as anchovies and mackerel caught as far away as South America. As dictated by the second law of thermodynamics (Chapter 2), only 1 kilogram of farmed salmon is produced for every 3 to 4 kilograms of feed fish. This is a poor use of fish protein and leads to the reduction of fish stocks elsewhere.

Social dimensions. Most profits from production go to five multinational companies that control 80 per cent of the industry in BC. As a result, a high percentage of the economic benefits attached to salmon aquaculture are exported out of the province. Increased mechanization is leading to lower employment figures, further limiting the economic benefits accruing to local communities. It is also feared that further growth in the industry will be detrimental to the wild fishery and reduce the health of communities dependent on wild fish. Increased supply of farmed salmon may continue to depress the price of BC's wild salmon.

Human health. To turn the white flesh pink, farmed salmon are fed artificial colouring. The most commonly used colourants are synthetic astaxanthin and canthaxanthin. In 2003, the European Union reduced the amount of canthaxanthin that can be fed to salmon by two-thirds because of concerns over retinal damage caused by ingesting too much of the chemical. One study found that farmed salmon contained 11 times the amount of toxic contaminants found in wild salmon (Hites et al., 2004). Recent studies have also drawn

Small fish farm on the Broughton archipelago, Vancouver Island, British Columbia.

links between farm-raised salmon and cancer, likely due to the high levels of carcinogens in salmon feed.

Most of these problems are not insurmountable. Salmon can be produced in closed, land-based systems that all but eliminate some of the problems. One large grocery chain on Vancouver Island, Thriftys, now buys salmon from closed-pen systems for approximately 20 to 30 per cent more than for salmon from net-pen fish but sells them at roughly the same price in order to promote more sustainable practices. The main factor in why more environmentally and socially sound farming techniques are not being more widely adopted is the consumer. If people were willing to pay more for salmon produced using techniques that avoided the problems outlined above, then producers would not be so resistant to adopting these more sustainable systems (Box 8.9). At the moment, however, the environment pays those extra costs.

In response to these concerns and vocal opposition from many communities, the BC government announced in 2008 that salmon aquaculture would not be allowed to expand to the north coast of the province. The moratorium remains in place today, although production has increased and the industry is pressuring governments to allow for major expansion. The main challenge to the aquaculture community is how to resolve the problems raised above so that salmon aquaculture can play an important role in meeting the food needs of the future.

Implications

Ocean health is now a major concern. Scientific efforts have intensified, and understanding has increased, yet much remains to be done. The very visible collapse of fishing stocks around the world and on the east and west coasts of Canada has helped to direct a little more political attention to oceans in general and fisheries in particular. Commitments have been made at both international and national levels to adopt more sustainable ocean practices, including encouraging and enabling sustainable fisheries, limiting pollution, and establishing systems of marine protected areas. At the moment, most of these measures are in the embryonic stage. Some plans, such as Canada's Oceans Strategy, have shown little progress. Only time will tell whether international and national commitments will be successful in turning around the trends described in this chapter.

ENVIRONMENT IN FOCUS

BOX 8.9 | What You Can Do: Supporting Healthy Oceans and Sustainable Fisheries

1. Fish are an important dietary component for many people and a healthy one. However, it is important that the fish you eat are not endangered or caught with a method that involves killing other species as bycatch. Use Canada's Seafood Guide produced by Sustainable Seafood Canada to inform your consumption (www.seachoice.org).
2. Buy only certified brands where they are available, such as dolphin-free tuna. Better still, do not eat tuna, but eat what tuna eat, sardines!
3. If you buy farmed seafood, consider paying a little more for products that have been produced using low-impact methods. For example, Thrifty Foods in BC sells farmed salmon produced using land-based, closed-system methods.
4. Ensure that you dispose of any toxic materials in the correct manner, not down the drain.
5. Use natural cleaners, such as vinegar and water, rather than commercial cleaners.
6. Using less water for your own needs leaves more water in rivers for fish such as salmon.
7. Support NGOs, such as Oceans Blue, Living Oceans, and the Canadian Parks and Wilderness Society, which are working for ocean conservation and the development of marine protected areas.
8. Whenever you do something that involves carbon emissions, whether travelling or buying a product, your actions are leading to ocean acidification. The car you drive and the coral reef in the South Pacific are intimately connected.

Summary

1. Throughout history, the resources of the oceans have been thought of as vast and undiminished. The past decade has furnished conclusive proof that this view is far from correct. More than 70 per cent of global fisheries are now at or over their maximum exploitation levels.
2. Oceanic ecosystems are controlled by the same general principles that influence terrestrial ecosystems, but their manifestations may be different. There may be up to 5,000 species of fish still awaiting discovery.
3. The carbon balance of the oceans is of great interest because of its relationship with global climatic change.
4. Ocean fisheries supply about 20 per cent of the world's annual animal protein. Catch statistics showed very large increased catches over the past 55 years, but they have now levelled off considerably.
5. Fish of the same species are smaller than they used to be and the species caught now are at lower trophic levels than in the past.
6. The oceans are the ultimate sink for many pollutants, and about 80 per cent of ocean pollution comes from activities on land.
7. The number of oxygen-deficient dead zones in the oceans is growing as a result of eutrophication and increasing sea temperatures.
8. More than 60 per cent of global oil production originates under the oceans. Exploration, drilling, transporting, and processing this oil is a major source of contamination.
9. Half of the world's population lives within 100 kilometres of the coast, a proportion expected to increase to 75 per cent by 2100.
10. Global climatic change will lead to increases in average sea level of 15–95 centimetres and 0.9–1.6 metres in the Arctic during this century. This will create severe challenges for many coastal communities.
11. Canada will experience greater impacts from the influence of global climate change on the oceans than most countries due to higher than average sea level and temperature rises, and greater vulnerability to ocean acidification.
12. There are many international agreements and programs on ocean management. Most have yet to fulfill their potential in improving oceanic conditions.
13. Marine protected areas have been endorsed by the scientific community as necessary to improving ocean conservation, but establishment at both international and national levels lags far behind targets.
14. Canada has the longest coastline of any country and the second-largest continental shelf, equal to 30 per cent of Canada's land mass.
15. The east coast fisheries have experienced profound changes over the past couple of decades with the total collapse of the northern cod stocks.
16. Management of Aboriginal use of marine resources is an important concern on all coasts.
17. Exploitation of offshore hydrocarbons in Canada has taken place over the past two decades, mainly off the east coast. Increased attention is now being given to the Arctic.
18. Pollution levels of many substances have declined over recent years. However, a recent study concluded that the killer whales of Georgia Strait in BC are among the most polluted animals on the planet.
19. Canada passed a comprehensive Oceans Act in 1998, but it has been ineffectual because of a lack of political support and funding.
20. Three federal programs establish marine protected areas (MPAs) in Canada, yet less than 1 per cent of the area of Canada's marine environment is protected.
21. Aquaculture accounts for almost 30 per cent of the volume and 39 per cent of the value of global fish landings. Aquaculture is the fastest-growing food production sector in the world.
22. BC has Canada's largest share of the total value of aquaculture production, focused mainly on salmon. Although economically important to some communities, salmon farming also raises concerns over escapement, disease, proliferation of sea lice, killing of predators, energetics, and pollution.

Key Terms

acidification
aquaculture
bottom trawling
bycatch
carbon balance
coral bleaching
coral polyps
ecotourism
endocrine disruption
exclusive economic zones (EEZs)
fishing down the food chain
hypoxic
illegal, unreported, and unregulated (IUU) fisheries
incentive-based
longline
marine protected areas (MPAs)
prey switching
serial depletion
shifting baseline
thermocline
thermohaline circulation
total allowable catch (TAC)
zooxanthellae

Questions for Review and Critical Thinking

1. In what ways are oceanic and terrestrial ecosystems the same, and in what ways do they differ?
2. What are the most biologically productive areas of the ocean?
3. What is thermohaline circulation, and why is it important?
4. Give an example of a positive feedback loop related to global climate change and the oceans. Are there any negative feedback loops?
5. Explain the concepts of shifting baselines, serial depletion, and fishing down the food chain.
6. Give an example of the destructive effects of bottom trawling.
7. What are the two main forms of chemical pollutants in the oceans, and what are their main effects?
8. What are some of the main international conventions concerning ocean management? How effective have they been?
9. What are the jurisdictional arrangements for ocean management in Canada?
10. Discuss the principal reasons behind the collapse of the Atlantic groundfish stocks and some of the lessons to be learned from this experience.
11. Outline some of the challenges involving the Aboriginal use of marine resources in Canada.
12. Discuss the differing approaches of Halifax and Victoria to ocean pollution resulting from sewage.
13. What are the main principles underlying Canada's Oceans Strategy?
14. Outline the three federal programs for creating marine protected areas in Canada and their similarities and differences.
15. Discuss the positive and negative aspects of aquaculture production.
16. What are the main interactions between global climate change and the oceans?

Related Websites

Canadian Parks and Wilderness Society (CPAWS)
www.cpaws.org

David Suzuki Foundation: Oceans (fishing, aquaculture, MPAs)
www.davidsuzuki.org/issues/oceans

Endeavour Hydrothermal Vents: Canada's First Marine Protected Area
www.dfo-mpo.gc.ca/oceans/marineareas-zonesmarines/mpa-zpm/pacific-pacifique/endeavour-eng.htm

Fisheries and Oceans Canada: Aquaculture
www.dfo-mpo.gc.ca/aquaculture/aquaculture-eng.htm

Marine protected areas, Canada
www.dfo-mpo.gc.ca/oceans/marineareas-zonesmarines/mpa-zpm/index-eng.htm

Marine Protected Areas Research Group (UVic)
mparg.wordpress.com/

NCEAS: Marine Ecology and Resources Management
www.nceas.ucsb.edu/ecology/marine

Notes from Sea Level
www.jonbowermaster.com/

Save Our Seas Foundation
www.saveourseas.org

Seafood Consumption Choices
www.seafoodchoices.com; www.oceantrust.org; www.seachoice.org/page/resources; www.legalseafoods.com; www.montereybayaquarium.org/cr/seafoodwatch.aspx

The Starving Ocean (fisheries crisis)
www.fisherycrisis.com

UN Food and Agriculture Organization, Fisheries and Aquaculture Department
www.fao.org/fi/default_all.asp

University of British Columbia Fisheries Centre
oceans.ubc.ca

Watershed Watch Salmon Society
www.watershed-watch.org

World Wildlife Fund Canada, Oceans
wwf.ca/conservation/oceans

Further Readings

Note: This list comprises works relevant to the subject of the chapter but not cited in the text. All cited works are listed in the References at the end of the book.

Bavington, D. "Marine and freshwater fisheries in Canada: Uncertainties, conflicts and hope on the water," in B. Mitchell, ed., *Resource and Environmental Management in Canada*, 5th edn. Don Mills, ON: Oxford University Press, 221–245.

Beaugrand, G., M. Edwards, and L. Legendre. 2010. "Marine biodiversity, ecosystem functioning, and carbon cycles," *Proceedings of the National Academy of Science* 107: 10120–4.

Bennett, N., and P. Dearden. 2013. "Why local people do not support conservation: Community perceptions of marine protected area livelihood impacts, governance and management in Thailand," *Marine Policy* 44: 107–116.

Bertazzon, S., P. D. O'Hara, O. Barrett, and N. Serra-Sogas. 2015. "Geospatial analysis of oil discharges observed by the National Aerial Surveillance Program in the Canadian Pacific Ocean," *Applied Geography* 52: 78–89.

Cosandey-Godin, A.C., and B. Worm. 2010. "Keeping the lead: How to strengthen shark conservation and management policies in Canada," *Marine Policy* 34, 5: 995–1001.

Favaro, B., J. D. Reynolds and I.M. Côté. 2012. "Canada's weakening aquatic protection," *Science* 337: 154.

Forbes, D.L., ed. 2011. *State of the Arctic Coast 2010—Scientific Review and Outlook.* International Arctic Science Committee, Land-Ocean Interactions in the Coastal Zone, Arctic Monitoring and Assessment Programme, International Permafrost Association. Geesthacht, Germany: Helmholtz-Zentrum Geesthacht Centre for Materials and Coastal Research.

Hutchings, J.A., C. Minto, D. Ricard, J.K. Baum, and O.P. Jensen. 2010. "Trends in the abundance of marine fishes," *Canadian Journal of Fisheries and Aquatic Sciences* 67: 1205–10.

Intergovernmental Panel on Climate Change. 2014. *Climate Change 2014 Synthesis Report. Summary for Policymakers.* http://www.ipcc.ch/pdf/assessment-report/ar5/syr/AR5_SYR_FINAL_SPM.pdf.

Pinskya, M.L., O.P. Jensen, D. Ricard, and S.R. Palumbi. 2011. "Unexpected patterns of fisheries collapse in the world's oceans," *Proceedings of the National Academy of Science*. doi: 10.1073/pnas.1015313108/

Powles, H. P. 2011. "Assessing risk of extinction of marine fishes in Canada—The COSEWIC experience," *Fisheries* 36: 231–246.

Rickels W., et al. 2014. "How healthy is the human-ocean system?" *Environmental Research* 9: 044013.

Ricketts, P.J., and L. Hildebrand. 2011. "Coastal and ocean management in Canada: Progress or paralysis?," *Coastal Management* 39: 4–19.

Safina, C. 1997. *Song for the Blue Ocean*. New York: Henry Holt.

Sciberras, M. et al. 2013. "Evaluating the biological effectiveness of fully and partially protected marine areas," *Environmental Evidence* doi: 10.1186/2047-2382-2-4

Vaquer-Sunyer, R., and C.M. Duarte. 2010. "Thresholds of hypoxia for marine biodiversity," *Proceedings of the National Academy of Science* 105: 15452–7.

Watson, R.A., and D. Pauly. 2013. "The changing face of global fisheries—The 1950s vs. the 2000s," *Marine Policy* 42:1–4.

Weigel, J.Y., et al. 2014. "Marine protected areas and fisheries: Bridging the divide," *Aquatic Conservation: Marine and Freshwater Ecosystems* 24, S2: 199–215.

Go to www.oupcanada.com/DeardenMitchell5e to access additional learning tools on your smartphone, tablet, or PC.

CHAPTER NINE

Forests

Learning Objectives

- To understand what the boreal forest is, its significance to Canada, and the main threats it is facing
- To discuss the economic and non-economic values of Canada's forests
- To appreciate the management arrangements and different approaches for harvesting Canada's forests
- To understand some of the environmental and social aspects of forest management practices
- To discuss the theory and practice of "new forestry"
- To describe current directions for forest use in Canada

Canada's Boreal Forest

Canadian forests, particularly in the boreal region, are often perceived as being largely intact due to low population density, an overall small proportion of forest cleared for agriculture or urban settings, and the high share (~65%) of the forested area found in unfragmented blocks covering at least 1 Mha. Although not inaccurate, this perspective is incomplete: excluding the Arctic ecozones, more than one-fourth of Canada's landmass is within 500 m of human access or activity; outside the boreal region, less than 45% of the forested area is found in unfragmented blocks covering at least 50,000 ha; and even in the boreal region, more than 60% of the timber productive area has already been logged at least once. These features result mainly from wood harvest and associated forest roads, but also from other ubiquitous activities like mining, oil and gas exploration and exploitation, hydroelectric power generation, agriculture, and hunting/fishing/trapping. More than 40 years ago, the increasing northward human pressure led Hare and Ritchie (1972) to state that "[p]erhaps within the next decade—and

> certainly within what is left of this century—the Boreal forest of North America [...] will be massively altered by economic invasion." One thing is sure: even though most of Canada's pre-European settlement forests are still covered by trees, human land use does occur over millions of hectares within them. (Landry and Ramankutty, 2015: 83)

"Borealis," a term that literally means "of the North," comes originally from the Greek god of the north wind, Boreas. The term is now applied to many northern phenomena, perhaps the most famous being the *aurora borealis*, or northern lights. Many animal and plant species that live in the North have "borealis" as part of their Latin name, such as the delicate twinflower, *Linnaea borealis*, which is found all across the country. It is also the name used to characterize the great northern forests that stretch not only across Canada but all across the northern hemisphere.

The **boreal forests** also support commercial activities such as logging, wood fibre and sawlog production, pulp and paper mills, and fibreboard production. Its wealth of minerals supports prospecting, mining, and smelting activities (Chapter 12). There are large-scale hydroelectric developments, and the abundant fish and wildlife resources support subsistence, sport, and commercial harvesting activities, as well as a growing tourism industry. Recreation-related activities, such as canoeing, hiking, and birding in the Boreal, contribute more than $4 billion to the economy every year. In addition, more than 186 billion tonnes of carbon are stored in the Boreal's trees, soils, water, and peat—equivalent to 913 years' worth of greenhouse gas emissions in Canada. The global Boreal is the largest terrestrial carbon "bank account" on the planet, with values at least double those of tropical forests (Schindler and Lee, 2010). In fact, Anielski and Wilson (2009) show that the total market value of boreal resource extraction is only about 7 per cent of the value of the **ecosystem services**. Wells et al. (2010) calculated that Canada's boreal forest produces over $700 billion of ecosystem services to the world every year and urged enhanced protection of this globally important landscape.

Almost 50 per cent of the boreal forest is allocated to industry and is open to harvesting. Although the Boreal Shield is the largest of Canada's 15 terrestrial ecozones (Chapter 2), it has one of the lowest proportions of land (6 per cent) dedicated to protected areas in which all forms of industrial activity are prohibited. Globally, the boreal forests now have the highest rates of increase in forest-cover loss (Figure 9.1).

© All Canada Photos/Ron Erwin

The boreal forest in Newfoundland has bedrock outcrops, lakes, and muskeg.

randimal/Thinkstock

The *linnaea borealis*, or twinflower, can be found growing on the forest floor in boreal forests across Canada. Stretching 3,800 kilometres from the eastern tip of Newfoundland to western BC, the **Boreal Shield**, which is coterminous with the geological formation known as the Canadian or Precambrian Shield, houses roughly one-quarter of the world's remaining original forests. The Boreal is Canada's largest ecozone, covering almost 58 per cent of the country's land mass and stretching through all provinces except PEI, Nova Scotia, and New Brunswick. The forests are home to a wide diversity of terrestrial and aquatic wildlife, and 30 per cent of North America's bird population relies on the Boreal for breeding. Many Aboriginal people depend on the resources of the forests for subsistence, and more than 600 Aboriginal communities retain their roots in the forest.

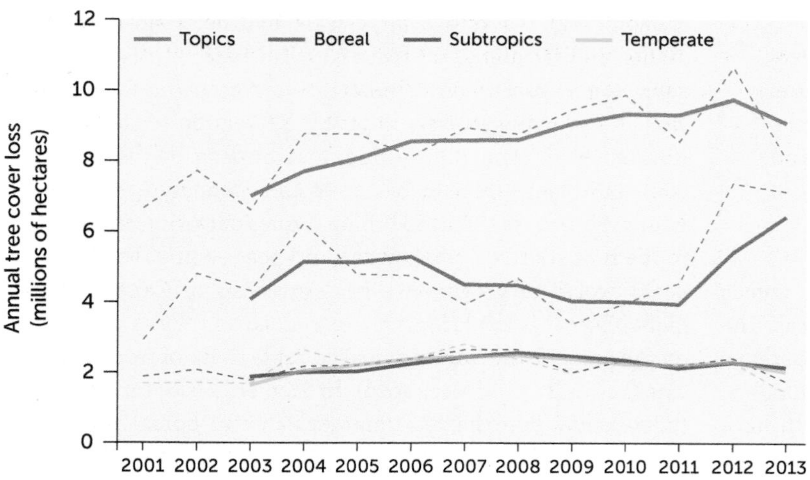

FIGURE 9.1 | Global tree-cover loss, 2001–2013.

Notes: Solid lines show trends; dotted lines show annual losses. Trend lines represent a three-year moving average. The trend may represent a more accurate picture of the data due to uncertainty in year-to-year comparisons.

All Figures are calculated with a 30 per cent minimum tree-cover canopy density.

Source: World Resources Institute, http://www.wri.org/sites/default/files/uploads/3-Boreal_increase_line_graph_0.jpg; based on data from Hansen et al. (2013: 850–853).

The Canadian Boreal Forest Agreement was signed in 2010 by 21 of Canada's largest forestry companies and nine national environmental organizations to ensure a more protected and sustainable boreal forest and a stronger, more competitive forest industry. Over 72 million hectares of land between Yukon and Newfoundland and Labrador have been included in the agreement. Forestry companies have committed to practise sustainable harvesting that will preserve large tracts of old-growth forest, a habitat necessary for the woodland caribou, an endangered species that has symbolized this agreement. In return, environmental organizations will end their campaigns against Canadian forest products. The six-goal agreement is shaping the forest industry to cater to environmentally conscious buyers and is the first of its kind in the world (Box 9.1). The challenge is a significant one, and two environmental groups, Greenpeace and Canopy, have withdrawn from the agreement, citing a lack of progress. However some progress has been made, and the latest developments can be followed at the website for the agreement (see "Related Websites").

The Canadian Boreal Forest Conservation Framework is another initiative, supported by more than 1,500 scientists and thousands of others, to gain permanent protection of at least 50 per cent of the Canadian Boreal and application of strict protective management standards in any other areas where development will occur. The framework has received significant support, including from more than 25 Aboriginal groups and some major forest companies, such as Domtar and Tembec. It is hoped that it will lead to some mitigation of the vast range of challenges now facing the Boreal, and some progress is already being made (Box 9.2).

Large areas of the Boreal are now experiencing serious environmental stresses. In many ways, these stresses are no different from those experienced elsewhere in Canada, and they epitomize the challenges of developing strategies for the management of Canada's sustainable forest ecosystems. This chapter outlines the main challenges and some of the strategies developed to address them.

An Overview of Canada's Forests

Canada is a forest nation. The symbol on our national flag is a maple leaf. Along with our northern latitude, the forests have provided part of the historical context for our national identity. Canada has one-tenth of the world's forests, and

ENVIRONMENT IN FOCUS

BOX 9.1 | Canadian Boreal Forest Agreement

The Canadian Boreal Forest Agreement has six strategic goals that encompass the needs for both conservation and economic development:

- Complete a representative network of protected areas that can serve as ecological benchmarks of the boreal forest
- Protect species at risk
- Reduce greenhouse gas emissions through the entire life-cycle of a forest product
- Develop sustainable forest-management based on ecosystem principles (see Chapter 5), active management (see Chapter 14), and third-party verification
- Improve the prosperity of the forest sector and associated communities
- Recognize the importance of consumers and investors

Source: *Canadian Boreal Forest Agreement* (2010).

these forests cover about 38 per cent of the nation's land area (Figure 9.2) and a much higher proportion of southern Canada, where most Canadians live. If surrounding ecosystems such as wetlands and lakes are considered, then almost two-thirds of Canada is dominated by forest ecosystems. These forests are relatively young, as almost the entire country was ice covered 21,000 years ago. Succession (see Chapter 3) occurred after the ice retreat, but it was not until about 5,000 years ago that the vegetation began to resemble that of today. Some 70 per cent of the treed area of Canada is now covered by coniferous forests, mostly spruce (*Picea*), followed by pines (*Pinus*) and fir (*Abies*), with 20 per cent mixed wood and 10 per cent deciduous forests, mostly of poplar (*Populus*), birch (*Betula*), and maple (*Acer*).

Canada has one-quarter of the world's temperate rain forests and more than one-third of the world's boreal forests. Furthermore, estimates suggest that more than half of Canada's forest area consists of as-yet undisturbed tracts of

ENVIRONMENT IN FOCUS

BOX 9.2 | Boreal Forest Conservation Framework

The Boreal Forest Conservation Framework is a shared vision to sustain the ecological and cultural integrity of the Canadian boreal forest in perpetuity.

The Boreal Forest Conservation Framework calls for conservation of at least 50 per cent of Canada's boreal forest in a network of interconnected, protected areas, and application of state-of-the art ecosystem-based resource management practices across the remaining landscape. It was developed by the Boreal Leadership Council (BLC), an unusual partnership of leading conservation organizations, resource companies, and Aboriginal groups, who joined together to promote the conservation and sustainable use of Canada's boreal forest region. Members of the BLC, convened by the Canadian Boreal Initiative, recognize that all who depend on the forest must come together to plan for its ecological, cultural, and economic future. The framework is based on the best available principles of conservation biology and land-use planning, and has been endorsed by 1,500 international scientists, 25 Canadian Aboriginal communities, international conservation groups, and major businesses with annual sales totalling over $30 billion. Some progress has been made toward the goals in the framework. Recent key land protection actions include the following:

- In 2010, the Ontario legislature passed a bill protecting over 445,000 km² of boreal forest and wetlands in the northern half of the province. The Far North Act is one of the largest wilderness protection efforts in the history of the province. It mandates that the entire area undergo conservation planning, and puts a minimum of 220,000 km² permanently off limits to development.
- In Quebec, Premier Jean Charest pledged in March 2009 to protect at least 50 per cent of the area covered by the Plan Nord; this commitment totals more than 645,000 km². However, in 2013 Quebec removed its deadline to protect half its northern forest by 2035 and has downgraded an interim goal of 20-per-cent protection by 2020 to 12 per cent.
- In the Northwest Territories, over 120,000 km² have been slated for protection since 2007; in April 2010, 33,000 km² were set aside for creation of a new national park around the East Arm of Great Slave Lake, the tenth-largest lake in the world.

Since 2007 the amount of land protected in the boreal forest has doubled to 12 per cent of the total area and now stands at 708,000 km². Although much remains to be done to ensure equal treatment of conservation, sustainable development, and Aboriginal rights across the region, progress is being made.

Sources: Wells et al. (2010); Los (2014); current news reports.

more than 50,000 hectares. More than one-third of Canada, however, is naturally treeless, and most of it occurs in the North. Together, Quebec, NWT, Ontario, and British Columbia account for almost two-thirds of the country's boreal forest. Canada clearly has a major international role to play in forest conservation and management.

Deforestation is the permanent conversion of forests to other land uses. In Canada the main process is conversion to agricultural land, with conversion to oil and gas use being the next main factor and the most rapidly growing. Forest degradation by unsustainable harvesting practices is another issue. Overall, the annual rate of deforestation is falling, dropping from 64,000 hectares in 1990 to around 50,000 hectares by 2013 (Natural Resources Canada, 2014a). However, it should be noted that this is an amount being lost each and every year.

Canada is also crucial to maintenance of global intact forest landscapes (IFLs). These are landscapes large enough to retain native **biodiversity** and contain no signs of fragmentation by logging and infrastructure such as roads, mining, and oil or gas development. Such areas are key for biodiversity protection as well as for ecosystem service provision. In fact, recent research shows that even small amounts of tree removal can have very significant effects on ecosystem service provision (Zhang et al., 2014). A recent global monitoring assessment of causes of IFL degradation (World Resources Institute, 2014) found that:

- Since 2000, 8.1 per cent of IFLs have been degraded.
- Almost 95 per cent of the world's remaining IFLs are in the tropical and boreal regions.
- The largest areas of IFL degradation have been found in the Northern boreal forest belt of Canada, Russia, and Alaska (47 per cent) and tropical forest regions such as the Amazon (25 per cent) and Congo (9 per cent) basins.
- Just three countries—Canada, Russia, and Brazil—together contain 65 per cent of the world's remaining IFLs. These countries also accounted for over half of all IFL degradation with road building, often linked to logging and extractive industries, being a key driver. Other drivers vary

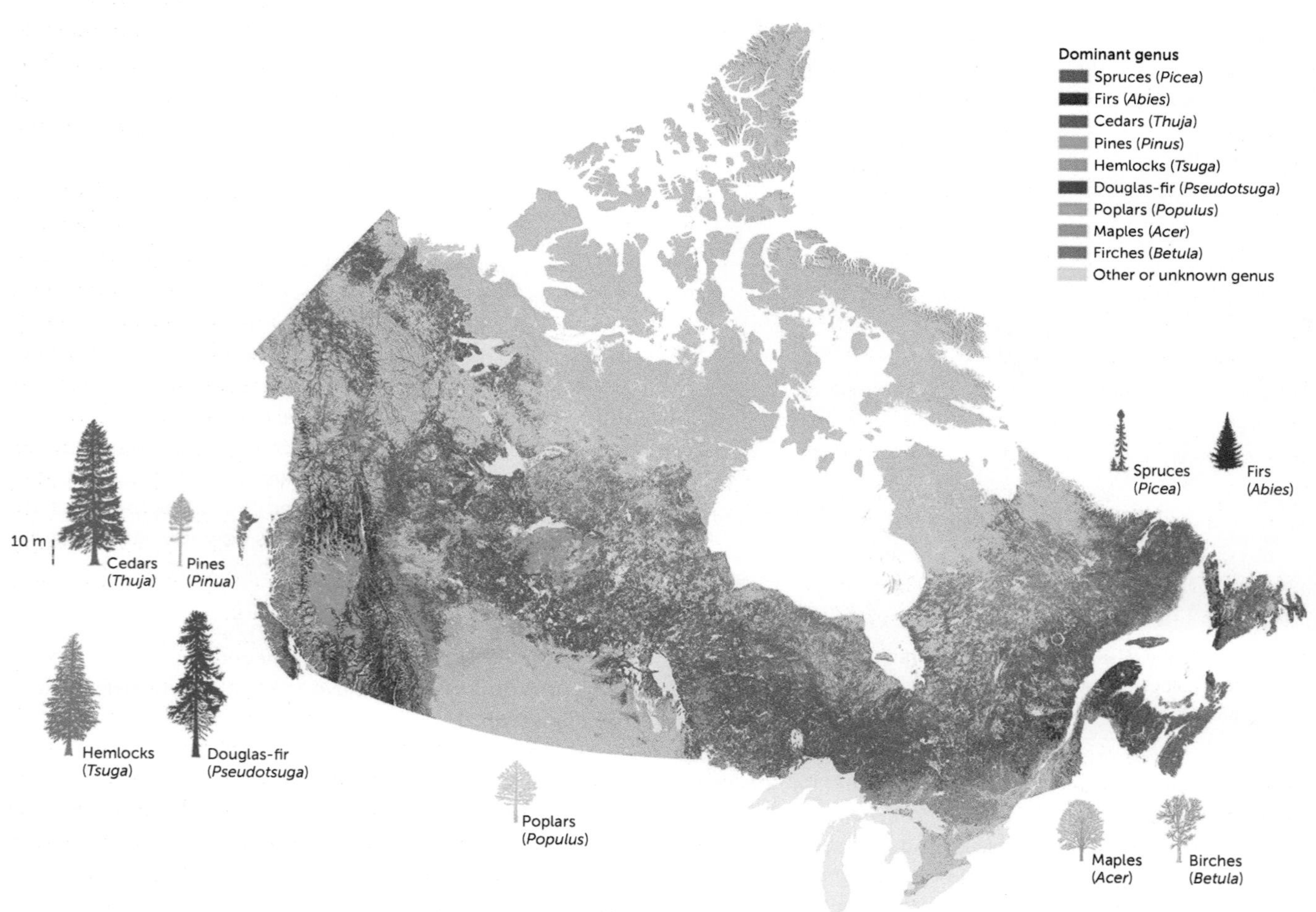

FIGURE 9.2 | Forest composition in Canada.

Sources: Natural Resources Canada (2014). Reproduced with the permission of the Minister of Natural Resources Canada, 2015. URL: http://cfs.nrcan.gc.ca/publications?id=35713

Philip Dearden

The use of wood products is an integral part of the livelihood of many Canadians, as illustrated by this local boat-building operation in Newfoundland.

significantly in different regions, from human-caused fires in Russia to agricultural conversion in Brazil.

The report goes on to identify Canada as the country responsible for most (21 per cent) of the IFL degradation in the world, mainly as a result of oil and gas exploration and development.

Forest Ecosystem Services and Products

Canada's forest ecosystems provide an array of beneficial services arising from ecological functions such as nutrient and water cycling, **carbon sequestration**, and waste decomposition. For example, plant communities are important in moderating local, regional, and national climate conditions. Biological communities are also of vital importance in protecting watersheds, buffering ecosystems against extremes of flood and drought, and maintaining water quality. The contributions of forest lands to the maintenance of ecological processes (Chapters 2 and 4) within Canada are substantial. However, the sheer scale of Canada's forests means that they are significant contributors on a global scale. It is estimated that 20 per cent of the world's water originates in Canada's forests. The forests are also major carbon sinks, with an estimated 50,000 million tonnes stored and a yearly accumulation of some 72 million tonnes. The role of ecosystem services in future forest management will be discussed later in the chapter.

Forests are also places of exceptional scenic beauty, and millions of Canadians travel each year to participate in nature-related recreational activities such as wildlife viewing in parks and protected areas, nature walks, and bird watching. The monetary value of these activities can be significant, especially to local rural economies.

Non-Timber Forest Products

In addition to the important "services" that forest ecosystems in Canada provide, forests are also a valuable source of commodities. Wild rice, mushrooms and berries, maple syrup, edible nuts, furs and hides, medicines, ornamental cuttings, and seeds—collectively known as **non-timber forest products (NTFPs)**—are typical examples. Their total value is unknown, but these products have the potential to generate $1 billion per year for the Canadian economy (Natural Resources Canada, 2010a). In 2013, Canada produced a record 59 million litres of maple products valued at $408 million. Similarly, 1.8 million Christmas trees generated $39 million, while blueberry exports were worth more than $207 million in 2014.

Some NTFPs are harvested commercially and are allocated by licence, while others are freely available and contribute significantly to recreational values, including tourism. These commodities are also important in sustaining First Nations communities. With careful management, NTFPs are renewable. Some inspection agencies have expressed concern about a lack of regulation over the harvesting, safety, and economic contribution of these products. In response, the Quebec NTFP association initiated a training program for harvesters to provide instruction on product identification, ethical harvesting, bush safety, and food storage and safety. A useful reference website on NTFPs in Canada is maintained by the NTFP Network (see "Related Websites").

Historically, non-timber products and services of Canada's forests have received little attention. However, as timber harvest levels have increased and the public has become more aware of and vocal about declines in these other forest values, forestry companies are being required to take these values into account in their cutting plans. In other words, they are being required to take a more ecosystem-based approach, as described in Chapter 5. NTFPs bring diversification to rural economies and can yield valuable economic returns. Some First Nation bands, for example, have succeeded in harvesting and marketing such forest products as mushrooms and wild rice, and the maple syrup industry in Quebec, which produces more than 90 per cent of the Canadian total, has become a significant business. However, Canada has a long way to go to catch up to most other countries in introducing this kind of product diversification to the forest land base.

NTFPs may be wild or managed and may come from both natural and managed forests. It is important to understand these differences if NTFPs are to play a fuller role in forest valuations and decision-making. For example, the harvesting of some wild stocks, such as mushrooms, from managed forests may conflict with timber production activities. However, harvesting some managed NTFPs can be encouraged alongside timber production and raise the overall level of return from the land. Such an approach has been adopted for blueberries in some areas of Quebec. It is an example of symbiotic

ENVIRONMENT IN FOCUS

BOX 9.3 | Canada's "Button" Mushroom

Pine mushrooms (also know as button mushrooms, matsutakes, or *Tricholoma magnivelare*) are found in the Pacific Northwest of North America, some northern parts of Europe, and select regions in northern Asia. Button mushrooms are mycorrhizal fungi that have a symbiotic relationship with nearby trees, making them difficult to produce outside of the forest. They are a highly priced delicacy in parts of Asia and Northern Europe and symbolize fertility and happiness. Their intense flavour and good omen mean these mushrooms have been known to generate upwards of $400 a kilogram in Japan. The industry has been estimated at $49 million annually, but the development of a substantial black market can skew approximations. Limited wild production and a high market value can drive tension between harvesters: those who simply enjoy mushroom-picking and others who are driven by the high value of this small forest product.

Button, or matsutake, mushrooms.

use between the different resources in which both kinds of resource use can benefit. We often see this approach used in agro-forestry ecosystems in the tropics but rarely in Canada.

Other kinds of relationships include complementary, competitive, and independent resource use. *Complementary* relationships occur when NTFPs and timber are extracted from the same land base in non-conflicting ways. Craftspeople, for example, may get improved access to their raw materials (e.g., tree bark, boughs) because of the development of logging roads. In contrast, *competitive* relationships often involve mutually exclusive uses. Logging **old-growth forests** in western Canada, for example, would devastate the lucrative pine mushroom industry. Finally, *independent* systems develop when the two uses operate on different units of land—for example, in commercial and non-commercial forests.

Besides tangible non-timber forest products, forests fulfill a host of less tangible values related to cultural and spiritual fulfillment and knowledge and understanding. Such values are difficult to assess, let alone manage. Our forested areas include some of our most scenic landscapes. Not just an attraction for tourists, they also offer recreational and spiritual satisfaction. Most provinces have introduced procedures for including assessments of aesthetic quality into harvesting plans. Unfortunately, many of these procedures still leave it up to the people in charge of timber extraction to decide what interests should be considered in assessing scenic value and what harvesting regime might follow. As a result, modifications to cutting plans to take aesthetics into consideration often tend to be minimal.

Timber Forest Products

Forest management paradigms over the past century have focused on the management of Canadian forests to supply wood. The economic benefits arising from timber products are substantial. For some 200 communities, the forest sector makes up at least 50 per cent of the economic base. Direct timber industry employment in 2013 totalled 216,500. Employment is concentrated in Quebec, British Columbia, and Ontario. The total number of people directly employed by the industry has been declining for over a decade and dropped 12 per cent between 2012 and 2013. Aboriginal peoples have a higher relative proportion (4.8 per cent) of the forestry workforce than they do in all other economic sectors (3 per cent) and are likely to suffer disproportionately from a declining workforce (Natural Resources Canada, 2014a).

Canada is the world's leading forest product exporter. In 2013, Canada's forests contributed a net $19.8 billion to national GDP (Table 9.1). The forestry industry is the largest single contributor to Canada's balance of trade, with exports totalling over $28 billion in 2012. British Columbia accounted for one-third of this, followed by Quebec and Ontario. The United States is still the largest buyer of Canadian forest products; however, its proportion is declining with strong growth in demand from China and South Korea. In 2009, the US purchased 71 per cent of all exports, and this had fallen to 63 per cent by 2013.

Most of these statistics are derived from the *State of Canada's Forests, 2014*, published by Natural Resources Canada, the

Perspectives on the Environment

A Selective Choice of Indicators

These indicators provide a clear picture of the interactions between forests and society, and of the status and trends of the main forest functions. They also show the successful results of more than 20 years of committed work in sustainably managing the country's forests. Canadians can feel confident that their forests are continuing to provide a broad range of benefits even though economic, environmental and social circumstances are constantly changing. Similarly, Canada's trading partners can feel confident that the Canadian forest products delivered to them come with strong environmental credentials from sustainably managed sources.

—Natural Resources Canada (2014: 15)

TABLE 9.1 | Canada's Forests

Total land	882.1 million ha
Total forest	348.7 million ha
Commercial forest	294.8 million ha
Managed forest	1.4 million ha
Harvested forest	0.6 million ha
Value of exports	$28.0 billion
Contribution to the GDP	$19.8 billion
Direct employment	216,500
Annual allowable cut	227 million m^3
Harvest (2012)	148 million m^3

All figures are 2013 unless otherwise noted.
Source: Natural Resources Canada (2014). Reproduced with the permission of the Minister of Natural Resources Canada, 2015. URL: http://cfs.nrcan.gc.ca/publications?id=35713

federal agency that oversees forestry in the country. There are 46 indicators that measure the health of Canada's forests and their relationship to Canadians. However, not all these are reported on, as explained in the "Perspectives on the Environment" box, but they are selected to showcase the positive aspects of the industry. The role of indicators in environmental reporting was discussed in more detail in Chapter 1. Indicators can play an invaluable role in assessing the health of any ecosystem or natural resource industry. In the late 1990s, Canada produced extensive compilations of a comprehensive selection of indicators. Many of these indicators revealed existing and growing problems. However, since that time the yearly production of indicator reports, such as the *State of the Forests* or *State of the Parks* reports, have become increasingly politicized and meant only as a political tool to report success, rather than an independent scientific monitoring.

The volume of wood produced per unit area differs across the country, rising to highs in excess of 800 cubic metres per hectare (m^3/ha) on the most productive sites in coastal British Columbia, where mild temperatures, deep soils, and abundant rainfall create some of the most productive growing sites in the world. The Canadian average volume is 136 m^3/ha. Volumes harvested also vary by province. For example, in 2013, British Columbia harvested over double the volume of any other province from less land area than in either Quebec or Ontario (Natural Resources Canada, 2014a).

ENVIRONMENT IN FOCUS

BOX 9.4 | Canada's Unique Forest Industry

Canada is the world's largest exporter of forest products. In the international marketplace, Canada has a number of assets, including:

- Of Canada's forest land, 93 per cent is publicly owned.
- The federal government is responsible for trade, the national economy, and federal lands.
- Eighty per cent of Aboriginal peoples live in forested areas.
- The federal government has constitutional, treaty, political, and legal responsibilities for Aboriginal peoples.
- Over 8 per cent of the total forest area is protected by legislation.
- Less than 1 per cent of forested land is harvested every year.
- By law, all harvested forests must be successfully regenerated.
- Over half of the energy used by the forest is bioenergy.
- Canada leads the world in exports of softwood lumber, newsprint, and wood pulp.
- By 2013, 150 million hectares of forest were certified as being sustainably managed.

Source: Natural Resources Canada (2014a).

"Brazil of the North" sign visible (left) as two protesters block the path of logging trucks during the 1993 protests in the region of Clayoquot Sound (right).

The Canadian forestry industry is also a frequent flashpoint of conflict. Names such as Carmanah, Temagami, and Clayoquot became well known across the country in the 1990s as they appeared in newspaper headlines and on national news broadcasts. All these conflicts revolved around whether particular areas should be logged or preserved. These conflicts reflected the increasing appreciation of the many values provided to society by forests besides economic benefits. Few of these non-economic values are easy to calculate in monetary terms and compare against the financial returns of the forest industry. However, these values are gaining increasing recognition on the part of the public and decision-makers as the process of converting old-growth forests across Canada into managed forests continues.

When considering the allocation of any resource to different uses, it makes good sense to evaluate the relative values that will result from the various allocation decisions. However, resources are commonly allocated in society with little appreciation of their true value. Anielski and Wilson (2009) assessed the total economic values of Canada's boreal forest and arrived at an annual figure of over $700 billion. They found that the value of the non-timber forest products outweighed that of the timber products by a ratio of 2.5 to 1, yet these values are rarely if ever taken into account in decisions about how to allocate the boreal forests among competing uses.

Forest Management Practices

The provincial governments are responsible for 77 per cent of the nation's forests, with the federal and territorial governments responsible for 16 per cent. The remaining 7 per cent of forests are managed by 450,000 private landowners. These figures are likely to change over the next decade as an increased number of land claims by Aboriginal peoples are settled and more land comes under their control. Areas under current land claims account for about one-quarter of large, intact forest landscapes in Canada. In mid 2014, Aboriginal people scored a major victory when the Supreme Court of Canada unanimously overturned an earlier appeal court ruling and recognized a First Nation's title to a specific tract of land. The case was brought by the Tsilhqot'in people in northern BC when land on which they had maintained traplines for centuries was allocated to a logging company. This was the Court's first ruling on Aboriginal title and will facilitate Aboriginal people establishing title over lands that they regularly use for fishing, hunting, and other activities. The future implications of this ruling for Aboriginal rights to land use will be very substantial.

Provincial governments manage forest resources on behalf of the public through agreements with private logging companies. Different forms of tenure exist, as discussed by Kevin Hanna in his "Domestic Guest Statement," but generally all involve the logging company submitting plans that outline where it intends to cut, the details of the harvesting process (including the location of roads), and **reclamation** plans. The governments provide regulations and guidelines for these practices and have the authority to ensure that they are followed.

Some 1.4 million hectares are currently managed for timber production. On these lands, forest ecosystems are being transformed from relatively natural systems to controlled systems, as described in Chapter 1, in which humans, not nature, influence the species that will grow there and the age that they will grow to. Over the past decade, increasing awareness of, and concern about, the environmental impact of forest harvesting has prompted questions about the environmental sustainability of forestry and about the different kinds of management approaches that might lead to sustainability. Key questions relate to the amount of forest protected from

DOMESTIC GUEST STATEMENT

Forest Ownership, Forest Stewardship, Community Sustainability | *Kevin Hanna*

Forest tenure refers to the conditions that govern forest ownership and use. Tenure is an important and fundamental element in determining forest policy and management. As this book points out, significant challenges face Canadian forest management and how we approach ownership, and ownership must play a role in realizing a more innovative and flexible forest industry and a greater sense of stewardship. But because tenure is a difficult and thorny subject, governments, industry, labour, and environmental groups have tended to ignore it. I would like to say this is beginning to change, but it is not.

About 95 per cent of Canada's forest land is owned by governments, largely the provinces, and about 80 per cent of Canada's private forest land is located east of Manitoba, most of it in the Maritimes. British Columbia has the highest level of provincial forest ownership, at 96 per cent. Compared to other major forest nations, Canada's tenure profile is unique. Our biggest competitors in the wood product export market are Finland and Sweden. Finland's forests are mainly privately owned. Individuals hold about 62 per cent of forest land, timber companies about 6 per cent, and the national government 31 per cent (most of which is in the far north). There are about 280,000 private forest holdings with an average size of 37 hectares. These small holdings are very productive and intensively managed. They supply the majority of Finland's domestic production, about 80 per cent of the stumpage income, and 80 per cent of annual growth and cut.

In Sweden, small-scale landowners have about 50 per cent of the forests, while the state and forest companies each have about 25 per cent. There are about 240,000 private forests in Sweden; and about 30 per cent of these are less than 50 hectares. They also provide a major part of Sweden's timber needs. In Canada, while production on private lands has grown, the great majority of timber still comes from provincial forests, and it most probably always will.

Swedish and Finnish forestry investment levels (regeneration, tending and harvesting techniques, and worker training) are relatively high, much higher than in Canada. The woods also hold a special place in the psyche of each nation. Public access, what the Swedes call *allemansrätten*, is an old concept simply meaning the right of access to the land. Except for an area nearest to a landholder's house and cultivated areas, anyone is free to traverse and enjoy the land of another, even to camp overnight. Intrinsic to this tradition is an appreciation and expectation of mutual respect. Stewardship is not only a policy concept, it is a cultural one. This is not to say that Scandinavian forestry is without its problems and controversies, but a strong culture of stewardship has endured and their forest sectors have created firms that are larger than their Canadian equivalents.

Many who work in Canada's forest industry would say that a culture of stewardship also exists here. Workers care about sustaining the resource on which their livelihoods depend. They might also suggest that it is really the short-term vision of companies and governments that limits the potential for such a culture to really flourish. But industry counters that tenures are unstable, the tenure times too short, or conditions too uncertain to see a significant increase in investment levels, to develop more non-timber forest products, or to follow forestry practices that clearly acknowledge the services that forests provide beyond timber. And despite a tenure model that has supported large companies, Canada has not been able to create the large, globally dominant firms that the Scandinavians have.

A solution offered at various times in Canada is to emulate the Scandinavian model. Large companies might be more willing to invest in innovative forestry practices if they owned the land. But there would not be much public support for selling provincial forests, certainly not to large companies, nor would many large firms necessarily want to buy forests or have the financial resources to do so. Another option is to increase the role of communities through community-held tenures. Yet another possibility is to offer better tenure opportunities for small firms and individuals, perhaps creating many small private forests, even if only leased from the province. But would small holdings, community forestry, or corporate ownership result in better forestry practices?

Experience in the US and Canada shows that some companies with private forests are not always good forest managers. Some have logged their lands quickly for short-term profit and made few investments in regeneration. But others treat their forests as the foundation of their long-term survival. Community tenures may also result in a more stable, long-term vision of forest management. Alternatively, some communities will support short-term timber production as the way to realize immediate employment and prosperity. Some individuals may also log their lands quickly for the sake of short-term profit. Small private holdings would require capacity-building and stable investment sources, but they offer the greatest promise and may be the best hope for reforming the industry and enhancing community sustainability. In Scandinavia, governments act to blunt some negative tendencies by regulating private forestry, requiring forest plans, setting cutting rates, and financing forestry renewal and management, all while supporting a strong private forest context.

In Canada, tenure reform will require a careful consideration of the lessons learned from other places. While we can look to other jurisdictions for information and experience, Canada's forests, geography, history, and culture are distinct. As part

Continued

of addressing Canada's forest management problems, tenure reform will require innovative approaches and leadership. The answers ultimately lie in creating a context that provides new opportunities for individuals, small firms, and stronger and more effective community-based tenures—all conditions that can encourage stable long-term business investments and support a more complex vision of what forests provide. Tenure reform must be part of realizing more sustainable forests and sustaining and growing our forest communities.

Kevin Hanna is in the Human Geography Department at UBC-Okanagan in Kelowna, BC. His research interests include community-based resource management environmental impact assessment, integrated resource and environmental management, climate change adaptation policy, natural resources policy in Canada and Northern Europe, and European Union environmental policy.

logging, the amount of fibre harvested over a specific period, the way in which it is logged, and what happens to the land after harvesting.

Rate of Conversion

The rate of conversion of natural to managed forests is one of the most controversial issues in Canadian forestry. Each provincial government establishes an **annual allowable cut (AAC)**, which is based on the theoretical annual increment of merchantable timber, after taking into account factors such as quantity and quality of species, accessibility and growth rates, and amounts of land protected from harvesting because of other use values, such as parks and wildlife habitat (Table 9.2). The AAC should reflect the **long-range sustained yield (LRSY)** of a given unit of land, or what that land should yield in perpetuity. This target is ultimately limited by the growth conditions, the biological potential of the site, and how that potential can be augmented by silvicultural practices. It is not sustainable to have an AAC that consistently exceeds this biological potential. Economists, however, often argue for the need to maximize the monetary return of the first cut in order to invest in other wealth-producing programs and to provide social services. The dominance of this line of thought has led to rates of conversion significantly higher than can be supported biologically. At the moment, for example, BC has an AAC of around 77 million m^3, mainly as a result of the over-logging to address the mountain pine beetle infestation. However, the LRSY is around 56 million m^3, meaning that massive scaling back will be necessary in the future to allow the missing trees time to regrow.

To calculate AACs, it is also necessary to know the rotation period for each forest type. This is the age of economic maturity of the tree crop and varies widely but usually falls within the 60- to 120-year range in Canada. Foresters call this the **culmination age**.

The AAC will also vary substantially depending on the proportion of old-growth to second-growth timber included in the proposed cutting unit. Old-growth forests have very high timber volumes—for example, up to 800 m^3/ha in BC's coastal forests. However, at the culmination age for **second growth** on these sites, volumes will be much lower, in the region of 500 m^3. This is known as the **falldown effect** and results in AACs up to 30 per cent lower as old-growth forests are eliminated.

For Canada, the total AAC is calculated by adding together all the provincial and territorial AACs where these figures are

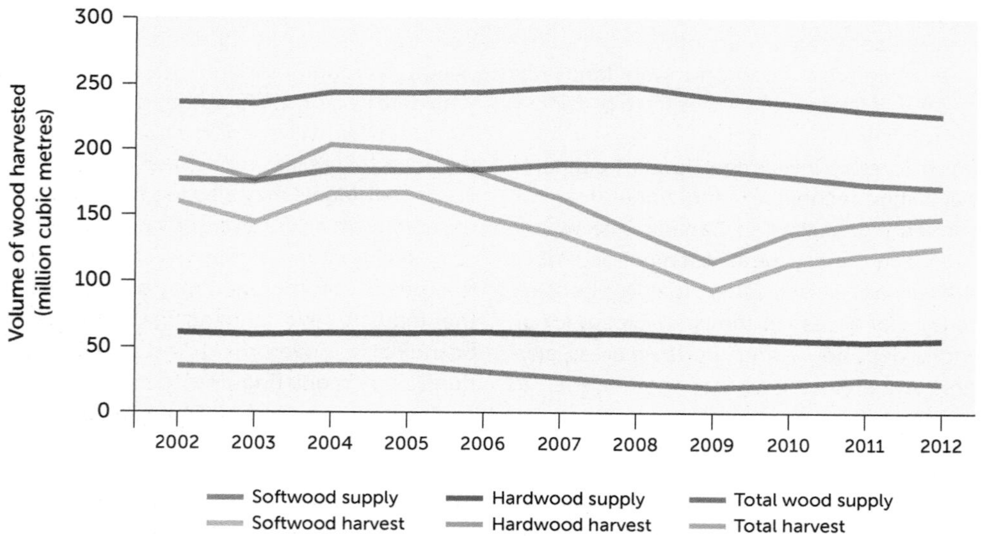

FIGURE 9.3 | Annual harvest versus supply deemed sustainable for harvest.

Source: Natural Resources Canada (2014a). Reproduced with the permission of the Minister of Natural Resources Canada, 2015. URL: http://cfs.nrcan.gc.ca/publications?id=35713

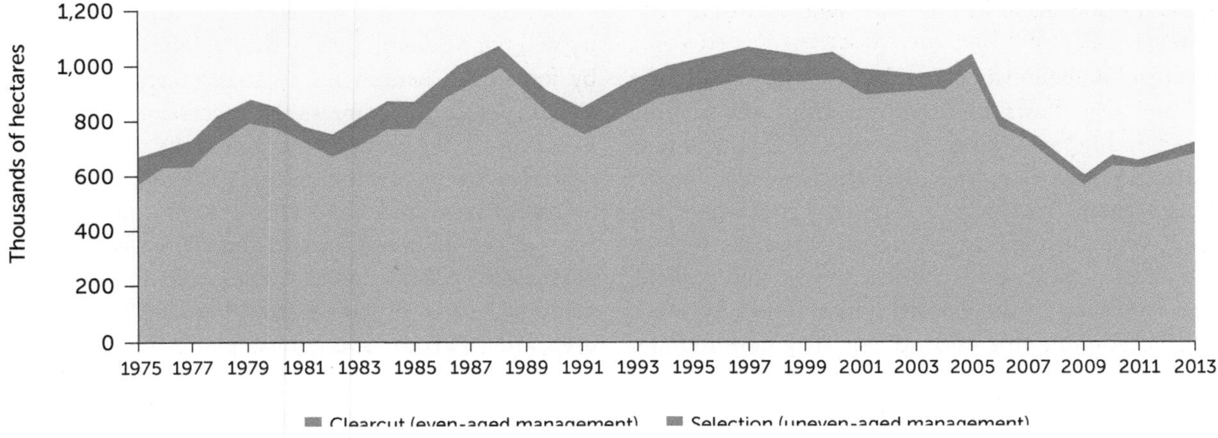

FIGURE 9.4 | Area harvested in Canada, 1975–2013, showing dominance of clear-cutting.

Source: National Forestry Database, Reproduced with the permission of the Minister of Natural Resources Canada, 2015. http://nfdp.ccfm.org/data/graphs/graph_61_a_e.php.

available. In 2013, the AAC stood at 227 million m^3, and 148 million m^3 of timber were harvested. The long-term harvesting trends and timber supply can be seen in Figure 9.3. Canada's wood supply is estimated by combining provincial AACs with the wood supply estimated for private, federal, and territorial lands. Harvest levels on these lands are not regulated by legislation, although the managers of these lands often set harvest targets. This means that wood supply from these lands can only be estimated based on the sum of these targets and, for lands where targets have not been set, the average of past harvest levels.

Silvicultural Systems

Silviculture is the practice of directing the establishment, composition, growth, and quality of forest stands through a variety of activities, including harvesting, reforestation, and site preparation.

Harvesting Methods

Perhaps no aspect of resource or environmental management has created as much conflict in Canada as the dominant forest harvesting practice of **clear-cutting**, and this method is used on much of the forest lands harvested in Canada (Figure 9.4). The size of the clear-cuts varies widely, from approximately 15 hectares to more than 250 hectares, and in some cases clear-cuts extend for many thousands of hectares. Although larger openings have few ecological advantages, it should not be assumed that more but smaller clear-cuts are necessarily superior to fewer, larger clear-cuts. More clear-cuts create more fragmentation and less undisturbed forest area, to the detriment of "interior" forest species.

Not only are clear-cuts aesthetically unappealing to many Canadians, but their environmental impact, especially cumulatively as they spread across the landscape, can be substantial. For example, Nova Scotia has implemented guidelines for the establishment of wildlife corridors to reconnect habitat. If clear-cuts are in excess of 50 hectares, the guidelines recommend that at least one corridor be created, with irregular borders and a minimum width of 50 metres. Furthermore, in 2010, Nova Scotia announced that whereas clear-cutting then accounted for 95 per cent of the harvested area, this would be reduced to 50 per cent by 2015, and they appear to be close to that figure (Canadian Council of Forest Ministers, 2014). These changes are a step in the right direction, but it is the implementation of such guidelines, not just their specification, that is important. British Columbia tried to take a tougher approach by legislating forest practices in detail through its Forest and Range Practices Act. Yet current government policy has seen considerable weakening in the implementation of the legislation as

davemantel/iStockphoto

The rate of conversion from natural to managed forests has alarmed many environmentalists, who claim that forestry companies have been allowed to extract too much wood too quickly. This will result not only in environmental problems but also in a lack of adequate fibre for industrial use in the future.

economic conditions have become less favourable to the forest industry.

Clear-cutting is the most economical way for wood to be extracted and also allows for easier replanting and tending of the regenerating forest. In certain types of forests, it may mimic natural processes more closely than selective or partial cutting systems. This may be especially true where natural fires have created even-aged stands of species such as lodgepole and Jack pine, black spruce, aspens, and poplars. Researchers working in the eastern boreal forest, however, have been questioning this assumption. They have found a dramatic decrease in fire frequency in this area over the past 150 years as a result of climatic change, and they suggest that this trend will continue into the future, leading to a higher proportion of old-growth forest in the landscape. In turn, this will lead to natural species replacement in these forests, with deciduous and mixed stands replaced by balsam fir and Jack pine by black spruce. Clear-cutting would counteract these changes rather than mimic natural processes and would lead to a dramatic decrease in stand diversity at the landscape level. In the future, forest management will have to employ mixed harvesting systems (Table 9.2) if forest management is to more closely emulate natural systems.

Reforestation

Until 1985, Canada's forests were considered to be so extensive that little effort was given to reforestation. Sites, once logged, might be burned to facilitate rapid nutrient return to the soil but then were abandoned in the hope that they would be recolonized by seeds from the surrounding area. Sometimes this was successful, but often it was not. Thus, with increased harvesting levels, the amount of land that no longer supported trees that could be harvested in the future gradually grew. In 2013, 0.6 million hectares of land were harvested, 8.6 million hectares were defoliated by insects, 4.2 million hectares were burned by fire, and yet only 357,600 hectares were planted and reseeded (Figure 9.5); the success of these plantings cannot be guaranteed. Given this annual deficit between what is cut and what is replanted, many conservationists have difficulty understanding further allocation of old-growth timber to the forest industry. Industry would counter that natural generation is the best way to regenerate in some environments, and in terms of cost effectiveness this is true. However, this was the argument they used to make about all lands, and the increasing proportion of planted lands shows it was often incorrect.

Site Preparation—Biocide Use

Biocides are used on forest lands in Canada to reduce competition for seedlings on replanted sites and to protect seedlings from insect damage. Sites regenerating from forest harvesting return to an earlier successional phase (Chapter 3), and under natural conditions a vigorous and diverse secondary succession takes place. However, for many years the community will not be dominated by the commercial species desired by foresters. Chemicals are used to suppress early successional species, to compress the successional time span, and to maximize the growth potential of the more commercially desirable species, usually conifers. Chemical use is generally quicker, easier, and more effective than using mechanical alternatives for weed suppression. Three herbicides (2,4-D, glyphosate, hexazinone) are registered for forest management in Canada. Glyphosate (or "Roundup"), the most widely used, affects a broad spectrum of plants but degrades quickly and is relatively non-toxic to terrestrial animals.

Early colonizers often compete more effectively for soil nitrogen than conifers. Where nitrogen is the most limiting factor, as it is in the boreal forest, this can inhibit conifer growth over the short term. However, the law of conservation of matter (Chapter 4) tells us that these nutrients have not disappeared—they are simply being held by different species. As these species die and decay, the nutrients will be returned to the soil and become available for uptake. Furthermore, by holding nutrients in this way, early colonizers often slow down the loss of nutrients from the site that might otherwise occur from leaching. They act as a biological sponge over the short term. Herbicide application may also eliminate species that are ecologically advantageous, such as nitrogen fixers like the red alder, exacerbating nutrient loss from logged sites.

The balance between these effects needs to be evaluated over long periods and probably differs from site to site. Lautenschlager and Sullivan (2002) reviewed the literature on the effects of forest herbicide applications on major biotic components of regenerating northern forests. They conclude that there is little evidence to support any long-term negative

Philip Dearden

Clear-cut logging in the Rocky Mountains. Not only is it visually unappealing in an otherwise spectacular landscape, but the scale and design of the clear-cuts have a drastic impact on the connectivity of natural habitat for forest-dwelling species.

TABLE 9.2 | Main Characteristics of Common Silvicultural Systems Practised in Canada

Clear-Cutting

The most commonly applied silvicultural system in Canada, clear-cutting involves the removal of all trees in a cutblock, in one operation, regardless of species and size. Some trees are left along riparian zones to protect streams. The objective is to create a new, even-aged stand, which will be regenerated naturally or through replanting.

Advantages	Disadvantages
• It is cost-effective. Clear-cut areas are easily accessed for site preparation and tree planting. • Stands of even-aged trees are created, producing wood products with more uniform qualities. • Newly planted seedlings quickly take root and grow in the sunlight reaching the ground. This can benefit certain animal species. • In some respects, clear-cutting simulates natural disturbances such as wildfire and insect disease outbreaks. • It is the safest harvesting method with the least risk of worker injury.	• Nutrients stored in the bodies of trees are removed from the ecosystem. • Habitat for some wildlife species is lost, as well as biodiversity. New vegetation does not maintain the complexity and stability of mature forests. • Clear-cutting in sensitive ecosystems can cause soil erosion, landslides, and silting, which can damage watersheds, lead to flooding, and inhibit successful fish reproduction. • Large gaps are opened up, fragmenting the forest and exposing more area to the edge effect. • It is aesthetically unattractive. Clear-cutting can conflict with other forest values. • No timber products are available for a long period of time (e.g., 50 to 70 years).

Seed Tree

Seed tree is a method of clear-cutting in which all trees are removed from an area in a single cut, except for a small number of seed-bearing trees, which are intended to be the main source of seed for natural regeneration after harvest. Tree species that have been managed under this system in Canada include western larch, Jack pine, eastern white pine, and yellow birch.

Advantages	Disadvantages
In addition to the above: • Next to clear-cutting, this system is the least expensive to implement. • The system can result in improved distribution of seedlings and a more desirable species mix, since the seed source for natural regeneration is not limited to adjacent stands.	In addition to the above: • Regeneration can be delayed if seed production and/or distribution are inadequate.

Shelterwood

Mature trees are removed in a series of two or more partial cuts. Residual trees are left to supply seed for natural regeneration and to supply shelter for the establishment of new or advanced regeneration. The remaining mature cover is removed once the desired regeneration has been established. Commonly, 30 to 50 per cent of the canopy is removed on the first cut. In Canada, this system has mainly been applied to conifers (e.g., red spruce in the East, white pine in Ontario, interior Douglas fir in the West).

Advantages	Disadvantages
• Trees left after the first cut grow faster and increase in value. • For eastern white pine, this system can be an effective management tool against white pine weevils, which are more attracted to pine shoots under full light exposure than under shade. • It is visually more appealing than clear-cutting.	• It is complex and costly to plan and implement. • Young trees can be damaged during removal of mature trees. • Windthrow is a serious concern. Uprooted stems can displace significant amounts of soil.

Selection

Involves the periodic harvest of selected trees of various ages in a stand. Trees are harvested singly or in groups as they reach maturity. Valuable, mature trees, along with poorly shaped, unhealthy, crooked, and leaning trees and broken or damaged trees, are selected for removal. The objective of this method is to create and maintain an uneven-aged stand. Small gaps created by harvesting leave room for natural seeding.

Advantages	Disadvantages
• This method is often favoured in areas where recreation or scenic values are important, since the harvested area is less visually offensive. • The method results in a continuous, regular supply of mature trees over time. Overall stand quality should improve after each harvest cycle. • Biodiversity loss is minimized.	• This system can only be successfully applied to stands containing shade-tolerant tree species (e.g., sugar maple, western red cedar, red spruce, balsam fir, eastern/western hemlock). • It requires skilled workers to implement successfully. • It can require more roads and skid trails per unit area. • It is complex and costly to plan and implement. • In some instances, landowners take the best trees in a forest, leaving poorly shaped and unhealthy trees to provide seed for the next generation, resulting in forest degradation over the long term.

Source: NRCAN (1995), Alberta Food and Rural Development (2001), Canadian Institute of Forestry (2003).

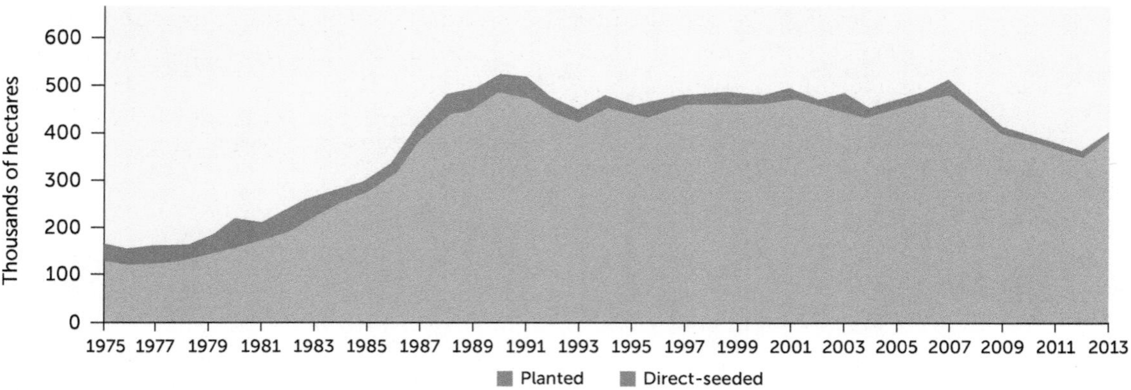

FIGURE 9.5 | Area planted or direct-seeded in Canada, 1975–2013.

Source: National Forestry Database, Silviculture: Area planted or direct-seeded, 1975–2013, Figure 6.6a. Reproduced with the permission of the Minister of Natural Resources Canada, 2015. http://nfdp.ccfm.org/data/graphs/graph_66_a_e.php.

consequences. Indeed, they suggest that, at the landscape scale, application of herbicides might help in the return to a more natural species composition in northern forests. This is because since colonization, hardwoods have expanded in these areas as coniferous species have been harvested. Use of herbicides may help to reverse this process. Nonetheless, Lautenschlager and Sullivan caution that we must overcome large gaps in knowledge before we can truly understand all the biotic implications of herbicide application.

Insecticides are used to attack pests such as the spruce budworm, Jack pine budworm, hemlock looper, mountain pine beetle (see Box 9.7), gypsy moth, and forest tent caterpillar. The amount sprayed varies, depending on the population dynamics of these insects, which changes in response to environmental factors (Figure 9.6). Most spraying has occurred in eastern Canada; the spruce budworm spraying program in the Maritime provinces is the best-known incidence of such spraying and has caused considerable controversy (Box 9.5). However, the total area treated with forest chemicals in Canada has steadily declined since 1990 (Figures 9.7 and 9.8).

Attention is being increasingly directed toward replacing synthetic insecticides with biological control agents such as *Bacillus thuringiensis* (Bt). Bt now accounts for almost all the insecticide used in Canadian forests and is non-toxic to humans and most wildlife, although it does affect moth and butterfly larvae of some non-target species. Plants also manufacture many chemicals themselves as protection against insects. Several of these chemicals appear to be good prospects for the development of insecticides for forestry use.

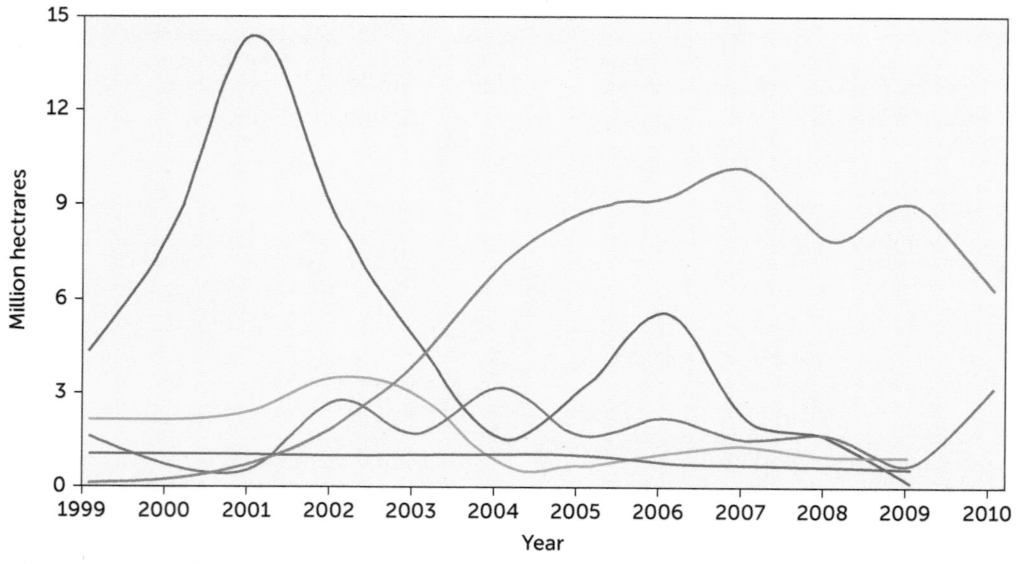

FIGURE 9.6 | Area of forest disturbed by fire, insects, and harvesting in Canada.

Sources: Natural Resources Canada (2013; 2014a). Reproduced with the permission of the Minister of Natural Resources Canada, 2015. National Forestry Database (2014).

Pheromones are volatile compounds, or "scents," used by insects of a given species to communicate with each other. Various types of pheromones serve different purposes—e.g., alarm, aggregation, territorial marking, tracking or recognition, and sexual attraction. Knowledge regarding the identification of pheromone components and determining how they are used by insects is being applied to developing synthetic pheromones that can be used for tracking and monitoring insect pests or for controlling such pests through mass captures or mating disruption.

Installing a few pheromone traps as opposed to systematically sampling trees substantially reduces the time spent on tracking and monitoring. This technique also makes it possible to increase the area covered at a cost lower than or equivalent to that of traditional sampling. The most common types of traps are sticky traps, the capacity of which is limited to the size of the sticky surface, and large-volume traps. Sticky traps are inexpensive and easy to use. Large-volume traps have a receptacle containing an insecticide that kills the insects that gather at the base of the trap.

Pheromones and biological control are among the approaches now being evaluated to address rapidly expanding areas of the emerald ash borer in Ontario and Quebec. This non-native species results in almost 100 per cent tree mortality within five years of infestation.

Intensive Forest Management

After a new crop of trees has been established and reaches a free-growing condition, future timber resource values can be further enhanced by intensive silvicultural practices. Activities undertaken by foresters to improve stand growth include:

- pre-commercial thinning (homogenizes the stand, increases mean tree size, and lowers the age at which the stand can be harvested)
- commercial thinning (attempts to recover lost volume production in a stand as a result of competition-induced mortality)
- scarification (physical disturbance of the forest floor to create improved seedbeds for natural regeneration)
- prescribed burning (removes slash and woody debris, sets back competing vegetation, provides ash as fertilizer, and increases nutrient mobilization and availability through increased soil temperatures)
- pruning and shearing (increases the value of individual trees by prematurely removing the lower branches so that clear wood, free of knots, is laid down around an unpruned knotty core)
- timber stand improvement (cutting down or poisoning all deformed and unwanted trees within older stands)

The long-term impacts of these activities are generally not well known. Structural simplification takes place that will benefit some species and have negative effects on others. There is little evidence to suggest that these techniques will have any greater impact than more traditional silvicultural activities.

Fire Suppression

In certain areas, fire is a frequent occurrence and necessary to the reproduction of forest tree species. Fire is part of the long-term dynamics of these ecosystems. Fire initiates secondary successions, renewing vegetation through regeneration involving a complete change of species, regeneration of the same species, or diversification of the species. Jack pine, birch, and trembling aspen are common in areas where fires have recently occurred. Fire suppression, viewed as essential to protect lives, property, and commercially valuable timber, has resulted in ecological changes not characteristic of fire-dominated ecosystems. For example, it has contributed to the very dense regeneration of almost pure Douglas fir in old-growth ponderosa pine stands in the interior of BC. Old-growth ponderosa pine stands are maintained by low-intensity, naturally occurring surface fires that burn brush and prevent maturation of the more shade-tolerant Douglas fir.

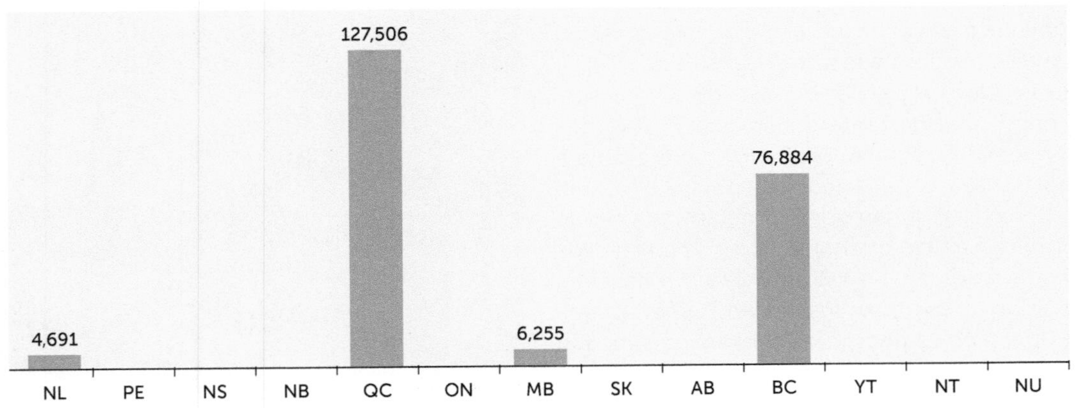

FIGURE 9.7 | Forest insecticide use by province, 2013 (hectares).

Source: National Forestry Database. Reproduced with the permission of the Minister of Natural Resources Canada, 2015. http://nfdp.ccfm.org/pest/quick_facts_e.php.

ENVIRONMENT IN FOCUS

BOX 9.5 | The Spruce Budworm Controversy

Since 1952, aircraft have been dousing the forests of eastern Canada, particularly New Brunswick and Nova Scotia, with an array of chemicals in the competition to see who would harvest the area's lumber—humans or the eastern spruce budworm. A native in Canada, the budworm feeds primarily on balsam fir but will also eat white spruce, red spruce, and, to a lesser extent, black spruce. Its range extends wherever balsam fir and spruce are found, from Atlantic Canada to the Yukon. Damage varies considerably from one stand to another. Mortality rates are related to stand composition and age, as well as site quality (soil, water, climate). Ordinarily, the influence of the insect goes unnoticed in a forest, but its impact occasionally reaches epidemic levels, with massive damage to the host trees. Outbreaks last between six and 10 years and have been documented for the past two centuries as the product of a long-term budworm–fir ecological cyclic succession. However, spruce budworm epidemics are occurring with increasing frequency as a result of human intervention related to forest harvesting. Human intervention has reduced the natural diversity of the forest through removal of preferred species such as white pine, creating a less diverse forest composed of large areas of mature balsam fir, the budworm's preferred food. Extensive mortality occurs in stands that have suffered defoliation for several years. In 1975, at the height of infestation, 54 million hectares of Canada's forest were defoliated, resulting in serious economic losses for the forestry industry.

Population levels of the spruce budworm have declined since that time, following a downward trend that started in 2003 and a precipitous drop in 2004. For the past several years outbreaks have been relatively small and localized. Manitoba had approximately 100,000 hectares infected from 1997 until a sharp drop in 2011. The spruce budworm is still present in central Canada (Figure 9.6). A 2006 outbreak in Quebec expanded to more than 600,000 hectares by 2010 and 2.7 million hectares by 2013. This trend of increasing infestations is expected to continue over the next five to ten years as habitat and environmental conditions become favourable.

The long-term ecological stability of the budworm–fir system does not match the shorter-term demands of the economic system dependent on the forests for products. As a result, the forests have been extensively sprayed to limit defoliation and mortality. When spray programs started in 1952, **DDT** was the chemical of choice, and some 5.75 million kilograms were sprayed in New Brunswick alone between 1952 and 1968, when use was suspended. Other chemicals replaced DDT, such as phosphamidon, aminocarb, and fenitrothion, until questions were raised about their ecological and health impacts. Phosphamidon, for example, is very toxic to birds. Up to 1985, 118.5 million hectares (mostly in New Brunswick) were sprayed, some areas annually. Continual spraying appears necessary once natural controls are disrupted.

The organophosphate fenitrothion then became the most popular chemical. It also became the source of heated controversy regarding its health and ecological impacts. In particular, there was concern over the link between the chemical and Reye's syndrome, a rare and fatal children's disease. As a result, and because of unfavourable reviews of the ecological impact of the chemical, particularly on songbirds, the use of fenitrothion in aerial applications was cancelled by 1998. The biological control *Bacillus thuringiensis* (Bt) is now being used more extensively. In some areas, it is supplemented by an insecticide called Mimic that kills the budworm through interruption of the moulting process, starving the larvae to death. Although Mimic is not a broad-spectrum biocide, it has the same lethal effect on the larvae of butterflies and moths. Nonetheless, it has been used in some areas, such as Manitoba, since 1998.

Attention is also being devoted to other less toxic approaches, such as species and landscape diversification, so that large stands of mature balsam fir do not dominate the landscape. Biological control is also being investigated with a parasitic wasp that attacks the larvae of the budworm.

Western provinces also use chemicals to try to limit damage from the spruce budworm. Manitoba, for example, uses dimethoate and malathion, and Bt is commonly used in Saskatchewan.

Management of spruce budworm outbreaks provides a graphic example of the challenges presented by the conflict between longer-term ecological cycles and shorter-term economic dependencies.

Spruce budworm.

In the absence of recurring fires, ground fuel may accumulate, increasing the risk of a major wildfire event. Overall, the Canadian fire regime is characterized by high-intensity crown fires at infrequent intervals, and the amount burned from year to year varies greatly. By 2050 it is estimated that the amount burned will increase 25 per cent, and 75 per cent by 2100, with the southern boreal forest experiencing many more fires as a result of increased temperatures and drier conditions due to global climate change (Balshi et al., 2009; Wotton et al., 2010; de Groot et al., 2013a; 2013b).

Environmental and Social Impacts of Forest Management Practices

Change in species and age distributions arising from forest management practices has a major impact on ecological processes such as energy flows, biogeochemical cycles and the hydrological cycle, and the habitat for other species. We have only a rudimentary knowledge of how forest ecosystems function. It is therefore difficult to be precise about the possible impacts of wholesale conversion from complex natural to more simple human-controlled systems. In addition, important differences occur among forest ecosystems. Some, such as the boreal forest, have naturally evolved with periodic disturbances such as fire or insect attack that stimulate forest renewal. Others, such as the rain forests of the west coast, have little history of disturbance. The difference between disturbance through forestry and natural processes (Box 9.6) must be considered against this background. One essential difference is that natural disturbances such as fire or insect attack do not result in the physical removal of the biomass from the site; it is merely converted from one form to another at that site, consistent with the law of conservation of matter (Chapter 2). In contrast, logging results in the physical translocation of nutrients from the site. The closer that forest harvesting approximates the conditions of natural perturbations, the less disturbing it will be to ecosystem processes. However, in an era when concerns over global warming are coming to dominate our thinking, it is also worth considering that the carbon in forest products, for example, the wood in your house, is stored there for a relatively long time. In contrast, both fire and insect attack result in a more rapid release of carbon back into the atmosphere as carbon dioxide. This is discussed in more detail later in the chapter.

Chapter 2 described how energy flows through ecosystems and is stored in various compartments. Trees, for example, represent energy stored in the autotrophic component of the ecosystem; deer represent storage in the herbivorous component. Thus, a forester may wish to maximize the energy storage in trees and minimize energy losses to herbivores, whereas a wildlife or recreation manager may wish to move the energy storage further up the food chain to support more wildlife. Conflicts therefore arise about where energy should be stored in ecosystems to optimize societal values. This section describes some of the environmental and social implications of forestry activities.

Forestry and Biodiversity

Most natural forest land is dominated by forests with old-growth characteristics, although the age of the trees and degree of structural and compositional attributes described for old growth vary greatly across Canada. Old-growth forests have ecological attributes that tend to be absent from forests that have been harvested. The age structure of old growth varies significantly by forest type and from one biogeoclimatic zone to another. The age at which old-growth forests develop their characteristic structural attributes varies according to forest type, climate, site characteristics, and disturbance regime.

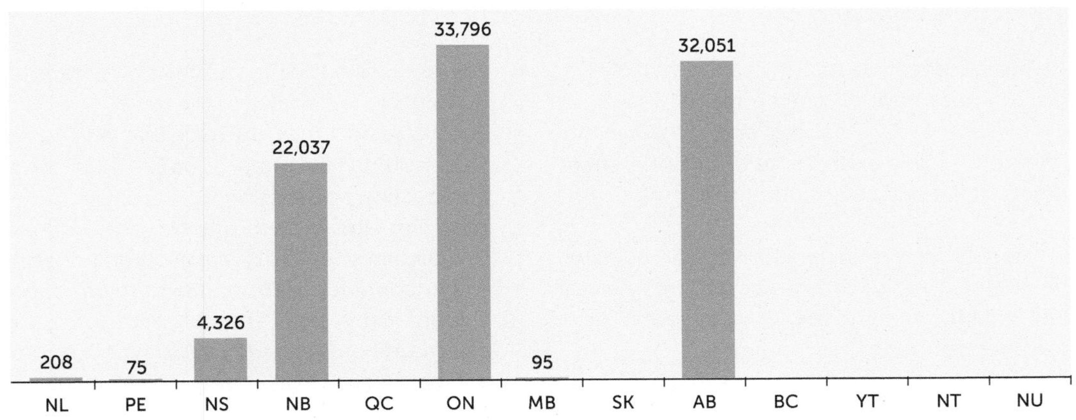

FIGURE 9.8 | Forest herbicide use by province, 2013 (hectares).

Source: National Forestry Database. Reproduced with the permission of the Minister of Natural Resources Canada, 2015. http://nfdp.ccfm.org/pest/quick_facts_e.php.

Old growth is typically distinguished from younger stands by at least several of the following attributes:

- large trees for species and site
- wide variation in tree sizes and spacing
- accumulations of large dead, fallen, and standing trees
- multiple canopy layers
- canopy gaps and understorey patchiness
- decadence in the form of broken tops or boles and root decay

Old-growth forests typically contain trees that span several centuries. Based on age, approximately 18 per cent of Canada's forests can be classified as old-growth. In Canada, the longest-lived tree species are yellow cedar on the west coast and eastern white cedar in central Canada. Trees of both these species may live more than 1,000 years.

Old-growth forests supply high-value timber, contain large amounts of carbon, contain a large reservoir of genetic diversity, provide habitat for many species, regulate hydrologic regimes, protect soils and conserve nutrients, and have substantial recreational and aesthetic values.

Logged forests undergo a number of changes, including modifications of the physical structure of the ecosystem and changes in biomass, plant species mixtures, and productivity. These changes affect biodiversity directly and indirectly by changing the nature of the habitat. Since more than 90,000 species depend on forest habitats in Canada, this is obviously of concern. The largest concentrations of these species are in the Carolinian forests of southern Ontario (see Box 2.10) and the coastal forests of BC.

Direct changes arising from forestry practices include the effects on the genetic and species richness of a biotic community. Most species contain a wide range of genetic variability that helps them adapt to changes in the environment (Chapter 3). As natural forests are replaced by plantations, this natural variability is reduced, since most plantation-grown trees are specially selected from the same genetic base to have desirable characteristics. This makes them more susceptible to pest infestations and disease and less able to adapt to future environmental changes (Box 9.7). For example, it has been suggested that the emergence of the spruce forest moth in central and eastern Canada since 1980 is at least partly due to the establishment of white spruce plantations. More than 92 per cent of the forest harvesting in Canada is done by clear-cutting. This does not destroy the ecosystem per se, in that an ecosystem still exists on that unit of land, but it does dramatically alter the attributes of that ecosystem. For vegetation, changes include removal of the previously dominant trees and their ecological influence, followed by the vigorous growth of other assemblages of plants (where herbicides have not been applied) as the successional process starts again.

Early successional species dominate in the immediate post-harvesting phase but are much reduced over time as the canopy closes. Tree species such as alder, birch, cherry, Jack pine, poplar, and aspen often fit into this category, along with semi-woody shrubs such as elderberry and blackberry, annual and short-lived perennial herb species such as members of the aster family, and various grasses and sedges. Other species that existed in low abundance in the original forest may survive the harvest and, freed from the competitive suppression of the harvested trees, may dominate the community

ENVIRONMENT IN FOCUS

BOX 9.6 | Forest Disturbance: Natural versus Clear-Cut

Some forests are more susceptible to disturbance than others, and different disturbances have differing impacts. There are similarities between some disturbances and clear-cutting, but important differences also exist. Some of the differences between the effects of fire and clear-cutting are:

- Openings created by fire are generally irregular in shape, with high perimeter-to-edge ratios that facilitate natural reseeding. Boundaries tend to be gradual rather than abrupt as in a clear-cut.
- Fires leave standing vegetation in wet areas that continues to provide habitat for wildlife and acts as a natural seed source. Clear-cuts remove all trees.
- Fires tend to kill pathogens; clear-cutting allows many pathogens to survive.
- Fire releases nutrients into the soil; clear-cutting removes nutrients in the bodies of the trees.
- Fire helps to break up rock that aids in soil formation; clear-cutting tends to physically disturb the site, leading to compaction and erosion.
- Fire stimulates growth of nitrogen-fixing plants that help to maintain soil fertility; clear-cutting does not.
- Fire encourages the continued growth of coniferous species in many areas through stimulating cone opening; clear-cutting often leads to dominance by shade-intolerant hardwoods. Ultimately, this changes species composition, as found in studies in Ontario where, in 1,000 sampled boreal clear-cut sites, regenerating poplar and birch had increased by 216 per cent and spruce had fallen by 77 per cent (Hearnden et al., 1992).

for some time. Trees such as red maple, yellow birch, and white pine often fall into this category in central and eastern Canada. As the canopy closes, most of these species will eventually be out-competed. Some species that survive the harvest or invade from surrounding areas may be found through all stages of succession. They have low light compensation thresholds, allowing survival under heavy shading. Balsam fir, hemlock, sugar maple, and beech fall into this category.

Once clear-cuts have had the opportunity to start regenerating, species diversity increases rapidly and usually results in a plant community that is more species-rich and diverse than the harvested community. The exception is where replanting takes place, which involves few species and where steps are taken to reduce competition for plantation trees. Herbicides such as Roundup are commonly applied to achieve this result, and may be applied consistently until the planted trees become established. Under these circumstances, an artificial lack of diversity is created, just as a farmer creates a similar system to maximize the amount of energy stored in the particular component that he or she wishes to harvest (Chapter 10).

Naturally regenerating clear-cuts may also produce a higher biomass of herbivorous species such as white-tailed and mule deer that require brushy habitats for at least part of the year. Both the quantity and quality of browse is greater in regenerating clear-cuts up to the time that the canopy starts to close, and is usually optimal during the first 8 to 13 years. In many parts of their range, white-tailed deer are more abundant than they were before European colonization, when the landscape was covered mostly in mature forest. However, even these species benefit most from a pattern of small clear-cuts, since they prefer edge habitats where the protective cover of the forest is not too far. Optimal clear-cut size for deer in southern Ontario, for example, is around 2 hectares.

Unharvested forests in most areas across Canada comprise a patchwork of forest stands of different ages and different diversities regenerating from the effects of various natural disturbances such as fire and insect attack. Clear-cutting at a certain rate and scale may not be inappropriate in some of these ecosystems. However, some forests, such as the coastal forests of BC and the mixed deciduous forests of southern Ontario and Quebec, are heavily influenced by the pattern of death of individual canopy trees. For example, more than half of the coastal rain forest is more than 250 years old, and much smaller interventions are required to mimic natural processes.

Some animal and bird species require forests with old-growth characteristics—for example, ample lichen growth for woodland caribou or the presence of dead trees to provide nesting cavities for birds such as woodpeckers. If forest harvesting takes place at a rate and scale that eliminates stands with these characteristics, these species will decline in numbers and may become extirpated. The case study presented in Box 9.8, the spotted owl, is a good example of the difficulties associated with maintaining populations of species dependent on old-growth habitat. Other species that have suffered in this regard include the woodland caribou, American pine marten, and marbled murrelet. There are 369 forest-associated species (species that require forest habitat to complete part of their life cycle) currently on the "at risk" list in Canada. Once species are identified as at risk of extinction, actions should be taken to protect them and ensure that they are moved progressively to less threatened categories and eventually off the list, as explained in more detail in Chapter 14. Unfortunately, this is not happening, and there is a marked tendency for forest-associated species to become progressively more, rather than less, endangered over time (Figure 9.9).

The pressure on high-profile species such as the grizzly bear is not the only concern in considering the destruction of old-growth forests; less well-known species, even unknown ones, and the kinds of ecological functions undertaken by these species are also at risk as the old-growth forests are cut away. Some 85 per cent of the species in some forests are arthropods such as insects and spiders. Only recently is the richness of this fauna being realized. There may be more than 1,000 species of invertebrates within a single forest stand. Many of these species are new to science, and we have little idea of their ecological role in maintaining healthy ecosystems. Specific spider species are associated with different stages of the successional process, and at least 30 years is required for the spider community to recover from clear-cutting. Studies of the upper branches of coastal forests in BC are revealing very complex predator–prey relationships among many different species. These relationships are not replicated in managed forests, suggesting that continued elimination of old-growth habitat will lead to species extinctions, a decrease in genetic diversity in these communities, and removal of natural controls on forest pests.

Philip Dearden

The impact of clear-cuts on biodiversity can be reduced by keeping them small, with irregular edges and retained forest patches within the clear-cut, such as this one on Vancouver Island.

ENVIRONMENT IN FOCUS

BOX 9.7 | The War against the Mountain Pine Beetle—Who is Winning?

The outbreak of mountain pine beetles in the interior forests of BC is one of the most dramatic changes ever to happen to BC's forest landscape. The mountain pine beetle epidemic has spread throughout BC's range of lodgepole pine forests as a result of a combination of natural beetle population cycles, continuous mild winters, and an abundance of uniformly mature pine stands. Since 1997, mountain pine beetles infested more than 18 million hectares of pine forests in BC, worth over $30 billion in lost forest products (Figure 9 .6). By 2015, the infestation had dropped to about 3 million hectares as all mature pine stands had been either consumed by the beetle or removed by industry. The beetles have spread into Alberta, and the government of Saskatchewan is supporting Alberta's efforts to stop the infestation moving further east. In the period 2000–2020, it is estimated that the affected forests will release 270 megatonnes of carbon per year to the atmosphere, equivalent to 75 per cent of the average annual forest-fire emissions from all of Canada in 1959–1999 (Kurz et al., 2008).

There is now concern that the beetles may spread all across the boreal forest. As the beetle spread eastward from central BC, it adapted to Jack pine from its main host, lodgepole pine. Jack pine is a main component of the boreal forest, creating the potential for the problem to become nationwide.

Bark beetles are small (rice sized), cylindrical insects that attack and kill mature trees by boring through the bark and mining the phloem (the layer between the bark and wood of a tree). The mountain pine beetle and other bark beetles are native species and natural and important agents of renewal and succession in the forest of the BC Interior. However, when the beetles reach epidemic levels, natural predators like woodpeckers cannot reproduce quickly enough to maintain the insect population at manageable levels.

The dead and dying trees are the source of controversy as government agencies try to combat the rate of infestation through increases in the annual allowable cuts for some areas, reductions in environmental regulations and planning requirements on treatment units, and reduced stumpage (fees paid for logging on public lands). Beetle-infested trees retain economic value and can be salvage-harvested, but since wood quality and value decline with time since attack, there is pressure to cut beetle-infested timber promptly to maximize the economic value of salvaged trees. The recommended size of clear-cut areas is set at 60 hectares in the BC Interior, but exemptions for salvage loggers have resulted in cutblocks as large as 1,300 hectares, more than 20 times the recommended maximum. The salvage clear-cuts can be placed adjacent to previously logged areas that have not yet regenerated, creating potentially very large contiguous openings. Furthermore, little attention has been devoted to the hydrological implications of suddenly deforesting large areas in the interior, and greater flood damage is predicted as a result.

Accelerated cutting of large attacked areas can prevent the decline of timber value in the short term, but a number of social and environmental costs are associated with this approach. Increases in AACs in response to insect infestations can disrupt forest plans, over-supply markets, cause short-term decreases in timber value, and affect employment levels when workers are no longer needed to support the temporary increase in harvest levels. Furthermore, the logging

Mountain pine beetle larvae and adult in pine tree bark, Smithers, British Columbia.

Forest in central British Columbia infested by mountain pine beetles.

industry has been using the pine beetle as an excuse to log areas not attacked by pine beetles. Between 2009 and 2013, for example, around the sawmill town of Houston in northern BC loggers took 29,000 logging truckloads more than they were allowed under a 2008 agreement. That wood was supposed to be still there for harvesting after the infestation had finished and provide a bridge to the newly planted stands still under culmination age. Such over-logging may keep mills running at elevated capacity in the short term, but over the long term it will lead to even more drastic job losses and economic difficulties for the surrounding communities.

The approach of the BC Ministry of Forests has received considerable attention from environmental groups, which view the response of government agencies as drastic. Environmentalists generally advocate natural control methods. Cold winters or fires will kill mountain beetle larvae. However, winters are now warmer than ever before, and many scientists point to the beetle outbreak as an indicator of the kinds of disturbance that will happen more commonly in the future (Woods et al., 2010).

In a further implication, in 2011 the US accused Canada of violating the 2006 softwood timber agreement by allowing lumber companies to sell off vast amounts of timber at cut-rate prices. Lumber that prior to the infestation would be sold to mills for as much as $\$18/m^3$ was sold for as little as 25 cents. This resulted in falling lumber prices all across North America. Although Canada claims the sales were only of damaged timber, the US claims that many good logs were included in the sell-off and their mills could no longer compete.

Despite nearly a century of active management of the mountain pine beetle, efforts to suppress the outbreaks across BC and other parts of North America have been largely unsuccessful. Why do you think this is? What approach would you recommend, given the value of lodgepole timber stands? Do you think provincial parks should be open to clear-cutting as a response to the beetle infestation?

From this brief review of the impact of forest harvesting activities on biodiversity, we can conclude that substantial changes can occur. These changes are beneficial to some species and detrimental to others. It is critical, therefore, to understand the complex ecological relationships involving forests if these changes are to be fully evaluated and taken into account in designing harvesting activities. And it is essential to leave some areas in their original state to maintain landscape biodiversity. Currently, about 8 per cent of Canada's forest area is protected from industrial exploitation by legislation.

Cameron (2006) has reviewed some of the interactions between protected areas and the so-called "working forest" in Canada and suggests:

- retaining or restoring natural climax forest species composition
- reducing edge contrast between working forest and protected areas
- maximizing protection of watercourses draining into protected areas
- planning road networks to minimize undesirable effects on nearby protected areas

Many conservationists do not like the term "working forest" to differentiate between logged and unlogged forests. They maintain that the unlogged forests are in fact working the hardest for society through means such as water storage and

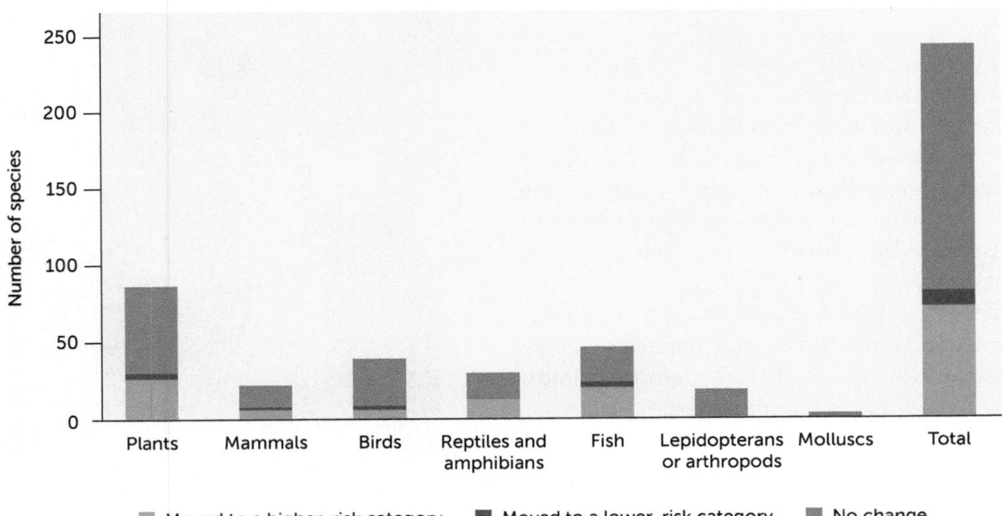

FIGURE 9.9 | Change in COSEWIC status of forest-associated species at risk, 1999–2013.

Source: Natural Resources Canada (2013). Reproduced with the permission of the Minister of Natural Resources Canada, 2015.

ENVIRONMENT IN FOCUS

BOX 9.8 | Case Study: The Northern Spotted Owl

In the latter part of the 1980s, the northern spotted owl in the western United States became the focal point of high-profile conflicts between conservationists and logging interests. The owl was accorded threatened status throughout its entire range in the US under the US Endangered Species Act. A "threatened status" designation means that the owl is likely to become an endangered species within the foreseeable future throughout all or a significant part of its range. This designation requires that critical habitat be identified and a recovery plan implemented. Because the owl depends on old-growth forests, this decision led to severe conflicts with forest harvesting activities. In 1994, the Clinton administration established reserves on more than 4 million hectares where harvesting would be severely restricted. Despite this protection, the numbers of the owl are continuing to decline and there is a move to reclassify the species from "threatened" to "endangered" in the US.

The spotted owl also is found in the old-growth forests of southwestern British Columbia. This northern extension of the range is important, since individuals at the extremes of a species's range are often the most important to protect because they may have the genetic diversity best suited for future adaptability. Furthermore, just as in the US, the old-growth forest on which the owl depends was allocated for harvest. The spotted owl therefore provides a good case study of the impact of forest harvesting on biodiversity.

Biology and Range

The northern spotted owl is found from northern California to southwestern BC. Scientists estimate that, historically, 500 pairs of spotted owls once inhabited the old-growth forests of southwestern BC. Between 1985 and 1993, some 39 active spotted owl sites were recorded, totalling a minimum of 71 adult owls. By 2003, research reported only 25 breeding pairs left in the province; by 2011, this number was down to 6. The historic range of the species in the province is probably not that much different from the current range, although the distribution of the owl within that range has changed significantly, primarily because of destruction of its prime habitat, old-growth forests.

Superior habitat for the owls has old-growth characteristics, such as "an uneven-aged, multi-layered multi-species canopy with numerous large trees with broken tops, deformed limbs, and large cavities; numerous large snags, large accumulations of logs, and downed woody debris; and canopies that are open enough to allow owls to fly within and beneath them" (Dunbar and Blackburn, 1994: 19). Main prey for northern spotted owls are small mammals such as the northern flying squirrel and dusky-footed and bushy-tailed wood rats. Both prey species are abundant in old-growth forests.

Threats

The greatest threat to the spotted owl is the logging of old-growth forests, leading to loss of suitable habitat. Estimates suggest that probably less than 50 per cent of the old-growth habitat that once covered the Lower Mainland of BC is suitable habitat, and much of it is highly fragmented. The provincial government has approved logging in as many as 6 of the 10 areas in which the owl was detected in 2003.

Provincial and regional parks provide some protection in two main blocks. Unfortunately, these blocks are about 85 kilometres apart, with little interconnecting habitat. It is extremely unlikely that the two populations will be able to interbreed. Provincial forests managed for timber production contain much larger amounts of suitable habitat, but much of this land is scheduled to be harvested over the next 100 years.

Management Options

The owl is listed as endangered by the Committee on the Status of Endangered Wildlife in Canada (COSEWIC) and resulted in the formation of a Spotted Owl Recovery Team in 1995 to develop a recovery plan for the species. The primary goal was to outline a course of action for stabilizing the current population, which in turn could improve the status of the species so that it could be removed from the endangered species category. The options range from banning all timber harvesting that could degrade suitable owl habitat within the

The northern spotted owl.

entire range of the owl to no owl management beyond existing parks and protected areas. Several attempts have been made to assist the recovery of the species, including various captive breeding projects. There are now 17 birds in captivity in BC, including five that were born in captivity.

An additional threat to the continued existence of the owls on both sides of the border has been identified. Competition from its larger cousin, the barred owl, is displacing the spotted owl from its habitat. "Removals" of barred owls (by killing them) from spotted owl habitat have shown that spotted owls re-occupy the habitat and thrive in the absence of the barred owl. A larger removal plan is being considered in the US to remove 3,600 barred owls at a cost of over $3.5 million. However, many biologists believe that any such plan would be ultimately unsuccessful because the numbers of barred owls are so large. Some groups are also arguing against the ethics of killing one species to protect another. They suggest that the problem is totally human caused. Spotted owl numbers were severely depressed through logging, and then barred owl numbers were enhanced through tree planting across the Midwest, making it easier for barred owls to migrate from their east coast homes. Others would argue that this is just a natural range expansion, and we should let nature take its course. What do you think?

carbon sequestration, and to imply that they are not working does not reflect modern scientific understanding of the ecosystem value of unlogged forests.

When enlightened forestry companies realize how whole forests work, they come up with innovative solutions. For example, in 2007 the Canadian Parks and Wilderness Society (CPAWS) and the forestry corporation Tembec negotiated a minimum 50-year halt on logging in an area used extensively by woodland caribou on the east side of Lake Winnipeg. The area is further protected under the Canadian Boreal Forest Agreement to ensure adequate conservation measures can be taken to protect the woodland caribou. Estimates suggest that the Manitoba woodland caribou population has decreased by 50 per cent since 1950, and in 2006 the species was listed as threatened under the Manitoba Endangered Species Act. The 26,000-hectare area in which harvesting is deferred is the "winter core zone" of the Owl Lake woodland caribou herd—in other words, the lands the herd uses most during Manitoba's cold months, the most critical time of year.

Forestry and Site Fertility

Forest harvesting removes nutrients from the harvested site (Figure 9.10). The amount of nutrients removed depends on the kind and extent of harvesting. Selective tree-length harvesting removes relatively few nutrients compared to large clear-cuts of complete-tree (above- and below-ground biomass) harvesting. The latter maximizes the short-term yield of biomass from the forest but may compromise the potential of that site over the long term to produce further harvests. **Complete-tree harvesting** is rare in Canada; however, **full-tree harvesting**, where trees are felled and transported to roadside with branches and top intact, is the most common system in use. Alternatively, **tree-length harvesting** involves felling, delimbing, and topping the trees in the cut-over area.

To judge the potential effects of forest harvesting on site fertility, it is necessary to consider the size of the soil nutrient pool, the amount of nutrients being removed, the net accretions and depletions of nutrients in the forests, and the ways in which these variables interact. The process of site impoverishment over time as a result of harvesting is shown in Figure 9.11. On some sites, the proportion of **nutrient capital** removed in the biomass will be relatively minor, while on others it may be substantial. This depends largely on the existing nutrient capital of the site. Areas with high soil fertility will be less affected. Some sites will recover quickly from harvesting and can sustain relatively short rotations. Other sites will not recover between rotations, and site nutrient capital will fall, making tree regeneration difficult and in some cases impossible. Thus, nutrient-deficient sites should have long rotations with just stem harvesting in order to maintain productivity.

The amount of nutrients removed by harvesting is influenced by tree species, age, harvesting method, season of harvesting, and other factors. Older trees contain larger amounts of nutrients—such as nitrogen, phosphorus, potassium, calcium, and manganese—than younger trees. There is also considerable variation among species in the amount of nutrients organically bound and the nutrients preferentially held by different species. The differences between whole-tree and stem-only harvests can also be significant. In a study

(a) Unmanaged Forest Ecosystem

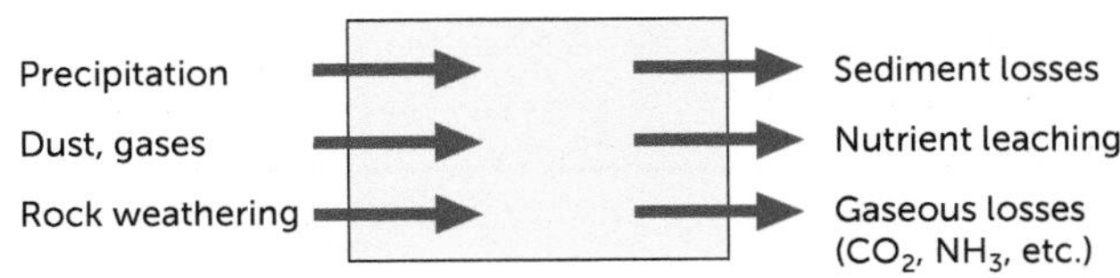

(b) Managed Forest Ecosystem

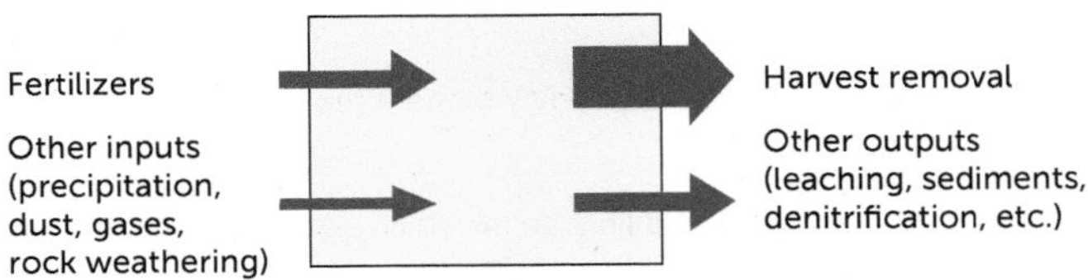

FIGURE 9.10 | Nutrient inputs and outputs from managed and unmanaged forest ecosystems.

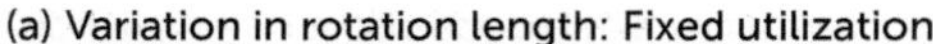

(a) Variation in rotation length: Fixed utilization

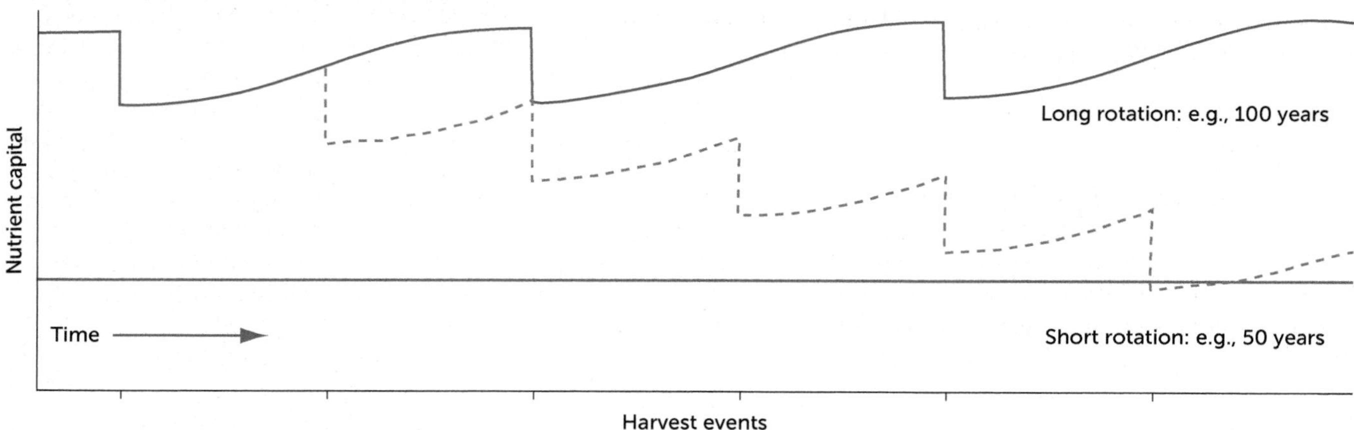

(b) Variation in utilization: Fixed rotation length

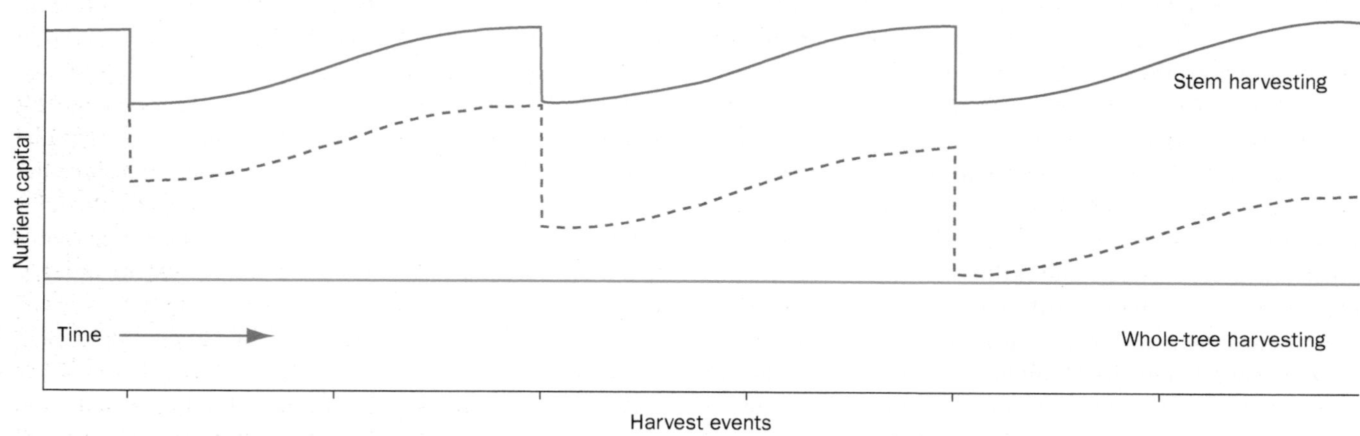

(c) Variation in rates of replacement of nutrient losses: Fixed rotation and utilization

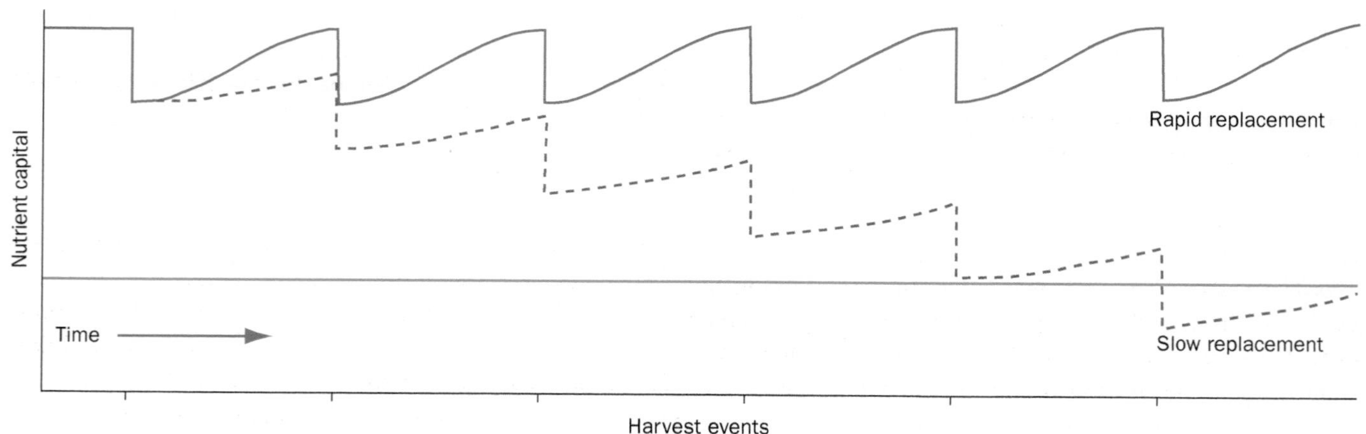

—— Extraction rate balanced by nutrient replacement

- - - Extraction rate in excess of nutrient replacement

—— Nutrient threshold limit below which site is incapable of supporting adequate tree growth

FIGURE 9.11 | Site impoverishment as a result of forest harvesting.

Source: Adapted from Kimmins (1977).

of black spruce in Nova Scotia, Freedman (1981) found an almost 35 per cent increase in biomass take for whole-tree harvesting. When deciduous trees are harvested, the loss of nutrients can be reduced significantly by cutting during the dormant period when leaves are not present.

Forest harvesting can also lead to dramatically increased rates of nutrient loss through **leaching** (the downward movement of dissolved nutrients) to the hydrological system. The amount of loss varies according to the intensity and scale of the harvest and the particular ecosystem. Loss of nitrate is of most concern, since it is not only often a dominant limiting factor (see Chapter 2) but also the nutrient lost most often in large quantities. One reason for this is disturbance in the nitrogen cycle (Chapter 4) by logging, which results in an increase in the bacterial process of nitrification, turning ammonium to nitrate. Nitrate is highly soluble, resulting in significant losses of nitrogen site capital in some ecosystems, particularly if the soil is not too acidic. Other factors, such as warmer soil temperatures, decreased uptake by vegetation, and abundant decaying organic matter on the forest floor, also contribute to increased losses of soluble nutrients following logging. In addition, younger stands (less than 145 years old) support a smaller biomass of lichens with nitrogen-fixing abilities compared to old-growth trees on the west coast of BC.

It is also important to consider nutrient inputs. Precipitation adds substantial amounts of nutrients over time. For a maple–birch stand in Nova Scotia, for example, Freedman et al. (1986) calculated that it would take 96 years of precipitation to replace the nitrogen lost through whole-tree removal, 83 years for potassium, 166 years for calcium, and 41 years for magnesium. Other nutrient inputs occur through dry deposition of gases and particulate matter, the weathering of minerals, and the fixation of atmospheric dinitrogen. Soil mycorrhizae are particularly important for the fixation of atmospheric dinitrogen (Chapter 4), but land treatments after clear-cutting, such as slash burning and pesticide use, may adversely affect fixation rates.

When an old-growth tree such as this giant Sitka spruce on the west coast of Vancouver Island dies, the nutrients it contains recycle to fuel new tree growth. When logging removes the whole tree, these nutrients are lost to the ecosystem.

Forestry and Soil Erosion

Besides its direct influence on nutrients, forest harvesting can have a substantial impact on soil through erosion, especially on steep slopes in areas of heavy precipitation (e.g., Goetz et al., 2014). Such losses also contribute to loss of site fertility, remove substrate for further regrowth, and contribute to flooding and the destruction of fish habitat. Poor road design and maintenance are often key factors behind accelerated soil erosion. Cutting roads across steep terrain exposes large banks of unprotected topsoil. Compacted road surfaces encourage overland flow with high erosive power. Many jurisdictions are implementing much stricter regulations on road construction. Other regulations to minimize soil erosion losses include leaving buffer strips along watercourses, using minimal impact logging techniques, and pursuing selective harvesting rather than clear-cutting.

Forestry and Hydrological Change

Forest harvesting can have a significant impact on hydrology. Under natural conditions, large amounts of water are returned into the atmosphere by the trees through transpiration (Chapter 4). Evapotranspiration includes transpiration plus evaporation from non-living surfaces. These processes are normally greatest during the summer. Removal of the trees significantly reduces this mechanism and other storage capacities, releasing large amounts of water into stream flow and often resulting in flooding during high-discharge periods. Furthermore, without the delaying mechanism of the trees, and with compacted soils from harvesting, the speed of flow is often increased, again raising the potential for flooding as well as increased erosion. In turn, sediment from erosion can damage fish spawning beds.

© Dan Lamont/Corbis

Logging has resulted in severe changes in the morphology of many coastal streams in BC, with large amounts of logging debris accumulating following flooding.

Forestry and Climate Change

Forests are a carbon sink. They take in carbon dioxide and convert it to wood, leaves, and roots. They are also a carbon source. They release stored carbon into the atmosphere when they decompose or burn. Because of this ability to both absorb and release huge amounts of carbon dioxide (a major greenhouse gas), forests play a major role in the global carbon cycle (Chapter 4), the exchange of carbon between the atmosphere and the biosphere. More carbon is stored in forest biomass (trees and other living plants), dead organic matter, and soil than is contained in the atmosphere. Forests are thus a key part of the global carbon cycle.

Large changes in forest carbon sinks and sources affect the climate by altering the amount of carbon dioxide in the atmosphere. As the climate changes, forest carbon storage will be affected. A warmer climate speeds up vegetation growth, which means more carbon storage. However, it also accelerates decomposition, resulting in more carbon emissions, and boosts the risk of drought, pest outbreaks, and fire, all of which can significantly reduce carbon storage. The extent of these effects is also influenced by the amount and/or timing of precipitation changes.

A rapidly changing climate has important implications for the forest sector and the communities whose livelihood is closely associated with forests. One example is the effects on timber supply. Growth and yield databases used in timber supply forecasting will need to be re-evaluated because of changing tree growth and productivity (e.g., see "Domestic Guest Statement" in Chapter 3). Long-term timber supply planning also needs to take into account changes in species composition over time. More frequent large-scale disturbances will cause timber supply fluctuations and result in more salvage-harvesting of trees killed by disturbances, which affect fibre quality.

Wood continues to store carbon even after it is made into products (such as lumber and paper), and only a fraction of the carbon removed from the forest is actually emitted into the atmosphere. For example, in 2012 about 24 million tonnes of carbon was transferred from the forests to the construction industry in Canada. As well, some of the wood waste from product manufacture is burned to produce energy, offsetting fossil-fuel use. After harvest, 40 to 60 per cent of the carbon remains in the forest in the roots, branches, and soil and decomposes slowly, providing nutrients for the newly regenerating forest. Natural disturbances such as forest fires and insect infestations release large amounts of carbon dioxide into the atmosphere, although the areas affected and emission levels vary considerably from year to year. The area of forest burned each year is on average 2.5 times the area harvested and is projected to increase under warmer, drier climate conditions.

Canada's managed forests were a net carbon sink in 12 of the 23 years between 1990 and 2012 (Figure 9.12). Annual amounts ranged from a large *sink* of 174 million tonnes of carbon dioxide equivalents (CO_2e) in 1992 to a large *source* of 171 million tonnes of CO_2e in 1995, mostly because of wildfires. In 2012, Canada's forests were a net emitter of carbon (33 million tonnes of CO_2e).

Deforestation, the permanent conversion of land from forest use to other uses such as agriculture and urban and industrial use, has slowed over the years, although it remains a subject of major international concern and negotiations (Chapter 7). Worldwide, deforestation creates about 20 per cent of human-generated greenhouse gas emissions, more than is produced by the transportation sector. In Canada, deforestation accounts for less than 3 per cent of national emissions, a figure that is declining. In 2013, an estimated 50,000 hectares of forest were converted to other land uses, equivalent to approximately 20 million tonnes of CO_2e, down from 70,000 hectares (29 million tonnes) in 1990. However, this is still considerably in excess of the sink amount of roughly 1 million tonnes of CO_2e per year created by afforestation (planting forests on land previously used for other purposes, usually agriculture).

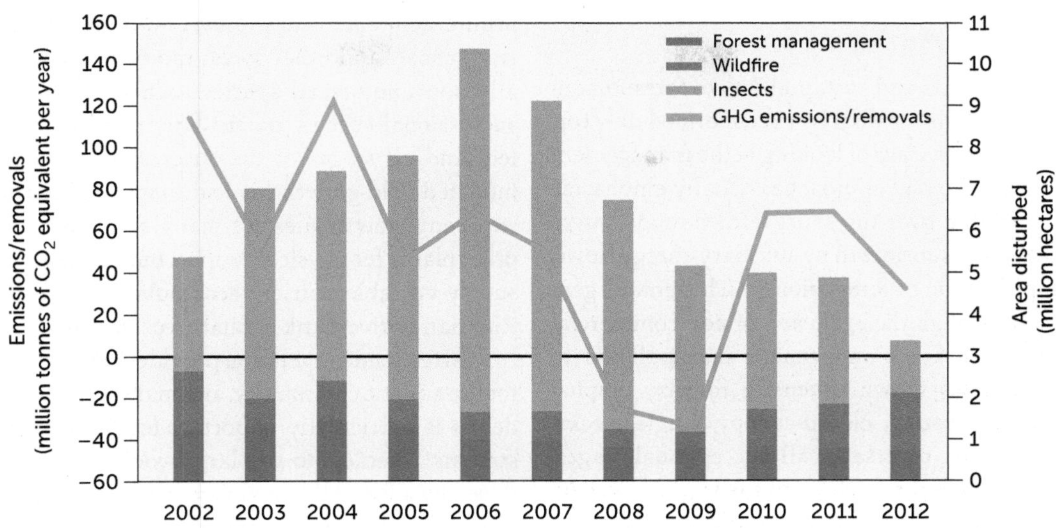

FIGURE 9.12 | Carbon emissions/removals in Canada's managed forests.

Source: Natural Resources Canada (2011: 29; 2014a: 29). Reproduced with the permission of the Minister of Natural Resources Canada, 2015.

Considering carbon sequestration in timber management might become a major factor in how we manage our forests. Neilson et al. (2007), for example, point out that hardwood stands in New Brunswick typically contain 10 to 20 per cent more carbon per hectare than a similar volume of softwoods of similar age. Forest managers might change their management practices as global climate change becomes more severe and thus shift to growing multi-aged hardwood stands that promote carbon sequestration instead of the single-aged softwoods that now dominate their thinking. However, research confirms that ultimately the most effective way to sequester carbon in forests is not to cut down the trees in the first place (Keith et al., 2014).

Other adaptations will also be required. Landry and Ramankutty (2015) discuss some of the longer-term implications of the need to address global climate change and the associated changes that will occur in forest management in Canada. They suggest five scientific principles (Table 9.3) and reflect on their relevance to some important management questions, such as the future response to mountain pine beetle infestation and suppression of natural disturbance events.

The importance of maintaining genetic diversity as a foundation for building species resilience was discussed in Chapter 3. Extensive work is being undertaken to try to document and understand the genetic diversity of major tree species in Canada. There is particular interest in genetic vulnerability and the factors that combine to make species, or a forest, more vulnerable to forest pathogens, climate change or pests as a result of its genetic composition (e.g., Beardmore et al., 2012). These results can also be used to inform human-assisted migration of species outside their historical range in anticipation of the new conditions expected under future climate change regimes. The Ministry of Forests in BC, for example, has a large trial underway for the assisted migrations of two high elevation pines that otherwise may be adversely affected by future conditions (see Pedlar et al., 2012, for a further discussion on assisted migration).

TABLE 9.3 | Five Scientific Principles Relevant for Canadian Managed Forests

P1	The disturbance regime, not a single disturbance event, modulates long-term carbon storage
P2	Disturbance-driven net carbon emissions can differ substantially from the gross emissions
P3	Even if initially beneficial, mitigation strategies requiring repeated fossil-fuel emissions can become detrimental over the climatically relevant millennial time horizon
P4	Climate regulation goes beyond carbon cycling, for disturbed and undisturbed forests
P5	Wood harvest cannot perfectly emulate natural disturbances

Source: Landry and Ramankutty (2015)

New Forestry

Concerns over the impacts and sustainability of forest practices have given rise to calls for what has been termed **new forestry**, which involves new ways of looking at the management of forest ecosystems. Current approaches usually emphasize economic maximization over the short term through intensive forest management subsidized by auxiliary energy flows, leading to a simplification of forest biology. This entails genetic simplification through the exclusion of non-commercial species from regrowth areas and genetic manipulation to homogenize the species grown. Intensive forestry emphasizes production of a young, closed-canopy, single-species forest, usually the least diverse of all successional stages. Moreover, the strength and reliability of the wood produced from such forests have been questioned, and these plantations are susceptible to **windthrow**, insect infestations, and gradual nutrient depletion. Structural simplification also takes place as the range of tree sizes and growth forms is reduced, snags and fallen trees are removed, and trees are regularly spaced to optimize growth. At the landscape scale, simplification occurs as old growth is removed and the irregularity of wind- and fire-created openings is replaced by the regularity of planned clear-cuts. Successional simplification also takes place, since intensive management aims at eliminating early and late successional stages from the landscape.

New forestry embraces an approach that mimics natural processes more closely, emphasizing long-term site productivity by maintaining ecological diversity. This includes rotation periods sometimes longer than the minimum economic periods, reinvesting organic matter and nutrients in the site through snag retention and stem-only harvesting, minimizing chemical inputs, and diversifying the range of tree species and other forest products. Growth of traditionally non-commercial species such as alder and other early successional species, particularly nitrogen fixers, is permitted, and all stages of the successional process are accommodated. Old-growth big-leaf maple, for example, provides excellent growth sites for many epiphytes (plants that use other plants for physical support but not nourishment), which supply valuable nutrient accumulation and water retention. Riparian or riverbank habitats receive special attention; litter from streamside vegetation provides the primary energy base for the aquatic community, and management of coarse woody debris is particularly important for the structure of smaller streams. Needless to say, large woody debris cannot be produced by a forest that no longer contains large trees.

New forestry also emphasizes the maintenance of non-timber parts of the forest community. Special attention is given to the impact of the size, shape, and location of forest patches on wildlife and how these patches can be connected to sustain populations. The ecological complexities of forests are only just starting to be revealed. Recent research, for example, suggests that the younger the forest, the less conifer seed production. Species that rely on these seeds, such as crossbills, also experience a decline. In western Canada, five species of crossbill have evolved, each specializing in a different species of conifer and even particular varieties of the same species. Protection of this diversity of crossbills will require protection of old-growth stands and an increase in rotation ages throughout the range of each conifer. Similar consideration must be given to the entire range of forest biodiversity if it is to be maintained into the future.

The kinds of changes suggested by new forestry make it unlikely that the dominant practices of today, such as extensive clear-cuts, can continue, and indicate that other harvesting systems (Table 9.2) will play a larger role as an ecosystem-based perspective becomes more widespread. However, a review of ecosystem-based forestry undertaken as part of the Canadian Boreal Forest Agreement described earlier in the chapter was not encouraging about the status of ecosystem-based management in Canada. In the context of forestry (see also Chapter 5), **ecosystem-based management** (EBM) was defined as "a management system that attempts to emulate ecological patterns and processes, with the goal of maintaining and/or restoring natural levels of ecosystem composition, structure and function within stands and across the landscape" (Van Damme et al., 2014: 1). They found a highly variable rate of adoption of ecosystem-based principles among the provinces, with Ontario and Quebec appearing to be the most advanced and BC and Manitoba the least. Conclusions include:

- Most provinces are still working to develop clear standards for implementing EBM in forest management practices.

New forestry would devote much more attention to tending stands on commercial sites, such as this birch stand, where limbing and thinning enhance growth.

- Few provinces have integrated land-use planning and/or cumulative effects assessment capacity.
- Poor quality of input data limits meaningful planning outputs for EBM (e.g., forest inventory, roads data).
- There are limited government resources for foundational science/policy work.
- The lack of integration (and significant challenges for achieving it) between the forestry and energy sectors in some provinces poses a significant barrier to EBM.
- There are high costs of implementation associated with aspects of EBM (e.g., large-scale restoration, prescribed burning).
- Ecosystem resilience (capacity, bounds) has largely remained undefined within the current state of knowledge.

New forestry may not suit the need for short-term economic return on the part of the large corporations now dominating the industry, and it is likely that more, smaller, community-based companies will emerge (Box 9.9). Monetary returns over the short term will probably fall as less wood fibre is extracted from the forest. Proponents of new forestry argue, however, that these changes will have to occur anyway. Continuing the old approaches will simply lead to an abrupt decline in the amount of timber available and consequently will diminish future prospects. This way of thinking is gaining wider acceptance. The development of Canada's National Forest Strategies, described in the next section, is one result.

ENVIRONMENT IN FOCUS

BOX 9.9 | New Forestry in Action

The ideas of new forestry must be put in motion if change is to occur. Several examples of alternatives to the dominant way of managing our forests are already in operation, both regarding individual woodlots and management of more extensive areas by communities.

At the individual scale, one well-known example is Merv Wilkinson and his 55-hectare woodlot, Wildwood Forest, on southern Vancouver Island. From 1936 until his death at the age of 97 in 2011, Wilkinson practised **sustained yield** forestry, and despite the removal of more than 4,000 m^3 of timber, his woodlot still contains as much wood as it did when it was first assessed in 1945. His practice involves removal of forest products by cutting in five-year rotations. The straightest, most vigorous trees with good foliage and abundant cone production are left as seed trees, including some estimated to be as old as 1,800 years. There is no clear-cutting, slash burning, or use of chemicals. The canopy is left intact to shield seedlings but thinned a little to promote good growth. Sheep are used for brush control. Wilkinson's model may not apply everywhere, but it worked for him and offers a good example of how a forest can be maintained while still retaining its essential ecological characteristics.

At a regional scale, attention has focused on "community forests." Decisions on forest use are often made in boardrooms at the dictates of international capital. Such decisions may not benefit the local communities dependent on the forests for their livelihoods. Concern over this situation has prompted interest in how to manage forests to maximize the benefits to local communities.

Many types of community forests exist in Canada, with different forms of land tenure and administrative arrangements. However, they are all aimed at achieving benefits for the community and encouraging local involvement in decision-making. In BC, for example, the provincial government amended the Forest Act in 2009 to create Community Forest Agreements (CFAs), a new form of tenure designed to enable more communities and First Nations to participate directly in the management of local forests. The BC government has a number of objectives for the program:

- Provide long-term opportunities for achieving a range of community objectives, values, and priorities
- Diversify the use of and benefits derived from the CFA area
- Provide social and economic benefits to British Columbia
- Undertake community forestry consistent with sound principles of environmental stewardship that reflect a broad spectrum of values
- Promote community involvement and participation
- Promote communication and strengthen relationships between Aboriginal and non-Aboriginal communities and persons
- Foster innovation
- Advocate forest worker safety

To 2015, 50 CFAs had been issued provincially, and more partnerships are being made with Aboriginal communities in BC. The government has harvesting agreements with 172 Aboriginal groups, covering 55 million m^3 and producing more than $243 million in revenue annually.

Alternative approaches to conventional forestry do exist. It is essential, however, to specify the goals of forestry activities before the most appropriate approach can be chosen, as emphasized in the framework in Chapter 1. Current models have evolved to maximize economic returns over the short term; the alternatives described above have different goals, more consistent with the demands of today. However, as Bullock and Hanna (2008) point out, community forestry is not a panacea for resolving conflict in forest management.

Canada's National Forest Strategies

During the 1980s, it became increasingly clear that forestry in Canada could not continue as it had in the past; new ways had to be found to develop more sustainable management practices. This realization resulted in the formation of a *National Forest Strategy* (NFS)*: Sustainable Forests: A Canadian Commitment (1992–7)*. It was revised and extended in a second strategy covering 1998 to 2003. The National Forest Strategy Coalition (NFSC), composed of 52 governmental and non-governmental agencies, was formed to oversee implementation of the strategy. The strategy made 121 commitments under nine strategic directions to move Canada along the road to a more sustainable use of forest ecosystems.

Such an approach is only useful, however, if the commitments are meaningful and progress is made to achieve them. An independent evaluation concluded that there had been substantial progress on 37 commitments, some progress on 76 commitments, little progress on six commitments, and no progress on two commitments. The evaluation commended Canada for showing international leadership but suggested a simplification of any future strategy, as well as the inclusion of clear targets and timetables.

In 2003, a further five-year strategy was adopted, along with a commitment on the part of the NFSC partners to work toward its completion. However, Alberta, Quebec, and the Forest Products Association of Canada did not sign the strategy. Eight themes were outlined, each of which specifies an objective and action items to be undertaken. Two noteworthy themes were the urban forest, which emphasized the need to engage more of Canadian society in forest questions, and recognition of the importance of private woodlots to sustainability. The latter is particularly important in the Maritime provinces, where more than half of the forests are in private hands and not subject to provincial forestry regulations. Overcutting and neglect of these lands have been problems in the past, and the action items in the strategy included providing more incentives and support for landowners to manage their woodlots on a sustainable basis.

The objectives of the 2003–8 NFS were highly laudable and seemed to herald a new and progressive approach to forest management in Canada. However, both the Sierra Club and the Ontario Federation of Anglers and Hunters withdrew from the program, feeling that inadequate attention was being devoted to non-timber values in the forests and that the situation was really "business as usual."

An evaluation of the ecosystem-based forest management aspects of the NFS was undertaken in 2007 by an independent team of evaluators who were generally critical of the NFS. They found an overall lack of engagement and financial support. For example, only 15 out of 66 coalition members attended the 2007 annual meeting. They were also highly critical of the evaluation system designed by the NFS (KBM Forestry Consultants, 2007).

The report identifies some positive trends in Canadian forestry, but "these trends would no doubt continue with or without an NFS." The main conclusion is that "the NFS is successful at communicating a consistent pattern of behaviour of Canada's forest jurisdictions for the benefit of its citizens and its trading partners around the world" (KBM Forestry Consultants, 2007: 50). Unfortunately, what this statement seems to indicate is that rather than the NFS creating real progress in forest management in Canada, it is mainly a communication vehicle. Understandably, NGOs interested in generating real change may feel a little co-opted by such a process, as in the selection of indicators for the *State of the Forests* reports mentioned earlier in this chapter.

Both the Sierra Club and the independent evaluation indicate that the future trend of the federal government seems to be to limit inclusivity and return more to a top-down process of input to forest land decision-making. The 2008–18 strategy confirms this approach, with the Canadian Council of Forest Ministers reassuring Canadians that they will lead the process "on behalf of all Canadians" (CCFM, 2008: ii) and therefore will not need the participatory approach adopted previously. The new strategy has two themes: transforming the forest sector, and mitigating and adapting to climate change. There seems to be little appetite for re-engaging in the more detailed aspects of forest management change that emanated from the previous strategy.

The Model Forest Program

One commitment from Canada's 1992–7 National Forest Strategy that has borne fruit is to develop a system of model forests in the major forest regions. The objectives of the program are:

- To increase the development and adoption of sustainable forest management systems and tools within and beyond model forest boundaries
- To disseminate the results of and knowledge gained through Canada's Model Forest Program at local, regional, and national levels
- To strengthen model forest network activities in support of Canada's sustainable forest management priorities
- To increase opportunities for local-level participation in sustainable forest management

Proposals were solicited for areas between 100,000 and 250,000 hectares where partners would develop a management structure to facilitate cooperation and include a vision and objectives to balance a variety of values, as well as actions to demonstrate sustainable forest management. Key attributes of model forests include:

- A partnership that includes principal land-users and other stakeholders from the area
- A commitment to sustainable forest management, using an ecosystem-based approach
- Operations at the landscape or watershed level
- Activities that reflect stakeholder needs and values
- A transparent and accountable governance structure
- Commitment to networking and capacity-building

Eleven model forest agreements in six forest regions across the country were initiated, each with a unique management structure designed to address the particular situation. Each model forest is an independent, not-for-profit organization, and in 2006 the Canadian Model Forest Network became an independent, not-for-profit organization, although Natural Resources Canada remains a key partner and supporter. Core issues relate to ecosystem-based management, Aboriginal participation, public participation, science and innovation, and the integration of non-market values into decision-making. Regular updates on network activities are provided in the *Forestry Chronicle* journal.

Model forests have a deliberate strategy of intra- and inter-site demonstration and networking. This strategy has expanded internationally, with sites in Mexico, Chile, Argentina, China, the US, Japan, Indonesia, Thailand, Myanmar, the Philippines, and Russia as part of an International Model Forest Network. These initiatives have been supported by Canadian aid programs totalling more than $11 million, with additional support from other donors of more than $7.5 million. This support reflects recognition that the programs constitute a tangible demonstration of the value of cooperatively working together toward sustainability. They illustrate many of the approaches outlined earlier in Chapters 5 and 6.

Global Forest Strategies

Most of this chapter has concentrated on the Canadian situation, but as outlined in Box 9.10 challenges also exist at the global level. Between 2000 and 2012, total global forest loss was 2.3 million km^2. Forests now occupy some 31 per cent of the Earth's land surface. There is some good news, in that the rate of deforestation declined from 0.20 per cent a year in the 1990s to 0.13 per cent in the first decade of the twenty-first century. The challenge is to reverse that figure so that, overall, forests are increasing and not declining as emphasized by Professor Oliver Coomes in the "International Guest Statement" on page 318. However, it should be noted that these figures are based on self-reported statistics and that they also include all lands growing trees, such as oil palm plantations, that might add to forest cover but do little for biodiversity.

Significantly, some of the most influential and far-reaching social movements in the world have arisen out of local concerns regarding unsustainable forestry practices by major logging interests. The Chipko Movement—also known as the "Hug the Trees" Movement; *chipko*, in Hindi, means "embrace" or "cling"—began in the Himalayan forest region of northern India in the 1970s when local people sought to protect local forests and in protest encircled trees to stop the logging that was destroying local ecosystems and ways of life, as well as causing erosion and flooding. Similarly, the Green Belt Movement in Kenya has fought against multinational interests by involving half a million schoolchildren, thousands of farmers, and thousands of local women in planting trees and creating hundreds of tree nurseries for reforestation in the effort to halt desertification and provide for the livelihood of entire communities. The leader of this movement, Wangari Maathai, received the Nobel Peace Prize in 2004.

One of the major disappointments of the United Nations Conference on Environment and Development (UNCED) in 1992 was the failure to establish an international convention on forests. Some legally binding outcomes related to forestry did emerge from UNCED, in particular the Convention on Biological Diversity, which committed signatories to prepare and adhere to a national biodiversity strategy, including the designation of representative samples of their forest

Philip Dearden

In Thailand sometimes conservationists will ordain trees as sacred to Buddhism to protect them from cutting.

lands as protected areas and ensuring that forest management does not impair biodiversity. Chapters 2 and 14 discuss these commitments.

Forests were also included in Agenda 21, the non-binding principles that emerged from UNCED and set an agenda for development in the twenty-first century. In 2000, the United

ENVIRONMENT IN FOCUS

BOX 9.10 | Forests: A Global Perspective

- Some 40 per cent of the land surface of the Earth supports trees or shrubs while 30 per cent is fully forested.
- Five countries—Canada, Russia, the US, Brazil, and China—contain more than 50 per cent of the world's forests while 10 countries have no forest at all.
- Each year, about 13 million hectares of the world's forests are lost to deforestation, but the rate of net forest loss is slowing down, thanks to new planting and natural expansion of existing forests.
- From 2000 to 2012, total forest loss was 2.3 million km^2, and total forest gain was 0.8 million km^2.
- In 2013, 18 million hectares were deforested globally, a 5.2 per cent increase over the 2000–2012 average loss.
- In 2011–2013, Russia and Canada topped the list for losses (mostly due to forest fires), jointly accounting for 34 per cent of total loss.
- Deforestation accounts for up to 20 per cent of the global greenhouse gas emissions that contribute to global warming.
- Primary forests comprise over one-third of all forests but lost over 40 million hectares since 2000 through deforestation or selective logging.
- Plantation forests are established at a rate of 5 million hectares per year.
- Plantations cover more than 264 million hectares (7 per cent of total forested area).
- The 10 countries with the largest net forest loss per year between 2011 and 2014 were Russia, Canada, Brazil, the US, Indonesia, Democratic Republic of the Congo, China, Malaysia, Argentina, and Paraguay.
- Estimates suggest that more than 80 per cent of the world's terrestrial species are found in forests. The tropical forests are our richest terrestrial biome. Tropical rain forests occupy only 7 per cent of the world's land area, but they contain more than half of the world's species.
- Developing countries consume more than 80 per cent of their wood as fuel; in developed countries, only 16 per cent goes to fuel, with the rest being processed as wood products. Approximately 1.5 billion tonnes of wood is harvested for fuel annually worldwide.
- Most wood products (85 per cent) are used domestically.
- Wood products are valuable, worth over US$100 billion annually.
- Global forests provide wage employment and subsistence equivalent to 60 million work-years annually worldwide, 80 per cent of which is in developing countries. More than 1.6 billion people depend to varying degrees on forests for their livelihoods (e.g., fuelwood, medicinal plants, and forest foods).
- People in developing countries consume much fewer wood products (30 m^3 per 1,000 people) and less paper (12 tonnes per 1,000 people) than people in developed countries (300 m^3 of wood products per 1,000 people and 150 tonnes of paper per 1,000 people).
- Thirty per cent of the world's forests are designated for production, with just 8 per cent for protection and 12 per cent for conservation.
- Worldwide, an estimated 460 million hectares of forested land are designated for the protection of biological diversity. However, of 200 areas of high biological diversity, 65 per cent are threatened by illegal logging. Illegal logging is estimated to cost governments approximately $15 billion annually.

Philip Dearden
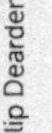

Philip Dearden

Can tropical forests, such as these in Sri Lanka, sustain the needs of both the people and animals that depend on them?

Sources: FAO (2014a); Hansen et al. (2013).

Nations Forum on Forests (UNFF) was created, with the objective of promoting the forest principles focusing on sustainable management contained in Agenda 21. In 2006, at its sixth session, the UNFF finally agreed on four shared Global Objectives on Forests:

- Reverse the loss of forest cover worldwide through sustainable forest management (SFM), including protection, restoration, afforestation, and reforestation, and increase efforts to prevent forest degradation
- Enhance forest-based economic, social, and environmental benefits, including by improving the livelihoods of forest-dependent people
- Increase significantly the area of sustainably managed forests, including protected forests, and increase the proportion of forest products derived from sustainably managed forests
- Reverse the decline in official development assistance for sustainable forest management and mobilize significantly increased new and additional financial resources from all sources for the implementation of SFM

In 2007, another breakthrough was achieved with agreement on the UN Non-legally Binding Instrument on All Types of Forests. This was the first time that member states had agreed to an international instrument for sustainable forest management, and it is expected to have a major impact on international cooperation and national action to reduce deforestation, prevent forest degradation, promote sustainable livelihoods, and reduce poverty for all forest-dependent people (FAO, 2013). A stronger initiative has emerged in the EU, where a legally binding agreement is under development, setting objectives for sustainable forest management.

Other global initiatives are expanding, especially certification (see Box 9.11). The two largest **certification** organizations worldwide are the Forest Stewardship Council (FSC), a membership organization dedicated to sustainable development principles (about one-third of the global certifications), and the Programme for the Endorsement of Forest Certification (PEFC), a voluntary initiative led by the forest industry to promote an internationally credible certification framework (about two-thirds of the global total). There is some overlap between the two certification schemes, with the area of double certification increasing annually. Both organizations develop principles and criteria for SFM using stakeholder participation and accredit third-party auditors to verify compliance through annual audits. Certifiers may issue a Forest Management Certificate for forest stewards or a Chain-of-Custody Certificate for forest product manufacturers and distributors. Consumers can then identify certified wood products through a certification logo. The area of certified forest increased from 3.24 million hectares in 1995 to 180.44 million hectares as of July 2013. The annual growth rate is relatively constant since 2005, only once falling below 10 million hectares. Nearly two-thirds of the certified forest area is within natural forests (65 per cent), more than a quarter (28 per cent) semi-natural and mixed (plantation and natural) forests, and less than a tenth plantations (8 per cent).

Although the early proponents of forest certification hoped to target tropical deforestation, the temperate and boreal forests of industrialized countries account for the vast majority of all certifications. Some argue that this is because certification is not conducive to forest management schemes involving communities or small enterprises, which are typical in developing countries. However, tropical forest certifications in the developing world are continuing to grow.

Perhaps the biggest factor that might affect the way we look at global forests is their role in mitigating the impact of global climate change. This has been recognized in global climate change negotiations and has resulted in a program to Reduce Emissions from Deforestation and Degradation (REDD). Initiated in 2005, the REDD program was a result of continuing conversion of tropical forests and efforts to provide incentives to halt, or at least slow, conversion to other uses. Based on projections of continued deforestation, developing nations are rewarded for slowing those rates through mechanisms specified under the United Nations Framework Convention on Climate Change (UNFCCC). In 2007 at the thirteenth session of the Conference of the Parties (COP-13), the scope of REDD was expanded to include sustainable forest management and conservation objectives (known as **REDD+**) and now includes: (1) reducing emissions from deforestation; (2) reducing emissions from forest degradation; (3) conservation of forest carbon stocks; (4) sustainable management of forests; and (5) enhancement of forest carbon stocks. However, despite these good intentions and the piloting of schemes in many parts of the world, as yet there is no final framework, nor the financial means to implement it, at the global level.

Implications

Forestry is "at a watershed" in Canada in terms of how forests, their value, and their management are viewed. The next decade will be crucial in determining whether Canadians will still consider themselves a forest nation in another 20 years. Although society in general and government and industry in particular have a much greater appreciation of the changes needed in the industry to move toward more sustainable practices, actually making these changes will take some time. However, the world is watching, and the power of consumers to effect change is evident. Box 9.12 offers some suggestions on things you can do in this regard. Large companies such as IKEA and Home Depot have reacted to consumer pressure by agreeing not to sell products from forestry operations not certified as sustainable. One can only hope that similar changes in other areas of forest product use will occur.

INTERNATIONAL GUEST STATEMENT

The Amazon Rain Forest | *Oliver Coomes*

Flying over the Amazon basin, far from the deforestation frontiers in Brazil and the Andes, one sees a green mottled carpet of forest stretching to the horizon, dissected by twisting ribbons of muddy rivers and dotted by the occasional riverside cluster of raised huts and the ubiquitous soccer field—a landscape so vast, remote, and lightly populated that surely much of the basin remains today untouched by humans. Indeed, the lowland Amazon rain forest with its multi-storied canopy, massive trees, and palms that reach up to 35 metres above the forest floor would seem to be exemplary of pristine nature. The largest intact extension of lowland tropical forest in the world, the rain forests of Amazonia cover over 5.5 million km^2 and are home to an estimated 40,000 species of plants, 430 species of mammals, 1,500 bird species, and 2,500 species of fish. And yet to ethnobotanists, anthropologists, and geographers, the forest bears the imprint of millennia of human occupation and use that has profoundly modified Amazonian environments. Evidence is mounting of large-scale pre-Columbian settlements, earthworks, canals, raised fields, and geoglyps in many areas of the basin. The spatial distributions of useful palms and trees species today along rivers and inland on the terra firme point to past human settlement and extensive forest modification. The rich black soils—or Amazonian dark earths (ADE) (terra preta)—found in patches under the forest over large areas are considered to be anthropogenic in origin. And even some river and stream courses are known to have been modified by human action. Indeed, so pervasive has been the influence of people since pre-history that some scientists believe, not without controversy, that no place in the Amazon basin remains untouched and "pristine."

The Amazon rain forest continues to be modified today, in old ways and new. Indigenous and folk people living along the rivers and interfluves of the basin shape their forest environment as they have for generations in subtle and complex ways, practising swidden-fallow agroforestry ("slash-and-burn" agriculture discussed in Chapter 4), flood plain agriculture, and extraction of timber and non-timber forest products—their livelihoods relying on the rich biological diversity and traditional ecological knowledge of the forest ecosystem. In sharp contrast, extensive rain forest clearing continues along the "arc of deforestation" in Brazil for cattle ranching and indirectly for soya bean production as both industries expand to meet demand of markets in Europe and China. In western Amazonia, smaller-scale colonist settlement, ranching, and oil palm expansion are claiming forests along roads leading down from the eastern slopes of the Andes. And accelerating urbanization in the basin—more than 50 per cent of the population now lives in towns and cities—is driving further forest clearing and resource harvesting, impoverishing the forests and rivers of the urban hinterland.

Recent experience in Brazil and elsewhere in Latin America, however, suggests that the fate of Amazonian forests may not be as dim as many observers projected. To date, about 12 per cent of the basin's upland forest has been lost, and in Brazil—the largest global forest-holder and deforester—rates of deforestation have fallen sharply, by some 70 per cent since 2004, faster than anywhere else in the tropical world. This impressive decline in forest clearing has been due to multiple, interacting factors including a moratorium imposed on "high-deforestation" beef and soy; the creation of new,

Philip Dearden

Ample water and heat promote lush growth through much of the Amazon forest.

extensive protected areas, indigenous territories, and sustainable development (extractive) reserves; satellite monitoring coupled with enforcement of laws and regulations governing deforestation; the rise of concern over deforestation both in Brazilian civil society and national environmental politics; and international pressure through NGOs, multilateral agencies, and governments. Numerous initiatives are also being planned to provide positive incentives for farmers, ranchers, and local governments to avoid deforestation through the payment for ecosystem services under REDD+ initiatives, as discussed earlier in this chapter.

In addition, as shown elsewhere in South and Central America, forests are returning—through secondary regrowth and tree planting—and moving regions through a "forest transition," from high rates of deforestation to net reforestation. Although Brazil continues to lose very large areas of lowland tropical forest by global standards—some 6,000 km^2 each year—the rate of net deforestation is slowing as secondary forests are reclaiming unused, fallowed, or abandoned land. Re-growing secondary forest now covers an area estimated between 90,000 and 160,000 km^2 in the Brazilian Amazon. Although secondary forests hold far less biological diversity than irreplaceable primary rain forests and thus are of lower conservation value, they do provide goods and services that are vital to the functioning of Amazonian ecosystems. Ongoing debate and speculation now focuses on whether current trends will persist and spare much of the remaining rain forest on the terra firme.

In the future, attention is likely to turn from the upland forests of Amazonia to development of the flood plains (*várzea*) of the Amazon River and its Andean alluvium tributaries. Wetlands cover about 30 per cent of the basin and the flood plain forests along the Amazon River, and its formative tributaries in the western basin are among the richest in species diversity—with over 1,000 known tree species—and the most productive in the world. The agricultural potential of the flood plains, which are replenished each year by fertile sediment borne by the annual flood from the Andes, has barely been tapped beyond the areas immediately around the major riverside towns and cities. The challenges of developing the flood plains are many, including the large seasonal variation in water levels, of 8–15 metres each year, the ever-shifting nature of the river course and its mudflats and levees, and the risk of exceptional floods and rapid river rises that flood crops, erode river banks, and destroy property, all of which may be sensitive to regional climate change. Nonetheless, just as pre-Columbian settlement was once concentrated on the river bluffs, drawing upon the rich aquatic and land resources below, future development in Amazonia is likely to focus on the flood plains—viewed by some observers as the last great agricultural frontier in Latin America.

Oliver T. Coomes is a professor of geography at McGill University. His research examines natural resource use, livelihoods, poverty, and adaptation to environmental change among forest peoples of the Peruvian Amazon and elsewhere in the Neotropic ecozone (www.geog.mcgill.ca/faculty/coomes).

Forestry will no longer be the main or only economic backbone for many communities, as it was in the past, because mills continue to close. Some places will be hit harder than others. In BC, which accounts for over 50 per cent of Canada's lumber production, the annual timber harvest is expected to drop by one-third over the next decade. This decline is partly due to the mountain pine beetle, but much is also due to the failure of forest management to heed warnings about

Philip Dearden

Philip Dearden

Chemainus, Vancouver Island, BC, was once a thriving mill town, but its fortunes collapsed along with the timber supply. As part of a bold new economic development plan, Chemainus commissioned many large murals to be painted around town celebrating its history and providing an attraction for a new, now flourishing, tourist industry.

overcutting during previous decades. It is to be hoped that changes will arise as a result of this situation and help to generate a more sustainable industry in the future.

Some changes are already evident. The United Steelworkers Union, representing thousands of forestry workers, is now joining with environmental groups such as the Western Canada Wilderness Committee—new allies that were bitter foes 10 years ago—in demonstrations to draw attention to the situation. Communities like Ucluelet, Port Alberni, and Port Hardy on Vancouver Island, which in the past strongly resisted attempts to preserve forest lands for other values such as recreation, are now looking at forests with a much greater appreciation of the multiple values they contain. Similar changes are occurring across the country. Forestry will continue to play a role in many economies, but the days of the one-industry town are gone.

ENVIRONMENT IN FOCUS

BOX 9.11 | The Seal of Approval

Increasingly, customers for wood products around the globe are asking for guarantees that the products they buy come from forests managed and logged according to ecologically responsible standards. The trend toward responsible consumerism is supported by certification and labelling, a process in which an independent audit of a forestry company is conducted to assess whether it meets internationally and/or nationally recognized guidelines for responsible forest management. Certification enables consumers and participants to measure forest management practices against approved standards and also provides forest owners with an incentive to maintain and improve forest management practices.

In Canada, there are three main certification systems:

- Forest Stewardship Council (FSC)
- Canadian Standards Association (CSA)
- Sustainable Forestry Initiative (SFI)

Important differences exist among these certification systems related to standards, policies, procedures, and on-the-ground results. The FSC is an international system with strict standards; the others are largely generated and controlled by the forest industry. One independent report (ÉEM Inc., 2007) found that the FSC had the only system prohibiting the use of genetically modified trees, preventing the conversion of natural forests to plantations, and requiring a precautionary approach to the management of areas with high conservation value. Although it found that certification systems often mentioned similar requirements, the study raised concerns that, under some systems, it was left to the individual forest manager to decide what to do on the ground. The study identified the FSC as generally more rigorous in its performance requirements, and this conclusion has been subsequently supported by a further audit (Masters et al., 2010).

Forest certification systems are designed to link environmentally and socially conscious consumers with like-minded producers, retailers, and distributors and typically involve:

- independent third-party auditing
- **chain-of-custody** procedures (verification of compliance from the forest through to the final product)
- on-the-ground inspections of forested areas to determine whether they are managed according to established sets of environmental and social standards
- certified product labelling
- multi-stakeholder involvement

The range of issues considered in defining responsible forest management includes wildlife habitat protection, endangered forests identification and maintenance, riparian and water utility protection, indigenous peoples' rights, and the equitable sharing of benefits with forestry-dependent workers and communities. For example, the FSC advocates that all functions of a forest ecosystem remain intact after an area is logged. This requires that a mix of tree species of different ages still remains standing after the forest is logged and that the functions of trees and other plant species also remain intact.

Forest products given the seal of approval should give consumers confidence that the products they purchase are derived from responsibly managed forests. As of 2015, about one-third of Canada's forests were certified under one or more of the main certification systems listed in Figure 9.13. In 2015 the province of Nova Scotia committed to achieving FSC certification for all public lands in western Nova Scotia, following independent reports on logging practices. Currently, over 50 million hectares of land, across all forest types, is FSC certified in Canada.

More and more, Canadian companies are trying to meet international standards. One company operating mainly in the boreal forest of northeastern Ontario has earned the FSC logo for voluntarily meeting its high standards for forest management. Clear-cutting once dominated the 2-million-hectare forest managed by Tembec Inc., but today considerable patches of trees are left standing, large tracts of old-growth forest are being protected, and selections of all forest types are being set aside to serve as wildlife habitat. Tembec is a leader in environmental forestry and now has almost 10 million hectares of FSC-certified forest in Canada.

Tembec has demonstrated that it is possible to dramatically improve forest management practices to attain the coveted FSC logo. In a climate in which consumers are becoming more concerned about environmental and social issues surrounding primary resource extraction, securing a seal of approval from a highly rated certification program will become increasingly important.

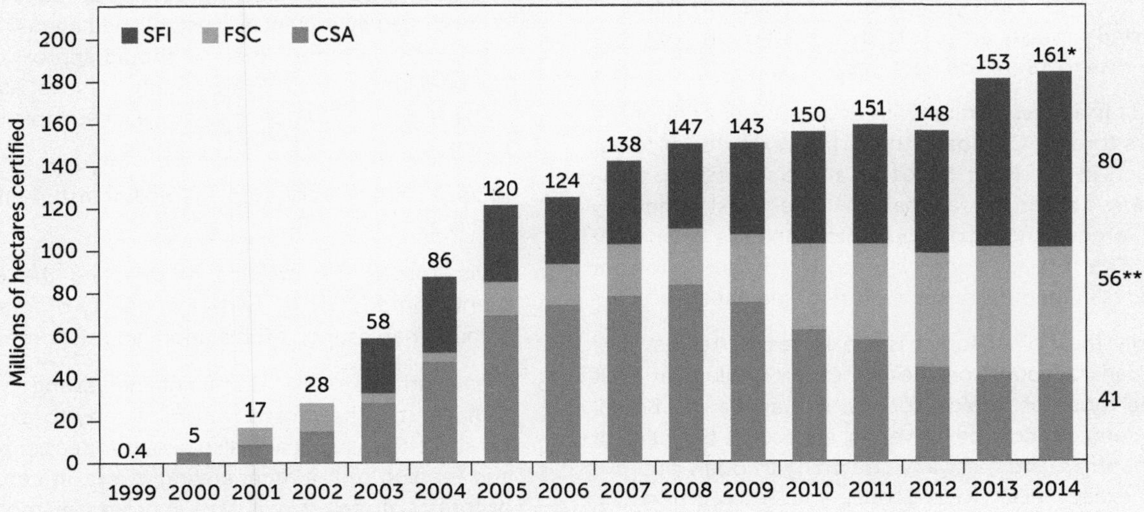

FIGURE 9.13 | Forestry certifications in Canada, 1999–2014.

Sources: Natural Resources Canada (2011: 34); Certification Canada (2014).

ENVIRONMENT IN FOCUS

BOX 9.12 | What You Can Do: Protecting the Health of Forests

A number of environmental stresses threaten the health of Canada's forests, but individuals can help.

1. Reduce your consumption of paper products. For example, use all available space on your paper (write in the margins and on both sides); carry fabric with you and use it instead of paper tissues, towels, and napkins; resist the temptation to print materials from the Internet—read online instead; insist that no unsolicited flyers be delivered to your home.
2. Recycle paper products and purchase recycled paper products.
3. Choose unbleached paper products whenever possible. Unbleached paper is less harmful to the environment, since it does not require the toxic chemicals used to whiten paper.
4. Purchase certified wood products. Make an effort to purchase wood that has been certified by at least one certification agency. This will help to ensure that the wood you purchase comes from a logging company that has introduced measures to promote long-term ecological, social, and economic sustainability.
5. Reduce the risk of human-caused fires. Many forest fires are started by human carelessness. Obey fire restrictions when visiting parks and protected areas, and do not discard fire accelerants (e.g., cigarettes) along highways.
6. Join one of the NGOs that support sustainable use of forest resources.
7. Write or phone your MP or provincial or territorial representative, and/or e-mail a letter to the editor of your local newspaper. Canadians own Canadian forests. If you are unhappy about how forests in your province or territory are being managed, voice or otherwise publicize your discontent.
8. Visit Global Forest Watch (http://www.globalforestwatch.org/) for live monitoring of global forest cover using the latest satellite technology and increase your awareness and involvement of global forest loss issues.

Summary

1. Some 40 per cent of the land surface of the Earth supports trees or shrubs. Four countries—Canada, Russia, the US, and Brazil—contain more than 50 per cent of the world's forests. Each year, about 13 million hectares of the world's forests are lost to deforestation In 2013, this figure rose to 18 million hectares.
2. Canada is a forest nation with about 10 per cent of the world's forests. Canada is the largest exporter of forest products in the world. In 2013, Canada's forests contributed $19.8 billion to national GDP. The forestry industry is the largest single contributor to Canada's balance of trade. The forests, along with the North, are dominant elements in the history and culture of the nation.
3. Globally the boreal forest is the largest terrestrial carbon "bank account" on the planet, with values at least double those of tropical forests. In Canada the Boreal is the largest ecozone, covering almost 58 per cent of the country's land mass and stretching through all provinces except PEI, Nova Scotia, and New Brunswick. Calculations suggest that Canada's boreal forest produces over $700 billion of ecosystem services every year. Currently Canada is the world leader in the fragmentation of intact forest landscapes. Most of this is occurring in the Boreal as a result of oil and gas exploration. The Boreal has the largest increase of any global ecozone in tree-cover loss from 2011 to 2013.
4. Ecosystems provide an array of beneficial services arising from ecological functions such as nutrient and water cycling, carbon sequestration, and waste decomposition. Forests are also places of exceptional scenic beauty, and millions of Canadians participate in nature-related recreational activities each year.
5. Forests are also a valuable source of commodities. Non-timber forest products contribute millions of dollars to the Canadian economy and are also an important aspect of Aboriginal peoples' subsistence economies. Despite government recognition that Canadian forests provide a broad range of values, forest management paradigms have traditionally focused on the management of forests to supply wood.
6. The provincial and territorial governments are responsible for 77 per cent of the nation's forests and the federal government for 16 per cent on behalf of the owners, the people of Canada. The remaining 7 per cent is owned privately. Governments enter into contract arrangements with private companies in which they can specify the forest management practices to be followed.
7. Approximately 143 million hectares are currently managed for timber production. On these lands, forest ecosystems are being transformed from relatively natural systems to control systems in which humans, not nature, influence the species that will grow there and the age to which they will grow.
8. The rate of conversion from natural to managed forest is controlled by provincially established annual allowable cuts (AACs). In theory, the AAC should approximate what the land should yield in perpetuity. It is not sustainable to have an AAC that consistently exceeds this biological potential.
9. In 2012 Canada harvested 148 million m^3 of timber. The AAC is 227 million m^3.
10. Silviculture is the practice of directing the establishment, composition, growth, and quality of forest stands through harvesting, reforestation, and site preparation.
11. Clear-cutting is the dominant harvesting system in Canada. It is the most economical way to extract fibre for short-term profit and also allows for easier replanting and tending of the regenerating forest. In certain types of forests, it may mimic natural processes more closely than selective or partial cutting systems. However, clear-cutting may not be the most appropriate way to harvest timber in some areas. Clear-cuts are aesthetically unappealing to many Canadians, and their environmental impact can be substantial.
12. Biocides are used in forestry to control populations of vegetation and insect species that compete with or eat commercial species. Several high-profile conflicts have arisen over application of chemicals. Concern over spraying to control the spruce budworm in the Maritime provinces is one of the most significant. The biological control agent *Bacillus thuringiensis* is increasingly being used against insect attacks in Canada.
13. Intensive forest management techniques are used to further enhance future timber resource values. Intensive silvicultural practices include pre-commercial thinning, commercial thinning, scarification, prescribed burning, pruning and shearing, and timber stand improvement. The long-term impacts of these activities are not well understood.
14. Fire suppression has resulted in ecological changes not characteristic of fire-dominated ecosystems, and has led to a gradual increase in the area burned over the past 30 years.
15. Various environmental impacts are associated with current forestry management systems, including changes to ecosystem, species, and genetic diversity; changes to biogeochemical and hydrological cycles; and soil erosion.
16. Timber harvesting can significantly alter species composition and abundance as the proportion of forest with old-growth characteristics is reduced. Species such as

the woodland caribou and marten that depend on old-growth characteristics decline in abundance. Other species, such as deer, may increase as regenerating cut areas produce more forage for them.

17. The spotted owl is perhaps the best-known example of the impact of logging on biodiversity. The spotted owl requires old-growth forests to maintain populations, but logging in BC's old-growth forests continues to threaten this endangered species, as does competition from the barred owl, which has now invaded the spotted owl habitat in many areas.

18. Forest harvesting removes nutrients from the site. The significance of this for future growth varies, depending on the nutrient capital of the site and type of harvesting system used. Sites with abundant capital and/or selective harvesting systems that leave branches behind will suffer less growth impairment of future generations than nutrient-poor sites or sites that are clear-cut with complete-tree removal.

19. Forest harvesting may also contribute to increased soil erosion and water flows.

20. Forests are a carbon sink. They take in carbon dioxide and convert it to wood, leaves, and roots. They are also a carbon source. They release stored carbon into the atmosphere when they decompose or burn. Because of this ability to both absorb and release huge amounts of carbon dioxide (a major greenhouse gas), forests play a major role in the global carbon cycle.

21. Canada's managed forests were a net carbon sink in 12 of the 23 years between 1990 and 2012. Annual amounts ranged from a large sink of 174 million tonnes of carbon dioxide equivalents (CO_2e) in 1992 to a large source of 171 million tonnes of CO_2e in 1995, mostly because of wildfires. In 2012 Canada's forests were a net emitter of carbon (33 million tonnes of CO_2).

22. Carbon sequestration was not considered in timber management in the past, but it might become a major influence on how we manage our forests. Hardwood stands in New Brunswick, for example, typically contain 10 to 20 per cent more carbon per hectare than a similar volume of softwoods of similar age. Forest managers might well change management practices in the future as global climate change becomes more severe and, therefore, grow multi-aged hardwood stands that promote carbon sequestration instead of the single-aged softwoods that now dominate thinking. The most effective way to sequester carbon in forests is not to cut down the trees in the first place.

23. Forests produce many values for Canadians. In the past, attention focused almost exclusively on the monetary returns from forest harvesting. However, as the amount of forest brought under management has increased and as the public becomes increasingly aware of the changes occurring in Canadian forests, more attention is being devoted to the assessment and management of other values besides timber production. An ecosystem perspective is being adopted.

24. Concern over the impact and sustainability of forest practices has given rise to calls for what has been termed "new forestry." Such an approach embraces an ecosystem and adaptive management perspective that seeks to mimic natural processes more closely and give greater attention to the full range of values from the forests.

25. Management of Canada's forests is directed by a National Forest Strategy, developed by provincial and territorial forest ministers and the Canadian minister of Natural Resources. The aim is to develop and implement more sustainable management practices. Independent reviews of the NFS have found many weaknesses. Despite this, Canada continues to boast of its international leadership in sustainable forest management.

26. Canada's Model Forest Program is one commitment arising from Canada's 1992–7 National Forest Strategy. Eleven model forest agreements were developed in six forest regions across the country, but the program was terminated in 2007. Core issues relate to ecosystem management, Aboriginal participation, public participation, science and innovation, and the integration of non-market values into decision-making.

27. Canada's Boreal Forest Agreement committed environmental groups and forestry companies to innovative approaches for managing 72 million hectares of Canadian boreal forest. The agreement aims to develop a strong, sustainable forest industry while better protecting ecosystems.

28. Internationally, the Convention on Biological Diversity commits signatories to prepare and adhere to a national biodiversity strategy, including the designation of representative samples of their forest lands as protected areas and ensuring that forest management does not impair biodiversity.

29. The United Nations Forum on Forests has agreed on four shared Global Objectives on Forests relating to reversing the loss of forest cover worldwide through sustainable forest management, enhancing forest-based economic, social, and environmental benefits, increasing the area of sustainably managed forests, and reversing the decline in official development assistance for sustainable forest management.

30. Certification of forest practices has become a more common practice both nationally and internationally. Certification is designed to enable consumers and participants to measure forest management practices against approved standards and also provides forest owners with an incentive to maintain and improve forest management practices.

Key Terms

annual allowable cut (AAC)
biocides
biodiversity
boreal forest
Boreal Shield
carbon sequestration
certification
chain-of-custody
clear-cutting
complete-tree harvesting
culmination age
DDT (dichlorodiphenyltrichloroethane)
ecosystem-based management
ecosystem services
falldown effect
forest tenure
full-tree harvesting
leaching
long-range sustained yield (LRSY)
new forestry
non-timber forest products (NTFPs)
nutrient capital
old-growth forests
pheromones
reclamation
REDD+
second growth
silviculture
sustained yield
tree-length harvesting
windthrow

Questions for Review and Critical Thinking

1. Outline some of the ways in which forests are important to Canada.
2. What is the Boreal and why is it so important nationally and internationally?
3. How is forestry an ecological process?
4. What is an AAC, what is the LRSY, and how do the two relate to each other?
5. Outline some of the advantages and disadvantages of clear-cutting.
6. Is Canada reforesting all lands that are harvested? What are some of the issues associated with current replanting schemes?
7. Outline some of the pros and cons of using chemical sprays to control insect infestations in Canada's forests.
8. List all the different values that society realizes from forests. What do you think the priorities should be among these different and sometimes conflicting uses?
9. Name some species that might increase in abundance as a result of forest harvesting and others that might decline. What are the characteristics of these species that would encourage this response?
10. What are the impacts of forest harvesting on site fertility, and how do they differ between sites?
11. What attributes of old-growth forests appear to explain their use by spotted owls?
12. What are the implications of global climate change for forest management in Canada?
13. How is forest management administered in Canada? What are the main strengths and weaknesses of this approach? What alternatives might you suggest? Do examples of such alternatives exist in your region?
14. What is "new forestry"?
15. What tools are used to evaluate the sustainability of Canadian forests? Are these tools adequate to the task?

Related Websites

A Vision for Canada's Forests, 2008 and Beyond
www.ccfm.org/pdf/Vision_EN.pdf

BC Ministry of Forests
www.for.gov.bc.ca/hfp/sof

Boreal Songbird Initiative
www.borealbirds.org

Canadian Boreal Forest Agreement
http://cbfa-efbc.ca/

Canadian Forest Service, State of Canada's Forests
cfs.nrcan.gc.ca/series/read/90

Canadian Institute of Forestry
www.cif-ifc.org

Canadian Model Forest Network
www.modelforest.net

Canadian Parks and Wilderness Society (CPAWS)
www.cpaws.org

Certification Canada
www.certificationcanada.org

David Suzuki Foundation: Forests
www.davidsuzuki.org/cgi-bin/mt1/mt-search.cgi?IncludeBlogs=14&tag=forests&limit=10

Food and Agriculture Organization of the United Nations: Global Forest Resource Assessment
www.fao.org/forest-resources-assessment/en

Forest Stewardship Council
www.fsccanada.org

Global Forest Watch Canada
www.globalforestwatch.ca

Government of Manitoba: Forestry Branch
www.gov.mb.ca/conservation/forestry/health/index.html

National Forest Information System
www.nfis.org/

National Forestry Database
http://nfdp.ccfm.org

National Forestry Database: Silvicultural Terms in Canada
http://nfdp.ccfm.org/terms/intro_e.php

Natural Resources Canada: Forestry in Canada
www.nrcan.gc.ca/forests/canada/13161

Non-Timber Forest Products Network of Canada
http://ntfpnetwork.ca/

Pacific Forestry Centre
cfs.nrcan.gc.ca/centres/read/pfc

Parks Canada: Species at Risk
www.pc.gc.ca/eng/nature/eep-sar/index.aspx

United Nations Forum on Forests
www.un.org/esa/forests/index.html

Wilderness Committee
www.wildernesscommittee.org

Further Readings

Note: This list comprises works relevant to the subject of the chapter but not cited in the text. All cited works are listed in the References at the end of the book.

Brandt, J.P., M.D. Flannigan, D.G. Maynard, I.D. Thompson, and W.J.A. Volney. 2013. "An introduction to Canada's boreal zone: Ecosystem processes, health, sustainability, and environmental issues," *Environmental Review* 21: 207–226.

Canadian Boreal Initiative. 2005. *The Boreal in the Balance: Securing the Future of Canada's Boreal Region*. Toronto: Canadian Boreal Initiative.

Cyr, D., et al. 2009. "Forest management is driving the eastern North American boreal forest outside its natural range of variability," *Frontiers in Ecology and the Environment* 7: 519–24.

Elgie, S., G.R. Mccarney, and W.L. Adamowicz. 2011. "Assessing the implications of a carbon market for boreal forest management," *Forestry Chronicle* 87, 3: 367–81.

Hanna, K. 2015. "The enduring importance of Canada's forest sector," in B. Mitchell, ed., *Resource and Environmental Management in Canada*, 5th edn. Don Mills, ON: Oxford University Press, 267–292.

McCarty, J. 2005. "Neoliberalism and the politics of alternatives: Community forestry in British Columbia and the United States," *Annals, Association of American Geographers* 96: 84–104.

Pimm, S.L., N. Roulet, and A. Weaver. 2009. "Boreal forests' carbon stores need better management," *Nature* 462: 276.

Rayner, J., and M. Howlett. 2007. "The National Forest Strategy in comparative perspective," *Forestry Chronicle* 83: 651–7.

Wulder, M.A., J.C. White, and N.C. Coops. 2011. "Fragmentation regimes of Canada's forests," *Canadian Geographer* 55: 288–300.

Go to www.oupcanada.com/DeardenMitchell5e to access additional learning tools on your smartphone, tablet, or PC.

CHAPTER TEN

Agriculture

Learning Objectives

- To understand the environmental and social impacts associated with the growth of agriculture
- To appreciate the global food situation and some of the factors that influence it
- To understand agriculture as an ecological process
- To understand the nature and importance of biofuels and some of their advantages and disadvantages
- To gain an understanding of the role of energy inputs in agriculture and the Green Revolution
- To realize the main trends in Canadian agriculture and Canada's contribution to the global food supply
- To know some of the main environmental implications of agriculture in Canada
- To appreciate the contributions of agriculture to global climate change
- To understand some of the main problems arising from the use of agricultural chemicals
- To analyze the implications of a diet with a high level of meat consumption
- To discover some of the changes needed to move toward more sustainable modes of agricultural production

Introduction

The food we grow and eat represents the most intimate interaction between humans and the natural world. Those of us lucky enough to have sufficient food will eat three or more times a day: consuming food and, along with it, all the energy, chemicals, and organisms that have gone into producing it. Like much of the world, our agricultural system has shifted dramatically over the past centuries, altering the way we produce, consume, and think about our food. Unfortunately, many people think about food all the time, because they are not getting enough. We tend to hear about large famines on the news and aid programs are often the result. However, for many people, lack of food is a day-to-day reality that they must face.

The origins of agriculture date back 9,000–11,000 years to a few regions where societies domesticated both plant and animal species. Through domestication, such desired traits as increased seed/fruit concentration and fleshiness, reduced or increased seed size, controlled seed dispersal, and improved taste could be achieved. Various agricultural practices—seedbeds, improved animal nutrition, and water management—also were devised. In turn, the increased availability of food, feed, and fibre provided the impetus for societies to prosper and support a larger non-farming population. Societies around the globe flourished by improving their capacity to expand agricultural production (Box 10.1).

The domestication of plants and animals continues today but under a much different set of social, economic, and environmental conditions than existed even a century ago. Agriculture is a dominant influence on the global landscape outside the major urban centres, if not the dominant influence. Three main kinds of agricultural land are generally distinguished by organizations such as the Food and Agriculture Organization of the United Nations (FAO, n.d.):

- **arable land** (13,812,040 km^2), occupied by crops that require annual replanting or fallowland or pasture used for such crops within any five-year period
- **permanent cropland** (1,484,087 km^2), where crops (such as coffee, tea, fruit) do not require annual replanting
- **permanent pastures** (33,556,943 km^2), which are used primarily for grazing livestock

The area included in each category is shown in parentheses, totalling to one-third of the land area of the world. As can be seen, considerably more of the world is dedicated to pasture land than to crop land. Canada ranks seventh in the world in terms of amount of arable land (Statistics Canada, 2014a).

Historically, agricultural output has been increased by bringing more land into production. However, the opportunity for further geographic expansion of cropland is small because of the comparatively limited amount of land well suited for crop production, the increasingly concentrated patterns of human settlement, and growing competition from other land uses. Global climate change will increase the area suitable for

ENVIRONMENT IN FOCUS

BOX 10.1 | Social Implications of the Development of Agriculture

- Agriculture has had a profound influence on society, which in turn has further implications for ecosystems.
- More reliable food supplies permitted growth in populations.
- A sedentary life became more possible as a result of these food supplies and the ability to store food; this allowed the establishment of larger, permanent settlements.
- Permanent settlements allowed greater accumulation of material goods than was possible in a nomadic lifestyle.
- Agriculture allowed food surpluses to be generated so that not all individuals or families had to be involved in the food-generating process and specialization of tasks became more clearly defined. One result is that only some 4 per cent of Canada's population is directly involved in food production today, permitting the rest of the population to direct their energies to other tasks, historically, the processing of raw materials into manufactured goods, thereby increasing the speed of flow-through of matter and energy in society. As indicated in Chapter 4, this high rate of throughput is at the core of many current environmental problems.
- The creation of food surpluses and more material goods promoted increasing trade between the now sedentary settlements. This led to the development of road and later rail connections to facilitate the rapid transport of materials, involving the consumption of large amounts of energy.
- Land and water resources became more important, leading to increased conflict between societies for control over agricultural lands.
- Aggregation of large numbers of people together in sedentary settlements also served to concentrate waste products in quantities over and above those that could be readily assimilated by the natural environment. Today we call this pollution.

Philip Dearden

Stone cities such as Machu Picchu in Peru could not have been built without the surplus labour created through the development of agriculture.

© AP Photo/Jerome Delay/CP

Children play in the United Nations High Commissioner for Refugees Ifo extension camp in eastern Kenya. In summer 2011, the camp registered more than 1,000 newcomers a day: refugees displaced by the drought in the Horn of Africa, which triggered the worst famine the region had seen in a generation.

agricultural production in some countries, especially in northern latitudes, but also lead to declines elsewhere, particularly in the tropics where future food demand will be the highest. South America may lose anywhere from 1 per cent to 21 per cent of its arable land area, Africa 1–18 per cent, Europe 1–17 per cent, and India 2–4 per cent (Zhang and Cai, 2011).

The intensification of production—obtaining more output from a given area of agricultural land—is hence a key development strategy. World grain production has tripled since 1961, as farmers harvest more grain from each hectare (Figure 10.1). On average, humans get about 48 per cent of their calories from grains, a share that has declined just slightly, from 50 per cent, over the past four decades. Grains, particularly corn, in conjunction with soybeans, also form the primary feedstock for industrial livestock production. Global grain stocks in 2015 were projected to reach a record high (Figure 10.2).

However, future capacity to deliver agricultural outputs also depends on the continuing ecological viability of agro-ecosystems and the increase in intensification associated with the **Green Revolution**. The Green Revolution includes a number of approaches to increase the productivity of agricultural lands with emphasis on hybridization and use of auxiliary energy flows in the form of fertilizer, both of which are discussed in more detail later in the chapter. However, the Green Revolution also carries with it a number of significant long-term negative environmental impacts that will ultimately lead to long-term productivity losses. Despite past successes, affordably feeding the current world population—and the more than 80 million people per annum by which that population will continue to grow over the next 20 years—remains a formidable challenge (Box 10.2). Many regions will face difficulties in meeting the growing demand for agricultural products while also preserving the productive capacity of their agro-ecosystems as discussed in the "International Guest Statement" in this chapter. Global climate change will be an additional stress. In more than 40 developing countries, mainly in sub-Saharan Africa, cereal yields are expected to decline, with mean losses of 15 per cent by 2080 (Fischer et al., 2005). Grain yields are likely to decline by 10 per cent for every 1°C increase over 30 years. Increased carbon dioxide and higher temperatures may promote lush growth, but they are deadly at the pollination stage, reducing some yields by 30 per cent. The International Rice Research Institute has found that the fertility of rice flowers falls from 100 per cent at 34°C to virtually zero at 40°C (Sanchez, 2001). In addition, warm, wet weather promotes diseases such as blight, and pests survive warmer winters, meaning that longer growing seasons lead to an increased incidence of pest attacks. There is now strong scientific consensus that the aggregate effects of climate change are going to be strongly negative on global grain supply, with impacts being felt in the next couple of decades, but most strongly in the latter part of the century and in tropical countries (Challinor et al., 2014).

World agricultural GDP is expected to fall by an average of 16 per cent as a result of climate change. However, these impacts are not evenly distributed, with a 20 per cent decline in less developed countries compared to a 6 per cent decline in industrial countries (Cline, 2007). Agricultural prices also will be affected, with price increases of up to 40 per cent expected if temperature increases more than 3°C (Easterling et al., 2007). Distribution will remain a major problem. For example, output per person for grain varies dramatically by region, standing at roughly 1,230 kilograms per year in the United States, most of which is fed to livestock, compared to 325 kilograms in China and just 90 kilograms in Zimbabwe.

Philip Dearden

Intensification has resulted in a doubling of grain production over the last 40 years. One of the main goals has been to increase the amount of grain produced per plant, as with these short-statured rice plants in the middle Himalayan region.

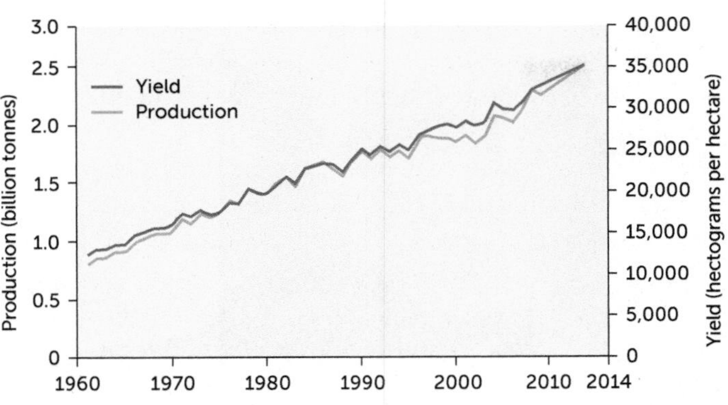

FIGURE 10.1 | World grain production and yield, 1961–2014.

Source: Adapted using data from Worldwatch Institute (2011: 56). Data from 2014: http://faostat3.fao.org.

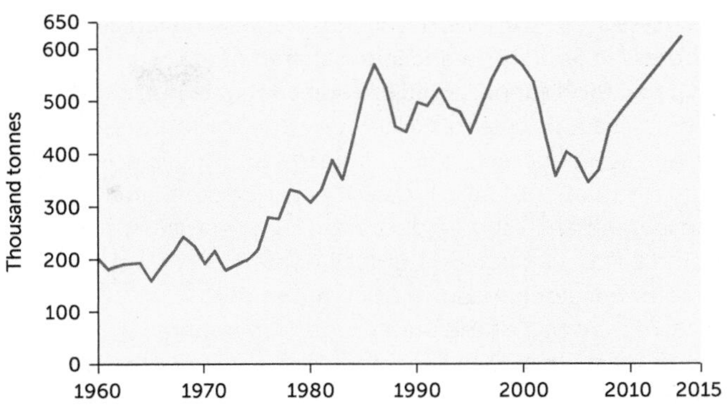

FIGURE 10.2 | World grain stocks, 1960–2015.

Source: Adapted using data from Worldwatch Institute (2011: 56). Data from 2014: http://faostat3.fao.org.

The very large subsidies involved in global agriculture are a major confounding factor in examining food production capabilities. Industrial nations collectively pay their farmers more than $300 billion each year in subsidies, and this amount goes to the largest farmers in the richest countries, promotes chemical dependencies, inhibits change, and discriminates against producers in less developed countries. However, in 2008, World Trade Organization members agreed to significant commitments. One obliges the European Union to eliminate agricultural subsidies, but a time frame was not set, and France's agriculture minister estimated that European export subsidies might not be finally eliminated until 2015 or 2017.

As the world becomes more crowded and as pressures on biological systems and global biogeochemical cycles mount (Chapter 3), it is no longer sufficient to ask whether we can feed

ENVIRONMENT IN FOCUS

BOX 10.2 | Hunger

Agriculture provides approximately 94 per cent of the protein and 99 per cent of the calories consumed by humans. On average, people need about 2,500 calories per day, although this amount varies from person to person depending on weight, age, level of activity, and other factors. For example, an adult woman normally needs about 2,000 calories per day, while an adult male needs 2,500 to 2,800 per day. Young children usually need less than 2,000 calories each day. North American and European adults on average consume 3,400 calories per day. Conversely, over 1 billion adults consume under 1,800 calories, and are classified as chronically hungry. Calories come mainly from carbohydrates, such as potatoes and rice, but to remain healthy, humans also need protein, vitamins, fatty acids, and minerals. Fatty acids are essential for hormonal control, and minerals are necessary for bone formation and growth.

People are considered undernourished if their caloric intake is less than 90 per cent of the recommended level for their size and level of activity. When people meet only 80 per cent of their recommended caloric intake requirement, they are considered severely undernourished. Malnourished people have adequate caloric intake but are deficient in other requirements. Protein deficiencies in children are obvious in their pot-bellied, skinny-limbed, and undersized appearance. TV news coverage of famines, mainly in Africa, have made such images very familiar to us. Vitamin deficiencies lead to many diseases, depending on the vitamin that is lacking. The deficiency can be fatal, such as the vitamin B deficiency that causes beriberi disease. Other effects include blindness, loss of hair and teeth, and bow-leggedness. Malnourishment also increases susceptibility to other diseases. Vitamin A deficiency, for example, impairs the immune system and is a significant contributor to the 1.5 million deaths from diarrhea each year. Over 3 billion people, about 40 per cent of the world's population, suffer some from some form of micronutrient deficiency.

The effects of malnutrition cross generations as well. Infants of malnourished, underweight women are likely to be small at birth and more susceptible to disease and death. Overall, 60 per cent of women of child-bearing age in South Asia, where half of all children are underweight, are themselves underweight. In Southeast Asia, the proportion of underweight women is 45 per cent, in sub-Saharan Africa, 20 per cent. Globally, the proportion of underweight children under five declined by one-fifth over the period 2009–2013. However, if current trends continue, the Millennium Development Goals target of halving the proportion of underweight children will

Continued

be missed by 30 million children, largely because of slow progress in South Asia and sub-Saharan Africa.

Global food supply could provide adequate nutrition for the entire global population. However, 805 million people were chronically undernourished in 2012–14. This is a reduction of more than 100 million over the last decade, and 209 million lower than in 1990–92. Undernourishment has also fallen from 18.7 to 11.3 per cent globally, and from 23.4 to 13.5 per cent for developing countries in this period.

More than half of the undernourished people (65 per cent) live in Asia, while sub-Saharan Africa accounts for almost a quarter (24 per cent). However, sub-Saharan Africa has the highest prevalence of hunger—one in four people are malnourished. Hunger is most pronounced where there are natural disasters and where warfare is ongoing. Every year, more than 3 million children die as a result of starvation. In stark contrast, the World Health Organization (WHO) reports that more than 300 million people are clinically classified as obese, and about half a million people die from obesity-related diseases every year. Obesity rates have tripled since 1980. The gross inequity between starvation and obesity rates suggests that hunger is a problem of distribution. Regardless of increasing global production levels, rising food prices and heavy agriculture subsidies result in food remaining inaccessible to many of the world's poorest people.

The 1974 World Food Summit promised to eradicate hunger within the next decade. The 1996 summit was a little more realistic and promised to cut the number of hungry people in half by 2015. The United Nations Millennium Development Goals aimed to cut the proportion of hungry people in half by 2015. The FAO was optimistic that this goal would be reached, and 63 countries below that level in 1992 have already surpassed this target (FAO, 2015), with greatest progress in Latin America and the Caribbean. African, Latin American, and Caribbean heads of state made commitments in 2014 to make their regions hunger free by 2015. World population is expected to increase from 7.2 billion in 2014 to 9.6 billion in 2050, as already discussed in Chapter 1. Almost all growth (97 per cent) is projected to occur in the less developed regions, where a large majority of the world's people live today. This will pose significant challenges for global food production systems. In many countries, more than half of family income goes to food, and with a doubling of food prices, people will have few options.

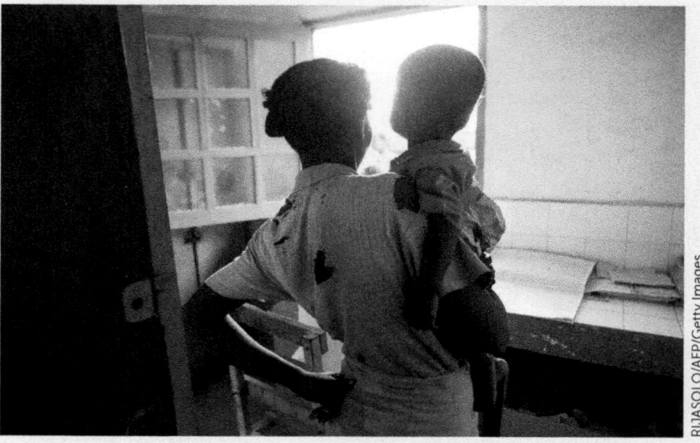
RIJASOLO/AFP/Getty Images

Despite the progress in reducing global levels of malnourishment, hunger continues to be a daily reality for many of the world's children, often as a result of wars or natural disasters. Here an undernourished 15-month-old baby and his mother wait for medications at a local health centre in southern Madagascar. An exceptional drought in 2015 destroyed crops in the region and left as many as 200,000 people—including 40,000 children—close to starvation.

No single solution can address the challenge of increasing the quantity and quality of affordable foods. The solution will involve a variety of approaches, including exploration of new marine and terrestrial food sources; continued research to increase yields of existing crops; improvements in the efficiency of natural resource use; family planning programs aimed at reducing population growth rates; elimination of global agricultural tariffs; more efficient food distribution systems to address chronic hunger; and a moderation in demand on the part of the already overfed countries.

Sources: FAO (2015); von Braun (2007); Pappas (2011); *Science Daily* (2011).

the planet. We need to ask ourselves more difficult questions. Can the world's agro-ecosystems feed today's planet and remain sufficiently resilient to feed tomorrow's hungrier planet? Will intensive production systems cause some agro-ecosystems to break down irreversibly? Presuming we can maintain current food production, are we paying too high a price in terms of the broader environmental effects of agriculture?

In answer to these questions, researchers using remote sensing and computer model techniques (Foley et al., 2011) have suggested the following steps to feed the global population, while still maintaining ecosystems:

- Halt farmland expansion, especially in the tropical rain forests, through development of incentives such as ecotourism and payment for ecosystem services
- Close yield gaps where land is not meeting its potential agricultural productivity through improved use of existing crop varieties, better management, and improved genetics
- Use inputs such as water, nutrients, and agricultural chemicals more effectively
- Shift diets to de-emphasize meat production and dedicate more lands to direct human food production
- Reduce waste, as one-third of the food produced ends up discarded, spoiled, or eaten by pests

As with many environmental challenges, we have a good idea about what needs to happen; the difficulty is designing appropriate management systems to ensure that it does happen. This is a good reminder of the importance of the ideas in Chapters 5 and 6. Agriculture is fundamentally an ecological

INTERNATIONAL GUEST STATEMENT

Life at the Crossroads for African Pastoralists: How Climate Change Threatens the Existence of the Maasai | *Philip Osano*

Pastoralism is a major livelihood system in the arid and semi-arid lands of the African continent. Recent estimates indicate that pastoral farming occupies an area of 3.66 million km^2, more or less equally distributed over the Sahel, the Horn of Africa, and southern Africa, and together contains 37.5 million cattle.

Drought, disease, and violence are major risks to pastoral communities. Drought in particular has become extremely prevalent in the Horn of Africa region and the Sahel, devastating pastoral livelihoods in multiple ways—it reduces milk production, halts herd growth, and leads to large livestock losses—and its effect lingers on after the rains recover. As an example, from 2008 to 2009, a devastating drought hit areas inhabited by Kenya's Maasai pastoralist community, destroying three-quarters of their cattle and two-thirds of their small stock—mainly sheep and goats. The drought was the worst the Maasai had experienced in decades, despite the fact that it followed recurrent droughts brought about by climate change.

The Maasai are pastoralists that live in the arid and semi-arid land areas (ASALs) in the southern part of Kenya and northern Tanzania, which are characterized by low and erratic rainfall with high evaporation rates, and limited soil moisture—conditions that render the drylands fragile and unsuitable for rain-fed agriculture. In this tenuous ecosystem, pastoralism is the most suitable form of land use and livestock forms the principal source of livelihood for the Maasai; an estimated 75 per cent of the total household income among the Maasai is generated from livestock.

Although the Maasai have a reputation of rigid adherence to their traditional means of living, in recent years, myriad changes in land tenure, land-use intensification, sedentarization, institutional changes, and climate change have forced the Maasai to abandon their old ways. Thus the majority of Maasai households are increasingly adopting agro-pastoralism, or shifting from natural resource–based livelihoods to non-farm activities, which often involve relocation to cities.

Two major factors are fuelling the transformation of the pastoral livelihoods of the Maasai: fragmentation of once-intact grasslands that reduce the scale of the pastoral landscape; and climate change, which is increasing the variability and frequency of rainfall perturbations in drylands. Climate change has been particularly devastating to the Maasai because of the negative effects of recurrent drought, leading to increased food insecurity, starvation, and poverty.

Climate change is expected to occur at a faster rate, culminating in new weather patterns that are likely to result in increased suffering among the Maasai. It is anticipated they will be affected in several ways: climate change variability will induce droughts that will disrupt the traditional seasonal migration of herders, livestock, and wildlife to critical water and nutrient resource points. The disruption of livestock and wildlife migration patterns will constrain the space for co-existence between humans and wildlife, as competition for scarce resources increases. As this competition intensifies, the possibility of violent conflicts between herders and farmers will also likely increase. More frequent droughts and floods will also limit capacities to diversify into crop farming because of increased risk of crop failure. Floods will also limit abilities to relocate to other areas.

Similarly, negative factors induced by climate change, such as drought, erratic rainfall, and lack of access to watering points, will result in poor nutrition for livestock because the quality and quantity of grass the animals feed on will be compromised. As well, climate change–induced conditions will worsen the severity and distribution of livestock diseases and pests.

The challenge of climate change and other drivers of change affecting the Maasai, are manifested at a larger scale across pastoral systems in Africa, and have resulted in several policy actions at national and regional levels. In 2013, the African Union responded to these challenges by developing a continental policy framework for pastoralism in Africa, which, among other measures, seeks to promote risk management rather than the short-term emergency response that has been the dominant approach to drought in pastoral areas.

Philip Dearden

Climate change in southern Kenya is creating drought, erratic rainfall, and restricted access to watering points, and places pressure on the land and livestock that are critical for the traditional pastoralist ways of the Maasai people.

Continued

A key focus of interventions to address drought and related risks affecting pastoralists has been to improve resilience of their livelihood and production systems in the ASALs. In the Horn of Africa, the Intergovernmental Authority on Development (IGAD) has developed a regional framework—the IGAD Drought Disaster Resilience and Sustainability Initiative (IDDRSI)—which aims at addressing the effects of drought and related shocks in the region in a sustainable and holistic manner. IDDRSI identifies seven priority intervention areas where the necessary investment and action will help build resilience through reducing the vulnerability of target pastoral communities to climatic and economic shocks. These areas include actions to ensure equitable access and sustainable use of natural resources, while improving environmental management and improving disaster risk-management capabilities and preparedness for effective response.

Some of the ongoing, more innovative interventions that can strengthen resilience of pastoral livelihood and production systems include payments for ecosystem services (PES), which is a practice of giving incentives to pastoralists in exchange for administering their land for some ecological service that promotes conservation. Typically, pastoralists who participate in a PES scheme for example, may voluntarily agree not to cultivate, fence, or subdivide their land in return for a fee paid directly to them, so that they can keep the land open for livestock and wildlife grazing. A section of the land can be reserved as a conservancy grass bank, an area of natural grassland that pastoralists agree to set aside for the benefit of wildlife and as a safety net during periods of drought. The provision of insurance to pastoral communities, most of whom lack access to insurance services despite the vulnerability posed by climate change to their livestock is another promising intervention. Index-based livestock insurance, for example, is being implemented in northern Kenya and southern Ethiopia in partnership with private industry and covers periodic drought that dries up the natural rangeland vegetation, leading to livestock mortality. Insurance payouts are made to herders who have bought annual insurance contracts.

There is no doubt that the dynamic pastoral ecosystems will be changing as a result of climate change, and now is the time to start implementing strategies that will lead to resilient livelihoods for the people in the future.

Courtesy Philip Osano

Philip Osano is a research fellow at the Stockholm Environment Institute (SEI) Africa Center and a non-resident fellow at the Africa Center for Technology Studies (ACTS). He graduated from McGill University, Canada, with a PhD in geography in 2013. He has conducted research on the impact of payments for ecosystem services (PES) on poverty among pastoral communities in East Africa's drylands.

Source: Based on an article first published in 2011 by the Africa Initiative (AI) and The Centre for International Governance Innovation (CIGI) on the Africa Portal (www.africaportal.org). Reproduced here with permission of the author, AI, and CIGI.

process as solar radiation is converted through one or more transformations into human food supplies. Rapid growth in human population has entailed increasing disruption of natural systems in order to feed burgeoning populations and, particularly in developed countries, growing appetites. The next section provides some context for this ecological process and the development of modern farming systems before considering some of the environmental challenges facing global and Canadian agriculture.

Agriculture as an Ecological Process

Agriculture is a food chain, with humans as the ultimate consumers. Energy flows through this food chain in a manner similar to the way it does in natural food chains. Thus, the second law of thermodynamics is also important to agricultural food chains—the longer the food chain, the greater the energy loss (Chapter 2). This fact is one of the arguments for a vegetarian diet. By eating at the lowest level on the food chain as herbivores, humans will maximize the amount of usable energy in the food system. There are, however, other aspects of food production at higher levels of the food chain that should also be considered.

Food meets more than energy requirements alone. Important protein and mineral demands must also be satisfied. Animal products, by and large, are the main suppliers of these proteins and minerals, including such elements as calcium and phosphorus. Areas currently used as rangeland to support animal production often cannot be used as cropland. They may be too dry or otherwise ecologically marginal, and severe problems, such as excessive soil erosion, may have arisen in the past when humans tried to bring such lands under cultivation. Thus, it is not always correct to presume that rangelands could produce more food under tillage. Furthermore, grazing animals in many parts of the world provide not only food supplies but also other products and services, such as their energy as draft animals and their hides and other animal parts for clothing.

However, there are many valid arguments from an ecological, health, moral, and spiritual point of view for reducing meat consumption in favour of a diet with a higher vegetable content, especially in industrialized nations. For instance, while Canada's Food Guide recommends that the average adult consume 54 kilograms of protein per year (including meat, fish, nuts, and seeds, as well as the protein acquired from plant products), Canadians consume 90 kilograms of meat per capita each year (Statistics Canada, 2010). Meat consumption still varies widely by region and socio-economic status. For instance, in the developing world, people eat about 32 kilograms of meat per year, compared to an average of 85 kilograms per person in the industrial world.

Researchers have calculated that about 40 per cent of global crop calories are used as livestock feed, and this will rise to 48–55 per cent by 2050. On average, about 4 kilocalories of crop products are used to generate 1 kilocalorie of animal products, although it can rise as high as 10 kilocalories. If global diet trends continue, the demand for global livestock feed will double by 2050 (Pradhan et al., 2013).

The domestication of plants and animals thousands of years ago led to profound changes to the global land base. Complex natural systems that once dominated the landscape have been replaced by relatively simple control systems in which humans are in command of the species and numbers that exist in a given area. However, unlike the process that took place during the Industrial Revolution, these changes occurred over an extended time period, allowing greater potential for adaptation. Furthermore, until the past 150 years or so, energy inputs were largely limited to photosynthetic energy from the sun, the energy of domesticated draft animals such as oxen, camels, and horses, and human energy input. It was not until the Industrial Revolution unlocked past deposits of photosynthetic energy in the form of coal and later oil that industrial agriculture began and energy inputs and environmental impacts increased dramatically. Indeed, only during the latter half of the twentieth century did some of the most damaging impacts of agriculture come into play.

One of the most significant impacts is in the concentration of greenhouse gases (GHGs) in the atmosphere. Research on atmospheric trace gas concentrations has revealed that even early agriculture had a significant impact (Ruddiman, 2003). An increase in atmospheric carbon dioxide (CO_2) concentration of 20 to 25 parts per million between 8,000 and 2,000 years ago appears to be related to increased forest clearing for agriculture. About 5,000 years ago, there was an increase of 250 parts per billion in atmospheric methane (CH_4) concentration, coinciding with the adoption of "wet rice" farming in Asia. These changes demonstrate that even with low populations, small changes over long periods can be as important as large changes caused by high populations over a short time.

Since cropland cultivation began in Canada, an estimated 1 billion tonnes of soil organic carbon has been lost. Early cultivation would have removed most of it, and further losses continued as a result of intensive tillage, biomass burning, and removal of residues. Canada also has extensive grasslands, much of which is used for seasonal grazing. If pastures are overgrazed, they store less carbon. Paradoxically, grazing stimulates growth up to a point; grazing that does not reach that threshold can shorten vegetative growth, producing the same effect as overgrazing. Since cultivation began, up to 30 per cent of the carbon originally present in the surface soil layer has been lost. However, the rate of loss appears to be falling because of smaller amounts of land being converted into cropland, decreases in summer fallow, increases in no-till farming, and increased fertilizer use in the Prairie provinces (Hengeveld et al., 2008).

Horse power is one form of auxiliary energy used in agricultural production, but the environmental impacts of this system of plowing with horses in British Columbia are much less than those resulting from the fossil-fuelled, mechanical processes favoured by most Canadian farmers.

Of course, CO_2 is not the only GHG affected by land-use change (Chapter 7). Fertilizers have a significant impact, as discussed in Chapter 4, as do the decomposition of crop residues and soil organic matter and the transport of nitrogen off-farm through leaching, runoff, and evaporation. Livestock is also a significant source, particularly of CH_4 and nitrous oxide (N_2O). Up to 10 per cent of feed energy is lost in ruminant animals through belching and other gaseous contributions, and additional amounts come from manure. The agricultural contribution of these gases has been increasing, and by 2005 the sector accounted for 66 per cent of Canada's N_2O emissions and 25 per cent of CH_4 emissions (Desjardins et al., 2008). Of this, 33 per cent is emitted from Alberta. These changes are driven mainly by increases in livestock numbers, discussed later in the chapter. In total, agriculture accounted for 10 per cent of Canada's GHGs by 2012 (Environment Canada, 2013b).

Perspectives on the Environment

Demitarianism

When we've seen people urged to be vegetarians I've personally seen that that can lead to a backlash because many people want to eat meat. From the environmental point of view, it's not about whether you eat meat or dairy, it's about how much.

—Professor Mark Sutton, a demitarian, quoted in *The Guardian*, 2 May 2014

Given the environmental significance of the rapidly increasing amount of reactive nitrogen from human activities, as discussed in Chapter 4, the European Union has been studying the sources of nitrogen. Agriculture is a main source, representing around 80 per cent of reactive nitrogen emissions from all sources to the EU environment. These losses occur in the form of ammonia to the air, of nitrate to ground and surface waters, and of the powerful greenhouse gas nitrous oxide (see Chapter 7). There are large differences between agricultural products in the amount of nitrogen lost, with livestock accounting for 79–88 per cent of the total (Leip et al., 2013). Compared with cereals, beef produces roughly 25 times the amount of nitrogen per unit of food protein, and for pig and poultry meat, eggs, and dairy, the losses are 3.5 to 8 times those from cereal. Countries with high meat intakes per capita also have a much larger nitrogen footprint per capita. Given that current protein intake in the EU is 70 per cent higher than World Health Organization recommendations, there is clearly room to reduce global impacts and also improve personal health by moving to a less meat-intensive diet (Westhoek et al., 2014). Many people may find this an easier transition than becoming pure vegetarian, and **demitarians** aim to reduce their consumption of meat and dairy products by half.

Opportunities to reduce the contributions of agriculture to global warming are many, but an obvious one is to reduce the numbers of livestock by eating less meat. Carbon sequestration in soils can be improved through such measures as no-tillage cultivation and reducing summer fallow, as discussed later in the chapter. Planting perennial crops such as trees also helps. On grasslands, grazing intensity can be reduced and productivity increased by adding nutrients and water. However, fertilizer has to be applied more precisely than in the past to ensure that the amounts added are taken up by the crops and will not denitrify into N_2O.

The complexity of finding the optimum solution for reducing GHG emissions from agriculture is illustrated by the fact that where soils are fine and it is relatively humid, such as in eastern Canada, no-tillage agriculture may result in increased N_2O emissions as a result of higher surface temperatures (Rochette et al., 2008). However, reducing no-tillage agriculture conflicts with the desire to maintain soil carbon levels through no-tillage systems. On the Prairies, because of the drier environment and heavier soils, no-tillage is a very appropriate way to reduce overall GHG emissions from agriculture. Solutions obviously have to take such geographical differences into account.

Modern Farming Systems in the Industrialized World

The Green Revolution

Dramatic changes in food production systems have occurred through a variety of technological advances that were in turn influenced by changes in demographics (e.g., increases in population densities), social structure (e.g., urbanization, social stratification), and economic conditions (e.g., global trade). Early food production systems were small scale and were largely dictated by fixed environmental conditions—the quantity and quality of food produced depended heavily on existing local climatic conditions (e.g., annual rainfall), native vegetation (i.e., plants indigenous to the region), and availability of human and/or animal labour. Soil fertility was maintained or enhanced by using locally available, natural elements such as manure, bones, and ashes.

Today, local conditions are manipulated to improve both the quantity and quality of outputs. The amount of food produced per unit of land has increased dramatically as a result of a variety of technological advances, including **hybridization**, genetic engineering, greater mechanization (e.g., tractors for plowing and seed sowing, mechanized food processing), and the creation of auxiliary energy flows, as discussed in Chapter 2. The package of inputs or agricultural techniques, which together are referred to as the Green Revolution, includes the introduction of higher-yield seeds (e.g., shorter maturation, drought resistance) and a reliance on auxiliary energy flows.

The development and commercialization of higher-yielding seeds through hybridization led to significant gains in grain yields throughout the world. In the 1940s, scientists developed a "miracle wheat seed" that matured faster, producing wheat that was shorter and stiffer than traditional breeds and less sensitive to variation of daylight. India more than doubled its wheat production in five years with the new technology, and other Asian and Latin American countries recorded similar productivity increases. Miracle rice seeds and high-yield maize (corn) were developed by scientists soon afterwards, and their use has diffused rapidly around the world.

Were it not for these developments, there would no doubt be many more people in the world suffering chronic food shortages. However, they also pose challenges. Most of the new hybrid seeds grew better than their native counterparts only if fertilizers and **biocides** were applied with sufficient frequency and in sufficient quantity. As these chemicals became more expensive, many poorer farmers were unable to take advantage of the high-yield seeds. The Green Revolution also encouraged a narrowing of the genetic base of the crop, and with each farmer growing exactly the same strain, any disease or pest that managed to adapt to the strain had an almost unlimited food supply.

Today, critics of the Green Revolution point to stagnation in scientific progress—the gains that can be made through technology have already been made, and the damage done to agro-ecosystems by modern production systems will limit the ability of farmers to increase yields significantly. For example, macronutrients in the soil, such as nitrogen, phosphorus, and potassium, can be replenished by fertilizers, but many of the micronutrients required in trace amounts cannot be replaced. As we take out more crops from the soil, these nutrients may become exhausted, leading to greatly diminished returns in the future. Signs of such declines are already appearing in some areas. The increasing cost of fossil fuels also leads to increasing fertilizer costs.

However, some advances are still being made. In 2001, for example, a new rice strain, called NERICA, was produced from hybridization of African and Asian rice varieties. According to the United Nations Development Programme (UNDP), the project's main supporter, NERICA produces 50 per cent more yield, uses less fertilizer, is richer in protein, and is more resistant to drought, disease, and pests. It was also developed in full consultation with farmers and consumers and is now being successfully grown in a wide range of African countries. In Guinea, thanks to the success of NERICA varieties, farmers are now able to gross US$65 per hectare with minimal inputs and $145 per hectare with a moderate level of inputs. The country saved more than US$13 million on rice imports in 2003. NERICA is now being used as a "success story" for the Millennium Development Goals (see http://www.mdgmonitor.org/goal1-eradicate-poverty-hunger/). However, there are also serious counter claims that the benefits have been exaggerated by agribusiness (for example, see http://www.grain.org/article/entries/111-nerica-another-trap-for-small-farmers-in-africa).

The development of these "miracle seeds" relied only on genetic combinations found in nature. The development of **genetically modified organisms (GMOs)**, on the other hand, involves combining genes from different and often totally unrelated species. Such genetic manipulation is now a multi-billion dollar industry, and Canada is one of the world's leading participants (Box 10.3).

The reliance on large auxiliary energy flows in modern industrialized agricultural systems is one of the main differences between natural and agro-ecosystems. Auxiliary energy flows include natural and chemical fertilizers, biocides (insecticides, herbicides, fungicides), fossil fuels, and irrigation systems. These energy subsidies have significantly increased crop yields over the past century, particularly over the past three decades. **Subsistence farming**, in which the production of food is intended to satisfy the needs of the farm household, relies on natural energy supplies and may produce 10 food units for every unit of energy invested. However, in the most energy-intensive food systems, such as those in Canada and the US, 10 times as much energy on average needs to be invested through auxiliary energy flows for every unit of food produced.

Improved water management, a key component in Green Revolution technologies, helped to boost worldwide productivity or output of "crops per drop" by an estimated 100 per cent since 1960 (FAO, 2003). Agriculture accounts for 70 per cent of fresh water withdrawn from natural sources for human use and as much as 90 per cent in many developing countries. The water needs of humans and animals are relatively small—the average human drinks about four litres a day. But producing the same person's daily food can take up to 5,000 litres of water. For example, it takes 1,000 tonnes of water to produce one tonne of grain. When countries import a tonne of grain, they are also importing 1,000 tonnes of water. This is the important concept of **virtual water**, discussed in more detail in Chapter 11.

Although agriculture is not Canada's largest user of water in terms of withdrawals, it is its largest consumer. Withdrawal is the amount of water removed from a source for a particular use. Consumption is the difference between the withdrawal and the amount returned to the source. Agriculture removes significant quantities of water from the landscape, tying it up in agricultural products or evaporating it back into the air rather than returning it directly to streams or groundwater; therefore, consumption is high. Agriculture relies on a reliable supply of good-quality water for growing crops, raising livestock, and cleaning farm buildings. Approximately 75 per cent of all agricultural water withdrawals in Canada occur in the semi-arid prairie region. More than 780,000

Philip Dearden

Philip Dearden

This deep well on the northern edge of the Sahara produces enough water for mixed crops when used wisely

ENVIRONMENT IN FOCUS

BOX 10.3 | Genetically Modified Organisms

Yields of many crops in the developed world will not increase significantly with conventional agricultural techniques, even those related to the Green Revolution. Instead, farmers are turning to biotechnology, or the genetic modification of crops, to increase production. The technology already dominates the production of a few crops in several countries, yet other countries ban its use. Some nations require labelling of foods that have been genetically modified, while others, such as Canada, have rejected this openness. Why are there such differences in approach toward this new "genetic revolution"? Before we answer that question, it is necessary to explain what GMOs entail.

Advances in understanding of DNA have shown that the basic building blocks of life are all very similar. Traits controlled by single genes can be transplanted from one species to another. Transgenic crops are produced when a single species contains pieces of DNA from at least one other species. One of the most common examples is the implantation of genes containing the toxin produced by *Bacillus thuringiensis* (Bt). For years, farmers have sprayed this naturally occurring toxin on their fields as an insecticide. Geneticists were able to isolate the toxic gene in the bacteria and are now inserting it into crops such as corn and soybeans. The crops then produce their own toxin. The other common genetic modification is to produce crops with genes that make them resistant to a particular herbicide. When a farmer sprays the crop, all competing plants are killed but the crop is unharmed.

The use of such transgenic crops has grown very rapidly. At the time of the Earth Summit in Rio de Janeiro in 1992, production of transgenic crops had not yet begun, but it now stands at over 180 million hectares (Figure 10.3). In 2014, the US, followed by Brazil, Argentina, India, and Canada, continued to be the principal adopters of biotech crops globally, with 73.1 million hectares planted in the US and 11.6 in Canada. Although in 2006 most of the area devoted to biotech was in industrial nations, by 2014, 90 per cent of all biotech farmers were in developing countries.

Soybeans (82 per cent biotech), maize (30 per cent), cotton (68 per cent), and canola (25 per cent) are the four leading biotech crops. About 47 per cent of the total area planted with these crops is now devoted to genetically modified varieties, and two traits—insect resistance and herbicide tolerance—dominate. Throughout the world, several thousand GMO field tests have been conducted or are underway, and many more crop–trait combinations are being investigated, with greater focus on virus resistance, quality, and in some cases tolerance to abiotic stresses.

In Canada, scientists at the University of Victoria have developed a potato that resists bacteria and fungi, allowing it to be stored for 10 times longer than "normal" potatoes. In Guelph, Ontario, scientists have engineered a pig that produces manure 20 to 50 times lower in phosphorus content than that of "regular" pigs. Since phosphorus is a main cause of eutrophication (Chapter 4), the number of pigs that can be kept in a given area is often limited. The new pig can be stocked in higher densities.

The global value of the biotech crop market was projected at more than $15.7 billion for 2014. There is no doubt that

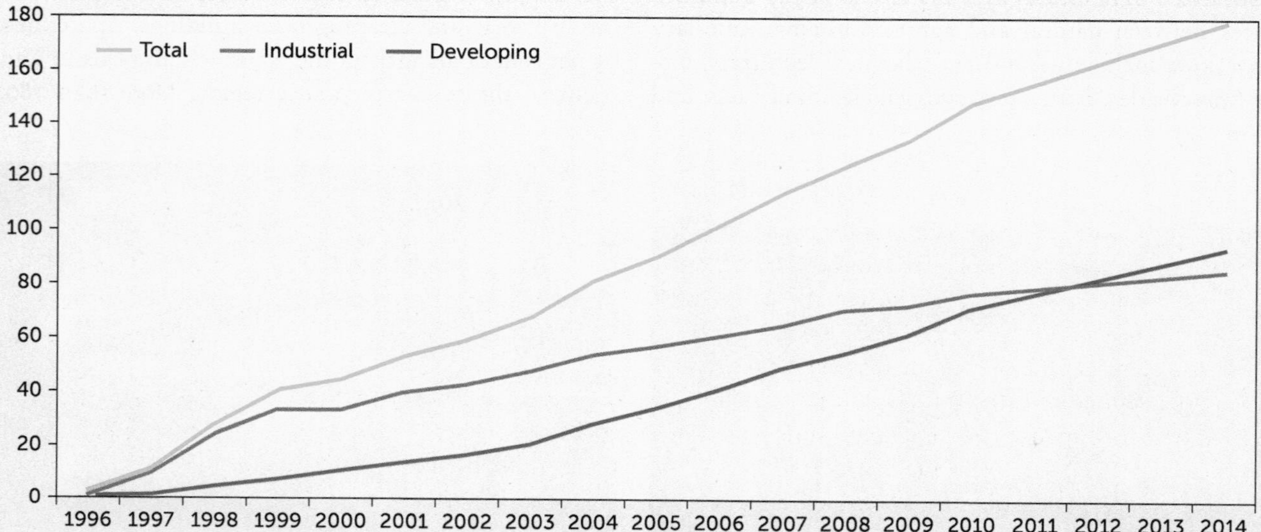

FIGURE 10.3 | Global area of biotech crops, industrial and developing countries (million hectares).

Source: Data to 2010 adapted from James (2010). Data to 2014 from authors.

GMOs hold great potential for the future. However, development has been very rapid, and several areas of uncertainty regarding their effects remain:

- *Pleiotropic effects*: These are unexpected side effects that might be suffered by the target organism as a result of incorporation of the new gene. For example, there may be a change in the toxins produced or the nutrient content.
- *Environmental effects*: There will be impacts on natural processes, such as pollination and biogeochemical cycles, as a result of creating new crops. It is also feared that there may be unanticipated gene flow to other organisms and perhaps interbreeding with wild relatives. This has the potential to produce "superweeds," as has happened in Canada with canola, where the biocide-resistant superweeds are now growing in wheat fields. The only way to get rid of them is to resort to broad-spectrum herbicides, those that will kill everything.
- *Unintentional spread*: Pollen and seeds from transgenic crops may spread onto lands where they are not intended to grow. This is already a problem for organic canola and honey producers on the Prairies, who can no longer guarantee that their products are transgenic-free.

There is little consensus among governments, consumers, farmers, and scientists concerning the benefits and risks associated with biotechnology or genetic engineering. A lack of perceived benefits for consumers and uncertainty about their safety have led to total bans in some countries, limited their adoption in other countries, while others have developed legislation requiring mandatory labelling on genetically modified foods. Canada has chosen not to do so despite the introduction of several private member's bills into Parliament, the latest in 2013, even though polls suggest that a large majority of Canadians would prefer to have a choice. What is your view? Do you think GMO food products should be explicitly labelled?

Source of statistics: James (2014).

hectares of cropland in Canada are under irrigation, and the amount is increasing. Alberta accounts for 63 per cent of the national total. Alberta has the largest irrigated field crop and irrigated hay and pasture areas. Most of the vegetable irrigation is in Ontario, with 45 per cent of the total irrigated vegetable area. British Columbia applies most of the irrigation to keep fruit areas, such as the orchards in the Okanagan Valley, thriving. As a whole, the province accounts for 52.8 per cent of total irrigated fruit area in the country.

Fertilizers are also important inputs to modern farming systems. Every crop that comes out of the earth is produced by nutrients. As more crops are taken, more nutrients are removed, and without the input of fertilizers, the soil would become depleted and unable to produce further crops. Originally this deficiency was met by the input of organic fertilizers, the feces of animals and other organic residues. However, given the intensity of modern farming, this is no longer adequate in many situations and chemical fertilizers, particularly nitrogen, phosphorus, and potash, are added to most croplands. New strains of crops, such as wheat, will produce superior yields only if fertilized adequately. The global consumption of fertilizer increased from 116 kilograms per hectare (kg/ha) of arable land in 2005 to over 140 kg/ha by 2012 (World Bank, 2015).

In Canada there was a 4 per cent increase in fertilized area between 2001 and 2011. Fertilizer is applied on 69 per cent of crop farms in Canada, with relatively little variability across the country (Statistics Canada, 2013b). The largest fertilized areas are in the Prairies: the Assiniboine–Red watershed (7,496,870 hectares), the South Saskatchewan watershed (5,195,829 hectares), and the North Saskatchewan watershed (4,499,229 hectares). These areas also have the highest proportions of land fertilized.

The *amount* of fertilizers applied *per hectare* (kg/ha) in Canada has increased considerably since the early 1970s, although the rate of increase has slowed since the mid 1980s. In 1970, 1980, 1990, and 2000, fertilizers were applied at a rate of 18.4, 42.4, 45.1, and 54.2 kg/ha, respectively. The rate rose to 81 by 2011 but has since fallen to 74 kg/ha (Statistics Canada, 2014a). These rates are not high by international standards, as can be seen in comparison with the global figures given above. In the United States the current rate is 131 kg/ha (World Bank, 2015). Fertilizer application is of environmental concern because fertilizers are a main contributor to the speed of the eutrophication process (Chapter 4) as well as to groundwater pollution in some areas (Chapter 11).

Philip Dearden

In poorer areas of Asia, water buffalo are still integral to the rice production system as they both till and fertilize the soil. In richer areas they have been replaced by mechanical tillers and chemical fertilizers.

A central strategy in improving agricultural output is to limit losses from the effects of pests and diseases and from weed competition. Since the mid 1990s, the approach to crop protection has relied increasingly on the use of biocides (insecticides, nematocides, fungicides, and herbicides). Pesticides should be referred to as biocides, since their application often affects more than just the target species. Biocides are applied to boost yields. Yields are improved by reducing the amount of energy flowing to the next trophic layer of the food chain through the respiration of heterotrophs (often insects) and by eliminating non-food plants that compete with the crop plants for available growth resources.

Biocide use continues to increase, indicating that farmers find biocides cost-effective from a production perspective, particularly where alternative forms of crop protection are labour-intensive and labour costs are high. Currently, about two million tonnes per year of biocides are used globally, of which 45 per cent is used by Europe and 25 per cent by the US. In Canada between 2001 and 2011 there was a 3 per cent increase in the area of farmland treated with herbicides, 42 per cent with insecticides, and 114 per cent with fungicides. The Prairie provinces have the largest amount of land treated; however, the fruit-growing Okanagan-Similkameen area of southern BC shows the highest proportion of application of insecticides and fungicides per area of cultivated land (Statistics Canada, 2014a). The large increases in the application of agricultural biocides over the past 20 years both globally and in Canada have profound environmental implications, as will be discussed in more detail later.

Raeside Cartoons

Ethanol is often made using crops such as sugarcane and corn. While ethanol can reduce the amount of fossil fuels used to run vehicles, its production can also reduce the amount of arable land devoted to the production of food, leading to increased food prices.

The Biofuel Revolution

Biofuels are solids, liquids, or gases that have been derived from recently dead biological material and are processed into an oil that acts as a petroleum replacement. As they are derived from plants and other organic material, they seem to have great potential to help curb global greenhouse gas emissions. About one-quarter of GHG emissions are produced by the transport sector, and biofuels, including ethanol and biodiesel, are the only existing renewable fuels compatible with the current transportation infrastructure. Biofuels generate a fraction of the pollutants of traditional petroleum-based fuels, and the plants that produce them remove carbon, a climate-altering GHG, from the atmosphere. Biofuels also have the potential to reduce foreign oil dependency, lower fuel prices, increase income for farmers, and provide a host of new jobs. Nations that develop domestic biofuel industries will be able to purchase fuel from their own farmers rather than spending scarce foreign exchange on imported oil.

Biofuel production is growing at a rate of roughly 15 per cent per year, more than 10 times that of oil, although oil still accounts for 95 per cent of the global transportation fuel market. Biofuels include two main types. The first, ethanol fuel, is ethyl alcohol (the same type of alcohol found in alcoholic beverages) and is used usually as a biofuel additive for gasoline. The production process starts with the growing of crops, such as sugar cane or maize, which are then fermented into alcohol. Most cars in the US (the world's largest producer) can run with up to 10 per cent ethanol added to their gas. In Brazil (the second-largest producer), it is mandatory to have ethanol fuel mixed with gas, and the approved rate is 25 per cent. The growth in world ethanol production is shown in Figure 10.4. The United States produces almost 90 per cent of global ethanol, followed by Brazil, Europe, China, and Thailand.

Biodiesel, the second main component of biofuels, is a vegetable oil processed from oils derived from soybeans, oil palm, and canola, among other crops, and it can be used in standard diesel engines or as a heating oil or mixed with regular diesel. For example, in 2004 Halifax began to run its buses entirely on a fish oil–based biodiesel. The trend in biodiesel production is shown in Figure 10.4. Europe is currently the leading producer of biodiesel.

Canada is not a large producer of biofuels in the global context, and the federal government introduced the ecoAGRICULTURE Biofuels Capital Initiative (ecoABC), a $200-million, four-year program to stimulate production that ended in 2012. The program provided repayable funding for the construction or expansion of transportation biofuel production facilities. Funding was conditional on investment in the biofuel projects by agricultural producers and the use of agricultural feedstock to produce the biofuel. However, the program faced many challenges, as outlined by Kedron (2014) and has not proven to be a good investment of public funds.

In view of its advantages, why are there so many critics of biofuels? One issue relates to the inputs used to grow many of the crops used for biofuels. Fossil fuels are invested in

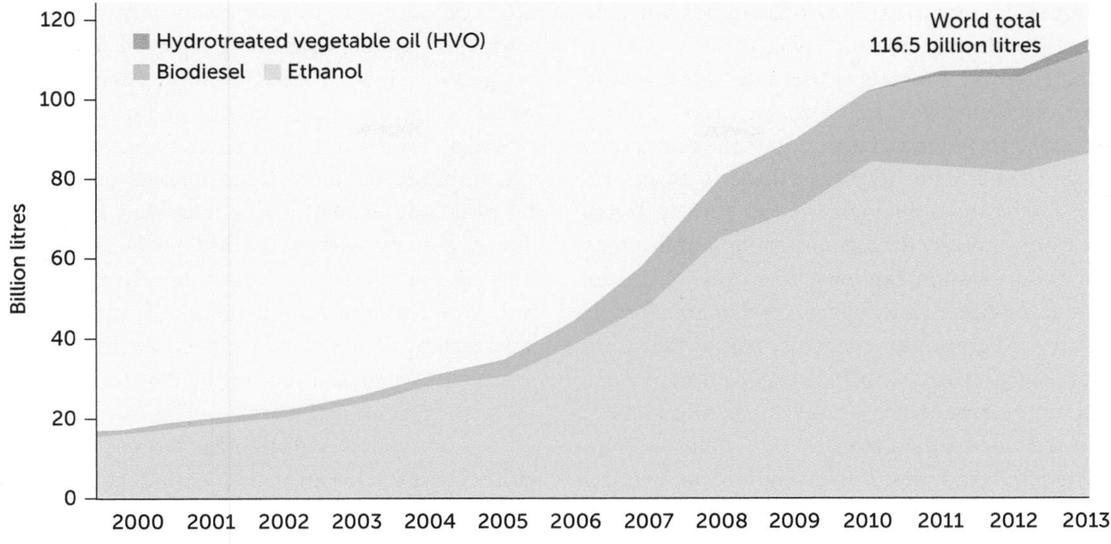

FIGURE 10.4 | Ethanol, biodiesel, and HVO production, 2000–2013.
Source: REN21 (2014).

fertilizers, pesticides, machinery, and processing, and the second law of thermodynamics (Chapter 2) warns us that energy is lost in each of these energy transformations, which contributes to global warming. Furthermore, nitrogen, a key fertilizer applied to biofuel crops, turns into nitrous oxide (N_2O), a greenhouse gas that is over 296 times more powerful than CO_2. Some scientists report that to produce ethanol from maize will cause 0.9 to 1.5 times as much GHG emissions as an equivalent amount of fossil fuels (Crutzen et al., 2007).

Concerns around the effects of biofuels on global warming are compounded by the land conversion associated with expanding biofuel crops. Biofuel crops displace existing agriculture, which in turn requires the conversion of natural ecosystems to maintain food production levels. Scientists have noted that converting rain forests, peatlands, savannahs, or other biologically diverse habitats for biofuel production results in a total contribution of CO_2 that is between 17 and 420 times higher than from fossil fuels (Fargione et al., 2008). Indonesia and Malaysia account for 86 per cent of the world's palm oil, and accelerating demand is prompting the conversion of tropical rain forests, contributing to GHG emissions and threatening biodiversity.

Another problem is that with the increased profit to be made from land used for growing biofuel inputs, land is being taken away from food production. The cars of the wealthy may end up consuming the food of the poor. The International Food Policy Research Institute projects that a drastic increase in biofuel production in sub-Saharan Africa will result in an 8 per cent decline in calorie availability (von Braun, 2007). A figure like that raises concern around the global capacity to produce both biofuels and food sufficient to meet growing demand. In 2007, interest in biofuels was high and corn prices doubled, causing social unrest in Mexico, where corn tortillas are a dietary staple. Unrest continued in many countries as food prices remained high into 2011. Overall, deeper analysis is needed to understand the global and local impact of expanded biofuel demand on food prices.

One possible answer to both the challenges of energy inputs into biofuel production and competition with food crops is to produce ethanol from non-food sources. Cellulosic ethanol is made from a wide variety of plant materials, including wood wastes, crop residues, and grasses, some of which can be grown on marginal lands not suitable for food production. The process for converting these materials to fuel is often more efficient, because plant material rather than fossil fuels can be used to provide heat and power. As a result, cellulosic ethanol has an energy yield at least four to six times the energy expended during production and can

Aerial view of sugarcane plantations abutting rain forest near Ribeirao Preto, São Paulo State, Brazil.

reduce greenhouse gas emissions by 65 to 110 per cent relative to gasoline (Worldwatch Institute, 2007).

A further challenge for biofuels is that large-scale biofuel production can threaten biodiversity, as seen recently with oil palm plantations in Indonesia and sugarcane plantations in Cambodia that are encroaching on forests. In Brazil, the Cerrado, a vast landscape of biologically rich forests, brush, and pasture just south of the Amazon, is coming under pressure as sugarcane cultivation expands. One response to this threat has been to convince decision-makers that areas rich in biodiversity may yield greater long-term returns by being preserved for ecotourism rather than bulldozed for sugarcane. For example, the government of Uganda had been supporting a proposal for a 7,000-hectare sugarcane concession in the supposedly protected Mabira Forest Reserve near Lake Victoria. However, a study by the conservation group NatureUganda showed that the financial benefits of protecting the forest and encouraging ecotourism vastly outstripped the potential of biofuel crops. The commercial value of tourism and carbon capture in Mabira was estimated at more than $316 million a year, whereas sugarcane production would be worth less than $20 million. However, it should be remembered that tourism can also generate additional stresses on the environment, such as the GHG emissions generated by flying long distances.

Despite associated challenges, it seems that biofuels will be part of a portfolio of options to deal with global warming that also includes dramatic improvements in vehicle fuel economy, investment in public transportation, better urban planning, and many other aspects discussed in Chapter 13. The long-term potential of biofuels is probably in the use of non-food feedstock. Following the model of Brazil's sugarcane-based biofuels industry, cellulosic ethanol could dramatically reduce the carbon dioxide and nitrogen pollution that results from today's biofuel crops.

Modern industrial cropping systems that rely on auxiliary energy flows and other inputs are responsible for the production of a large percentage of the cereals, pulses, oil crops, roots and tubers, fruits, and sugar crops produced and consumed worldwide. Together, these crops represent only 60 per cent of the total value of output from the world's agro-ecosystems. Livestock production is responsible for the remaining 40 per cent, and this proportion is growing.

The Livestock Revolution

Hundreds of years ago, livestock (e.g., cattle, sheep, goats) raised for local consumption were permitted to graze on surrounding natural vegetation. Stocking densities were dictated by surrounding environmental conditions—i.e., the availability of water and food supplies on a given unit of land and the ability of the local environment to assimilate animal wastes. As a result, farms were typically small, with fewer than 100 animals. However, as the industrialized world's appetite for meat continues to grow exponentially, traditional livestock production systems are being replaced with industrial technologies and intensification. Livestock are now increasingly raised in high densities and confined spaces with inputs, such as food and water, supplied directly to them. Worldwide, meat consumption has more than doubled since 1977, and over the past half-century it has increased fivefold. Production of beef, poultry, pork, and other meats has risen to nearly 43 kilograms per person per year, more than twice as much as in 1950. However, there are major global differences, with average consumption in the developed world being over 76 kilograms per capita and that in the developing world less than half that amount (FAO, 2015).

The **Livestock Revolution** has led to a number of changes with respect to how animals are brought to market. In industrialized countries such as Canada, the desire to supply the phenomenal growth in demand for protein has led to a reliance on industrial feedlots, which now produce more than half of the world's pork and poultry and 43 per cent of the world's beef. Livestock production requires high water inputs and accounts for over 30 per cent of the water used by the agricultural sector globally. Technology, capital, and infrastructure requirements are based on large economies of scale, and production efficiency is high in terms of output per unit of feed. As the world's main providers of eggs, poultry, beef, and pork at competitive prices, intensive farm operations (or "factory farms") meet most of the escalating demands for low-cost animal products.

Agricultural production of livestock has grown across Canada, while the number of farmers has declined and the size of the average farm has increased. New farms are often capital-intensive operations with very large numbers of livestock. Farms with 3,000 or more pigs or 1,200 cattle are increasingly common, and some farms in Ontario and Quebec house in excess of 10,000 animals. For pigs, herd size grew by 76 per cent between 2006 and 2011, and average herd size is now 1,720 pigs per farm. The number of pig farms decreased by 35 per cent over this time period. Between 2006 and 2013, dairy cattle herd size decreased by 5 per cent and beef by 21 per cent (Agriculture and Agri-Food Canada, 2013).

As the livestock industry expands and becomes more intensive, health and environmental concerns over livestock manure are growing, particularly when livestock are produced in large numbers under confined conditions such as beef feedlots and intensive hog and poultry barns. In feedlots, animals are typically fed grains, which have undergone extensive energy and chemical inputs. Furthermore, at such high densities, animals easily acquire and transmit diseases and require extensive antibiotic treatments. Again, the second law of thermodynamics suggests that this may not be an efficient system. The social and environmental impacts associated with intensive farming operations will be discussed in greater detail later.

Agriculture's Impact on the Global Landscape

Various impacts are associated with the development of agriculture and, more specifically, with the development and spread of modern farming systems:

- Humans, rather than natural selection, have become the primary influence on the number and distribution of species. In modern agriculture, the dominant mechanism for production is through **monoculture cropping**, in which crops are often made up of a single species with each individual having exactly the same genetic code. New species have been created for the purpose of maximizing the output of food for humans, while native species have been displaced. Domesticated plants and animals greatly increase in number and range, but wild species are drastically reduced.
- Energy flows are increasingly directed into agricultural as opposed to natural systems. It is estimated that humans now appropriate some 40 per cent of the net primary productivity of the planet.
- Biogeochemical cycles are interrupted as natural vegetation is replaced by domesticates that are harvested on a regular basis. Auxiliary energy flows in the form of fertilizer are used in an attempt to replenish some of the nutrients extracted through harvesting.
- Auxiliary energy flows used in modern agricultural systems to supplement the natural energy flow from the sun are often in excess of those derived from natural sources.
- In many areas, agriculture involves supplementing rainfall with irrigation to provide adequate water supplies. This has led to large-scale water diversions and to changes in groundwater, soil characteristics, precipitation patterns, and water quality.
- Soils are altered not only chemically through fertilizer and biocide inputs but also physically through plowing. There is no natural process that mimics the disturbance created by plowing.
- Natural food chains are truncated as humans destroy and replace natural consumers and predators at higher trophic levels.
- Natural successional processes are altered to keep agricultural systems in an early seral stage; auxiliary energy flows in the form of herbicides and mechanical weeding are often used to accomplish this.
- The stocking densities of domesticated herbivores are often much higher than that of natural herbivores, leading to a reduction in standing biomass and changes in the structure and composition of the primary production system.
- The industrial system of livestock production acts directly on land, water, air, and biodiversity through the emission of animal waste, use of fossil fuels, and substitution of animal genetic resources. It also affects the global land base indirectly through its effect on the arable land needed to satisfy its feed concentrate requirements. The industrial system requires the use of uniform animals of similar genetic composition, contributing to within-breed erosion of domestic animal diversity.

Trends in Canadian Agriculture

Approximately 7 per cent of Canada's total land area (65 million hectares) is agricultural land, of which 46 million hectares are cropland, pasture, or summer fallow. Between 1971 and 2011, farm area in Canada declined by roughly 4 million hectares (6 per cent), roughly the size of Vancouver

VichoT/iStockphoto

Agriculture has had a profound impact on the distribution of species. Large areas of the agricultural landscape are dominated by monocultures—in this case sunflowers—in which each plant has the same genetic makeup.

© Mcmaster Studio/Alamy Stock Photo

Big Muddy Valley, about 200 kilometres south of Regina, Saskatchewan. The Prairie provinces contain 83 per cent of the agricultural land base of the country.

ENVIRONMENT IN FOCUS

BOX 10.4 | Urbanization of Agricultural Land

Despite the fact that Canada is the second-largest country in the world and one of the biggest exporters of foodstuffs worldwide, only 64.8 million hectares, less than 7 per cent of Canada's overall land mass, are used for agricultural production. The amount of arable land free from severe constraints on crop production is even smaller, totalling less than 5 per cent of the land base. This land is classified as "dependable agricultural land" by Statistics Canada and constitutes classes 1 through 3 of the Canada Land Inventory (CLI). The CLI classified agricultural land in Canada into seven classes based on soil and climate characteristics, with Class 1 having few or no limitations for agriculture through to Class 7 where agriculture is not possible. Lands in classes 4 to 6 have important limitations for crops (Environment Canada, 1972). About 40 per cent of agricultural activities occur on marginal or poorer-quality land, which may not be dependable for long-term agricultural activity (Statistics Canada, 2001).

Most of the prime agricultural land is in southern Canada, where 90 per cent of Canadians live. In Ontario, for example, more than 18 per cent of Class 1 farmland is now being used for urban purposes. This juxtaposition of prime agricultural land and the main urban centres has meant that suburban expansion invariably leads to losses in agricultural land. By 2001, half of Canada's urbanized land was located on dependable agricultural land, and 7.5 per cent was on our very best agricultural land (Hofmann et al., 2005).

Between 1966 and 1986, 301,440 hectares of rural land were converted to urban use. Furthermore, some 58 per cent of the converted land was of prime agricultural capability. To replace the productivity of this land would require bringing twice as much land under cultivation on the agricultural margins. One study found that urbanization had consumed 15,200 km^2 of surrounding lands between 1971 and 2001, an increase of 96 per cent in the total amount of urban land over the period. In Ontario alone, urbanization increased by 4,300 km^2, a growth of almost 80 per cent (Hofmann et al., 2005). Between 2001 and 2011, the farm area located on dependable agricultural land in Canada declined by 969,802 hectares, and settlement on these lands increased by 19 per cent (Statistics Canada, 2014a). At the same time, agriculture on lands with significant limitations increased. Canada is exchanging its very best agricultural lands for some of the most challenging as urban growth continues to spread, a challenge also addressed in Chapter 13.

Although much of this urban expansion has been in Ontario, other areas have also been greatly affected. For example, in the Calgary–Edmonton corridor, research showed that 60 per cent of the urban expansion between 1988 and 2010 was on to previously agricultural lands. However, the amount of agricultural land overall expanded, as new lands with significant limitations for agriculture were brought into production (Martellozzo et al., 2014). In other words, this case study mirrors exactly the national trend.

Urbanization of agricultural land often affects specialty crops that have a limited ability to flourish in Canada. These crops often represent an important resource to local economies (e.g., the fruit belts in the Niagara and Okanagan regions). Cities also affect the use of surrounding lands in indirect ways—golf courses, gravel pits, and recreational areas are often located on agricultural land in areas adjacent to urban areas, and as a result, the effects of urban areas extend beyond their physical boundaries.

In an effort to slow the rates of conversion, several provinces have enacted legislation regarding the protection of agricultural lands. In 1972, for example, British Columbia enacted the Agricultural Land Reserve (ALR). At the time of its inception, some 6,000 hectares of prime agricultural land were being lost to urbanization each year. The annual loss has now fallen to less than one-seventh of that amount. The ALR initially covered 4.7 million hectares (5 per cent of BC); despite boundary changes over the decades, its current area remains

AnikaSalsera/iStockphoto

Most Canadian cities of any size are surrounded by good agricultural lands. As the cities increase in size, they invariably encroach on the surrounding lands, as seen here in Quebec.

approximately the same. A similar program exists in Quebec. In 1978, the Quebec government introduced the Agricultural Land Preservation Act, which now protects more than 63,000 km² of prime agricultural land.

However, these programs do have their problems. Often, farmers whose lands fall within the program and cannot be sold for non-agricultural uses cannot compete with cheap agricultural imports from elsewhere. Hence, they cannot make a decent living in agriculture and yet cannot sell their lands for non-agricultural purposes. And as a nation, should we be concerned about becoming increasingly dependent on other countries for our food? What do you think?

Island in British Columbia, mainly as a result of urbanization (Box 10.4). The Prairie provinces contain 81 per cent of the agricultural land base, while Quebec, Ontario, and BC account for 17 per cent, with the remaining 2 per cent in Atlantic Canada.

The agriculture and agri-food sector is a $103 billion industry, exporting more than $43 billion in products annually (Statistics Canada, 2013b; Agriculture and Agri-Food Canada, 2013), making Canada the world's fifth-largest exporter. The number of farms has declined since the early 1970s, with almost 171,555 farms in Canada in 2013, a decline of 31 per cent since 2001. At the same time, average farm size has been increasing. The largest farms are in Saskatchewan (average of 675 hectares), an increase of 15 per cent from 2006–2011, and the smallest in Newfoundland (average of 65 hectares).

Wheat is still the dominant crop in Canada, although the area dedicated to wheat production is declining. Saskatchewan grows 46 per cent of Canada's wheat. Other traditional grains, such as barley and oats, are also declining. The production of pulses (e.g., dry field peas, lentils, field beans, soybeans) has increased since the late 1970s and now accounts for almost 8 per cent of national crop area. Soybeans, the second-largest oilseed crop grown in Canada after canola, are a major field crop in eastern Canada, along with grain corn. The area under soybean production in 2013, more than 1.2 million hectares, has grown eightfold since 1976, mostly as a result of strong demand for the crop and of breeding that has produced more cold-tolerant varieties with short growing seasons. The high-protein, high-oil beans are used as food for human consumption, animal rations, and edible oils as well as in many industrial products. They are also nitrogen fixers and help to replenish the soil (Chapter 4).

Over 70 per cent of the food Canadians bought in 2010 was produced domestically. Canada is particularly self-sufficient for meat, dairy (including eggs), breads, and cereals. Many Canadians have access to a ready supply of fresh produce year round. Innovations include a thriving greenhouse subsector, as well as advanced storage technologies. Other technologies have increased the availability of fresh food through production techniques that improve yields. Yield-enhancing technologies include mechanization, fertilizers and biocides, and genetic research. Canada is a main producer of food for the global market. Undoubtedly, there will be changes in these trends as the impacts of climate change become more pervasive. Some of these trends will benefit certain areas and agricultural sectors; others will not, as emphasized in the "Perspectives on the Environment" box and discussed in Chapter 7. Unfortunately, many of the innovations and technologies employed by Canadian farmers have negative implications for ecosystem health. These implications will be discussed in more detail in the next section.

Perspectives on the Environment

Climate Change Impacts on Agriculture

The net medium-term outlook is for a likely modest increase in agricultural food production. Longer and warmer growing seasons would allow higher-value warmer-weather crops to be grown further north (where soil conditions permit), lengthen outdoor feeding seasons for livestock, and allow the maple syrup industry to expand northward. However, there will likely be new pests and diseases, as well as more severe outbreaks of current ones, and challenges associated with extreme weather events and the reduced predictability of inter-annual weather variability that could negatively affect production.

—Warren and Lemmen (2014b: 3)

Environmental Challenges for Canadian Agriculture

Land Degradation

Land degradation reduces the capability of agricultural lands to produce food. As agricultural activities have intensified with increased cultivation and addition of agricultural chemicals to produce better yields, so has pressure on the soil resource.

Soil Erosion

Soil erosion is a natural process whereby soil is removed from its place of formation by gravitational, water, and wind processes. In Canada soil erosion is a serious land degradation problem resulting in reduced yields and higher costs. In some parts of southwestern Ontario, erosion has caused a loss in corn yields of 30 to 40 per cent. Further costs are incurred off the farm when sedimentation blocks waterways, impairs fish habitat, lowers water quality, increases the costs of water treatment, and contributes to flooding.

stevegeer/iStockphoto

Large areas of tilled soil are particularly vulnerable to erosion.

Under natural conditions in most ecozones, soil erosion is minimal, since the natural vegetation tends to bind the soil together and keep it in place. Agricultural activities may totally remove this natural vegetation and replace it with intermittent crop plantings, thereby exposing the bare soil to erosive processes, or keep the land under full vegetation for grazing purposes. The latter approach provides much better protection for the soil but may still result in erosion, particularly under conditions of high livestock density.

The rate of soil formation varies as a function of different environmental factors. Because of Canada's latitude, soil formation is slow, with an average annual rate of 0.5 to 1.0 tonne per hectare. Any soil erosion above this amount will result in some loss of productive capacity. Losses in excess of 5 to 10 tonnes per hectare per year may lead to serious long-term problems. These figures have often been exceeded, and 30 tonnes per hectare loss has been recorded in BC's Fraser River Valley under row crops, while 20 tonnes per hectare is not uncommon in Prince Edward Island. Wind erosion is more difficult to measure but is a significant problem in the Prairie provinces, where high wind speeds, dry soils, and cropping practices often leave the soil unprotected. One study in Saskatchewan detected a net output of soil of 1.5 tonnes per hectare on a near-level field as a result of wind erosion, whereas a field with a greater incline (three degrees) was found to lose 6.6 tonnes per hectare, with water and wind erosion combined. However, recent research suggests that programs to reduce soil erosion in the Prairie provinces are having some impact as there is a measurably reduced amount of particle matter in the air (Fox et al., 2012).

Soil Compaction

Soil compaction occurs from frequent use of heavy machinery on wet soils or from overstocking with cattle. Compaction breaks down the soil structure and inhibits the throughflow of water. Crop yields can be reduced by up to 60 per cent in such conditions. Soil compaction is a problem mainly in the lower Fraser River Valley in BC and in parts of central and eastern Canada.

Soil Acidification and Salinization

Acidity in soils can occur naturally but can also be augmented by fallout from acid precipitation (Chapter 4) and the use of fertilizers. Nitrogen fertilizers undergo chemical changes in the soil that result in production of H+ ions, causing greater acidity. In the Maritime provinces, where significant declines in soil pH have been measured, it is estimated that 60 per cent of the change can be attributed to fertilizer use and 40 per cent to acid precipitation. In the Prairies, concern over acidity is relatively recent because the substrate is generally alkaline. However, increased use of fertilizer has led to acidification in some areas. Excess acidity reduces crop yields and leads to nutrient deficiencies and the export of soluble elements such as iron and aluminum into waterways. The yields of crops such as barley and alfalfa fall sharply at soil pH of less than 6. Liming is a common agricultural practice to combat the effects of acidity.

Salinization is the deposition of salts in irrigated soils. Soil salinization is a major problem in many areas of the world where irrigation is common as it leaves soil unfit for growing most crops. As water evaporates, it leaves behind dissolved salts. Over time, these salts can accumulate in sufficient quantities to render the land unusable. Ancient civilizations that designed complex irrigation systems were unable to counter the effects of salinization, contributing to their eventual decline. Estimates suggest that 50 to 65 per cent of irrigated croplands worldwide are now less productive due to salinization.

Alkaline soils occur naturally in areas of western Canada that have high sodium content and shallow water tables. Salinization can also be exacerbated through cropping practices that remove natural vegetation and increase the rate of surface evaporation, leading to greater salt concentration at the surface. Summer fallow has this effect. **Summer fallow** is a practice common on the Prairies in which selected land is kept bare to minimize moisture losses through evapotranspiration. On the Prairies, crop yields have been reduced by 10 to 75 per cent as a result of salinization. Despite the increased use of fertilizers, it is estimated that in some regions, salinization is increasing in area by 10 per cent every year. However, summer fallow decreased by 25 per cent between 2001 and 2006. The economic need to keep arable land productive, along with diversified and extended crop rotations, improved seeding and tilling methods, and proper use of herbicides, have all contributed to the reduction in summer fallow.

Organic Matter and Nutrient Losses

Cultivation involves a continuous process of removing plant matter from a field. In so doing, both the organic and nutrient content of the soil are reduced. Organic matter is critical for maintaining the structure of the soil, influencing water filtration, facilitating aeration, and providing the capacity to support machinery. It also helps to maintain water and nutrient levels.

On the Prairies, current organic matter levels are estimated to be 50 to 60 per cent of original levels, representing a probable annual loss of about 112,000 tonnes of nitrogen (Figure 10.5). This nitrogen is replaced by the addition of synthetic fertilizers, which in turn contribute to the problem of acidification. An alternative way to replace the nitrogen is by the growth of leguminous crops to enhance biological nitrogen fixation (BNF), discussed in Chapter 4. It is estimated that before the increased use of fertilizers began in the 1960s, nitrogen exports from prairie grain exceeded fertilizer applications by more than tenfold, and phosphate removals exceeded inputs by threefold. Current estimates still show depletion of the soil but with nitrogen now reduced to double the exports over inputs and phosphorus inputs to about 50 to 60 per cent of the export.

Soil degradation, including erosion and nutrient depletion, is undermining the long-term capacity of many agricultural systems worldwide and is estimated to affect nearly 40 per cent of the world's agricultural land. This degradation will likely have serious implications for future generations, since the production of food in sufficient quantity and quality requires a healthy natural resource base.

Biocides

Biocides have helped to boost yields throughout the world to meet the food demands of rising populations (many more people would be starving without their use), and biocides have also saved countless lives throughout the world by assisting in the control of various diseases through attacking vectors, such as malaria-carrying mosquitoes. But scientific evidence indicates that many chemicals have profound negative impacts on ecosystems. The possible environmental and health impacts may be delayed, in some cases for decades. Despite various risks such as pest resistance, non-selectivity, chemical persistence, biocide mobility, biomagnification, and bioaccumulation, biocide use continues to grow on a global scale.

Resistance

Part of the scientific debate on crop protection relates to the ability of pests, weeds, and viruses to develop resistance to biocides. When a population of insects, for example, is sprayed with a chemical, individuals within the population will react in various ways. If the biocide is effective, most of the population will be killed, but it is likely that a small number of individuals will have a higher natural resistance and survive the chemical onslaught. This remnant resistant

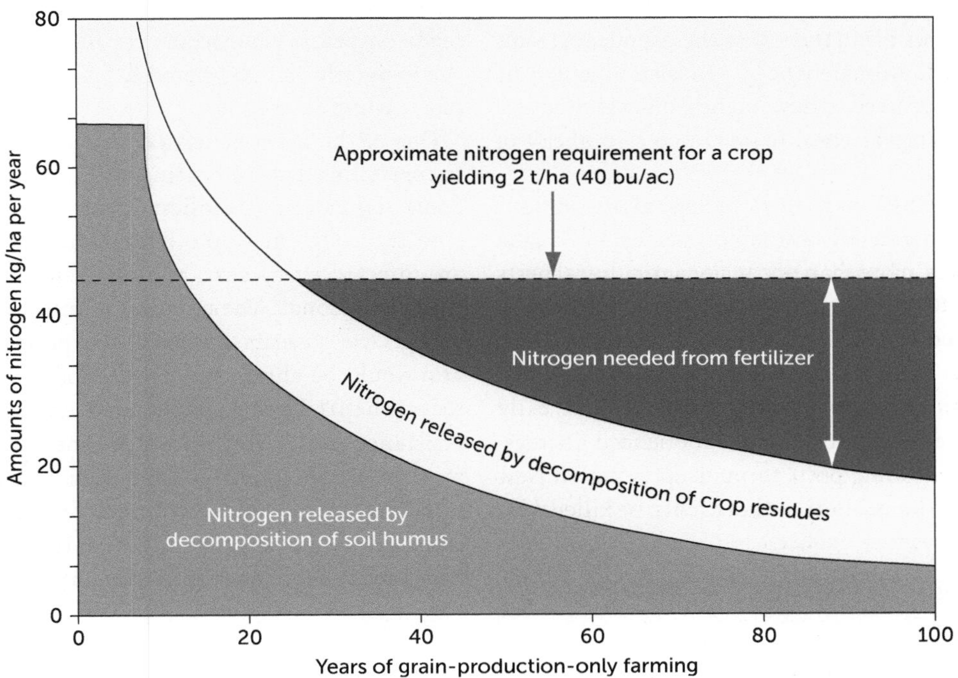

FIGURE 10.5 | Diagrammatic illustration of approximate sources of nitrogen needed to maintain grain yields of about 2 tonnes per hectare (40 bushels per acre) of barley under a system of continuous grain production in the prairie region. Note that this diagram illustrates plant requirements, not supply—i.e., the amount of fertilizer nitrogen applied would normally be greater than the plant requirements because of losses due to denitrification and/or leaching.

Source: Bentley and Leskiw (1985).

TABLE 10.1 | Major Types of Pesticides

Type	Examples
Insecticides	
Chlorinated hydrocarbons	aldrin, chlordane, DDT, dieldrin, endrin, heptachlor, mirex, toxaphene, kepone, methoxychlor
Organophosphates	malathion, parathion, diazinon, TEEP, DDVP
Carbamates	aldicarb, carbaryl (Sevin), carbofuran, propoxur, maneb, zineb
Botanicals	rotenone, nicotine, pyrethrum, camphor extracted from plants, neonicotinoids
Microbotanicals	bacteria (e.g., Bt), fungi, protozoans
Fungicides	
Various chemicals	captan, pentachlorphenol, methyl bromide, carbon bisulphide
Fumigants	
Various chemicals	carbon tetrachloride, ethylene dibromide (EDB), methyl bromide (MIC)
Herbicides	
Contact chemicals	atrazine, paraquat, simazine
Systemic chemicals	2,4-D; 2,4,5-T; daminozide (Alar); alachlor (Lasso); glyphosate (Roundup)

population may then grow rapidly in numbers, a result of the lack of competition from all the dead insects. Seeing a resurgence of the pest insect, the farmer sprays again and is again successful in killing a proportion of the population but not as high a proportion as before, since the natural resistance has been passed on to a larger proportion of the population. As this process repeats itself, the use of the chemical creates a population that will ultimately be quite resistant to it. This results in a continuous need to develop new biocide products (or pest-resistant plant varieties) to keep one step ahead of biological adaptation.

The "biocide treadmill" has led to biological adaptations resistant to most commercially available biocides. In Canada and the United States, more than 900 major agricultural pests are now immune to biocides, including some 500 insects and mites, 270 weed species, and 150 plant diseases (UNEP, 2002). As a result, more frequent applications are needed today to accomplish the same level of control as in the early 1970s. Across Canada, farmers have experienced increasing difficulty in controlling pests through spraying. In New Brunswick, Colorado potato beetles that used to be killed with one spraying a season now must be sprayed five or six times, and they still cause substantial damage. New approaches to controlling beetle damage have involved hybridization with a naturally resistant wild variety, illustrating the value of maintaining as wide a spectrum of wild species as possible. In British Columbia, the pear psylla, an aphid-like insect that feeds on pears, has become resistant to the five main synthetic pyrethroids registered for use against it, and another one is being developed.

One of the main beneficial impacts of biocides has been in controlling disease-bearing organisms such as mosquitoes. Some of the world's deadliest diseases, including malaria, are spread through mosquito bites. More than 1 million people are infected every year, and one person dies from malaria every 30 seconds. The numbers of infections and deaths are rising. Over 50 years ago, medical experts predicted that malaria would be eliminated because of the control of mosquitoes with DDT. Unfortunately, the mosquitoes soon developed resistance to DDT, and since that time have become resistant to virtually all control mechanisms. Given global warming trends, it is possible that tropical diseases such as malaria could invade Canada. The advent of West Nile virus may well be a forerunner of what is to come in the future.

Perspectives on the Environment

Silent Spring

It was a silent spring without voices. On the mornings that had once throbbed with the dawn chorus of robins, catbirds, doves, jays, wrens, and scores of other bird voices, there was now no sound; only silence lay over the fields and woods and marsh.

—Rachel Carson, ***Silent Spring*** (1962)

Non-Selective

Many biocides are popular because they are broad-spectrum poisons. In other words, there is no need to identify the specific pest, because a broad-spectrum poison will kill most insects. Unfortunately, they tend to eliminate not only the pest species but also other, valuable species, including some that may act to control the population of the pest. This outcome may result in a population explosion of the resistant members of the pest population after spraying due to the reduced abundance of their predators. Similarly, the lack of predators may allow new pest problems to develop that were previously kept in check by natural predators.

Many biocides are also extremely toxic to species other than those directly targeted, such as soil micro-organisms, insects, plants, mammals, birds, and fish (Box 10.5). For example, in PEI more than 20 instances of fish kills since 1994 have been attributed to pesticides, with up to 35,000 dead fish collected in each incident (Commissioner of the Environment and Sustainable Development, 2003). The government instituted new buffer zone regulations as a result of excessive kills; however from 2011 to 2014, there were four incidents in which large kills occurred, with pesticide runoff identified as the primary cause. Non-target organisms poisoned by biocide use may be beneficial to agriculture or other human economic activities, and as part of biodiversity, they are valued by society for recreational, cultural, ethical, or other reasons.

37 MILLION DEAD BEES

"Once the corn started to get planted our bees died by the millions..."

Europe got the message. When will we?

An outreach poster from Seattleorganicrestaurants.com draws attention to the 600 hives and 37 million bees of farmer Dave Schuit of Elmwood, Ontario, which died immediately following the planting of a GMO-corn field treated with neonics next to his hives (Seattle Organic Restaurants, n.d.).

Insect pollination is needed for about 75 per cent of the world's food crops and is estimated to be worth about 10 per cent of value the entire food supply of the world (Potts et al., 2010). However, pollinators are declining dramatically in both numbers and diversity throughout the world. A classic example that attracted a lot of attention in 2014 and 2015 is the death of honey bees related to use of neonicotinoid pesticides. A normal death rate for beehives over winter is around 15 per cent. It has risen to an average of 25 per cent, and over 50 per cent in Ontario. In that province, beekeepers have filed a class action suit for damages against the makers of neonicotinoid pesticides. In Europe, researchers in Germany as far back as 2008 documented the toxic effect of neonicotinoids on bees, and a team of Italian researchers has more recently documented how the chemical makes bees more susceptible to fungal attack through suppression of the immune system (di Prisco et al., 2013). Another study from the Netherlands has implicated the chemicals in widespread bird deaths (Hallmann et al., 2014). There is now a moratorium placed on the use of the chemicals by the EU; the Canadian government, however, has failed to take any action.

Neonicotinoids are very popular, and in Ontario, all corn and canola, and most soybean seeds are coated with neonics to protect the plants from insects. However, probably only 10 to 20 per cent of the corn and soybean acreage requires neonics, and the Ontario government is planning to restrict sales to farmers who have the greatest need to apply the chemicals. Need must be verified by a third party, and the farmers must take a special course in applying the chemical. The pesticide is also used by growers of flowers, fruits, vegetables, and sod, and they would not be affected by the ban.

Mobility

The purpose of biocides is to reduce the impact of a particular pest species (or several species) on a particular crop in a particular area. However, the effects of the chemical application are often felt over a much wider area, sometimes spanning thousands of square kilometres, because of the mobility of the chemicals in the Earth's natural cycles, particularly the hydrological cycle, and the manner in which chemicals are applied (Figure 10.7). The US Department of Agriculture estimates that aerial spraying of insecticide results in less than 2 per cent reaching the target and for herbicide applications, less than 5 per cent. The remainder finds its way into the ecosystem where it may contaminate local water supplies or be transported by atmospheric processes to more distant sites (Box 10.5).

Places with well-developed agricultural sectors and frequent use of chemicals might find that the entire environment is becoming contaminated. In PEI tests on airborne pollution found every sample to be contaminated. Even tests taken at the end of a wharf, far from any farms, showed chemicals. One of the most heavily used chemicals on the island, chlorothalonil, has been identified by the US government as a potential carcinogen, and its effects can be detected in air samples two hours after spraying has taken place. For

Philip Dearden

Malaria kills many people a year but receives little funding because it has little impact on the richer countries of the North. This is an educational sign in Sri Lanka showing villagers how to minimize the risks.

ENVIRONMENT IN FOCUS

BOX 10.5 | Carbofuran and Birds

Carbofuran is a carbamate (Table 10.1) that was registered for agricultural use in Canada. It was available either as a liquid or in granular form, on particles of grit, and was often applied in the latter form during seeding to protect recently germinated seedlings from insects. Considerable amounts of the chemical (up to 30 per cent of that applied) are often exposed on the soil surface following application. These granules are highly attractive to many birds that ingest grit in their gizzards to grind seeds. The chemical is highly toxic to birds, and the consumption of just one grain can be fatal to small seed-eaters. Carbofuran also contaminates invertebrates such as earthworms, which in turn will poison organisms higher on the food chain. Flooded fields are also highly dangerous, since the chemical goes into solution. This is particularly serious in acidic fields, where the breakdown of carbofuran is very slow.

There have been many documented bird kills as a result of the use of carbofuran, including 1,000 green-winged teal in flooded turnip fields in BC in 1975 and more than 2,000 Lapland longspurs in a canola field in Saskatchewan in 1984. Estimates suggest that the chemical has killed between 17 and 100 million birds annually in North America. It has also been recently implicated in the death of more than 70 lions killed by poachers in Kenya, which was brought to global attention through a television documentary.

Of particular concern is the impact of carbofuran on one of Canada's designated threatened species, the burrowing owl. The owl nests on the Prairies in abandoned mammal burrows, feeding on small mammals and insects. Two-thirds of the Canadian breeding population nests in Saskatchewan, where breeding numbers declined by 50 per cent in the south-central region between 1976 and 1987. Carbofuran spraying for grasshopper infestations is suspected to be the main cause. There were significant declines in nesting success and brood size with increasing proximity of carbofuran spraying to the nests. A high percentage of adult owls also disappeared after spraying. There were particularly severe infestations of grasshoppers in the early 1980s, and in Saskatchewan alone more than 3 million hectares were sprayed in 1985, 40 per cent of the area with carbofuran.

Several factors besides the chemical likely have an impact upon burrowing owl recovery, including loss of nesting holes as other creatures which make the holes (such as ground squirrels and prairie dogs) decline in population, lack of prey, and loss and fragmentation of native and non-native grassland habitats. Only 23 pairs were reported in 2013 in Saskatchewan, significantly down from the 79 pairs reported in 2009. In 2008, Canada and the EU banned the use of carbofuran; however, it is still being used widely by farmers and poachers in the developing world.

Missing35mm/iStockphoto

The burrowing owl is an endangered species that has been particularly threatened by the use of agricultural biocides.

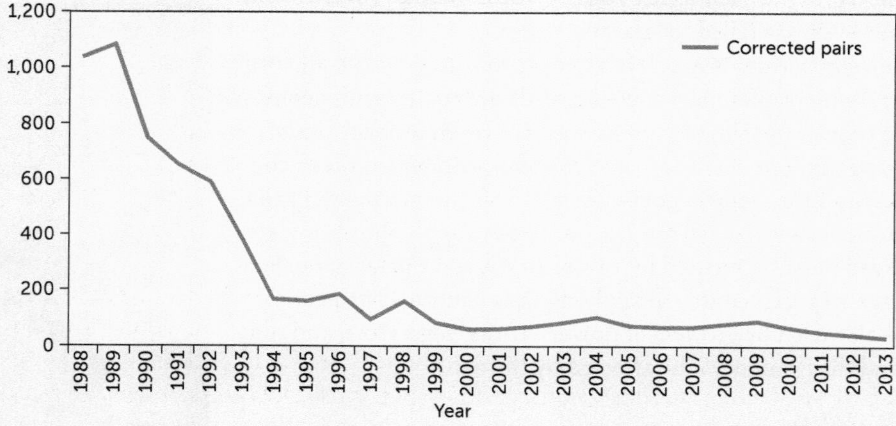

FIGURE 10.6 | Estimated pairs of burrowing owls reported by Operation Burrowing Owl sites. In 2013, there was a 41 per cent decrease from the 39 pairs reported by participants in 2012.

Source: Nature Saskatchewan (n.d.)

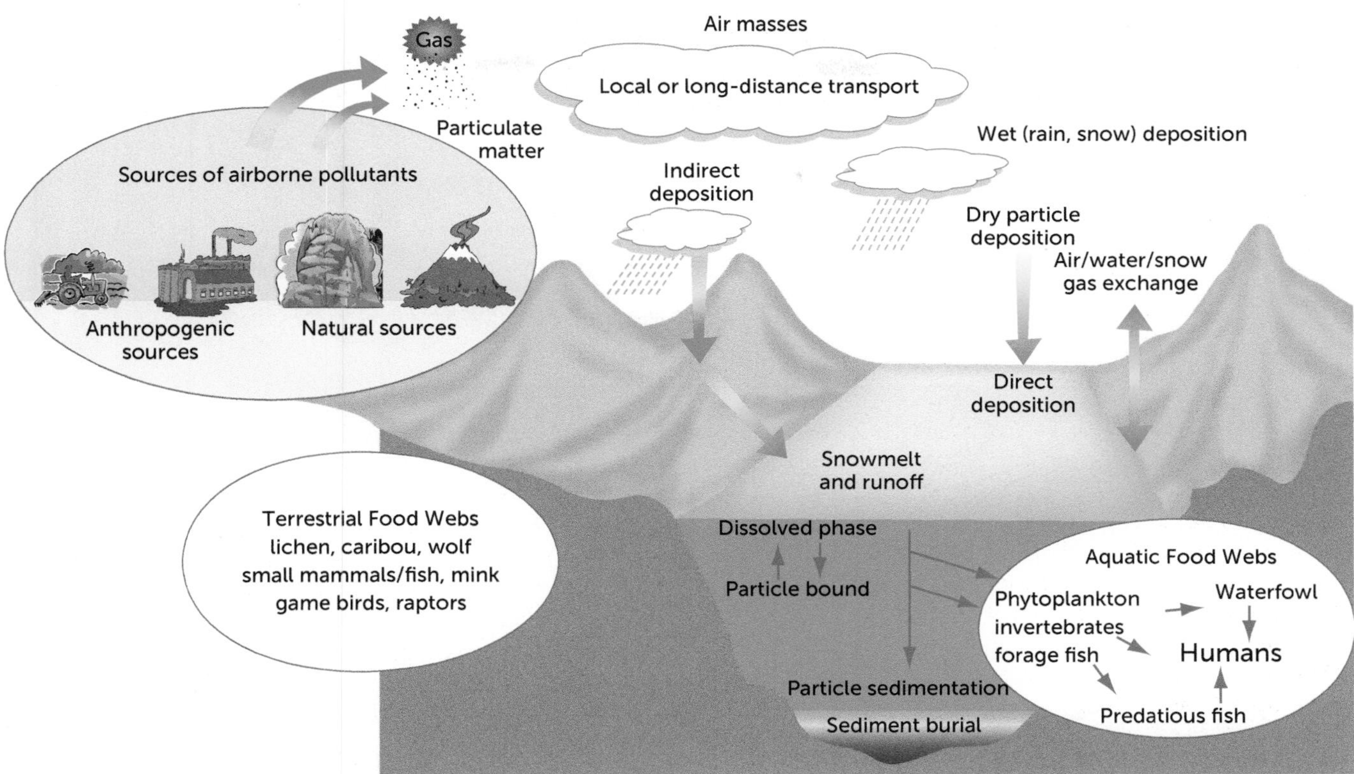

FIGURE 10.7 | Pesticide transportation in the environment.
Source: Adapted from Indian and Northern Affairs Canada (1997b).

the fourth time in four years in 2014, PEI Environment officials found themselves investigating a large fish kill of over 1,000 fish caused by biocide runoff.

Persistence

Not only do biocides spread over vast areas, they also continue to contaminate through time, as many are very persistent. DDT is one of the best-known insecticides. First synthesized more than 100 years ago, it was not until the 1940s that DDT became widely used, first in health programs in World War II to control disease vectors and later as an agricultural chemical. Production peaked by 1970, when 175 million kilograms were manufactured. By that time, the environmental effects of DDT were becoming better understood, and its use, but not manufacture, was banned in the US in 1972. It was not until 1985 that registration of all DDT products was discontinued in Canada. More than 7 million kilograms of DDT were sprayed on forests in New Brunswick and Quebec between the early 1950s and the late 1960s. DDT is extremely persistent. Even now, there are still considerable residues of DDT and its main breakdown product, DDE, in the environment. Because it is soluble in fat, DDT may also gradually accumulate over time in the tissues of organisms. This is known as **bioaccumulation** (Figure 10.8).

Organisms with long lifespans are particularly susceptible to bioaccumulation. In British Columbia, for example, HCH, once used as a timber preservative and agricultural spray and banned in the late 1970s, is still being found in geoducks, a type of clam, off the west coast of Vancouver Island and in Puget Sound. These large clams are filter-feeders that may live as long as 140 years. They are therefore very susceptible to bioaccumulation, and concentrations have been sufficient to have the clams refused by processing plants. In another example of the persistence of biocides in aquatic environments, researchers have detected high levels of toxaphene in trout in Bow Lake in Banff National Park, Alberta. The toxaphene had been applied in 1959 to rid the lake of what were then seen as undesirable fish species. DDT and other chemicals have been detected in trout in many of the lakes in Waterton, Banff, Jasper, and Yoho National Parks.

Biomagnification

The Arctic has generally been viewed as one of the few unpolluted regions of the world. But a closer look reveals a different story. High concentrations of persistent organic pollutants (POPs) such as organochlorine biocides have been detected in top predators of the Arctic food chain, including indigenous peoples. The ability of biocides and other toxic chemicals to traverse long distances, combined with the ability of biocides to concentrate and accumulate in the lipids of pelagic marine organisms (e.g., Atlantic cod, whales, seals), is

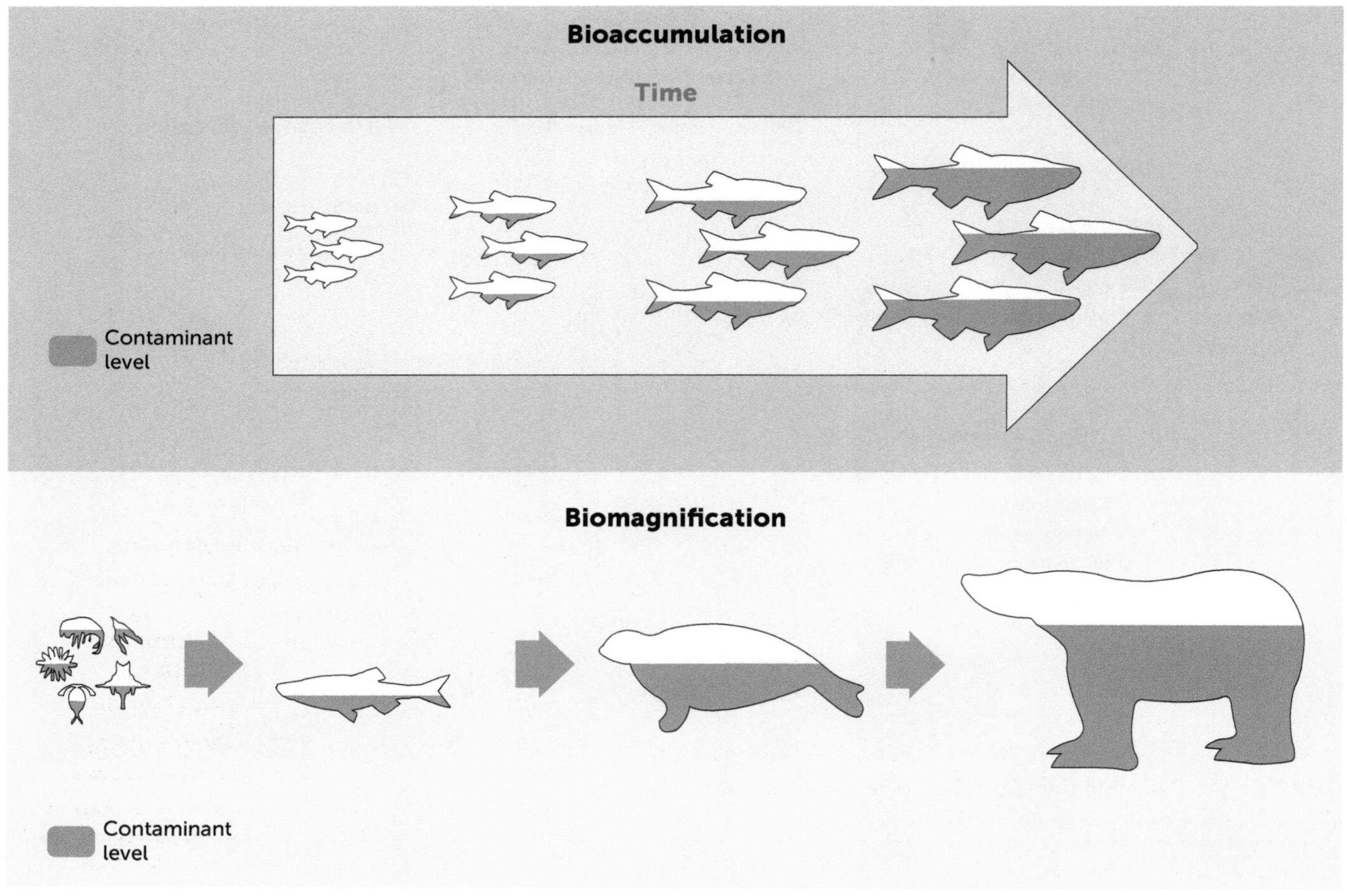

FIGURE 10.8 | Bioaccumulation and biomagnification.
Source: Adapted from Indian and Northern Affairs Canada (1997a).

ENVIRONMENT IN FOCUS

BOX 10.6 | The Grasshopper Effect

Imagine for a moment, if you will, the emotions we now feel: shock, panic, grief—as we discover that the food which for generations nourished us and keeps us whole physically and spiritually is now poisoning us. You go to the supermarket for food. We go out on the land to hunt, fish, trap, and gather. The environment is our supermarket. . . . As we put our babies to our breasts, we feed them a noxious chemical cocktail that foreshadows neurological disorders, cancers, kidney failure, reproductive dysfunction. That Inuit mothers—far from areas where POPs [persistent organochlorine pesticides] are manufactured and used—have to think twice before breastfeeding their infants is surely a wake-up call to the world.

—Sheila Watt-Cloutier, President, Inuit Circumpolar Conference (Canada) (2000)

We tend to think of the Arctic as "pristine wilderness." However, research has indicated that this is far from the truth. At Ice Island, for example, a floating ice-research station 1,900 kilometres above the Arctic Circle, concentrations of a family of pesticides called hexachlorocyclohexanes (HCHs) have been measured that are twice as high as those in agricultural southern Ontario. Yet there is not a single pesticide-dependent product grown in the North! How did the chemicals get there?

The so-called **grasshopper effect** is one reason behind Arctic pollution. Indeed, atmospheric transport and deposition is a major pathway of contamination. After chemicals are introduced into an environment, they are absorbed into the soils and/or plant tissues or deposited into rivers, lakes, and wetlands. Persistent and volatile pollutants evaporate into the air in warmer climates and travel in the atmosphere toward cooler areas, condensing out again when the temperature drops. The cycle then repeats itself in a series of "hops" until the pollutants reach climates where they can no longer evaporate. Chemicals released in southern Canada, for example, may go through the grasshopper cycle several times and take 10 years to reach the Arctic. Extremely volatile chemicals will travel farther and recondense in greater concentrations. For example, biocides such as lindane and HCH are quite volatile compared to DDT and therefore usually reach the North in greater quantities.

However, if only air transport were responsible, then the pollutants should have a fairly even distribution across the Arctic. Researchers found this not to be the case, with marked concentrations in some areas, particularly near bird colonies. These birds, such as fulmars, are at the top of the food chain and serve to concentrate the chemicals before excreting them on the local landscape, where concentrations can be 60 per cent higher than in the surrounding landscape.

The implications of this long-distance transport are serious. Arctic ecosystems are more vulnerable to toxic chemicals because they last longer in the North. Degradation processes are inhibited by low temperatures and reduced ultraviolet radiation from the sun. The cold also condenses the toxins, keeping them locked up and slowing evaporation rates. There are measurable concentrations of DDT, toxaphene, chlordane, and PCBs in the Arctic, and when fish and other species ingest these chemicals, they travel up the food chain, accumulating in the fatty tissue of animals at the top of the food chain.

Concentrations of several **persistent organochlorine pesticides (POPs)** remain high in many aquatic food webs in Canada. This has serious implications for the Inuit in particular because of their high consumption of wildlife. More than 80 per cent of Inuit consume caribou, almost 60 per cent consume fish, and almost 40 per cent consume marine mammals. Because of bioconcentration, the consumption of traditional foods places the Inuit at greater risk for developing several ailments related to toxic chemical exposure, including endocrine disruption, reproductive impairment, and cancer. These concerns are not restricted to the Arctic, since large concentrations of toxic chemicals have also been found in the mountains of British Columbia. Fish in alpine lakes have chemical levels that make them toxic to eat in large quantities.

Since POPs travel great distances, a global approach to tackle the issue is required. Various initiatives have been undertaken to control or eliminate POPs, including the Global POPs Protocol in 2000. Signatories, including Canada, agreed to a global ban of 12 chemicals, including the pesticides aldrin/dieldrin, endrin, DDT/DDE, HCH/lindane, chlordane, heptachlor, chlordecone, mirex, and toxaphene. Canada is also a signatory to the United Nations Economic Commission for Europe (UNECE) POPs Protocol, which lists 16 chemicals for phase-out. But while governments around the globe have a significant role to play in reducing Arctic pollution, consumers also share the responsibility. Chemicals used in consumers' everyday environment can end up polluting some of the most "pristine" environments on Earth. Consumers must make an effort to phase out domestic use of toxic chemicals.

Philip Dearden

People have the perception of the Arctic and Rockies as pristine wilderness areas. Marketers use this image to sell products such as water. In reality, these cold environments can have high toxic burdens due to the grasshopper effect.

to blame for the introduction of contaminants into the Arctic food web (Box 10.6). Concentrations of POPs multiply five- to tenfold with every step in the food chain. This process, known as **biomagnification**, is illustrated in Figure 10.9, showing the concentration of DDT and its derivatives along a food chain in the North Pacific Ocean. The relatively low concentrations at the lower end of the food chain are magnified many times by the time they reach top fish-eating predators. Most of the visible effects of POPs on animals are related to the ability to conceive and raise young. Malformations in reproductive organs, fewer young, and even complete failure to reproduce are some of the detrimental signs of high contaminant levels. Animals with a high load of organic contaminants are also more susceptible to infections, and POPs are suspected of being responsible for increased rates of malignant tumours in wildlife.

Some species build up very large concentrations. The beluga whales of the St Lawrence estuary, for example, showed concentrations of 70,000 to 100,000 parts per billion of DDT. Populations fell to less than 10 per cent of the original population in the area, and individual lifespans were about half the normal lifespan for the species, indicating that

Philip Dearden

Although Prince Edward Island is known for its beautiful rural landscape, the intensity of agricultural production has left large biocide residues, even in ocean sediments.

this level of toxic burden exceeded their level of tolerance (Chapter 2). Scientists examined 73 carcasses that washed ashore between 1983 and 1994 and found that 20 per cent of them had intestinal cancer. Of the 1,800 whales washed ashore and examined in the US, scientists found cancer in only one. Cancer has never been reported in Arctic belugas.

The toxic burdens of the belugas have now fallen significantly. A major component of the toxic burden for the belugas was mirex and its by-products. Mirex is a biocide, now banned, which was never produced along the St Lawrence. Biologists think that the source was Lake Ontario, where American eels accumulate the chemical. During their downstream migration, these eels constituted a significant part of the whales' food supply.

Biomagnification was largely responsible for the drastic population reductions of many birds during the 1960s and 1970s. Birds of prey such as ospreys, peregrine falcons, and bald and golden eagles and fish eaters such as double-crested cormorants, gannets, and grebes were particularly affected by the widespread use of insecticides. Some birds were killed directly through bioaccumulation and biomagnification, while many others were unsuccessful in breeding. DDT affects the calcium metabolism of these species, resulting in thinner eggshells and leading to breakage and chick mortality. The banning of DDT and similar chemicals has led to a recovery of many of these species in temperate countries (see Chapter 14). However, the continued use of the chemicals in some tropical countries still affects populations in these areas as well as the populations of migratory species such as peregrines.

© James Gritz/Alamy Stock Photo

The beluga whale population has declined rapidly in the St Lawrence, and the toxic burden from biocides appears to be one cause.

Together, biomagnification and bioaccumulation are often known as **bioconcentration**. Humans are exposed to the harmful effects of biocides through bioconcentration. They may come into contact with chemicals through contaminated water supplies and ingestion of food products, in their workplaces, and/or through domestic use (Box 10.7). Researchers found, for example, that women involved in farming in Ontario's Essex County have a risk of developing breast cancer nine times greater than non-farm women.

A greater dependence on fish or game birds for food may elevate the risk of biocide exposure, since fish and game birds may have already concentrated significant amounts of toxic matter in their fat deposits. Many indigenous communities are highly dependent on marine fish and mammals and may be particularly at risk. For example, levels of the biocide chlordane are significantly higher in the breast milk of Inuit women in the North than in women in southern Canada (UNEP, 2002).

Synergism

When chemicals are tested for their harmful effects, they are tested individually in controlled situations. When applied on farmers' fields, however, the chemicals are free to interact with each other and the environment in myriad ways. A single biocide may contain up to 2,000 chemicals, and as the chemicals break down, new ones are created that may again react with each other in unpredicted ways. The combined effects are often greater than the sum of their individual effects. This is called synergism, and it can result in many unanticipated effects.

Biocide Regulation

The concerns related to the use of biocides—resistance, non-selection, mobility, persistence, bioaccumulation, biomagnification, and synergism—are significant. However, the economic value tied to the use of biocides is also very significant. Because the use of biocides will likely continue to grow in the foreseeable future, there is a pressing need to strengthen the regulatory and enforcement mechanisms governing biocide import, production, and use.

In Canada, an estimated 1,000 new chemicals are introduced annually, adding to the more than 20,000 already in

ENVIRONMENT IN FOCUS

BOX 10.7 | Biocides and You

Although most biocides in Canada are used by commercial producers, large amounts are also used domestically in homes and on gardens and lawns to control unwanted organisms. How people use, store, and dispose of these chemicals is very important in terms of minimizing environmental damage. Here are a few tips.

- Use chemicals only as a last resort. Ask yourself why you need to kill the organism. If it is just for aesthetic reasons, such as dandelions on your lawn, then maybe you need to change your perceptions rather than automatically reaching for a chemical solution. For each pest or weed, there are usually several other approaches you can take as part of your own integrated pest management strategy. You can find out about more specific strategies from government ministries such as the ministry of agriculture in your area.
- Use the safest chemicals available in the minimum quantities. Many plant nurseries now sell products that are less toxic than traditional biocides. Often, they need more skill in application, but they are less environmentally damaging than regular chemicals. Examples include the "Safer Soap" line of products.
- Apply all chemicals in strict accordance with the manufacturer's instructions.
- Store unused chemicals so that they do not leak and cannot be accidentally upset.
- Dispose of chemicals and containers in a safe manner. Contact your local Ministry of Environment to see what programs are in place in your province for safe disposal. Some provinces, for example, have specific sites where biocides and other toxic chemicals can be disposed. If your province does not have such a program or acceptable alternative, start lobbying for one!

You should also protect yourself against the risk of ingesting chemicals that have been applied to food.

- Grow your own food; do not use chemicals.
- Buy organically grown produce whenever possible.
- Fruit and vegetables that look perfect often do so because they have had heavier applications of fertilizers and pesticides. Choose products that show more natural blemishes; this is a sign that chemical use has not been as high.
- Carefully wash all produce in soapy water.
- Remove the outer leaves of vegetables such as cabbage and lettuce, and peel all fruit.

industrial, agricultural, and commercial use. New chemicals cannot be introduced onto the market without undergoing scientific tests regarding their capacity to cause cancer, birth defects, and mutations. The Pest Management Regulatory Agency (PMRA), a branch of Health Canada created in 1995, has the primary responsibility for regulating biocides. Other Health Canada branches and other federal departments and agencies that play important roles in biocide management include Agriculture and Agri-Food Canada, the Canadian Food Inspection Agency, Environment Canada, Fisheries and Oceans Canada, and Natural Resources Canada. The federal government shares the responsibility for managing biocides with provincial, territorial, and in some cases municipal governments (Box 10.8). About 5,000 biocides are currently registered for use in Canada.

To predict the effectiveness of biocides and their risks to human health and the environment, the PMRA relies on the expertise and judgement of the agency's scientists and managers. Evaluation of a new biocide ends with the approval of the biocide label, which describes the biocide's hazards and its proper use. This process, however, has not been foolproof.

In 2003 a report titled *Managing the Safety and Accessibility of Pesticides* was released by the commissioner of the Environment and Sustainable Development. This report documented the adequacy (or lack thereof) of regulatory practices in Canada to approve biocide use, as well as the health and environmental standards relating to compliance, the government's commitment to research, and monitoring. The commissioner published a follow-up audit in 2008,

Biocides and human health.

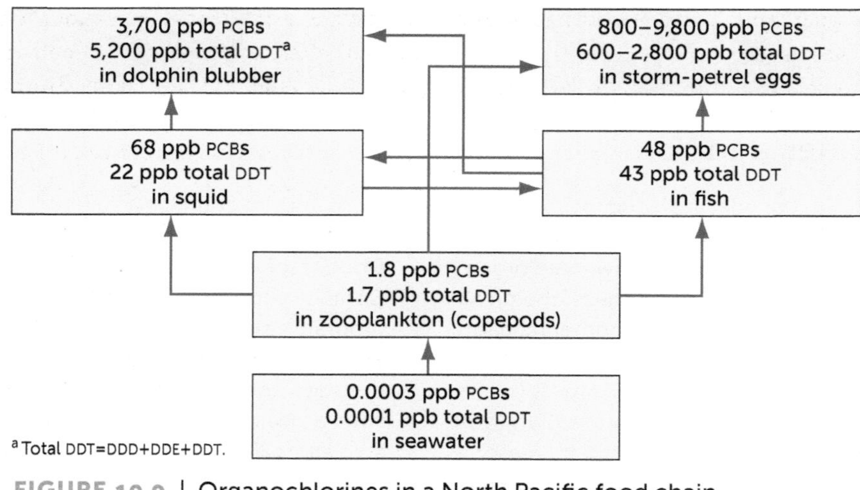

FIGURE 10.9 | Organochlorines in a North Pacific food chain.
Source: Nobel (1990).

concluding that the PMRA procedures had improved, as had procedures for re-evaluating chemicals, although there was still a considerable backlog and no action plan to deal with it. The Canadian Food Inspection Agency had also broadened the range of residue tests on fresh fruits and vegetables (Commissioner of the Environment and Sustainable Development, 2008: ch. 2).

Lack of compliance is partly due to problems with pesticide labels. Some agricultural pesticides may have 30 or more pages of directions in fine print, while other label instructions are difficult to follow. For example, labels are often ambiguous, and application therefore depends on the applicator's interpretation. Ambiguous, vague terms used on pesticide labels include:

- *Appropriate* buffer zones should be established between treatment areas and aquatic systems, and treatment areas and *significant* habitat.

ENVIRONMENT IN FOCUS

BOX 10. 8 | Cosmetic Use of Pesticides

The proportion of households using pesticides on their lawns and gardens in Canada dropped from 47 per cent in 1994 to 21 per cent in 2011. Municipalities also use substantial amounts of pesticides. Figures are difficult to obtain, but in Ontario in 1993, the amount was estimated at 1.3 million kilograms, about one-quarter of the amount used in agriculture in that province.

Because of potential negative impacts on human health, the Standing Committee on Environment and Sustainable Development (2000) recommended a ban on the use of biocides for cosmetic purposes—i.e., lawn care—but the federal government refused to endorse the recommendation (see cartoon on previous page). The government preferred to take a voluntary, educational approach to reducing the cosmetic use of pesticides and launched a Healthy Lawns Strategy to address the issue.

However, the government's educational approach did not satisfy all Canadians, particularly residents of a small community in Hudson, Quebec. Residents were worried about the health consequences of lawn and park applications of herbicides and insecticides, particularly on children. The community wanted the municipal government to enact a bylaw that would ban the cosmetic use of pesticides, but chemical companies won the first battle, arguing that municipal governments lacked the authority to introduce such bylaws. The community took the matter to court, and in June 2001, Canada's Supreme Court unanimously ruled that towns and cities have the right to enact bylaws banning the purely cosmetic use of pesticides. The Supreme Court ruling grants municipalities across the country the right to impose similar pesticide restrictions. In 2002, Halifax became the first large city to ban pesticide use. Today, more than 130 communities in Canada have bylaws banning the use of chemicals for cosmetic lawn purposes, including the entire province of Quebec. Toronto's Board of Health has endorsed a similar bylaw, initiating steps to phase out the use of pesticides on lawns for cosmetic purposes. In 2009 the province of Ontario followed suit and instigated a strict ban against cosmetic pesticide use, banning over 250 products for sale and 95 for use on lawns, gardens, patios, driveways, cemeteries, parks, and schoolyards.

- Do not apply in areas where soils are *highly* permeable and groundwater is *near* the surface.
- Do not apply *near* buildings inhabited by humans or livestock.
- Do not apply where fish and crustaceans are *important* resources.

Failure to follow label instructions could increase the risks to consumers and the environment, but it is difficult to apply pesticides appropriately when the directions are unclear. Many poisonings have been attributed to inappropriate application, and this is one reason why farmers in Ontario have welcomed mandatory biocide safety courses dealing with the use, mixing, handling, and transportation of biocides as well as laws governing their use. The certificate from these courses must be renewed every five years, and it must be presented in order to buy agricultural chemicals.

The federal Pest Control Products Act came into force in 2006. The Act requires that all pesticides be re-evaluated every 15 years against the most current health and environmental standards. A lack of transparency in the Act led to a petition in 2011 demanding that Health Canada release information on evaluation and approval of pesticides, specifically concerning health issues and pesticides used for cosmetic purposes. Health Canada responded with a full outline of procedures, which can be found through the Office of the Auditor General (http://www.oag-bvg.gc.ca/).

Intensive Livestock Operations

Livestock farming can have significant and far-reaching environmental implications. The production of livestock manure has both environmental benefits and drawbacks. Although manure is a valuable fertilizer for crop production, it can also become a source of pollution if not managed properly.

Manure consists of a variety of substances, including nitrogen, phosphorus, potassium, calcium, sodium, sulphur, lead, chloride, and carbon. Manure also contains countless micro-organisms, including bacteria, viruses, and parasites. Some of these micro-organisms are pathogenic, and therefore direct consumption or recreational use of water containing these organisms can lead to a variety of illnesses and even death. The contamination of drinking water with *E. coli* that killed seven residents of Walkerton, Ontario, in May 2000 was related to livestock manure (Chapter 11). Pathogens from manure that have reached watercourses also have the potential to spread disease to livestock. The spread of bovine spongiform encephalopathy (BSE), commonly referred to as "mad cow disease," is an example of an inter-species disease transmission. BSE is thought to cause Creutzfeldt-Jakob disease among humans.

Other risks to human and ecosystem health arise from air pollution. Odour and air pollution are identified as serious environmental and human health concerns related to **intensive livestock operations (ILOs)**. High concentrations of noxious gases such as methane, hydrogen sulphide, carbon dioxide, and ammonia are often found in manure pits and confinement barns. Pigs and poultry, for example, excrete some 65 and 70 per cent of their nitrogen and phosphorus intake, respectively. Nitrogen, under aerobic conditions, can evaporate in the form of ammonia (Chapter 4). Ammonium nitrate and ammonium sulphate emitted to the air from animal housing can be harmful to human and animal health. Foul odours emitted by ILOs are a significant problem for neighbours, and studies have shown an increase in chronic respiratory diseases reported by people who live in close proximity to a large animal farm. Ammonia can also have toxic and acidifying effects on ecosystems. Ammonia in high concentrations in the air can have a direct effect on plant growth by damaging leaf absorption capacities, but its indirect effect on soil chemistry is even more important—ammonia acidifies the soil, interfering with the absorption of other essential plant elements.

Issues also arise from the storage and use of livestock manure. Problems arise when storage systems are inadequately built or when they are sited too close to water supplies. Liquid manure stored in lagoons, for example, may overflow during periods of heavy rainfall, or the lagoons can fail to prevent the leaching of organic and inorganic materials into the surrounding environment.

Raw, well-rotted manure is often spread onto farm fields as fertilizer, a reasonable environmental practice as long as farmers have sufficient cropland to absorb the manure of their livestock. However, new large-scale farms produce vast quantities of manure and often do not have correspondingly large areas of farmland. In 2011 Canadian livestock produced an estimated 152 million tonnes of manure, containing over 1 million tonnes of nitrogen, 255,000 tonnes of phosphorus,

Aerial view of mixed breeds of cattle in pens at a large, modern beef feedlot with a 12,500-head capacity in Alberta.

and 524,000 tonnes of potassium. Over 50 per cent of manure production occurred in the South Saskatchewan and Assiniboine–Red drainage regions located in the Prairies and the Great Lakes drainage region in Ontario (Statistics Canada, 2014a). The hogs in Ontario currently produce as much raw sewage as the province's people.

If manure and commercial fertilizers are misused, spilled, or applied in excessive quantities, the result is contamination of soil and water by nitrogen, phosphorus, and bacteria. Although crops take up the bulk of added nutrients, a portion—the nutrient surplus—remains in the field. For all agricultural land in Canada, annual inputs of nitrogen and phosphorus from commercial fertilizers and livestock manure exceed annual outputs. There is a national surplus of approximately 0.3 million tonnes of nitrogen and 56,000 tonnes of phosphorus, or 8.4 kg/ha of nitrogen and 1.6 kg/ha of phosphorus. Fertilizers, whether organic or synthetic, are viewed as essential to maintain crop yield and soil health, but their application in excess of what crops can utilize can have significant implications for human and environmental health.

Nutrient loading can result in runoff to streams, rivers, lakes, and wetlands, spurring additional growth of algae and other aquatic plants. Accelerated eutrophication results in loss of habitat and changes in biodiversity (Chapter 4). For example, long-term exposure to elevated nitrate concentrations has contributed to the recent decline in frog and salamander populations in Canada. Concentrations of nitrate greater than 60 milligrams per litre in water kill the larvae of many amphibians. Reporting on fish kills from accidental spills/discharges of nutrient-related compounds is currently voluntary, so they are believed to be widely under-reported.

Factors influencing the effect of manure and commercial fertilizers on the environment include soil type, climate, precipitation, topography, and the quantities of manure produced. Most of these factors are beyond the farmer's control. However, manure management practices also influence the magnitude and extent of ecological impacts. Unfortunately, the environmental laws governing manure management were created when small operations were the norm, and therefore they fail to address the environmental and health risks that come with more intensive livestock operations. For example, in Ontario there are no legally binding standards for constructing manure storage facilities or for the application of manure. Nor are there any monitoring mechanisms to ensure that farmers use best practices for managing manure.

Sustainable Food Production Systems

The future capacity to deliver agricultural outputs depends on the continuing ecological viability of agro-ecosystems, yet significant stresses are imposed on them by intensification. The challenge is to foster agro-ecosystem management practices that will meet growing food, feed, and fibre needs while providing more environmental protection.

Improving agro-ecosystem management so that all levels of agricultural production can be associated with better environmental performance requires new knowledge and better skills, which can be achieved by improvements in technology, natural resource management systems, and landscape planning, as well as by policies and governance arrangements that help to integrate environmental values into agricultural investment and management decisions. Examples include integrated pest management, integrated plant nutrient systems, no-till and conservation agriculture, and permaculture. These approaches seek to meet the dual goals of increased productivity and reduced environmental impact.

Integrated Pest Management

Integrated pest management (IPM) seeks to avoid or reduce yield losses caused by diseases, weeds, insects, mites, nematodes, and other pests while minimizing the negative impacts of pest control (resistance, non-selection, mobility, persistence, bioconcentration, etc.). Originally used to reduce excessive use of pesticides while achieving zero pest incidence, the concept has broadened over time. The presence and density of pests and their predators and the degree of pest damage are monitored, and no action is taken as long as the level of pest population is expected to remain within specified limits.

IPM considers the crop and pest as part of a wider agro-ecosystem, promoting biological, cultural, and physical pest management techniques over chemical solutions to pest control. Combinations of approaches are used, including:

- bacteria, viruses, and fungi (pathogens)
- insects such as predators and parasites (biological management)
- disease and insect-resistant plant varieties
- synthetic hormones that inhibit the normal growth process
- behaviour-modifying chemicals and chemical ecology products (such as pheromones, kairomones, and allomones)

If pesticide use is deemed essential to pest control, only pesticides with the lowest toxicity to humans and non-target organisms are applied.

The adoption of IPM practices has economic and other benefits for farmers, but it requires more expertise than simply applying chemicals. For this reason, Ontario has established a formal system of IPM for agricultural commodities. Producers can obtain expert and current advice on these products, their pests, and optimal courses of action by phone. Ontario has also introduced a formal accreditation program for companies and facilities wishing to be IPM certified. Increased adoption of IPM and alternative pest control strategies, such as border sprays for migratory pests, mating disruption, alternate row spraying, and pest monitoring, are major reasons for these large declines. Internationally, some countries have developed aggressive IPM programs; Indonesia, for example, has managed to cut pesticide use by as much as 90 per cent, while Sweden has adopted a similar aggressive approach, reducing pesticide use by 50 per cent.

Integrated Plant Nutrient Systems

Agricultural production removes plant nutrients from the soil, reducing its organic and nutrient content. Imbalances in nutrient availability can lead to excessive depletion of nutrients that are in short supply, with corresponding reductions in crop yield. The goal of **integrated plant nutrient systems (IPNSs)** is to maximize nutrient use efficiency by recycling all plant nutrient sources within the farm and by using nitrogen fixation by legumes (Chapter 4) to the extent possible. Soil productivity is enhanced through a balanced use of local and external nutrient sources, including manufactured fertilizers. Fertilizers supplied in excess can pollute soils and waters, as discussed in Chapter 4, so IPNSs also seek to minimize the loss of nutrients through the judicious use of external fertilizers. IPNSs aim to optimize the productivity of the flows of nutrients passing through the farming system during a **crop rotation**. The quantities of nutrients applied are based on estimates of crop nutrient requirements—i.e., knowledge of the quantities of nutrients removed by crops at the desired yield level.

No-Till/Conservation Agriculture

To destroy weeds and loosen topsoil to facilitate water infiltration and crop establishment, agricultural land is plowed, harrowed, or hoed before every planting. Topsoil disturbance of this magnitude and frequency destabilizes the soil structure, leading to soil erosion and soil compaction, negatively affecting productivity and sustainability. The economic and ecological costs associated with conventional tillage systems are becoming more apparent, leading farmers to search for alternative land preparation techniques, such as **no-till/conservation agriculture (NT/CA)**. NT/CA (or zero, minimum, or low tillage) protects and stimulates the biological functioning of the soil while maintaining and improving crop yields.

Essential features of NT/CA include minimal soil disturbance restricted to planting and drilling (farmers use special equipment to drill seeds directly into the soil instead of plowing); direct sowing; maintenance of a permanent cover of live or dead plant material on the soil surface; and crop rotation, combining different plant families (e.g., cereals and legumes). Crops are seeded or planted through soil cover with special equipment or in narrow cleared strips. Soil cover inhibits the germination of many weed seeds, minimizing weed competition and reducing reliance on herbicides. Soil cover also reduces soil mineralization, erosion, and water loss, builds up organic matter, and protects soil micro-organisms. Crop sequences are planned over several seasons to minimize the buildup of pests or diseases and to optimize plant nutrient use by synergy among different crop types, and these sequences involve alternating shallow-rooting crops with deep-rooting ones to utilize nutrients throughout various layers of the soil. Other advantages associated with NT/CA include increased yields in the order of 20 to 50 per cent higher than with conventional tillage practices; reduction in the variability of yields from season to season; significant reductions in labour costs; and lower input costs, particularly for machinery (e.g., smaller tractors can be used, reducing fuel costs).

In Canada no-till increased to 56 per cent of the area tilled in 2014 from 29.7 per cent in 2001. The area worked with conventional tillage, which had historically been the most popular tillage method, dropped to 19 per cent in 2014 from 40.5 per cent in 2001. Conservation tillage—the midpoint between conventional and no-till, dropped from 29.8 per cent of tilled area to 25 per cent over the same fifteen-year period.

The increased popularity of no-till and decline in area of summer fallow have turned Canadian cropland into a greenhouse gas (GHG) sink rather than a source. In 1990, cropland was a source of 12 megatonnes (Mt) CO_2 equivalent GHG to the atmosphere, while in 2012 net removals of GHGs by cropland was 5 Mt CO_2 equivalent (Statistics Canada, 2014a).

Farms in Canada use various soil conservation methods. Crop rotation is the most common and is an important means of recharging soil nitrogen through use of legumes such as alfalfa and clover. Grassed waterways are used to control overland flow of runoff, thereby controlling the formation of gullies on exposed soil surfaces. **Contour cultivation** involves cultivating the soil parallel to the contour of the slope, which serves to reduce the speed of runoff by catching soil particles in the plow furrows. More than 16 per cent of PEI and Saskatchewan

Strip farming in Saskatchewan.

cropland is protected in this way. **Strip cropping** is a similar technique in which different crops may be planted in strips parallel to the slope. While one crop may be harvested, leaving bare soil, the other crop serves to provide some protection. This technique is commonly used against wind erosion and is most prevalent in western Canada. The soil surface can also be protected in winter through growth of a winter cover crop. This is effective not only for wind erosion in winter but also to protect the soil from intense rainfall in the spring.

Organic Farming

Approaches to sustainable agriculture such as IPM, IPNS, and conservation tillage each consider only one aspect of the farming system components—pest ecology, plant ecology, and soil ecology, respectively. Organic agriculture, however, combines these and other management strategies into a single approach, focusing on food web relations and element cycling to maximize agro-ecosystem stability. Organic agriculture is a production management system that aims to promote and enhance ecosystem health. It is based on minimizing the use of external inputs and represents a deliberate attempt to make the best use of local natural resources while minimizing air, soil, and water pollution. Synthetic pesticides, mineral fertilizers, synthetic preservatives, pharmaceuticals, genetically modified organisms, sewage sludge, and irradiation are prohibited in all organic standards (FAO, 2001; Canadian General Standards Board, 2003).

Organic agriculture encompasses a range of land, crop, and animal management procedures designed to:

- Enhance biological diversity within the whole system
- Increase soil biological activity
- Maintain long-term soil fertility
- Recycle wastes of plant and animal origin in order to return nutrients to the land, thus minimizing the use of non-renewable resources
- Rely on renewable resources in locally organized agricultural systems
- Promote healthy use of soil, water, and air as well as minimize all forms of pollution that may result from agricultural practices
- Handle agricultural products with emphasis on careful processing methods in order to maintain the organic integrity and vital qualities of the product at all stages
- Become established on any existing farm through a period of conversion, the appropriate length of which is determined by site-specific factors such as the history of the land and the type of crops and livestock to be produced

For example, organic practices that encourage soil biological activity and nutrient cycling include manipulation of crop rotations and strip cropping, the use of **green manure** and organic fertilizer (animal manure, compost, crop residues), minimum tillage or zero tillage, and avoidance of pesticide and herbicide use. Organic agriculture significantly increases the density of beneficial invertebrates, earthworms, root symbionts, and other micro-organisms essential to maintaining soil health. For example, the biomass of earthworms in organic systems is 30 to 40 per cent higher than in conventional systems.

Organic farming systems are also more energy efficient per unit crop than conventional farming techniques, since organic systems resemble closed or semi-closed nutrient cycles. Organic land management permits the development of a rich weed flora, and a versatile flora attracts more kinds of beneficial insects. Organic farming systems are also better at controlling erosion, since organic soil management techniques improve soil structure. Organically grown foods also benefit human health, since they contain fewer pesticide residues than foodstuffs grown under intensive farming methods.

In 2012 there were 37.5 million hectares of organic agricultural land globally, with the largest areas of organic agricultural land being Oceania (Australia and the Pacific, 32 per cent of the world's organic agricultural land) and Europe (30 per cent) followed by Latin America (18 per cent), Asia (9 per cent), North America (8 per cent), and Africa (3 per cent). By country, Australia has the most, followed by Argentina and the United States. About two-thirds of the organic land is in grasslands. Overall, less than 1 per cent of the agricultural land of 164 reporting countries is organic (Willer and Lernoud, 2014).

Canada has national organic standards, regulations, and inspection and certification systems that govern the production and sale of foods labelled as "organic." In 2007, federal regulations were introduced for organic certification, and were revised in 2009 to ease the way for organic trade of produce between provinces and other countries. These standards are again under review, with a report on updated standards available by the end of 2015.

In 2009, agricultural land under certified organic management averaged 1.7 per cent of total agricultural land in Canada, compared to 5.6 per cent of total agricultural land in the EU, 1.7 per cent in Australia, and 0.7 per cent in the United States (Willer and Lernoud, 2014). In most developing countries, agricultural land reported under certified organic production is less than 0.5 per cent, although the extent of non-market, non-certified organic agriculture may be considerable. For example, an estimated one-third of West African agricultural produce is produced organically (Willer and Lernoud, 2014).

More than 15,000 farm operations in Canada (6.8 per cent) reported at least one type of organic product in 2006 and there were almost 4,000 certified organic farms by 2009. (Agriculture and Agri-Food Canada, 2015). However, the number of producers is declining overall, with the highest declines in Manitoba and Saskatchewan (Holmes and Macy, 2014). The highest number of certified organic producers is now in Quebec. Non-certified organic production is also common, with the most likely application being animal products. The total acreage in certified production, including both annual and perennial crops, forages and pasture, is estimated at 825,079 hectares. Field crops such as buckwheat, oats, barley and flax dominate certified Canadian organic production. Canada is among the top five world producers of organic grains and oilseeds. By 2012, organic food sales contributed $3 billion a year to the Canadian economy, representing a tripling in value since 2006 (Holmes and Macy 2014). The domestic organic market is strongest in British Columbia, Alberta, Quebec, and Ontario. Nevertheless, Saskatchewan has the highest proportion of certified organic producers, with 38 per cent of the national total.

An organic farm food market near the urbanized area of Markham, Ontario. In Canada, demand for most organic products continues to exceed supply.

Consumer health and food quality concerns (e.g., concerns about growth-stimulating substances, genetically modified [GM] food, dioxin-contaminated food, and livestock epidemics such as bovine spongiform encephalopathy and foot-and-mouth disease) continue to drive demand for organic products in Canada and around the globe. Organic food production systems are considerably more respectful of the environment than chemically intensive farming practices, but chemical-intensive farming systems still dominate.

In the absence of governmental support for the expansion of organic production, farmers may be reluctant to convert to organic farming for several reasons. Conversion from conventional, intensive systems to organic production causes a loss in yields, the extent of which varies depending on the biological attributes of the farm, farmer expertise, the extent to which synthetic inputs were used under previous management, and the state of natural resources. Yields can be 10 to 30 per cent lower in organic systems, and it may take several years (e.g., three to five) to restore the ecosystem to the point where organic production becomes economically viable. In addition, production costs per unit of production (e.g., labour, certification and inspection fees) and marketing expenses can be higher with organic produce, but once produce qualifies as *certified* organic, some costs can be offset by price premiums. In developed countries, retail organic products can command 10 to 50 per cent more than conventional prices for the same commodity. In many places, rising fuel costs and depleting supplies have increased the costs of agricultural inputs, making organic agriculture a more economically viable alternative. In Canada, demand for most organic products continues to exceed supply, despite the higher prices charged for certified organic produce. Consumers in industrialized countries are willing to pay a premium for organic food because they perceive environmental, health, or other benefits.

In Canada and elsewhere, cases are emerging in which organic production is constrained or no longer feasible because of the advent of GM crops. Organic farmers in Canada can no longer grow organic canola (i.e., oilseed rape) because of GM canola contamination in Saskatchewan.

In many places, demand for organic foods cannot be met with the current supply. As a result, supermarkets are beginning to offer organic produce, increasing the availability of these foods for the general population. In fact by 2010, 54 per cent of organic food products were sold by mass-market retailers. Many mass-market retailers rely on large quantities of food products from a high production source—increasing the incentive for intensified organic agriculture. Most small farmers cannot compete with the impossibly low prices offered by intensified organic agriculture, and are threatened by these developments. If you walk through the organic section in a supermarket, how many products are available from your local area? From Canada? Should we have more local products available?

Local Agriculture

Canada currently imports over 70 per cent of its food. The majority of domestic products that feature a "Made in Canada" label contain imported ingredients (CFIA, 2010). The global food system allows us to eat bananas while there is snow on the ground, but this also dramatically increases our food miles. **Food miles** measure the distance your food must travel from where it was produced to reach your plate. As food miles increase, greenhouse gas emissions, rural unemployment, and local food insecurity grow correspondingly. For instance, the average food item in Toronto travels close to 4,500 kilometres before it is consumed (Toronto Public Health, 2007). The development of local food systems can contribute to reducing the impact of agriculture on the environment and local agricultural economies.

Local agriculture often consists primarily of small farms, characterized by diverse crops, low capital, and, consequently, low energy inputs and high levels of human labour. This is in stark contrast with the high energy inputs common to producing a single crop in most industrial agricultural practices. Many small farms have a greater yield per hectare than large farms, in part due to the human labour involved. The amount of food produced and consumed in a region can influence the food security of the area, which is highly variable both spatially and temporally (Morrison et al., 2011).

The logic for eating locally seems very persuasive and gave popularity to the "100 mile diet," a term coined by two Vancouverites who in 2005 decided to spend a year only eating food that was demonstrably produced within 100 miles of that city (Smith and MacKinnon, 2007). Their book was an instant success and helped cultivate further the **locavore** movement that was emerging elsewhere, especially in North America. Locavores are people who are interested in eating locally produced food. In fact, this is most often the case for many poorer people around the world and, even in Europe, there is still a much greater and ongoing tradition for eating locally produced food. However, to new generations in North America, the idea seemed novel and attracted many adherents.

Eating locally is a good, simple idea, but things in reality are more complex. If the goal is just to support local farmers and protect farmland, then it works admirably. However, when the goal is extended to aspects of food production such as minimizing environmental impacts, then many other factors have to be taken into account besides the "food miles" involved in transport. For example, one study of lamb consumption in the UK found that eating lamb imported from New Zealand actually had a lower impact than eating locally reared animals. The New Zealand sheep were raised on grass, compared with the grain-fed UK sheep. Thus, the second law of thermodynamics (Chapter 2) once again triumphs, as the extra energy transition steps involved in growing the grain ensure that the final energy input into the UK sheep is much higher than for the sheep from New Zealand. Transport costs are often only a small component (about 10 per cent on average) of the final energetic cost of food production. This does not mean that being a locavore is not a good thing to do; it just illustrates that if the main goal is to reduce environmental impact, then eating locally may not achieve that goal. Organic and local is a better combination.

While there are challenges associated with local food consumption, various solutions have emerged as people aim to decrease their impact on the environment and increase their food security. For example, urban agriculture is being practised throughout Canada in the form of community gardens, rooftop gardens, or growing peri-urban crops. In Montreal, a group of eager gardeners has collaborated to offer city-wide tours of urban agriculture ventures featuring the unique practices employed by each. One practice used in many urban agriculture centres is **permaculture**. Permaculture agricultural designs are based on ecological relationships with the fundamental principle of minimizing wasted energy. In these systems, the wastes of one component become the inputs for another. Some rooftop permaculture catches rainwater to feed plants that are strategically positioned to ward off pests, capture nutrients, and provide shelter.

Implications

Agricultural modification is arguably the main impact that humans have had on natural ecosystems. It is, however, also one of the oldest and one that is basically a modification of ecological systems to benefit humans. Over centuries, natural and human-modified agricultural landscapes have existed and transformed from one state to the other with little lasting damage to planetary life-support systems. However, as additional auxiliary energy flows were applied to boost the productivity of agriculture, the differences between these two ecological systems became more distinct, and the impacts of agriculture on natural ecosystems increased. Agricultural production (certainly in Canada's commercial agricultural sector) is now more similar to industrial production than to the natural ecosystems from which agriculture was derived.

This industrialization has led to many environmental challenges for agriculture. Yields are declining in some areas as crops become less responsive to fertilizer input, biocides continue to eliminate many natural enemies of pests, and soils are eroded, salinized, and compacted. In response, researchers are suggesting that a fundamental restructuring is required in how agriculture is undertaken, with the emphasis changing from maximizing productivity to ensuring sustainability.

Achieving sustainability and resilience will require greater attention to the agro-ecosystem and particularly to the soil base that sustains agriculture. In addition, the socio-economic and regulatory dimensions will need to be integrated into systemic change. Organic farming will not be successful, however, unless customers are willing to pay for the produce, not only as a benefit to themselves but also to sustain and nourish healthier ecosystems overall. In addition to buying organic produce, we can do a number of things as individuals to ensure that we at least do not exacerbate the challenges now facing agricultural systems (Box 10.9).

Various countries collaborated at the World Food Summit in 1996 and stated that food security exists "when all people, at all times, have physical and economic access to sufficient, safe, and nutritious food to meet their dietary needs and food preferences for an active and healthy life" (WHO, n.d.). The implications of this statement on food security both globally and in Canada are reviewed in the "Domestic Guest Statement" below by researchers from the University of Guelph. Further Canadian perspectives are provided by Wakefield et al. (2014).

DOMESTIC GUEST STATEMENT

Perspectives on Food Security | *Ashley McInnes and Evan D.G. Fraser*

Global Food Security Perspectives

While many agree that population growth and climate change are causing a "food crisis," few agree on the best solutions (Fraser, 2013). For instance, some focus on what is described as "sustainable intensification," namely developing technologies to boost production by 70 per cent while reducing agriculture's impact on the environment (Godfray et al., 2010). Other experts argue that the food crisis has very little to do with production and is actually a crisis of food distribution (Tomlinson, 2010). Arguments about distribution go back to at least the 1980s, when scholars and aid workers concerned with food security began to consider food access (defined as whether people can obtain the food that is present in a given location) along with food availability (defined in terms of the food that is present in a location).

Amartya Sen won a Nobel Prize in economics for his work on food distribution. Sen (1981: 1) argues "starvation is the characteristic of some people not having enough to eat. It is not the characteristic of there not being enough food to eat." Sen uses the Bangladesh famine of 1974 to illustrate this point by showing that of all the years between 1971 and 1975, food production was highest in 1974. Yet, 1974 was the year that famine hit. The cause for the famine was floods, which meant that farm labourers lost their jobs and were unable to purchase the food the country was producing (Sen, 1981; see also Fraser, 2007 for a review of a series of other famines).

Scholars critical of the need to produce more food often cite data from the United Nations Food and Agriculture Organization that show the world produces over 2,800 dietary calories per person per day, which is more than enough (FAO, 2015); yet, over a billion people are overweight or obese while almost a billion are undernourished (Popkin, Adair, and Ng, 2012). Furthermore, about 30 per cent of the world's food is wasted (Gustavsson, Cederberg, Sonesson, van Otterdijk, and Meybeck, 2011). Finally, recently published work shows that promoting gender equality, clean water, sanitation, and women's education are more effective at reducing childhood food insecurity than measures to boost production (Dougill, Fraser, and Reed, 2011; Smith and Haddad, 2015). As a result, many scholars worry that if we focus on sustainable intensification we risk proposing technological solutions to problems that are political and economic in nature (Holt-Gimenez, 2014).

Canadian Food Security Perspectives

These global-scale debates are just as relevant in Canada. As noted elsewhere in this chapter, the food system plays an important role in the Canadian economy. Yet scholars suggest that Canadian food and agriculture policy has prioritized production and economic growth at the expense of producers and consumers (Eaton, 2013). For instance, while our farms are producing more food than ever before and corporations are experiencing record profits, farmer incomes hover near zero and almost all the $795 billion generated in farm production revenues between 1985 and 2010 was transferred from family farms to transnational corporations (Qualman, 2011). Simultaneously, food bank use is rising and nearly 2.5 million Canadians are classified as "food insecure" (Wiebe and Wipf, 2011).

Arguing that these issues are exacerbated by high production, many Canadian scholars focus on political, rather than technological, solutions (Wittman, Desmarais, and Wiebe, 2011). For these scholars, these issues occur because we have adopted a "cheap food" policy (MacRae, 2011) that encourages farmers to overproduce certain commodities (such as corn and soy) that are grown in monocultures and used primarily in unhealthy processed food, causing environmental and human health problems. Food is "cheap" largely because social (e.g., declining rural communities), economic (e.g., health care) and environmental (e.g., soil and water quality) costs are "externalized" or not taken into account (MacRae, 2011).

Arguing for a "joined-up" food policy, MacRae (2011) suggests that integrating all relevant policy domains (agriculture, environment, health, social and economic development) will allow for more informed policy decisions. Such a broad shift is unlikely in the short term, given the current political culture (sometimes referred to as "neo-liberal restructuring") that emphasizes deregulation of social and environmental protection and increasing market-friendly policies such as trade liberalization.

Other academics argue that equitable and sustainable policies should include establishing higher environmental regulations to narrow the gap between high-quality food produced at voluntary standards (such as organic or fair-trade food) and low-cost food produced at existing regulations (Friedmann, 2005). Another proposed area of policy reform is to help family farmers through support for marketing boards to ensure farmers receive fair prices for produce (Magnan, 2011). A third strategy is to reward farmers (through grants or subsidies) for using "ecological production practices" and technologies that promote more crop diversification and better soil health (Benton, Dougill, Fraser, and Howlett, 2011). Not only would such measures benefit the

Continued

environment, they would also make farms more resilient to droughts and pests, which should reduce demands placed on government-funded safety nets such as crop insurance (MacRae, Frick, and Martin, 2007).

Focusing on the Canadian North, social issues become even more apparent in that the decline of traditional Inuit hunting has meant that many Northern communities have lost all "food sovereignty" and have become dependent on imported, expensive, and often unhealthy foods (People's Food Policy Project, 2011). This problem is being tackled by the federal government's Nutrition North Canada program that aims to make nutritious food more affordable in Nunavut. Unfortunately, some argue that this program has been ineffective due to a lack of transparency and power for those who depend on the program, since there is no required monitoring to guarantee subsidies are passed onto consumers (Splawinski, 2015). While political change is necessary, so is promoting indigenous food production capacity through learning and sharing programs that link traditional knowledge with permaculture technologies and practices (Morrison, 2011). Properly designed, such programs should reduce dependence on imported food. Hence, even in Canada's far North, we see the tension between those who promote a technical perspective on food availability versus those who focus on the politics of food access.

Ashley McInnes is a PhD candidate in the Department of Geography at the University of Guelph. Her research focuses on sustainability transitions in the context of the Canadian food system. She currently is co-chair of the Guelph-Wellington Food Round Table.

Evan Fraser is a Canada Research Chair and a professor of geography at the University of Guelph. He leads a multidisciplinary research program on global food security both in Canada and in the global South. For more information, see feeding9billion.com.

ENVIRONMENT IN FOCUS

BOX 10.9 | What You Can Do: Food Awareness

Although the challenges facing agriculture at the global and national levels are immense, there are still some ways in which individuals can help.

1. Eat less. This entails finding out about good nutritional habits so that we consume only the food that we really need.
2. Eat lower on the food chain. Most North Americans eat far too much meat. Eating more vegetables will benefit not only the global food situation but your own health.
3. Feed your pet lower on the food chain. Dogs and cats will also be healthier if fed on balanced grain pet foods rather than meat.
4. Waste less food. Studies indicate that as much as 25 per cent of food produced in North America is wasted.
5. Grow at least some of your own food. If Canadians were to devote a fraction of the time and resources on growing food that they spend on their lawns, it would allow more food for others elsewhere.
6. Support local food growers and food co-ops. This helps to protect agricultural land in Canada from being transformed to other uses.
7. Learn what foods are in season in your area, and try to build your diet around them.
8. Ask the manager or chef of your favourite restaurant how much of the food on the menu is locally grown, and then encourage him or her to source more food locally. You can do the same at your local supermarket or school cafeteria.
9. Take a trip to a local farm to learn what it produces.
10. Host a harvest party at your home or in your community that features locally available and in-season foods.
11. Produce a local food directory that lists all the local food sources in your area, including farmers' markets, food co-ops, restaurants emphasizing seasonal cuisine and local produce, and farmers willing to sell directly to consumers year round.
12. Buy extra quantities of your favourite fruit or vegetable when it is in season and experiment with drying, canning, jamming, or otherwise preserving it for a later date.
13. Join one of the NGO groups that specializes in rural development in less developed countries.

Summary

1. Agriculture originated at least 9,000 years ago, when societies domesticated both plant and animal species. Societies around the globe flourished by improving their capacity to expand agricultural production.

2. Over much of history, agricultural output has been increased by bringing more land into production. Today, intensification of production—obtaining more output from a given area of agricultural land—has become a key development strategy in most parts of the world to meet the increased demand for foodstuffs. The future capacity to deliver agricultural outputs depends on the continuing ecological viability of agro-ecosystems.

3. Enough food is produced to fulfill the daily calorific requirements of everyone on Earth. However, over 800 million people are chronically undernourished. This number is falling over time, particularly through successful food programs in Latin America, the Caribbean, and China.

4. Agriculture is a food chain, with humans as the ultimate consumers. The second law of thermodynamics dictates that the shorter the food chain, the more efficient it will be.

5. The Green Revolution and the Livestock Revolution have led to profound changes to the global land base. Complex natural systems have been replaced by relatively simple control systems in which humans are in command of the species and numbers that exist in a given area.

6. The Green Revolution relies on auxiliary energy flows, such as fertilizers, biocides, fossil fuels, and irrigation systems, to increase yields. Yields have risen tremendously over the last 30 years but are falling in many of the poorest parts of the world because of soil exhaustion and the rising price of fertilizers. Industrial systems of livestock production also depend on outside supplies of feed, energy, and other inputs to satisfy growing worldwide demand for meat.

7. Genetically modified organisms (GMOs) have potential to boost yields in many areas, but also have many undesirable side effects.

8. Global climate change will have a strong overall negative impact on global food production, especially in tropical countries.

9. Biofuels have great potential to be part of adaptation to reducing GHGs and creating higher values for agricultural products in many underdeveloped countries, but they also create challenges in terms of competition with food supply and encourage greater transformation of biodiversity-rich forests into agricultural land. Cellulosic production seems to have the greatest potential to address these problems in the future.

10. There has been a major increase in livestock production in many parts of the world to meet dietary demands accompanying economic growth. Livestock production has many undesirable environmental impacts, ranging from contributions to global climate change through to water pollution.

11. Agriculture is an important industry in Canada, accounting for 8 per cent of gross domestic product, 12 per cent of employment, and about 6 per cent of total merchandise export earnings. Many of the innovations and technologies employed by Canadian farmers to produce agricultural products have extraordinary implications for ecosystems.

12. The area of agricultural land in Canada is declining, largely as a result of urbanization on the most productive agricultural lands.

13. Large increases in fertilizer inputs have occurred in Canada over the past three decades.

14. Land degradation includes a number of processes that reduce the capability of agricultural lands to produce food. One study suggests that such processes cost Canadian farmers more than $1 billion per year.

15. Soil erosion is estimated to cost $707 million per year in terms of reduced yields and higher costs. Soil formation in Canada is slow. A rate of 0.5 to 1.0 tonnes per hectare (t/ha) per year may be considered average. Losses of 5 to 10 t/ha are common in Canada, and figures of 30 t/ha have been recorded in the Fraser River Valley.

16. Increasing acidity as a result of the application of nitrogen fertilizers and acid deposition is also a problem that reduces crop yields. Salinization occurs where there are high sodium levels in the soils and shallow water tables, such as in the Prairie provinces. One estimate suggests that salinization causes economic losses four to five times as great as losses due to erosion, acidification, and loss of nitrogen.

17. Cultivation involves a continual process of removing plant matter from a field. In the process, both the organic content and nutrient content of the soil are reduced. On the Prairies, current organic matter levels are estimated to be 50 to 60 per cent of the original levels.

18. Biocides are applied to crops to kill unwanted plants and insects that may hinder the growth of the crop. They have boosted yields throughout the world and helped feed many hungry mouths. There is also clear scientific evidence that they have serious negative impacts on ecosystem health.

19. Biocides promote the development of resistance among target organisms. Over the past 40 years, more than 1,000 insects have developed such resistant populations. These chemicals are non-selective and tend to kill non-target as well as target organisms. They may also be highly mobile and move great distances from their place of application. In addition, they may persist for a long time in the environment and accumulate along food chains. Such biomagnification has resulted in drastic reductions in the populations of some species at higher trophic levels, such as ospreys and bald eagles.

20. Chemicals, and their constituents as they break down, may interact synergistically.

21. Attention is being devoted to sustainable food production systems that maintain or enhance environmental quality, generate adequate economic and social returns to all individuals/firms in the production system, and produce a sufficient and accessible food supply. Integrated pest management is becoming more popular, and several provinces have such programs.

22. Organic farming is growing rapidly but is still a relatively small part of overall agricultural production.

Key Terms

arable land
bioaccumulation
biocides
bioconcentration
biofuels
biomagnification
contour cultivation
crop rotation
demitarian
food miles
genetically modified organisms (GMOs)
grasshopper effect
green manure
Green Revolution
hybridization
integrated pest management (IPM)
integrated plant nutrient systems (IPNSs)
intensive livestock operations (ILOs)
Livestock Revolution
locavore
monoculture cropping
no-till/conservation agriculture (NT/CA)
organic farming
permaculture
permanent cropland
permanent pastures
persistent organochlorine pesticides (POPs)
salinization
Silent Spring
soil compaction
soil erosion
strip cropping
subsistence farming
summer fallow
virtual water

Questions for Review and Critical Thinking

1. How do the laws of thermodynamics apply to agriculture?

2. Indicate how the concepts of "limiting factors" and "range of tolerance," discussed in Chapter 4, can be applied to agriculture.

3. Considerable interest is being directed toward ecosystem management. What is the relevance of this concept, if any, for agriculture?

4. Do you think that biofuels have an important role to play in agricultural systems in the future? How would you try to mitigate some of the challenges presented by biofuels?

5. What do you think might be the main challenges facing the global agricultural supply in five years?

6. In this chapter, mention was made of the resilience of farm systems. In Chapter 6, in relation to adaptive management, attention was also given to resilience. What value do the concepts of resilience and adaptive management have regarding agriculture?

7. How would you go about identifying and assessing the impacts (environmental and social) of agricultural policies and practices in Canada? What ideas from Chapter 6 might be helpful in this exercise?

8. If you were a commercial farmer in Canada, to what extent would it be important for you to consider the implications of climate change for your farming operations?

Related Websites

Agriculture and Agri-Food Canada
www.agr.gc.ca

Agriculture and Agri-Food Canada: Sustainable Development
www.agr.gc.ca/eng/about-us/planning-and-reporting/sustainable-development/?id=1175526032952

Consultative Group on International Agricultural Research (CGIAR)
www.cgiar.org

Environment Canada
www.ec.gc.ca

FAO Statistics Division
http://faostat3.fao.org/home/E

Food and Agriculture Organization of the United Nations (FAO)
www.fao.org

Hinterland Who's Who: Pesticides and Wild Birds
www.hww.ca/en/issues-and-topics/pesticides-and-wild-birds.html

World Wildlife Fund: Causes for Concern: Chemicals and Wildlife
panda.org/downloads/toxics/causesforconcern.pdf

Further Readings

Note: This list comprises works relevant to the subject of the chapter but not cited in the text. All cited works are listed in the References at the end of the book.

Calvert, K., and W. Mabee. 2015. "More solar farms or more bioenergy crops? Mapping and assessing potential land-use conflicts among renewable energy technologies in eastern Ontario, Canada," *Applied Geography* 56: 209–21.

Campbell, I.D., D.G. Durant, K.L. Hunter, and K.D. Hyatt, 2014. "Food Production," in F.J. Warren and D.S. Lemmen, eds, *Canada in a Changing Climate: Sector Perspectives on Impacts and Adaptation*, Ottawa: Government of Canada, 99–134.

FiBL and International Federation of Organic Agriculture Movements (iFoam). 2014. *The World of Organic Agriculture: Statistics & Emerging Trends 2014*. Germany: Medienhaus Plump.

Iizumi, T., and N. Ramankutty. 2014. "How do weather and climate influence cropping area and intensity?" *Global Food Security*. DOI:10.1016/j.gfs.2014.11.003

Koning, N., and M.K. Van Ittersum. 2009. "Will the world have enough to eat?" *Current Opinion in Environmental Sustainability* 1: 77–82.

Go to www.oupcanada.com/DeardenMitchell5e to access additional learning tools on your smartphone, tablet, or PC.

CHAPTER ELEVEN
Water

Learning Objectives

- To recognize the water endowment in Canada
- To understand the hydrological cycle
- To know the environmental and social impacts associated with water diversions
- To appreciate various perspectives related to water export from Canada
- To understand the significance of point and non-point sources of pollution
- To learn about the concept of "water security"
- To gain an understanding of the concept of a "multi-barrier approach" to drinking water protection
- To understand the challenges and opportunities regarding water security on Aboriginal reserves
- To appreciate the distinctions among supply management, demand management, and the soft path approach
- To understand the concepts of "virtual water" and "water footprint"
- To realize that water is both a resource and hazard
- To appreciate the difference between structural and non-structural approaches to flood damage reduction
- To understand the significance of droughts
- To appreciate the significance of heritage related to protection of aquatic systems
- To understand the importance of hydrosolidarity and integrated water resource management (IWRM)
- To appreciate the evolving ideas related to "water ethics"
- To understand perspectives related to the issue of "water as a human right"

Introduction

Environment Canada (2012) reports that in terms of water, although Canada has just 0.5 per cent of the world's population, Canadians have access to almost 20 per cent of the global stock of fresh water, and Canada has 6.5 per cent of the total flow of renewable water. Nevertheless, this apparent natural bounty is often taken for granted, it seems, since Canadians are among the highest consumers of water in terms of per capita water use (251 litres/capita/day in 2011), second only to citizens of the United States (333 litres/capita/day in 2010). This high use was characterized some time ago by Foster and Sewell (1981: 7) as due to a "myth of superabundance."

With or without a myth of superabundance, Canada has a relatively and absolutely generous endowment of water. In contrast, countries in the Middle East and Sahelian Africa usually experience significant water deficits that are a major impediment to overcoming poverty and facilitating development. Furthermore, some experts caution that the likelihood is high for violent conflict between nations due to shortages of fresh water in the near future. Rapid population growth, climate change, and food shortages could combine to exacerbate tensions related to scarcity of fresh water.

The seventh annual Canadian Water Attitudes Study, completed in early 2014 (RBC, 2014: 6), stated that water supply and pollution were ranked fifteenth and sixteenth in terms of the most important issues for Canada. In contrast, the following were ranked ahead of water: first, the economy (20 per cent); second, health care (18 per cent); eighth, energy prices; and ninth, the impact of climate change.

Hydrological Cycle

Water or aquatic resources are one component of a system that includes the atmosphere, cryosphere, biosphere, and terrestrial components. Evaporation from surface water (rivers,

Wetlands of the Hudson Bay Lowland—Mansel Island.

Perspectives on the Environment

Future Conflict over Fresh Water Shortages?

Water resources in themselves have rarely been the sole source of conflict or war. Unfortunately, our global water situation is changing rapidly and may soon no longer resemble anything that has existed on Earth before. The tensions and conflicts over water of the kind that have typically occurred in the past will soon represent only one of many emerging explosive hydro-climatic issues that are likely to bring sovereign nations into internal and external discord that could erupt in violence.

—Bob Sandford, water policy expert (quoted in Perkel, 2011)

Perspectives on the Environment

Water-Stressed Countries

In 2014, the World Resources Institute (Reig, Maddocks, and Gassert, 2014) reported that 36 of 180 nations had "extremely high" levels of baseline water stress. This meant that in those countries over 80 per cent of water accessible for agricultural, domestic, and industrial users was being withdrawn each year. Reig et al. also stated that another 31 countries had "high" (40 to 80 per cent of accessible water being withdrawn annually) baseline water stress.

Most of the countries in the extremely high stress category were in the Caribbean, adjacent to the eastern Mediterranean, the Middle East, North Africa, or South Asia. Canada was ranked in the second-lowest category, of "low to medium stress" (ratio of total withdrawals to total renewable water supply between 10 and 20 per cent).

It was noted that because a country was assessed as having an extremely high level of baseline water stress does not mean it would automatically experience scarcity. Singapore was placed in the "extremely high" category of water stress, and even though it has a high population density, is without freshwater lakes or aquifers, and has demand that significantly exceeds natural water supplies, it meets its water needs. Reasons for its avoiding vulnerability include significant investments in technology, international agreements, and high-quality management. For example, Singapore uses advanced rainwater capture techniques to provide 20 per cent of its water supply, imports water from Malaysia for 40 per cent, uses grey water for 30 per cent, and uses desalinization for the other 10 per cent.

lakes, wetlands) and transpiration from plants release water vapour into the atmosphere, which condenses and forms clouds while moving upward. The tiny droplets of water in clouds eventually fall to the Earth as rain, fog, hail, or snow. After reaching the surface, the water evaporates back into the atmosphere; moves into rivers, lakes, or oceans; or percolates into the soil to become groundwater. Chapter 4 provides a more detailed discussion of the hydrological cycle.

About 12 per cent of Canada (1.2 million km^2) is covered by lakes and rivers, with only 3 per cent of that area located in inhabited regions. There are more than 2 million lakes, with the largest being the Great Lakes shared between Canada and the United States. Other large lakes are Great Bear Lake and Great Slave Lake in the Northwest Territories and Lake Winnipeg in Manitoba. Lake water represents about 98 per cent of the surface water available for human use. Canada has more than 8,500 named rivers, and the Mackenzie River, with an average surface flow of 8,968 cubic metres per second (m^3/sec), has the highest volume. There are more than 1,000 named *glaciers*, an important source of fresh water for rivers and lakes.

Various types of **wetlands** exist, all being hybrid aquatic and terrestrial systems. They are a key habitat for waterfowl and also store and gradually release water, thus serving as an important "sponge" to aid in reducing flooding. Wetlands, found in the greatest number and extent in the Prairie provinces and in northern Ontario, cover about 14 per cent of the land area in Canada. Canada has about 25 per cent of the wetlands in the world, the largest amount of any country.

Groundwater is a key source of water for rivers and lakes and is created by surface water passing into the ground and becoming contained in sand and gravel as well as in pores and cracks in bedrock. During dry periods, many rivers receive much of their water via base flow from groundwater aquifers.

Sprague (2007: 23–5) observed that the belief of many Canadians about an abundance of water most likely stems from the apparent large volume of fresh water contained in lakes across the country, totalling about 20 per cent of the water in all the lakes of the world. He emphasizes, however, that water contained in lakes is not the same as what is considered a "renewable" supply. The latter is based on precipitation that falls and then runs off into rivers, often being held in lakes before draining to the ocean or moving downward into aquifers. The flows associated with precipitation or snowmelt should be identified as the renewable supply. As Sprague (2007, 24) states: "To use a financial analogy, the water sitting in lakes and aquifers is comparable to a capital resource of money that can be spent only once. The rivers running out of the lakes would represent interest and dividends that could be used every year for an indefinite time."

More specifically, Sprague highlights that the apparent bountiful abundance of water in Canada is due to: (1) a few very large lakes and many shallow, small lakes; (2) a cool climate; and (3) low evaporation of water. Calculations suggest that Canada ranks between third and sixth in terms of **renewable water supply**. The leaders are Brazil, with more than 12 per cent of the global renewable supply, followed by Russia with 10 per cent. After that, Canada (6.5 per cent) is in a virtual tie with Indonesia (6.5 per cent), the United States (6.4 per cent), and China (6.4 per cent). The next four on the list, ranging from 5 to 2 per cent of the global renewable water supply, are Colombia, Peru, India, and the Democratic Republic of Congo.

Some 60 per cent of Canada's water flows northward to Arctic and Subarctic areas in which few people live. Such northward-flowing water is generally not available to southern Canada, which is where most people live and work. Consequently, when considering the renewable water supply available to southern Canada, the proportion drops from 6.5 to 2.6 per cent of the global supply. Sprague argues that it is the 2.6 per cent figure that citizens, managers, and political leaders should keep in mind, and remarks that "notably, the figure [of 2.6 per cent] is tenfold lower than the frequently used and mythical 'one-quarter of the world supply.'"

Thus, the world and Canada face significant challenges related to water, and, yet, opportunities for innovation exist. In the following "Domestic Guest Statement," Oliver Brandes highlights such opportunities.

Human Interventions in the Hydrological Cycle: Water Diversions

Given that water is often not in the right place at the right time, humans modify aquatic systems to store, divert, or modify flows. There are more than 900 large dams in Canada and about 60 large interbasin diversions. Quebec has 333 large dams, followed by Ontario with 149 and British Columbia with 131 (Environment Canada, 2010c). **Diversions** are completed for one or more of the following reasons:

- To increase water supplies for a community or in a region, as illustrated by the St Mary Irrigation District in Alberta. While diversions for irrigation are important in the southern Prairies, this type of diversion is not as typical of the Canadian experience as it is for countries such as India and the United States.
- To deflect watercourses away from or around areas to be protected, such as the Portage Diversion in Manitoba. Here, the purpose is not to move water to a place of need but to protect a community from flood damage. Other reasons are to drain land to allow agricultural production or to drain a mine site.
- To enhance the capacity of a river so that it can be used to support activities such as floating logs or to allow passage

DOMESTIC GUEST STATEMENT

Thinking Like a Watershed: Fresh Ideas, Laws, and Institutions in a Changing Water World | *Oliver M. Brandes*

> Water is life. Water is our relation. Water bonds us across time and place to our ancestors, to our descendants, and to our land. Water nourishes, replenishes, cleanses, and refreshes. It is the source of food, sustains our salmon, supports our rich environment, and powers our economy. It is critical to our community and economic prosperity.
>
> —Watersheds 2014 Forum Consensus[1]

This eloquent statement is the core message from a recent national forum held on the west coast. Participants came from diverse backgrounds, including First Nations, different levels of government, academia, community watershed managers, and industry, and included international thought leaders. The statement captures an emerging sentiment about the importance of water and many of the central themes discussed in this chapter.

The community of water managers, researchers, and experts has long realized that water is society's most critical and strategic asset. Yet, fresh water and its sustainable management are increasingly under threat. Many global challenges—including growing consumption, pollution, urbanization, and rapid resource development—are also manifesting across Canada.

The prospect of a changing climate causing fundamental shifts in the structure and processes of the hydrological cycle only exacerbates these problems. Witness the increasingly common extreme weather events leading to flooding and prolonged droughts that stress ecosystems and social systems. The themes discussed in this chapter capture the freshwater challenges ahead and also provide hope and optimism. The ideas presented not only deepen our understanding of the critical water issues, but also offer fresh thinking and solutions for the future of water management.

The water issues facing British Columbia are a microcosm of those facing us all. In the West, we are perched on a precipice—at a true watershed moment. The province is poised to plunge into a new regime based on a strengthened water ethic focused on stewardship, water security, and an explicit recognition of an uncertain water future. Fundamental is the realization that addressing water governance will be the priority going forward. As discussed in Chapter 5, governance refers to the complex processes of collective choices and decision-making. It involves both the *whom* and the *how* of making decisions and, importantly, how those making decisions will be held to account.

Mounting water challenges have driven the reform of water laws in the majority of the four western provinces. These reforms tend to resituate the notion of "water for nature" from an afterthought to an emerging priority. BC's Water Sustainability Act, 2014, acknowledges this priority: water for nature can trump other uses in times of drought or threat to fish populations. It also allows for thinking outside the usual "water box" by recognizing the value of community-based planning and that actions which happen upstream or throughout a river basin or catchment have significant impacts downstream. The legislation contemplates issues of power dynamics around water by creating opportunity for innovative forms of governance that enable sharing of power and decision-making across new scales—from communities and local watersheds to whole-of-basin thinking.

However, stubborn inertia and a mindset of taming rivers for human benefit keep many large-scale water diversions and interventions locked in place. Mega-dams, like the now-approved Site C on the Peace River, or the development of a labyrinth of hydrologic fracturing (fracking) infrastructure in the northeast of the province, represent the essence of a twentieth-century approach to water management with the built environment and a notion of "humans over nature" at its heart.

The status quo, however, is being challenged. In some places, water conservation is being viewed as the best source of "new" water; green infrastructure is emphasizing healthy rivers and lakes as source protection; and rainwater management is promoting functioning urban streams, wetlands, and

Jennifer Swift

The three-day forum Watersheds 2014 was held on Cowichan Tribes territory in Duncan, BC in January 2014. Watershed groups, researchers, professional resource managers, and decision-makers at all levels of government, including First Nations, came together to re-envision the way we use, share, and respect our fresh water and watershed resources.

Continued

Jennifer Swift

Designated as both a BC Heritage River and a Canadian Heritage River, the Cowichan River is also an internationally known fishing destination.

permeable surfaces. Recent decisions by the Supreme Court of Canada lend credence to the urgency of reconciliation with Aboriginal peoples. Ensuring that constitutionally protected Aboriginal rights, such as hunting, fishing, and even self-determination, are intimately linked with the sustainable management of both land and water is foundational to any manifestation of those rights.

The view of water as our relative and as so much more than just a resource to be extracted and managed for current human benefit, is driving the next generation of water laws and new nested forms of watershed governance. The reality is that an increasingly dynamic and uncertain water future is upon us; our water laws, governance systems, and approaches to management must in turn evolve. Water is limited and precious. If we want to take water politics, security, and sustainability seriously, we must accept that limits exist and begin living within them.

POLIS center, University of Victoria

Oliver M. Brandes is an economist and lawyer by training and a trans-disciplinarian by design. He serves as co-director of the Centre for Global Studies' POLIS Project on Ecological Governance at the University of Victoria and leads the Water Sustainability Project. His work focuses on water sustainability, sound resource management, public policy development, and ecologically based legal and institutional reform.

Note:

1. The *Watersheds 2014 Forum Consensus* was collaboratively produced and endorsed at the three-day watershed governance forum Watersheds 2014, held on Cowichan Tribes territory in Duncan, BC, in January 2014. See http://poliswaterproject.org/sites/default/files/watersheds2014/Watersheds2014Consensus_FINAL.pdf.

of ships, disposal of wastes, or sustaining of fish. For example, dams on the Ottawa River were designed partly to facilitate the moving of logs downriver to sawmills.

- To combine or consolidate water flows from several sources into one channel or route in order to facilitate hydroelectric generation, such as the James Bay Project in northern Quebec. Canada is a global leader in water diversions for hydroelectricity generation, and diversions for hydropower purposes dominate overwhelmingly in both number and scale of diversions in Canada (Day and Quinn, 1992: 10–11).

While diversions can create positive capacity, they also can cause negative environmental impacts and impose costs on people or regions not benefiting directly from them. The James Bay Cree and their homeland in northern Quebec represent a case in point.

Perspectives on the Environment

Water Diversions in Canada

Interbasin diversion projects are found in almost all provinces, and the total flow of water diverted currently between drainage basins is enormous—approximately 4,500 m³/sec. No other country diverts nearly as much water or concentrates so much flow for a single function—hydroelectric power generation.

—Quinn et al. (2004: 3)

The James Bay Hydroelectric Project

Governments and private corporations have pursued many **megaprojects** in Canada to meet energy demands, and virtually every region in the country has experienced such megaprojects (Figure 11.1). One that has garnered a great deal of national and international attention is the **James Bay Project** in Quebec. Other huge hydroelectric developments include Churchill Falls in Labrador, the Nelson–Churchill river system in Manitoba, and the Columbia and Nechako Rivers in British Columbia. Nuclear power plants in Ontario, the development of oil fields off the coast of Newfoundland, the Sable Island natural gas exploration off Nova Scotia, and the exploitation of the oil sands in northern Alberta are among other major Canadian energy projects and are discussed in detail in Chapter 12.

Background

In 1971, Quebec Premier Robert Bourassa proposed hydroelectric development using the rivers on the eastern side of James Bay. The purpose was to satisfy future electricity needs in Quebec. The cost was estimated at $2 billion. The decision was to develop La Grande River basin to double the flow in that river by diverting water from adjacent catchments

(Figure 11.2). Other river systems north and south of La Grande were to be developed in later phases.

Two major diversions channelled water into La Grande basin. These diversions added an average of 1,635 m^3/sec to La Grande, almost doubling the natural flow in that river. Over a 15-year period, the cost increased to $14.6 billion, compared to the $2 billion estimate in 1971.

In Phase I of the development, three hydroelectric plants (LG2, LG3, LG4) with a combined 10,283 megawatt (MW) capacity were built. The first electricity was generated from LG2 in 1979, and LG4 was completed in 1986. Construction of LG1 and other dams was deferred to Phase II.

The scope and magnitude of the James Bay development has been described as "breathtaking." It produces electricity from rivers flowing in a 350,000-km^2 area of Quebec, more than one-fifth of the province or an area equivalent to France. The provincial government and Hydro-Québec justified the James Bay development on the grounds of jobs to be created, industrial growth to be attracted to the province, and stability to be generated. However, in the enthusiasm over the perceived benefits from hydroelectricity, little regard was given to the fact that the area was the homeland of about 10,000 Cree and Inuit whose people had lived and hunted in the region for centuries.

James Bay and Northern Quebec Agreement

The **James Bay and Northern Quebec Agreement** is the first "modern" Aboriginal land claims agreement in Canada. However, when Premier Bourassa first announced the construction of the hydroelectric megaproject, no systematic environmental or social impact assessments had been completed. The Cree people in northern Quebec soon organized themselves to fight the project. The outcome was the agreement, signed on 11 November 1975 and subsequently approved by the government of Canada and Quebec's National Assembly.

The agreement, although complex and often ambiguous, provided for land rights and guaranteed a process to deal with future hydroelectric developments. The agreement included provisions for environmental and social impact assessment for future developments, monetary compensation, economic and social development, and income security for Cree hunters and trappers.

James Bay II

When Premier Bourassa announced Phase II in 1985, he explained that the development would (1) generate revenue for Quebec through exports of electricity to the United States

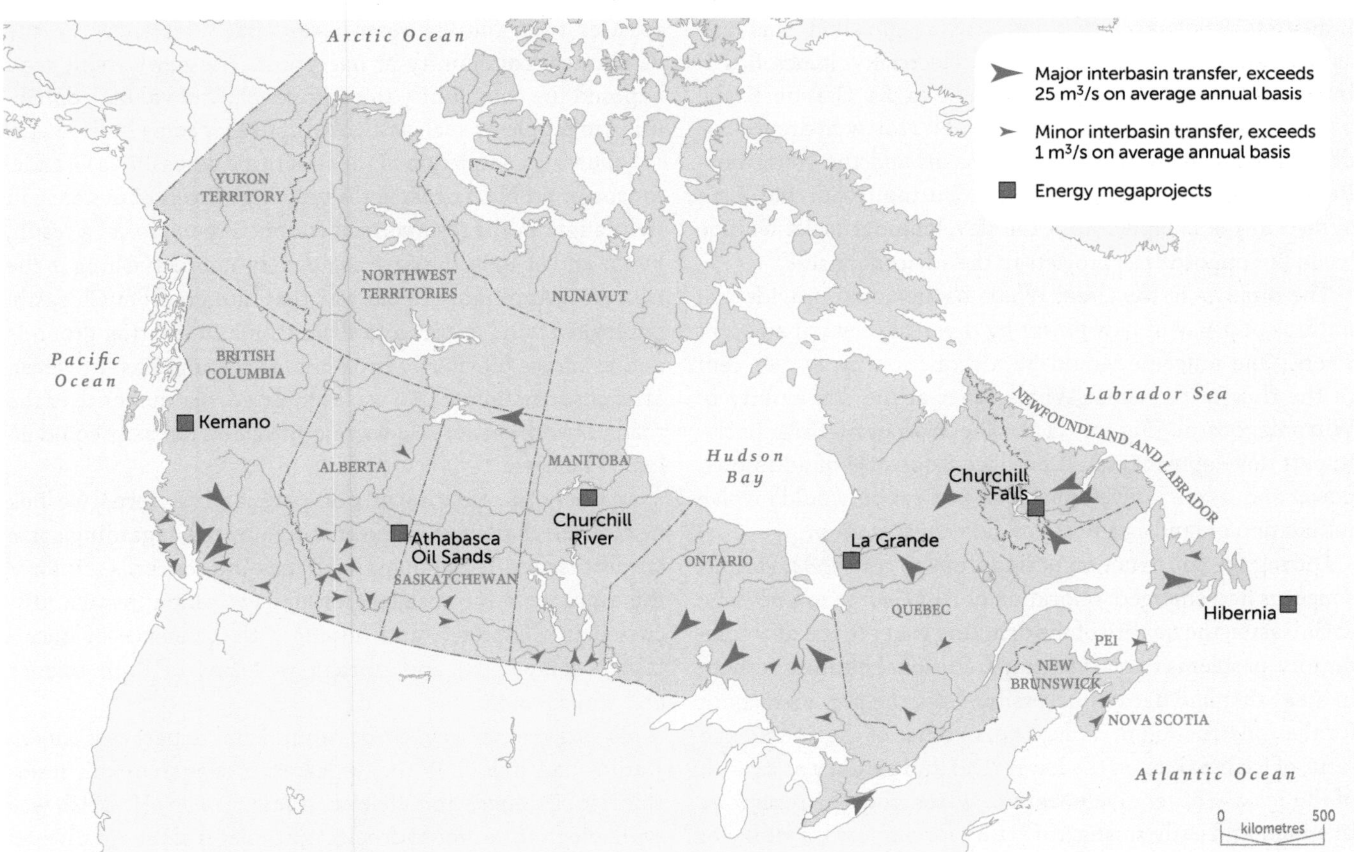

FIGURE 11.1 | Hydroelectric megaprojects in Canada.
Source: Adapted from Day and Quinn (1992: 16).

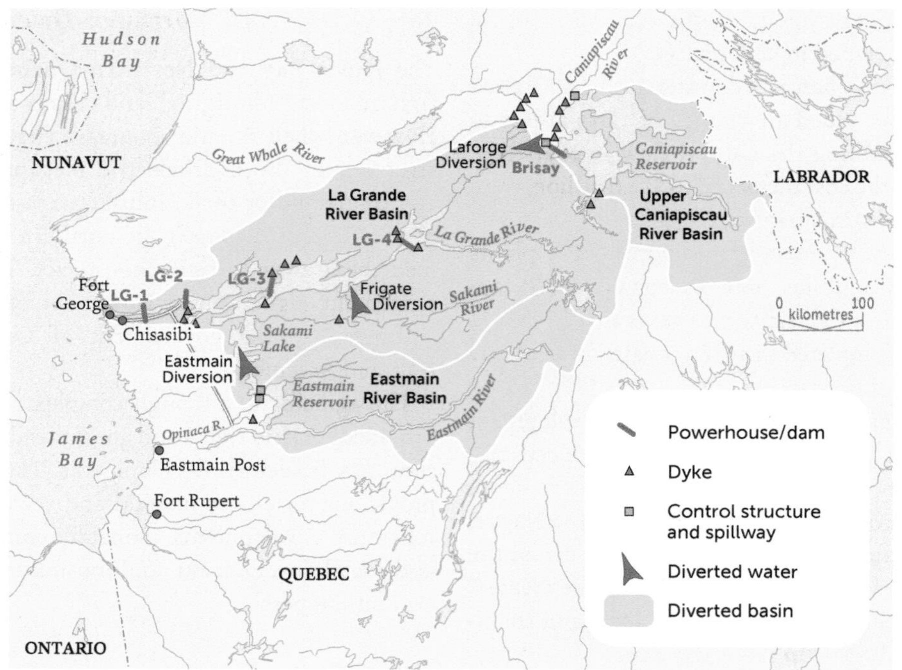

FIGURE 11.2 | La Grande River hydroelectric development project, Phase 1.
Source: Day and Quinn (1992: 134).

under long-term contracts and (2) attract energy-intensive industries (such as aluminum and magnesium smelters) as a result of competitively priced electricity. James Bay II involved completion of development in La Grande basin, particularly the building of LG1, as well as new hydroelectric development in the Great Whale basin and the Nottaway–Broadback–Rupert river systems. During 1986, the Cree agreed to the completion of the development in La Grande basin but opposed the projects in the adjacent basins.

The projects in the Great Whale basin would provide just under 3,000 MW of new power by diverting several adjacent rivers. One outcome would be a reduction by 85 per cent in the flow of the Great Whale River at the community of Whapmagoostui (Figure 11.3). The Nottaway–Broadback–Rupert development would produce 8,000 MW of additional power and, as with development on La Grande, would involve inundation of land as a result of dam construction.

During the construction period from 1974 to 1984, various concerns had emerged: relocation of Fort George to a new site at Chisasibi, the quality of the drinking water in the new community, problems in maintaining traditional hunting activity in areas that had become accessible from the new roads built for the construction of dams, and, because of the altered patterns of ice breakup on the lower river and **estuary** as a result of the release of relatively warmer water from the reservoirs in winter and early spring, difficulty for hunters travelling to the northern coastal area across the river from Chisasibi.

At the community level, other concerns emerged. For example, increased erosion along the banks of La Grande, the result of fluctuating water levels in the river caused by releases from the upstream reservoirs, threatened the site of the new community at one point. The newly built road exposed the community to other people and values, contributing to problems such as alcohol abuse for some individuals.

Following completion of the first three dams on La Grande, the major problem became the very high levels of mercury in fish caught in the reservoirs or connecting rivers. As a result, by the end of 1985, the Cree completely stopped fishing in the LG2 area. Another problem was that hunters from Chisasibi purchased vans to travel to distant inland hunting grounds and to access previously little-hunted populations. However, after construction of LG4 was completed, maintenance of the road network east of LG4 was stopped, and the vans could no longer be used.

Against this changing mix of issues and concerns, we look next at the challenges of estimating impacts regarding some specific issues. These changing issues and concerns reinforce the arguments for an adaptive management approach, discussed in Chapter 6, and highlight the presence of uncertainty, complexity, and change in terms of both science and management.

Mercury in reservoirs. No environmental impact assessment studies had predicted the appearance of mercury in reservoir fish. Evidence about elevated mercury levels in fish was available from earlier hydroelectric projects at the Smallwood Reservoir in Labrador and from Southern Indian Lake in Manitoba, but such impacts apparently were dismissed as short-lived and not significant for La Grande.

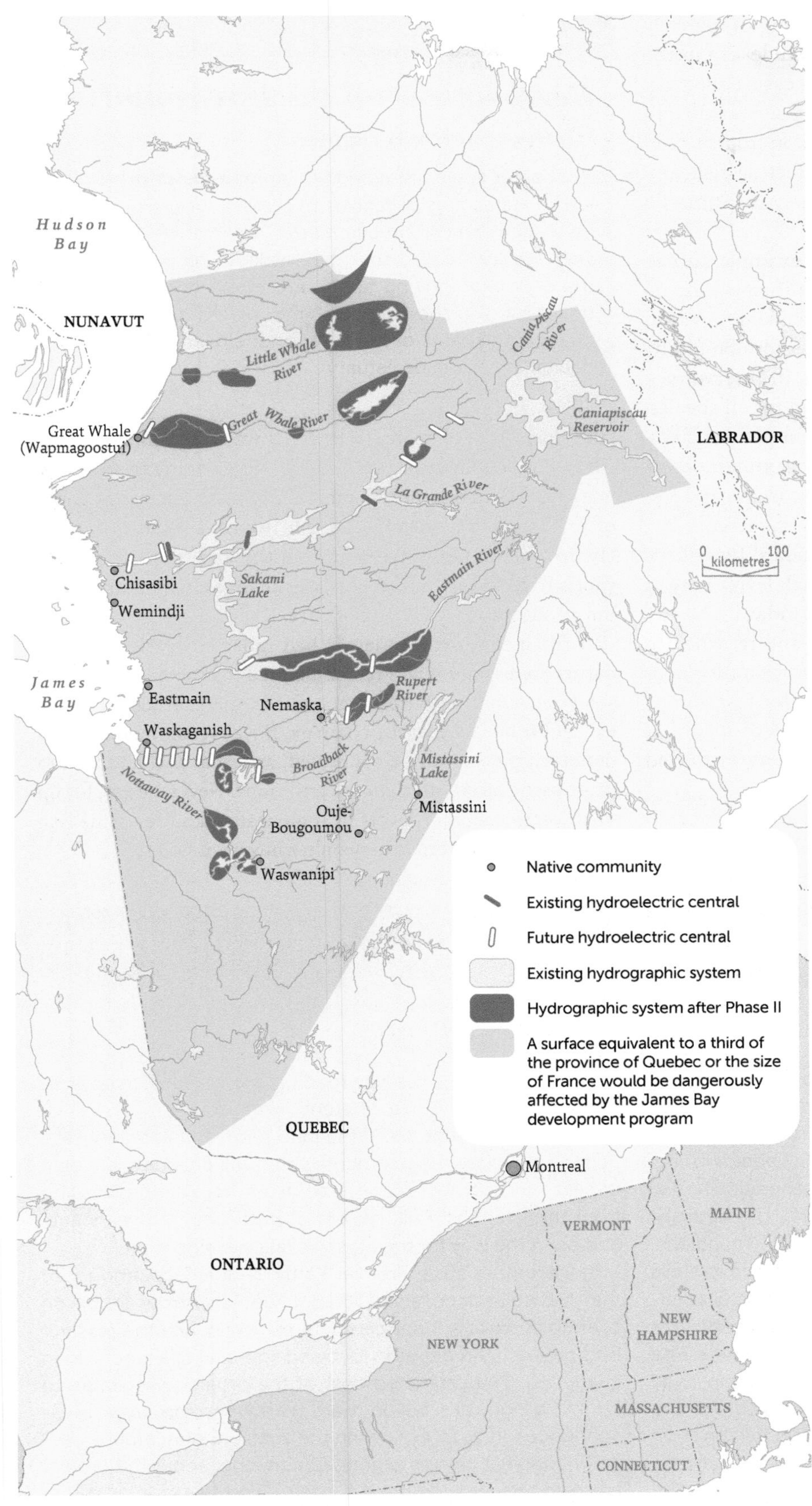

FIGURE 11.3 | The Great Whale project.

Source: Diamond (1990: 32).

Mercury is common in rocks throughout the North in an insoluble form. However, when such rocks are inundated by a reservoir, bacteria associated with the decomposition of organic material in the reservoir water transform the insoluble mercury into methyl mercury that vaporizes, is released into the atmosphere, and returns to the water. Once in the water, the mercury enters the food chain and through biomagnification reaches the highest trophic levels in fish species. Such predator fish had been an important source of high-quality protein food for the local people. Berkes (1988) indicated that in most years, about one-quarter of the total community wild food harvest came from fishing, averaging about 60 kilograms per year for every man, woman, and child.

In new reservoirs, a burst of decomposition often accelerates the release of mercury. In the La Grande River system, initially few trees were removed prior to the flooding of the reservoir area, so there was a lot of organic matter to decompose. (In later stages of the massive project, tree removal was done—with much of the timber going to Cree-operated sawmills.) Downstream from the dams on La Grande, levels of mercury in fish climbed to six times their normal levels within months of completion of the dams. By the sixth year following the impoundment, concentrations of mercury were four to five times higher in all species sampled. A 1984 survey of the Cree at Chisasibi showed that 64 per cent of the villagers had unsafe levels of mercury in their bodies.

It was expected that as time passed and the drowned vegetation completely decomposed, the release of mercury would return to normal (and safe) levels. Monitoring, as reported by Chevalier et al. (1997) and Dumont et al. (1998), focused on the species most often consumed by the Cree people. The results indicated that 15 years after the impounding of the LG2 reservoir, the concentrations of methyl mercury were higher than in natural lakes but also that they were decreasing in both predatory and non-predatory species.

Hydro-Québec (2013) reported on monitoring of mercury levels from 1978 to 2012 related to "La Grande Complex." Sampling was conducted at 97 stations to measure mercury levels in natural lakes, reservoirs, portions of rivers immediately downstream from reservoirs, diversion routes, and reduced flow rivers, and to examine the effect on fish consumption related to piscivorous (eating solely or primarily fish) and non-piscivorous species.

The effect on mercury levels varied. For example, in natural lakes, mercury levels in fish varied significantly, by up to a factor of four for a given species of a given length within a given lake. Also, levels normally were lower for non-piscivorous than piscivorous species. In contrast, in reservoirs, a significant increase in mercury was recorded for all species, by a factor of two to eight relative to those in natural lakes. More significantly, it took 4 to 11 years for maximum levels of mercury to be reached in non-piscivorous species, and 7 to 14 years in piscivorous species. For the former, mercury levels often remained below the Canadian standard for fishery products, but for piscivorous species the peak levels ranged from three to nine times higher than the standard. The elevated levels were found to be "temporary," and returned to normal levels in natural lakes after 10 to 20 years for non-piscivorous species and after 20 to 30 years for piscivorous species. Regarding diversion routes, it was determined that mercury was exported from reservoirs and then transferred to fish inhabiting downstream waters.

In terms of implications for fish consumption, levels of mercury were tracked for whitefish, northern pike, walleye, and lake trout. At peak mercury levels, it was recommended consumption be reduced to specified levels, ranging from two to one or less than one meal per month, compared to a maximum of four meals per month for fish from most natural lakes. Hydro-Québec (2013) reported that the local population and sports fishers were informed about changes in mercury levels in various ways. By the end of 2012, Hydro-Québec concluded that the mean mercury levels had fallen to levels found in natural lakes, and it was recommended that people follow the same consumption patterns as applied to natural lakes. Finally, except for one lake in the complex, it was recommended that monitoring need not be continued, as levels had returned to those associated with natural conditions. Nevertheless, for up to 30 years, mercury levels in some waters and for some fish species were dangerous to people who consumed fish.

Perspectives on the Environment

Limiting Factor Principle

In Chapter 2, we discussed the **limiting factor principle**, which states that all factors necessary for growth must be available in certain quantities if an organism is to survive. We also noted that the weakest link is known as the dominant limiting factor. Are these ideas helpful in understanding the impact of interrupting river flow and changing patterns of ice cover on the overwintering fish habitat in La Grande estuary?

ENVIRONMENT IN FOCUS

BOX 11.1 | Hydroelectricity on the Lower Churchill River

In November 2010, Premier Danny Williams of Newfoundland and Labrador announced a $6.2-billion project to develop hydroelectricity on the Lower Churchill River, in partnership with Nova Scotia, subject to ratification by the Labrador Innu. The planned project would include a power-generating facility at Muskrat Falls with capacity to produce 824 MW of electricity, a subsea transmission link from Labrador to Newfoundland, and a 180-kilometre subsea link from Newfoundland to Nova Scotia. Nova Scotia would receive 170 MW of electricity annually for 35 years, about 10 per cent of its total power needs, with additional capacity transmitted to New England markets. The decision to plan for the costly underwater transmission route was driven by ongoing conflict between Newfoundland and Labrador and the Quebec government over the transmission of power to southern markets from the Churchill Falls hydroelectric project (built 1967–71) via Hydro-Québec lines. The 1969 agreement favoured Quebec, and when Hydro-Québec baulked at offering a significantly better deal for transmitting Muskrat Falls power, the Newfoundland and Labrador government opted to move in a different direction.

At the end of June 2011, the Innu people of Labrador ratified the New Dawn Agreement, which will provide them with benefits and compensation, both from the new project and from the Churchill Falls project of more than 40 years ago, and open the way for the Muskrat Falls development.

In December 2013, Premier Kathy Dunderdale announced that Newfoundland and Labrador would borrow $5 billion over 40 years at 3.8 per cent interest to finance the Muskrat Falls project. This decision followed approval of a federal loan guarantee. The estimated cost of the project was stated to be $7.7 billion, $1.5 billion more than when the project was announced in 2010. Following the 2013 announcement, several Aboriginal groups expressed concerns about the project and said they would fight it. Construction began in 2013 and is expected to take four to five years to complete, with power to be produced in 2017.

La Grande estuary fish. The pre-construction impact assessments indicated that the estuarine fishery in La Grande was unlikely to survive development of the dams and reservoirs. The impact study predicted that when the reservoirs began to fill behind the dams, with the resulting absence of ice cover to dampen the impact of ebb and flow of the tidal water from James Bay, salt water would move farther up into the river. The consequence would be elimination of the freshwater overwintering fish habitat for species important for the local fishery. On the other hand, if the river water flow were reduced *after* the formation of ice cover, then saltwater intrusion would be impeded and a critically important pocket of fresh water could be maintained in the key habitat area.

Partly as a result of pressure exerted by local fishers, the river flow was not cut off until after an ice cover had formed on the river. Monitoring revealed that this action resulted in the creation of the necessary freshwater pocket, which remained in place throughout the winter. Thus the predicted fish kill did not occur, and subsequent fish populations were about the same as in the pre-construction period.

Water Exports, Diversions, and Other Options

Growth and development in the US Southwest has the potential to lead to water scarcity in that region. One "supply management" solution would be to look to Canada as a source and to import water in bottles, by ship, or via pipeline. Canada exports oil and natural gas to the United States, so why not water?

As Day and Quinn (1992: 41–2) and Quinn (2007) have explained, those who support the export of water to the United States argue that water is just another resource with value and can be exchanged on the open market, Canada has more water than it needs to meet its foreseeable needs, substantial income could be earned from selling water to the US and elsewhere, jobs would be created through the necessary major construction projects such as pipelines, and some of the diverted water could be sent to regions in Canada facing shortfalls. These reasons, identified nearly 30 years ago, continue to be promoted by those advocating export of water (Boyer, 2008; Katz, 2010).

Those opposing the export of water emphasize that the scale or magnitude of the proposed water diversion projects would be much larger than any previous project, creating significant risks and uncertainty. Once the taps are turned on, it would be virtually impossible to turn them off, since receiving areas would become dependent on the diverted water. In addition, negative environmental and social impacts could be significant and irreversible (Nikiforuk, 2007; Lasserre, 2009).

During the 1960s, various southern state governments in the US considered the feasibility of large-scale water diversions through pipelines from one or both of the Columbia and Mississippi river systems. The northern states that would be the source of these diversions strongly opposed the proposals. One outcome was that some states and private companies began to consider whether water from Canadian river or lake systems could be diverted southward. Two examples illustrate such proposals (Day and Quinn, 1992: 40).

North American Water and Power Alliance (NAWAPA)

Conceived by the Ralph M. Parsons Company in California, NAWAPA would store the headwaters of the Yukon, Skeena, Peace, Fraser, and Columbia Rivers in the Rocky Mountain Trench in eastern British Columbia. The stored water would be diverted to both the Canadian Prairie provinces and the western states by pipeline. The Canadian federal and provincial governments strongly opposed major water diversions from Canada to the US, rejecting Parsons's basic assumption that water in Canada was a "continental resource."

Grand Recycling and Northern Development (GRAND) Canal

Thomas Kierans, a Canadian engineer, proposed a major diversion involving a dyke across James Bay, creating a reservoir in the bay, and then pumping water up 300 metres into the Great Lakes basin, from which it could be moved by pipeline to the southwestern states. The eight states (Minnesota, Wisconsin, Michigan, Illinois, Indiana, Ohio, Pennsylvania, New York) and two provinces (Ontario, Quebec) in the Great Lakes basin all opposed this proposal.

Other Options

Water exports do not have to take place only via pipelines or major diversions. Some exports come about between adjacent communities on either side of the Canada–US border. In such situations, water supply systems are shared between communities, such as St Stephen, New Brunswick, and Calais, Maine; or Coutts, Alberta, and Sweetgrass, Montana. In these arrangements, water often flows in both directions, the volumes are modest, and mutual accommodation is achieved.

Another type of diversion involves movement of water between national and boundary waters. For example, in northern Ontario, diversions from Ogoki Lake and Long Lac move water from Ontario rivers into Lake Superior in order to increase power-generating capacity. In the United States, a channel was constructed at Chicago to divert water from Lake Michigan to the Illinois–Mississippi river system to facilitate navigation southward from Chicago. While the amounts of water involved are modest in the Chicago Diversion, there is concern that it could be regarded as a precedent for larger-scale diversions from Lake Michigan for other purposes. There is also always a risk that diversion channels between watersheds can lead to introduction of invasive species from one to the other.

Tanker shipment represents another option. Containerized vessels would take fresh water from coastal rivers to destinations as close as California or as distant as Middle East nations. One arrangement would use ships bringing petroleum to Canada from the Middle East to transport fresh water on the return journey, after suitable cleaning of holds. Another option would be to use tanker ships dedicated to carrying only water. A third option, still under development, would be floating bags or membranes towed behind a ship. The volumes of water would be relatively small, and the cost of collection and transportation would have to be competitive with alternatives available at the destinations, such as desalinization.

El Ayoubi and McNiven (2006) analyzed possible export of water by tanker from the Annapolis Valley in western Nova Scotia to Brownsville, Texas. They concluded that the project was unprofitable: "Pricing policies and alternate technologies will probably mean that the utility of tanker-based projects will remain only a future possibility. The unprofitability of such projects is likely the reason why there have been so few examples of bulk water exports in the world and not because of the political opposition to them" (El Ayoubi and McNiven, 2006: 14).

Export of water in bottles or similar containers is a possibility. It does not raise concerns on the same scale because the quantities involved would not be significant and such trade could be stopped or modified with minimal consequences, unlike turning off the water passing through a major pipeline.

Reactions and Responses

The situation in the US is evolving. For example, Lasserre (2007: 152) observed that "water demand has been stagnating in the United States for the past two decades." Several reasons account for this pattern. First, although still relatively low, water prices in the US have been steadily rising. Second, water-short cities are relatively wealthy compared to the agricultural sector and have been able to drive reallocation of water from agriculture to urban areas. Third, agriculture in the US is facing growing competition from producers in Mexico and Asia, leading to reduced crop production. As a result, Americans appear more likely to look to other solutions than to Canada for bulk imports.

In Canada and in the Great Lakes states, however, concern has persisted. This concern was reflected during 1985 when the Ontario and Quebec premiers joined the governors of the eight Great Lakes states in signing the Great Lakes Charter. Those signing agreed to notify and consult each other regarding any possible diversion. In addition, they agreed that no jurisdiction would start a new diversion or increase an existing one involving more than 5 million gallons per day without seeking the consent of all Great Lakes states or provinces that would be affected. An annex to the charter was signed in 2001, and the intent of both the charter and the annex continues through the Great Lakes–St. Lawrence River Basin Sustainable Water Resources Agreement, signed in December 2005, and the Great Lakes Compact, signed in 2008 by the eight US governors and two Canadian premiers.

The Canadian government has taken various actions to curtail water export, drawing on its authority for international and interjurisdictional matters. The first major initiative was the federal water policy introduced in November 1987. In that policy, the government prohibited "large-scale" export by interbasin water diversions to the United States.

A different challenge emerged in the late 1980s when free-trade negotiations between Canada and the US were at their final stage. Concern was expressed that provisions for free trade would make it impossible for Canada to prohibit export of water to the United States. Reflecting this concern, the government of Ontario introduced a bill entitled the Water Transfer Control Act to prohibit all forms of water export from Ontario, except for bottled water, and it became law in 1989.

In 1998, however, the Ontario government of Premier Mike Harris awarded a licence to the Nova Group to export water from Sault Ste Marie, Ontario, to Asia. There was an immediate uproar across Ontario and in the Great Lakes states, which led the Ontario government to reverse its decision. The Ontario government's original willingness to approve water exports raised doubts about the capacity of the Great Lakes Charter to prevent such decisions.

One outcome was that the federal government in 1999 announced a three-part strategy to address water exports from Canada. First, the **International Joint Commission** was asked to provide a legal opinion regarding exports from the Great Lakes basin. Second, the provincial governments were urged to pass laws that would ban water exports. This was viewed as necessary, since provinces own the water within their boundaries. And third, a federal law was to be designed to restrict exports.

With the exception of New Brunswick, all provinces subsequently passed legislation to prevent bulk water diversions or exports outside their borders. The door was still left open for other types of exports, such as bottled water. The risk is that if one province allows what might be viewed as significant water exports, then under the North American Free Trade Agreement (NAFTA), all provinces might be compelled to treat water as a "tradable good."

Rather than passing a law, the federal government chose a different approach (Lasserre, 2007). The choice was based on a feature of the river basins associated with the international border. Nearly all the large basins are located either entirely in Canada or entirely in the US, with only a few systems, such as the Great Lakes and the Columbia River, straddling the border. Given this physical reality, if provinces prohibited transferring water out of their jurisdiction, water exports to the US would be effectively stopped. This arrangement could be reinforced by the federal government restricting interbasin transfers because of negative environmental impacts.

Thus, Canada did not need to have a direct policy or law prohibiting water exports to the United States, either of which might be challengeable under NAFTA.

The federal government also approved an amendment to the International Boundary Waters Treaty Act during December 2002. The amendment prohibits bulk water exports from river basins if they exceed 50 m³/day. It was also intended to deter the diversion of water out of the Great Lakes basin, since the International Joint Commission's legal position in response to Canada's request for guidance was that diversions from boundary waters could occur only if they were authorized by the appropriate governments with jurisdiction over the water.

In the US, some initiatives have been undertaken to restrict large-volume diversions from the Great Lakes. In 2000, the US government stipulated that any diversion of water from the Great Lakes system by any state or federal agency or private organization for use outside of the Great Lakes basin is prohibited unless the governors of each of the eight Great Lakes states give approval. Further support for this policy came in December 2005 when the eight governors and two premiers, through the Council of Great Lakes Governors, agreed on a set of principles to review proposals for transfers of water from the Great Lakes. Any proposal would be authorized only if:

- No reasonable alternative to the proposed transfer exists
- Withdrawals are limited to reasonable volumes for specified uses
- All withdrawn water, after an allowance for consumption, is returned to the Great Lakes basin from which it was removed
- For "major" proposals, an explicit conservation plan has been prepared

The 2005 agreement by the Council of Great Lakes Governors effectively banned major water exports or diversions from the Great Lakes basin but left open the option for low-volume transfers that might be anticipated between adjacent communities on either side of the border.

Water Quality

Humans can adversely affect water quality in numerous ways, and water quality is one of Environment Canada's three main Environmental Sustainability Indicators (Environment Canada, 2014b). Water quality is assessed according to an index to measure the ability of surface waters to protect aquatic life at selected river and lake locations within Canada (Environment Canada, 2014c). Based on information between 2009 and 2011 regarding its water quality indicator, Environment Canada (2014c) reported that:

> Of 172 sites (compared to 379 sites in 2006), 3 sites were rated poor for water quality, 30 marginal, 60 fair, 69 good, and 10 excellent.
>
> Of 101 sites, 12 showed improved quality, 4 declining quality, and 84 no change.

More generally, the Conference Board of Canada (2014b: 1) stated that Canada ranked fourth of 17 OECD countries regarding water quality. Sweden, Norway, and Austria were ranked higher. The greatest risk for water quality in Canada was attributed to poorly treated municipal waste, industrial effluent, and agricultural fertilizer runoff. Those three sources generate most of the nitrogen and phosphorus entering into water systems, as discussed in Chapter 4. Release of nitrogen and phosphorus is noted to be "common," even though stiff regulations are applied to control release of toxic effluents (Conference Board of Canada, 2014b: 2).

High concentrations of nitrogen and phosphorus can cause eutrophication, a serious matter for the Prairie provinces, southern Ontario, and Quebec. The Prairie provinces have an additional challenge, with high natural levels of nitrogen and phosphorus exacerbated by intensive agriculture. The Great Lakes have been negatively affected by release of nitrogen and phosphorous from municipal sewage, farms, and industrial plants in southern Ontario.

The Conference Board of Canada (2014b: 2) reports that water quality in Canada has improved since the mid 1980s, although nitrogen discharges increased during the mid 1980s to mid 1990s and phosphorous discharges dropped. For example, in 1999, tonnes of total nitrogen released into surface waters across the country were estimated to have increased by 24 per cent relative to 1983, while for the same period phosphorous releases decreased by 44 per cent. However, since the late 1990s, phosphorous releases began to climb, while nitrogen releases fell.

Notwithstanding the data provided above based on federal government monitoring programs, we need to be careful in using such information. As the commissioner of the Environment and Sustainable Development (2010: 3)

Bruce Edwards/Edmonton Journal

Syncrude's Mildred Lake settling basin sits near Fort McMurray, Alberta. It has been polluted by the oil sands, resulting in the deaths of hundreds of ducks.

reported, "Environment Canada is not adequately monitoring the quality and quantity of Canada's surface water resources. . . . The Department is not monitoring water quality on the majority of federal lands and does not know whether other federal departments are doing so."

The most important issue is pollution from various sources but especially from industrial and other urban wastes and from agricultural runoff. The first two are easier to identify because they are usually associated with *point sources*, such as manufacturing plants or sewage treatment plants. Agricultural runoff is more challenging, since it is usually diffuse pollution from *non-point sources*, such as fertilizers, herbicides, and pesticides from farm fields. Some types of urban runoff, such as oil and salt from road surfaces, also are non-point, since they cannot be identified with specific places.

Point Sources

Urban waste water can receive up to three levels of treatment: (1) *primary*, which removes only insoluble material; (2) *secondary*, which removes bacterial impurities from water previously having received primary treatment; and (3) *tertiary*, which removes chemical and nutrient contaminants following secondary treatment.

In 2006, 79 per cent of Canadians lived in dwellings serviced by municipal sewer systems providing at least secondary treatment, compared to 56 per cent in 1983. By 2009, 82 per cent of households were connected to municipal sewer systems, while 13 per cent used private septic systems and 1 per cent used communal septic systems. Furthermore, in 2009, about 65 per cent of waste flows into municipal waste systems originated in households, with another 18 per cent from industrial, commercial, and institutional sources and 8 per cent from stormwater. The balance came from groundwater infiltration. In 2006, municipalities spent $3.9 billion on sewage collection and disposal (Statistics Canada, 2013a).

Discharges from industrial sources can be challenging, given the mix of contaminants. To illustrate the complexity and uncertainty that must be addressed, the following detailed case study of the Sydney Tar Ponds is provided.

Sydney Tar Ponds, Cape Breton Regional Municipality, Nova Scotia

Background

Sydney, Nova Scotia, merged in 1995 with other communities to form the Cape Breton Regional Municipality (CBRM), is located on the northern part of Cape Breton Island (Figure 11.4). Extensive deposits of coal and iron ore in the CBRM area resulted in a long history of coal mining and steel production. These resources, in addition to a coastal fishery, forestry, and a striking natural landscape, formed the economic base for the community.

In the late nineteenth century the Industrial Revolution was powered by coal. Geologists knew that Cape Breton Island and mainland Nova Scotia had substantial coal deposits. Shafts were sunk, and coal production steadily grew. Shortly after 1891, annual coal production had grown to 1.5 million tonnes. By 1893, the numerous small coal mines joined together as the Dominion Coal Company (DOMCO), and output continued to grow—to more than 6 million tonnes annually by 1913.

The steady expansion of rail lines in North America led to a high demand for steel, prompting the American owner of DOMCO to create the Dominion Iron and Steel Company (DISCO). In 1899 construction started on the new steel plant located along Muggah Creek. A few years before the start of World War I, Cape Breton had become the source of nearly half of all the steel produced in Canada, with Sydney's Dominion Iron and Steel Company having the largest share (Lahey, 1998: 38). A supply of coal was readily available, but more iron ore was needed, and it was procured from the iron ore mines at Wabana, Bell Island, Newfoundland.

If coal deposits contain too much sulphur, however, inferior coke is the result. Low-grade iron ore also requires larger quantities of limestone to remove the impurities. To assess the quality of the basic inputs to the steelmaking process, science is essential. However, such science was ignored when arrangements were being made for the basic raw materials—the beginning of a pattern. As Barlow and May (2000, 11–12) observed:

> In a rush to begin full operation, they failed to run the most basic tests on their coals and ores.
>
> The coal from Cape Breton seams was very high in sulphur, so far more coal had to be baked to produce usable coke. The iron ore from Wabana was full of impurities, such as silica and rock, so far more limestone was required to pull out the impurities as slag. The unusually large amounts of limestone required in the blast furnaces caused the furnace linings to deteriorate rapidly. . . .
>
> The poor quality of the basic ingredients led to higher costs, less marketable and inferior products, and far more waste. In what had been Muggah Creek, the slag would eventually create a mountain range of waste, stretching hundreds of feet high and reducing the mouth of the estuary by nearly a mile.

The coal and steel operations continued for almost a century, under various owners. The coke ovens, used to produce a higher-quality fuel source for the steel mill's open-hearth blast furnaces, were closed in 1988 (see photo, next page). The steel plant stopped operating in 2001. The closure of these operations was a serious blow to the economy of the CBRM. However, even after the coke ovens closed, millions of tonnes of toxic sludge remained. For decades, air pollution originating from the coke ovens and open-hearth furnaces also had been clearly evident. Nevertheless, the implications of the air pollution were in some cases unknown and in other cases poorly understood.

The "tar ponds" area was created from the deposit of chemical by-products from the coking process, runoff of water used for cooling in the coke ovens and the steel mill, leaching from contaminated soil at the coke and steelmaking plants, a garbage dump site in the upper catchment, and discharge of raw sewage from residential and commercial areas of Sydney. Other contaminants came from a cement factory, a gas and oil company, and a brick factory. The outcome was a chemical- and bacteria-laden river system, including the estuary full of contaminated sediments, the latter called the tar ponds, a 2-kilometre stretch of contaminated water and sludge referred to by federal officials at the time as "the largest chemical waste site in Canada" (Lahey, 1998: 37). Various government surveys identified polycyclic aromatic hydrocarbons (PAHs), polychlorinated biphenyls (PCBs), and other chemicals and metals among the pollutants. Muggah Creek and the estuary empty into Sydney Harbour, and discovery of PAHs in those waters resulted in closure of the lobster fishery. The surveys confirmed that the soil on the coke ovens site was highly contaminated.

The tar ponds are in the lower part of the Muggah Creek watershed, and since Dominion Iron and Steel built its plant in 1899, what was once a navigable waterway and a habitat for fish and birds became a highly contaminated narrow tidal outlet. A causeway and bridge divided what used to be an estuary into north and south ponds. Surveys by governments and consultants revealed that the two ponds contained about 700,000 tonnes of sediment contaminated with PAHs, including 45,000 tonnes also containing PCBs at concentrations above 50 parts per million (ppm).

Challenges for Epidemiological Studies

Various studies revealed that citizens of Sydney were suffering serious health problems, including higher cancer rates compared to the rest of Canada. Health and Welfare Canada expressed concerns about the possible link to the toxic wastes from the coke ovens. One study found that the life expectancy for both male and female residents in Sydney was as much as five years less than for the Canadian population as a whole. The primary causes were significantly higher levels of cancer and cardiovascular disease. Yet another study indicated that rates of major birth anomalies were significantly higher among Sydney residents relative to the rest of Nova Scotia.

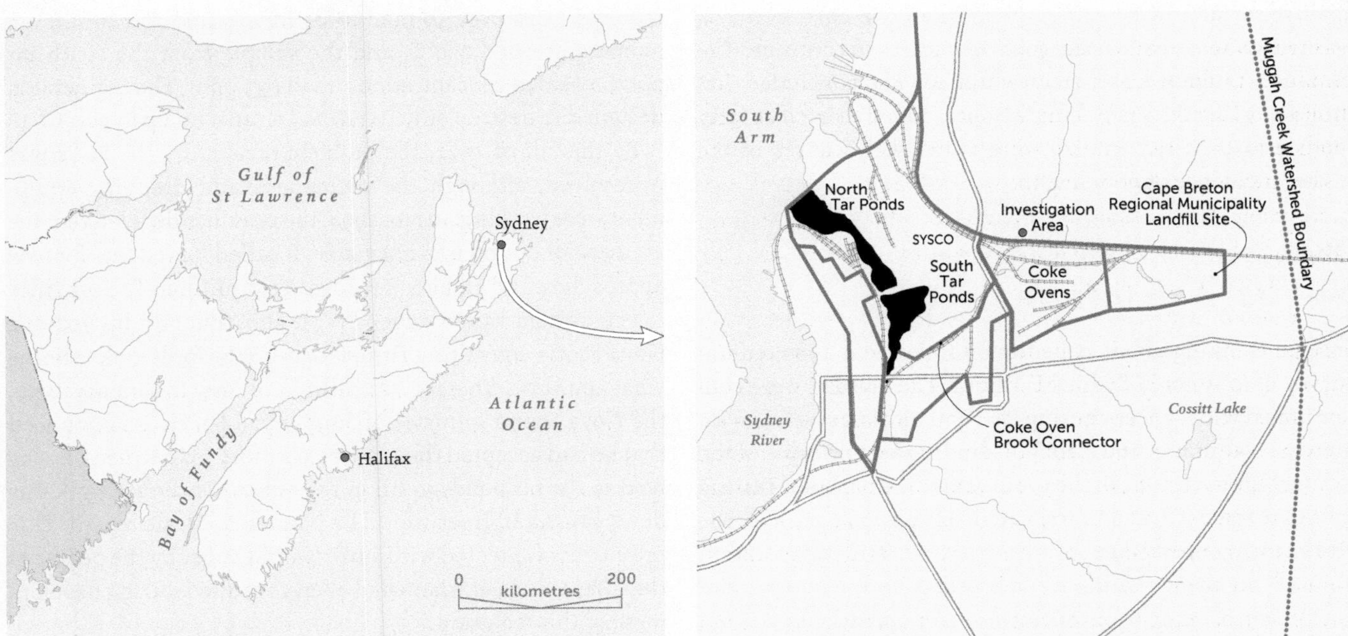

FIGURE 11.4 | On the detailed map (right), the highway that curves around Cossitt Lake and meets the Glace Bay Highway, which bisects the figure horizontally, now extends onward and links with a road, SPAR (an acronym for Sydney Port Authority Road), on the other side of the CBRM landfill site. It then continues past the coke ovens site and into the main cleanup area. It was built to facilitate easier access to the cleaned-up area for industrial and commercial purposes.
Source: Rainham (2002: 27), from Joint Action Group, Sydney, Cape Breton (1999).

Coke Ovens, SYSCO, 1987, G. Langille, 90-221-19653, Beaton Institute, Cape Breton University

Sydney, Nova Scotia, coke ovens, 1987. Aerial view of the coke ovens, showing the quenching plant with steam at left, coal pocket and batteries between exhaust stacks, centre, and conveyor leading from pocket to blending plant, right. By-product building is large brick structure, foreground. Smaller buildings are pump house, carpenter shop, and oil house (Coke Ovens, SYSCO, 1987, 90–221–19653, Beaton Institute, University College of Cape Breton, Sydney, NS).

In the mid 1980s, Health and Welfare Canada alerted the Environment Canada Atlantic regional office about health concerns, which then contacted its provincial counterpart. However, the epidemiologist for Nova Scotia stated that the hazard depended on long-term exposure and that balanced against social and economic benefits of the coke ovens, it was reasonable to allow the coke operations to continue. The province conducted its own investigation and concluded that unhealthy lifestyles (smoking, alcohol, poor diet such as fatty foods and high salt intake) were more likely causes of the higher incidence of poor health.

Problems When Science Is Not Used to Inform Decisions

Serious thinking about remediation followed a 1980 federal survey of lobsters in Sydney Harbour. The lobsters were contaminated with cancer-causing PAH chemicals, as well as with mercury, cadmium, and lead. This finding led to closure of the lobster fishery in 1982 in the south arm of the harbour. Testing by Environment Canada indicated the obvious source—the steelmaking operations of the Sydney Steel Corporation (SYSCO), an agency of the Nova Scotia government that had taken control of the failing private-sector operations.

In 1984, the consulting firm Acres International was contracted to determine the scope of the pollution and recommend options. Initial testing indicated that the tar ponds contained the equivalent of 540,000 tonnes (dry weight) of toxic waste, including 4.4 to 8.8 million pounds of PAHs. The sludge on the bottom of the estuary was judged to be between 1 and 4 metres deep. Acres focused on the challenges represented by the PAHs. PCBs had been identified in the earlier study of lobsters, but were not considered a problem because random sampling in the estuary revealed only small quantities of PCBs.

Acres identified three options: (1) leave polluted sludge in place and cover it; (2) remove sludge and store it somewhere else; and (3) remove sludge and incinerate it. Acres estimated that incineration would destroy 99.99 per cent of the PAHs. However, PCBs are virtually indestructible at extreme temperatures and when burned are transformed into airborne dioxins and other poisons. Given the estimate of the high proportion of PAHs that would be destroyed by incineration and the almost 1,500 person-years of work to be generated by incineration, the provincial government selected that option.

In 1987, federal and Nova Scotia ministers of Environment announced a $34.3 million package for excavation and incineration of the toxic waste. Workers in the coke ovens had first opportunity for employment in the cleanup. At the press conference, the ministers stated that the tar ponds were the worst toxic waste site in Canada, and the second-worst in North America.

The incinerator was supposed to be operational by 1990. However, as 1992 began, the project was behind schedule and over budget. Also, further testing was to be conducted to better understand the contaminants. In October 1992, testing identified a "hot spot" of PCBs in the south tar pond, indicating it had 4,000 tonnes of sludge contaminated with PCBs. Canadian law requires PCBs over 50 ppm to be incinerated at a minimum temperature of 1,200°C, and the sample from the south tar pond revealed concentrations up to 633 ppm. The incinerator, designed to destroy only PAHs, had a capacity up to 900°C.

By the fall of 1994, the problem created by the PCBs was unresolved, although the incinerator and dredging equipment were working. In late 1994, the province decided that the incinerator option was not viable. It called for tenders for new approaches, and all bids were over $100 million. The province rejected them as too expensive. It subsequently invited one Nova Scotia consulting firm, Jacques Whitford, to determine what could be done for $20 million or less. In January 1996, the Nova Scotia minister of Supply and Services announced that he had accepted the Jacques Whitford plan to use the slag next to the tar ponds to fill in the ponds. Once that work was done, grass and trees would be planted to create a park. This proposal was greeted with surprise and anger by the people of the CBRM, none of whom had been consulted during development of this "solution."

Jacques Whitford started the first phase of its work, more sampling to determine the extent of the PCBs. Ten years had passed since the federal and provincial governments had announced the cleanup, and under federal law, PCBs cannot be buried. The intent was to identify the PCB-contaminated sludge and remove it to a disposal site in Quebec. Throughout the spring, the sampling continued, and by midsummer the estimate was that 45,000 tonnes of PCB-contaminated sludge existed, leaving Jacques Whitford to express reservations about its proposal. The outcome was that the "encapsulation" option was rejected. To this point, $60 million had been spent, and a viable solution had not emerged.

The federal and provincial governments then announced that they would pursue a more open and participatory approach and established a community–government committee to develop a cleanup plan. The committee was named the Joint Action Group (JAG). In 1998, an agreement was reached to clarify the relationship of JAG with the three levels of government, and $62 million was committed to complete studies, designs, and other preparations for the cleanup. In 2000, another consulting firm, Conestoga-Rovers and Associates, was hired to manage the agreement intended to lead to the cleanup of the tar ponds as well as the coke ovens site. Over the next few years, a sewer system was built to divert tonnes of raw sewage flowing daily into the tar ponds, the derelict structures on the coke oven site were demolished and removed, and the old Sydney landfill was closed and capped.

Next Steps

In 2007, a $400-million cleanup of the tar ponds was announced by the federal and provincial governments to reclaim the 97 hectares of the industrial land. This was the fourth major initiative to deal with the legacy of pollutants in the tar ponds. The press release from the governments of Canada and Nova Scotia stated that the solution would involve solidification, containment, and capping of contaminated soils, to be followed by site development and long-term and ongoing monitoring and maintenance. Incineration would not be used. The recommendation not to use incineration was based not on advice from scientists or consultants, but on strong rejection by the community. In announcing the cleanup initiative, the governments emphasized that the remediation proposal had been reviewed through an environmental assessment process that started during 2005. The independent Environmental Assessment Panel strongly recommended that remediation should focus on containment and capping of all materials in the tar ponds rather than incinerating some materials and containment and capping of the remainder. And, to ensure engagement with the public, a Community Liaison Committee was established. Its membership reflects six sectors in the community, and it is a forum to provide information about remediation progress, and to receive feedback from the community.

In the late spring 2007, building began on more than 2 kilometres of channels through the tar ponds to allow clean water from the Coke Oven Brook and Wash Brook to flow through the ponds without becoming contaminated. Subsequently, in the spring and summer of 2008, sediments from the old channel of the Coke Oven Brook were removed and moved elsewhere on the site to be stabilized and solidified. High-density polyethylene liner was then placed on the bed of the brook and covered with gravel to allow water to drain off the site without becoming contaminated. Between 2008 and 2012, sediments in the tar ponds were stabilized, solidified, and

Sydney Tar Ponds Agency

Sydney Tar Ponds Agency

Tim Babcock

An aerial view of the Sydney Tar Ponds site (top) shows the scope of the cleanup project, and an artist's rendering (middle) and close-up of tennis courts (bottom) give an on-the-ground view of some of the remediation work.

Photo courtesy AECOM

Open Hearth Park opened in August 2013.

capped. The finished surface was then planted with grass and other vegetation. And, after 2012, the provincial government initiated a long-term monitoring program of water quality in the harbour, and governments engaged with the community regarding future uses on the remediated sites.

The cost was shared by the federal government ($280 million) and the provincial government ($120 million) for the cleanup. Full opportunity for participation in the remediation was provided to local companies and to Aboriginal businesses. Thirty per cent of the contracts for the coke ovens site were a part of the Aboriginal set-aside program. An environmental training program was also initiated to develop environmental remediation skills for Aboriginal workers.

In late August 2013, the 39-hectare Open Hearth Park, which has sports fields, walking trails, art installations, and a playground, was officially opened. The park is situated 2 metres above the contaminated sediment that was contained and covered. At the opening, many expressed satisfaction and happiness with the reclamation outcome, and were pleased to know that $15 million had been allocated for long-term maintenance and monitoring. However, some expressed concern about whether the approach would totally contain the contaminated material.

Looking forward, the federal and provincial governments hired a consulting firm, Ekistics Planning and Design, to develop a Tar Ponds and Coke Ovens Land Use Plan. The Sydney Tar Ponds Agency (n.d.) stated that the intent was to create a "phased land use plan" to be logical and achievable but also visionary and transformative to "leave a lasting legacy for the entire region" by (1) creating lands for public purposes, (2) facilitating new sustainable economic development initiatives, (3) integrating surrounding communities, and (4) reinforcing and reflecting the cultural history of the area. In addition to the facilities opened in the late summer of 2013, future components might include an outdoor concert ground, wildlife watching stations, urban forests, trail networks, bridges, boardwalks, docks, rest areas, interpretative stations, outdoor exercise stations, outdoor interpretative pavilion, new roads and sidewalks to serve as connectors to the adjacent communities, an innovative business campus, and commercial development along an adjacent road.

At least three lessons stand out from this experience. First, when basic science is not used from the outset to inform policy decisions related to environmental issues, effective solutions will probably not be identified. Second, even when science is used, understanding can be incomplete, and decisions will be taken in the face of considerable uncertainty. Third, when local stakeholders are not included in the process, challenges can be expected to proposed solutions.

A growing concern is that many wastewater treatment facilities are old and need expensive maintenance, upgrading, or replacement. The Canadian Water and Wastewater Association calculated that $5.4 billion in new investment would be required *each year* between 1997 and 2012 to modernize and upgrade all existing water and wastewater treatment facilities, as well as to provide such facilities to communities without them. Such investment did not occur.

© US Environmental Protection Agency, Great Lakes National Program Office

Point-source, end-of-pipe type of water pollution, Great Lakes Basin.

Ammonia and nitrogen represented more than 94 per cent of the total releases to water. Other chemicals such as mercury are released in much smaller amounts but have serious negative impacts on human and aquatic system health. Mercury bioaccumulates and biomagnifies (see Chapter 10) in the liver, kidneys, and muscles of affected organisms, and chronic exposure can result in brain and kidney damage. Mercury levels in the Canadian environment continue to rise. Main sources are metal mining and smelting, waste incineration, and coal-fired power plants.

Runoff from urban areas either flows directly into water bodies from roads and other non-point sources or can be channelled by stormwater systems. Stormwater can contain various contaminants such as suspended solids, sediment, and grit; nutrients, including different forms of phosphorus and nitrogen; toxic metals, including copper, lead, and zinc; hydrocarbons, including oil, grease, and polycyclic aromatic hydrocarbons; trace organic contaminants, including pesticides, herbicides, and industrial chemicals; and fecal bacteria. Stormwater should therefore be treated in municipal wastewater plants. Unfortunately, such treatment does not always occur.

A third important source of wastes into water bodies is agricultural activity, but this is more appropriately discussed under the category of non-point sources.

Non-Point Sources

As discussed in Chapter 10, crop and livestock production has increased significantly as a result of more effective farm machinery, new genetic crops, agrochemicals, and irrigation. The latter two also contribute to environmental impacts, especially through fertilizers, pesticides, and herbicides being carried in runoff from farm fields, which ends up in streams, rivers, and lakes. In this section, we examine the experience with diffuse pollution in the Great Lakes basin.

Diffuse pollution is a policy issue in the Great Lakes basin. Since the early 1960s, interest has evolved from concern about sedimentation from soil erosion and eutrophication from phosphorus and nitrate loading to persistent toxic chemicals. As the definition of the problem has evolved, so have ideas regarding appropriate responses.

What has been learned about the strategic implications of how the problem has been defined? A key lesson is that diffuse pollution represents a "layered" problem. Too often, attention does not go beyond the first layer, where concern focuses on *environmental degradation* and the *economic costs* imposed on downstream users. The motivation for defining the problem in this manner appears to be that people will see the connection between diffuse pollution and loss of economic production or increased costs for economic production. A second layer, now receiving increased attention, is the link between diffuse pollution and negative impacts on *ecosystem health* or *integrity* and especially on *human health*. It is believed that making the connection to human health should create a powerful image in the minds of both policy-makers and residents regarding diffuse pollution. A third layer is diffuse pollution as a problem touching on human *values, beliefs, attitudes, and behaviour*. From this perspective, the fundamental problem is behaviour by individuals and groups, driven by inappropriate values, beliefs, and attitudes. If attention is focused on this third level, then the prescription to resolve diffuse pollution is certainly different from what it would be if attention were limited to the first level. You may wish to re-read Box 1.5 about the Drivers-Pressures-State-Impact-Response (DPSIR) framework discussed in Chapter 1 with regard to the implications of diffuse pollution.

What mechanisms have been effective in achieving recognition of diffuse pollution as a policy issue? First, there is a need for *credible science* to document the problem.

Credible Science and Institutional Commitment

Appreciation of diffuse pollution as a policy issue has been encouraged in Canada and the Great Lakes basin by a combination of science, institutions, and individuals. Several initiatives by the International Joint Commission (IJC), a bilateral institution created in 1909 to manage interjurisdictional water issues between Canada and the United States, have been significant.

During the 1960s, the media declared that "Lake Erie is dying," a reference to the highly eutrophic state of that lake (see Chapter 4). In 1972, the governments of Canada and the United States entered into an agreement to restore and enhance water quality in the Great Lakes. Initial attention focused on reducing phosphorus loading from municipal sewage treatment plants and other point sources. Initiatives were effective, but it was suspected that non-point sources might also be significant. However, data were not available regarding such sources.

Under the 1972 agreement, the IJC was asked "to conduct a study of pollution of the boundary waters of the Great Lakes System from agricultural, forestry, and other land use activities." Subsequently, the International Reference Group on Great Lakes Pollution from Land Use Activities, known as PLUARG, examined two major pollution problems: eutrophication from elevated nutrient inputs, and increasing contamination by toxic substances. PLUARG studied the pollution potential from various land uses, including agriculture, urbanization, forestry, transportation, and waste disposal, as well as natural processes such as lakeshore and riverbank erosion.

PLUARG concluded that the "combined land drainage and atmospheric [non-point] inputs to individual Great Lakes ranged from 32 per cent (Lake Ontario) to 90 per cent (Lake Superior) of the total phosphorus loads (excluding shoreline erosion). Phosphorus loads in 1976 exceeded the recommended target loads in all lakes" (International Reference Group on Great Lakes Pollution from Land Use Activities, 1978: 4–5). The PLUARG study findings, the first credible science to document the contribution of non-point sources to phosphorus loading, were difficult to ignore. The report also stated that toxic substances such as PCBs (polychlorinated biphenyls) were entering the Great Lakes system "from diffuse sources, especially through atmospheric deposition. Through land drainage, residues of previously used organochlorine pesticides (e.g., DDT) are still entering the boundary waters in substantial quantities." In terms of the sources, it was reported that "intensive agricultural operations have been identified as the major diffuse source contributor of phosphorus." In addition, "Erosion from crop production on fine-textured soils and from urbanizing areas, where large-scale land developments have removed natural ground cover, were found to be the main sources of sediment. Urban runoff and atmospheric deposition were identified as the major contributors of toxic substances from non-point sources" (ibid., 6).

The PLUARG report and other analyses led to renewal of the Great Lakes Water Quality Agreement in 1978 and to the signing in 1987 of a protocol amending the 1978 agreement. The 1987 amendments extended the scope of the agreement, but diffuse pollution was still recognized as a priority problem. Specifically, Annex 13 of the protocol focused exclusively on "pollution from non-point sources" and identified "programs and measures for abatement and reduction of non-point sources of pollution from land-use activities" in order "to further reduce non-point-source inputs of phosphorus, sediments, toxic substances, and microbiological contaminants contained in drainage from urban and rural land, including waste disposal sites, in the Great Lakes System" (Canada and Ontario, 1988: 55).

The PLUARG study commissioned by the International Joint Commission, along with the IJC's prestige and watchdog role, was significant in helping elected officials and the public to understand the severity of the diffuse pollution problem in the Great Lakes. Without such a credible voice to draw attention to the issue, it is unlikely that action would have been forthcoming.

Agricultural Non-point-Source Pollution

After the PLUARG studies were completed, Canada and the United States agreed to deal with the issue of high phosphorus loadings from rural non-point sources. In Canada in 1987, the federal and Ontario governments created a cost-shared program—the Soil and Water Environmental Enhancement Program, or SWEEP. The purpose was to meet, by 1990, the target reduction for Canada of 200 tonnes per year of phosphorus loading in Lake Erie from non-point sources.

SWEEP involved various programs. The first, focused on technology evaluation and development, was intended to stimulate adoption of soil management and cropping practices to improve water quality and to reduce soil erosion and degradation. A second thrust focused on pilot watershed programs, local demonstrations, and technical assistance at the farm level. In the pilot watershed program, the effects of using different practices on all farms in three experimental watersheds were compared with conventional practices in three control watersheds regarding water quality, hydrology, soil quality, crop production, and economics. A third component involved informing the public about the nature and consequences of soil and water quality problems and about the SWEEP objectives. Cressman (1994: 421), whose consulting firm was actively involved in the pilot watershed studies, later remarked that "It was during this time that interest in, and the practice of, conservation tillage grew significantly among Ontario farmers."

In parallel with SWEEP, the Ontario Land Stewardship Program was introduced. This $40 million program provided financial incentives for first-time adoption of conservation measures on farmland, such as protecting soil structure, building structures to ameliorate soil erosion, purchasing conservation equipment, and obtaining technical training. Funds also were dedicated to research projects related to stewardship practices. The SWEEP program overlapped with the National Soil Conservation Program, a $150 million shared-cost program. When SWEEP and the National Soil Conservation Program both terminated in the early 1990s, a newly elected federal government introduced another program—the Green Plan—for soil conservation and diffuse pollution control. However, by that time attention had shifted from soil erosion, sedimentation, and eutrophication to toxic substances. One observer remarked to one of the authors that in his view, the three programs had been developed with little consultation among key agencies, resulting in duplication and overlap and a time frame not long enough to allow measurement of program impacts.

Some positive results were achieved nevertheless. In the Lake Erie and Lake Ontario basins, the loads from phosphorus were reduced significantly. The main initiatives for non-point sources helped farmers modify how their land was cropped, especially by encouraging conservation tillage to reduce erosion and thereby reduce sediment and toxics placed into aquatic systems. The main actions regarding point sources involved upgrading municipal sewage treatment plants, and regulations were established to reduce phosphorus in laundry detergents.

Water Security: Protecting Quantity and Quality

A central concern in water management is to ensure a sufficient quantity of water of adequate quality for human use. By the middle of the second decade of the twenty-first century, more than one in six people on the Earth did not have access to safe water supplies, and two out of five did not have access to adequate sanitation, notwithstanding substantive efforts during the United Nations International Drinking Water Supply and Sanitation Decade (the 1980s) to improve conditions.

Current per capita water use extends from as little as 20 litres to more than 500 litres each day. Only 4 per cent of the world's population use water in the range of 300 to 400 litres per person per day, with people in the United States, Canada, and Switzerland being the highest per capita users. In contrast, about two-thirds of the global population use fewer than 50 litres for each person daily. In Canada, the average residential use during 2009 was 274 litres per capita per day (Lcd), a decrease from 327 in 2006 (Environment Canada, 2011b). Canada has been consistently ranked among the world's highest per capita water users. In 2009, the lowest provincial and territorial uses were in Prince Edward Island (189 Lcd), Manitoba (199 Lcd), and Alberta (208 Lcd), while the highest were in Newfoundland and Labrador (395 Lcd), New Brunswick (394 Lcd), and the territories (391 Lcd).

Most humans become thirsty after losing only 1 per cent of their bodily fluid and are in danger of death once the loss approaches 10 per cent. The minimum water requirement to replace loss of fluid for a normal healthy adult in an average temperate climate is about 3 litres each day. In tropical or subtropical conditions, the minimum amount becomes about 5 litres per person per day. A general rule of thumb is that an adult in average health in average climate conditions will die within three days without water, whereas the same person would live for up to three weeks without food.

Most Canadians receive their drinking water from the 4,000 municipal water treatment plants across the country, but a significant number depend on private wells or other arrangements. About 9 million Canadians, most living in small towns or rural areas, draw on groundwater for their drinking water.

The relative abundance of water in Canada, the high levels of water use, and the myth of superabundance, all referred to at the beginning of this chapter, made most Canadians complacent about the adequacy and safety of their water supplies. For many, this all changed in mid May 2000 when the town of Walkerton in southwestern Ontario, population about 5,000, experienced contamination of its water supply system by deadly bacteria, *Escherichia coli* O157:H7, or ***E. coli***, and *Campylobacter jejuni*. Seven people died and more than 2,300 became ill. Some individuals who became sick in Walkerton, especially children, may experience effects for the rest of their lives. For example, 10 years after the "Walkerton event," a medical team at the University of Western Ontario reported that adults from Walkerton who developed acute gastroenteritis in May 2000 and had been monitored between March 2002 and August 2008 showed higher probabilities of developing hypertension, kidney problems, or cardiovascular disease compared to adults who had not become ill or who had become mildly ill (Clark et al., 2010).

The concern generated by the Walkerton experience was reinforced during March 2001 in North Battleford, Saskatchewan, a community of 14,000, where thousands of residents suffered from contamination of the municipal water system by the parasite *cryptosporidium*. The parasite got into the water supply system over three weeks following routine maintenance at the treatment plant. Residents were under a boil-water order for three months. An inquiry ordered by the provincial premier concluded that the Saskatchewan government had not been effective in safeguarding drinking water in the province.

Perspectives on the Environment

Groundwater Quality and Contamination

Groundwater contaminants come from two categories of sources: point sources and distributed, or non-point, sources. Landfills, leaking gasoline storage tanks, leaking septic tanks, and accidental spills are examples of point sources. Infiltration from farm land treated with pesticides and fertilizers is an example of a non-point source.

Among the more significant point sources are municipal landfills and industrial waste disposal sites. When either of these occurs in or near sand and gravel aquifers, the potential for widespread contamination is the greatest.

Other point sources are individually less significant, but they occur in large numbers all across the country. Some of these dangerous and widespread sources of contamination are septic tanks and leaks and spills of petroleum products and of dense industrial organic liquids.

Contamination can render groundwater unsuitable for use. Although the overall extent of the problem across Canada is unknown, many individual cases of contamination have been investigated . . . . In many cases, contamination is recognized only after groundwater users have been exposed to potential health risks. The cost of cleaning up contaminated water supplies is usually extremely high.

Contamination problems are increasing in Canada primarily because of the large and growing number of toxic compounds used in industry and agriculture. In rural Canada, scientists suspect that many household wells are contaminated by substances from such common sources as septic systems, underground tanks, used motor oil, road salt, fertilizer, pesticides, and livestock wastes. Scientists also predict that in the next few decades more contaminated aquifers will be discovered, new contaminants will be identified, and more contaminated groundwater will be discharged into wetlands, streams and lakes.

Once an aquifer is contaminated, it may be unusable for decades. The residence time . . . can be anywhere from two weeks or 10,000 years.

Furthermore, the effects of groundwater contamination do not end with the loss of well-water supplies. Several studies have documented the migration of contaminants from disposal or spill sites to nearby lakes and rivers as this groundwater passes through the hydrologic cycle, but the processes are not as yet well understood. In Canada, pollution of surface water by groundwater is probably at least as serious as the contamination of groundwater supplies. Preventing contamination in the first place is by far the most practical solution to the problem.

—Environment Canada (2010d)

The Walkerton Inquiry

A public inquiry by Justice Dennis O'Connor (2002a; 2002b) established that:

1. The *E. coli*, contained in manure spread on a farm near one well of the Walkerton water supply system, entered the system through that well.
2. The farmer who spread the manure followed proper practices and was not at fault.
3. The outbreak would not have occurred if the water had been treated. The water was not treated because the chlorination equipment was being repaired.
4. The provincial government's approvals and monitoring programs were inadequate.
5. In addition to lack of training, the operators of the well system had a history of improper operating practices.
6. When people began to fall ill, the general manager of the water system withheld from the public health unit critical information about adverse water quality test results. This resulted in delay of a boil-water advisory.
7. Budget reductions by the provincial government had led to closure of government laboratory testing services for municipalities, and private laboratories were not required to submit adverse test results to the Ministry of the Environment or to the medical officer of health.

Walkerton: Lessons and Recommendations

Justice O'Connor offered recommendations to ensure the safety of drinking water, which are relevant to all regions of Canada. Overall, he recommended a **multi-barrier approach**. In his words, "Putting in place a series of measures, each independently acting as a barrier to passing water-borne contaminants through the system to consumers, achieves a greater overall level of protection than does relying exclusively on a single barrier (e.g., treatment alone or source protection alone). A failure in any given barrier will not cause a failure of the entire system" (O'Connor, 2002b: 5). The key components of a multi-barrier approach are source water protection, effective treatment of drinking water, and secure distribution of treated water to consumers. Given that the first barrier involves selecting and protecting reliable, high-quality drinking-water sources, he recommended "a source protection system that includes a strong planning component on an ecologically meaningful scale—that is, at the watershed level" and said "the Province [should] adopt a watershed-based planning process" (ibid.: 6, 3). Within a watershed-based approach, he recommended using a comprehensive approach for all aspects in a watershed, and undertaking source protection planning as much as possible at a local (catchment) scale by those most affected (municipalities and other local stakeholders). The multi-barrier approach was subsequently endorsed by the federal and other provincial governments.

First Nations Water Security

The events at Walkerton and North Battleford drew attention to structural and human resource issues related to reliable and safe water supply systems in Canada, systems that most citizens had previously taken for granted. Events in October 2005 at the Cree First Nations community of Kashechewan close to the western shore of James Bay, however, highlighted

Bruce Mitchell

Bruce Mitchell

Walkerton water memorial.

Bruce Mitchell

Bruce Mitchell

Established in 2004 as an agency of the Ontario government, the Walkerton Clean Water Centre provides education and training on drinking-water systems and advises on research needed to maintain high-quality, safe drinking water.

the Third World conditions on many First Nation reserves across the country. This situation was verified by the commissioner of the Environment and Sustainable Development, who observed that "When it comes to the safety of drinking water, residents of First Nations communities do not benefit from a level of protection comparable to that of people who live off reserves" (Auditor General of Canada, 2005a: ch. 5, 1).

Health Canada (2015) reported that as of July 2015, 133 drinking water advisories were in place for 93 First Nations reserve communities south of 60°, excluding British Columbia. As of April 2013, Health Canada had transferred responsibility for advisories in that province to the new BC First Nations Health Authority, and one of its tasks is to track boil-water advisories. In 2014, there were 617 First Nation reserve communities across the country. This situation reinforces a conclusion by Harden and Levalliant (2008: 7): "The fact remains that unsatisfactory access to safe drinking water persists for many First Nations people despite numerous reports and policies."

Swain et al. (2006: 19) have explained that water systems in most First Nations communities share challenges common to small and remote systems:

> ... capital and operating costs for each connection are high; it is hard to find, train and keep qualified operators; exploiting the economies of scale that can save money and reduce risks by consolidating systems is usually impossible where capital is concerned, and very difficult where human and other resources are concerned, because of travel distances; getting emergency help and supplies during crises is difficult, slow and costly; many community members resist the idea of treatment, because they do not like the taste of chlorinated water and have drunk untreated water in the past without apparent harm; and capacity to manage and govern the system is often a concern. In addition, many small communities have source water that is scarce, hard to treat, or both.

Kashechewan, a community of 1,900 people located on the Albany River some 400 kilometres north of Timmins, Ontario, became a flashpoint for the poor water services in many remote and distant communities. Kashechewan was established by the federal government in 1958 on the flood plain of the Albany River near James Bay because supply barges were unable to travel through rapids on the Albany River to a site further upstream preferred by the Cree people.

Perspectives on the Environment

Boil-Water Advisories in Canada

In 2008, the Canadian Medical Association reported that 1,760 boil-water advisories were in place across the country, in addition to those in place on 93 First Nations reserves. The number of advisories by province, in descending order, were: Ontario, 679; British Columbia, 530; Newfoundland and Labrador, 228; Saskatchewan, 126; Nova Scotia, 67; Quebec, 61; Manitoba, 59; Alberta, 13; New Brunswick, 2; Northwest Territories, 1; Prince Edward Island, Nunavut, and Yukon, 0.

The advisories included those for communities, commercial facilities, and trailer parks. Some had been in place for at least five years.

The Federation of Canadian Municipalities estimates that about $31 billion is needed to upgrade water and waste water treatment facilities across the country.

—CBC and CTV News, 7 and 8 April 2008

A water treatment plant was built in 1996, with the intake located downstream from large sewage lagoons that leach continuously into the creek containing the water supply intake. Furthermore, tidal action from James Bay pushes waste-laden water into the creek, past the water intake. A further challenge was that the plant was run by local operators who did not have sufficient background or expertise to recognize serious problems.

A contributing factor to the contamination of Kashechewan's drinking water in October 2005 was the failure of a chlorine pump. An emergency backup system should have taken over but did not because it had not been connected. In most modern plants, an emergency paging system alerts operators to a system malfunction, but such a system had not been installed. Thus, the sequence of events leading to contamination was similar to that at Walkerton, where chlorine equipment was not working and operators did not have the necessary training to realize the implications.

On 12 October 2005, Health Canada discovered unacceptable levels of *E. coli* in the treatment system but did not alert the band office for two days. Once a qualified contractor arrived at the treatment plant, it took about six hours to have the equipment operating properly, and safe potable water was being provided by 22 October. Nevertheless, nearly 1,000 community members experienced negative side effects. All 1,900 residents needed vaccinations for hepatitis A and B. Furthermore, many residents had scabies and impetigo because of the ongoing poor water quality, conditions exacerbated by high chlorine levels.

A further concern was that in 2003, the Ontario Clean Water Agency had alerted the government about problems with the water treatment system at Kashechewan. The next year, the provincial minister of Health and the minister of Community Safety visited the community, but no action was taken. The view of the provincial government was that because First Nation reserves are under the jurisdiction of the federal government, it was the responsibility of federal departments, specifically Health Canada, and Indian and Northern Affairs.

The short-term solution was to evacuate residents needing treatment and care. The evacuation began on 26 October, and by 2 November 815 people had been removed to Ottawa (245), Sudbury (251), Cochrane (206), Timmins (50), Attawapiskat (43), and Moosonee (20). The cost of the evacuation was estimated at about $16 million. The provincial minister of Natural Resources, David Ramsay, attributed the delay in evacuating people to "a jurisdictional misunderstanding as to who should have the lead on this." In addition to the evacuation, other interim steps were taken to ship bottled water to the community, send certified water treatment operators to assess and repair the treatment plant, evaluate the quantity and quality of the water in the river from which the treatment plant takes water, and assess the state of the sewage treatment lagoon.

Subsequently, the federal government examined various long-term solutions, including a $200-million package over five to seven years to reinforce a dyke to reduce flood damage vulnerability as well as to construct better drainage systems to protect low-lying areas; a $200-million project to relocate the community to Timmins; or a $500-million initiative to move the entire reserve to a new location on higher ground. At the end of July 2007, the federal minister of Indian and Northern Affairs announced that his government would rebuild and redevelop the low-lying reserve on its present location, since relocation was too expensive.

As a result of the Walkerton experience in 2000, the federal government initiated a First Nations Water Management Strategy in 2003, with a budget of $600 million spread over five years. The main purpose was to improve the quality and safety of drinking water on First Nation reserves through developing comprehensive policies, guidelines, and standards; educating on-reserve residents about drinking water issues; clarifying roles and responsibilities; building and upgrading water systems to meet standards; improving operation and maintenance; providing training to operators; and expanding water testing. The federal budget in 2008 included over $330 million for a renamed First Nations Water and Wastewater Management Action Plan for two years, and in the 2010 budget the plan was extended. Given what happened at Kashechewan and continuing conditions on many other First Nations reserves, it appears that much more needs to be done.

Perspectives on the Environment

Flooding in Kashechewan in 2008

On 25 April 2008, Kashechewan was again evacuated, this time because of flooding. Hundreds of the most vulnerable residents were evacuated by plane and were housed in motels, hotels, or other types of accommodation in Cochrane, Greenstone, Kapuskasing, Hearst, Sault Ste Marie, and Thunder Bay. Subsequently, about 1,900 people were evacuated from Kashechewan and Fort Albany, with 1,000 sent to Stratford and nearby communities such as St Mary's, Mitchell, and Milverton. The plan was to accommodate them for up to three weeks, but many were able to return in less than a week.

This was the fourth evacuation caused by flooding for Kashechewan since 2004 and the first for Fort Albany.

Subsequent evacuations happened in 2012 and 2013 due to flooding, becoming the fifth and sixth evacuations since 2004. In 2012, 250 residents in Kashechewan and Fort Albany were evacuated in late March, and in early May 2013, 901 people from Kashechewan were evacuated, as well as 160 from Moosonee.

Dan McCarthy

Tributary joining the Albany River at Kashechewan, Ontario.

Dan McCarthy

Dyke and drain control between the Albany River and Kashechewan, Ontario.

Dan McCarthy

New water treatment plant beside the dyke, Kashechewan, Ontario.

Perspectives on the Environment

Monitoring of Fresh Water on Reserves

. . . there are unacceptable gaps in the federal monitoring of fresh water—notably, that Environment Canada has water quality monitoring stations on only 12 of some 3,000 First Nations reserves.

—Commissioner of the Environment and Sustainable Development (2010: 2)

Supply Management, Demand Management, and Soft Path

Water security can be achieved through various approaches. The best known are supply management and demand management, but an emerging approach is called soft path, and all three will be reviewed in following section.

Supply Management

Supply management is the traditional approach. When a water shortage is anticipated, the solution is to develop a new source of supply, normally accomplished through either augmenting an existing supply (e.g., raising the height of a dam in order to be able to impound more water) or developing a new supply (e.g., a new dam and reservoir, new wells, a pipeline to a new source [a lake or river], a desalinization plant). The rationale is that populations will grow and the economy will expand, and each requires additional water supplies. Without incremental water, human well-being and development will be impeded.

Supply management has served societies well when it has resulted in an adequate supply of suitable-quality water available to meet demands. There are also some downsides. If people believe that additional supplies will always be found

Perspectives on the Environment

Uncertainty and Choices

Water problems (scarcity, flooding, pollution) have no single solution: options to deal with scarcity include supply augmentation through the mobilization of more resources through capital-intensive projects; efforts to conserve water; or redefining allocation to users. All these options have political and financial implications. They all come with risks, costs, and benefits, private or public, which strongly shape what solutions particular stakeholders are likely to push for.

—Molle (2007: 361)

to meet demands, little incentive exists to avoid wasteful water use or to adopt water conservation measures. One consequence is that a society may invest more money than would otherwise be required. Such additional costs may be significant, since the low-cost sources have usually already been developed. Another consequence is that the construction of new dams and reservoirs or pipelines may have significant environmental or social impacts at local and regional scales.

Given the above mix of benefits and limitations, it is worthwhile to consider other approaches that can be used in combination with or in place of supply management.

Demand Management

While supply management manipulates the natural system to create new sources of supply, **demand management** seeks to influence human behaviour so that less water is used.

Various methods can be used to influence human behaviour in water use. The most basic is pricing. It signals to users that water has a cost and that by using less water, people can save money. Volume-based pricing can be designed so that as consumers use more water, they pay an increasingly higher per unit charge. For this system to work, all use, whether in homes, offices, institutions, manufacturing plants, or farms, has to be metered. However, significantly higher prices for water could disadvantage the poorest members of a society, who may find it difficult to pay for minimal amounts to meet basic needs. To avoid inequities, other social policies must be in place to ensure that vulnerable people are not in jeopardy. This is particularly important with regard to water, because there is no alternative to water for meeting basic needs.

Another incentive is to offer price rebates for the purchase and installation of water-saving devices such as low-flow showerheads or toilets. Low-flow toilets, for example, use on average about 75 per cent less water per flush than a "regular" toilet. Since showers and baths account for 35 per cent and toilet flushing 30 per cent of water used in Canadian households, reducing volumes of water for them can lead to significant reductions in water. Further savings can be realized if previously used water, or grey water, is used for waste disposal, rather than using drinking-quality water for toilet flushing.

A third incentive is to restrict outside water use (watering of lawns, flower beds) by regulation during the hottest months when water use peaks. If the high peaks of water use in summer can be reduced, there would be no need to invest in additional capacity only required during a few days or months each year.

A fourth measure in demand management is to inform and educate water users so that, over time, they reduce water use. For example, people can be educated to turn off the faucet when brushing their teeth except when rinsing the toothbrush or to turn off the water in a shower except when initially soaking or rinsing off soap. Other practices include running a dishwasher or washing machine only with a full load.

Demand management is not a new concept, but it has been introduced often as a second-level approach after decisions focused on supply management have been taken. An ideal approach would combine the two in a well-integrated system.

Soft Path

The **soft path** approach extends demand management. Soft path aims to improve water use efficiency by challenging basic patterns of consumption. While demand management emphasizes the question of "how" to do the same with less water, the soft path approach raises the question of "why" water is even used for a function.

In the words of Brandes and Brooks (2006: 9):

- Why . . . do we use water to carry away our waste? Demand management would urge low-flow toilets, but waterless systems are available—perhaps not for homes (because of the need for regular maintenance) but certainly for larger buildings.
- Why do we use half the potable water piped to a house in the summer for watering lawns and gardens—and sidewalks? Demand management would urge more efficient sprinklers with automatic shut-offs, maybe even water restrictions. The soft path goes further: recycling water from bathtubs and washing machines or, better yet, drought-resistant greenery that requires little or no watering once it is established.

The soft path approach is based on four basic principles (ibid., 10–13):

1. *Water is treated as a service rather than as an end.* In the soft path, water is not viewed as the final product, other than for a few human uses (drinking, washing)

Perspectives on the Environment

How to Reduce Water Use in the Home

So, where do we start? The first step is to identify where we use water in the home. Then we need to decide on what to do to reduce the amount of water we use, either by eliminating wasteful practices and habits, or improving the efficiency of our water using fixtures and devices. Since we waste so much, this should be a relatively easy and painless process. The prime area to target is the bathroom, where nearly 65 per cent of all indoor water use occurs. . . . Based on the three rules of water conservation—reduce, repair, and retrofit—a typical household can reduce water consumption by 40 per cent or more, with no effect on lifestyle.

—Environment Canada (2009a: 10–11)

and for support of ecosystems. Instead, water is viewed as a means to accomplish specific functions, including sanitation, farm production, and yard maintenance. For example, the end is not to flush toilets or irrigate crops but to dispose of wastes or to grow food.

2. *Ecological sustainability is fundamental.* Ecosystems are viewed as legitimate users of water and also as one foundation of economies. Consequently, ecosystem health and ecosystem resilience must be considered when calculating the cost–benefit ratio of solutions to meet water demand. One result is that environmental needs are identified from the outset, and the amount of water required to satisfy such needs is subtracted from what is available to meet human needs.
3. *Quality of delivered water is matched to an end-use requirement.* While high-quality water is necessary for human consumption, the quality may vary significantly for other uses. The soft path seeks to match water quality to what is needed to accommodate an end use. One implication is recognition of "cascading water systems": waste water from one use becomes the supply for another use needing less stringent quality. Examples include using water from a washing machine on a garden or shower or bath water for toilet flushing.
4. *Determine the desired future condition, and plan back to the present.* Conventional planning for water takes the present as its starting point. Future needs are projected, and then decisions are taken to meet these needs. The soft path focuses not on the most probable future but instead on the most desirable future. Once the attributes of the desirable future are defined, decisions are taken about the most appropriate means to meet desired ends—without assuming that the way water is used now will be the same in the anticipated desirable future. This approach is referred to as backcasting, discussed in Chapter 5.

Brooks and Holtz (2009: 164–6) examine how soft path analysis was applied in Nova Scotia's Annapolis Valley. They concluded that water-use practices mean that available surface water will be inadequate to meet annual demand at least once every 12 years, and nearly every second year during summer seasons. Also, groundwater will not meet annual demands in two years out of every five. Based on that assessment, it was proposed that a mix of demand-management measures, such as high-efficiency technologies (low-flush toilets; crop, golf course, and lawn irrigation; industrial procedures), drip irrigation or high-efficiency sprinklers, repair of leaks in municipal water mains, and capping of artesian wells, along with soft path measures, such as waterless technologies or practices (toilets, cooling systems, industrial systems), rainwater/runoff storage, and water/wastewater recycling and reuse, be introduced. They also offer the following insight:

> The analysis underlying soft path planning does not generally yield a single, best path. Different policy and program combinations will lead us to the desired future. Soft path analysis can identify possible paths, describe the advantages and disadvantages (where quantifiable, the benefits and costs) and determine the likely social appeal. It is up to the society at large, with decision making that employs community consultation and participation, to choose the path most appropriate to its values. (Brooks and Holtz, 2009: 163)

Water security, both quantity and quality, should be achieved through a mix of supply management, demand management, and soft path approaches. The goal should be to use an integrated strategy drawing on all three.

Virtual Water

Increasing water scarcity, whether shortages of quantity or inadequate quality, may damage economic development, human livelihoods, and well-being. A relevant concept is **virtual water**, which has grown out of recognition of the importance of water for agriculture and food production. Aldaya et al. (2010: 942) explained the virtual water concept:

> The virtual water content of a product (a commodity, good or service) refers to the volume of water used in its production . . . virtual water "trade" represents the amount of water embedded in traded products. A nation can preserve its domestic water resources by importing water intensive products instead of producing them domestically. . . . Thus, virtual water "import" is increasingly perceived as an alternative source of water as well as an opportunity to preserve environmental flows in water-stressed nations, and is slowly changing the prevailing paradigms of water and food security.

Allan (2011: 2–3) provides examples of virtual water related to some Western breakfast foods: slice of toast, 80 litres; bacon, 480 litres; eggs, 120 litres; glass of milk, 240 litres; and espresso coffee, 140 litres. Those amounts reflect the water needed to grow, produce, package, and ship those products. To visualize the total amount, it is the equivalent of about three bathtubs filled with water. And about two-thirds of the total reflects the water related to animal products: milk, eggs, and bacon. As Allan (2011: 3) notes, "the average non-vegetarian diet in the US or Europe consumes about 5 cubic metres of water each day. That is 15 bathtubs, each and every day. . . ."

By pursuing a virtual water strategy, national governments in water-stressed countries can plan to meet food security needs even if their nation has a limited water endowment.

For example, the net virtual water import by Egypt, as a percentage of its own water resources, has been calculated to be about 23 per cent (El-Sadek, 2010: 2445). Given that a water shortage within that country has been a barrier to expanding cropland, Egypt benefits by importing crops that require significant amounts of water to grow. However, as El-Sadek comments, before adopting an explicit virtual water approach, "Egypt needs to be assured that it can have fair and secure trade with water-abundant nations" (ibid.).

A virtual water strategy does have the potential to ameliorate water shortages at a national level. Nevertheless, as with all concepts or strategies, and as already indicated above, it has limitations. First, if a nation decided to cut back significantly on domestic production of crops demanding a large amount of water and import them from other countries, many local farmers might lose their livelihoods. One outcome could be migration of poor rural people into urban areas, where they would probably become part of a growing marginalized group. Second, a relatively poor nation would not likely have the foreign currency to purchase food products requiring significant water inputs. Third, a nation might be reluctant to become dependent on other countries for food needs. Liu et al. (2007: 86) have commented that with regard to China: "For food security, the government pays more attention to food self-sufficiency than to water use efficiency. Food self-sufficiency is overwhelmingly favoured by the Chinese government, which regards reliance on international food markets as a threat to domestic security." And fourth, use of virtual water might mask or obscure the reality of in-country water shortages and lead to delays or inaction regarding policy changes providing environmental and social as well as economic benefits.

Perspectives on the Environment

Professor Tony Allan and Virtual Water

Emeritus Professor John Anthony Allan of the Department of Geography in King's College, London, and the School of Oriental and African Studies received the 2008 Stockholm Water Prize for his pioneering work in developing the concept of virtual water. The Stockholm Water Prize, established in 1990, is awarded annually by the Stockholm Water Foundation. It is conferred for "outstanding water-related activities."

Perspectives on the Environment

Singapore and Virtual Water

Singapore has only 5 per cent of the water it needs. Yet there is no hint of water shortages, nor of the constrained economic development that many feel ought to be inevitable for a seriously water-short island economy. Ninety per cent of the total water need is brought in through trade in food commodities. The other non-native 5 per cent has until recently been imported across the straits from Malaysia. This dependence is now being reduced by investment in desalinization, an increasingly affordable technology.

—Allan (2011: 53)

Perspectives on the Environment

Limitations of the Virtual Water Concept

Estimates of "virtual water flows" are helpful in generating public awareness regarding the volume of water required to support production and consumption activities. However, the true policy relevance is gained only by considering information regarding the scarcity of water . . . in a given region or country. . . . The policy relevance . . . will be greater where scarcity values (opportunity costs) are substantial.

—Wichelns (2010: 2204)

Nevertheless, virtual water provides an option for consideration. For example, a virtual water assessment was conducted by Brown et al. (2009) in British Columbia to understand the virtual water requirements and contents for crops and livestock within watersheds of wet and dry regions to create a foundation for water conservation management strategies. The Okanagan Basin was chosen as a dry region and the Lower Fraser Valley as a wet region. The virtual water content in both areas related to fruits was higher compared to the average for Canada, and was 50 per cent higher compared to global averages. Regarding grain and field crops, 55 per cent were above Canadian averages and 68 per cent were above global averages. Brown et al. (2009: 2694) concluded: "Some major decisions will need to be made on how to reduce water consumption in order to accommodate future anticipated growth. The data generated is a first step in providing science based information to assist decision makers in strategic choices of reallocation and conservation of water use."

What are your views on virtual water? Does it offer promise to address water security challenges? Or does it have the potential to disadvantage people already vulnerable and benefit those who enjoy a relatively high standard of living?

Water Footprints

If virtual water relates to the volume of water used to produce a commodity, good, or service, a **water footprint** serves as an indicator of water consumption by tracking both direct and indirect water use by a consumer or a product (Water Footprint Network, 2011). As Hockstra and Chapagain (2007: 36) observed, the water footprint is analogous to the ecological footprint, discussed in Chapter 1. More specifically, they commented: "The water footprint of a nation is defined as the total volume of freshwater . . . used to produce the goods and services consumed by the people of the nation. Since not all goods consumed in one particular country are produced in that country, the water footprint consists of two parts: use of domestic water resources and use of water outside the borders of the country."

Hockstra and Chapagain calculated that the global water footprint is 7,450 cubic gigametres per year (Gm^3/year; a gigametre is 10^9 metres). In terms of direct factors determining a water footprint, they identify (1) volume of consumption (related to gross national income), (2) consumption patterns (such as high versus low meat consumption), (3) climate, and (4) agricultural practice (water-use efficiency). The relative importance of the four factors varies from country to country. To illustrate, at the start of the twenty-first century, the footprint of the US was high (2,480 m^3/capita/year) due to high consumption of meat and industrial products. Iran also had a relatively high footprint (1,624 m^3/capita/year), mainly due to low crop production yields and high evapotranspiration rates.

In terms of water footprint measured by total water use, India (987 Gm^3/year, or 13 per cent), China (883 Gm^3/year, or 12 per cent), and the US (696 Gm^3/year, or 9 per cent) are the largest consumers of global water resources; Canada's total footprint is 62.8 Gm^3/year. However, if the measure is water use per capita, tracking both direct and indirect water use by a consumer or a product, the largest footprint is that of the US, as noted above, followed by Italy (2,332 m^3/capita/year) and Canada (2,049 m^3/capita/year). In contrast, India's per capita footprint is 980 m^3/capita/year and China's is 702 m^3/capita/year, both relatively small footprints.

Various options exist to reduce water footprints. Improved technology that reduces the amount of water needed per unit of product is one. A second is to adopt consumption patterns that require less water, such as reduced consumption of meat. Third, behaviour can be altered through a mix of pricing, raising awareness, labelling of products, or other incentives to encourage behaviour that uses less water. And, fourth, production can be shifted away from low productivity per unit of water to high productivity, through altering trading patterns and thereby achieving global water-use efficiency.

Water as Hazard

Flooding

Humans settle adjacent to rivers and lakes for many reasons. Proximity provides access to potable water, a place to dispose of wastes, and sometimes, a source of power and a means of transportation. The relatively flat land beside many rivers and lakes facilitates construction of roads, homes, and places of business. The aesthetic quality—serenity, beauty, natural appeal—of a river or lake view also often means that waterfront lots command a premium price. However, the term "**flood plain**" exists for a reason. From time to time, rivers and lakes extend beyond their normal limits to cover adjacent areas or flood plains. Flooding is a normal hydrological function. Indeed, many species of flora and fauna depend on flooding to survive and flourish. In addition, humans often benefit from flooding, as when flood plains are enriched by the deposit of silt that then supports agriculture.

When flooding occurs, the result is often only a minor inconvenience, and this was usually the case when settlements were relatively small. However, as population concentrations on flood plains increase, the potential of flood damage goes up. Examples of major floods and serious associated damages in Canada include:

- lower Fraser River Valley, BC, 1948
- Manitoba, 1950
- southern Ontario—Hurricane Hazel, 1954 (more than 80 deaths and millions of dollars in damage)
- Fredericton, 1973
- Cambridge, Ontario; Maniwaki, Quebec; Montreal, 1974
- Saguenay River Valley, Quebec, 1996 (10 deaths and $800 million in damage)
- Manitoba, 1997 (estimated $300 million in damage)
- eastern Ontario; Quebec; Saint John River, New Brunswick, 2008
- Manitoba, 2009 (estimated $40 million in damage)
- Manitoba, 2011 (estimated minimum of $550 million in damage)
- Souris River, southern Saskatchewan; Richelieu River, Quebec, 2011 (the worst in 150 years, forcing more than 1,000 people to evacuate their homes)
- southern Alberta, 2013 (record flooding; the most expensive natural disaster in Canada)
- Toronto, 2013 (record flooding; the most expensive natural disaster in Ontario)

In his "Domestic Guest Statement" in Chapter 5, Dan Shrubsole states the costs were $7.6 billion and $1.2 billion respectively for the 2013 floods in Alberta and Toronto.

The southern Alberta flooding in June 2013 was driven by over 200 millimetres of rain during two days, falling on ground already saturated. Four people drowned, and over 100,000 people were displaced from their homes. The flooding on the Bow and Elbow Rivers was three times greater than the previously worst flooding in 2005, which caused $400 million in damages.

In Calgary, over 75,000 residents of 26 neighbourhoods received mandatory evacuation orders during 20–21 June.

THE CANADIAN PRESS/Jonathan Hayward

Aerial shot of flooded downtown Calgary in June 2013.

In High River, all 13,000 residents were ordered to evacuate their homes. In addition to Calgary and High River, nine other municipalities declared a state of emergency. In Calgary, the central business district remained inaccessible until 26 June, and residents in Banff and Canmore were cut off due to flooding and mudslides that closed parts of the Trans-Canada Highway.

During November 2013, the Alberta provincial government announced it would examine several structural mitigation measures to protect communities. For High River, a channel to divert water around the municipality would be considered, and for Calgary, a dry off-stream dam near Springbank would be considered for the Elbow River, as well as an underground diversion tunnel through Calgary. Shortly after the announcement, some Springbank residents expressed opposition to the off-stream dam, which would affect up to 14 local landowners, and argued for other options to be examined.

THE CANADIAN PRESS/Winston Neutel

GO train service was severely affected during the 2013 Toronto floods, leaving hundreds of passengers stranded on board for hours before rescue teams arrived.

In Toronto, on 8 July 2013, some 126 millimetres of rain fell in a two-hour period, an amount significantly higher than the average rainfall of 74.4 millimetres for the entire month of July. The downpour triggered flash flooding out of sewer drains, which flooded basements of homes, closed roads, and stranded commuters on GO trains. Over 350,000 people were without power, a non-trivial issue for residents living in high-rise apartment or condominium towers in the central city.

After this event, the Ontario provincial government announced it would spend \$3.1 billion over 10 years to improve wastewater and stormwater collection systems as mitigation measures. Please read the "Domestic Guest Statement" in Chapter 13 by Meg Holden for further insights about how major urban areas can respond to such disasters.

Humans have various ways of reducing flood damage potential, as noted by Dan Shrubsole in his "Domestic Guest Statement" in Chapter 5. *Structural approaches* modify the behaviour of the natural system by delaying or redirecting flood waters. Common methods are upstream dams and storage reservoirs, protective dykes or levees, and deepening or straightening river channels to increase their capacity. All these measures provide protection. However, because they are designed and built with a standard in mind, such as the magnitude of flooding that may occur once in 100 years, a flood of greater magnitude will eventually occur (such as a flood that occurs once every 200 or 500 years). If people perceive the structural measures as "protecting" the flood plain, resulting in more development on it, then when the inevitable flood event greater than the design capacity of the structural measures does happen, potential and actual flood damage will be greater.

A *non-structural approach* focuses on modifying the behaviour of people. Methods include land-use zoning to restrict or prohibit development in flood-prone areas, relocation of existing flood-prone structures, information and education

Perspectives on the Environment

Flood Management

The present practice of flood management in Canada is characterized by at least three realities. First, it is impossible to provide absolute protection to people and communities. Second, a mix of structural and non-structural adjustments that cover the entire range of protection, warning, response, and recovery is needed to effectively protect lives and property. Third, implementation of flood adjustments requires the effective participation of all levels of government and the public.

— Shrubsole (2001: 462)

programs to alert people to the hazard of occupying flood plains, and insurance programs to help people deal with the costs of flood damage. Ideally, an integrated combination of structural and non-structural measures should be used.

Canadians will continue to live and work on flood plains for the reasons mentioned at the beginning of this section. In that context, the comments of Shrubsole in the above Perspective box deserve consideration.

Droughts

If flooding represents situations with too much water, droughts represent the opposite problem—insufficient water. Flooding is immediate and apparent. The beginning or end of a **drought** is more difficult to determine, since droughts reflect a lack of precipitation, along with temperature, evaporation, evapotranspiration, capacity of soil to retain moisture, and resilience of flora and fauna in dry conditions.

Consequently, as Gabriel and Kreutzwiser (1993) noted, a significant challenge when seeking to identify "drought-prone" areas is to define what is meant by "drought." As they noted, interpretations are based on causes and effects. Regarding those based on *causes*, a meteorological drought is due to a prolonged deficiency of precipitation, which reduces soil moisture. This type of drought can trigger a second type (hydrological drought, an effect that then becomes a cause), manifested by reduced stream flows and lowered **water table** and/or lake levels. In terms of *effects*, an agricultural drought results in reduced crop yields due to lack of moisture. An urban drought happens when there is insufficient water, because of lower stream flows or water tables, to support all demands in the community.

Droughts, as Gabriel and Kreutzwiser (1993: 119) explain, reduce the amount of water for use by depleting soil moisture and groundwater reserves as well as by lowering stream flows and lake levels. These reductions can start a "depletion cycle": less than normal rainfall leads to low soil moisture, triggering demand for irrigation development, in turn depleting non-recharging surface and groundwater supplies. The high evapotranspiration rate associated with hot, dry periods also contributes to depleting soil moisture and surface water supplies, which are not restored to normal levels without unusually high rainfall.

What has been the experience with drought in Canada, where the Prairies, the interior of British Columbia, and southern Ontario and Quebec are most vulnerable?

The Prairie provinces, especially in that area of southern Alberta and Saskatchewan and extreme southwest Manitoba known as **Palliser's Triangle** (Figure 11.5), experience the most severe drought conditions. This area is named after Captain John Palliser, sent by the British government and the Royal Geographical Society to explore the territory between the Laurentian Shield and the Rocky Mountains from 1857 to 1860 and to determine the nature of the soil, its capacity for agriculture, the quantity of its timber, and the presence of coal or other minerals.

Palliser divided the area into two sections—a fertile belt and a semi-arid area. He considered the southern or semi-arid area unfit for settlement. Palliser commented that this area "has even early in the season a dry patched look. . . . The grass is very short on these plains, and forms no turf, merely consisting of little wiry tufts. Much of the arid country is occupied by tracts of loose sand, which is constantly on the move before the prevailing winds" (Mackintosh, 1934: 11). Palliser concluded: "There is no doubt that the prevalence of a hard clay soil derived from the cretaceous strata which bakes under the heat of the sun, has a great deal to do with the aridity of these plains, but it is primarily due more to want of moisture in the early spring" (ibid., 34). Indeed, the average annual precipitation in this area is only 380 millimetres. Thus, almost 160 years ago, Palliser identified the drought-prone nature of the southern Prairies.

Over the past two centuries, there have been about 40 droughts, with multi-year ones in the 1890s, 1910s, 1930s, late 1950s and early 1960s, 1980s, and 1999–2005. The worst drought in 100 years occurred on the Prairies from 1929 to 1937, affecting 7.3 million hectares of agricultural land. The lack of precipitation also led to significant soil erosion due to wind. As a result of the drought in the 1930s, several responses occurred. Most notably, the Prairie Farm Rehabilitation Administration (PFRA) was created by legislation in 1935. Its purpose was to facilitate financial and technical support to farmers, especially to build dugouts (small ponds) and small dams. In addition, sub-marginal land was taken over by PFRA, was re-grassed, and became community pastures. Government tree nurseries also provided free trees to farmers to be planted to counter wind-driven soil erosion. PFRA and the three Prairie provincial governments collaborate to support adaptation through soil and water conservation initiatives, irrigation, and structural infrastructure (reservoirs and pipelines).

The period from 1999 to the spring of 2004 also was one of significant drought, and from 2001 to 2002 drought extended across the south of the country from British Columbia to the Maritimes.

Figure 11.6 illustrates that "in 2002, drought-stricken areas covered over three-quarters of the Prairies (including the northeastern part of British Columbia)" (Statistics Canada, 2003b: 13). While there were many impacts, the most pronounced was inadequate water to support agriculture. Yields of spring wheat, barley, and canola fell significantly during 2002 relative to the average yields between 1991 and 2000, which were non-drought years.

Livestock were also affected negatively. The greatest impact was in Alberta, where the inventory dropped by 605,000 cattle, a decrease of 10.4 per cent between January 2002 and

January 2003. At the same time, declining supplies of cattle feed, a result of the drought conditions, pushed up feed prices and led many ranchers to reduce herds.

Another indicator of the drought conditions was the drying up of many dugouts, potholes (small natural ponds), and sloughs. By September 2002, 80 per cent of Prairie farms were in regions in which dugouts were half empty, and 20 per cent reported their dugouts were completely dry. The drying up of potholes and sloughs not only affected agriculture. They are also critically important habitat for migratory wildfowl, which were adversely affected (Statistics Canada, 2003b: Table 10.4, regarding the effect of drought on wetlands).

While droughts represent an extreme condition related to water shortages, we also should be aware that for some regions of Canada the historical record indicates that water availability, even over many previous decades, may not be a good guide regarding what should be expected as "normal" water availability in natural systems. For example, Wolfe et al. (2011) examined the record for more than 5,200 years at Lake Athabasca and came to some startling conclusions, as noted in the "Perspectives on the Environment" box.

In Ontario, drought can occur in any season but is most likely in the summer when demand for water is usually the highest. Compared to the Prairie provinces, droughts in Ontario tend to last not as long, affect a smaller area, occur less frequently, and be less intense. Southwestern Ontario is most vulnerable, especially in the summer and early autumn. Extended dry periods for more than a month are unusual, but shorter droughts are not uncommon. For example, dry periods of at least seven consecutive days occur at least once a month during the agricultural growing season in southern Ontario, and short-term (10 to 20 days) dry spells occur every year. Longer droughts (more than four weeks) happen once in three years.

Lake levels are affected by dry periods, and the Great Lakes illustrate this effect. The variation between minimum and maximum lake levels is 1.2 metres on Lake Superior, 1.8 metres on Lakes Huron and Erie, and 2 metres on Lake Ontario. Low levels affect shipping, especially in terms of cargo tonnages, which have to be reduced so that ships do not run aground. To reduce the draft by only 2.5 centimetres requires a reduction of up to 90 tonnes on most ships and more than 180 tonnes on ships between 244 and 305 metres in length.

In Ontario, many streams are almost totally supplied by groundwater discharges during low rainfall periods. In average conditions, groundwater discharge provides 20 per cent of the water for streams and rivers in most of Ontario. For some rivers or streams, the contribution can be up to 60 per cent, extending up to 100 per cent in the summer months. Thus, depletion of groundwater reserves resulting from drought can have a serious impact on surface flows, especially for smaller streams. The lowering of water tables due to drought can also lead to the drying up of wells dependent on shallow aquifers.

In the following "International Guest Statement," Kathryn Bellette shares insight from Australia related to strategies there for both droughts and floods.

Perspectives on the Environment

Historical Perspective on Natural Water Availability in the Athabasca River System

. . . a new 5,200-year record of Lake Athabasca water-level variations, which serves as a sensitive gauge of past changes in alpine-sourced river discharge, reveals that western Canadian society has developed during a rare period of unusually abundant water "subsidized" by prior glacier expansion. As the "alpine water tap" closes, much drier times are ahead. Future water availability is likely to become similar to the mid-Holocene when Lake Athabasca dropped 2–4 metres below the twentieth century mean. Regions dependent on high elevation runoff (i.e., western North America) must prepare to cope with impending water scarcity of a magnitude not yet experienced since European settlement.

—Wolfe et al. (2011: 1)

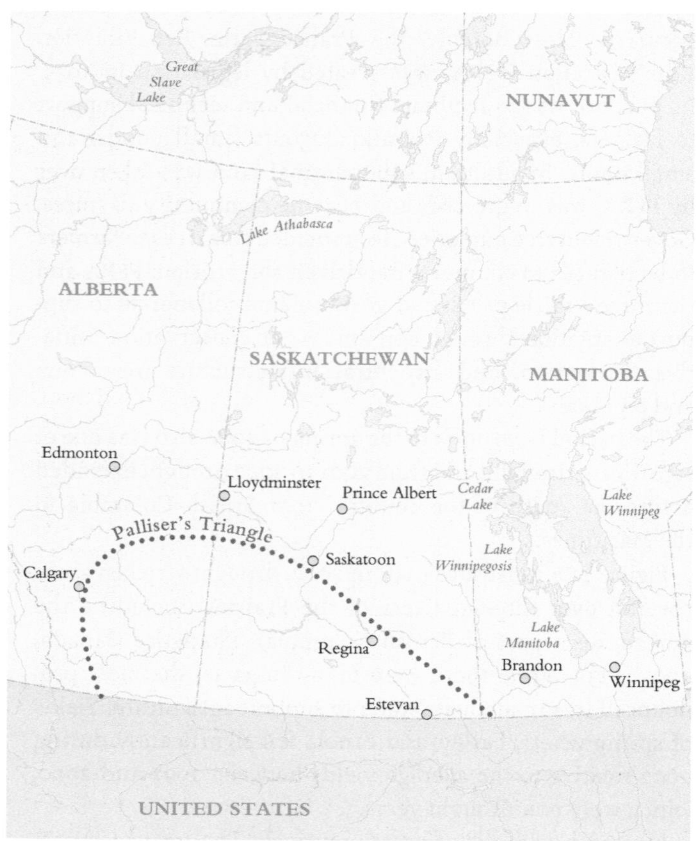

FIGURE 11.5 | Palliser's Triangle.
Source: Adapted from Bone (2005: 410).

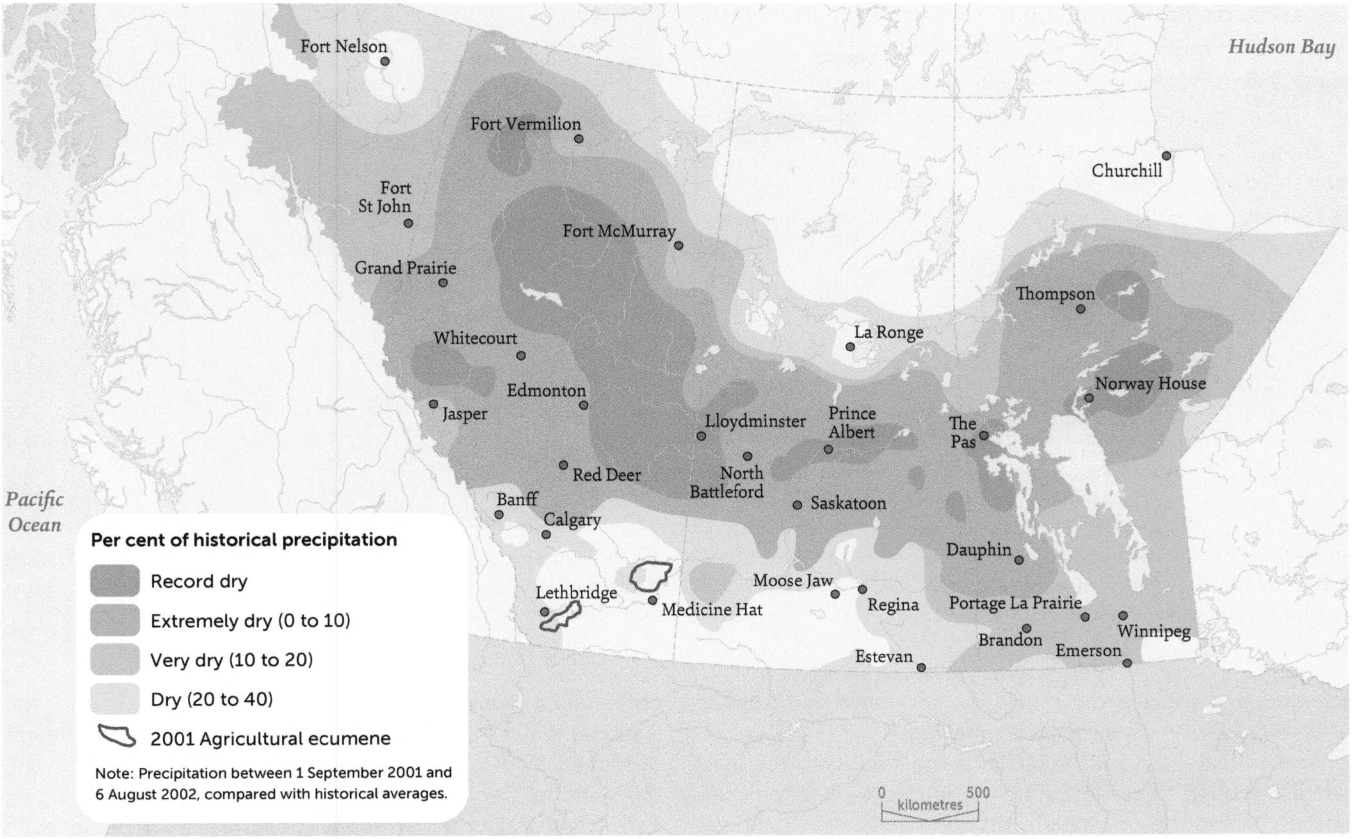

Per cent of historical precipitation

Record dry

Extremely dry (0 to 10)

Very dry (10 to 20)

Dry (20 to 40)

2001 Agricultural ecumene

Note: Precipitation between 1 September 2001 and 6 August 2002, compared with historical averages.

FIGURE 11.6 | Precipitation below historical averages, 2002.

Source: Statistics Canada (2003b: 13).

A Land of Flood and Drought | *Kathryn Bellette*

Picture a continent where the average annual rainfall is 455 millimetres, with 88 per cent lost through evapotranspiration. Around 10 per cent of this rainfall is available as surface runoff, of which 91 per cent is limited to the northeastern coastal fringe of the continent and an island to the south. A significant proportion of the central south part of the continent has an annual average rainfall of less than 200 millimetres, where it is not unusual for rain not to fall at all for a number of years.

This geologically old, flat land is Australia. When it does rain, particularly in the monsoonal north, it often floods; it is a land of flood and drought.

Water in significant catchments such as the Murray-Darling Basin is allocated by a share of the available flow each year rather than as a set amount–such is the unpredictability of the water source availability both within and between seasons. Droughts have been known to last beyond 10 years, and there is a growing climate change signal.

During what is described as the "millennium drought" (1997–2009) in southeastern and southwestern Australia, significant investments were made in water policy development. The National Water Commission was established to lead a national water initiative and a reform agenda, which included water planning, markets, and regulation. The central issue is determining how much water is available and how it should be shared: How much for the environment, and how much for consumptive use? How much for each environmental asset and how much for each alternative consumptive use? Nationally agreed policy objectives were water security, water-use efficiency, water for the environment, sustainable supply, and tradability of water. Addressing these objectives required better metering and accounting of water, better

Continued

© Commonwealth of Australia

The flooding of towns is a consequence of significant flood events breaking across rivers and moving across flood plains and beyond due to relatively flat topography. These events can occur over a range of climates across the northeastern State of Queensland to the towns of the Murray-Darling Basin in southeastern Australia and settlements and station homesteads in arid central Australia.

Photo by Diana Love

The millennium drought saw such a decline in the flow of the Darling River that land-based activities such as grazing could occur across parts of the river bed.

scientific and socio-economic input, and more participation of stakeholders in water decision-making.

Within Australia, South Australia is the state with the least rainfall, dubbed "the driest state in the driest inhabited continent." During the millennium drought, South Australia was placed on water restrictions. A water security plan, labelled "Water for Good," was developed, better financed and more detailed than the previous "Waterproofing Adelaide" plan. Major differences were the seriousness with which alternative water sources were considered in the mix and enabling funding that became available for implementation. The Goyder Institute for Water Research was established in 2010, and research on the optimal water resources mix to supply metropolitan Adelaide was among the first priority projects. Water sources now available to the water supply pool for the Adelaide Metropolitan region include surface water, groundwater, desalinated water, stormwater, roof- or rainwater, recycled water, and River Murray water piped to Adelaide Hills storage reservoirs. Determining an optimal mix of water supply options requires considering trade-offs among multiple objectives such as supply security, economic costs (financial and externalized), social preferences/resistance, and environmental impacts.

The millennium drought broke in the summer of 2010–11, when the world experienced one of the strongest La Niña episodes on record. Widespread flooding occurred through southeastern Australia, and the Murray-Darling Basin experienced its largest annual rainfall on record. Some of us have advocated that this period of relative plenty is the ideal time to plan for future droughts.

But by 2014–15, support for water research was at a low, with some authorities, centres, and research institutions reaching the end of their funding cycle with little prospect of continuity of support. For instance, research funding for the National Water Initiative dried up, the Australian government proposed to disband the National Water Commission, and the National Centre for Groundwater Research and Training had its Australian government funding greatly reduced. In South Australia, the role of commissioner for water security was eliminated in 2013, with the state government Water Resources minister stating "The job is no longer required. The position was established during the most unprecedented drought . . ." And future funding for the Goyder Institute for Water Research was uncertain.

Some of us call the tendency of authorities to move after a drought breaks into a mode of policy and planning apathy as part of the "hydro-illogical cycle" (drought leads to awareness, to concern, to panic, and then it rains, and then an apathy sets in). We should ask, why have we not invested as a state and nation in reflections from the last drought? What did we learn? What should we do differently next time? Are we prepared? The psychology and sociology of water policy development is a niche wide open for contributions, and also may be relevant to other enduring resource issues.

Courtesy Kathryn Bellette

Kathryn Bellette has a background in environmental science and environmental management, policy development, and regulation. She has undertaken leadership roles in catchment management, framing and forming sustainable development policy, and associated cross-portfolio/sector strategic planning, bridging across disciplines and sectors. She has held executive positions in a number of South Australian government portfolios and is a past and present member of a number of state government boards, ministerial advisory committees, and a local government development assessment panel.

Heritage Rivers

The purpose of the Canadian Heritage Rivers Program (CHRP) is to "recognize, conserve and manage, in a sustainable manner, Canada's designated **heritage rivers** and their natural qualities, cultural/historical heritage, and recreational values" (Canadian Heritage Rivers System, 2014). The CHRP is overseen by a board with representatives from the federal, provincial, and territorial governments. However, Quebec withdrew in 2006, and has not had any rivers designated. The Ottawa River has been considered for nomination, but since it forms much of the border between Ontario and Quebec, it has not been put forward. In contrast, the Upper Restigouche River in New Brunswick was designated in 1998, as that could be done even though the downstream portion of the river is in Quebec.

A new charter for the Canadian Heritage Rivers System was signed on 24 December 2013, and is in effect from 1 April 2011 until 1 April 2031. In the charter, the vision states that "the Canadian Heritage Rivers System is a model of stewardship, cooperation and participation; one that engages society in valuing the natural and cultural heritage of rivers and river communities as essential to the identity, health and quality of life of Canadians" (Canadian Heritage Rivers System, 2014).

A set of nine principles is identified in the Charter, including: (1) voluntary participation in the heritage system, (2) jurisdictional powers maintained by participants regarding rivers designated in the system, (3) Aboriginal peoples, community, landowner and individual rights and interests are respected in the nomination, designation and management of heritage rivers, (4) the spirit of the heritage and recreational selection guidelines identified by the Canadian Heritage Rivers Board is reflected by rivers, or portions of rivers, incorporated into the system, (5) appropriate provincial, territorial and federal ministers approve nominations and designations of rivers, and (6) the federal lead agency, giving technical and financial support for nominations and designations, and for coordinating monitoring of designated rivers, is Parks Canada.

The French (French River Provincial Park in Ontario) and the Alsek (Kluane National Park in Yukon) were the first two rivers designated under this program in February 1986. By 2014, 38 had been formally designated, totalling over 9,000 kilometres, and four others had been nominated, totalling nearly 11,000 kilometres (Figure 11.7)

For almost a decade after the beginning of the program, designated rivers were located in federal or provincial parks, the territories, or in areas within provinces with relatively few people. Designation thus involved rivers primarily on Crown land, avoiding the complication of having to deal with private landowners and municipalities, often suspicious of the Heritage Rivers Program, viewing it as possible intrusion into property or municipal rights.

Perspectives on the Environment

Rivers as Heritage

Rivers teach valuable lessons about renewal. It is said, and it is true, that you cannot enter a river at the same spot twice; because, of course, the river "rolls along." This very character of rivers generates health and well-being. It also connects one part of the waterway to another.

—Harry Collins, chairperson, Canadian Heritage Rivers Board, 2002

However, in 1994, the entire Grand River basin, located in southern Ontario and with most of its land in private ownership, was designated. Other rivers in highly settled areas have since been designated, such as the Humber River in Toronto and the Thames River and the Detroit River in southwestern Ontario.

In the Fraser River basin in British Columbia, a Charter for Sustainability, which outlines what is needed to achieve sustainability for the Fraser River and its watershed, has been signed by federal, provincial, and municipal governments, as well as by First Nations and other organizations. A Fraser Basin Council, a not-for-profit organization, was created and provides oversight for activities to achieve the future identified by the charter.

These examples illustrate the types of initiatives being taken as part of the management strategies for designated heritage rivers. All are oriented to protecting the integrity and health of the ecosystems, ranging from biophysical to cultural components. In September 2007, a 10-year Canadian Heritage

Bruce Mitchell

Grand River, Cambridge, Ontario. A former factory has become a park setting adjacent to the river, making the river accessible to the public while retaining a sense of heritage.

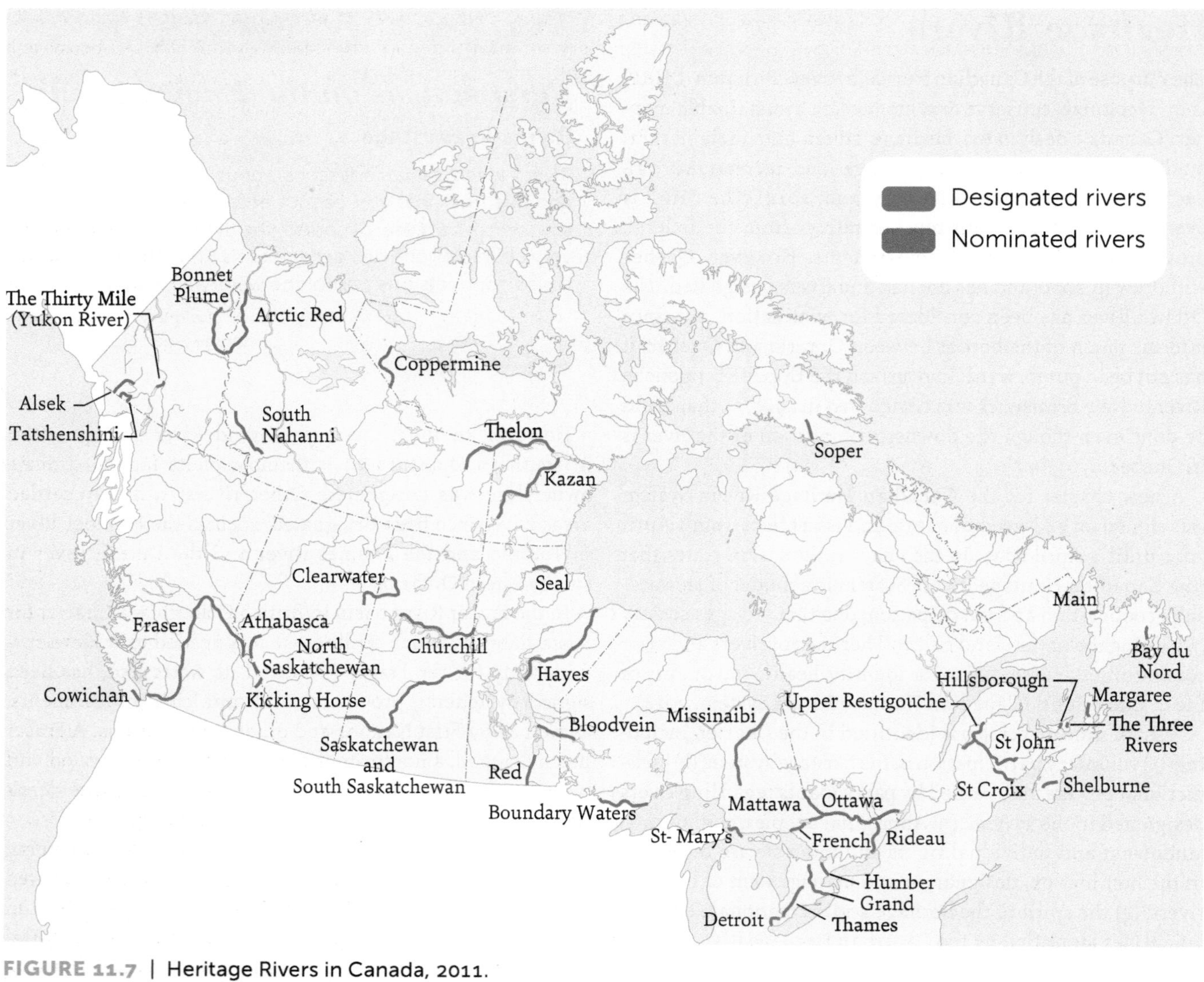

FIGURE 11.7 | Heritage Rivers in Canada, 2011.
Source: Parks Canada, 2015. http://www.chrs.ca/en/rivers.php

Rivers System strategic plan was approved, and the plan will be in place until March 2018. Four priorities are in this plan: (1) build a comprehensive and representative system that recognizes Canada's river heritage; (2) conserve the natural, cultural, and recreational values and integrity of designated Canadian heritage rivers; (3) engage communities and partners to maximize the full range of benefits associated with the Canadian Heritage Rivers Program; and (4) foster excellence in river management.

Hydrosolidarity

Hydrosolidarity refers to an approach that recognizes interconnections among aquatic, terrestrial, and other resource systems, leading to integrated, participative, collaborative, coordinated, and shared management, whether at local, provincial/state, national, or international levels. The challenges of achieving hydrosolidarity increase when moving from local to international situations. Notwithstanding such difficulties, hydrosolidarity is most often evoked as necessary in international settings (International Water Resources Association, 2000). Hydrosolidarity contrasts with more traditional approaches to international rivers or lakes in which sovereign states claim control over the water within their boundaries without regard for the implications for countries sharing the resource, especially downstream users.

Best practice associated with hydrosolidarity reflects the reality of aquatic systems, including that (1) water flows downhill, leading to differing upstream and downstream interests; (2) interconnections exist between water and land systems, meaning that land-based activities can have significant implications for water quantity and quality; and (3) the multiple uses that water can serve range from drinking, to crop and industrial production, to supporting migratory bird habitats and recreation. As a result, best practice regarding hydrosolidarity includes management by (1) normally using river basins as the spatial unit for planning and management; (2) ensuring attention to upstream–downstream issues; (3) recognizing the interrelationships among water, land, and other resource systems; (4) engaging stakeholders in a collaborative and participatory manner; and (5) acknowledging the needs of biophysical and human systems.

Consistent with hydrosolidarity is the concept of **integrated water resource management (IWRM)**, which the Global Water Partnership (2000: 22) defined as "a process which promotes the co-ordinated development and management of water, land, and related resources in order to maximize the resultant economic and social welfare in an equitable manner without compromising the sustainability of vital ecosystems."

The motivation for IWRM is to overcome the challenges arising from various groups having interest in and different organizations being responsible for water and related resources, along with the reality that they each often focus only on their own interests and responsibilities. One result, for example, can be a ministry of agriculture providing support for farmers to drain wetlands in order to expand land in agricultural production, while a ministry of natural resources in the same jurisdiction provides support to farmers to expand wetlands in order to extend migratory bird habitat and enhance capacity to slow the release of flood waters. As Dale and Newman (2007: 59–60) observed, an integrated approach seeks to overcome the silos, stovepipes, and solitudes often characterizing the approaches of governmental organizations responsible for water, land, and other related resources.

Ideally, IWRM drives managers to consider integration at several levels, including:

1. Integration of various dimensions of water, such as quantity and quality, surface and underground, and upstream and downstream. Use of river basins or watersheds for planning and management is recognized as often the most appropriate spatial unit to achieve this.
2. Integration of water considerations with those for terrestrial and other related resources. This involves recognizing that many water problems, such as pollution and flooding, originate from or are exacerbated by land-based activities. Here again, the river basin or catchment is the most appropriate unit to facilitate attention to a range of interconnected resource systems.
3. Integration of water, as part of the environmental system, with aspects related to economic and social systems. Regional land-use planning, environmental impact assessments, and strategic sustainability assessments are used to connect environmental, economic, and social considerations.

The rationale for IWRM is intuitive: water is but one subsystem, and therefore managers need to take an ecosystem approach to ensure linkages and connections are addressed. However, the challenges to implementing IWRM can be formidable, because human behaviour is often competitive rather than cooperative, some individuals focus on narrow interests without concern for the consequences for others today or in the future, and understanding complex natural and human systems can be very difficult (Biswas, 2004, 2008; Rahman and Varis, 2005; Lenton and Muller, 2009; Butterworth et al., 2010).

The following example illustrates the opportunities and challenges in implementing a hydrosolidarity approach.

Great Lakes Water Quality Protocol

In 1972, the governments of Canada and the United States signed the Great Lakes Water Quality Agreement (GLWQA). As previously mentioned, the agreement was amended in 1978, 1983, and 1987. It focused on the Great Lakes ecosystem, defined to include the interacting components of air, land, water, and living organisms, including humans. The purpose was to restore and maintain the chemical, physical, and biological integrity of waters in the Great Lakes ecosystem. In September 2012, a Great Lakes Water Quality Protocol was approved to amend the GLWQA and took effect in February 2013. The Protocol reaffirmed the commitment to protect, restore, and enhance water quality in the Great Lakes. It also specified the need to address four challenges: (1) threats to water quality, especially from aquatic invasive species, nutrients, and chemical substances, (2) discharges from vessels, (3) climate change impacts, and (4) loss of species. The Protocol also stipulates that 16 principles and approaches will be applied, including sustainability, ecosystem approach, science-based management, adaptive management, polluter pays, precaution, prevention, coordination, and public engagement. Performance is to be tracked relative to 14 indicators regarding chemical (7), biological (5), and physical (2) integrity, as well as two indicators regarding performance effectiveness (International Joint Commission, 2012a; 2012b).

The objectives of the 1972 agreement were to reduce nuisance conditions and discharge of substances toxic to humans, animals, and aquatic life, as well as to reduce phosphorous loadings in Lakes Erie and Ontario. During 1978, an amendment specified that an ecosystem approach would be used, with attention directed to both human health and environmental quality. Furthermore, it was specified that the intent was to virtually eliminate persistent toxic substances.

In 1983, further amendments stipulated increased effort to reduce phosphorous inputs into each lake. During 1987, a key change was to identify "areas of concern," significantly degraded nearshore areas for which rehabilitation efforts would be pursued (Hartig and Zarull, 1992). In addition, new initiatives would address non-point pollution sources and create lake-wide management plans, as well as deal with contaminated sediment, airborne toxic substances, and contaminated groundwater.

Despite impressive progress, 20 years later the Agreement Review Committee (2007: 8) remarked that "there are still serious threats to the physical, biological, and chemical integrity of the Ecosystem. Many scientists have voiced concern that the Great Lakes are exhibiting symptoms of stress from a variety of sources and impacts, including nutrient loadings, toxic contaminants, invasive species, and land use changes." The drivers behind some of these challenges were viewed to include climate change, urbanization, long-range transport of toxics, and inadequate approaches to stop invasive species.

Perspectives on the Environment

Different Views on the Great Lakes Water Quality Agreement and Protocol

Often cited as one of the most forward-thinking diplomatic achievements for the environment, the Agreement has served as a model for other international agreements to protect and restore environments elsewhere in the world. Its strengths include the establishment of common objectives and commitments for protecting and restoring the waters of the Great Lakes Ecosystem, the facilitation of information sharing, and cooperation on research and monitoring.

—Agreement Review Committee (2007: 6–7)

In some respects it could be argued that leadership in the Great Lakes governance regime forgot how to learn and adapt. . . . Matters of accountability, transparency, distributed governance, and shared decision-making are all absent from the current GLWQA, leading to the threat that if not addressed in a new agreement, an implementation deficit is nearly certain.

—Krantzberg and Manno (2010: 4274, 4275–6)

The IJC recommends that the governments develop their Progress Report of the Parties using a core set of indicators related to the objectives for the 2012 Agreement. Such core indicators provide the public and policy makers with scientifically sound information to make better monitoring, restoration and prevention decisions.

Although there is research and management value in having many indicators, having a core set provides a focus for monitoring, analysis, public communications and enables the tracking of progress for the lifetime of the updated Agreement. Targets, goals or standards should be developed for each of the core indicators and resources should be provided for protection and restoration actions to achieve the goals.

—International Joint Commission (2012b: 13)

The spirit of hydrosolidarity is that upstream and downstream jurisdictions work together collaboratively to ensure that initiatives in upstream parts of an aquatic system do not cause significant damage in downstream parts. The IJC was created for exactly that purpose and is viewed as a model of how transjurisdictional resource issues can be addressed. Certainly, when a nation agrees to participate in mechanisms and processes to deal with cross-border problems, it acknowledges that it is sacrificing some autonomy in order to reach decisions that benefit all nations.

Water Ethics

Water is a necessity of human life. There is no substitute. Furthermore, many needs and interests compete for their share of water. Given this situation, it is puzzling that more attention has not been given to development of **water ethics** to establish principles on which water management decisions could be based. UNESCO has published some relevant reports (Selbourne, 2000; Priscoli et al., 2004), but study focused on water ethics has been paltry.

Matthews et al. (2007) have addressed the matter of water ethics, and the following comments are based on their work. They remind us that an ethic normally is a statement of principles or values to identify appropriate behaviour by individuals or groups. At the same time, a set of ethics cannot provide all the answers needed or resolve all dilemmas. Frequently, uncertainty and complexity make outcomes difficult to predict, contributing to fuzzy understanding about what might happen. Also, different ethical principles, each desirable, can sometimes conflict, making it unclear as to which path to pursue.

Notwithstanding the above difficulties, Matthews et al. (2007: 350–3) offer six "imperatives" for a new water ethic:

- Meet basic human needs to enhance equity today and for the future
- Safeguard ecosystems by allocating sufficient water resources
- Encourage efficiency and conservation of water resources
- Establish open and participative decision-making processes
- Respect system complexity and emphasize precaution
- Seek multiple sustainability benefits from water-centred initiatives

We encourage you to think about these six imperatives and to decide whether they provide a reasonable foundation for a water ethic. If you conclude that they do not, then decide what should be changed or added. For help, you may wish to review the reports by Armstrong (2009), Graenfeldt (2010), and Sandford and Phare (2011).

Regarding the first imperative of the proposed water ethic (meet basic human needs to enhance equity today and for the future), the UN Human Rights Council has sought to have water and sanitation recognized as a basic human right and to establish an international monitoring organization to track actions of nations. The council met in 2008 to address this and other matters, the third time in six years that the UN had attempted to have human rights to water and sanitation recognized. Canada opposed the resolution for **water rights**, which had been proposed by Germany and Spain. Russia and the United Kingdom also did not support it. Nevertheless, it was generally agreed that Canada led the opposition.

Canada had been consistent in its opposition. During a Human Rights Council meeting in 2002, Canada was the only one of 53 nations voting against a motion to appoint a special rapporteur on water. And in October 2006, Canada voted against a resolution to have the Human Rights Council conduct a study on the right to water.

Canada's lack of support appears to be driven by a belief on the part of federal politicians that Canadian sovereignty over its own water is ambiguous under NAFTA. In that trade agreement, water could be viewed as a commodity or service comparable to any other. As a result, if Canada were to support the principle that water is a basic human right, some believe that it could become vulnerable to claims from the United States that since Canada has more water than it needs and places such as Atlanta and the US Southwest face water shortages, then Canada has a moral duty to share its water through bulk water transfers or other means. In contrast, others argue that the Human Rights Council resolution explicitly excluded transborder water issues and therefore Canadian sovereignty over its water would not be threatened.

Another reason undoubtedly has influenced the federal government. If it were to support the concept of a human right to water, liability issues could emerge related to the many small communities across Canada under boil-water advisories. If water were prescribed to be a basic human right, could the federal or provincial governments become liable to lawsuits when sufficient quantities of potable water are not provided to communities? The federal government would be especially liable regarding Aboriginal communities, since under the Canadian Constitution, the federal government is responsible for their reserves.

Bruce Mitchell

A sign requests donations toward clean and clear water at a local park.

As you think about the matter of water as a human right, consider that Article 25.1 of the Universal Declaration of Human Rights, adopted by the UN General Assembly on 10 December 1948, states that "Everyone has the right to a standard of living adequate for the health and well-being of himself and his family, including food, clothing, housing, and medical care and necessary social services. . . ." If food, clothing, and housing are viewed as basic human rights, why could not "water" be included in this statement?

In 2002 the UN Committee on Economic, Social and Culture Rights (CESCR) issued "General Comment No. 15," or GCN15, in which the following words appear: "The human right to water entitles everyone to sufficient, safe, acceptable, physically accessible and affordable water for personal and domestic uses. An adequate amount of safe water is necessary to prevent death from dehydration, reduce the risk of water-related disease and provide for consumption, cooking, personal and domestic hygienic requirements." The CESCR is explicit that this statement is an "interpretation" rather than a "treaty," and as result is not legally binding on member states. However, it reflects a powerful moral position (Debreuil, 2006: 8).

On 28 July 2010, the UN General Assembly adopted a resolution recognizing access to clean water and sanitation as a human right. The vote was 122 nations for, none against, and 41 abstentions. Bolivia's representative, who introduced the resolution, argued that the resolution was needed because a human right to water was not fully recognized despite being referred to in various international instruments. Countries abstaining, including Canada, the US, the UK, Australia, Denmark, Greece, Ireland, Israel, Japan, Kenya, the Netherlands, New Zealand, Poland, and Sweden, took the position that this matter was being examined by the Geneva-based Human Rights Council, and, as a result, such a resolution was premature until that council's work, which is intended to clarify the scope of such a right, is concluded.

What is your position related to water as a human right? As you consider this question, you may find the insights of Debreuil (2006), Jayyousi (2007), Khadka (2010), and Llamas, Martínez-Cortina, and Mukherji (2009) helpful.

Implications

Canada has a relative abundance of high-quality water, even though some areas experience scarcity in terms of quantity and/or quality. As a society, however, we have placed stress on aquatic systems, sometimes degrading them significantly. As shown in this chapter, considerable scientific understanding can be drawn upon to assist in the management of water systems. And there have also been significant improvements, confirming that individuals, groups, communities, and societies can reverse degradation and deterioration.

Each of us has opportunities to modify our basic values and change behaviour to help protect our water resources and to maintain the integrity and health of aquatic ecosystems. Table 11.1 identifies actions that individuals and/or governments can take to contribute to improved water resources in Canada.

Perspectives on the Environment

A Public Policy Matter

Ultimately, if we are to sustain Canada's water supplies, we all have to better understand how we use water as individuals, as communities and as consumers. Water management is not just a government problem or an industry problem. Rather it is one of the most important public policy issues facing the world today—with the key word in that phrase being "public."

—Taylor (2009: 47)

TABLE 11.1 | What You Can Do: Ten Water Conservation Initiatives

Focus	Problem	Solution	Challenges	Savings
1. Educate	Lack of understanding about need for and potential benefits of water conservation	Introduce outreach and education programs beyond information dissemination to change behaviour	Engaging community members in meaningful education that changes view of "water abundance"	Many experts agree 50 to 80 litres of high-quality water per capita per day is needed for a good standard of living
2. Design communities for conservation	Municipal-level decisions too often have negative impacts on watersheds	Limit urban sprawl, reduce "green lawn syndrome," promote "green" infrastructure, expect land-use decisions to be judged for their impacts on watersheds	Belief that water-sensitive urban design is much more expensive than standard approaches	Conservation-oriented urban design can save 50 per cent of outdoor water use
3. Close urban water loop	All municipal water treated to drinking-water quality but more than two-thirds used for non-drinking functions	Reclaim, reuse, and recycle to ensure better match of water quality to end uses	Possibility that lower water prices may make reuse and recycling less financially attractive; risks associated with reused and recycled water	Up to 50 per cent water savings can be achieved by reusing or recycling water for toilets and outdoor irrigation
4. Use rainwater	Rainwater not usually viewed as source of water for homes, businesses, etc.	Use decentralized infrastructure to harvest rainfall and create xeriscaped landscapes that rely on rainfall	Building and plumbing code restrictions; financial cost of rainwater harvesting infrastructure for homeowners and businesses	Rainwater harvesting and xeriscaping can lead to 50 per cent savings in outdoor water use and up to 40 per cent savings for indoor use for toilet flushing and clothes washing
5. Plan for sustainability	Too many conservation programs viewed as short-term solutions until next supply source can be developed	Plan with 10- to 50-year time horizon, involve all stakeholders, and place ecological health in central position	Looking beyond the three- or four-year electoral cycle and investing in programs that provide long-term returns; engaging the community	Effective water conservation plans can lead to water savings ranging from 20 to 50 per cent
6. Adopt appropriate pricing	Normal water pricing rates encourage wasteful use	Use "full cost" pricing with volume-based pricing structures	Need to implement metering and gain political support; need to ensure full accessibility to meet basic needs for water	Effective pricing can lead to 20 per cent reduction in water use over the long term

TABLE 11.1 | *Continued*

Focus	Problem	Solution	Challenges	Savings
7. Link conservation to development	Present arrangements for funding urban water infrastructure promote neither conservation nor innovation	Connect conservation to development by requiring water infrastructure funding and development permits to depend on use of demand management	Local resistance to conditional funding arrangements; capacity for enforcement and follow-up on conditions	Water savings from 20 to 30 per cent can be achieved by using "off the shelf" technologies and modest water pricing reforms
8. Make managing demand part of regular business	Demand-management approaches often not comprehensive or part of daily business in most communities	Implement permanent water conservation measures and hire full-time staff with appropriate skills	Reluctance of utilities to commit financial resources to hire demand-management professionals and implement long-term demand-management programs	Depending on how aggressive and creative demand-management programs are, "the sky is the limit" in terms of potential savings
9. Stop flushing the future	Inefficient fixtures and appliances common in most homes	Install water-efficient toilets, faucets, and showerheads as well as water-saving dishwashers and washing machines	Permissive building and plumbing codes and lack of incentives and resources to promote efficient technologies	Efficient fixtures and appliances can achieve 33 to 50 per cent indoor water savings with payback within two years in most instances
10. Fix leaks and reduce waste	Significant water loss from leaks, often due to old infrastructure	Detect and repair leaks by regular water audits and maintenance programs	Financial challenges on utilities of up-front costs for integrated metering, detection, maintenance, and monitoring programs	Fixing leaks can easily result in 5 to 10 per cent water savings, and up to 30 per cent savings are possible with older infrastructure

Source: Based on Brandes et al. (2006: 6–42); see also Casselman (2011)

Summary

1. While comprising only 0.5 per cent of the world's population, Canadians have access to almost 20 per cent of the global stock of fresh water and 7 per cent of the total flow of renewable water. About one-fifth of the Canadian population relies on groundwater for daily water needs.

2. Canada's per capita demands on water resources are the second-highest in the world and have been calculated at about 250 litres per person per day at home.

3. Canada is a global leader in terms of water diversions for hydroelectric generation, and diversions for hydro power dominate overwhelmingly in both number and scale of diversions.

4. Canada has used many megaprojects to meet energy demands, and virtually every region in the country has energy megaprojects. One of the most significant is James Bay in Quebec, while others are Churchill Falls in Labrador, the Nelson–Churchill river system in Manitoba, and the Columbia and Nechako Rivers in British Columbia.

5. Various major projects have been proposed, such as NAWAPA and the GRAND scheme, to transfer large volumes of water from Canada to the United States. They all have significant financial costs and environmental implications.

6. Free-trade agreements, such as stipulations under NAFTA, trigger concern that water could become a tradable commodity.

7. Pollution involves point and non-point sources, with the latter being the most challenging to manage.

8. Progress regarding diffuse pollution has been associated with *credible science* to document the nature of the problem.

9. The governance of the Great Lakes is evolving, and key aspects include a shift from an exclusive command-and-control emphasis to voluntary measures and from top-down management to environmental partnerships.

10. At the start of the second decade of the twenty-first century, one in six people worldwide did not have access to a safe water supply, and two out of five people did not have access to adequate sanitation.

11. Many Canadians have been complacent about the adequacy and safety of their water supplies. For many, this changed in mid May 2000 when Walkerton, Ontario, experienced contamination of its water supply system by deadly bacteria. Seven people died, and more than 2,300 became ill.

12. The judge who conducted a public inquiry into the Walkerton tragedy recommended a "multi-barrier approach" to drinking water safety.

13. The water crises at Kashechewan have highlighted the often unsatisfactory water supply infrastructure on First Nation reserves as well as in many other rural communities in remote regions. Water supply systems in such places are often more like those in developing countries.

14. Increasing attention is being given to determining the most appropriate mix of supply management, demand management, and soft path approaches to provide water to communities. The soft path approach shifts attention from questions about *how* to meet needs to questions about *why* needs are met by using water.

15. The concept of "virtual" water encourages nations to determine whether it would be more sensible to import water-intensive crops than to grow them in their own countries. This sometimes leads to conflict between two desirable goals: food self-sufficiency and efficient water use. The concept of "water footprint" complements the idea of virtual water, and helps to educate people and communities about the impact of their use of water.

16. Floods along rivers and lakes are normal occurrences. Humans adapt to flooding through some mix of structural and non-structural approaches.

17. Droughts are a function of precipitation (or lack thereof), temperature, evaporation, evapotranspiration, capacity of soil to retain moisture, and resilience of flora and fauna in dry conditions.

18. The most drought-prone areas in Canada are the southern Prairie provinces, south-central British Columbia and southern Ontario.

19. The Canadian Heritage Rivers Program recognizes the significance of rivers in the identity and history of Canada and is intended to ensure that their natural, cultural, and recreational values are protected.

20. Hydrosolidarity and integrated water resource management promote an ecosystem approach to water management in which attention is given to connections among water, land, and other resources, relationships between upstream and downstream parts of a basin, and linkages between surface and groundwater.

21. The Great Lakes Water Quality Agreement contains many elements of best practice related to hydrosolidarity.

22. Principles have been developed related to a water ethic to guide decisions regarding water allocation, development, and use.

23. International dialogue continues related to the idea of "water as a human right."

Key Terms

demand management
diversions
drought
E. coli
estuary
flood plain
heritage rivers
hydrosolidarity
integrated water resource management (IWRM)
International Joint Commission
James Bay and Northern Quebec Agreement
James Bay Project
limiting factor principle
megaprojects
multi-barrier approach
Palliser's Triangle
renewable water supply
soft path
supply management
virtual water
water ethics
water footprint
water rights
water table
wetlands

Questions for Review and Critical Thinking

1. Does the "myth of superabundance" adequately account for the high per capita water use by Canadians?
2. Why do some believe that Canada has 20 per cent of the world's renewable water supplies while others suggest that this number is 2.6 per cent?

3. What are the main reasons for water diversions in Canada?
4. Why is the likelihood of pressure emerging in the United States to import bulk water supplies from Canada relatively low?
5. Explain the significance of the "limiting factor principle."
6. Explain the significance of bioaccumulation and biomagnification of chemicals in the food chain and what role water plays in it.
7. Why is diffuse pollution from non-point sources a challenge for managers?
8. What is meant by "water security"?
9. What are the implications of the experience with contaminated drinking water in Walkerton, Ontario, and North Battleford, Saskatchewan?
10. What is the significance of the failure of the water supply system in Kashechewan?
11. Explain the distinctions among supply management, demand management, and soft path approaches.
12. What is the relationship between "virtual water" and a "water footprint"?
13. What is the significance of structural and non-structural approaches for reducing flood damages?
14. What lessons were learned from major floods in Canada in the past five years?
15. How do we know when a drought begins and ends?
16. What are the most significant flood and drought-prone areas in Canada?
17. Which criteria and indicators should be used to identify the natural, cultural, and recreational value of rivers?
18. Are there river systems in your region that could be candidates for nomination as heritage rivers?
19. Explain the relationship between the concepts of "hydrosolidarity" and "integrated water resource management."
20. What is the significance of the Great Lakes Water Quality Agreement in terms of best practice associated with hydrosolidarity? What are the implications of the amendments to the agreement that took effect in 2013?
21. What principles should underlie a "water ethic" to guide decisions about allocation and use of water?
22. What are arguments for and against the proposition that water should be a basic human right? What is your view about this proposition?

Related Websites

Agriculture and Agri-Food Canada: Drought Watch
www.agr.gc.ca/eng?id=1326402878459

Atlantic Coastal Action Program
www.unep.org/gc/gc23/documents/Canada-ACAP-AF8-REV.pdf

Atlantic Coastal Action Program: Saint John
www.acapsj.org

Atlantic Coastal Action Program: Cape Breton
www.acapcb.ns.ca/

Canadian Council of Ministers of the Environment
www.ccme.ca

Canadian Water and Wastewater Association
www.cwwa.ca

Canadian Water Resources Association
www.cwra.org

Centre for Global Studies
www.uvic.ca/research/centres/globalstudies/

Clean Annapolis River Project
www.annapolisriver.ca

Environment Canada: Canadian Pollution Prevention Information Clearinghouse
www.ec.gc.ca/cppic

Environment Canada: National Water Research Institute
www.ec.gc.ca/inre-nwri/

Environment Canada: State of the Great Lakes Reporting
www.ec.gc.ca/grandslacs-greatlakes/default.asp?lang=En&n=70FFEFDF-1

Environment Canada: Water
www.ec.gc.ca/eau-water

Environment Canada: Water Quality Objectives and Guidelines
www.ec.gc.ca/eau-water/default.asp?lang=En&n=F77856A7-1

Environment Canada: Water Survey of Canada
www.ec.gc.ca/rhc-wsc/

Experimental Lakes Area
www.iisd.org/ela

Fisheries and Oceans Canada: Freshwater Institute
www.dfo-mpo.gc.ca/science/aah-saa/Freshwater-Institute-eng.html

Freshwater Quality Monitoring Program
www.ec.gc.ca/eaudouce-freshwater/Default.asp?lang=En&n=6F77A064-1

Great Lakes Information Network
www.great-lakes.net/lakes

International Joint Commission
www.ijc.org

Statistics Canada: Human Activity and the Environment Annual Statistics
www.statcan.ca/bsolc/english/bsolc?catno=16-201-X&CHROPG=1

Sydney Tar Ponds Agency
www.tarpondscleanup.ca/

UNESCO Water e-Newsletter
www.unesco.org/water/news/newsletter

WaterAid Canada
www.wateraidcanada.com

Water Footprint Network
www.waterfootprint.org

Further Readings

Note: This list comprises works relevant to the subject of the chapter but not cited in the text. All cited works are listed in the References at the end of the book.

Bakker, K., and C. Cook. 2011. "Water governance in Canada: Innovation and fragmentation," *International Journal of Water Resources Development* 27: 275–89.

Benson, D., A. Gain, and J. Rouillard. 2015. "Water governance in a comparative perspective: From IWRM to a 'nexus' approach?" *Water Alternatives* 8 (1): 756–73.

Bower, S.S. 2011. *Wet Prairie: People, Land and Water in Agricultural Manitoba*. Vancouver: University of British Columbia Press.

Clancy, P. 2014. *Freshwater Politics in Canada*. Toronto: University of Toronto Press.

Collins, L.M. 2007. *Implementing the Human Right to Water in Canada: A Discussion Paper*. Ottawa: United Nations Association in Canada, March.

Desbiens, B. 2013. *Power from the North: Territory, Identity, and the Culture of Hydroelectricity in Québec*. Vancouver: UBC Press.

Furimsky, E. 2002. "Sydney Tar Ponds: Some problems in quantifying toxic waste," *Environmental Management* 30, 6: 872–9.

Global Water Partnership Technical Committee. 2014. *Water Security: Putting the Concept into Practice*. Stockholm: Global Water Partnership.

Guernsy, J.R., et al. 2000. "Incidence of cancer in Sydney and Cape Breton County, Nova Scotia, 1979–1997," *Canadian Journal of Public Health* 91, 4: 285–92.

Lavoie, R., F. Joerin, and M.J. Rodriguez. 2014. "Incorporating groundwater issues into regional planning in the Province of Quebec," *Journal of Environmental Planning and Management* 57: 516–37.

Leahy, S. 2014. *Your Water Footprint*. Richmond Hill, ON: Firefly Books.

Mannix A.E., W.L. Adamowicz, and C. Dridi. 2014. "Solutions to the high costs of future water restrictions for new oil sands industry along the Athabasca River," *Canadian Water Resources Journal* 39: 395–408.

Mysiak, J., C. Pahl-Wostl, C. Sullivan, J. Bromley, and H.J. Henrikson, eds. 2009. *The Adaptive Water Resources Management Handbook*. London: Earthscan.

Olsson, G. 2015. *Water and Energy: Threats and Opportunities*. London: IWA Publishing.

Organisation for Economic Co-operation and Development. 2013. *Water Security for Better Living*. Paris: OECD Publishing.

Pentland, R., and C. Wood. 2013. *Down the Drain: How We Are Failing to Protect Our Water Resources*. Vancouver, Greystone Books.

Perkel, C.N. 2002. *Well of Lies: The Walkerton Water Tragedy*. Toronto: McClelland & Stewart.

Plummer, R., D. de Grosbois, D. Armitage, and R.C. de Loë. 2013. "An integrative assessment of water vulnerability in First Nations communities in southern Ontario, Canada," *Global Environmental Change* 23: 749–63.

Swain, H., S. Louttit, and S. Hrudey. 2006. *Report of the Expert Panel on Safe Drinking Water for First Nations*, vol. 1. Ottawa: Department of Indian Affairs and Northern Development.

von der Porten, S., and R. de Loë. 2014. "Water policy reform and Indigenous governance," *Water Policy* 16 (2): 222–243.

Walker, T.R. 2014. "Environmental effects monitoring in Sydney Harbour during remediation of one of Canada's most polluted sites: A review and lessons learned," *Reclamation* 24 (13): 103–117.

Walker, T.R., D. MacAskill, T. Rushton, A.H. Thalheimer, and A.P. Weaver. 2013. "Monitoring effects of remediation in natural sediment recovery in Sydney Harbour, Nova Scotia," *Environmental Monitoring and Assessment* 185 (10): 8089–8107.

Walters, D., N. Spence, K. Kuikman, and B. Singh. 2012. "Multi-barrier protection of drinking water systems: A comparison of First Nations and non First Nations communities in Ontario," *International Indigenous Policy Journal* 3 (3). http://ir.lib.uwo.ca/iipj/vol3/iss3/8.

Go to www.oupcanada.com/DeardenMitchell5e to access additional learning tools on your smartphone, tablet, or PC.

CHAPTER TWELVE

Minerals and Energy

Learning Objectives

- To understand characteristics of non-renewable resources relative to the renewable resources discussed in previous chapters
- To appreciate the significance of minerals and energy for Canada
- To understand the management issues associated with non-renewable resources in general and minerals and energy in particular
- To identify the relative importance of different minerals for the Canadian mining industry, as well as Canada's importance in global mining trade
- To discover how science is used in environmental assessments
- To appreciate how energy resources can be both renewable and non-renewable
- To learn the potential of alternative, renewable energy sources, particularly wind and solar
- To understand the significance of non-renewable energy resources, including offshore petroleum and natural gas, the Athabasca oil sands, and nuclear power
- To know how to have a lighter "footprint" related to use of minerals and energy

Introduction

Previous chapters focused on **renewable or flow resources**, those renewed naturally within a relatively short period of time, such as water, air, animals, and plants. Other renewable resources are solar radiation, wind power, and tidal energy. Given this mix, a distinction is often made between renewable resources not dependent on human activity (e.g., solar radiation) and those that renew themselves as long as human use allows reproduction or regeneration (e.g., fish).

Figure 12.1 highlights that flow or renewable resources can exist in critical or non-critical zones. Those in the critical zone can be harvested or exploited to exhaustion. The most vulnerable depend on biological reproduction for renewal.

Whether through overhunting, overfishing, polluting, or destroying habitats, humans can create conditions such that renewable resources cannot replace or replenish themselves. Indeed, the "collapse" of the northern cod in the northwest Atlantic (see Chapter 8) is a classic case of overharvesting leading to depletion.

In this chapter, emphasis is mostly on **non-renewable** or **stock resources**, which take millions of years to form. As a result, from a human viewpoint, such resources are for practical purposes fixed in supply and therefore not renewable. However, Figure 12.1 indicates that non-renewable or stock resources are not homogeneous. Some are consumed through use, whereas others can be recycled. Those consumed by use are best illustrated by fossil fuels (coal, oil, natural gas). Once used, they are effectively not available to humans, even though they do not really disappear but are changed into another form, often pollutants. In contrast, stock resources such as metals can be recycled many times, so the stock in the ground is not the only source. However, recycling often requires significant amounts of energy, so the recycling of one type of stock resource (e.g., aluminum) may hasten the depletion of another (coal, oil, or natural gas) stock resource.

Our attention here focuses on both minerals and energy. And to emphasize that non-renewable resources are not homogeneous, the discussion of energy examines wind and solar power, usually viewed as renewable or flow resources. In addition, attention is given to non-renewable types of energy resources, such as offshore petroleum and natural gas, the Athabasca oil sands, and nuclear power.

Mineral and energy resources are important for Canada. Canada is the fifth-largest producer of energy and the seventh-largest user of primary energy (commercially traded fuels) in the world. Such a high level of use is attributed to Canada being a large country with long travel distances, as well as its cold climate, an energy-intensive industrial base, relatively low energy prices, and a high standard of living. Regarding minerals, Canada is a major global exporter. More details about energy and minerals will be provided later in the chapter, but the key message here is that both are important for regional and national economies in this country.

Framing Issues and Questions

The challenge for renewable resources is to manage them so that they remain sustainable and resilient. For non-renewable resources, however, extraction usually results in absolute depletion in any time frame other than a geological one. Given the characteristics of non-renewable resources, management issues are usually different from those associated with renewable resources. Specifically, concerns focus on how to:

1. Use the proceeds from resource extraction to generate new wealth, to benefit generations today and in the future
2. Conserve mineral or fossil-fuel assets to extend the longevity of reserves and how to identify substitutes for use in the long run
3. Minimize negative environmental impacts at each stage in the life cycle of use: exploration, extraction, transformation, consumption, recycling, and final disposal
4. Create improved socio-economic relationships with stakeholders, especially communities located in a mining area
5. Manage recyclable non-renewable resources—i.e., many metals and minerals—as a renewable or flow resource

What would motivate mining and fossil-fuel firms to engage in environmental management, given that their priority is to maximize profits and remain competitive in international markets? As Hilson (2000: 203) noted, if done systematically, enhanced "environmental management practices and extended social responsibility almost always generate some kind of economic return on investment for business, although usually over the long term. A documented reduction in effluent discharges, for example, leads to a reduction in costly government inspections and auditing practices."

The main environmental issues for the mining and energy sectors include **acid mine drainage**, **sulphur dioxide emissions**, and **metal toxicity**.

1. *Acid mine drainage.* Most non-ferrous metals exist as sulphides and usually are accompanied by iron sulphides. When ore minerals are separated from minerals without economic value, significant quantities of waste rock and tailings are created, and they contain iron sulphides that can readily oxidize to become sulphuric acid. When exposed to precipitation (rain or snow), sulphuric acid can dissolve residual metals, leading to acidic drainage, which can continue for centuries. Liabilities in the Canadian mining industry related to acidic drainage are estimated to range between $2 billion and $5 billion.

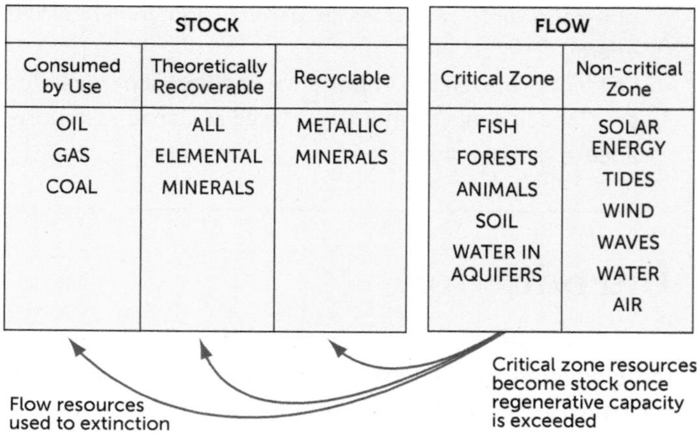

STOCK			FLOW	
Consumed by Use	Theoretically Recoverable	Recyclable	Critical Zone	Non-critical Zone
OIL GAS COAL	ALL ELEMENTAL MINERALS	METALLIC MINERALS	FISH FORESTS ANIMALS SOIL WATER IN AQUIFERS	SOLAR ENERGY TIDES WIND WAVES WATER AIR

Flow resources used to extinction

Critical zone resources become stock once regenerative capacity is exceeded

FIGURE 12.1 | A classification of resource types.

Source: Rees (1985: 13).

2. *Sulphur dioxide emissions*. One outcome of smelting sulphide ores is the release of huge quantities of sulphur, mainly in the form of dioxides, into the atmosphere, thereby creating acid precipitation, as discussed in Chapter 4. The Canadian mining sector is the main contributor to sulphur dioxide emissions in Canada. The burning of fossil fuels is also a major source of atmospheric emissions of sulphur dioxides, creating pressure for alternative sources of energy.
3. *Metal toxicity*. The mining industry is being challenged about the toxic effects of metals on human and ecosystem health. For example, many uses of asbestos are now not acceptable because of connections established between it and cancer. Lead is also toxic. Emissions from smelting and steelmaking processes can also threaten health.

To these three issues can be added challenges related to energy:

- Disruption of remote ecosystems due to exploration, test drilling, and operation of oil fields or gas wells, ranging from habitat degradation to disruption of nesting, denning, and migration patterns of birds and animals
- Disturbance to aquatic ecosystems from escape of waste heat produced from nuclear energy production
- Threat to human and ecosystem health from radioactive waste associated with nuclear energy production over thousands of years
- Alteration to ecosystems from building hydroelectric dams and generating stations

These issues, individually and collectively, provide a strong rationale for increased attention to environmental aspects and management in the mining and fossil-fuel sectors.

"Best practice" related to environmental management for mining and fossil-fuel firms in Canada should include a combination of basic scientific research to ensure understanding of natural and social systems that can be affected by operations and design of appropriate mitigation measures, environmental impact assessments and reporting, environmental audits, corporate policies that explicitly include environmental aspects, environmental management systems, and life-cycle assessments.

Non-Renewable Resources in Canada: Basic Information

According to Natural Resources Canada (2009a), Canada was severely affected by the global economic and financial crisis in 2008–9, with negative consequences for the mining and mineral processing industries. As the global economic downturn intensified, demand for many commodities declined, leading to lower prices, quantities, and value of production, reduced investment in exploration, and decreased workforces. To illustrate, in 2008 the gross domestic product for Canadian mining and mineral processing industries was almost $40 billion, or 3.2 per cent of Canada's total GDP. In 2009, the GDP for mining and mineral processing industries fell to just under $32 billion, or 2.7 per cent of the total Canadian GDP.

Notwithstanding the challenges associated with the 2008–9 financial crisis, Canada has maintained its position as a global leader in exports of minerals and metals. More than 200 active mines produce more than 60 minerals and metals (Natural Resources Canada, 2014b). Important exports from Canada are aluminum, copper, nickel, potash, uranium, and zinc, as well as diamonds, gold, and silver. Gold generated the most value from exports of metallic minerals, earning $16.9 billion in 2012 and $17.7 billion in 2013, while potash was the leader for both non-metallic and metallic minerals even though its value decreased 3.8 per cent between 2012 and 2013 (Natural Resources Canada, 2014d). During 2011, the Canadian mining industry accounted for $64 billion, or 3.9 per cent, of the national GDP (Natural Resources Canada, 2014b).

Reductions in the value of metal produced in Canada have often reflected mostly a drop in commodity prices rather than decreased output. Exceptions to this pattern have been gold and uranium. The increase in value of gold primarily has reflected higher prices. The increase in value of uranium reflected a significant increase in volume of production along with higher prices. Despite a strong performance by the uranium sector, Canada dropped to second place behind Kazakhstan as the leading global producer of uranium in 2009, a position it retained in 2013 when Kazakhstan produced 38 per cent, Canada 16 per cent, and Australia 11 per cent.

Perspectives on the Environment

Diversification in Export of Minerals and Metals

The United States continued to be Canada's main partner in the trade of mineral commodities in 2013, accounting for 50.2% of mineral exports. The European Union (EU) (19.1%), China (7.3%), and Japan (4.4%) were the next most important destinations for Canada's mineral exports.

While the United States remains Canada's leading trading partner, the percentage of mineral exports to the US has been steadily declining since 1999 and the percentage destined for other countries has been growing. In 2000, less than 2% of Canada's mineral exports went to China, but in 2013, that proportion had increased to 7.3% ($6.4 billion). Exports to Brazil, valued at $1.11 billion in 2013, have more than quadrupled since 2000.

—Natural Resources Canada (2014b)

Potash in Saskatchewan

The potash industry began in Saskatchewan during the early 1960s and expanded steadily during the 1970s and 1980s. Potash had been discovered in the 1940s during exploratory drilling for petroleum. In 2014, 10 potash mines owned by three companies operated in Saskatchewan.

In 2013, Canada was the second-largest producer of potash in the world, second to Russia. Third to fifth places were held by Belarus, China, and Germany. Canada has 46 per cent of global potash reserves, and in 2013 produced 9.53 million tonnes (up from 8.14 million tonnes in 2012), second only to the 13.88 million tonnes from Russia (Potash Investing News, 2014).

"Potash," a generic term, covers different kinds of potassium salts. The most important type is potassium chloride. Potassium, a necessary ingredient for plant growth, has become one foundation of modern fertilizers. Some 95 per cent of potassium production is used in fertilizers. In southern Saskatchewan, potassium is located at depths of more than 1,000 metres beneath the surface. Estimated reserves are sufficient to meet global demand for several hundred years, assuming current levels of use. In addition to massive supply, the quality of the potash is very high. Situated in flat beds, the potash can be mined efficiently, and the mines in Saskatchewan are considered to be among the most efficient in the world.

The potash industry in Saskatchewan attracted significant attention during the second half of 2010 due to a takeover bid by the Anglo-Australian mining giant BHP Billiton to purchase Saskatchewan's Potash Corporation, one of the world's largest producers of potash, for $38.6 billion. The takeover bid, considered hostile, would have been the biggest takeover in Canadian history. The provincial government, led by Premier Brad Wall, argued that jobs and revenues in Saskatchewan would be at risk if a foreign owner controlled Potash Corp.

© The Canadian Press/Troy Fleece

In early November 2010, federal Industry Minister Tony Clement decided that the takeover bid "did not likely present a net benefit to Canada." Subsequently, Billiton withdrew its takeover bid. The decision by Clement caused much speculation as to the "real reasons" for rejection of the bid, given that the federal Conservative government had been explicit earlier in 2010 that one of its key principles was commitment to free trade and Canada being open to foreign investment.

Some suggested that, with a federal election likely in 2011, with 13 of the 14 federal seats in Saskatchewan held by the Conservatives, and with fierce and emotional opposition from Saskatchewan to the takeover, the decision reflected partisan politics. The political concern for the Conservatives was undoubtedly heightened by support for Saskatchewan from the premiers of Alberta (Conservative), Manitoba (NDP), and Quebec (Liberal). This example highlights that many considerations often influence decisions related to resource and environmental management.

Canadian mineral production not only is exported but also is used within the country. For example, coal and uranium are the basis for one-third of electricity production. Alberta, Saskatchewan, and Nova Scotia depend on coal for more than 50 per cent of their electricity. Coal deposits occur across the nation, with active mining and production based in Alberta, British Columbia, and Saskatchewan. While production of coal has continued to rise since the early 2000s, domestic consumption has fallen significantly due to governments' policies to reduce use of coal to generate electricity. Thus, in 2012, for example, Canada exported more than 50 per cent of the coal it produced, in contrast to 2003 when it consumed all the coal produced. In 2013, over 80 per cent of coal exports went to Asia, especially Japan, China, and South Korea, and about 9 per cent to the Americas, including the US. Canada also imports coal from the US (US Energy Information Administration, 2014). Given that use of coal in generating electricity is a major contributor to greenhouse gas emissions, what is your view about the role of coal in the future Canadian economy?

In the following sections, we look at how science has been incorporated into initiatives to remediate landscape degradation associated with mineral extraction and how it has been used in understanding and mitigating environmental impacts when a new mining venture is being designed. Finally, we consider the role of science in exploring alternatives to fossil-fuel energy sources.

Developing a Diamond Mine: Ekati, NWT

In 1991, after over a decade of exploration, two Canadian geologists discovered minable diamonds underneath Lac de Gras in the Northwest Territories, leading to the opening in

1998 of the first diamond mine in Canada by BHP Diamonds Inc., after an investment of $700 million. Called Ekati, the mine is 200 kilometres south of the Arctic Circle. A second diamond mine, Diavik, began producing in 2003 after a $1.3 billion investment by Rio Tinto/Aber Resources. In November 2014, it was announced that a fourth diamond pipe at Diavik would be developed, at an estimated cost of $400 million. Production of diamonds is expected to begin from it in 2018, but the overall Diavik operation is scheduled to close in 2023.

In 2003, the Nunavut Impact Review Board conditionally approved Canada's third diamond mine, the first in Nunavut. The mine was operated by Vancouver-based Tahera Corporation, and its Jericho mine, located 420 kilometres northeast of Yellowknife began commercial production in July 2006 (Tahera Diamond Corporation, 2008). However, while more than 786,000 carats of gem-quality diamonds were produced from the Jericho mine between 2006 and the winter of 2008, Tahera closed the mine in February 2008 and put it up for sale in early 2010. It cited high operating costs, especially due to the high value of the Canadian dollar and increasing energy costs, which made the mine unprofitable. De Beers, a South Africa–based mining multinational, began producing diamonds from a fourth mine at Snap Lake, NWT, in January 2008, 220 kilometres northeast of Yellowknife. Snap Lake is Canada's first completely underground diamond mine. It is expected to operate for 20 years.

A fifth mine, Gahcho Kué, owned jointly by De Beers and Mountain Province Diamonds, was approved by the Mackenzie Valley Environmental Impact Review Board in July 2013 and by the federal government in October 2013, subject to conditions to minimize impacts on the Bathurst caribou herd and its habitat. Located about 280 kilometres northeast of Yellowknife, the mine is expected to begin operations in late 2016 or 2017. It will be a large, open-pit mine.

In addition to exploration and diamond production in NWT and Nunavut, major exploration is underway in Alberta, Saskatchewan, Manitoba, Ontario, and Quebec, and has yielded results. The Victor diamond mine, another De Beers operation, is located about 500 kilometres north of Timmins in the Hudson Bay Lowland of Ontario and began production in 2008. Three **impact benefit agreements** and one working agreement were signed by First Nations in the area and the company between 2005 and 2009. One of the largest bodies of diamond-bearing ore in the world has been found in the Fort à la Corne forest in central Saskatchewan, 65 kilometres northeast of Prince Albert. Shore Gold had indicated that diamonds could be mined from its holdings in Saskatchewan by 2016, with the expectation that the mine would operate for 20 years. However, by May 2015 Shore Gold had not started development of a mine at the site, but test drilling continued.

The story of Ekati is part of Canadian mining lore. In 1980, geologists Chuck Fipke and Stewart Blusson noticed alluvial traces of pyrope garnet, ilmenite, and chrome diopside—all indicator minerals associated with diamonds—while working near the border of Yukon and the Northwest Territories. These indicator minerals had been dispersed during the last ice age 10,000 years ago, and Fipke and Blusson realized that their presence did not mean diamonds were close by. Analysis of paleoglaciation and drainage patterns led them to believe that they would have originated in **kimberlite pipes** somewhere in a 65-million-km^2 area of tundra to the east.

They began an extensive program of exploration, collecting thousands of alluvial samples and examining each for traces of indicator minerals. By 1983, they observed that, as they moved east, the concentration of indicator minerals increased, and more significantly, the crystals had less alluvial wear. By 1989, the trail of indicator minerals had led them some 640 kilometres to the east, and other geologists also were searching. In that year, although no diamonds had been found, Fipke and Blusson staked claims on 1,800 km^2 of tundra. Later that year, travelling by helicopter, they noticed that Point Lake was circular and much deeper than other lakes in the area. They sampled along its shoreline and discovered a chrome diopside crystal with no alluvial wear, suggesting a kimberlite pipe was close by, perhaps even underneath the lake.

A partnership was arranged with a major Australian mining company, BHP World Minerals, and in 1991, core samples from Point Lake yielded the first diamonds found in Canada. The subsequent public announcement, required under Canadian law, triggered a mineral rush, with 260 companies from eight nations staking claims totalling 194,000 km^2. Following an environmental impact assessment review spanning 1994 to 1996, Canada became a major producer of diamonds in October 1998 when the Ekati diamond mine started up. The Ekati mine is expected to produce a gross value of $9.5 billion over its projected 25-year life.

Perspectives on the Environment

Kimberlite

Diamonds are a crystalline type of carbon, stable at depths of 150 kilometres or more beneath the Earth's surface. Kimberlite is a rare igneous rock found at the same or greater depth. Eruptions of kimberlite can transport diamonds to the surface of the Earth. Diamond content can be highly variable in a carrot-shaped kimberlite pipe, ranging from nothing to economic concentrations. Because of glaciation in Canada's North, the top part of the diamond-yielding kimberlite pipes often have been scoured out, leaving a circular depression. Glacial alluvium and water then fill the depression, creating a circular lake over the kimberlite pipe, as was the case at what has become the Ekati mine.

—Rylatt (1999: 39); Voynick (1999); Couch (2002: 267)

The Environmental Context

A claim was staked by BHP for an area of 3,400 km² some 300 kilometres northeast of Yellowknife (Figure 12.2). The mining activity is located mainly in the Koala catchment, which drains into Lac de Gras and then northward into the Coppermine River and on to the Arctic Ocean. The mine is in the Low Arctic ecoclimate region in which the average annual temperature is −11.8°C. The temperature range is large, with daily temperatures in summer reaching 25°C and winter temperatures often falling below −30°C. Precipitation is low, averaging only 300 millimetres, most as snow.

The BHP claim area is in the tundra region, 100 kilometres north of the treeline. About one-third of it is covered by some 8,000 lakes, and the landscape has continuous permafrost, with permanently frozen subsoil and rock up to 250 metres deep, and an overlayer of about 1 metre that thaws during summer. The main vegetation includes stunted shrubs and grass tussocks, with willows and scrub bush in low areas. Wetlands include water sedges and sedge-willow communities.

The area supports the Bathurst caribou herd and grizzly bears. The caribou herd, estimated to be approximately 350,000 animals during the mid 1990s, moves around a range of about 250,000 km². They spend the winter south of the treeline, and then in the spring migrate northward to calving grounds near Bathurst Inlet on the Arctic Ocean. The grizzly bear, because of low numbers, density, and reproduction rates, has been designated as vulnerable (see Chapter 14).

Economic and Social Context

The economic aspects of the Ekati diamond mine are significant. The total project capital cost is estimated to be $1.2 billion, the contribution to the Canadian gross national product will be $6.2 billion, and the direct, indirect, and induced benefits to the NWT will be $2.5 billion (60 per cent being wages and benefits). The mining company's policy has been to hire NWT Aboriginal people first, then non-Aboriginal NWT

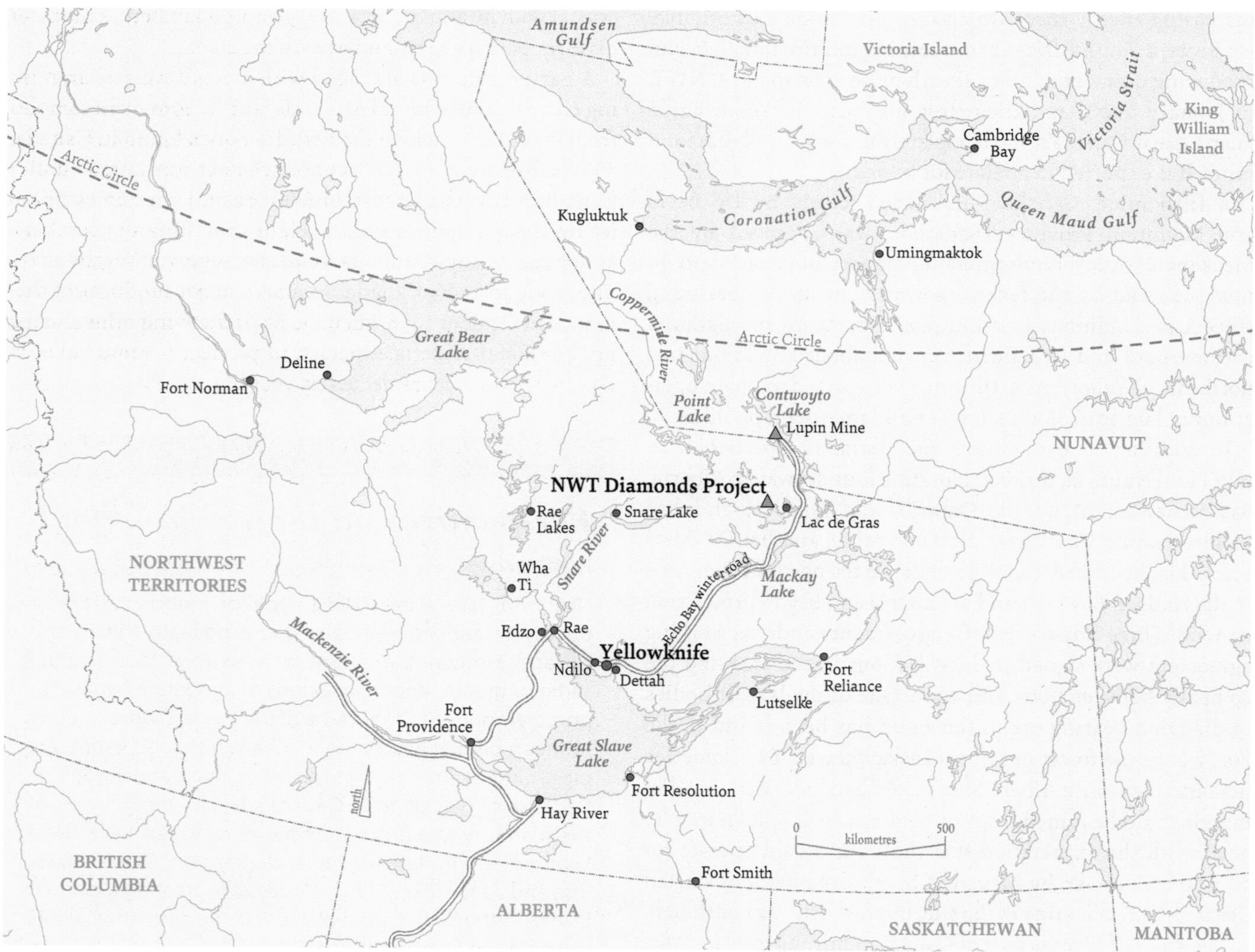

FIGURE 12.2 | Location of NWT Diamonds Project.

Source: Canadian Environmental Assessment Agency (1996: 6). Reproduced with the permission of the Minister of Public Works and Government Services, Canada, 2005.

residents, and finally other Canadians. When Aboriginal people do not have the necessary skills, the company has provided education and training. The company also committed to give preference to businesses owned by Aboriginal people for contracting and to establish scholarship programs and on-the-job training programs for Aboriginal students, and cross-cultural training in the workplace.

Assembling Data Related to Environmental Impacts

The mining company, BHP, collected baseline data during 1992, with systematic and intensive field sampling begun in 1993. The sampling program addressed biological, cultural, and socio-economic issues. Various federal government departments provided comments about the field sampling design. The most significant comment focused on the need for BHP to incorporate traditional knowledge into the collection of conventional scientific data.

In response, BHP observed that it faced serious challenges to include traditional knowledge into its research program. First, the Treaty 8 and Treaty 11 Dene groups were in the midst of land claim negotiations and thus reluctant to release traditional knowledge into the public domain because the knowledge was important for their negotiation strategy. Second, Aboriginal people expressed concern about traditional knowledge being used outside the context of the cultures and broader system of knowledge that gives it meaning. Third, not one set of traditional knowledge existed, since the Inuit, Métis, and Dene each has its own traditional knowledge, which do not always coincide. Fourth, traditional knowledge was viewed by Aboriginal people as their intellectual property, meaning its use and management had to remain within their control. And fifth, there was no documented baseline of traditional knowledge, nor any generally accepted standards or methods to guide traditional knowledge research.

By permission of Independent Environmental Monitoring Agency

Panda Pit.

© GNWT/A. Gunn, ENR

Barren-ground caribou.

Mining Tailings

Management of mining tailings is necessary because of potential impact on downstream water quality. During mining operations, 35 to 40 million tonnes of waste rock are excavated annually. The ore is crushed, and diamonds are separated through physical means. The crushed rock or tailings are being placed in the Long Lake tailings impoundment basin for the first 20 years and then in one of the mined-out pits for the final five years of the project.

The capacity of Long Lake was increased by building three perimeter dams. Each dam has a central core of frozen soil saturated with ice and bonded to the natural permafrost. The core is surrounded with granular fill to ensure both stability and thermal protection. A frozen core and permafrost foundation ensures that no water can escape through the dams as long as the soil remains saturated with ice (Figure 12.3). The frozen core dam design was chosen because impervious fill needed for a conventional dam was lacking, the climate is conducive to a frozen core design, and previous experience with frozen core designs in Canada and Russia could be drawn upon.

The design has the tailings gradually consolidating and becoming permafrost. Once a frozen crust has formed over a cell, it is covered with waste rock and topped with fine granular soil. Such a covering is thick and moist enough to create a new active layer in the new permafrost system. Subsequently, the soil is revegetated, with the ultimate purpose of creating a wetland.

Migratory Caribou

BHP conducted and supported research on the Bathurst caribou herd, the largest in the NWT (Figure 12.4); the value of the harvest, based on meat replacement costs, is estimated to be $11.2 million annually (Canadian Environmental Assessment Agency, 1996: 39).

Baseline data were collected in 1994 and 1995 to determine the numbers of animals using the Lac de Gras area during migrations, the location of migration corridors, and the use of habitat. The migration patterns differed during the two baseline years, reflecting natural variability in caribou migration and use of habitat. The government of the

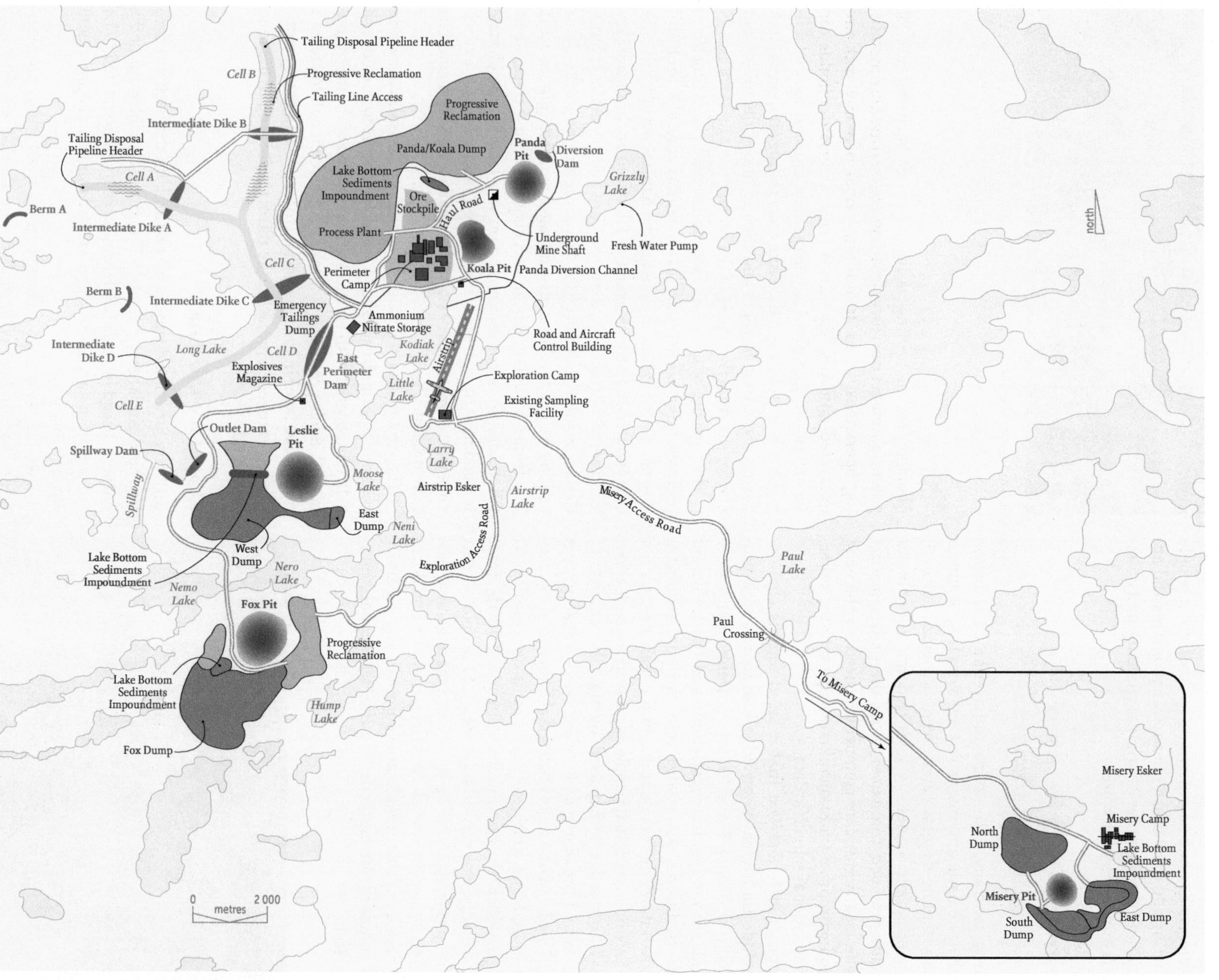

FIGURE 12.3 | Development plan area, NWT Diamonds Project.

Source: Canadian Environmental Assessment Agency (1996: 7).

Northwest Territories agreed that the ability to predict, on an annual basis, the timing and numbers of caribou in the vicinity of the proposed mine was low (Canadian Environmental Assessment Agency, 1996: 39).

Since the caribou herd does not follow the same migration route each year and the areas affected by mining activity represent less than 0.01 per cent of the range of the herd, it was believed that mining would have a very small impact. Attention was also given to the possible effects of roads and the new airport landing strip. It was concluded that these developments would not cause problems.

A 2006 survey of breeding females revealed that the Bathurst caribou herd had been declining by about 5 per cent annually between 1995 and 2005 (NWT, 2006). In 2006–7, the Independent Environmental Monitoring Agency (IEMA) commented on the lack of progress on understanding the regional and cumulative effects on caribou and recommended increased action on the part of territorial governments. The results of a photographic survey conducted during June 2009 on the calving grounds by the NWT Department of Environment and Natural Resources showed the estimated number of

The Panda Pit frozen core dam.

FIGURE 12.4 | Distribution of Bathurst caribou herds.

Source: Canadian Environmental Assessment Agency (1996: 40).

breeding females had fallen from 55,600 in 2006 to 16,000 (plus or minus 4,500 animals). The minister of Environment and Natural Resources stated that size of caribou herds does traditionally cycle, but the low numbers and dramatic decline in 2009 indicated intervention would be necessary to ensure recovery by the herd. However, the reasons for the precipitous fall in the herd size could not be determined.

The Department of Environment and Natural Resources (2014) reported later that the Bathurst herd had declined from about 186,000 animals in 2003 to 128,000 in 2006, to 32,000 in 2009 and then slightly upwards to 35,000 in 2012. Management actions were initiated in 2010 to help the herd. For example, at the start of 2010, all resident, commercial, and outfitted harvesting of Bathurst caribou was halted, while only 300 bulls were allowed for harvesting by Aboriginals. Such restrictions continue.

A protocol for monitoring, assessing, and managing cumulative impacts on the herd was developed. A survey in June 2014 showed the herd had continued to decline. The drop is not attributed to the diamond mines, but concern exists about viability of the herd. Decreases also have been documented for caribou herds in the George River grounds in northern Quebec and Labrador as well as on Baffin Island and on Nunavut's Southampton Island.

Finally, modelling indicated that the water in the tailings impoundment would be within federal guidelines for protection of livestock (and therefore of wildlife). According to the BHP Billiton Environmental Agreement annual report in 2001, "the undisturbed lakes and streams around Ekati are very clean." Results from water quality monitoring downstream from the mine site indicated balanced levels of zooplankton and phytoplankton, indicators of healthy lakes and streams. The slight fluctuations in pH and nitrate levels in the Koala catchment are not viewed as a threat to fish.

Water Issues

Water flow changes will be caused by draining lakes to facilitate open-pit mining as well as by diversion of flows around the pits and by the infilling of Long Lake with tailings. In total, 15 lakes will be affected. Drainage of the lakes prior to open-pit mining will be managed so that flows will not be greater than 50 per cent of the mean annual flood levels in any downstream water system containing fish. As a result, the main consequence will be to extend the peak spring flows for a longer period of time. Because the connecting channels between the lakes are both wide and braided, the effects of the extended period of higher flow were judged to be negligible.

Regarding the potential impact of mining operations on water quality, a primary concern was that contaminants from the mining operation could affect downstream consumers of fish and drinking water in the Coppermine River basin. The main issue was whether the tailings impoundment in Long Lake would ultimately release water of acceptable quality. Analysis focused on three water quality variables (suspended solids, total nickel, total aluminum). During the impact assessment process, it was agreed that the design should meet all regulatory standards for water quality.

Concern also arose about possible contamination from toxicity of kimberlites, acid generation from waste rock, and nitrogen from blasting. Analysis led to agreement that such contamination would be controlled satisfactorily. Effects on groundwater also were addressed. Baseline data were collected, and a long-term monitoring program was established to track effects on hydrogeology.

Fish

Fish are in 12 of the 15 lakes affected by the mining. In addition, 43 connecting streams, outflow streams, and inflow streams are affected. The main species is lake trout, followed by round whitefish, Arctic grayling, and burbot. Fisheries and Oceans Canada (DFO) has a policy of "no net loss" of productive capacity of fish habitat, meaning whenever fish habitat is degraded or lost, DFO expects a counterbalancing habitat replacement.

BHP has compensated for the lost fish habitat in streams by creating a diversion channel between two key lakes, making the channel a quality fish habitat. The cost of this initiative was $1.5 million.

Costs

Couch (2002: 274) reported that the initial scientific research funded by BHP cost more than $10 million. In addition, the environmental assessment review process cost the Canadian government about $1 million, with another $255,000 for participant funding. These amounts do not include costs incurred by various federal departments and by the government of the Northwest Territories. In Couch's view, "in comparison with the Project's capital cost, the anticipated profits to BHP Diamonds Inc., and the tax revenue to governments, this outlay was very small" (ibid.).

Environmental Assessment Process

Beginning in 1992, BHP began research to understand the impact of the proposed mining activity and to develop mitigation measures. Company representatives visited all communities in the project area. BHP made public presentations, organized field trips, held community meetings and open houses, facilitated cultural exchanges and workshops, and sent a group of Aboriginal people to its mines in New Mexico, where 76 per cent of its employees were Native Americans.

In 1994, the minister of Indian Affairs and Northern Development referred the mining project for an environmental assessment, and in 1995 BHP submitted its environmental impact statement. From late January to late February

1996, an environmental assessment panel appointed by the minister of Environment held public meetings, and its report was submitted to the federal government in June 1996. In 1997, the federal government gave formal approval, and construction started. In January 1999, the first diamonds from Ekati were sold in Antwerp, Belgium.

Agreements and Arrangements

Emerging from the process outlined above were several agreements.

Environmental Agreement. The Environmental Agreement is legally binding and requires BHP to (1) prepare a plan for environmental management during the construction and operation of the diamond mine; (2) submit annual reports related to the environmental management plan; (3) prepare an impact report every three years related to the project; (4) establish a monitoring program for air and water quality and for wildlife; (5) submit a reclamation plan for approval; (6) establish a security deposit ($11+ million) for potential land impacts and a guarantee of $20 million for potential water impacts; and (7) incorporate traditional ecological knowledge into all environmental plans and programs.

In addition, the Independent Environmental Monitoring Agency (IEMA) was established by the two governments and BHP as a public watchdog. The IEMA, a non-profit organization, (1) prepares annual reports on the project's environmental implications; (2) reviews impact reports; and (3) provides a public document repository at its Yellowknife office.

The IEMA report in 2014 has three versions: technical report, plain language report, and summary (all available at http://www.monitoringagency.net). The reports note that on 1 April 2014, devolution began in the NWT. The implication is that many tasks handled by the Canadian federal government became the responsibility of the NWT government. The agency also noted that in the previous year the Ekati mine was sold to the Dominion Diamond Ekati Corporation (DDEC). The agency also observed that the funds set aside by DDEC to cover costs if the mine were to be closed early are not sufficient relative to the approved closure plan, a matter it states needs to be resolved. More positively, the agency commented that at Ekati two new pipes will be mined (Lynx and Jay-Cardinal pipes). Finally, the agency provided data and observations about handling of waste water and waste rock, water and fish, air quality, and wildlife, as well as about closure planning, cumulative effects, and traditional knowledge and community engagement. The comments identify progress and where further effort is required to minimize impacts on both natural systems and people living in the area.

Socio-economic Agreement (SEA). This agreement between BHP and the government of the Northwest Territories addressed commitments beyond statutory requirements. The concern was economic benefits and social impacts related to all NWT residents, not just traditional users of the project area. The agreement covered matters such as preferential hiring of NWT residents (with a target of 62 per cent northerners and 31 per cent Aboriginal peoples), criteria to guide recruitment, overall employment targets, employment of local contractors, training programs, and employment support. Targets were also specified for awarding contracts to and purchases from northern businesses.

Although not part of the agreement, a noteworthy initiative was the establishment of diamond cutting and polishing businesses in Yellowknife. The traditional centres for polishing are Antwerp, Tel Aviv, New York City, and India. In 1999, a small Vancouver-based diamond-polishing company opened a facility in Yellowknife, recruiting a South African diamond cutter from Antwerp. Shortly afterward, another company opened, with cutters recruited from Armenia. Other firms opened facilities as well, and local people began learning the trade under the guidance of cutters from Europe, Israel, and Africa.

However, in June 2009, two companies went into receivership, laying off 52 people and owing more than $42 million to creditors. Almost $6 million was owed to the NWT government, which had taken over the buildings in which diamond cutting was done. The explanation for the closure was the global recession had caused a significant drop in diamond sales. Subsequently, the NWT government named Deepak International Ltd. an Approved NWT Diamond Manufacturer, with exclusive use of the Polar Bear Diamond trademark, after its owner agreed to purchase the buildings used by the closed firms. Deepak International indicated it would open a new diamond cutting and polishing facility in the spring of 2013, but that did not happen, and several other opening dates have come and gone without the new firm beginning work. And, in early 2015, a lawsuit was started in Ontario against Deepak International by several firms that had helped finance purchase of the buildings in Yellowknife.

Impact and Benefit Agreements. In 1994, BHP began negotiations with the four Aboriginal groups. Each was involved in land claim negotiations, and BHP did not want to get entangled in those processes. **Impact and benefit agreements (IBAs)** address community and industry relations in mining or other extractive resource activities. They are voluntary agreements, beyond formal impact assessment requirements, intended to facilitate extraction of resources in a way that contributes to the economic and social well-being of local people and communities, and to create opportunities for communities to participate in the management, monitoring, and mitigation of impacts. Such matters were all addressed in the IBAs between BHP and the four Aboriginal groups.

Managing Change and Conflict

Mining activity often generates conflicts relative to other land uses. The following example illustrates the challenges.

Ring of Fire

Some 500 kilometres north of Thunder Bay, a wilderness area of just over 5,000 km^2 is the traditional homeland of the Marten Falls First Nation. Geological exploration has revealed massive deposits of chromite, used in making stainless steel, with the deposits believed to be sufficient to maintain mining for 150–200 years. This area has been labelled the "Ring of Fire," named by a mining company executive who also is a fan of Johnny Cash. If the deposits are developed, massive change will occur in the area, ranging from a new 350-kilometre railway, a processing plant, jobs for Aboriginal people for several generations in an area with few employment opportunities, and significant tax revenue to the Ontario provincial government.

The world's supply of chromite primarily comes from South Africa and Zimbabwe, which have 70 per cent of the world's reserves. Its discovery in the Hudson Bay Lowland was accidental. Geologists were examining the area near Marten Falls and McFaulds Lake for diamonds when they discovered massive deposits of copper, nickel, and platinum. During the follow-up exploration, chromite was discovered in an area of wetlands and bush. Its value has been estimated to be $50 billion. The nickel, copper, and other metals were estimated to be worth another $10 billion.

However, in November 2013, Cliffs Natural Resources, the largest US iron producer, whose intent had been to spend $3.3 billion to mine the chromite, process it in a plant near Sudbury, and create the necessary transportation infrastructure to move the finished product to market—all of which would create 1,200 jobs—announced it was stopping the project and closed its company offices in Thunder Bay and Toronto. Cliffs indicated the main reason was the growing risks related to creation of necessary infrastructure, especially in the context of dropping prices for metals. Other concerns were delays due to negotiations with the Ontario government related to the environmental review process resulting from challenges by Aboriginal groups, and concern about lack of progress by the provincial government in reaching agreement with local First Nation communities about their role in the mining initiatives. A further concern was the ruling by a provincial agency against an all-weather road to transport the ore. On the latter point, the provincial government committed to spend $1 billion to build the necessary transportation infrastructure, but the road would be built through hundreds of kilometres of wilderness area, which would most likely be contested.

One positive sign was that in early 2014, Noront Resources, a mining company based in Toronto, completed required studies for an environmental assessment regarding the so-called Eagle's Nest deposit of high-grade copper, nickel, platinum, and palladium, estimated to be worth some $700 million.

The Ring of Fire highlights the multiple dimensions often associated with a proposed mining operation. It emphasizes that, in addition to addressing technical issues, decision-makers normally have to resolve conflict and uncertainty for and among stakeholders. What would you recommend for the Ring of Fire, based on the experience of the Ekati diamond mine, as well as the planning concepts discussed in Chapters 5 and 6?

Energy Resources

Energy resources are classified as renewable and non-renewable. Renewable resources can be replenished in a relatively short time period. Figure 12.5 identifies three renewable energy sources; one of these, gravity, is ongoing and widespread but remains as only potential energy unless associated with significant motion, such as tides or river flow. Geothermal heat also is persistent and widespread but at great depths below the surface. Manifestations of geothermal heat at the surface or shallow depths, for example, in Iceland and in parts of New Zealand, are much more limited and are usually associated with heat being carried by water or steam, so the renewability of geothermal heat depends on a reliable and ongoing supply of water. Solar supplies come from continuous emission of radiation from the sun, but it arrives discontinuously on the surface of the Earth because of diurnal and seasonal variation as well as cloud cover. As a result, renewable, solar-based energy supplies are intermittent and often cyclic, meaning that they usually must be supplemented by other sources.

Biomass energy sources are frequently used in rural areas in developing countries and can take the form of millions of people and their draft animals doing subsistence work. Metabolic energy (muscle power) is supplemented by heat created from burning firewood, from crop and animal wastes in basic biogas converters, and from direct sunlight used to dry and preserve agricultural or marine products (e.g., dried fish). Biomass energy is renewable as long as the rate of use and capacity to produce biomass are balanced.

Non-renewable sources cannot be replenished over a period of time short enough to support humans. These sources result from geological processes over millions of years, which lead to solid (coal) and liquid (oil) fuels, natural gas, and nuclear fuels. While they all share the characteristic of offering high energy content per unit of weight or volume, they also differ. Solid fuels are mined, both labour-intensive and requiring expensive infrastructure. For efficient transport, they must be carried in bulk or batch containers, such as rail cars or ships. When burned, solid fuels release gaseous and particulate matter in large quantities. In contrast, oil and natural gas can be produced with facilities requiring relatively little labour but capital-intensive refineries or processing plants. Once processed, the product can be transported continuously through pipelines or in batches (trains, ships, trucks). Nuclear fuels contain the highest content per unit of weight but require sophisticated facilities and highly skilled human resources. They are used only to generate electricity and demand careful handling in processing and waste disposal. Given these different attributes, appropriate sources of energy will vary depending on circumstances. Box 12.1 highlights the different variables to be considered when making a choice, and the "International Guest Statement" by Gavin Bridge highlights the wide-ranging considerations needing attention related to energy.

Energy Transition and Social Power | *Gavin Bridge*

Redefining society's relationship to energy is one of the "grand challenges" of the twenty-first century. Concerns about the security of energy supply, energy poverty, and the environmental consequences of energy systems now frame decision-making at scales from the personal (e.g., carbon footprints) to the geopolitical (e.g., military interventions to control supply, or the UN Framework Convention on Climate Change). At the same time, long-standing social concerns—such as the alleviation of poverty or international peace and security—are being re-interpreted in ways that place energy at their core: the UN's *Decade of Sustainable Energy for All* initiative (2014–24), for example, describes energy access as "the golden thread that weaves together economy, environment and equity" (UN, 2012) and a precondition for achieving the Millennium Development Goals, discussed in Chapter 1.

Global carbon emissions, regional electricity blackouts, urban plans for "energy descent" from a high-energy society to low-energy future, and household fuel poverty suggest some of the different ways (and scales) in which energy is now a policy focus and an agenda for social movements. "Energy transition" is an active political and economic project in many parts of the world, with the goal of transforming the technical and/or social and environmental performance of energy infrastructure. However, improving efficiency, alleviating poverty, enhancing security and promoting a low-carbon economy often push and pull energy policy in different directions. How these contending agendas play out at local, national, and international scales shapes the intensity and character of energy flows (e.g., how much pollution is emitted for each unit of energy consumed), and the geographical and organizational form of energy infrastructure. At stake, for example, is whether energy security is pursued by "hardening" supply systems or enhancing social resilience; whether cultural practices of energy consumption (norms around thermal comfort and mobility, for example) are considered acceptable arenas for intervention; and the allocation of investment between fossil and renewable energy sources.

Several unconventional "energy landscapes" have emerged in response to concerns about energy security and climate change. These include intimate spaces of home (via smart metering for energy efficiency and carbon monitoring); urban rooftops (for solar thermal and photovoltaic energy); biofuel plantations and offshore wind farms; boreal forests (as spaces of both unconventional oil development and carbon management); and the Arctic for oil and gas exploration. The messy process of incorporating these diverse "frontiers" into systems of energy provisioning illustrates energy's entanglement with a broad range of social concerns that include democracy and public participation, indigenous rights, and regulation of public and private space.

Energy, then, has slipped its traditional moorings within the engineering and physical sciences and is now an increasingly prominent issue for the social sciences and humanities. Yet many conventional concepts for energy and resource analysis owe a debt to the science and practical art of resource management, and do not reflect developments in contemporary social science. For example, we most readily associate "energy" with natural resources or technologies of energy conversion, such as turbines, tar sands, pylons, and petroleum. Social scientists, however, recognize how such material objects reflect and sustain social relations. Their significance, meaning, and status as resources and technologies (implying particular end-users, forms of economy, and time horizons) derive from the way they are connected to other stakeholders and structures within society. This insistence on the interrelatedness of social and technical aspects of energy is a hallmark of a "socio-technical approach" to understanding large technical systems and a characteristic of critical resource geography. As crude oil flows along a pipeline from wellhead to refinery, for example, it reproduces a series of economic and political relationships: between places that extract and export oil and those consuming it; between banks and investors financing the pipeline's construction and landowners over whose property the pipeline passes; and, between contemporary generations who reap the energy services—mobility, heat—that oil provides and future generations and other living creatures which must bear environmental costs of its extraction and combustion.

Energy systems, then, create and sustain geographical relationships that are also relations of social power. Canada's pursuit of "energy superpower" status by expanding oil, gas,

Continued

and electricity exports has required reworking its interior geographies (via the re-regulation of land and water access, state and provincial challenges to the exercise of sovereign rights by indigenous peoples, and infrastructure investment to accelerate the flow of resources to tidewater ports, for example), and external trade and investment relations (for example, via transnational inward investment in "national" energy projects and expanding energy export infrastructure). A relational perspective demonstrates how projects of energy transition are about more than shifting the fuel mix or changing technologies of energy conversion. It highlights the "techno-political" character of energy systems and how, for example, an energy transition toward decarbonization will require challenging those forms of social power sustained by the promotion of fossil fuels.

Gavin Bridge is professor of economic geography at Durham University in the United Kingdom. His research focuses on the political economy and political ecology of extractive industries (oil, gas, and mining) and he is a founder member of the Energy Geographies Working Group of the Royal Geographic Society–Institute of British Geographers. He is the co-author of *Oil*, published by Polity Press (2013), and co-editor of the Routledge *Handbook of Political Ecology* (2015).

Energy Use and Issues in Canada

The US Energy Information Administration (2014) stated that Canada is the seventh-largest consumer of energy at a global scale, following China, the United States, Russia, India, Japan, and Germany. The main explanations are a growing population and economic growth, while other important factors are long, cold winters; large travel distances; and an economy reliant on high energy-consuming industries. The region with the greatest increase in energy use has been Alberta, attributable to high population growth and an economy based on energy-consuming industries. In energy production, Canada is ranked fifth, after China, the United States, Russia, and Saudi Arabia (US Energy Information Administration, 2014). The major source of energy has been fossil fuels (refined petroleum products, natural gas, and coal).

Regarding primary energy production in Canada, Statistics Canada (2014b) indicated that between 2011 and 2012 crude oil accounted for the largest proportion (42.9 per cent), followed by natural gas (34.9 per cent), primary electricity (9.9 per cent), coal (8.9 per cent), and other (3.6 per cent). In terms of demand, the National Energy Board (2014) reported that in 2011 industry accounted for 48 per cent of total energy demand in Canada, driven by a small number of energy-intensive industries such as iron and steel, aluminum, cement, chemicals and fertilizers, pulp and paper, petroleum refining, mining, and oil and gas extraction. The transportation sector was second, at 25 per cent, followed by residential (14 per cent) and commercial (13 per cent) sectors. Statistics Canada (2014b) also indicated that national energy consumption decreased 0.6 per cent in 2012, following a 7.5 per cent increase in 2011 after declines in each of 2008 and 2009 before increasing in each of 2010 and 2011. Three provinces (Ontario, Alberta, and Quebec) accounted for 74.7 per cent of energy consumption in 2012. In four provinces, energy consumption increased relative to 2011:

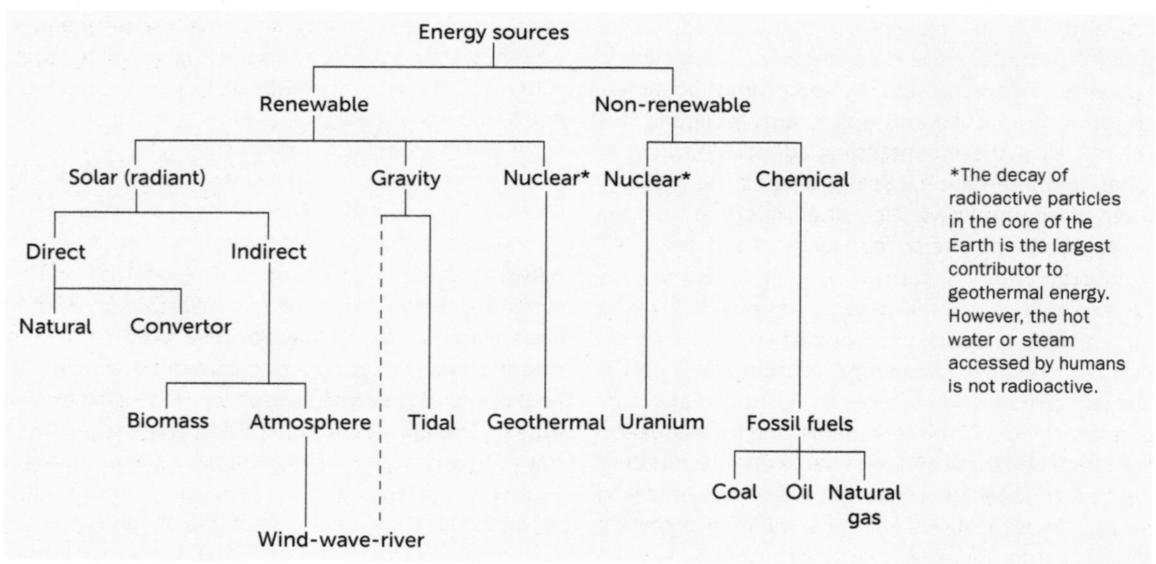

FIGURE 12.5 | Energy sources.
Source: Chapman (1989: 4). Reprinted with permission of the author.

ENVIRONMENT IN FOCUS

BOX 12.1 | Choosing among Energy Sources

1. *Occurrence.* Many energy sources are confined to specific environments and locations and are only available at other locations when transport systems exist. Even physically present sources may not actually be available because of technical, economic, or other constraints.
2. *Transferability.* The distance over which an energy source may be transported is a function of its physical form, energy content, and transport technology.
3. *Energy content.* This is the amount of usable energy by weight or volume of a given source. Low-energy-content sources are inadequate when demand is large and spatially concentrated.
4. *Reliability.* Uninterrupted availability gives one source an advantage over an intermittent source.
5. *Storability.* To meet interruptions of supply or peaks of demand, a source that can be stored has an advantage over one that cannot.
6. *Flexibility.* The greater the variety of end uses to which a given source or form may be put, the more desirable it is.
7. *Safety and impact.* Sources that may be produced or used with low risk to human health and the environment will be preferred over less benign sources.
8. *Cleanliness and convenience.* The cleaner and more convenient source will be preferred over the dirty and the cumbersome.
9. *Price.* The less expensive source or form will be preferred over the more expensive.

Source: Chapman (1989: 5).

Manitoba, 5.7 per cent; Alberta, 4.7 per cent; Saskatchewan, 1.5 per cent; and BC, 0.8 per cent. The other six provinces experienced decreases in consumption: Nova Scotia, −10.7 per cent; Newfoundland and Labrador, −9.9 per cent; PEI, −7.6 per cent; New Brunswick, −6.0 per cent; Ontario, −3.3 per cent; and Quebec, −2.8 per cent.

Perspectives on the Environment

Energy and Climate Change

In June 2006, the [National] Round Table [on the Environment and the Economy] released its advice to the federal government on a long-term strategy on energy and climate change. It noted that significant greenhouse gas emission reductions could take place in Canada in mid-century only if energy is used more efficiently and if it is produced while emitting less carbon. It pointed to the need to increase energy efficiency, to perfect carbon capture and storage, and to transform energy generation to clean coal technology, co-generation, and renewable energy, particularly wind power.

—Auditor General of Canada (2006)

Note: The government of Canada announced in its 2012 budget that the National Round Table on the Environment and the Economy would no longer be funded, and it was closed at the end of March 2013. The National Round Table had been created to serve as an independent policy advisory agency to the government of Canada, and had operated for 25 years.

Wind Power

Natural Resources Canada (2006c) explains that wind energy converts kinetic energy available in wind to forms of energy more useful to humans, such as mechanical energy or electricity. Furthermore, wind energy is "a pollution-free, sustainable form of energy. It doesn't use fuel; it doesn't produce greenhouse gases, and it doesn't produce toxic or radioactive waste."

Humans have used wind energy for centuries, beginning with windmills to provide mechanical energy for pumping water and grinding grain. Sailing ships also depend on the power of the wind. Frequent contemporary uses of wind energy are electricity production and water pumping.

Capacity to generate power from wind depends on several variables, the most important being wind speed. Wind turbines are located in the windiest areas, and usually are situated on high spots, since wind speed increases with elevation above the surface. Exceptions are "wind tunnel" areas at lower elevations.

In terms of global production of **wind power**, in 2013 China was the leader, accounting for 91,424 megawatts (MW) or 28.7 per cent of production, followed by the United States with 61,108 MW (19.2 per cent), Germany with 34,250 MW (10.8 per cent), Spain (7.2 per cent), India (6.3 per cent), United Kingdom (3.3 per cent), Italy (2.7 per cent), France (2.6 per cent), Canada with 7,698 MW (2.5 per cent), and Denmark (1.5 per cent) (Global Wind Energy Council, 2014). At the end of 2013, wind power provided about 3 per cent of Canada's electricity demand. The leading provinces at the end of 2013 were Ontario and Quebec, each with an installed capacity of about 2,500 MW (Canadian Wind Energy Association, 2014).

A continuing issue is some public opposition to wind farms because of noise and aesthetics, and concern about health implications. In Ontario, for example, opposition has included lawsuits, marches, and protests in rural areas adjacent to proposed or approved wind farms. In some cases, protesters lodged lawsuits against wind farms, while wind power companies alleged complainants were distributing false and misleading statements. The courts consistently have upheld approval of the wind farm projects. For example, in late December 2014 an Ontario Divisional Court dismissed appeals from four families seeking to have the Green Energy Act declared unconstitutional regarding review and approval of large-scale wind farms. The cases focused on the proposed $850 million project near Goderich involving 140 wind turbines, a 92–wind turbine farm near Kincardine, and a 15–wind turbine farm near Seaforth. In explaining their decision, the judges stated that no conclusive proof had been provided that wind turbines were a human health hazard.

In early March 2015, it was announced that four wind farm companies were seeking $340,000 in damages against the four families, a claim that a lawyer representing the families labelled as "intimidation." The lawyer argued that the companies were aiming to discourage future claims, while the companies argued that they were seeking compensation for the significant legal resources needed to defend safe projects. A week later, the Divisional Court determined that the four families would be required to pay a total of $67,000 to the companies. The Court explained that, in its view, while the families had a direct interest in the litigation, there also was a "public interest" component to their appeal. As a result, the reduced amount awarded to the companies was deemed to reflect the "public interest component."

Lawyers for groups opposing wind farms also have argued that the legal system creates a challenge because opponents must prove wind farms damage health. In contrast, proponents of wind farms argue that opponents are unwilling to accept approvals of wind farms after authorized processes have been used, causing uncertainty and risk for such projects because of the drawn-out nature of the appeals process.

Research is being conducted on the impact of wind farms. For example, Vyn and McCullough (2014) examined the impact of wind farms on property values in Melancthon Township and 10 adjacent townships between January 2002 and April 2013, an area where wind turbines have been installed in southern Ontario. They examined the sales of 5,414 rural residential properties and 1,590 farmlands over that period, with regard to proximity of properties to turbines and level of visibility of turbines. Regarding both variables, their analysis indicated no significant impact on property values.

In response to continuing concern about perceived negative impacts of wind farms, Health Canada and Statistics Canada collaborated in a $2.1 million study that started in 2012 to examine the health impacts of wind farms in Prince Edward Island and Ontario (Health Canada, 2014). The study involved interviewing a sample of residents in 1,238 households from both provinces (with a participation rate of 78.9 per cent) at varying distances from wind turbine installations, collecting information (hair cortisol, blood pressure, sleep quality), and documenting over 4,000 hours of wind turbine noise (WTN) in the study areas.

Preliminary findings, reported in early November 2014, showed the following were not associated with exposure to wind turbine noise: (1) self-reported sleep problems (e.g., general disturbance, use of sleep medication, diagnosed sleep disorders); (2) self-reported illnesses (e.g., dizziness, tinnitus, prevalence of frequent migraines and headaches) and chronic health conditions (e.g., heart disease, high blood pressure, diabetes); and (3) self-reported stress and quality of life. However, a statistically significant relationship was found between increasing levels of wind turbine noise and annoyance, regarding various wind turbine characteristics (e.g., noise, shadow flicker, blinking lights, vibrations, and visual impacts). Community annoyance was found to decrease in Ontario at distances between 1 and 2 kilometres from wind farms and in PEI at distances beyond 500 metres. It was also observed that "Annoyance was significantly lower among the 110 participants receiving personal benefit from wind farms, such as rent, payments or other indirect benefits from having wind turbines in their area."

In terms of the measured data, the findings were similar to the self-reported results from the survey. That is, wind turbine noise was not statistically associated with hair cortisol concentrations, blood pressure, resting heart rate, or measured sleep.

Oppose Belwood Wind Farm Association (OBWF) is a community effort to prevent the installation of industrial wind turbine projects until all long-term effects on health of residents living near such installations have been studied and addressed.

Not surprisingly, opponents and proponents of wind farms each claimed aspects of the Health Canada study supported their positions. The *Toronto Star* reported that a lawyer for clients opposing wind farms stated that the study was a breakthrough because it confirmed what he said were serious adverse health effects. In contrast, the Canadian Wind Energy Association said it was pleased with the findings since they did not show a significant relationship between wind turbine noise and self-reported illnesses and chronic conditions (Aulakh and Spears, 2014). As you reflect on the discussion in Chapter 6 about stakeholder engagement and dispute resolution, what ideas do you have related to how different perspectives related to the impacts of wind turbine farms should be addressed?

Debate and conflict can be expected to continue, since wind energy has advantages and disadvantages.

Advantages of Wind Power

- Wind power does not require fuel, create greenhouse gases (GHGs), or produce toxic or radioactive wastes.
- Production of wind energy is quiet and not a significant hazard to birds or other wildlife.
- When large wind farms are established, containing many wind turbines, they require 2 per cent of the land area, making the balance available for farming, livestock, and other uses.
- Payment is made to landowners, providing another source of income.

Disadvantages of Wind Power

- Wind is not constant, meaning that there will be times when no power is generated.
- When wind turbines are built, conflict often arises because landowners view them as a negative feature on the landscape.
- With a large wind farm containing many wind turbines, noise from the turbines may be intrusive for nearby landowners.

These advantages and disadvantages can be considered with reference to the "criteria" for sustainable energy options introduced at the beginning of the chapter.

Environmental Impacts of Wind Turbines

With regard to the significance of wind turbines in terms of birds, habitat, noise, safety, and aesthetics, Dillon Consulting Ltd (2000) and Kuvlesky et al. (2007) examined the possible impacts and reached conclusions outlined below.

Wildlife

Kuvlesky et al. concluded that research has focused on the impact of wind farms on birds and bats, with emphasis on mortality due to collisions with turbines. A key aspect of their conclusions can be summarized with the words "it depends." That is, layout of a wind farm, specific attributes of turbines, topography, weather conditions, and types and numbers of birds and their behaviour all affect impact.

Most research has focused on passerines, especially nocturnal migrants, which suffer the highest mortality, regardless of the type of habitats on which wind farms are constructed. Nevertheless, they still concluded that "generally collision fatalities are not thought to be substantial enough to impact bird populations because few birds collide with turbines" (Kuvlesky et al., 2007: 2488). In contrast, they note justifiable concern about impact on raptor populations because substantial raptor fatalities occur due to wind farms. Despite such concerns, their overall view was that raptor populations were not affected by collisions with wind turbines.

Another finding, with significance for waterfowl, is that their collision rates are higher for offshore wind farms than with those on terrestrial sites. In addition, offshore facilities have been shown to divert migration routes of sea ducks from traditional migration paths, but the consequences are not clear.

The above findings indicate that research results are mixed, but in general it appears as if wildlife populations are not significantly adversely affected by wind farms.

Habitat Loss and Change

Loss of habitat is a greater threat to bird, mammal, and herpetofauna populations. Wind farms often render habitats unsuitable for birds. The fragmentation of habitats due to wind farms or related infrastructure (roads, electric transmission lines) can create challenges for wildlife. Another negative impact associated with related road construction and maintenance is the introduction and range expansion of exotic species, as well as increased probability of mortality from collisions with vehicles.

Nevertheless, the conclusion is that disruption from wind farms is significantly less than from other types of energy extraction, such as oil and gas exploration or extraction, or surface mineral mining.

Noise

Disturbance from noise is influenced by many variables, including distance from source, type of background noise, and attributes of the source (frequency, time pattern, intensity). All noise levels from wind turbines during operation are lower than what is experienced in a quiet residential area and similar to what is experienced inside an average home. Dillon Consulting (2000) concluded that given the normal background noise in an average suburban residence, the noise from a wind turbine would be inaudible at a distance of 260 metres. However, it should be noted that Dillon's research focused primarily on volume (decibels). The frequency (hertz) of sound, or pitch, is another key variable, and can affect health and well-being.

Safety

The main safety concern is ice thrown from turbine blades or falling off the tower. Proactive steps can be taken to ensure public safety. First, setback criteria can be used to ensure that people are kept at a reasonable distance from a wind turbine tower and the rotating blades. Second, temperature sensors as well as sensors to monitor the balance of blades can provide early information about ice buildup. Once ice accumulation is detected, the wind turbine can be shut down and not restarted until conditions are safe.

Aesthetics

Some people view a wind turbine or wind turbine field as an unwelcome visual intrusion on the landscape, especially if they feel the turbines are not in keeping with an area's historical, cultural, or natural values. In contrast, others may enjoy the look of a wind turbine, appreciating its modern, futuristic appearance as well as the symbolism and educational role of a visible environmentally benign technology. The challenge, as Dillon Consulting (2000: 44) observed, is that "Given the conformity of view that windmills are a good thing but that they should be placed 'somewhere else' and not 'here,' and the recognition that everyone's 'somewhere else' is someone else's 'here,' a balanced answer is needed."

Research regarding wind turbines or windmills in Europe and North America has indicated that prior to windmills' construction, nearby residents usually have concerns. However, after the wind turbines are operating, their views normally became either neutral or positive. If the homes receive electricity from the turbines, attitudes are likely to be more positive.

Summary

Evidence indicates that wind turbines have minimal adverse environmental effects. However, issues of health and well-being are often a source of concern for nearby residents. And, compared to conventional fossil-fuel energy sources, wind turbines are still relatively expensive, but that could change as the technology becomes less costly and/or fossil-fuel supplies become more expensive. Their increased use in the future will require governments to be proactive and create requirements or incentives for energy suppliers to include renewable sources in their mix of sources. Furthermore, in weighing the cost of alternative sources against that of conventional sources, the total costs of each source should be considered, including the costs entailed in emissions into the atmosphere. If such comprehensive costing were done, the gap between conventional sources and renewable energy sources would not be as large as it seems to be at the moment.

Solar Power

Solar power is another renewable energy option. Energy generated by the sun travels to the Earth as electromagnetic radiation. The solar energy available at any place on the Earth is a function of several variables, the most important being how high the sun is in the sky and the degree of cloud cover. There are three general uses for solar energy: heating/cooling, production of electricity, and chemical processes. The most widespread uses are for heating of space and water.

The end use for solar power varies from country to country. For example, in China, Taiwan, Japan, and Europe, the main use is for heating water and space. In contrast, the dominant use in the US and Canada is for heating swimming pools. Europe has the most diverse and sophisticated market for solar power, with end uses ranging from heating water, space heating for single- and multi-family houses and hotels, and large-scale plants for district-scale heating, as well as air conditioning of homes along with cooling and industrial uses.

Based on total installed solar power capacity, the five leading countries at the end of 2013 were Germany (32.41 gigawatts [GW]), Italy (16.36 GW), China (8.3 GW), USA (7.78 GW), and Japan (6.01 GW) (Energy Informative, 2014). Canada is well down the list, with 819 MW in 2011 and an annual average growth in capacity since 2000 of 9.5 per cent (Natural Resources Canada, 2014d). British Columbia, Ontario, Quebec, and the Prairie provinces have the most installed solar capacity. In Canada, solar power has become a key source of power in northern communities, since many of them otherwise depend on expensive diesel fuel to generate electricity.

In considering prospects for solar energy, Renewable Energy World.Com (2014) compiled the advantages and disadvantages of solar photovoltaic (PV) power relative to conventional energy sources.

Advantages

- PV panels generate no harmful greenhouse gas emissions.
- Solar energy, provided by nature, is available almost anywhere sunlight is present.

Enbridge/Ryan Szulc

Covering 384.4 hectares of farmland, the Sarnia Photovoltaic Power Plant in Sarnia, Ontario, is one of Canada's largest photovoltaic power plants, producing enough energy to power more than 12,000 homes.

Perspectives on the Environment

Solar Power Potential in Canada

The potential for solar energy varies across Canada. The potential is lower in coastal areas, due to increased cloud coverage, and is higher in the central regions. . . . In general, many Canadian cities have a solar potential that is comparable internationally with that of many major cities. For instance, about half of Canada's residential electricity requirements could be met by installing solar panels on the roofs of residential buildings.

—National Energy Board (2009a: 5)

- Solar energy is most suitable for smart energy networks involving distributed power generation.
- The cost of solar panels has been dropping significantly.
- PV panels are silent and therefore appropriate for urban and residential areas.

Disadvantages

- Intermittency issues exist, due to cloudy or rainy conditions, and at night.
- Intermittency and unpredictability make solar energy panels less reliable than some other energy sources.
- PVs require incremental equipment, inverters, to convert direct electricity to alternating electricity, and storage batteries usually are needed.
- PV-panel installations need relatively large areas, and the necessary land space is normally committed for 15 to 20 years or longer.

Offshore Petroleum

About three-quarters of the surface of the Earth is covered by oceans. As land-based reserves of petroleum and gas become depleted, exploration has moved to offshore locations. The outcome is that about three-fifths of global production of petroleum is from offshore facilities in waters adjacent to more than half of the world's coastal nations. The extraction of offshore petroleum is also increasingly occurring in highly challenging environments, including at greater depths (e.g., 2,500 metres below the surface in the Gulf of Mexico off the coast of Louisiana) or in extreme climate conditions (e.g., storms in the North Sea; hurricanes in the Gulf of Mexico; high winds and waves, cold temperatures, ice and icebergs, and fog in the northwest Atlantic east of Newfoundland).

With Pacific, Atlantic, and Arctic coastlines, Canada is an offshore producer. Offshore petroleum production started in 1992 southwest of Sable Island, off the coast of Nova Scotia. Production continued there until 1999. However, the main area for offshore oil production is the Jeanne d'Arc Basin, off the eastern coast of Newfoundland and Labrador. In 2013, light crude oil production from the different fields in this basin totalled 229,000 barrels daily (bbl/d) (US Energy Information Administration, 2014: 3). The first major production in this basin started in mid-November 1997 at the Hibernia field on the Grand Banks, about 315 kilometres south–southeast of St John's in Newfoundland. The fixed production platform used at Hibernia is anchored on the seabed at a depth of 80 metres. Because of the prevalence of icebergs, the outer edge of the platform is serrated. A support vessel is stationed near the production platform, with one task—to tow small and medium-sized icebergs away from the platform. Tankers take the petroleum from the production platform to an inshore storage terminal near an oil refinery at Come By Chance. In 2013, 135,000 bbl/d of production came from the Hibernia field.

Located 350 kilometres east-southeast of St John's and discovered in 1984, the Terra Nova project is Canada's third field and began production in January 2002. The Terra Nova field, the second-largest after Hibernia, is estimated to hold 440 million barrels of recoverable petroleum. Producers use a floating facility with capacity for production, storage, and offloading. The floating facility design was chosen in light of the harsh environment, and it can be disconnected relatively quickly from its mooring system and moved off-location in case of an emergency. The hull was designed to withstand the force of an iceberg weighing up to 100,000 tonnes or sea ice covering up to 50 per cent of the ocean surface around the platform. Other protective measures include subsea wells within "glory holes" (excavations on the seabed) to protect the wellheads from icebergs that scour the ocean bottom and flexible pipes to take oil from the wells so that oil can be flushed out of them and replaced by sea water if an approaching iceberg might damage the pipes.

Hibernia originally had an expected production life of 25 years and Terra Nova 15 or more years. In 2006, the Canada–Newfoundland and Labrador Offshore Petroleum Board revised its estimate of Hibernia's recoverable reserves at 1,244 billion barrels, an increase of 379 million barrels from the previous estimate. This upward revision means that Hibernia is expected to be in production until about 2030.

In 2005, a fourth field containing both petroleum and gas, named White Rose, was brought into production. It is located about 50 kilometres from the Hibernia and Terra Nova fields, on the northeastern part of the Grand Banks. The White Rose field extends over 40 km^2 at a depth of 120 metres and is estimated to contain 250 million barrels of recoverable oil. By 2013, production from both the Terra Nova and White Rose fields had declined significantly from amounts in the previous decade. However, production started in 2010 from the North Amethyst field, a satellite of White Rose, which is expected to offset declining production from the older fields.

And production is anticipated to begin in 2017 from another satellite field (Hebron, 350 kilometres southeast of St John's) (Smith and Rosano, 2014: 36).

White Rose received regulatory approval in 2001 following an environmental impact assessment. The federal minister of Environment concluded significant negative environmental effects were unlikely as long as mitigation measures were used. The environmental assessment report, completed in 1997, concluded that extreme weather and ice regimes at the production site would be the most serious challenges (Canada–Newfoundland and Labrador Offshore Petroleum Board, 1997). The Environmental Assessment Panel believed that a floating production system, by allowing avoidance strategies in the face of extreme conditions, reflected the *precautionary approach* that should underlie all aspects of the project. Notwithstanding its confidence in the capacity for avoidance of possible environmental dangers to the production platform, the panel recommended continuing effort to improve operational forecasting capacity regarding both weather and iceberg trajectories.

The panel also observed that the developers of White Rose could not be held responsible for the effects of subsequent development projects on the Grand Banks. The possibility of future projects, however, made it clear to the panel that significant difficulties and uncertainties exist in terms of calculating *cumulative effects* from various offshore projects. As one step to respond to this dilemma, the panel recommended a systematic and peer-reviewed monitoring system.

Beyond the possibility of a major oil spill, the panel noted that discharges of oil-based drilling mud, various chemicals, and product water (used in processes to extract and produce oil, as well as general cleaning) into the ocean were the project's biggest environmental hazards. If a major oil spill were to occur, the panel believed mitigative measures were unlikely to be effective because of the fragile environment. Consequently, the panel argued that it was "absolutely essential" that prevention be the top priority.

The possible impact of light oil on seabirds was recognized. A specific risk to seabirds would arise when oil is moved from the production site to the shore refinery. An oil spill close to the shoreline could threaten the large seabird colonies on the Avalon Peninsula. The panel recommended development of a systematic coastal zone management regime for the Avalon Peninsula shoreline.

Regarding natural gas, the coastal continental shelf adjacent to Nova Scotia contains significant gas fields. In the 1970s, recoverable reserves were discovered in various locations near Sable Island, some 100 kilometres from the Canadian mainland. During 1979, a drill rig successfully identified a commercial field. By the mid 1990s, improvements in drilling technology and increased prices for natural gas made commercial extraction feasible. A consortium of oil and gas extraction companies began developing the gas fields in 1996, and production began from the Sable Island Project during 1999. This was the first offshore natural gas project in Canada.

The project has two components. The initial one focused on extracting gas from six fields near Sable Island and constructing a pipeline to take the product for further processing near Goldboro, Nova Scotia. The second component involved building the Maritimes and Northeast Pipeline to move processed gas from the Goldboro plant to a transfer point at the border between Canada and the United States.

Given the possible environmental impact of these projects, various federal and provincial departments collaborated on an environmental impact assessment process (Canadian Environmental Assessment Agency, 2003). A five-member assessment board was created in 1996 and completed its report in 1997. Subsequently, all appropriate regulatory agencies gave approval, subject to adoption of recommendations in the assessment report. It was estimated that the Sable Island Project would produce for up to 25 years, with royalty payments to the province ranging between $1.6 and $2.3 billion.

In 2013, Newfoundland and Labrador produced nearly 17 per cent of Canada's crude oil and equivalent. However, significant discoveries of oil and gas have been made in the Beaufort Sea off the coast of the Northwest Territories. Production will likely begin there once a Mackenzie Valley pipeline has been built to move the oil and gas to southern markets. There also are estimates of significant oil and gas reserves off the coast of British Columbia, but a federal moratorium on exploratory drilling has been in place there since 1972 (Hull et al., 2004; Natural Resources Canada, 2014f).

The moratorium affecting the waters off the British Columbia coast reflects at least the following concerns: jurisdictional uncertainty regarding whether the federal or

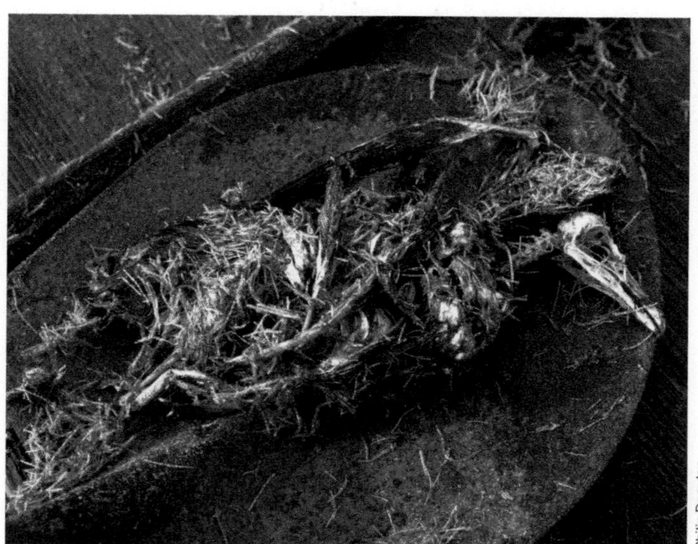
Philip Dearden

A cormorant killed by an oil spill.

ENVIRONMENT IN FOCUS

BOX 12.2 | The BP Oil Spill, Gulf of Mexico, April 2010

The risk of offshore oil extraction was highlighted on 20 April 2010 when an explosion occurred on an offshore drilling rig, the *Deepwater Horizon*, operated by British Petroleum (BP) in the Gulf of Mexico, killing 11 workers and resulting in an uncontrolled wellhead blowout and the worst offshore oil spill in the deep ocean in North American history. The flow of oil into the Gulf affected states from Florida to Texas. Major negative economic impacts were caused to fishing (especially shrimping) and tourism industries. It will take decades to understand the long-term effect on the Gulf ecosystem. Another consequence was a moratorium placed on deepwater offshore drilling in US waters.

After many unsuccessful tries, on 15 July a temporary cap was placed over the wellhead, nearly 4 kilometres beneath the surface of the Gulf of Mexico, and on 19 September 2010, five months after the blowout began, a permanent cap had been installed. It was estimated that the costs for cleanup, government fines, lawsuits, and damage claims will be well over $40 billion. Some experts suggested the final costs could be up to $200 billion.

A seven-member US presidential commission reported that the oil well blowout was caused by cost-cutting and time-saving business decisions by BP and its partners (National Commission on the BP *Deepwater Horizon* Oil Spill and Offshore Drilling, 2011). In the view of the commission, without significant reform in business practices and government policy, more such spills are likely.

© AP Photo/Gerald Herbert/CP

The *Deepwater Horizon* oil rig burning after an explosion in the Gulf of Mexico, off the southeast tip of Louisiana on 20 April 2010.

© AP Photo/Dave Martin/CP

Tourists look on as a worker cleans oil from the sand along a strip of beach in Gulf Shores, Alabama, two months after the initial *Deepwater Horizon* explosion.

provincial government owns the seabed, Aboriginal land and related ocean claims, and environmental risks. The oil spill from the tanker *Exxon Valdez* in 1989 in Alaskan waters highlighted the vulnerability of BC coastal waters to environmental risk. Some 10.8 million US gallons of unrefined crude oil were released into Prince William Sound from the tanker, the largest oil spill to that time in North American waters. The oil eventually covered more than 1,900 kilometres of rocky shoreline and caused the death of tens of thousands of birds, a thousand sea otters, several hundred seals, and unknown numbers of fish and other sea life. Exxon had 10,000 workers on site in the summer of 1989 for the cleanup work, which ultimately cost US$2.2 billion. Additional costs were a US$1 billion fine payable to the US and Alaskan governments and several billion dollars for damage experienced by fishers, property owners, and others.

The potential for offshore oil and gas (estimated to be up to 25 per cent of the globe's undiscovered oil and gas) and mineral deposits has led the "Arctic Five" countries—Canada, Denmark, Norway, Russia, and the United States—to make political claims to seabed resources in the Arctic. For example, in August 2007, a remote-controlled Russian mini-submarine was used to plant a Russian flag on the seabed at the North Pole. This was a symbolic gesture by Russia to claim rights to the Lomonosov Ridge, an underwater mountain range extending 1,995 kilometres, as part of Russia's continental shelf. One month later, Russia stated that initial analysis of samples collected by one of its scientific teams proved that the mountain range beneath the Arctic Ocean was an extension of its continental shelf. The consequence of Russia asserting this area as part of its economic zone would be to give itself rights to the resources on the ocean floor in that area. Shortly after that flag-planting event, Danish scientists travelled to the Arctic to search for evidence supporting Denmark's claim that the Lomonosov Ridge is an extension of the continental shelf of Greenland, which would place it under the control of Denmark.

Canada's prime minister declared in 2007 that the Northwest Passage was "Canadian internal waters" rather than an "international waterway." In international law, foreign ships can travel through an international waterway that is within a nation's territorial waters without permission, but foreign warships must obtain permission. The complication is that the Northwest Passage consists of a number of linked channels situated between Canadian-owned Arctic islands, and some countries do not recognize Canada's jurisdiction over these waters. For example, the United States has never accepted the Canadian claim that the Northwest Passage consists of internal or territorial waters, instead arguing that it is "international waters," meaning US warships can use the Northwest Passage without seeking Canada's permission. As Dyer (2007: A9) commented, "There is a scramble for the Arctic, but it is not military. It's about laying claim to potentially valuable resources."

Athabasca Oil Sands

Background

Extensive and intensive development is occurring in northeastern Alberta, focused on the oil sands located north of Fort McMurray along both sides of the Athabasca River. The Athabasca oil sands are one of three deposits, the others being in the Peace River and Cold Lake areas (Figure 12.6). Together, the three deposits extend under an area of 149,000 km², almost one-quarter of Alberta and larger than the state of Florida. The oil sands make Canada third after Saudi Arabia and Venezuela for oil sands reserves, and second only to Saudi Arabia in terms of global oil reserves. Alberta accounted for 78 per cent of all Canadian oil production in 2013, and some 80 per cent of Alberta's contribution was from the oil sands (US Energy Information Administration, 2014: 4).

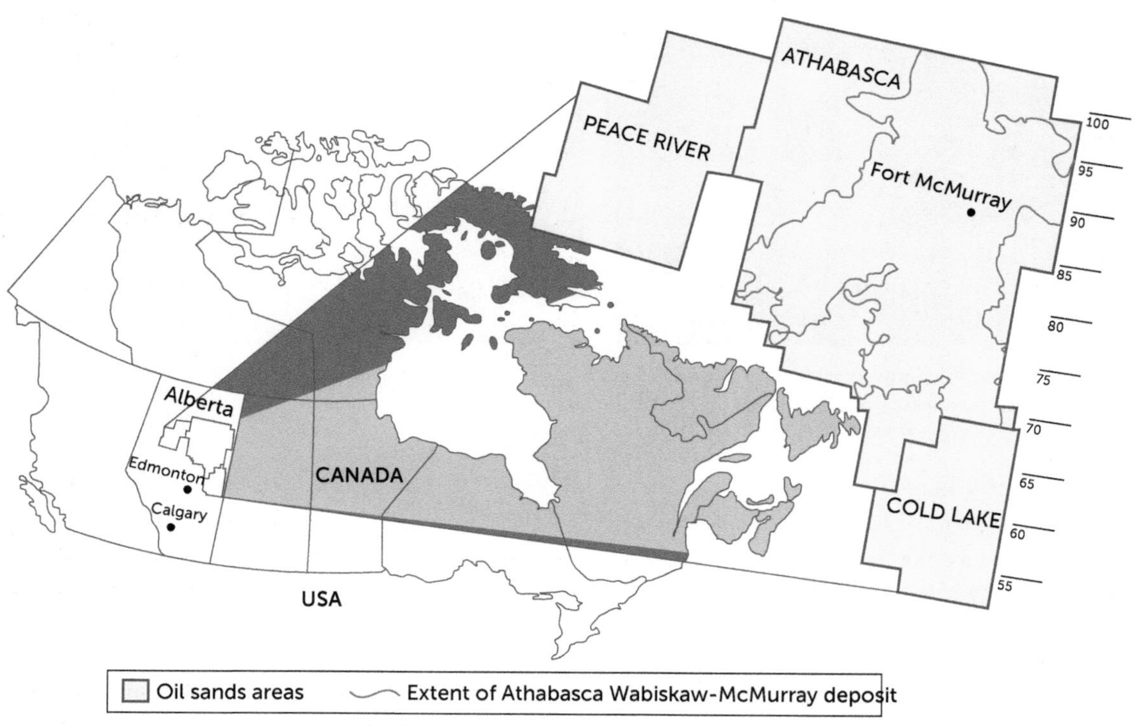

FIGURE 12.6 | Athabasca oil sands region.

Source: ERCB ST98-2011: Alberta's Energy Reserves and Supply/Demand Outlook.

Alberta has proven oil reserves of 170 billion barrels, based on an estimated 168 billion barrels of bitumen or oil sands and 1.7 billion barrels of conventional crude oil. In 2013, Alberta produced about 1.9 million barrels of oil daily (Alberta Government, 2014: 1) and until 2013 about 767 km^2 had been affected by mining activity.

Development of the oil sands started during the mid 1960s, but it was not until the mid 1990s that it became financially viable as a result of improving technology, preferential financial arrangements (low provincial royalties and federal tax concessions), and strong demand as well as rising prices for oil. In 2013, the forecast was for production to be 3.7 million and 5.2 million barrels a day in 2020 and 2030, respectively (Alberta Energy, 2014). This level of output brings major economic benefits to Alberta and to Canada. Nevertheless, the development also has implications for the integrity of the northern boreal forest as well as for air quality, water in the Athabasca River, and land-based resources. Each of these aspects is considered here, while the implications for greenhouse gas emissions are addressed in Chapter 7.

Before considering the implications for oil sands production on the environment, it is appropriate to consider price changes for oil in 2014 and 2015. Since December 2011, the average price for a barrel of Brent crude, the international benchmark, had been about US$108/barrel, but between June and November 2014 it fell to below US$80/barrel, a 30 per cent drop. By the end of December 2014, the price had fallen further to below US$54, and in the first week of January 2015 it dropped to just above US$48. On 5 January, when the price went below US$50/barrel for the first time, the Toronto Stock Exchange dropped 2.5 per cent due to a sell-off of energy stocks, which had fallen in value by 6.5 per cent. The New York Stock Exchange had comparable drops.

Various reasons accounted for the drop in price, including a strengthening US dollar, a drop in demand due to a sluggish global economy (especially the economies of China, Japan, and some Western European countries), and, perhaps most importantly, the significant increase in oil production from shale deposits in the US. As a result, the oil market toward the end of 2014 was over-supplied by about 2 million barrels a day. Historically, over-supply would be addressed by OPEC countries, which account for about a third of global oil production, through decreasing their output in order to maintain prices. However, increasing supplies from countries outside OPEC made that a less effective strategy. Indeed, when the 12 OPEC countries met in Vienna in late November 2014, they decided to maintain their daily oil output at 30 million barrels/day. Their rationale was that, if OPEC cut production, other countries such as the US and Russia would fill the gap, and hence OPEC would lose some market share, which it was determined to protect. In addition, by maintaining production, OPEC nations would contribute to reduced oil prices, which, it was argued, would make oil produced from fracking and the oil sands in Alberta less competitive.

There are serious economic implications for Canada, as the federal government as well as the provincial governments in Alberta, Saskatchewan, and Newfoundland and Labrador generate significant revenue through taxes on oil production. Indeed, in late January 2015 the Conference Board of Canada predicted that if the oil prices did not go back up in 2015 the federal government would lose $4.3 billion in tax revenue and the oil-producing provinces would lose about $10 billion due to reduced royalties and taxes. In addition, it has been suggested that many oil sands operations in Alberta are economically viable only when the price for a barrel of oil is above US$110. If the global price stays at about half the level it was in mid 2014, some operations are unlikely to be profitable, and would likely be scaled back and/or new operations will not be developed. For example, in May 2014, Total E&P Canada and its partner Suncor Energy decided to defer their joint $11 billion Joslyn North oil sands mine because it was not viewed as economically viable. Furthermore, the Canadian Association of Petroleum Producers reported in January 2015 that investment in the oil industry was expected to fall from $69 billion in 2014 to $40 billion during 2015. It also suggested in 2014 that future production in Alberta would be scaled back to 4.8 million barrels from the earlier target of 5.2 million barrels of bitumen oil per day by 2030, a drop of almost 8 per cent. As an example of such cutbacks, in early 2015 Calgary-based Suncor announced it was cutting 1,000 jobs and its capital budget by $1 billion, both due to the dropping oil price. This situation highlights that uncertainty is an important factor for those making production decisions, and often they do not control the circumstances behind the changing conditions.

In contrast, provinces with a significant manufacturing base, such as Ontario and Quebec, benefit significantly from lower oil prices, as do individual consumers when buying gas for their vehicles and homes. In addition, the reduced value of oil contributed to a significant drop in the Canadian dollar relative to the US dollar, creating a competitive edge for manufacturers to export to the US. Indeed, at the end of December 2014 the Canadian dollar was valued at US$0.86 and by late September 2015 it was valued at about US$0.75 cents. In contrast, in November 2007 the Canadian dollar was worth US$1.10.

Several implications are clear. First, Canada can be either a winner or a loser when global prices for petroleum go up or down. Second, within Canada, some provinces gain and some lose when petroleum prices are either higher or lower.

Context

In 2001, production of **crude bitumen** (a thick and heavy oil) surpassed production of conventional crude oil in Alberta. In 2013, production from the oil sands represented about 55 per cent of total crude oil production in Canada.

Extracting Oil from Oil Sands

The oil sands consist of about 10 to 12 per cent **bitumen** mixed with sand, silt, clay, and water. The oil removed from the oil sands is termed crude bitumen, and because it is thick and heavy, it cannot flow toward a well. As a result, two different methods are used for extraction. If the bitumen is not more than 100 metres below the surface, it is removed through surface or strip mining from open pits. Subsequently, mined oil sands are mixed with hot water, which washes the bitumen out of the sand. The other method, used at depths greater than 100 metres, is **in situ recovery**, and the specific technique is **steam-assisted gravity drainage**, or SAGD. This method is used for more than 90 per cent of the oil sands. The usual approach is to inject high-pressure steam into the oil sands to separate the bitumen from the sand, silt, and clay. Once exposed to the steam, bitumen can flow to a well from which it can be pumped to the surface.

The surface mining method results in about 90 per cent of the bitumen being recovered. In contrast, in situ oil sands extraction recovers 60 to 80 per cent of the bitumen. After recovering the bitumen, subsequent processing stages involve producing the final synthetic crude oil and then transporting it to final destinations in Canada or the US. The removal of the bitumen from the oil sands and the production of synthetic crude oil require significant energy inputs.

Pipelines move most of the oil to markets in Ontario, BC, and Washington state as well as in Rocky Mountain and Midwest states. A pipeline (Northern Gateway) from Alberta to a marine terminal in Kitimat, BC, to export the synthetic oil to China and other Asian markets as well as to California, was approved by the federal government in June 2014, but subject to over 200 conditions. The pipeline is strongly opposed by some First Nations bands over whose territories the pipeline would cross, and legal challenges are anticipated.

Athabasca oil sands, north of Fort McMurray.

Calgary-based TransCanada Corp. also has proposed the 1,897-kilometre and $8-billion Keystone XL pipeline, from Alberta to the Gulf coast in Texas, where the raw bitumen would be upgraded and refined, then much of it exported overseas. Prime Minister Harper and then–Natural Resources Minister Joe Oliver argued that such a pipeline would benefit the Canadian economy through profits from selling oil to the US and other countries as well as the creation of construction jobs. They also argued that oil from Canada would be a reliable source of energy for the US. In November 2011, after large-scale protests centred on the possible negative impacts of the pipeline route through Nebraska, where it would cross a large aquifer providing water to several Great Plains states, the US State Department announced that TransCanada would be required to examine rerouting the pipeline. President Obama supported the US State Department decision, and said it "could affect the health and safety of the American people as well as the environment."

TransCanada developed an alternative route to avoid sensitive areas in Nebraska, but President Obama indicated that a decision would not be taken until a full environmental assessment of the new route was completed, which would take until the end of 2014. In November 2014, Republicans introduced a motion in the Democratic-controlled US Senate to have the Keystone XL pipeline approved, but were one vote short, and, even if they had been successful, faced the prospect of a presidential veto.

At the end of January 2015, the US Congress passed a bill to approve building the Keystone XL pipeline, the first congressional approval since discussion began about this project seven years earlier. The reason the bill passed was that beginning in January 2015 the Republicans had a majority in the Senate and thus obtained the required three-fifths majority vote: 62 for and 36 against. However, the bill still needed presidential approval to become law, and 67 votes were necessary to negate the option of a presidential veto. President Obama had been consistent and explicit in stating that it was not Congress's role to determine what was an acceptable transboundary infrastructure project. Furthermore, the US courts consistently have supported the decision-making authority of the president and cabinet on such matters.

President Obama had argued that the US should be a leader in reducing greenhouse gas emissions, and he had often observed that heavy oil from Alberta contributed to higher levels of emissions than conventional crude. He also expressed concern that much of the crude oil from Alberta would not be used in the US, but would be exported to other countries, so would not help to provide energy security to the US. Finally, after the January 2015 vote in Congress, the US Environmental Protection Agency wrote to the US State Department, questioning the latter's statements that oil from Alberta would reach US markets by other means if the pipeline were not built, and thus challenged the State Department's view that the pipeline would not change the contribution of Alberta's heavy oil to greenhouse gas production.

In late February 2015, Obama vetoed the bill to approve the Keystone XL pipeline. Republican leaders of the Senate and House of Representatives indicated they would continue to seek its approval. And the Canadian government also indicated it would continue to advocate for approval of the pipeline. Indeed, it was reported that Greg Rickford, the federal minister of Natural Resources, stated that "It is not a question of if this project will be approved: it is a matter of when" (Panetta, 2015: A4).

Environmental Impacts

Oil sands operations have impacts on the boreal forest system and on water and water levels in the Athabasca River and Lake Athabasca, which feeds into the Mackenzie River system, as well as on air quality and wildlife. The consequences of the development are also significant in relation to *cumulative impact assessment*, discussed in Chapter 6.

Boreal Forest and Wetlands

A major impact of oil sands development is fragmentation of boreal forests. Fragmentation is significant because boreal ecosystems, involving a mix of forest and wetlands, are habitat for many species of wildlife and also support the highest diversity of breeding bird species in North America. Furthermore, the boreal forest system is valuable in the context of global climate change because it is a reservoir for storage of carbon. Fragmentation occurs when forests and wetlands are removed through either surface or strip mining or in situ extraction of bitumen, as well as building of roads and above-ground pipelines. The breaking up of continuous areas of extensive woodland and wetlands into smaller and separated patches means reduced habitat for wildlife, as well as constraints on movement of wildlife from patch to patch.

Reclamation programs have been designed, but they have limitations. For example, the eventual reclaimed landscape will usually be different from the mix of forest and wetlands altered by mining. It will consist mainly of dry, forested hills, more lake area arising from the end-pit lakes used in oil sands production, and absence of peatlands. The latter take thousands of years to develop and so cannot readily be replicated by reclamation. After reclamation, an estimated 10 per cent of the wetlands in the original boreal ecosystem in the region will be gone forever. The loss of wetlands will have several consequences because they:

- Provide habitat for rare plants and wildlife
- Regulate surface and groundwater flow through retaining snowmelt and summer storm flows
- Recharge aquifers
- Serve as natural filters, removing contaminants from waters that flow through them

Photo by Nancy Groce. Courtesy of the Ralph Rinzler Folklife Archives and Collections, Smithsonian Institution.

Athabasca River north of Fort McMurray, with the town of Fort McMurray in the background. The road leads to the oil sands operations.

Athabasca River

Impacts on aquatic systems occur from draining or removing wetlands, dewatering aquifers, withdrawing water from the Athabasca River, and storing tailings.

The Athabasca River is about 1,540 kilometres long, starting in Jasper National Park and emptying into Lake Athabasca through the Peace–Athabasca Delta in Wood Buffalo National Park, a major nesting and staging area for migratory birds. The national park has been designated as a World Heritage Site (discussed in Chapter 14). Given the demand for water for oil sands production, large quantities of water are being removed from the Athabasca River. Such withdrawals pose a potential threat to the Peace–Athabasca Delta, which requires minimum flows from the river as well as natural fluctuations.

In addition, the river supports fish species. The natural flow in the river fluctuates seasonally, with lows in winter and highs in spring. Fish such as northern pike, walleye, and burbot that occupy the river during the winter are vulnerable if flows drop below their minimum needs. The challenge, then, is to determine "instream flow needs," or the minimum threshold for water flow needed to sustain a healthy aquatic ecosystem.

Woynillowicz and Severson-Baker (2006: 4) note that withdrawal of water from the Athabasca River to support production from the oil sands is challenging because such operations "return very little water to the Athabasca River." They also highlight that oil sands operations are by far the largest withdrawers of water from the river. Future anticipated oil sands production will increase the withdrawals.

Water quality issues also have been identified. David Schindler, an ecologist at the University of Alberta, and a group of colleagues published results from research focused on determining the relative contribution of natural sources and the oil sands industry regarding elements and polycyclic compounds in the Athabasca River. They concluded, "Contrary to claims made by industry and government in the popular press, the oil sands industry substantially increases loadings of toxic PPE [priority pollutants] to the AR [Athabasca River] and its tributaries via air and water pathways" (Kelly et al., 2010: 5).

The federal minister of Environment appointed an Oil Sands Advisory Panel on water monitoring for the lower Athabasca River and associated water systems in September 2010, and directed it to report on two aspects: (1) reviewing and assessing current scientific research and monitoring, and (2) identifying strengths and weaknesses in the scientific monitoring and the reasons for these. The panel submitted its report in December 2010, observing that:

> Despite the myriad programs ongoing in the oil sands region . . . there was no evidence of science leadership to ensure that monitoring and research activities are planned and performed in a coordinated way, and no evidence that the vast quantities of data are analyzed in an integrated manner. (Oil Sands Advisory Panel, 2010: 34)

The panel concluded that there was not a first-class, state-of-the-art monitoring system for the oil sands, but emphasized that such a system could be created and offered recommendations.

In October 2011, the commissioner of the Environment and Sustainable Development (2011: 79) reported on an audit focused on cumulative environmental effects of oil sands projects, and observed: ". . . that incomplete environmental baselines and environmental monitoring systems . . . have hindered the ability of Fisheries and Oceans Canada and Environment Canada to consider in a thorough and systematic manner the cumulative environmental effects of oil sands projects in the region." Thus, work is needed to ensure capacity exists to monitor and assess environmental conditions related to oil sands development. Environmental monitoring is discussed further in a later section.

In late 2014, Wiklund et al. reported on research contradicting the work described above by Schindler and colleagues. Wiklund and his group recognized that lack of information about pre-disturbance conditions in aquatic systems relative to oil sands production had limited the Regional Aquatics Monitoring Program (RAMP) designed to track pollution in the Athabasca River. Consequently, they drew upon data about pre-industrial reference metal concentrations in river bottom sediments deposited in downstream lakes in the Athabasca Delta between 1700 and 1916, prior to extraction of oil sands, with data collected by RAMP between 2010 and 2013 for downstream sites of the Athabasca River and its tributaries. With reference to seven different pollutants, they detected "little to no evidence of pollution by the oil sands development in downstream surficial bottom sediments of the Athabasca River." They believed these findings were significant, given concerns expressed about possible negative impacts of oil sands extraction related to water for both the Athabasca Delta and the downstream community of Fort Chipewyan. This study, and the one previously mentioned by Schindler's team, reminds us that scientific evidence can lead to different conclusions as well as implications for management decisions, as discussed in Chapter 6.

Air Quality

Development of the oil sands is a major contributor to air pollution emissions in Alberta. They represent 5 per cent of Canada's total GHG emissions and are the fastest-growing source (Gosselin et al., 2010: 7).

Particular attention has been directed to "criteria air contaminants," or CACs. These contaminants are the ones most commonly emitted by heavy industry using fossil fuels, and negatively affect health. They include nitrogen oxides (NO_X), sulphur dioxide (SO_2), volatile organic compounds

Courtesy M.C. English

Oil sands operation in Alberta. The Athabasca River is in the far background, adjacent to the end of the plant. In the foreground are large (soccer-field-sized) cakes of yellow sulphur, a by-product of the upgrading process.

Perspectives on the Environment

Greenhouse Gas Emissions from the Oil Sands

Greenhouse gas (GHG) emissions from the oil sands . . . are a major environmental issue. Although substantial progress has been made in reducing the quantity of GHG emitted per unit of production (emissions intensity) by the oil sands industry, and future reductions in emissions intensity will occur, the rapid pace of growth in bitumen production means direct oil sands GHG emissions have grown substantially. With current and projected developments, direct GHG emissions will continue to grow at a time when Canada has accepted targets for substantial overall reductions.

—Gosselin et al. (2010: 4)

(VOCs), and particulate matter ($PM_{2.5}$)—all released from oil sands operations.

Oil sands technology has improved, leading to a reduction in the volume of pollutants emitted per barrel of oil produced. Nevertheless, the emissions from producing synthetic oil from bitumen are higher than they are in conventional oil production processes. Furthermore, the rapid expansion of oil sands production has meant that overall emissions continue to increase even though emissions per barrel have decreased.

Modelling of air pollution based on approved future oil sands production expansion indicates that maximum emissions of NO_X and SO_2 will exceed provincial, national, and international standards. VOCs are also of concern because in 2002 Alberta was one of the top four states or provinces in North America in terms of emissions, and these emissions are predicted to go up. Any additional development will make the situation worse. In contrast, forecast emissions related to $PM_{2.5}$ show that although they will increase, they will remain below accepted thresholds.

In early 2008, the federal Conservative government announced a "green" plan that would allow GHG emissions from the oil sands to triple from 25 million to 75 million tonnes a year over the next decade, a period when the national goal is to reduce overall emissions by 150 million tonnes. The economic value of the oil sands development appears to override environmental concerns, even in regard to issues as serious as global climate change, as discussed in Chapter 7.

Wildlife

On 28 April 2008, ducks landed on a 12 km^2 tailings pond operated by Syncrude Canada in association with its oil sands operations, and 1,600 died. Syncrude was charged under provincial and federal regulations for failing to deter the ducks from landing in the tailings pond. The government's view was that it should have been apparent to Syncrude that deterrent systems (air cannons, scarecrows) to discourage landings by birds should have been in place in the spring as soon as reasonably possible. The lawyer for Syncrude argued that the company had followed all regulations, and finding the company guilty would have a serious negative impact on the entire oil sands industry.

Photos of the oil-covered ducks quickly appeared in the global media. Many died because they could not get themselves out of the thick "goop" on the surface of the tailings pond. Photos showed some being eaten alive by ravens while stuck on the surface, while others sank and drowned. Such images generated criticism, claiming the environmental costs of extraction from the oil sands were too high.

In June 2010, a Provincial Court judge found Syncrude guilty, and assigned $3 million in penalties. The cost was broken down into a $500,000 provincial fine, a $300,000 federal fine, $1.3 million to support research on how to deter birds from oil sands operations, and $900,000 for habitat restoration. Some funds for habitat restoration were used to purchase wetlands to the east of Edmonton, to be managed by conservation groups. Also, one-half of the provincial fine supported an environmental diploma program at Keyano College in Fort McMurray.

Environmental Monitoring and Assessment

During February 2012, the federal and Alberta governments indicated they would develop a joint implementation plan for monitoring the oil sands (Environment Canada and Alberta Environment, 2012). The initial work would occur between 2012 and 2015, build on existing monitoring capacity, and be designed to create "a scientifically credible, integrated approach to environmental monitoring, including an improved understanding of how the different types of impacts—on air, water, land, and biodiversity—affect one another" (Environment Canada and Alberta Environment, 2012: 1).

The governments indicated that the incremental costs beyond what they spent at that time were estimated to be initially about $50 million annually, to be funded by industry. It was expected that subsequently the annual costs would decrease. To achieve greater effectiveness and efficiency, the existing constellation of monitoring programs would be rationalized and integrated into one program, jointly managed by both governments.

To ensure transparency, an annual report would be made available to the public, and the monitoring system would be peer reviewed after the third year, and subsequently at five-year intervals. Further transparency would be achieved through creation of a data management framework to make information freely and publicly available.

The two governments stated that the extraction of oil sands creates two basic kinds of environmental impacts: release of contaminants (from industrial stacks, open mine faces, tailings ponds) with potentially harmful effects, and direct disturbance of the environment. Both of these impacts need to be monitored in an integrated manner since they can interact to cause cumulative effects. As a result, it had been decided that the monitoring program would be holistic, in order than that "the results are interpreted and linked across environmental media to relate emissions and habitat disturbance to cumulative, long-term effects on receptors, both ecosystems and human health" (Environment Canada and Alberta Environment, 2012: 6). In that context, the following would be monitored: (1) air quality (from the point of emission to the point of deposition in both aquatic and terrestrial ecosystems), (2) acid-sensitive lakes and accumulated aerial deposition, (3) water quantity and quality, (4) aquatic system health, including fish status and health, benthic invertebrates and other aquatic biota, (5) wildlife toxicology, and (6) terrestrial biodiversity and habitat disturbance.

The first annual report related to oil sands monitoring covered 2012–2013. In the second report, covering 2013–2014, Environment Canada and the Alberta Environmental Monitoring, Evaluation and Reporting Agency (2014) reported that:

- A funding formula had been developed with the Canadian Association of Petroleum Producers (CAPP) for monitoring. A total of $48.13 million of industry funding was targeted for the second year.
- In December 2013, Alberta passed the Protecting Alberta's Environment Act, which created the Alberta Environmental Monitoring, Evaluation and Reporting Agency (AEMERA) as the provincial agency responsible for environmental monitoring. Its mandate is to collect and provide access to scientific data and information related to the condition of the environment in Alberta, including indicators as well as cumulative effects, both provincially and in specific areas. AEMERA was proclaimed on 28 April 2014 and became the provincial lead for oil sands monitoring.
- Engagement was facilitated with Aboriginal peoples, industry, scientists, and stakeholders. Multi-stakeholder forums were used to share information and obtain feedback related to objectives, priority audiences, and areas for focus. A key lesson from the sessions was that "the forums were better suited for sharing information with a large group of people than for meaningful engagement on technical/monitoring planning" (2014: 14). This led to creation of several "Component Advisory Committees" focused on technical/monitoring planning. The CACs suggested monitoring be broadened to include groundwater and wetlands (2014: 15).
- An explicit commitment had been made to deliver a monitoring program which included traditional ecological knowledge (TEK) and created mechanisms to incorporate advice from Aboriginal peoples. However, it was noted that by the end of the reporting period, "to date, no agreement has been reached on the inclusion of TEK into the Joint Oil Sands Monitoring Program" (2014: 12).
- The two governments had committed to provide training and participation of members of local Aboriginal communities related to monitoring activities. During May 2013, training in basic monitoring techniques was provided to First Nations and Métis individuals from the Fort Chipewyan community.
- A Canada–Alberta Oil Sands Environmental Monitoring Information Portal was launched to provide transparent access.

Natural Gas

Although having a small share (67 trillion cubic feet [Tcf]) of proven global natural gas reserves, Canada in 2012 was ranked fifth in its production, following the United States, Russia, Iran, and Qatar (US Energy Information Administration, 2014: 14). All of Canada's exports are to the United States, transported through pipelines.

Most of Canada's natural gas reserves are of the conventional kind in the Western Canada Sedimentary Basin (WCSB), extending from British Columbia to Manitoba and to the Northwest Territories. However, significant deposits exist in unconventional reserves as coal-bed methane, shale gas, and tight gas. It has been estimated that Canada has 573 Tcf of recoverable shale gas (US Energy Administration, 2014: 13), with five large deposits in British Columbia (Horn River, Cordova Embayment, Liard) and Alberta (Colorado Group), and the Deep Basins in both provinces. Other reserves of shale gas are in Saskatchewan, Manitoba, Quebec, and Nova Scotia.

The term **hydraulic fracturing**, or **fracking**, describes removal of natural gas from rock formations well below the Earth's surface. Holes are drilled thousands of metres below the surface, first vertically and then horizontally. Water and chemicals are forced at high pressure into impermeable shale deposits. The product is often called shale gas. Fracking allows vast quantities of gas, previously inaccessible, to be extracted. The US is a leader in fracking. That procedure is expected to make the US an energy exporter and eliminate its reliance on energy imports. Generally, shale gas is viewed as a replacement for the depleting reserves of gas in more conventional geological formations.

As with all technologies, fracking has challenges. Concerns exist about the toxicity of chemicals being injected with water to release the gas from shale. Concerns also are expressed about the large volumes of water required, as well as for potential groundwater contamination, degradation of air quality, triggering of earthquakes, and surface and noise pollution.

To illustrate, a Liberal government was elected in New Brunswick during September 2014, with a key campaign promise being to impose a moratorium on fracking for existing shale gas sites. A further complication in New Brunswick is that First Nations and their supporters have been protesting about fracking of shale gas on the principle that provincial governments have a duty to consult and accommodate Aboriginal peoples when proposed development is on their traditional lands.

Another example is from Newfoundland and Labrador, whose provincial government imposed a moratorium on fracking for oil and gas operations in inshore areas. However, in early 2015 opposition arose related to possible fracking just outside the boundary of Gros Morne National Park, designated in 1987 as a World Heritage Site by UNESCO. Opponents called for an anti-fracking zone around the park, arguing that fracking adjacent to the park could have serious negative impacts within the park.

Coal

In 2013, metallurgical coke (used in production of iron and steel) and coke exports went up by 12.5 per cent, but the value fell by 15.5 per cent, to $5.1 billion, due to lower prices. Exports of coal also decreased modestly (-0.3 per cent) as did the value of those exports (-0.9 per cent) to $0.7 billion (Natural Resources Canada, 2014b: 2). Coal is mined in British Columbia, Alberta, and Saskatchewan and is a key ingredient in production of electricity in Alberta and Saskatchewan.

In 2003, Canada used all the coal mined in country, some 69 million short tons (62.6 million tonnes). However, 10 years later, the consumption pattern changed significantly, with only 46 of the 73 million short tons (41.7 and 71.7 million tonnes) produced being consumed within the country, due to government policies discouraging coal-fired electricity plants as well as development of alternatives to coal. Coal is used primarily for electricity generation, and accounts for over 50 per cent of power generation in Canada. The main provinces reliant on coal for electricity production are Alberta, Saskatchewan, and Nova Scotia (US Energy Information Administration, 2014: 17). Regarding exported coal, over 80 per cent goes to Asian countries, with less than 10 per cent being shipped to the Americas.

A challenge related to use of coal as a resource to power electricity relates to generation of greenhouse gases. In the following "Domestic Guest Statement," Emily Eaton explains an innovative approach introduced in Saskatchewan related to coal and greenhouse gases.

Uranium and Nuclear Power

Uranium

The main use of uranium, once processed, is for fuel in nuclear reactors to generate electricity. When exploration for uranium began in the early 1940s, however, the demand for uranium was not for nuclear reactors, because none existed. Instead, uranium was required for atomic weapons then being developed. During World War II, the federal government established a Crown corporation, later known as Eldorado Nuclear Ltd. For a short time, it was the only company approved to mine radioactive material. After the end of the war, other firms were approved to mine and process uranium, and by the late 1950s more than 20 uranium mines were operating. The largest were near Elliot Lake, Ontario, and Uranium City, Saskatchewan. When commercial nuclear reactors became available in the 1960s, further exploration led to discovery of major new deposits of uranium in northern Saskatchewan. One outcome was the closure of the lower-grade mines in Elliot Lake and Uranium City.

Uranium mining and production is controversial. The mining process results in tailings that need careful storage to prevent leakage into aquatic systems. After being used in power plants, the nuclear fuel wastes are highly radioactive, generating challenges for long-term containment and storage. From an economic perspective, however, uranium mines have provided jobs for skilled workers in remote regions of the country where jobs have not been plentiful.

Canada produced the most uranium of all countries for many years, but in 2009 became second to Kazakhstan. It now contributes just over one-fifth of world output, with the largest operation at the McArthur River mine in northern Saskatchewan.

All production in Canada is from mines in northern Saskatchewan. McArthur River, an underground mine, is the largest uranium mine in the world, and McClean Lake began as an open-pit mine and subsequently became an underground mine. They began production in 2000 and 1999, respectively. Previous mines at Key Lake, Rabbit Lake, and Cluff Lake are no longer in production.

In 2014 production began at the Cigar Lake mine, anticipated to have a life of at least 30 years. Its construction started in 2008 with the intent to begin production in 2011. Underground flooding delayed progress, and production did not begin until 2014, at which point the initial cost estimate of $660 million had increased to about $2.6 billion (World Nuclear Association, 2014a: 5).

The provincial government in Saskatchewan supports uranium mining, subject to appropriate safeguards for the environment. AREVA (2007), operator of the McClean Lake mine, has stated that the "industry's long-term goal is to return all operations, as close as possible, to a natural state suitable for future uses. All uranium mine site operators must post bonds with the federal government to ensure adequate funds are available for proper decommissioning of each site after the reserves have been mined out."

Another mine, called Midwest, in northern Saskatchewan is expected to begin operations in the future. The comprehensive environmental impact assessment for it was started in 2006, and federal approval was given in August 2012.

DOMESTIC GUEST STATEMENT

Capturing Carbon for Enhanced Oil Recovery: A Climate Change Strategy?

Emily Eaton

On 2 October 2014 Saskatchewan's Crown-owned power utility SaskPower opened its carbon capture and storage (CCS) project at Boundary Dam, a coal-fired power plant in the southeast of the province. Touted as the world's first and largest commercial-scale CCS initiative, the project promises to capture 90 per cent of the greenhouse gas emissions from one of the six units at Boundary Dam and transport the liquefied CO_2 by pipeline to a nearby oil field where it will be used by Calgary-based oil company Cenovus Energy Inc. to push more oil out of its aging Weyburn oil field. In an information sheet, SaskPower (2012) boasts that it "is leading the way to make a viable technical, environmental and economic case for the continued use of coal." As students of environmental change, what are we to make of this "clean coal" strategy? Can it be understood as a climate change mitigation strategy? If so, how should it be evaluated?

Carbon capture and storage is very much in its experimental phase. Geologists and engineers are still studying what happens to the liquefied carbon injected into formations deep underground, including whether it has the potential to migrate and contaminate groundwater sources and which formations are best for sequestration. If we assume that all of the CO_2 injected underground stays sequestered, SaskPower's projection of capturing 90 per cent of the emissions produced at the 110-MW unit seems like a net positive effect for the climate. Yet, a host of other details should be taken into account when investing in CCS as a climate change mitigation strategy.

First, the Saskatchewan government's stated purpose to promote CCS as "clean coal" further delays the transition to renewable energy sources and locks in a huge amount of public investment and infrastructure into coal mining and coal-fired production (coal-fired production accounts for 47 per cent of Saskatchewan's electricity). The CCS project cost the Crown corporation $1.4 billion, $240 million of which came from the federal government. In fact, the steep costs associated with CCS infrastructure have been cited as one of the greatest barriers to its widespread adoption (Gibbins and Chalmers, 2008). While SaskPower has signed a 10-year contract to supply 1 million tonnes of liquefied CO_2 per year to Cenovus Energy Inc. at an undisclosed price, the selling of 1 million tonnes of CO_2 per year is not expected to pay for the investment over the 20-year projected lifespan of the project (Mandryk, 2014). This view has led local groups, such as Saskatchewan Community Wind, to argue that the large public investment would have been better spent on wind energy. Its analysis shows that over a 20-year lifespan, wind energy could generate the same amount of electricity as the coal-fired CCS project, while saving ratepayers $301 million in capital and operating costs (Saskatchewan Community Wind, 2014).

On top of the costs associated with preempted transitions to renewable energy, Saskatchewan's CCS project ought to be evaluated based on its total contribution to reducing GHG emissions. The capture technology affixed to the one unit at Boundary Dam means that just 9 per cent of the total coal-fired production in Saskatchewan is subject to CCS. Moreover, the process of capturing carbon from the plant is energy intensive itself. According to journalist Bruce Johnstone (2014), 21 per cent of the energy generated will go to capturing the CO_2.

Finally, an assessment of Saskatchewan's CCS project should include the GHG emissions associated with the end use of the captured CO_2. Climate change will only be arrested if total world GHG emissions are reduced. The fact that the liquefied CO_2 will be used to produce crude oil further entrenches the province's reliance on carbon extractive industries. Importantly, fully one-fifth of the province's GHG emissions are attributed to "fugitive emissions" from the oil and gas industry (Environment Canada, 2013b). Fugitive emissions are essentially waste, and include emissions from venting and flaring associated gas, and from pipeline and wellhead leaks. Moreover, significant GHG emissions are associated with the consumption of petroleum. If Saskatchewan plans to implement CCS technology across all of its coal-fired plants, even more petroleum production will be enabled. Unfortunately, it is difficult to estimate the total GHG implications of using the CO_2 for enhanced oil recovery. Nevertheless, the story of CCS in Saskatchewan is much more complicated than SaskPower or the Saskatchewan government acknowledges.

Courtesy Emily Eaton

Emily Eaton, PhD, is an associate professor in the Department of Geography and Environmental Studies at the University of Regina. Her research concerns natural resource economies, including those based on oil and agriculture.

Production was initially planned to begin in 2011, but the starting date has been reset several times, partially reflecting a 50-per-cent increase in the estimated capital costs of $435 million. Millennium, another mine in Saskatchewan, and Kiggavik, in Nunavut, are the next likely mines to be opened. And, in addition to exploration continuing in northern Saskatchewan, surveys are underway in Labrador, Nova Scotia, Quebec, Ontario (Elliott Lake area), and Nunavut (World Nuclear Association, 2014a: 5–12).

Nuclear Power

A made-in-Canada experimental nuclear reactor was developed at Chalk River, Ontario, and began producing power in 1947. That reactor became the forerunner of the CANDU (Canada Deuterium Uranium) pressurized heavy-water reactors used around the world.

Canada produces about 15 per cent of its electricity from **nuclear power**, and its production ranks Canada sixth in the world, after the US, France, Russia, South Korea, and China. At a global scale, just over 12 per cent of electricity is generated from nuclear power (Nuclear Energy Institute, 2014: 1). In Canada, some 19 reactors produced 96.4 billion kilowatt-hours (kWh) of power in 2012, out of a total of 646 billion kWh from all sources (World Nuclear Association, 2014b: 1). Ontario, the province most dependent on nuclear power (over 50 per cent and with 15 active reactors in late 2014), has used it since the early 1970s. Quebec (Gentilly) and New Brunswick (Point Lepreau) each has a single-unit CANDU plant.

Ontario has commercial nuclear reactors in operation in three multiple-unit locations (Pickering and Darlington, both on the shore of Lake Ontario, and Bruce on the shore of Lake Huron). During the early 1990s, nuclear reactors generated about two-thirds of Ontario's electricity. This dropped to just over 50 per cent by 2014. Part of the reason is that several units at the Pickering and Bruce plants have been taken out of service for long periods for safety reasons, and then for refurbishing.

All three provinces using nuclear reactors have refurbishing programs to extend their life. Refurbishing was expected to be less expensive than building new plants, but cost overruns in some instances have been significant—over twice the estimated costs. For example, refurbishing of the Pickering and Bruce plants has been labelled "a cautionary tale (and classic industry case study)" (World Nuclear Association, 2014b: 4). The two plants were shut down for several years to allow design problems to be resolved and operating systems to be upgraded. At Pickering, some $200 million was spent to extend the plants for 10 years. At the Bruce stations, the entire refurbishment had been calculated to be $5.25 billion, but in 2010 the cost had increased to $6.8 billion. In New Brunswick, refurbishing had been estimated to be $1.4 billion, but went about $2 billion over budget and took 54 months rather than 18. Quebec decided in August 2008 to refurbish the Gentilly 2 reactor to extend its life to 2040. The estimated cost was $1.9 billion, including development of a radioactive waste facility. Work was to begin in 2011 but was deferred, and then in September 2013 a new provincial government decided to close the plant at the end of 2013 (World Nuclear Association, 2014b: 4–8).

Arguments in favour of refurbishing existing reactors or building more nuclear power capacity include that nuclear power has less short-term environmental impact than coal- or petroleum-fuelled power plants and operates at a lower cost. As Ontario Power Generation (2010) has stated, nuclear power "has two major benefits—low operating costs and virtually none of the emissions that lead to smog, acid rain or global warming."

Looking forward, the World Nuclear Association (2014b: 8–12) states that several proposals have been considered regarding new nuclear reactors in Canada. Two are for Ontario, one for New Brunswick, and one, or perhaps up to four smaller reactors, for Alberta. The motivation in Alberta is different than in other provinces. The driver there is the high cost of extracting bitumen from oil sands. Current procedures rely on natural gas, which are expensive and emit significant greenhouse gases (GHG). Nuclear power reactors are perceived to be more cost effective and emit much fewer GHGs for necessary steam to extract bitumen from oil sands. However, in late 2011 the idea of nuclear plants for Alberta was shelved.

Management of Used Nuclear Fuel

A major issue for nuclear energy is radioactive waste. The federal government created the Nuclear Waste Management Organization (NWMO) to identify options for storage and disposal of **nuclear wastes.** Canada has used nuclear fuel to generate electricity for decades, and the Low-Level Radioactive Waste Management Office (2012: ii) reported that, at the end of 2011, the national inventory of nuclear fuel waste was 9,400 m^3 and the projection to 2050 was for 20,000 m^3.

Used fuel bundles from nuclear plants are stored in regulated facilities on the sites at which they are produced, always viewed as a short-term arrangement, with a need to determine a long-term solution. In June 2007, the federal government announced that the NWMO would apply an **adaptive phased management** approach regarding long-term management of used nuclear fuel. The intent is to contain and isolate used nuclear fuel in one or more deep geological depositories. More details are provided below.

The NWMO (2014a) has explained that an adaptive phased management approach involves (1) centralized storage of used nuclear fuel in a deep underground depository; (2) a series of steps and decision points, adapted as learning occurs; (3) people and communities having opportunity to be involved throughout the process; (4) long-term stewardship through ongoing monitoring of used fuels; (5) capacity to retrieve and

ENVIRONMENT IN FOCUS

BOX 12.3 | Implications of Nuclear Crisis in Japan

The earthquake (9.0 on the Richter scale) in Japan, and the associated tsunami that devastated the northeast coast of that country on 11 March 2011 had major impacts. Over 25,000 people lost their lives, more than 500,000 had to evacuate homes, an estimated 2 million households were left without electricity, and 1.5 million households had no water. The impact on the Fukushima Daiichi nuclear complex on the coastline some 240 kilometres north of Tokyo particularly drew attention since the combined natural disasters left the plant without the capacity to cool three nuclear reactors due to structural damage, loss of electricity, and swamping of backup generators by the tsunami. Commentators around the world suggested that this event was a wake-up call and should create a critical reassessment of the role and potential vulnerabilities of nuclear power plants.

In early November 2014, the Governor of Japan provided final approval for the restarting of two reactors at the Sendai nuclear power station in the south of Japan, the first to restart operating under new safety rules developed after the Fukushima meltdown. All 48 working reactors in Japan had been offline to allow safety checks since the March 2011 disaster, except for two that had operated for approximately a year. By late 2014, significant quantities of contaminated water continued to leak from the damaged Fukushima reactors.

The impact of the problems at the Fukushima nuclear power plant is illustrated by a decision subsequently taken almost halfway around the world. In May 2011, Chancellor Angela Merkel announced that Germany would abandon its nuclear energy program over an 11-year period and turn more to renewable energy sources, especially solar, wind, and hydroelectricity. All 17 of Germany's nuclear power plants are to be shut down by 2022. This decision represented a remarkable shift in policy, as in 2010 Germany had announced a plan to extend the lifespan of its nuclear reactors, with the last one to go offline about 2036.

Damage to the unit 4 nuclear reactor building at the Fukushima Daiichi nuclear plant.

remove the used waste to take advantage of new technologies; and (6) sufficient long-term funding to support long-term care of the fuel.

The NMWO (2014c) developed a set of principles to guide the program. These include (1) safety of people and environment being first and foremost; (2) an informed and willing host community for the waste repository; (3) long-term well-being of the host community; (4) all those who will be potentially affected to be involved, including relevant provincial governments; and, (5) Aboriginal rights, treaties, and land claims, including unresolved claims, to be respected.

Nine steps are included in the siting process, including (1) publishing and explaining the process, and responding to questions; (2) inviting communities to express interest and to learn more, followed by an initial screening; (3) for interested communities, completing a preliminary assessment to determine if a site could meet requirements, and encouraging such communities to communicate with adjacent communities; (4) completing detailed assessments of sites in communities which expressed interest, and engaging with adjacent communities which might be affected; (5) once confirming suitable sites, determining willingness of relevant communities to accept a project, and under what terms and conditions; (6) developing an agreement between the NWMO and the community with the preferred site; (7) assessing the proposed site by regulatory authorities, verifying all requirements are met, and giving approval; (8) constructing and operating an underground demonstration facility; and, (9) constructing the deep geological repository and beginning operations (NWMO, 2014b).

In the spirit of "fairness," the NWMO concluded that it would focus on the provinces directly involved in nuclear fuel—Saskatchewan, Ontario, Quebec, and New Brunswick. Twenty-two communities were identified through the second step in the process: three were in Saskatchewan and 18 were in Ontario. After completion of the initial screenings, in November 2013 four communities were dropped, followed by two more in January 2014, and one more in the summer of 2014, leaving 15. One of those was in Saskatchewan (Creighton) with the remainder in northern and southwestern Ontario.

The NWMO (2013: 3) explained its intent for the five-year period from 2014 to 2019 is to complete the first phase of preliminary assessments of potential host communities, identify communities that offer strong potential to host a repository site and complete more detailed assessments, and then identify one or two communities and sites for further assessment. Thus, by 2019, the goal is to have reached the fourth or fifth step. At this rate, the nine steps will take considerable time to complete.

Sustainable Energy Pathways

Figure 12.7 illustrates how major sources of primary energy, over time and around the world, have evolved from muscular and biomass energy to coal, to oil and natural gas, and to nuclear fuels. Some countries, such as Japan, have moved rapidly from Phase I to Phase IV. In contrast, many developing countries struggle to move beyond Phase I except in their major cities. Canada is now well into Phase IV. What might a Phase V look like?

We encourage you to use an *explicit* set of criteria to assess which options or pathways are most appropriate in the future. When using such criteria, you should decide whether all of them have equal value or whether to weight them in terms of relative importance. All of us, as citizens, should know the basis upon which assessments of energy options are made. This is important, because every option has a different mix of strengths and weaknesses, and, ultimately, these factors will affect our lives now and for the generations to come.

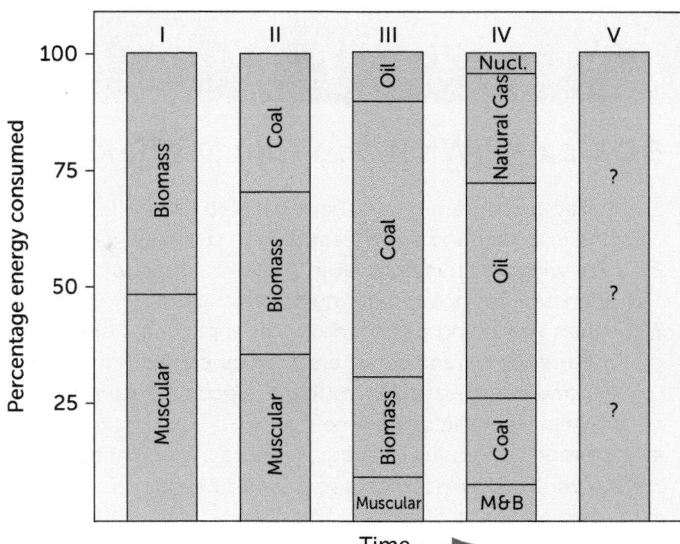

FIGURE 12.7 | The evolution of energy consumption mixes by source.

Source: Chapman 1989: 6). Reprinted with permission of the author.

Implications

If our ecological footprint is to become lighter in terms of our use of minerals and energy, individuals, institutions, and societies will have to change. Consumers complain that manufacturers do not provide enough choice of "green cars," while manufacturers say that customer demand does not indicate that green cars are wanted in sufficient quantity to justify producing them. Thus, if change is to occur, adjustments are needed at all levels, with individuals taking initiative to reduce consumption of energy and mineral products, governments providing greater incentives to both individuals and manufacturers to embrace green products, and manufacturers showing leadership to market green products effectively.

In the meantime, what can you do? No simple recipe or formula will lead readily and easily to a society less materialistic and energy intensive. However, small steps identified in Box 12.5 can effect significant change. Perhaps most important, thinking about and taking such actions are first steps in shifting basic beliefs and values.

ENVIRONMENT IN FOCUS

BOX 12.4 | Compact Fluorescent Bulbs

During 2007, the federal Conservative government announced it would ban incandescent light bulbs and support compact fluorescent bulbs, since the latter require less energy, and develop a plan for mandatory recycling of the compact fluorescent bulbs, which contain mercury, a toxic element.

In November 2014, without publicity, the federal government posted regulations for a voluntary recycling code of practice for companies selling compact fluorescent bulbs. In 2013, Home Depot had stopped accepting such bulbs for recycling, indicating their customers should take them to third-party operations. In contrast, Rona accepts such bulbs, receiving 370,000 of them in 2013.

In terms of managing waste and protecting public health, do you think such a product should require the merchants who sell them to accept them for recycling, or that a voluntary recycling program should be used? What are the advantages and limitations of required and voluntary recycling codes of practice? In general, do you think one is better than the other?

ENVIRONMENT IN FOCUS

BOX 12.5 | What You Can Do: Taking Action to Reduce Energy Use

1. Install a programmable thermostat to have a lower setting in winter and a higher setting in summer.
2. Use window shades to let in sunlight during winter days and keep out hot sun during summer days.
3. When not being used, ensure all appliances, entertainment systems and other electronics are turned off. Use a power strip to allow multiple electronic items to be turned off at the same time.
4. Change light bulbs to use only energy-efficient types.
5. Lower the thermostat on your water heater.
6. Wash full loads of clothes and dishes.
7. Air dry clothes when possible. Air dry dishes rather than using the drying cycle of a dishwasher.
8. Install low-flow taps and shower heads. Reduced water use means reduced energy use.
9. Check and change furnace and air conditioner filters regularly.
10. Check for air leaks around windows and doors, and seal them.
11. Avoid aggressive driving (e.g., speeding, rapid acceleration, and braking), all of which wastes fuel.

Sources: Energy.gov (2014); Alliance to Save Energy (2012).

Summary

1. Non-renewable or stock resources take millions of years to form. Consequently, from a human viewpoint, they are for all practical purposes fixed in supply and therefore not renewable.
2. If done systematically and correctly, enhanced environmental management practices and extended social responsibility with regard to non-renewable resources almost always generate an economic return on investment for business, although usually over the long term.
3. The main environmental issues for the mining and energy sectors include acid mine drainage; sulphur dioxide emissions; metal toxicity; disruption of remote ecosystems as a result of exploration, test drilling, and operation of oil fields or gas wells; disturbance to aquatic ecosystems from escape of waste heat produced by nuclear energy production; and threats to human and ecosystem health from radioactive waste associated with nuclear energy production over thousands of years.
4. "Best practice" for environmental management in mining and fossil-fuel firms in Canada should include a combination of basic scientific research to ensure understanding of natural and social systems that can be affected by operations, design of appropriate mitigation measures, environmental impact assessments and reporting, environmental audits, corporate policies that explicitly include environmental aspects, environmental management systems, and life-cycle assessments.
5. Canada is one of the top producers in the world of aluminum, diamonds, nickel, platinum, group metals, potash, uranium, and zinc.
6. In 1998, BHP's Ekati mine, located 200 kilometres south of the Arctic Circle in the Northwest Territories, became the first diamond operation in Canada.
7. At the Ekati diamond mine, tailings are held in a lake. As the tailings settle, consolidate, and evolve to permafrost, rocks and soil will be spread over the surface. Revegetation will be started, with the goal of having the entire holding area become a wetland once the mining is completed.
8. Serious challenges were encountered by Ekati in incorporating traditional ecological knowledge into environmental research: (1) two Aboriginal groups were in the midst of land claim negotiations and as a result were reluctant to release traditional knowledge into the public domain because this knowledge was important for their negotiation strategy; (2) concern was expressed by Aboriginal people about using traditional knowledge outside of the context of their culture and broader system of knowledge that give it meaning and value.
9. The Bathurst caribou herd is the largest one in the NWT. Since the caribou herd does not follow the same migration route each year and the areas affected by the Ekati mine represent less than 0.01 per cent of the range of the herd, it was believed that the mining activity would have a very small impact.
10. Beginning in 1992, BHP Billiton initiated scientific research to understand the impact of the proposed Ekati mining activity and to develop mitigation measures. In July 1994, the minister of Indian Affairs and Northern Development referred the mining project for an environmental assessment. An environmental assessment panel held public

meetings and in June submitted its report to the federal government. In February 1997, the federal government gave its formal approval. In January 1999, the first diamonds from Ekati were sold in Antwerp.

11. Impact and benefit agreements were pioneered in Canada and are intended to ensure that Aboriginal communities benefit from mining projects and that if they contain compensation provisions, the communities are compensated for the negative impact on their communities, their land, and their traditional way of life.
12. The "Ring of Fire" area in northwestern Ontario highlights types of conflict that can emerge when exploration and/or extraction of minerals is pursued in remote areas viewed to have high biodiversity value and to be traditional lands used by Aboriginal peoples.
13. Canada is ranked as the sixth-largest user of primary energy in the world. Fossil fuels are the main type of energy consumed by Canadians.
14. The combustion of fossil fuels emits greenhouse gases, such as carbon dioxide and nitrous oxide, which accumulate in the atmosphere and contribute to climate change.
15. Alternative energy sources are solar, geothermal, hydro, tides, and wind.
16. Wind power is the fastest-growing sector in the world's energy market. Canada is ranked ninth in the world in terms of installed wind power.
17. Wind turbines have minimal impact on flying birds, but various factors influence the seriousness of collisions with wind turbines. Fragmentation of habitats often is the most disruptive characteristic of wind farms, reflecting the cumulative effects of wind turbines along with related infrastructure (electrical transmission lines, roads).
18. There are growing complaints from individuals and communities about the noise and negative health impacts believed to be caused by wind farms.
19. Europe has the most diverse end uses of solar power. In Canada and the US, the main use of solar power is to heat water in swimming pools.
20. In Atlantic Canada, offshore oil production is based in the Hibernia, Terra Nova, White Rose, and North Amethyst fields off the coast of Newfoundland, and natural gas extraction occurs near Sable Island, Nova Scotia. The Hebron oil field is expected to begin production in 2017.
21. Discoveries of petroleum and gas below the Beaufort Sea off the coast of the Northwest Territories and off the coast of British Columbia offer potential for development. However, there is a prohibition on transporting petroleum by ship along the coast of British Columbia because of the *Exxon Valdez* spill in 1989 and a moratorium in place since 1972 prevents exploration and production off the BC coast.
22. The oil spill from the *Deepwater Horizon* drilling rig explosion and wellhead blowout in the Gulf of Mexico in April 2010 highlighted the environmental risks associated with extraction of oil from significant depths on the ocean floor.
23. Various nations are challenging Canada's claims to Arctic sovereignty, not only for strategic military reasons but also to establish ownership over fossil fuels on the sea floor.
24. The Athabasca oil sands represent the second-largest reserve of petroleum in the world, outranked only by the reserves in Saudi Arabia.
25. Extraction of the bitumen from the oil sands is having negative environmental impacts on the boreal forest and wetland systems, the Athabasca River, and air quality.
26. A joint Canada–Alberta Implementation Plan for Oil Sands Monitoring was initiated in 2012.
27. The monitoring plan is designed to take a holistic approach in order to track variables that generate cumulative effects, and also to incorporate traditional ecological knowledge into the monitoring protocols.
28. Canada is ranked fifth in the world as a producer of natural gas.
29. Hydraulic fracturing, or "fracking," has made natural gas in shale deposits, which were previously inaccessible, feasible to extract. Debate exists related to the environmental costs associated with fracking.
30. Use of coal in Canada dropped significantly between 2003 and 2013; domestic use of all coal produced in the country fell to just over 60 per cent of mined coal. The main reasons are government policies to shift producing electricity from coal to other sources of energy.
31. Canada produces about one-fifth of the world's uranium; most of that production is from two mines in northern Saskatchewan whose reserves appear to be extractable for 40 years.
32. Canada is the sixth-largest producer of nuclear energy in the world.
33. Twelve to 15 per cent of electricity in Canada is supplied from nuclear power plants in Ontario (17 reactors), Quebec (1 reactor), and New Brunswick (1 reactor).
34. The earthquake and tsunami that struck Japan in March 2011 and disabled nuclear power plants is pointed to as a reason why societies need to pause and reassess the vulnerability of nuclear power systems.
35. Most concern about nuclear energy focuses on how to dispose of used nuclear fuel.

36. Adaptive phased management is being used by the Nuclear Waste Management Organization to identify one or more sites in which to store used nuclear fuel waste.
37. A nine-step process is being used to identify a site in which to store used nuclear fuel waste, but it will likely be well into the 2020s before such a site is constructed and in operation.

Key Terms

acid mine drainage
adaptive phased management
bitumen
crude bitumen
fracking
hydraulic fracturing (fracking)
impact and benefit agreements (IBAs)
in situ recovery
kimberlite pipes
metal toxicity
non-renewable or stock resources
nuclear power
nuclear wastes
renewable or flow resources
solar power
steam-assisted gravity drainage
sulphur dioxide emissions
wind power

Questions for Review and Critical Thinking

1. What are the implications of non-renewable or stock resources for strategies related to "sustainable development" or for "resilience"?
2. How important are non-renewable resources for the Canadian economy?
3. What have been elements of "best practice" related to the opening of diamond mines in the Canadian North?
4. What was learned from the environmental assessment for the Ekati mine regarding incorporation of local knowledge into scientific understanding of impacts?
5. Why is Canada so dependent on fossil fuels? What would have to change for there to be less dependence?
6. What are the main uses of primary energy in Canada?
7. What are the advantages and disadvantages of alternative energy sources?
8. What are the main objections from individuals and communities located adjacent to wind farms related to health? What scientific evidence exists related to health matters associated with wind turbines and wind farms?
9. What is the main use of solar power in Canada?
10. What are the greatest environmental risks associated with extracting fossil fuels from the seabeds of the Atlantic, Pacific, and Arctic oceans?
11. What is the significance of the *Exxon Valdez* incident off the coast of Alaska in 1989 and the *Deepwater Horizon* oil spill in the Gulf of Mexico during 2010 in terms of the development of offshore oil resources?
12. Why did the Russians plant a flag on the seabed at the North Pole in August 2007?
13. Why is fragmentation of the boreal forests and wetlands in the area of the Athabasca oil sands of concern in terms of biodiversity?
14. Why does removal of water from the Athabasca River to support oil production pose a threat to the Peace–Athabasca Delta?
15. What are the strengths and weaknesses of the newly introduced integrated monitoring system for the oil sands region, and what key changes might be made to improve monitoring?
16. What are the best strategies for facilitating the economic benefits related to oil production from the Athabasca oil sands while minimizing negative environmental impacts?
17. Why is "fracking" controversial? What are the main arguments for and against fracking?
18. Why are some provincial governments deciding to move away from use of coal to produce electricity, and instead use other sources?
19. What are the main controversies associated with mining of uranium?
20. Why did the earthquake and tsunami in March 2011 in Japan lead to calls for a review of the safety of nuclear power plants around the world?
21. Why are there concerns about storing used nuclear fuel on the sites of nuclear power plants?
22. What are the characteristics of "adaptive phased management" in relation to spent nuclear fuel?
23. What changes should be made by individuals, organizations, businesses, and governments to reduce energy and mineral use?

Related Websites

Canadian Wind Energy Association
www.canwea.org

Danish Windpower Organization
www.windpower.org/en/

Environment Canada: Canadian Wind Energy Atlas
www.windatlas.ca/en/index.php

European Wind Energy Association
www.ewea.org

Global Wind Energy Council
www.gwec.net

Independent Environmental Monitoring Association: A Public Watchdog for Environmental Monitoring of Ekati Diamond Mine
www.monitoringagency.net/Home/tabid/36/Default.aspx

Mining Association of Canada
www.mining.ca/

MiningWatch Canada
www.miningwatch.ca/index.php

Natural Resources Canada: Canadian Minerals Yearbook
www.nrcan.gc.ca/mining-materials/markets/canadian-minerals-yearbook/8426

Natural Resources Canada: Office of Energy Efficiency
www.nrcan.gc.ca/energy/offices-labs/office-energy-efficiency

Natural Resources Canada: Wind Energy
www.nrcan.gc.ca/energy/renewables/wind/7299

Nuclear Waste Management Organization
www.nwmo.ca/home

Ontario Wind Resistance
www.ontario-wind-resistance.org

Society for Wind Vigilance
www.windvigilance.com

Solar and Sustainable Energy Society of Canada
www.landstewardship.org/resources/agency/30/

Wind Power Methods
www.wpm.co.nz

Further Readings

Note: This list comprises works relevant to the subject of the chapter but not cited in the text. All cited works are listed in the References at the end of the book.

Adachi, C.W., and I.H. Rowlands. 2010. "The effectiveness of policies in supporting the diffusion of solar photovoltaic systems: Experiences with Ontario, Canada's Renewable Energy Standard Offer Program," *Sustainability* 2, 1: 30–47.

Global Wind Energy Council. 2014. *Global Wind Energy Outlook 2014*. Brussels and Amsterdam: Global Wind Energy Council and Greenpeace,.

Heisler, K.G., and S. Markey. 2014. "Navigating jurisdiction: Local and regional strategies to access economic benefits from mineral development," *Canadian Geographer* 58, 4: 457–68.

Henderson, C. 2013. *Aboriginal Power: Clean Energy and the Future of Canada's First Peoples*. Erin, ON: Rainforest Editions.

International Energy Agency. 2014. *Key World Energy Statistics, 2014*. Paris: International Energy Agency.

Levant, E. 2010. *Ethical Oil: The Case for Canada's Oil Sands*. Toronto: McClelland & Stewart.

Nikiforuk, A. 2010. *Tar Sands: Dirty Oil and the Future of the Continent*, rev. edn. Vancouver: Greystone Books and David Suzuki Foundation.

Schindler, D.W. 2010. "Tar sands need solid science," *Nature* 468, 7323: 499–501.

Go to www.oupcanada.com/DeardenMitchell5e to access additional learning tools on your smartphone, tablet, or PC.

CHAPTER THIRTEEN

Urban Environmental Management

Learning Objectives

- To understand the nature and significance of urbanization
- To understand the quality of environmental conditions in Canadian cities
- To become aware of impacts of urban areas on the environment
- To understand the vulnerability of urban areas to natural and human-induced events
- To become aware of best practices related to urban environmental management
- To identify strategies to reduce the impact of urban areas on the environment

Introduction

The United Nations Population Fund (2007a: 1) indicated the world passed a significant milestone during 2008, with more than half the global population, some 3.3 billion people, living in urban areas for the first time. Looking forward to 2030, it is estimated that almost 5 billion people will be urban residents. The greatest changes will occur in Africa and Asia, where urban populations are expected to double between 2000 and 2030. Canada is highly urbanized. Indeed, the 2011 Canadian census revealed that 81 per cent of Canadians lived in urban centres with 35 per cent in one of three census metropolitan areas (Toronto, Montreal, and Vancouver).

William Rees (2010: 73), one of Canada's foremost ecologists, has written that "the city might be described as a livestock feedlot." While in some regards cities do function as feedlots for humans, we differ from cattle and pigs in that we are not so willing to live in the muck we create, and humans have the capacity—and perhaps the willpower—to do something about it. Here, we examine the nature of sustainable and resilient urban development at global and Canadian scales, determine impacts of cities on the environment, examine how urban areas become vulnerable to environmental variability, and consider strategies for cities to become part of the solution rather than the problem regarding environmental quality, sustainable development, and resilience. In other words, we want to learn not only "what is the right thing to do" but also "how to do the thing right."

> ### *Perspectives on the Environment*
> **Urban Sustainability and Greenhouse Gases**
>
> A large share of global greenhouse gas emissions is attributable to cities. The International Energy Agency (IEA) estimates that urban areas currently account for more than 71 per cent of energy-related global greenhouse gases and this is expected to rise to 76 per cent by 2030. . . .
>
> —Hoornweg et al. (2011: 208)

Sustainable Urban Development

The National Round Table on the Environment and the Economy (NRTEE, 2003c: 3), later disbanded by the federal government, defined urban sustainability as "The enhanced well-being of cities or urban regions, including integrated economic, ecological, and social components, which will maintain the quality of life for future generations." Achieving sustainable urban development requires attention to at least four key factors: *urban form*, *transportation*, *energy*, and *waste management*. Each is considered below.

Urban Form

Urban form refers to the type and distribution of infrastructure (e.g., buildings, roads) and is a key factor influencing environmental quality. For example, the configuration of roads and other transportation networks has a major impact on energy use for travel within cities. Furthermore, regulations related to buildings influence their energy efficiency. Energy use by both transportation and in buildings is a major contributor to GHG emissions.

> ### *Perspectives on the Environment*
> **Urban Sustainability**
>
> . . . at the heart of most definitions is the notion that a city is sustainable only if it meets the social and economic needs of its residents without undermining its ecological continuity over time. Meeting social and economic needs entails ensuring that economic opportunities are fairly distributed among the population, that all citizens have an adequate standard of living (e.g., in terms of education, housing, health care, and food), and that everyone has access to opportunities for participation in community and political life. Ecological continuity means that urban development does not overwhelm the capacity of local and global ecosystems to absorb waste and contaminants, deplete the store of resources that cities depend on, or undermine local, regional or global ecological processes.
>
> —Tomalty (2013: 2)

Finally, **urban sprawl** contributes to loss and disruption to, or degradation of, adjacent agricultural land, environmentally sensitive areas, natural habitats, and water and air quality.

A compact urban form is more environmentally desirable than the "sprawl" typical of many North American cities. And the trend continues to be toward sprawl. The External Advisory Committee on Cities and Communities (2006) reported various trends 10 years ago, which continue to be relevant:

- The average home in Canada is farther away from a city centre than it was a decade ago.
- The proportion of low-rise, low-density homes, except in major cities, is expanding steadily.
- While house sizes have increased, the number of people in households has decreased, resulting in space and energy use per person increasing significantly.
- Commuting times have increased, with traffic congestion costs estimated at $2.3 to $3.7 billion each year, with obvious negative consequences for productivity.
- Sprawl causes higher servicing and infrastructure costs and less effective public transit service, displaces large tracts of habitat and prime agricultural land, and contributes to water quality degradation.

The External Advisory Committee (2006: 52) concluded that "the principal land use challenge . . . is to reduce sprawl in our growing places." Urban areas with a high population density in their cores lead to more efficient and effective land use than in lower-density areas. They are also much more likely to provide effective public transit. In addition, it is normally cheaper to provide services such as water supply and waste removal in higher-density areas. Later in this chapter, we examine alternative ways of reducing or minimizing urban sprawl and other important aspects of urban sprawl.

Adventure_Photo/iStockphoto

Urban sprawl.

Transportation

Negative consequences of low-density urban development are at the heart of many serious critiques of automobile-dependent cities and adverse environmental impacts of cities. The strong relationship revealed by many studies between more compact, mixed-use urban form and reduced car use is reflected in efforts to reduce urban sprawl and create more transit-oriented communities.

Several variables affect energy used for transportation in cities: distance travelled, vehicle loading, and vehicle mode. Each is significantly affected by urban form. Other influential variables are density of the urban area, urban structure, mixes of land use, and street patterns. All affect the number, length, and type of trips. The more spread out a city, the farther people have to travel between places. The lower the population density, the more challenging it is to provide high-quality public transit services. The usual outcome is higher reliance on automobiles, resulting in greater energy use.

Transportation is a major contributor to GHG emissions because fossil fuels power most vehicles. In contrast, for commercial and industrial buildings, the source of energy for heating, cooling, and lighting is often cleaner, such as natural gas or hydroelectricity. In Canada, almost 60 per cent of the energy used in transportation is for moving people, with automobiles accounting for the largest share. The National Round Table (2003c: 13) stated that "transit is a more environmentally sustainable form of urban transportation than the automobile." However, the National Energy Board reports that between 1990 and 2006, "passenger-kilometres," a measure of one passenger over a distance of 1 kilometre and therefore representing the total annual distance travelled by on-road passengers in Canada, increased by 1.8 per cent annually. Furthermore, the NEB (2009b: 5) stated that:

> Over time, Canadians have become more dependent on their automobiles. The number of Canadians aged 18 and over who travelled everywhere by car . . . rose from 68 per cent in 1992 to 74 per cent in 2005, and the number of people that made a trip under their own power by bicycle or on foot declined from 26 per cent in 1992 to 19 per cent in 2005.

MCCAIG/iStockphoto

Commuter traffic.

Springer and Burda (2014) compared rapid transit systems in Toronto, Montreal, Vancouver, Calgary, and Ottawa regarding level of service and responsiveness to urban growth. Toronto had the highest per capita transit ridership, with residents averaging 133 transit trips annually. However, Toronto had less rapid transit infrastructure relative to Calgary, Ottawa, and Montreal. Calgary had the greatest per capita rapid transit infrastructure. In contrast, Vancouver had built the most rapid transit infrastructure (44 kilometres) during the last 20 years, followed by Calgary and Toronto with 18 kilometres each. In the last decade, Calgary and Vancouver had built the most rapid transit, whereas Montreal led regarding access to rapid transit. Thirty-seven per cent of its population lived within walking distance of a rapid transit stop, followed by Toronto, which had 34 per cent within walking distance. This information reminds us that multiple metrics are needed to characterize urban transit arrangements, and different features provide different benefits to users.

Various strategies can reduce energy use by transportation within cities. They include: (1) facilitating teleworking and teleservices to reduce travel time; (2) ensuring parking arrangements encourage reduced car travel (providing ample parking adjacent to public transit departure nodes; setting appropriate [higher] charges for parking cars near workplaces); (3) encouraging development of ride-sharing programs; (4) initiating transit pass programs to provide a seamless public transit system, such as systems in Hong Kong and various European cities that allow a single pass to be used on buses, trains, and ferries; and (5) facilitating use of bicycles and other means with a small ecological footprint.

Energy Use

Promoting green design, construction, renovation, and operation of buildings could cut North American greenhouse gas emissions more deeply, quickly, and cheaply than any other measure (Commission for Environmental Cooperation, 2008). Buildings in North America release more than 2,200 megatonnes (Mt) of CO_2 into the atmosphere annually, about 35 per cent of the continent's total. Rapid market uptake of available and emerging advanced energy-saving technologies could result in a reduction of more than 1,700 Mt by 2030 from emissions projected for that year under a business-as-usual approach.

In terms of end use, residential, commercial, and industrial buildings account for over 60 per cent of GHG emissions in Canada, and most of it occurs in urban areas. For the residential and commercial sectors, energy in buildings is used mostly for heating water and space and for cooling space. Indeed, for residential buildings, these three end uses are responsible for 80 per cent of energy use.

Energy use in residential buildings is influenced by construction materials, shape, and orientation of the building, internal temperature settings, internal use activity, and climate conditions. Urban form also is an important influence. For example, townhouses and apartments are usually more energy efficient than single detached houses. As the National Round Table (NRTEE, 2003c: 20) observed, "overall energy use is inversely related to the density of development: more compact, mixed-use cities, which support greater use of sustainable forms of transportation and less energy-intensive building types, tend to use less energy." More advanced green buildings routinely reduce energy usage by 30, 40, or even 50 per cent over conventional buildings, with the most efficient buildings performing more than 70 per cent better than conventional properties. Despite proven environmental, economic, and health benefits, however, green building today accounts for a small fraction of new home and commercial building construction (Commission for Environmental Cooperation, 2008).

Paul Parker

This residential house in Waterloo, Ontario, features a BIPV (Building Integrated PV 7.6kW system). The system uses roof vents and pipes to draw warm air down through the ground in order to cool it before it re-enters the house, thus avoiding the need for air conditioning. The clothesline on the deck is another example of energy saving.

Waste Management

Various factors affect per capita amounts of waste generated. For residential areas, key factors include demographic characteristics such as household size, age structure, and annual income, as well as type of dwelling unit, geographical location, and time of year (Maclaren, 2010: 385). Some of these factors are affected by urban form. For example, presence or absence of yard wastes influences the amounts and composition produced by households. Apartment dwellers generate lower per capita wastes than single-family dwellings because the former do not have yards and instead often share a common area adjacent to the apartment building.

An integrated approach to waste management strives to divert as much waste as possible away from disposal through the 3Rs: source **reduction**, followed by **reuse**, **recycling** and biological treatment, thermal treatment (usually with energy

MarcusPhoto1/iStockphoto

Paper-recycling depot.

recovery), and land treatment. Energy recovery is often challenging because it involves incinerating waste. Establishing an incinerator facility is usually controversial, since most people are not enthusiastic about having one nearby. The other well-known option is disposal in a landfill site. Finding such sites can also be controversial, since they, along with incinerators, are viewed as LULUs (locally unwanted land uses) that trigger **NIMBY** (not in my backyard) reactions.

Urban Canadians are recycling and composting, but with significant variability (Statistics Canada, 2007b). For example, in Montreal and Calgary, less than one-third of waste is diverted from landfill sites. Toronto diverts just over 40 per cent. In contrast, in Halifax about 55 per cent of waste is diverted and in Markham, Ontario, about 70 per cent. Markham officials attribute its success to collecting recyclable (**blue boxes**) and organic waste (**green bins**) twice as frequently as garbage. Furthermore, Mustapha (2013) reported 61 per cent of households in Canada participated during 2011 in some kind of composting compared to 38 per cent during 1994. Of those, 45 per cent of households stated that they composted kitchen waste while 68 per cent with lawns or gardens composted yard wastes. In census metropolitan areas (each with a total population of at least 100,000 with 50,000 or more in the urban core), the leading CMA composting kitchen and/or yard waste rates were Halifax (93 per cent), Guelph (87 per cent), Kingston (83 per cent), Saint John (83 per cent), St Catharines-Niagara (82 per cent), and Oshawa (80 per cent). By province, the best kitchen and/or yard waste composting rates were in Prince Edward Island (96 per cent), Nova Scotia (94 per cent), Ontario (75 per cent), and British Columbia (64 per cent). The overall Canadian provincial average rate was 61 per cent.

Urban form, transportation, energy, and wastes are closely interrelated. As Kenworthy (2006: 67) noted, "Not only do urban form, transportation systems, and water, waste, and energy technologies have to change, but the value systems and underlying processes for urban governance and planning need to be reformed to reflect a sustainability agenda."

Moving Forward

The National Round Table (NRTEE, 2003c: 31) developed a sustainability checklist for location and site design of buildings which offers useful ideas (Box 13.1).

Environmental Issues in Cities

Air Pollutants

The World Health Organization (2014) reported that, in 2012, about 7 million people died as a result of exposure to air pollution. That means one in eight of total global deaths were due to air pollution. The implication, as noted by the World Health Organization (2014), is that air pollution had become "the world's largest single environmental health risk."

Concentrations of some common air pollutants in Canadian cities have been decreasing. The main reason is stricter regulation of emissions from automobiles combined with enhanced regulations regarding industrial emissions. One anomaly to this trend is ground-level ozone (also referred to as photochemical **smog** or summer smog) created when nitrogen oxides and volatile organic compounds combine in sunlight. There has been a striking increase in the number of "smog advisory days" in many of Canada's major cities,

ENVIRONMENT IN FOCUS

BOX 13.1 | Sustainability Checklist for Location and Site Design of Buildings

Location

- Use of existing buildings in already urbanized areas before new construction on **greenfields** (undeveloped land, as opposed to brownfields, or previously developed properties)
- Easy access to good transit service
- Potential for walking and cycling access by employees and visitors
- Proximity (walking distance) to amenities and services for workers (e.g., restaurants, personal services, and daycare)
- Potential to link to a community energy system
- Potential to contribute to the regeneration of economically depressed urban areas

Site Design

- Maximized building density
- Integration with transit facilities (e.g., covered walkways connecting transit to the facility)
- Facilities (racks and showers) for bicycle riders
- Minimization and appropriate treatment of parking (e.g., creation of underground or structured parking lots; landscaping lots to maintain street frontages)
- Maximized site permeability
- Easy pedestrian access to facilities
- Integration of other uses into facilities (e.g., restaurants, services, amenities, and residences)

Derek Shapton Photography

Sign in Michigan protesting imports of Toronto garbage.

especially in southern Ontario. The principal explanation is more ground-level ozone. Nevertheless, urban outdoor air quality is improving, as indicated in a 2011 report from the World Health Organization (2011) showing urban air quality in Canada as third-best of 91 countries.

Environment Canada and other federal agencies monitor air quality through four measures: fine particulate matter ($PM_{2.5}$), ground-level ozone, sulphur dioxide, and nitrogen dioxide. Respiration and heart rates can be increased by ground-level ozone. Other health problems can be asthma attacks, bronchitis, and emphysema. Children are usually most vulnerable.

Environment Canada et al. (2006: 5) report that at a national level during the period 1990 to 2004, an average annual increase of 0.9 per cent for ozone occurred as well as year-to-year variation. In urban areas, triggers for ozone, such as nitric oxide and volatile organic compounds (VOCs), generated from local emissions, have dropped. The main explanation is improved quality of fuels and better emission control technology in vehicles. Nevertheless, over the same period there was an increasing trend in southern Ontario, which had "the highest concentrations and fastest rise of all regions monitored" (ibid., 6) as well as about 30 per cent of Canada's population. Specifically, southern Ontario experienced an average annual increase of 1.3 per cent in ozone levels. Part of the explanation for this increase is proximity to the industrialized northeastern US, along with prevailing winds that result in long-range transport of ozone and its trigger chemicals.

Environment Canada (2014a) has provided comparative data for Canadian cities with populations over 1 million people (Calgary, Edmonton, Montreal, Ottawa–Gatineau, Toronto, Vancouver) relative to 26 similar-sized cities in the United States, Europe, and Australia. Regarding fine particulate matter, Vancouver had the lowest average concentration in both Canada and internationally, while Calgary had the highest concentration levels in Canada and was similar to Boston and Washington. Vancouver also had the lowest annual average concentration of ground-level ozone in Canada, and was second-lowest in the overall comparator group. In contrast, Toronto had the highest ozone levels in Canada, followed closely by Calgary, and each with a level similar to Prague and Lyon. For sulphur dioxide, Ottawa–Gatineau had the second-lowest level of all urban areas, whereas Toronto had the highest SO_2 in Canada and was similar to Boston and Madrid. Finally, for nitrogen dioxide, Ottawa–Gatineau had the lowest annual average concentration relative to all the cities, while Toronto had the highest concentration in Canada, similar to those in Berlin and Boston.

Urban Heat Island Effect

The **urban heat island** effect occurs due to increased temperatures in core urban areas relative to surrounding areas. It is not uncommon for the temperature in city centres to be 2–6°C higher than nearby rural areas. This effect can be reduced or countered by skilful creation of green areas, given their cooling effect within urban areas. A secondary benefit of reducing the urban heat island effect is a decrease in need for air conditioning of buildings, thereby reducing electricity use. Higher temperatures created by the urban heat island effect can also generate smog and enhance ground-level ozone, neither being confined to the urban area. The smog and ozone can drift to nearby rural areas and in some cases can reduce agricultural productivity, increase health risks, and contribute to triggering tornadoes and thunderstorms.

The urban heat island effect has encouraged "green roof technology," which involves creating a new roof or retrofitting an existing roof with a growing medium for plants, shrubs, or trees. Leaders in this technology include European countries and Japan. A 1°C reduction in the urban heat island effect is estimated to cause significantly reduced demand for electricity for air conditioning and refrigeration, which in turn results in lower GHG releases.

In addition to monitoring for energy savings, proponents of green roofs track their impact on stormwater retention. To deal with water runoff, Portland, Oregon, has used green roofs for some time. Most rain landing on a green roof is absorbed by plants and soil and eventually evaporates or transpires into the atmosphere. Almost all the summer rain in Portland is held by green roofs, and in the fall and spring, retention is between 40 and 50 per cent. In the winter months, retention drops to between 10 and 20 per cent. This retention

ENVIRONMENT IN FOCUS

BOX 13.2 | Human Deaths from Air Pollution

Researchers at the University of British Columbia and the University of Alberta concluded that up to 25,000 premature deaths annually in Canada are due to air pollution, hazardous chemicals, and pesticides. The associated costs to the health-care system are estimated at up to $9.1 billion related to illnesses such as cancers, respiratory diseases, heart problems, and congenital problems associated with pollutants, all with demonstrated connections to environmental contaminants.

They also concluded that such pollutants cause major disabilities and estimated that the types of pollution noted above cause between 1.1 million and 1.8 million "restricted activity days" annually for people with asthma and result in Canadians every year spending between 600,000 and 1.5 million additional days in hospital.

David Boyd, one of the researchers, commented that "In our cultural DNA, we think of Canada as a pristine nation, but this is at odds with our track record on the environment" (Mittelstaedt, 2007). Boyd argued that such deaths, impairments, and costs could be reduced if Canada introduced and enforced more stringent standards regarding air quality, drinking water, food, and consumer products.

significantly reduces peak runoff flows following rain events, reducing localized flooding (Dawson, 2002).

Murphy and Martin (2001: 69–70) observed that "solutions to heat island effects ultimately depend on reductions in energy consumption, pollution, and urban sprawl, but there are mitigation efforts that can work." In that regard, they suggest:

1. Design buildings and neighbourhoods to balance building structures with the geometric shapes and characters of the areas between buildings to reduce the amount of energy hitting the surface of buildings and roadways and thus the amount of energy re-radiated. North–south street orientations reduce the amount of energy reaching roads.
2. Use light-coloured surfaces and less thermally absorptive exterior facing on buildings (but this option reduces the potential for solar-based heating).
3. Provide vegetation surfaces in place of or to shade heat-absorbing surfaces. This can reduce the urban heat island effect by 25 to 80 per cent. However, negative effects can include obstructions to walking, hiding places for assailants, injuries from falling branches, and an increase in pollen and mould that trigger allergies.

Perspectives on the Environment

Urban Heat Island Effect in Canada

Regina and Saskatoon: The night temperatures in the city centres on average are three to four degrees warmer than those in the adjacent countryside. The heat island effect is greatest on calm and cloudless nights, when conditions are best for rural areas to cool more quickly than city surfaces.

—*Encyclopedia of Saskatchewan* (2007)

Winnipeg: The average low temperature at the Forks, in the centre of the city, is 2.73 degrees warmer than at the airport on the edge of the city. The comparable difference for the average warm high temperature is 1.56 degrees.

—Seymour (2007)

Toronto: The average summer temperatures are four to 10 degrees higher in the city centre compared to temperatures in nearby rural communities.

—World Weather Online, Toronto's Climate (n.d.)

In assessing the third option, Murphy and Martin (2001: 70) observe that "Ultimately, the question is about the relative short and long-term risks, costs, and benefits of an ecological mitigation of urban heat island effects versus doing nothing. We believe the cost of doing nothing is greater, especially since the benefits of ecological mitigation go beyond the urban heat island effect."

Hydrological Cycle

Urban areas affect the hydrological cycle regarding both quantity and quality of water.

Regarding quantity, an obvious impact is due to urban infrastructure creating an impervious surface. The implications are twofold. First, expansion of roads and construction of parking lots and buildings results in precipitation running off more quickly, since it is less likely to soak into the soil because of the impervious surface. Second, consequences become (1) surface flooding and (2) reduced recharge of aquifers. Both outcomes have stimulated initiatives to build retention ponds so that water can be collected during rainfalls and allowed to either percolate into the ground or be released

© Ken Josephson

The green roof of the Social Science and Mathematics Building at the University of Victoria is vegetated by native species such as sedums, yarrow, vine maples, sumac, grasses, wild flowers, wild strawberries, and wild rose. The roof results in a reduction of up to 95 per cent of the heat gain and 26 per cent of the heat loss, and adds 10 per cent R-value insulating properties. In terms of water, approximately 30 per cent is used by plants, 30 per cent percolates to aquifers, and 40 per cent is returned to the atmosphere with little to no surface runoff. For a typical urban non-green roof, 5 per cent goes to aquifers, 15 per cent to the atmosphere, and 75 per cent to surface runoff.

more slowly than would otherwise happen. These outcomes are also a reminder that urban sprawl, especially when suburbs are built on aquifer recharge areas such as moraines, can significantly affect the amount of water available in aquifers for human use. The following "International Guest Statement" by Mee Kam Ng highlights how a creative vision for urban waterways can be transformative in improving ecological, economic, and social well-being.

Water quality is negatively affected when pollutants such as oil and gas from vehicles and salt from winter applications (to make driving safer) get washed into surface streams and groundwater systems. The result is degraded water quality, with negative health consequences. Such negative outcomes have been summarized well by the United Nations

Perspectives on the Environment

Road Salt Challenges in Toronto

The GTA (Greater Toronto Area) is one of North America's fastest-growing regions, and serious questions are being raised regarding the environmental sustainability of the anticipated urban growth and the potential long-term impacts on the quality and quantity of ground and surface water resources. Degradation of groundwater quality by NaCl de-icing salt is the primary concern since there are no cost-effective alternatives to NaCl de-icing salt for large-scale use and there is little evidence that salt loadings to the subsurface can be significantly reduced (Howard and Maier, 2007). According to the City of Toronto (2014), the City gets about 130 cm of snow annually, has 1,000 City staff and 600 contractors involved in snow removal, and uses 130,000 to 150,000 tonnes of salt annually.

—Howard and Maier (2007: 147) and City of Toronto (2014)

Population Fund (2007a: 58): "Urban areas can affect water resources and the hydrological cycle . . . through the expansion of roads, parking lots, and other impervious surfaces, which pollute runoff and reduce the absorption of rainwater and aquifer replenishment."

The United Nations Population Fund (2007a) also noted another negative impact "through large-scale hydroelectric installations that help supply urban energy needs." This perspective provides a counterview to those who argue that hydroelectric installations are "clean" in terms of GHG emissions. Hydroelectric dams and reservoirs can inundate significant amounts of habitat, modify downstream flow regimes, and even out natural fluctuations in the hydrological cycle, which can affect both flora and fauna dependent on these fluctuations.

Brownfield Sites

Many cities have a legacy of abandoned or inactive industrial sites. Surface or underground soils can be contaminated through disposal practices accepted in earlier times before people appreciated the long-term consequences. Such contaminated sites are often referred to as **brownfields**.

One specific problem results from LUST, or "leaking underground storage tanks." Industrial sites and garages usually have underground tanks in which materials, including gasoline and chemicals, have been or are stored. While in active use, storage tanks often develop leaks, resulting in some contents being gradually released into surrounding soil. Alternatively, when an industrial plant or garage is closed, it was not uncommon for the contents to be left in the tanks or for the tanks to be

INTERNATIONAL GUEST STATEMENT

Revitalizing Urban Streams | *Mee Kam Ng*

Cheong Gye Cheon (CGC) (literally meaning "clear stream"), a 5.9-kilometre stream spanning an area of 51 km² in the heart of Seoul, South Korea, divides the city into north and south. According to early maps, the stream was fed by 23 tributaries flowing from the mountains around the city. During World War II and the Korean War, squatter settlements had polluted the CGC so much that the government decided in the 1960s to cover it with concrete and a four-lane overpass. The project was hailed as a symbol of modernity in post–World War II South Korea. Decades of subsequent development turned the area into a bustling haven of small businesses, but with a deteriorating urban environment and few green spaces. When the integrity of the aging concrete overpass became a safety concern, a group of professors at Yonsei University advocated restoration of the CGC. Not only did they use their interdisciplinary knowledge to examine the feasibility of demolishing the overpass and uncovering the urban stream, they also engaged a popular Korean novelist to help publicize the dream of restoring the CGC. The politician who adopted this dream as his political agenda won the mayoral election and succeeded in revitalizing the stream within two years. The renovation initiative became so successful and popular that similar projects were undertaken in Taiwan, Singapore, and Chinese cities such as Shenzhen and Guangzhou.

The Seoul experiment highlights the importance of invoking different knowledge domains in pursuing sustainable urban development: *hydrologists and ecologists* who helped understand the drainage system in order to "revitalize" the local hydrological cycle and bring biodiversity back to the dense urban environment; *historians and conservationists* who leveraged the project to revive the cultural and historical heritage of the area, by building of traditional bridges and making the place pedestrian friendly; *civil engineers* who removed the overpass, redirected the stream into a deepened above-ground channel to prevent flooding, and ensure its proper maintenance; *transport engineers* who advised on comprehensive arrangements to divert traffic and provide alternative means of transportation; *urban planners, designers, landscape architects and artists* who themed, designed, and added interest features and art work to different sections of the stream, as well as its connections to the surrounding neighbourhoods; and *politicians, government officials, and non-governmental organizations* forming partnerships and collaborating in the engagement of the general public throughout the planning, designing, and implementing processes.

TwilightShow/iStockphoto

Cheong Gye Cheon, Seoul.

The CGC experiment would be perfect if it had resulted in a revitalized natural stream. Unfortunately, covered box culverts were installed along the stream to intercept rainfall and waste water, which are treated before being pumped back to the CGC to maintain a steady water flow. Hence, while the project is an engineering success, it is not a full ecological restoration of the river. Nevertheless, the CGC revitalization has helped ameliorate the urban heat island effect by lowering the urban temperature. The water and ecological features also add interest and inspiration to the urban experiences of the local residents and numerous visitors.

Subsequent stream revitalization projects in other parts of Asia have tried to incorporate more ecological measures such as biotope or local habitat, to treat and cleanse polluted water. The important lesson is to place the urban stream in the natural context and examine how the whole region can be utilized to retain water and to install sustainable treatment facilities. For instance, localized rainwater can be harvested, cleansed, and retained through design features such as green roofs, vegetated swales, constructed wetlands, sedimentation basins, or even porous urban surfaces to achieve low-impact development. Besides renaturalizing urban streams, the planning and design of any new urban development should respect the drainage system it is embedded in. Natural streams should be retained as part of the urban development and every effort should be made to protect their ecological functions, especially in their riparian habitats.

Revitalizing urban streams reminds us about the importance of adopting a holistic view of the landscape in order to achieve sustainable urban development. Hence, urban stream revitalization needs to be part of a much bigger initiative of making urban development more environmentally friendly. And sustainable development goes beyond environmental concerns. However, some have argued that renaturalizing urban streams is very costly. Others go further to criticize that the restored

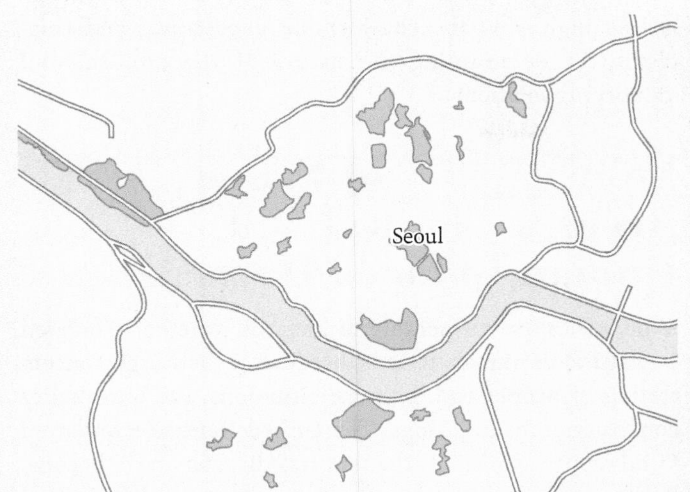

FIGURE 13.1 | Running through the heart of the city, the Cheong Gye Cheon is a prominent feature of Seoul, South Korea.

streamscape amounts to "greenwashing" which tends to increase land and property value and gentrify a place, displacing the poor and disadvantaged. Hence, urban stream revitalization has to be a collective effort by different stakeholders at the local level, not only to caution about and prevent profit-driven gentrification but also to learn and treasure the historical and ecological values and functions of their drainage basin in order to build a sustainable community and a vibrant local economy for the life and livelihood of its diverse residents.

Professor Mee Kam Ng, PhD, is vice-chair of the Department of Geography and Resource Management, the director of the Urban Studies Programme, and associate director of the Institute of Future Cities and the Hong Kong Institute of Asian Pacific Studies at the Chinese University of Hong Kong. She is a member of the Royal Town Planning Institute, a fellow of the Hong Kong Institute of Planners, and an academic adviser of the Hong Kong Institute of Urban Design.

filled with unwanted liquids. Eventually, many would develop leaks. Once out of the tanks, the liquids may move through the soil, often ending up in aquifers. When such aquifers are the source of well water, there is a risk to human health. Or if the contaminants are underneath fields on which crops are grown, the contaminants can be drawn into the plants by their root systems and eventually absorbed by the plant material, which is later consumed by humans or animals.

A similar contamination problem can occur through the burying of uncontained wastes under or on the property of a factory or production facility. The case study of the Sydney Tar Ponds in Chapter 11 highlights the huge cost of remediating large sites. As another example, the municipal government in Kitchener, Ontario, spent about $19 million to remove coal tar from beneath one square block in the centre of the city. The city had operated a coal gasification plant there from 1883 until 1958. Coal was heated in ovens, and the flammable gas was used to heat and light businesses and residences in the central part of the city. During the process of gasification, some coal became an oily tar, commonly called "coal tar." This waste by-product was placed in underground tanks or open pits and then buried under the property.

After the gasification plant was closed, a Canada Post building was constructed over the coal tar site, and roads were built and paved on each side of the old site. Over decades, the buried coal tar gradually seeped laterally through the fine-grained silt beneath the property. Some was discovered under an adjacent property, leading to a $5 million lawsuit against the city. The suit was dropped when the city agreed to remove the coal tar from under the old gasification plant site and purchase the property.

Kitchener ended up paying almost $15 million more than initially estimated for the remediation of the gasification site, an experience highlighting uncertainty involved with such contaminants. The first estimate for the cleanup was $5.6 million. This amount later increased to $9 million and then finally to $19.5 million. The reason for the extra cost? There was much more coal tar and much more of it was hazardous waste than originally estimated.

Initial estimates of the amount and kind of soil contaminated by coal tar were based on test drilling of boreholes between 1986 and 2004. The conclusion was that the contaminated soil was not more than 5.5 metres below the surface. The test drilling also indicated that none of the contaminated soil was hazardous. In estimating remediation costs, the consultants included an allowance of 1,500 tonnes of hazardous waste to be removed in case some was present.

Retention pond.

During May 2006, after work began on building a right-of-way to the site, it was discovered that the coal tar–contaminated soil extended at least 7 metres below the surface. As a result, new boreholes were drilled. The results verified that the contaminated soils extended to 7 metres but also that there were 13 times more hazardous contaminated soils than originally estimated, as well as almost twice as much non-hazardous contaminated soils.

The cost of removing hazardous soils ($156 per tonne) was about three times as much as for disposing of non-hazardous soils ($48.50 per tonne). The hazardous material was trucked to a site in Quebec with the capacity to handle hazardous soil. The remediation was completed during the summer of 2007, and about 2,500 truckloads of contaminated soil were removed.

Another unanticipated cost emerged. CDI College operated from a building near the remediated property. Students attending the college complained about the smell associated with the cleanup, and stated they experienced dizziness and nausea. CDI College, later renamed Everest College, initiated a lawsuit in April 2009 against the city for $800,000, plus interest and court costs, arguing the remediation had created "significant negative publicity" as a result of the "toxic nature" of the material being removed and also caused the college to be closed for two weeks. The College argued that its enrolment dropped and it lost nearly half a million dollars in tuition revenue. The lawsuit focused only on the inconvenience and impact, not on health matters.

In early February 2012, the City of Kitchener and Everest College jointly announced a settlement. Terms of the settlement were not provided, as both parties signed a confidentiality agreement.

The above example illustrates that the presence of brownfield sites within urban areas can be a major challenge. It also highlights the considerable uncertainty and complexity in determining the nature of the problem and identifying solutions.

Coal tar cleanup in Kitchener, Ontario.

Vulnerability of Urban Areas to Natural and Human-Induced Hazards

Many cities are vulnerable to hazards, whether triggered by natural or human actions, because of their high concentration of people and, in some situations, the low-quality construction of buildings. The United Nations Population Fund (2007a: 59) states that natural disasters have become both more frequent and more severe since 1990. The United Nations International Strategy for Disaster Reduction (2004: 59) further stated that more than 75 per cent of the 100 largest cities in the world are vulnerable to at least one natural hazard. And Gencer (2013: 12–13) reported that climate change is likely to increase exposure to hazards for many urban areas, especially those located adjacent to coasts due to rising sea level and associated coastal flooding, as well as heightened intensity and frequency of climatic events (e.g., extreme cold and heat as well as heavy rain and flash floods).

Canadians experience many natural disasters. Geophysical hazards such as earthquakes have stayed constant over the past 60 years, but weather-associated hazards have increased dramatically. Environment Canada (2003c: 2) has noted that the following factors make us vulnerable: population growth, urbanization, environmental degradation (e.g., removing timber from hillsides, leading to landslides), urban sprawl in hazard-prone areas, loss of collective memory about hazardous events because of increased mobility, aging infrastructure, and historical overdependence on technological solutions. Specifically, Environment Canada (ibid.) observed that "Higher concentrations of people living in urban areas mean that if disasters hit, they affect a larger number of individuals. Urban sprawl has led to more development in high-risk areas, such as flood plains."

McBean and Henstra (2003) provide further information and insight on why urban Canada is susceptible to hazards. One core factor is that about 60 per cent of Canadians live in urban areas of 100,000 or more people and about 80 per cent in cities of 10,000 or more. Earthquakes are a significant hazard, with the most vulnerable areas in British Columbia and the St Lawrence Valley. However, in their view, "about 80 per cent of the impacts are due to weather and weather-related hazards." Weather hazards include tornadoes, hailstorms, winter storms, and heat waves, while what are termed "weather-related hazards" are drought, storm surges, floods, and moving ice. In terms of specific weather and weather-related hazards, the probability of tornadoes and hailstorms is highest on the Prairies and in southern Ontario, storm surges are most frequent along the Atlantic coast, and winter storms are ubiquitous.

Godschalk (2003) has argued that resilient cities are most likely to be able to cope with natural hazards. Citing Foster (1997), Godschalk (2003: 139) suggested that characteristics of resilience include independence, diversity, renewability, and functional redundancy, along with "reserve capacity," achieved by duplication, interchangeability, and interconnections. Regarding such characteristics, Godschalk suggested resilient systems tend to be:

- *Redundant*, by having various functionally similar components so the entire system does not falter if one component fails
- *Diverse*, by containing several functionally different components to protect a system from threats
- *Autonomous*, by having capacity to function independently from external controls
- *Interdependent*, by ensuring system parts are connected and able to support one another
- *Adaptable*, through the ability to learn from experience and change
- *Collaborative*, by creating multiple opportunities and incentives for stakeholder engagement

The above principles provide a checklist against which a strategy for disaster resilience can be reviewed. In her "Domestic Guest Statement," Meg Holden provides further insight regarding resilient thinking for cities.

DOMESTIC GUEST STATEMENT

Managing for Urban Resilience: Recovery, Resistance, and "Bouncing Forward"

Meg Holden

In Chapter 1, the concept of resilience is examined. In his "Domestic Guest Statement" in that chapter, Ryan Plummer refers to the valuable role of resilience thinking in the context of watershed management and in other fields. In Canadian cities, too, resilience is taking over from other imperatives of planning and environmental management, such as climate change and urban sustainability. For good reason: it does not carry the political baggage of "climate change," which politicians can dispute endlessly and protest, "If we didn't break the climate, it isn't our job to fix it!"

Resilience shifts our thinking from disputable causes to our speed and effectiveness in responding to major disruptive events, sometimes called X-events (Casti, 2012), when they occur. Any responsible leader needs to act to save lives, infrastructure, and property when disaster strikes. Cities (meaning census metropolitan areas and census agglomerations, in Statistics Canada terms) are home to 82 per cent of Canadians. Cities and regions are responsible for crucial drinking water, local roads and transportation systems, storm and wastewater systems, and sewer infrastructure—the built structures of the city that we take for granted, until disruption cuts them off from our use (Canadian Infrastructure Report Card, 2012). In terms of resilience, these structures and systems that ensure our access to these essentials in the case of emergency are our anchors in the face of uncomfortable and disruptive change.

Canadians are coming to expect the unexpected, as we have lived through disasters such as the 2013 floods in Toronto and Calgary, Hurricane Juan that ripped up Halifax in 2003, the 1998 ice storm that left 1.2 million Canadians in eastern Ontario and Quebec in the dark for a week in January, not to mention Superstorm Sandy in 2012 and Hurricane Katrina in 2005, south of the border. The speed and effectiveness of cities' responses makes a huge difference to loss and preservation of life, property, and public infrastructure. What resilience thinking should also spur in urban environmental management is preparedness for disruptions and changes before they occur—resistance as well as recovery.

Many Canadian cities are pursuing resilience thinking and management. Approaches include resilience-asset mapping toward city-wide networks of resilience nodes related to different kinds of emergency events, visualizations of what different future scenarios of shocks and disruptions might entail, seeking information on the resilience capacity of neighbourhoods and communities, educating and coordinating volunteers prepared to mobilize when called upon in extreme events, and even creating a new job title, resilience manager, responsible for instituting systems-based resilience thinking. For an example of application of resilience thinking in Canada, visit the Rockefeller Foundation 100 Resilient Cities Project website to read about the approach in Montreal, the one Canadian city in the project (http://www.100resilientcities.org/cities/entry/montreal#/-_/).

Resilience management often means preparations, adaptations, and built-in "safe failure" of infrastructure, systems, and institutions. "Safe failure" means, for example, building underground parking structures that can serve as storm sewer overflow when all other systems fail, without risk to life or irretrievable damage. Resilience also can refer to response systems to longer-term urban trends, and a systems-oriented rather than linear approach to understanding risk and threats.

Continued

This kind of approach can be found in isolated instances long before the popularity of "resilience" as a planning concept. In Toronto, Hurricane Hazel in 1954 flooded the city's extensive ravine network, damaging neighbourhoods within the flood zone and killing 81 people. The long-term response was to ban new residential development in the ravines and to create the Toronto and Region Conservation Authority to maintain them (Fulford, 1996). Future waves of resilience thinking have led to additional innovative uses of the ravines, including the repurposing of an old brick factory as Evergreen Brickworks, a multipurpose environmental education, recreational, and conference facility, depicted below.

In Canada's northern communities, by contrast, melting permafrost is one prominent effect of climate change, causing extensive damage to roads, buildings, and other infrastructure. Adaptation strategies to permafrost instability in the North begin with infrastructure risk and vulnerability assessments, particularly for critical infrastructure, and scientific inventories of permafrost information, including different strategies for building and infrastructure construction and maintenance on permafrost (Governments of Nunavut, Northwest Territories, and Yukon, 2011). In the energy domain, district energy is considered to increase local resilience, as a solution that allows neighbourhoods to meet energy needs without reliance on the public energy grid.

More than the physical side of resilience needs attention. When talking about socio-ecological resilience in cities, we need to think about fostering and supporting social cohesion as a key means for people to prepare for disruptions—and to avoid loss when systems and institutions fail. Social cohesion represents people's ability to function and come together in a time of crisis to meet one another's daily needs.

A resilience approach to urban environmental management may also have a dark side. When our goal is resilience to threats and disruptions, are we forced to sacrifice visions of transformative change, or change to structures, systems, and institutions that will disrupt the status quo but ultimately be rewarding? For example, increasing urban density may reduce resilience when we consider the difficult task of organizing and evacuating large groups in time of disaster, the greater likelihood of spread of contagious disease in high-density environments, and the tendency for high-density living environments to lack the same social cohesion of lower-density and smaller-scale communities. At the same time, from a sustainability perspective, increasing urban density and social mix in communities have long been key planning goals to protect environmental resources and habitats, and even to offer culturally richer, more vibrant neighbourhoods.

Which priorities should prevail, if we want to build and maintain resilient communities that are able not merely to "bounce back" from disaster but also to "bounce forward" to more sustainable futures?

Courtesy of Meg Holden

Evergreen Brickworks, in Toronto, exemplifies an approach to building urban resilience through creative reuse of old buildings and infrastructure, such as an old brick factory at the bottom of the ravine, and incorporates green features for "safe failure" in times of flood.

Courtesy of Meg Holden

Meg Holden, PhD, is associate professor of Urban Studies and Geography at Simon Fraser University in Vancouver. Dr. Holden's published research crosses the domains of urban and social sustainability, sustainability and climate change policy and planning, sustainability and environmental assessment, and investigation of urban environmental pragmatism and social and policy learning. She also works within the realm of applied policy research and practice in the service of sustainable cities, particularly in the realm of sustainability assessment, measurement, and monitoring.

The following two subsections illustrate in more detail hazards that can be experienced by urban dwellers, and responses. We suggest you consider how the resilience characteristics outlined immediately above could be used to reflect on immediate responses and longer-term thinking about how to cope with them.

Hurricane Katrina and New Orleans; Superstorm Sandy and the Eastern Seaboard

About 65 per cent of urban areas with populations of 5 million or more are located in low-elevation coastal areas throughout the world. A striking example of a low-elevation coastal area damage from a natural disaster occurred on 29 August 2005 when Hurricane Katrina hit the Gulf coast of the United States. More than 2,800 people died, thousands of homes were destroyed, and hundreds of thousands were left homeless. New Orleans received the greatest damage, but almost 10 million people living in the Gulf coast states of Alabama, Louisiana, and Mississippi were affected by Katrina. In southeast Louisiana alone, 90 per cent of residents were evacuated.

In New Orleans, with slightly less than 50 per cent of the city below sea level, about 80 per cent was flooded two days after the hurricane struck, with some areas under 5 metres of water. Much flooding occurred because the levees built over four decades to provide flood protection had been breached. Levee construction had started in 1965 and was scheduled to be completed in 2015. The Superdome stadium became a "refuge of last resort," and by the evening of 28 August 20,000 to 25,000 people were staying there.

Human behaviour contributed to problems. Notwithstanding the mandatory evacuation order, many stayed in New Orleans, citing various reasons: belief that their homes were adequately protected, lack of access to transportation or sufficient money to leave, and conviction that it was necessary to "guard" their homes and possessions. Unfortunately, the third reason was valid. Within a day of Hurricane Katrina making landfall, violence and looting spread throughout many areas of New Orleans. Those who remained in their homes often became stranded when flood waters had risen. Clean water was not available from the municipal water system, and power outages were common. Significant time and resources were needed to remove stranded people.

What was learned? In November 2009, a federal judge stated that significant flooding had occurred because of negligence of the US Army Corps of Engineers, mainly responsible for the protective levees. Early in 2010, the federal government allocated billions of dollars for city hospitals and schools. A new city master plan was in place by the summer of 2010, and businesspeople were starting new businesses at a rate above the national average.

Associated Press (2014) reported that prior to Hurricane Katrina the population of New Orleans was about 484,000 people; by 2012 it was 360,400. The year after Katrina, over 70,000 people were living in Federal Emergency Management Agency (FEMA) trailers; by 2012, no one was living in FEMA trailers. Before Katrina, the US Army Corps of Engineers was upgrading flood defences to protect against a Category 3 hurricane. By 2012, the corps had mostly completed $14 billion worth of flood defences to provide protection against a Category 3 hurricane (Table 13.1).

The death toll in Louisiana related to the hurricane was 1,836 people, with 71 per cent being 60 years or older. In terms of economic costs, Amadeo (2014) reported that estimated total damage was between $96 and $125 billion (US), of which $40 to $66 billion were insured losses. Half the losses were from flooding in New Orleans, where 300,000 homes were estimated to have been destroyed or made uninhabitable, and a minimum of 505 million m^3 of debris had been created. A massive cleanup effort was required. Another estimate of losses, including the above damages plus disruption to 18 per cent of US oil production, impact on the Louisiana sugar crop, and general impact on national economic growth, was up to $250 billion.

New Orleans was severely flooded following Hurricane Katrina in August 2005.

On Halloween in 2012, Superstorm Sandy landed on the East Coast of the US. Amadeo (2014) reported that it caused $50 billion in damages. It was estimated that more than 650,000 homes were damaged or destroyed, with 8 million people losing power due to flooding of power stations and fallen trees breaking power lines. The New York Stock Exchange was closed for two days, the first two-day closure since 1888. About 50 million people were placed at risk, with 72 people dying as a direct result of the storm. A further

TABLE 13.1 | Saffir-Simpson Hurricane Scale and Wind Speeds (km/hour)

Category 1	119 to 153
Category 2	154 to 177
Category 3	178 to 208
Category 4	209 to 251
Category 5	252 and higher

Superstorm Sandy destroyed Casino Pier in Seaside Heights, New Jersey, causing the Jet Star roller coaster to fall into the Atlantic Ocean.

87 people died due to hypothermia from loss of power, carbon monoxide, or accidents.

This storm was a combination of a season's end Category 1 hurricane, a cold front, and a second storm, which led to torrential rain plus snow. The storm also hit land during a full moon, contributing to higher storm surges. The storm surge affected 965 kilometres along the Eastern Seaboard, with wind speeds as high as 128 km/hour. Waves almost 5 metres high crashed onto Battery Park in Lower Manhattan, and over 80 per cent of Atlantic City was covered by water. Amadeo stated that over 15,000 flights into New York and other Eastern Seaboard airports were cancelled, and all three New York City airports were closed. The subway system in New York was closed due to seawater flooding, the first time in 108 years of its operations. MTA bus systems also were shut down, along with AMTRAK trains.

Sandy was the second-most damaging storm in US history, following Hurricane Katrina. Prior to Sandy, the second-most damaging storm had been Hurricane Andrew, a Category 5 storm which affected Florida during 1995 and caused $55 billion in property destruction and damage. In contrast, Hurricane Hazel which affected Toronto in 1954 was a Category 4 storm and killed 81 Canadians and 95 Americans.

While Hurricane Katrina and Superstorm Sandy were extreme natural disasters, they emphasize that humans often are vulnerable because of where they live and work, sometimes by choice but more often because they have no alternatives or the means to relocate to a safer geographical area. Individuals living or working adjacent to rivers or shorelines are at risk of floods, just as those living in snow-prone areas are vulnerable to severe winter storms. The key message is that, as a species, humans have choices and often have not been attentive enough to the risks posed by natural hazards. Individually, those who suffer the greatest harm are often people from the lower rungs of society or in poorer countries—those living in substandard housing that cannot withstand an earthquake; those living in rural and low-lying areas with insufficient infrastructure to ameliorate flooding; those who have no way of escaping disaster before it strikes; and/or those living in a trailer park when a tornado sweeps through.

Earthquake and Haiti

Another dramatic example was the earthquake in Haiti on the late afternoon of 12 January 2010, with a magnitude of 7.0 on the Richter scale (Box 13.3). The epicentre was about 25 kilometres west of Port-au-Prince. This earthquake was the most powerful to hit Haiti in 200 years, and the impact was devastating. More than 230,000 people were killed, 180,000 homes were destroyed, and total damage was estimated to be between $7.9 and $11.5 billion (US).

More than 1.5 million people were left without homes, and were moved into 1,100 camps with limited water and sanitation services. Subsequent storms and floods created further challenges for those in the camps. Four years after the quake, tents and makeshift shelters continued to be home for 150,000 people.

The international community responded. However, getting support to those in need was challenging because infrastructure had been badly damaged. For example, air traffic control capacity was disrupted, as were ports and roads. Hospitals and communication systems were damaged. Regarding communications, social networking sites such as Facebook and Twitter became major conduits for many. Insufficient morgue facilities created difficulties, leading to mass burials. Confusion also occurred related to coordination and leadership of the overall relief effort, given the many foreign governments and NGOs involved.

Another challenge arose when a cholera outbreak began in October 2010. It extended across the entire country and caused 8,500 deaths as well as another 690,000 people to become ill. It was not determined how cholera was introduced

Haiti's 7.0-magnitude earthquake in January 2010 devastated this Caribbean country. (a) The destroyed capital city, Port-au-Prince. (b) Containing the crowds displaced by the earthquake.

ENVIRONMENT IN FOCUS

BOX 13.3 | Richter Scale

Earthquake severity is measured by *magnitude* (amount of energy released at the hypocentre of an earthquake, measured through the amplitude of earthquake waves) and *intensity* (observed effect of movement of the ground on people, buildings, and natural landscape features). The **Richter scale**, developed in 1935, is a measure of magnitude.

The Richter scale is logarithmic, which means that a whole-number increase (e.g., from 5 to 6) represents a tenfold increase in magnitude. Expressed in terms of energy released, the difference between two whole numbers is 31 times more energy. Earthquakes with a Richter number of up to 2.0 are not normally noticed by people and are only recorded on local seismographs. Quakes with a magnitude of 4.5 or higher are detected by seismographs around the world, and several thousand such events occur annually. Exceptionally high-magnitude earthquakes measure 8.0 or higher, and on average one such event happens each year. Examples are the 1906 earthquake in San Francisco, with an estimated Richter number of 8.3, the "Good Friday" earthquake centred in Alaska in 1964, which measured 8.6 and affected the west coast of British Columbia and Vancouver Island, and the 7.9 quake in Mindanao, Philippines, in 1976. Damage from an 8.0 earthquake usually extends over at least 300 kilometres. Theoretically, there is no upper limit to the Richter scale, but the largest measured events have been between 8.8 and 9.0. The movement of the earth due to a high-magnitude earthquake can cause serious damage and disruption, but often more damage is caused by fires triggered by ruptured gasoline lines and similar incidents. Most property damage in San Francisco after the 1906 earthquake was from fire.

Source: United States Geological Survey (2013).

into the country, but one possibility was that it was introduced by UN peacekeeping troops from Nepal. Donors have since promised $2.2 billion over 10 years to resolve conditions that triggered the outbreak. The focus will be upon improving sanitation, access to drinking water, and basic medical infrastructure.

The initial response focused on search and rescue, with support from sniffer dogs and high-tech heat sensors. Many foreign countries provided aid, and the initial needs were for food, water, medical supplies, and temporary shelters. Attention was also given to maintenance of law and order, so that aid could be distributed efficiently and equitably. In the longer term, about three-quarters of damaged buildings received inspections and then repairs, and 200,000 individuals received money or food after they worked on clearing away rubble and related work.

The capacity in Haiti to respond after the quake was limited. The nation has long been the poorest in the western hemisphere, and was ranked 149th out of 182 countries on the Human Development Index. As a result, many people were living in poverty prior to the quake. For example, before the quake some 70 per cent of the residents of Port-au-Prince lived in slums. Furthermore, building regulations did not exist, and many buildings had been constructed with poor workmanship and cheap materials. And no action plans had been developed to respond to earthquake damage.

Further challenges arose because basic infrastructure (e.g., roads, ports, fuel depots) was damaged. In addition, many key agencies—domestic and international—had lost staff and facilities because of the earthquake. When the United Nations launched an initial appeal for $575 million for emergency aid, the international community responded generously. Many countries sent rescue, relief, and medical workers. However, the influx of so many people from outside of Haiti created coordination challenges. Furthermore, arrival of aid workers who needed places to live pushed up rents. One result was that Haitians in the camps could not afford to move out because they could not afford the higher rents. It was also observed that, because foreign aid teams concentrated their facilities adjacent to the temporary camps, locals were encouraged to stay in the camps in order to have ready access to support.

During October 2013, the Haitian government announced its first national housing policy, with a goal to resolve the shortage of 500,000 new homes needed by 2020. A related challenge is to resolve landownership issues, since many Haitians do not have land titles and much land is controlled by a relatively few large landowners. No credible land registry system exists.

In March 2010, major donors committed $9 billion for a five-year reconstruction and development plan, to be supervised by the World Bank and to be overseen by a disaster management group co-chaired by former US President Bill Clinton and the prime minister of Haiti. One priority will be to construct earthquake- and hurricane-resistant homes, schools, and hospitals. Another initiative will be to provide education and training related to what to do during an earthquake or hurricane, since it was determined many Haitians did not know where to find safe places during the quake (Thomson Reuters, n.d.; Muskett, 2014).

Implications

Regarding earthquakes in Canada, Environment Canada (2003c: 3–4) has observed that:

> Although the only significant earthquake in Canada occurred off the east coast in 1929, triggering a tsunami that killed 28 people [on Newfoundland's Burin Peninsula], scientists predict that an earthquake in the Vancouver area is the most likely major disaster on our horizon. Since quakes occur where tectonic plates converge, only certain regions of the country are at risk: the West Coast, the St. Lawrence and Ottawa valleys, off the coast of Nova Scotia and Newfoundland, and certain parts of the Arctic.

What is the nature of risk from natural hazards in your community? To what extent is there awareness of natural hazards on the part of residents in your community? What are the main mitigation measures in place? What might be "next steps" to protect residents, buildings, and infrastructure? Which steps would best reflect the six characteristics developed by Godschalk and the ideas about resilience presented by Holden provided earlier in this chapter?

Inco's Superstack in Sudbury, Ontario, built to address issues of air pollution.

Urban Sustainability

In this section, we turn our attention to cities or communities taking action to establish an urban sustainability trajectory.

Sudbury, Ontario: Remediating Mined Landscapes

Located about 400 kilometres north of Toronto, Greater Sudbury at one time was "notorious across the country for the air pollution and the barren, blackened landscape created by its smelters" (Richardson et al., 1989, 4). Starting in the 1970s, however, initiatives began to rehabilitate its landscape and restructure the economy.

Sudbury was established in the early 1880s as a construction camp for the Canadian Pacific Railway. During building of the railway, copper and nickel deposits were discovered a few kilometres north of the construction camp. The camp evolved into a mining community, and Sudbury became the second-largest producer of nickel in the world. In addition to Sudbury, other mining communities such as Falconbridge were established in the 30 × 60–kilometre Sudbury basin (Figure 13.2).

ENVIRONMENT IN FOCUS

BOX 13.4 | LEED and CBIP

LEED stands for the Leadership in Energy and Environmental Design Green Building Rating System. It is a national standard, established in the US, related to the design, construction, and operation of "high-performance green buildings."

LEED provides benchmarks for performance related to five factors affecting human and environmental health: (1) sustainable site development; (2) water savings; (3) energy efficiency; (4) materials selection; and (5) indoor environmental quality.

CBIP, or the Commercial Building Initiative Program of Natural Resources Canada, is based on experience that new buildings can be designed to reduce significantly overall energy consumption. Performance better than 25 per cent above the minimum requirements specified in the Model National Energy Code for Buildings (MNECB) is a common target in the marketplace.

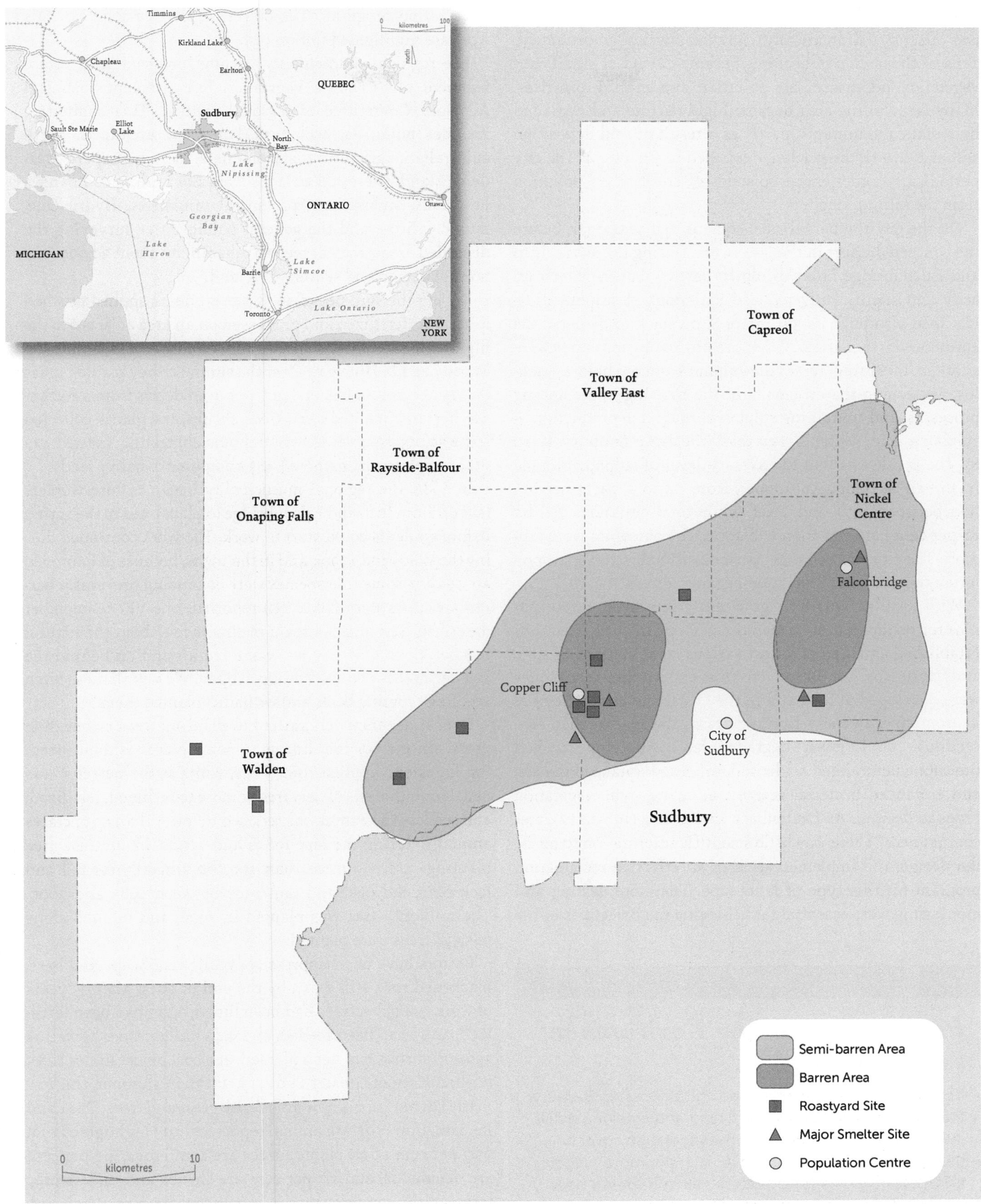

FIGURE 13.2 | Sudbury: Extent of barren and semi-barren landscape.

Source: Lautenbach (1985: 4). Copyright © 1995, Springer-Verlag New York Inc.

Strong economic growth, based on the mining industry, was offset by a dramatically degraded physical environment. Tens of thousands of hectares became devoid of significant vegetation because of air pollution and mining practices. Many lakes in the area became highly acidic and degraded by metal contaminants, partly as a result of acid deposition associated with the smelter, described in Chapter 4. The city periodically experienced episodes of choking air pollution from the mining smelters.

On the environmental side, some initiatives began before the concerted effort in the late 1970s. During the 1970s, Inco and Falconbridge Ltd. shut down part of their smelter capacity and significantly reduced emissions of sulphur dioxide. Inco also built its 381-metre Superstack to disperse the emissions farther afield. Other ore-processing measures were adopted, including "removing sulphur from ore before smelting, increasing the efficiency of the roasting and smelting processes, and containing sulphur through the production of sulphuric acid, which is then sold" (Clean Air Sudbury, 2005: 8). The result was that the average level of sulphur dioxide in the air at Sudbury dropped from 54 to 5 parts per billion between 1971 and 2002, while total emissions fell by 88 per cent between 1960 and 2002. The outcomes were tangible. The city was no longer periodically subjected to air pollution fumigations. Vegetation began to return.

With local air quality significantly improved, opportunities for restoration presented themselves. In 1971, scientists established small plots to test various combinations of soils and plant species. Based on this experience, techniques were developed at Inco and in the Department of Biology at Laurentian University to grow grass, clover, and then tree seedlings on formerly degraded land. Applying crushed limestone neutralized acidic soil, inhibited uptake of metals, and enhanced bacterial activity, allowing some vegetation types to do well. As Lautenbach and others (1995: 112) later commented: "There was little scientific information to guide the design and implementation of an effective reclamation program for this type of landscape. Therefore, testing and monitoring were essential for achieving the objectives of the reclamation program." The objectives and outcomes of this work are highlighted in Box 13.5.

The regional municipality became involved with establishment of VETAC—a Vegetation Enhancement Technical Advisory Committee of regional council. This committee includes botanists, ecologists, landscape architects, horticulturalists, agriculturalists, planners, fisheries experts, gardeners, and interested citizens from the mining companies, university and college, provincial ministries, Hydro One, municipalities, and the general public. After surveying the degraded areas, they agreed to rehabilitate about 30,000 hectares of barren and semi-barren land.

During the summer of 1978, 174 students applied crushed limestone, fertilizer, and grass seed on an area adjacent to the highway close to the airport and on another area beside the Trans-Canada Highway. Over the summer, they planted grass on 115 hectares of barren land; removed debris from a further 206 hectares; planted 6,000 trees, shrubs, and plants; collected some 30,000 samples for pH and nutrient testing; created 122 new test plots; and gathered 365 kilograms of native seeds.

In 1982, the regional municipality began to hire workers laid off from Inco and Falconbridge to plant trees in the spring before students could start to work. The work continued during the 1980s and 1990s, and in the 1990s, because of improved air quality, some tree species were colonizing previously barren areas. As Ross (2001: 60) reported, one VETAC member described how amazed team members felt about the natural regeneration: "One day we wandered around up behind the smelter, and our mouths dropped open. We saw all these birch seedlings coming back, and we hadn't planted them."

Over time, emphasis shifted to planting trees rather than grass, since trees could grow in some places without needing limestone applied first. Thus, while at the outset it was usual for hundreds of hectares or more to be limed, fertilized, and seeded, the extent was reduced to fewer than 50 hectares annually during the late 1980s and 1990s. In contrast, tree plantings grew to more than 100,000 annually for red and Jack pine, red oak, and tamarack between 1983 and 2000. The millionth tree was planted in 1990, and in 1998 alone 985,574 trees were planted.

Results have been impressive. While slag heaps and bare, blackened rock still exist, by the end of 2013, after 35 years of work, 3,445 hectares had been limed, 3,217 had been fertilized, 3,145 had been seeded, and 9.42 million trees as well as 159,496 shrubs had been planted, at a cost of just under $28.5 million (City of Greater Sudbury, 2013). In summer, this formerly barren land is now green with grass and trees. The Land Reclamation Program annual report for 2013 highlighted that 93.7 per cent of all planted trees are coniferous, 4.6 per cent are deciduous, and 1.7 per cent are shrubs and understorey trees. Of the coniferous trees, 75 per cent are pines (Jack, red, and white), while red oak trees represent 48.3 per cent of the hardwoods, followed by black locust (28 per cent) and maple

Perspectives on the Environment

Sudbury Barrens

Barrens: The areas within the City of Greater Sudbury that were impacted by past mining and smelting activities, resulting in virtually all of the vegetation cover being destroyed. Semi-barrens have slightly more vegetation cover than barrens, but are still considered heavily impacted.

—Greater Sudbury (2010: 1)

ENVIRONMENT IN FOCUS

BOX 13.5 | Objectives of the Grassing and Reforestation Activities in Sudbury

The objectives were to:

- Create a self-sustaining ecosystem requiring minimal maintenance
- Use plant species tolerant of acidic soils and low nutrient concentrations
- Use seed application rates allowing for natural colonization and thus increase species diversity
- Give preference to use of native species
- Restore nutrient cycles and pools by using species that fix nitrogen (legumes)
- Use species that attract and provide cover for wildlife
- Undertake initiatives that accelerate natural successional changes

(9.7 per cent). The aim has been to plant species believed to be main components of the original forests.

Given that the remediation initiative has been in part a research project, results have been documented. Monitoring was started during the early years regarding the survival and growth of tree seedlings, as was tracking the biodiversity/forest floor transplant plots. Identification of future planting sites was also systematically developed. Newer monitoring initiatives have included establishment of plots to evaluate the health of shrubs, long-term survival, and spring versus fall planting success, as well as wetland assessment and selection of future potential seed collection sites (Land Reclamation Program, 2007: 8).

Other benefits have emerged. Almost a century after elk disappeared from the local landscape, more than 150 were reintroduced and appear to be thriving in their traditional habitat south of Sudbury. Following an absence of 30 years, pairs of peregrine falcons now nest in Sudbury, and during the spring of 2000 a pair of trumpeter swans hatched cygnets.

Perspectives on the Environment

Biodiversity and Ecological Recovery in Sudbury

During 2009, a Greater Sudbury Biodiversity Partnership was created by 26 organizations (http://www.greatersudbury.ca/living/environmental-initiatives/biodiversity/). Its purpose is to facilitate information sharing, broader participation through group activities, and public awareness and education on biodiversity issues.

In the same year, a Biodiversity Action Plan was developed related to ecological recovery in the Greater Sudbury area. The plan (see above website), revised in January 2012, provides a vision and prioritizes goals for ecological recovery.

The positive results outlined above have attracted recognition for Sudbury. Among the 10 awards Sudbury has received from within Canada are the Lieutenant-Governor's Conservation Award from the Council of Ontario and an award from Canadian Land Reclamation. Outside Canada, Sudbury has been recognized through a United Nations Local Government Honours Award, an award from the Society for Ecological Restoration and a finalist certificate for the Bremen [Germany] Partnership Award for Global Responsibilities Through Local Action.

Perspectives on the Environment

Importance of Science and Community Involvement

The science isn't really complicated. First lime is scattered onto the soil to help deal with the acidity. And then fertilizer is added to provide the nutrients that plants need. In the first four to five years of research, Keith Winterhalder [Laurentian University professor and former VETAC chairman] and his colleagues learned what were effective mixtures of lime and fertilizer, what grasses would provide cover, what trees would survive and how best to plant them.

Everything had to be done by hand, by armies of people carrying bags of lime. And after that was done, they would walk the land with bags of grass and fertilizer.

Getting the community involved is what has sustained the program. About 25 per cent of the trees have been planted by community groups—Scouts, schools, Lions and Rotary Clubs. Some groups volunteer over and over again.

The continuity of individuals, their determination, and the recognition that everyone would work has helped make the project succeed.

—David Pearson, founding director of Science North, quoted in *Viewpoint: Perspectives on Modern Mining* (2008: 3, 4)

Best Practice for Urban Environmental Management

In the following subsections, best practice related to urban environmental management is highlighted. To begin, we present four of 10 principles in the Melbourne Principles for Sustainable Cities (United Nations Environment Programme, 2002), developed in April 2002 and endorsed at the 2002 Earth Summit in Johannesburg. They are:

- Recognize and build on distinctive characteristics of cities, including their human and cultural values, history and natural systems
- Empower people and foster participation: specifically, "Empowering people mobilises local knowledge and resources and enlists the support and active participation of all who need to be involved at all stages, from long-term planning to implementation of sustainable solutions."
- Expand and enable cooperative networks to work toward a common, sustainable future
- Provide a long-term vision for cities based on sustainability, intergenerational, social, economic, and political equity, and their individuality

The above principles offer a general direction to create sustainable and resilient cities, and also incorporate the ideas of Gencer (2013), provided earlier.

Complementary operational guidelines have been developed by the Canada Mortgage and Housing Corporation (CMHC, 2005: 1) regarding "smart growth" for cities, or in its words, "land use and development practices that limit costly urban sprawl, use tax dollars more efficiently, and create more livable communities." CMHC (2005: 2) uses the following "indicators" to assess whether a municipality is using smart-growth principles:

- Promote denser, mixed-use development in greenfield areas
- Intensify the existing fabric to moderate greenfield development
- Take advantage of specific intensification opportunities
- Increase transportation choice and reduce car usage
- Increase supply of new affordable housing
- Improve range of housing types
- Preserve agricultural lands
- Preserve lands essential for maintaining regional ecosystem functions
- Direct employment to strengthen the core and designated sub-centres
- Provide infrastructure to reduce ecological impacts of development

In the following five subsections, we consider spatial scale, parks and pathways, air quality, waste management, and transportation. Earlier in the chapter, we examined urban form or structure in some detail. In the final subsection, we review approaches in Vancouver, Calgary, Montreal, and Moncton.

Spatial Scale

The United Nations Population Fund (2007a: 53) noted that:

> fragmentation of the urban territory brings both administrative inefficiency and environmental setbacks. The boundaries of the city's administration rarely coincide with its actual area of influence. . . . Without some sort of regional entity, the administration of key services, such as water and transport, that cut across different boundaries, is very difficult. By the same token, fragmentation breaks up the contiguity that natural processes require. Fragmentation also makes it difficult to protect ecologically fragile areas or regulate for environmental integrity.

The challenges outlined by the UN Population Fund have been recognized for many years but are still difficult to overcome. Boundaries of urban municipalities usually reflect administrative or political, not ecological, considerations. For example, the cities of Ottawa in Ontario and Gatineau in Quebec are across from each other on opposite sides of the Ottawa River. Their urban boundaries do not reflect the reality that both are within the Ottawa River basin.

The most common way to achieve an ecosystem approach is by a "regional authority" based on landscape features to assist managers in considering the larger ecosystem within which a city is located. This is not a perfect solution, but is a first step. For instance, many cities within a region are often reluctant to give up their authority or autonomy. This can subsequently lead to conflicts and requires a high level of capacity to facilitate cooperation and negotiation.

Perspectives on the Environment

Importance of Spatial Scale for Governance Arrangements

In any dispute it is useful to ask about which interests and which processes are involved. The watershed scale is especially useful here, as it allows us to combine the biophysical and social dimensions of the resource, to highlight both their interdependencies and the cumulative layers of political involvement.

—Clancy (2014: 203)

Parks and Pathways

Public parks and pathways in urban areas contribute to physical fitness and well-being of residents. In addition, urban trees and other vegetation filter air pollutants, moderate the urban heat island effect, and help to enhance water quality and reduce flood damage potential. Thus, parks or informal "green spaces" offer considerable ecological value.

In addition to creating or enhancing parks, municipal governments can facilitate community gardens, ban use of pesticides for "cosmetic" reasons, and protect or restore wetlands and other natural areas. At the household level, residents can plant more trees and shrubs, which take up rainwater and help keep buildings cooler. Using native species for home gardens instead of lawns and imported plants is beneficial because native species are adapted to local climate conditions and therefore need less watering or fertilizing. Another choice is to have a vegetable garden or grow vegetables in an allotment garden, since locally grown vegetables do not contribute as much to energy use and emissions.

A community garden coordinated by Ecosource, an Ontario-based environmental organization that inspires the community to become more environmentally responsible through creative public education.

Air Quality

Municipal governments have options to enhance air quality. They can use more energy-efficient vehicles in their municipal fleets, reducing fuel consumption and GHG emissions. Furthermore, in terms of energy for buildings or other purposes, options exist for renewable energy sources, such as wind or solar power. In terms of urban form, sprawl can be constrained through land-use regulations and by providing convenient public transit. Finally, standards can be modified to improve energy efficiency of new or renovated buildings.

Individual urban residents also have choices. They can walk, cycle, or use public transit, all contributing to lower GHG emissions. Insulating or draft-proofing homes and switching to energy-efficient lighting and appliances will reduce draw on energy sources, thereby contributing to lower GHG emissions. Setting the furnace thermostat at a lower temperature and wearing a sweater in winter or setting the air conditioner to a higher temperature and wearing lighter clothing in summer reduces energy consumption and GHG emissions. Finally, purchasing food grown in the local area contributes to lower energy consumption. These ideas highlight the importance of disseminating information to help individuals understand the impact of behaviour, thus facilitating shifts in basic values, attitudes, and behaviour.

Waste Management

Municipal governments can enhance reduction of the waste stream by expanding types of items that can be placed in blue boxes and by providing blue box services to apartments and office buildings. Reduction also can be improved by requiring manufacturers to reduce packaging for products and by establishing deposit refunds for glass bottles. Recycling can be enhanced by searching for and developing more markets for recycled materials. More aggressive options include banning of certain products, as San Francisco did by banning plastic bags in larger supermarkets and pharmacies in 2006. Oakland, California, has banned polystyrene or Styrofoam containers, leading restaurants to use paper, cardboard, or recyclable plastic containers.

Individuals can become more disciplined in using blue and green boxes and using reusable coffee containers, water bottles, and shopping bags. Other options include purchasing products with minimal packaging, buying reusable instead of disposable products, and, when appropriate, reusing paper, bottles, and other material, and composting organic wastes.

Transportation

If people are to change behaviour, incentives are appropriate, and people need to understand why behavioural change is necessary. If it is clear that many people will continue to use automobiles, then they should be encouraged to use more fuel-efficient vehicles, which also would reduce GHG emissions.

What incentives might be provided to encourage people using fuel-efficient vehicles? Suggestions include charging a lower licence fee for such vehicles, providing free parking for them in municipal parking lots plus access to commuter lanes on highways normally reserved for buses or other vehicles with a minimum number of passengers. Another option is to encourage people to use transportation other than cars. For example, it could be made more expensive to drive a car into a city centre, as in London, England, where drivers pay a fee for driving in the central area during the day. And first in Paris and now in other major cities, people can rent a bicycle for a

ENVIRONMENT IN FOCUS

BOX 13.6 | Montreal's BIXI Public Bicycle Program

In Montreal, the first public bike program in Canada was initiated under the name BIXI (a combination of the words "bicycle" and "taxi") in May 2009. It also was one of the largest such bike programs in North America when it was started. In its first year, 3,000 bicycles were available on a self-service basis at 400 stations in three boroughs (Ville-Marie, Plateau-Mont-Royal, Rosemont–La Petite-Patrie). The next year, stations were extended into five more boroughs, and in 2012 BIXI reached Longueuil, south of the Island of Montreal. Users could purchase passes for 24 hours, 72 hours, a month, or a year, with a security fee also paid (Reid, 2015).

However, in January 2014, BIXI filed for bankruptcy protection (Woods, 2014). It was explained that the public bike program would continue in 2014, to avoid complications with many users who had already purchased subscriptions. It was emphasized that there could be no guarantee that the program would continue after the end of the 2014 rental season. The program had cost taxpayers in Montreal $40 million for loans for which there was no prospect of repayment.

In the summer of 2014, it was reported that BIXI had been operating in the red each year since 2009, and the City of Montreal had provided multiple bailouts (Sargeant, 2014).

small fee at one of many docking stations. When they are finished with the bicycle, they can leave it at any other docking station. Paris's Vélib program was popular from its beginning in July 2007, with 1 million customers during the first year. However, challenges also arose: 24,000 bicycles had been stolen by the summer of 2010, but by 2012 theft or vandalism to bicycles had decreased significantly. By 2014, 14,000 bicycles and 1,230 stations were available. And, in June 2014, 300 children's bicycles were introduced under the name of the P'tit Vélib program.

In December 2011, a Paris Autolib program was introduced, and by October 2013, there were 105,00 members and a fleet of 2,200 electric Bolloré four-seat cars available 24 hours a day, along with 4,300 charging stations. Membership can be for a day, a week, a month, or a year. Users pay a subscription fee to borrow a car. In the spring of 2014, the same firm introduced the Autolib program in Indianapolis, Indiana, with 500 cars and 1,200 charging stations.

What information and education programs do you think should be developed to help individuals understand the impact of travel behaviour on the environment? Why is it in everyone's interest to modify travel behaviour with the environment in mind?

Best Practice: Sustainable Development Strategies for Vancouver, Calgary, Montreal, and Moncton

Vancouver: Greenest City 2020

In early 2009, Mayor Gregor Robertson created a Greenest City Action Team, and directed it to determine necessary action to make Vancouver the greenest city in the world by 2020. In April 2009, the team identified 44 "quick start recommendations" focused on three aspects: jobs and the economy, greener communities, and human health (Vancouver, 2009a). Later the same year, the committee submitted a proposed action plan containing 10 long-term goals, as well as a set of targets for 2020 (Vancouver, 2009b). In February 2010, the city council accepted the recommended long-term goals, which reflected the following vision:

> The greenest city in the world will be a vibrant place where residents live prosperous, healthy, happy lives with a one-planet footprint, so as not to compromise the quality of life of future generations or people living in other parts of the world. (Ibid., 11)

The team also outlined the rationale for the vision and its recommendations:

> Why green? Because in the highly competitive, highly mobile modern world, the elements that make a community healthy also make it wealthy. Functionally, a compact, efficient city with a well-organized transportation system and a light environmental footprint is cheaper to run and easier to maintain. The bright, creative people who are the key to conceiving and expanding a globally competitive economy also gravitate to the most desirable—livable—cities. (Vancouver, 2009b: 6)

The team recognized that the 10 goals were ambitious and could take a generation (20 to 30 years) to achieve. To ensure initiatives were kept on track, each goal was accompanied by a measurable 2020 target. The long-term goals were divided into three categories, shown below.

A. Green Economy, Green Jobs

Goal 1. Gain international recognition as a mecca of green enterprise
Target: 20,000 new green jobs

Goal 2. Eliminate dependence on fossil fuels
Target: Reduce GHG emissions 33 per cent from 2007 levels

Goal 3. Lead the world in green building design and construction
Target: All new construction carbon neutral: improve efficiency of existing buildings by 20 per cent

B. Greener Communities

Goal 4. Make walking, cycling, and public transit preferred transportation options
Target: Make the majority of trips (over 50 per cent) on foot, bicycle, and public transit

Goal 5. Create zero waste
Target: Reduce solid waste per capita going to landfill or incinerator by 40 per cent

Goal 6. Provide incomparable access to green spaces, including the world's most spectacular urban forest
Target: Every person lives within a five-minute walk of a park, beach, greenway, or other natural space; plant 150,000 additional trees in the city

Goal 7. Achieve a one-planet ecological footprint
Target: Reduce per capita ecological footprint by 33 per cent

C. Human Health

Goal 8. Enjoy the best drinking water of any major city in the world
Target: Always meet or beat the strongest of BC, Canada, and World Health Organization drinking water standards; reduce per capita water consumption by 33 per cent

Goal 9. Breathe the cleanest air of any major city in the world
Target: Always meet or beat World Health Organization air quality guidelines, which are stronger than Canadian guidelines

Goal 10. Become a global leader in urban food systems
Target: Reduce the carbon footprint of our food by 33 per cent per capita

The team concluded by observing that the recommended actions offered "dividends in the form of better health, a more resilient economy, and a vibrant environment" (Vancouver, 2009b: 63). Further details about the Greenest City Action Plan, along with annual implementation update reports, can be found on the City of Vancouver's website (see "Related Websites" at the end of the chapter). What would be a comparable set of recommendations for your community?

Calgary

In 2004, the City of Calgary endorsed the Brundtland Commission's definition of sustainable development, discussed in Chapter 1. In January 2005 and lasting for 18 months, more than 18,000 Calgarians participated in developing a long-range urban sustainability plan for the city, termed *imagineCalgary*. A 100-year perspective was taken. The city was viewed as a whole system, with five interacting systems: (1) built environment, (2) economic, (3) governance, (4) natural environment, and (5) social. Goals, targets, and strategies were developed for each, with particular attention to the interaction among them. A total of 32 goals and 114 targets were identified (City of Calgary, 2006).

The vision for Calgary in *imagineCalgary* included four foundations:

> We are each connected to one another. Our diverse skills and heritage interweave to create a resilient communal fabric, while our collective spirit generates opportunity, prosperity and choice for all of us.
>
> We are each connected to our places. We treasure and protect our natural environment.
>
> We are each connected to our communities. Whether social, cultural or physical, these communities are mixed, safe and just. They welcome meaningful participation from everyone . . .
>
> We are each connected beyond our boundaries. We understand our impact upon and responsibility to others. (City of Calgary, 2006).

In addition to the *imagineCalgary* long-term plan, in 2005 the city initiated a **triple bottom line** policy, which considers social and environmental, as well as financial matters. Such an approach also is referred to as "profits, people and the planet," or the 3Ps (Slaper and Hall, 2011: 4). It was observed that the main challenge was not how to define the 3Ps concept but how to measure it.

In terms of moving forward to implement the vision and plan, a 10-year sustainability plan entitled the *2020 Sustainability Direction* was developed to ensure various initiatives were aligned (City of Calgary, 2013). Five principles were identified to guide action: (1) collaborate, (2) set the direction, be visionary and innovative, (3) make decisions and implement, (4) grow and reward, and (5) evaluate progress and learn from experience. The *2020 Sustainability Direction* plan provides goals, objectives, targets and indicators, and strategies for community well-being, a prosperous economy, a sustainable environment, smart growth and mobility choice, financial capacity, and sustainable corporations. Details can be found in the City of Calgary's report *Sustainability Direction* (2013). Below, details are provided regarding a sustainable environment. A striking omission from these topics, however, is flooding, given the major damage created by flooding in the summer of 2013.

Goal: Sustainable Development

Protection of air, land, and water is critical for achieving healthy ecosystems within Calgary, an understanding applied to the way we grow and operate as a city.

Objective 1: GHG Emission Reduction—GHG emissions are reduced by decreasing energy use, doing more with less energy, and developing and using energy from renewable or low-carbon sources.
Target 1: By 2020, greenhouse gas emissions reduced by 20 per cent from a 2005 baseline.

Objective 2: Brownfields—Brownfield remediation and redevelopment support efficient land use and environmental protection.
Target 1: By 2020, 25 per cent of current vacant former gas station sites (within an Area Redevelopment Plan) returned to productive community use.
Target 2: By 2020, fuel storage sites located within residential communities redeveloped within three years of the termination of their original use.

Objective 3: Air Quality—Calgarians recognize importance of air quality to their health and well-being and are working collaboratively to protect the airshed.
Target 1: By 2020, ambient air quality meets or surpasses national and provincial air quality standards, objectives, and guidelines.

Objective 4: Waste Management—Calgarians recognize waste is a resource and that effective waste management protects public health and the environment.
Target 1: By 2020, achieve 80 per cent diversion of waste from City-run landfills.

Objective 5: Biodiversity—Calgary's ecosystems are healthy, connected, and diverse and represent the breadth of our natural heritage.
Target 1: By 2020, no net loss of unique and environmentally significant habitats.
Target 2: By 2020, species at risk protected and with sustainable populations.
Target 3: By 2020, significant landscapes and habitats restored and/or reconnected.
Target 4: By 2020, an increase achieved in the use of native plant xeriscaping in Calgary parks.

Objective 6: Water Quality—Public health and the health of watersheds are protected by delivering safe and reliable drinking water, collecting and treating wastewater, and minimizing the impact of urban form.
Target 1: By 2020, drinking water and treated wastewater effluent continue to meet provincial regulations for quality 100 per cent of the time.
Target 2: By 2020, total loading targets continue to be met in the City's License to Operate.

Objective 7: Water Quantity—Long-term sustainability and resilience of Calgary's water supply meets current and future needs of a growing city and region.
Target 1: By 2020, accommodate Calgary's population with the same amount of water withdrawn from the river in 2003.
Target 2: By 2020, diversify future water supply to align with water demand.
Target 3: By 2020, per capita daily residential water demand of 210 litres per person per day.

The *2020 Sustainability Direction* indicates what the city will strive for over 10 years related to the 100-year vision in *imagineCalgary* (City of Calgary, 2013: 37). Annual monitoring and reporting will track progress, and ensure transparency and accountability.

Montreal

Sustainable development (*développement durable*) has been a centrepiece since Montreal's first Strategic Plan for Sustainable Development for the 2005 to 2009 period. Subsequently, through collaboration with more than 180 organizations in Montreal, its *Community Sustainable Development Plan, 2010–2015* was prepared. The second plan, shown below, is based on the same five orientations as the first.

The second sustainable development plan includes nine objectives, seven with specific targets. The city also recognized that the plan, by itself, was insufficient without systematic implementation initiatives. Below are the five orientations and nine specific objectives. For each objective, initiatives also were prepared. More details about the plan and its implementation can be found on the City of Montreal's website (see "Related Websites" at the end of the chapter).

Orientation 1: Improve Air Quality and Reduce Greenhouse Gas Emissions
Objective 1: Reduce Montreal's GHG emissions by 30 per cent by 2020 compared with 1990.

Perspectives on the Environment

Vision for Montreal's Community Sustainable Development Plan

Montreal is a city on a human scale, proud and respectful of its heritage, where everyone contributes to creating a vibrant, prosperous, united, viable, and democratic community. Montreal, its citizens and institutional leaders of the community are making sustainable development a priority.

—Montreal (2010)

Objective 2: Achieve the Canadian standard for fine particle concentrations in ambient air (30μg/m³) by 2020.

Orientation 2: Ensure Quality of Residential Living Environments
Objective 3: Reduce net migration between Montreal and suburbs by 25 per cent by 2012, mainly by targeting Montrealers aged 25 to 44 who each year leave the city.

Orientation 3: Manage Resources Responsibly
Objective 4: Reduce potable water production by 15 per cent by 2015 compared with 2000.
Objective 5: Improve quality of runoff water flowing into watercourses.
Objective 6: Recover 80 per cent of recyclables and organic materials; household hazardous wastes; construction, renovation, and demolition waste; and bulky refuse by 2019, as stipulated in Montreal's Municipal Waste Management Master Plan.

Orientation 4: Adopt Good Practices for Sustainable Development in Companies, Institutions, and Businesses
Objective 7: Become a North American leader in the environmental and clean-tech sector by 2020.
Objective 8: Increase number of environmental certifications and participation in voluntary environmental programs in Montreal by 30 per cent by 2030 compared with 2010.

Orientation 5: Improve Protection of Biodiversity, Natural Environments, and Green Spaces
Objective 9: Improve green infrastructure by increasing the canopy cover to 25 per cent from 20 per cent by 2025 compared with 2007.

In addition to the above five orientations, the plan includes a "Social Component," explained as "providing a place for family and the quality of the living environment." Specifically, the city government and administration committed to (1) showing solidarity, especially through international cooperation and the social economy, (2) demonstrating equity, by efforts to reduce poverty, social marginalization, and inequality, and (3) addressing succession planning by engaging with young Montrealers.

The city government acknowledges it cannot achieve sustainable development on its own, and therefore lobbies higher levels of government to develop complementary interventions. For example, Montreal calls on the province and federal governments to use fiscal or economic tools, such as a regulated carbon market, to facilitate greenhouse gas reduction in the transportation and building sectors, to provide programs to encourage electric forms of transportation, to adopt new regulations regarding quality of the atmosphere, and to create awareness-building programs and incentives supported by regulatory and financial instruments for sale and purchase of water-efficient equipment. It also commits the local government to build awareness and provide information to residents, and to report on progress every two years.

Moncton

Moncton states that "environmental sustainability is a top priority" for the city (Moncton, n.d.). In addition to a Sustainability Plan, the city also plans for sustainable transportation, energy conservation, waste and recycling, water, and environmental programs.

The Sustainability Plan has four objectives: (1) develop a long-term vision for a sustainable community, (2) consolidate existing sustainability goals and targets, (3) identify sustainability goals and targets for the short, medium and long term, and (4) prepare action, implementation, and monitoring plans for sustainability.

Moncton states that its Sustainability Plan is an "Integrated Community Sustainability Plan" (ICSP), characterized as a ". . . long term plan through which a community can realize the sustainability objectives it has for the environmental, cultural, social and economic dimensions of its identity" (Dillon, 2011: 3). Furthermore, the plan ". . . expresses Moncton's commitment to a sustainable future, with a particular focus on the sustainable outcomes of clean air, clean water, reduced greenhouse gas emission and an overall reduction of our environmental footprint" (Dillon, 2011: 3). Specifically, the plan focuses on five pillars of sustainability: environment, culture, society, economy, and governance. In addition, the Sustainability Plan contains 24 goals accompanied by indicators or targets and specified actions. All of those are in the context of a vision that states "Moncton is a green, healthy, vibrant, prosperous and engaged community where we proudly choose to live within the limits of the natural, social and built systems on which we depend."

The following discussion elaborates on the environmental pillar, based on an objective to be a green community. Being green, as explained in the Sustainability Plan, requires attention to energy, smart growth, water, transportation, materials

Perspectives on the Environment

Sustainability Related to Moncton

In a sustainable community the natural environment and natural resources are protected and managed to ensure that they are not degraded or depleted for future generations. Sustainable communities have strong, diverse economies that provide meaningful employment to residents and opportunities for businesses and entrepreneurs. They are welcoming and diverse communities, with strong social networks, excellent community services, a broad range of educational opportunities and rich cultural and artistic scenes. They also have a wide variety of amenities, transportation choices, housing and jobs.

—Dillon (2011: 2)

and solid waste, and ecosystems. Three different types of targets are used:

- *Specific targets*, when adequate baseline information existed (e.g., reduce municipal greenhouse gas emissions by 20 per cent below 2002 levels by 2017)
- *More general targets* through benchmarking, when baseline data were not available. Benchmarks were determined relative to similar communities, or relative to provincial or national comparisons (e.g., reduce waste generation to 800 kg/person/year, which is the national average).
- *Very general targets*, when neither baseline nor benchmarking data existed (e.g., increase the number of events hosted by Moncton in an eco-friendly manner)

Objective: Moncton Is a Green Community

Goal 1: Our energy system is sustainable, reliable, and flexible. Energy conservation is a priority.
Targets:

1. Lower energy use (kWh) to 20 per cent below 2002 levels by 2017
2. Reduce corporate GHG emissions by 20 per cent below 2002 levels by 2017
3. Reduce community emissions by 6 per cent below 2002 levels by 2017
4. Decrease per cent of energy use from non-renewable resources
5. Decrease municipal fleet emissions to 2002 levels by 2017
6. All newly constructed municipal buildings greater than 500 m^2 are LEED certified.

Goal 2: Moncton is a smart growth community. Our built environment is designed to facilitate choices in the everyday lives of residents and visitors.
Targets:

1. Increase the number of dwelling units within the downtown core by 500 for a total of 4,100 units by 2016
2. Reduce the percentage of greenfield development
3. Increase the number of community energy systems
4. Maintain/increase percentage of tree cover and forest owned by the city
5. Increase percentage of dwellings located within 2 to 5 kilometres of a variety of uses
6. Increase density of housing in Moncton
7. Improve quality of stormwater runoff
8. No new increases to the stormwater system

Goal 3: Moncton's water resources provide a healthy, dependable supply for long-term needs of our community and nature.
Targets:

1. 10 per cent reduction in per capita water use by 2020
2. No exceptions related to Health-based Canadian Drinking Water Quality Guidelines
3. Reduce number of water-related customer complaints

Goal 4: Residents and visitors have access to an affordable and convenient transportation system promoting sustainable and healthy choices.
Targets:

1. Increase transit ridership per capita
2. Decrease single-occupant vehicle modal share to 65 per cent by 2016
3. Increase amount (in kilometres) of each of on-street bike lanes, sidewalks, trails, and bus routes
4. Reduce city-wide transportation emissions

Goal 5: Materials and solid waste are managed to support the concept of a "zero waste" community.
Targets:

1. Reduce waste generation to 800 kg/person/year by 2020
2. Increase waste diversion rate to 60 per cent by 2015
3. All construction waste recycled or processed by approved landfills

Goal 6: Natural ecosystems—habitats, wildlife, and environmentally sensitive areas and natural areas—are enhanced, conserved, and healthy.
Targets:

1. Maintain or increase forest land area
2. Maintain riparian buffers in new developments
3. Preserve various habitat types
4. No exceptions to recreation-based water quality guidelines

In addition to sustainability plans, as illustrated by the Moncton example, New Brunswick has been a leader related to "sustainable community design." Principles, approaches, and methods are identified to help in development of new areas within a city, or "retrofitting" of existing areas. More details can be found in Kelley (2009) and Savard (2013); see as well "Related Websites" at the end of the chapter.

Initiatives in Vancouver, Calgary, Montreal, and Moncton illustrate various ideas for achieving sustainable development, whether for a specific area within a city or city-wide. Based on their ideas and experiences, consider what might be done in your community, whether for a designated area or for the entire community.

Using ideas for best practice from Vancouver, Calgary, Montreal, and Moncton, we challenge you to complete an inventory and assessment of sustainability initiatives in your community. How many best practices exist in your community? Of those used, how effectively have they been implemented? If one new initiative might be undertaken, which would you recommend?

To motivate you to think imaginatively, check out the accomplishments of Copenhagen in Denmark (Copenhagen,

Hans Laubel/iStockphoto

Cyclists wait at an intersection in Copenhagen, Denmark.

2007). Copenhagen, a city of almost 550,000 people, and expected to reach 637,000 by 2025, aims to become the world's Eco-Metropole by 2015, or the capital city with the best urban environment in the world. It was recognized as the European Green Capital for 2014 by the European Union (previous cities receiving that award were Stockholm, Sweden, 2010; Hamburg, Germany, 2011; Vitoria-Gasteiz, Spain, 2012; and Nantes, France, 2013). The award is open to all cities in Europe with 200,000 people or more, or the largest city in countries with smaller populations. Copenhagen's aspiration is a reminder that many cities seek to be recognized as the leading green city in the world.

> 20 years ago some Copenhageners suggested that it should be possible to swim in the city harbour—which was heavily polluted at the time. Politicians at the City Hall listened, nonetheless, did some analysis and implemented a cleaning plan. 10 years later the first "harbour bath" opened and several others have come along. The first harbour bath is now one of the most popular places in Copenhagen. This tells us that environmental improvement and green growth go hand in hand with liveability.
>
> —Frank Jensen, Lord Mayor of Copenhagen, and Ayfer Baykal, Mayor of the Technical and Environmental Administration in Copenhagen (European Commission, 2013: 7)

© imageBROKER/Alamy Stock Photo

Sunbathers relax at the harbour in Copenhagen, Denmark.

Thirty-six per cent of commuters and 55 per cent of Copenhageners cycle to work or schools or colleges along 359 kilometres of dedicated bike tracks and lanes. The intent was to increase that to 50 per cent of commuters by 2015 and also to reduce seriously injured cyclists by more than half. To achieve that ambition, about $40 million was spent between 2008 and 2011 on enhancing road arrangements for cyclists. And since 1995, Copenhagen has provided bicycles for use in the city. For a deposit of 20 Danish krone (a bit less than $5), people can use one of more than 2,000 city-provided bicycles between April and November. The bicycles can be picked up and dropped off at one of more than 100 city bicycle stations.

When the 50 per cent target of Copenhageners cycling to work or school each day is achieved, CO_2 emissions will have been reduced by 80,000 tonnes. CO_2 emissions were reduced by 24 per cent between 2005 and 2012, better than the goal of achieving a reduction of at least 20 per cent relative to 2005. Furthermore, Copenhagen's goal is to become the first city in the world to be "carbon neutral" by 2025, and progress indicates it is likely to achieve that goal.

Copenhagen reuses about 90 per cent of all building waste, and incinerates about 75 per cent of household waste. Less than 2 per cent of waste is sent to landfill sites, a reduction from 44 per cent sent in 1988. Energy from burning waste is used for both electricity generation and district heating. Ninety-eight per cent of households in Copenhagen are serviced by **district heating systems**. These draw energy from large co-generation plants, using 40 per cent of the annual waste produced in the city as fuel to generate electricity.

> The term "Copenhagenisation" is used to refer to the confiscation of defeated ships in sea battles—dating back to the 1807 Battle of Copenhagen. Now it has taken on a new usage, embodying "a design strategy centred around making a city more accessible to bicyclists and pedestrians, and less car dependent. . . ." Copenhagenisation is how to improve the quality of sustainable urban life. (European Commission 2013: 40)

What initiatives could or should be taken in your community to achieve "Copenhagenization"? Before you reflect on this, consider the ideas provided by Meg Holden in her "Domestic Guest Statement," especially her ideas related to resilience.

Implications

Our goal here has been to help you understand the implications of current values and behaviour regarding urban environmental management. Understanding implications is important in Canada because more than four of five Canadians live in urban areas. We have choices regarding urban form and design (sprawling or compact), transportation (private vehicles or public transit), energy consumption (fossil-fuel or hybrid engines for vehicles), waste generation, and green space. Choices have consequences for air and water quality, greenhouse gas emissions, and the health of humans and other species.

We invite you to develop a vision for urban sustainability and resilience for the community in which you live. If your community were on a trajectory toward sustainability and resilience, what would be different from today? What changes would you have to make as an individual? What choices would have to be made by the entire community? What would be the costs of making such changes? What would be the costs of not making changes? In the short term, however, individuals can take actions, as shown in Box 13.7.

ENVIRONMENT IN FOCUS

BOX 13.7 | What You Can Do: Greening Your Town or City

1. Support elected officials to promote and introduce land-use planning practices that minimize urban sprawl.
2. Use public transit, car-sharing, bicycling, and/or walking as alternatives to travelling alone in your automobile.
3. Find opportunities to reuse, reduce, and recycle household and work-related waste.
4. Determine how green building technology could be incorporated in a new home or when renovating.
5. Purchase and use energy- and water-efficient units at home and in the workplace.
6. Replace low energy-efficient with energy-efficient light bulbs.
7. Set your furnace thermostat at a lower temperature during winter and your air conditioner at a higher setting during summer.
8. Use native trees and shrubs for your gardens and yards.
9. Volunteer to help create and maintain community trails or walking paths.

Summary

1. Fifty per cent of the world's population live in urban areas; more than four out of five Canadians live in urban areas.
2. Urban sustainable development and resilience are based on four considerations: urban form, transportation, energy, and waste management.
3. Urban sprawl can be reduced by compact, mixed-use urban form and reduced private car use.
4. Private automobile use is a major contributor to greenhouse gas emissions. Shifting from cars to other forms of transit is the one action likely to have the greatest single impact on improving environmental quality in Canadian cities.
5. Advanced "green" buildings can save up to 50 per cent in energy use relative to conventional buildings.
6. Key activities in waste management are reduction, reuse, and recycling, followed by energy recovery.
7. Major environmental issues in cities include air pollution, urban heat island effect, poor water quantity and quality, and brownfield sites.
8. Many cities are vulnerable to natural or human-induced hazards. For Canada, notable hazards include earthquakes, storm surges, floods, droughts, and snow or ice storms.
9. Numerous natural disasters in recent years have highlighted the vulnerability of urban infrastructure and residents.
10. Vancouver, Calgary, Montreal, Moncton, and Copenhagen, Denmark, offer excellent examples of urban sustainability initiatives.

Key Terms

blue boxes
brownfields
district heating systems
green bins
greenfields
LEED
LUST
NIMBY
recovery
recycling
reduction
reuse
Richter scale
smog
triple bottom line
urban form
urban heat island
urban sprawl

Questions for Review and Critical Thinking

1. Why is Canada so urbanized? Why is urbanization a global phenomenon?
2. What are the principal attributes of urban sustainability or of urban resilience?
3. What is the significance of urban form, transportation, energy use, and waste management for urban sustainability and resilience. What are the key connections among them?
4. What are the 3Rs?
5. How can the site selection of urban buildings help to achieve urban sustainability and resilience?
6. Why is air pollution generally increasing in highly urbanized areas?
7. How can the urban heat island effect be reduced?
8. What impact does urbanization have on the hydrological cycle?
9. What is the significance of LULUs, NIMBY, and LUST for urban sustainability?
10. What are the general lessons from Hurricane Katrina and Superstorm Sandy related to the vulnerability of urban areas to natural and human-induced hazards?
11. What are the lessons from Sudbury, Vancouver, Calgary, Montreal, and Moncton regarding urban sustainability and resilience?

Related Websites

BCIT Centre for Architectural Ecology: Collaborations in Living Architecture, Acoustics and Building Science
www.commons.bcit.ca/greenroof

Canada Green Building Council
www.cagbc.org

Canada's Ecofiscal Commission
http://ecofiscal.ca

City of Edmonton: The Way Ahead
www.edmonton.ca/city_government/city_vision_and_strategic_plan/the-way-ahead.aspx

City of Greater Sudbury: Environmental Initiatives
www.greatersudbury.ca/VETAC

City of Moncton: Environment
www.moncton.ca/Residents/Environment.htm

City of Montreal:
Community Sustainable Development Plan:
http://ville.montreal.qc.ca/portal/page?_pageid=2762,3101662&_dad=portal&_schema=PORTAL

City of Montreal (*con't*):
Community Sustainable Development Implementation:
http://ville.montreal.qc.ca/portal/page?_pageid=2762,3101710&_dad=portal&_schema=PORTAL

City of Toronto: City Planning
www1.toronto.ca/wps/portal/contentonly?vgnextoid=ae9352cc66061410VgnVCM10000071d60f89RCRD

City of Vancouver: Greenest City Action Plan
http://vancouver.ca/green-vancouver/greenest-city-action-plan.aspx

European Commission: Copenhagen, European Green Capital
http://ec.europa.eu/environment/europeangreencapital/winning-cities/2014-copenhagen/

Foreign Affairs, Trade and Development Canada: Urban Environmental Management Applications
www.acdi-cida.gc.ca/cidaweb/cpo.nsf/vWebCCEn/712523A22AD0AD4E852572300041F9E9

International Green Roof Association: Greenroofs Project Database
www.greenroofs.com

New Brunswick: Community Sustainability Plans in New Brunswick
www2.gnb.ca/content/gnb/en/departments/elg/environment/content/community_sustainability_plans.html

New Brunswick: Environment and Local Government: Sustainable Community Design—Online Seminar
www2.gnb.ca/content/gnb/en/departments/elg/environment/content/sustainable_communitydesign.html

Paris Vélib Program
http://en.velib.paris.fr

Pembina Institute: Fast Cities
www.pembina.org/pub/fast-cities

Transport Canada: Environment
www.tc.gc.ca/eng/environment-menu.htm

United Nations Population Fund
www.unfpa.org

World Health Organization: Health and Environment Linkages Initiative: The Urban Environment—A General Directory of Resources
www.who.int/heli/risks/urban/urbenvdirectory/en/index.html

Further Readings

Note: This list comprises works relevant to the subject of the chapter but not cited in the text. All cited works are listed in the References at the end of the book.

da Costa Silva, G. 2014. "Climate change and the water-energy nexus: An urban challenge," *Journal of Water and Climate Change* 5 (3): 259–75.

Hollander, J., N. Kirkwood, and J. Gold. 2010. *Principles of Brownfield Regeneration: Cleanup, Design, and Reuse of Derelict Land*. Washington: Island Press.

Kenway, S.J., G.M. Turner, S. Cook, and T. Baynes. 2014. "Water and energy futures for Melbourne: Implications of land use, water use, and water supply," *Journal of Water and Climate Change* 5 (2): 163–75.

Lehmann, S. 2010. *The Principles of Green Urbanism*. London: Earthscan.

Winterhalder, K. 2002. "The effects of the mining and smelting industry on Sudbury's landscape," in D.H. Rousell and K.J. Jansons, eds, *The Physical Environment of the City of Greater Sudbury*. Ontario Geological Survey Special Volume no. 6. Toronto: Ontario Ministry of Northern Development and Mines, Mines and Minerals Information Centre, 145–73.

Go to www.oupcanada.com/DeardenMitchell5e to access additional learning tools on your smartphone, tablet, or PC.

CHAPTER FOURTEEN

Endangered Species and Protected Areas

Learning Objectives

- To understand why endangered species are important and the factors leading to endangerment
- To become aware of the extrinsic and intrinsic values of nature
- To learn why some species are more vulnerable to extinction than others
- To be able to discuss the main responses to endangerment at the international and national levels
- To appreciate the many roles played by protected areas
- To gain an international and a Canadian perspective on protected areas
- To know some of the main management challenges faced by protected areas in Canada

Introduction

Most people are aware that many more species are becoming **endangered** than is natural—that we have a "biodiversity crisis." What took hundreds of millions of years to evolve is disappearing in only generations. The United Nations declared 2010 as the International Year of Biodiversity to promote awareness and conservation of the biosphere, an essential component to ensuring functioning Earth-system processes, and this has been extended to a whole decade (2010–2020) to emphasize the importance of biodiversity. Biodiversity is the living underpinning of our lives: we depend on biodiversity for clear air, fresh water, many medicines, and the various resources we consume every day.

Extinction is occurring many times faster than natural rates. Rockström (2009) and his co-authors, in their global assessment of the resilience of key planetary systems, found biodiversity loss to be the most stressed process. A common perception, however, is that this problem is one more for the tropics than for countries such as Canada. Although it is true that threat levels and the numbers of endangered species are higher in the tropics, Canada also has plenty of challenges.

Canada has a long-established national parks system designed to protect species and their habitats, but parks do not necessarily afford adequate protection to all species needing it. The decline in turtle populations in Point Pelee National Park, Ontario, highlights some of the problems in our national parks and the challenges park managers face.

Turtles have evolved for hundreds of millions of years. Historically, their adaptations—terrestrial nesting, low adult mortality, late maturation, and longevity—have served them well. But these attributes are no longer adequate, and throughout the world many turtle species are experiencing dramatic declines. Historical records show that Point Pelee, the southern tip of Canada's mainland, at one time had seven different species of indigenous turtles. Research by Browne and Hecnar (2003) revealed that several species, including the stinkpot, map, and Blanding's turtles, now exist only in small populations, while other species may be headed toward extirpation—no spotted turtles were found in the park, and only one individual of the threatened spiny softshell turtle was recorded. Reasonably large populations exist for only one species, the painted turtle (Browne and Hecnar, 2007). The authors examined the age structures of the populations and found a preponderance of older animals for most species, indicating aging populations, especially for Blanding's and snapping turtles.

Although the populations are "protected" within the park, at least three problems threaten the long-term viability of turtle populations. Roads are implicated in two of the three and illustrate the need to minimize development within parks (discussed later). Roads are a source of direct mortality. Some species are attracted by the soft shoulders of roads for nesting, and while migrating across roads in search of suitable sites, many turtles are killed. In addition, roadside nesting sites were found to be very vulnerable to nest predation (100 per cent loss), compared to the 62 to 64 per cent loss in more remote areas of the park. Roadsides are a favourite scavenging area for predators such as raccoons. These and other predators, such as striped skunks and opossums, are reportedly at higher levels in the park than previously, and raccoons may be the dominant limiting factor (Chapter 2) on population growth.

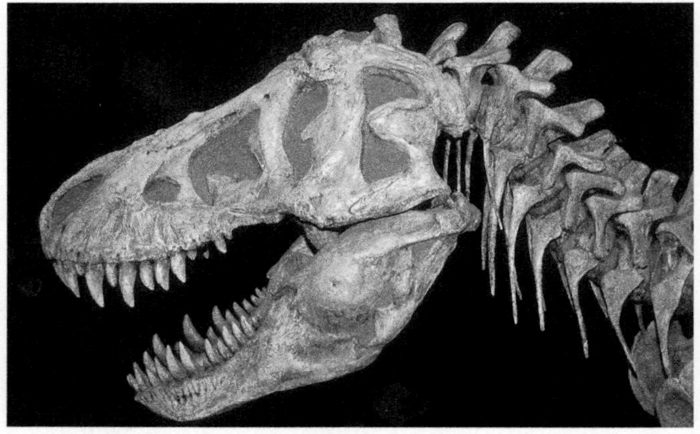

© Marvyn Rees/Alamy Stock Photo

Extinction is a natural process that has been occurring since life first evolved on Earth (the *Tyrannosaurus rex*, like this skeleton in the Royal Tyrell Dinosaur Museum near Drumheller, Alberta, disappeared during the Cretaceous-Tertiary extinction event approximately 65.5 million years ago). However, it is the speed of current extinction rates across many different forms of life that concerns scientists.

Stephen Belcher/Minden Pictures

The Javan rhinoceros was found throughout Southeast Asia until recently. It has now been confirmed that the one shot in Vietnam in 2010 was the last surviving rhino in Vietnam and almost certainly in mainland Southeast Asia. One small population remains in Indonesia. Extinction is very real and happening all the time.

Contaminants are also implicated in turtle population declines. There are still elevated levels of DDT and DDE (see Chapter 10) in areas of the park from past agricultural practices, illustrating the vulnerability of parks to threats from surrounding land uses.

This example illustrates the plight of many species to which we give relatively little attention. Plant and animal populations are often assumed to be "healthy," especially if they are within the boundaries of a national park. However, *no* national park—anywhere on the planet—is big or remote enough to exclude the impacts of modern society. This chapter focuses on endangered species and the factors behind endangerment. One of the main responses to endangerment is to protect habitats and species in park systems. The designation and management of park systems constitute the second main topic discussed.

But why should we be concerned about endangerment? Extinction is a natural process that has been taking place since life first evolved on this planet more than 4 billion years ago (Chapter 3). Consequently, concern for the extinction of species does not focus on the process itself but on the increasing rates of extinction—i.e., what humans are doing to speed up the process. Before looking at some of the pressures responsible for this increase, we need to understand why high extinction rates are undesirable.

Valuing Biodiversity

Changes in biodiversity due to human activities were more rapid in the past 50 years than at any time in human history, and the drivers of change that cause biodiversity loss and lead to changes in ecosystem services are either steady, show no evidence of declining over time, or are increasing in intensity.

Humans derive **extrinsic values** from other species. These values can be *consumptive* (i.e., the organism is harvested) or *non-consumptive* (i.e., the organism is not harvested or the resource is not destroyed). There is no universally accepted framework for assigning value to biological diversity, but various approaches have been proposed. For example, the value of biodiversity can be calculated by examining import and export statistics for products bought and sold in markets. However, it is often difficult to assign an economic value to biodiversity. How do you put a price tag on environmental services provided by biological communities, such as photosynthesis, protection of watersheds, or climate regulation? These services, not directly consumed by humans, are vital for survival.

While important, the extrinsic reasons for species protection should not be allowed to dominate our thinking. Such thinking could lead to the protection of a selection of species believed to be of higher value, while species with less use value are afforded little or no protection. Thus, arguments for biological conservation focus on the **intrinsic value** of nature—nature has value in and of itself, apart from its value to humanity. The following discussion outlines some of the key ecological, economic, and ethical reasons for conservation.

Ecological Values

The elimination of species affects ecosystem functioning such as the impact on coastal marine ecosystems on the Pacific coast when the sea otter was extirpated (discussed in Chapter 3). The important role species play in ecosystem functioning is another extrinsic value that humans derive from biodiversity. Species become **extirpated** when they have been eliminated from one part of their range but still exist somewhere else. A species is considered **ecologically extinct** in an area when it exists in such low numbers that it can no longer fulfill its ecological role in the ecosystem. For example, the eastern mountain lion may still exist in the Maritime provinces and has not yet been declared extinct, but if this species does persist, it exists in such low numbers that it no longer acts as a significant control for species in the preceding trophic level. The eastern mountain lion may therefore be considered ecologically extinct in this region.

Perspectives on the Environment

Keeping Every Cog in the Wheel

If the land mechanism as a whole is good, then every part is good, whether we understand it or not. If the biota, in the course of aeons, has built something we like but do not understand, then who but a fool would discard seemingly useless parts? To keep every cog and wheel is the first precaution of intelligent tinkering.

—Aldo Leopold, *Round River* (1953)

All species in a community combine to maintain the vital ecosystem processes that make human life possible on this planet—oxygen to breathe, water to drink, and food to eat. Humans are part of this web of life, but if we continue to eliminate components of the web, its strength will be compromised, with a significant impact on the ability of humans to

© Chris Fredriksson/Alamy Stock Photo

The great hornbill is found throughout the tropical forests of Southeast Asia where it has been extirpated from many areas by hunting. Even where it exists in small numbers, it is often considered ecologically extinct as there are no longer sufficient numbers to crack and distribute the seeds of many of the tree species. Ultimately, this will also cause changes in the tree species composition of the forests.

survive. As we noted in Chapter 2, the elimination of species from an ecosystem is similar to the removal of rivets from an airplane—the system may continue to function after losing a few components, but sooner or later the system will crash. One role of science is to understand how these systems work, but it is difficult to achieve this understanding if components are missing as a result of extinction.

In addition to the value of species in ecosystem functioning, species should be protected for their evolutionary value, their value to future generations. Species evolve, as discussed in Chapter 3, and as more species become extinct, genetic variation in the ecosphere on which to base future adaptability is reduced. Fewer species means a more impoverished biosphere on which to base evolutionary adaptability for future generations. The need to preserve species exemplifies the precautionary principle on a grand scale.

Economic Values

Another extrinsic value of biodiversity is the economic benefit derived from preservation of ecosystem components and functions. Countless products used in agriculture and industry originate in the natural world. Naturally occurring plants in the tropics are the source of 90 per cent of the world's food supply. Corn, or maize, feeds millions of people and is estimated to be worth at least $50 billion annually worldwide. Corn was first domesticated by indigenous people in Central America some 7,000 years ago.

More than 99.8 per cent of the world's plants have never been tested for human food potential. Some may become important food staples in the future, so preservation of their habitat is important. Furthermore, wild animals still provide an important source of food for millions of people worldwide, particularly indigenous peoples, including Canada's Aboriginal communities.

Other products besides food are also of economic importance. Many plant and animal products are used extensively in various industries. Rubber, for example, is an important commodity in the automotive sector. It is just one example of a chemical that tropical plants produce to prevent insect damage. Many other chemicals produced by plants are used in the pharmaceutical industry. Fifty-six per cent of the top 150 prescribed drugs in the United States contain ingredients from wild species, with an annual economic value of US$80 billion, according to the UN. In 2010, half of all synthetic drugs had been traced to natural ingredients. One drug, a compound derived from a sea sponge to treat herpes, is valued at up to $100 million annually.

However, less than 1 per cent of the world's tropical plants have been screened for potential pharmaceutical application. Next time you take an aspirin tablet, thank the white willow, the species in which the active ingredient was first discovered. Taxol, found in the bark of the western yew—a small understorey tree in the forests of the Pacific Northwest—was recently discovered as a treatment for cancer. Prior to the discovery, the species was of little commercial value, and it was routinely cut down in clear-cuts and left to rot.

It is difficult to assess the economic value of many products we derive from nature. For example, natural gene pools provide a source of material to aid in the development of new genetic strains of crops needed to feed the world's burgeoning human population. Wheat, the mainstay of the western Canadian agricultural economy, originated in Mediterranean countries, where most of its wild forebears have disappeared. But preservation of such wild strains is necessary to allow selective breeding based on the widest range of genetic material to continue.

Ecosystems also provide humans with a wide array of economically important services. Natural pollinators, for example, provide an essential service to commercial crops. Pollination of flowers by diverse species of wild bees, wasps, butterflies, and other insects—not just managed honeybees—accounts for more than 30 per cent of all food production that humans depend upon. Environment Canada (2003b)

Whether sold in a modern or a traditional pharmacy, many of our medicinal products are based on products found in nature.

has conservatively estimated the value of pollination services to crops in Canada at $1.2 billion annually. When New Brunswick switched from spraying its forests with DDT to fenitrothion in 1970 to control the spruce budworm (see Chapter 9), there was a devastating impact on pollination of the blueberry crop because fenitrothion is highly toxic to bees. The commercial crop fell by 665 tonnes per year, and growers successfully sued the government.

Natural predator–prey relationships also aid in food production. Woodpeckers, for example, provide an economically important service in the control of pests such as coddling moths in the orchards of Nova Scotia. Such predator–prey relationships can significantly reduce the need to apply biocides to control pests. Similarly, the natural toxicity found in some species can occasionally be refined into a natural biocide for use in agriculture. For example, a powerful insect repellent—trans-pulegol—was recently discovered in an endangered member of the mint family.

Other Extrinsic Values

The ecological and economic benefits mentioned above do not encompass all the values associated with protecting other species. How many of us are permanently enriched and emotionally uplifted by a wildlife encounter at some point in our lives? Wildlife contributes to the joy of life, but this joy often translates into a contribution to the economic values attached to wildlife. Viewing wildlife is a major reason for travel to some areas. The economic value attached to nature-based tourism can provide a significant impetus to conservation when managed so as to enhance biodiversity and educational values. This form of tourism can also provide a sustainable livelihood for local residents. The extrinsic ecological and economic values of biodiversity just discussed exemplify an anthropocentric view of life, a view that favours the protection of species providing a direct benefit to humans.

Ethical Values

Ethical arguments can be made for preserving all species, regardless of their use value to humans. Arguments based on the intrinsic value (value unrelated to human needs or desires) of nature suggest that humans have no right to destroy any species. In fact, humans have a moral responsibility to actively protect species from going extinct due to our activities. This philosophy reflects an ecocentric view—humans are part of the larger biotic community in which all species' rights to exist are respected. This view contrasts to the anthropocentric view of life presented in the previous section, and also discussed in Chapter 1.

In the past, extinction has been viewed simply as a biological problem. The points raised above emphasize the need to make links among the biological process of extinction and the ethical and economic reasons why extinction is undesirable. However, decisions to protect species and communities often become arguments over money—how much will it cost, and how much is it worth? All too often, governments demonstrate a willingness to protect biodiversity only when its loss is perceived to cost money. Unfortunately, standard economic systems tend to undervalue natural resources, and as a consequence, the cost of environmental damage often has been ignored and the depletion of natural resources frequently has been disregarded. Ecosystems are being destroyed and species are now being driven to extinction at a rate greater than at any time in the past. An economic system that undervalues natural resources is a main underlying cause of extinction. The Millennium Ecosystem Assessment (2005) suggests that the amount of biodiversity remaining on the planet in another

Philip Dearden

Philip Dearden

If the economic value attached to viewing wildlife is more than the value from killing wildlife, then this creates a financial incentive for conservation. Here snorkelers watch whale sharks off the coast of Cebu in the Philippines and provide an incentive for the sharks not to be killed for their fins.

100 years will reflect society's ability to understand and take into account the different values associated with biodiversity conservation (Figure 14.1). The next section reviews some of the main causes of biodiversity loss.

Main Pressures Causing Extinction

Chapter 3 described some human activities that have contributed to the increasing rates of extinction over the past 200 years. This section discusses some of the main pressures on biodiversity in greater detail. Rarely do these pressures act alone; they must therefore be seen as part of the overall stress that human demands are placing on the biosphere.

Humans expropriate more than 40 per cent of the net primary productivity (NPP) of the planet (Chapter 2). With global populations predicted to increase to 9.2 billion by 2050, this figure will only increase. As the amount of NPP increases to support one species—*Homo sapiens*—the amount available to support all other species decreases. The extinction vortex (Figure 14.2) is driven by these human pressures, manifested as habitat loss, overharvesting, pollution, and the introduction of exotic species (Chapter 3). These pressures result in small, isolated populations that become vulnerable to inbreeding and demographic instability. Unfortunately, there is a positive feedback loop (Chapter 3) between these factors and population decline. The more the population declines, the greater the impact of these factors, and ultimately this leads to extinction. The fragmented populations of the endangered mountain caribou in BC are a good example. As the populations have become progressively reduced and isolated, mainly because of logging, they become more vulnerable to extirpation through such factors as bad weather and increased predation, and fewer and fewer sites exist from which repopulation can take place. The vortex eventually spins down to extinction.

Most attention regarding extinction has been devoted to the tropical countries, mainly because they are "hot spots" for biodiversity and because they are experiencing many pressures responsible for increasing rates of extinction. Of the 10 to 15 million terrestrial species thought to be on Earth, up to 90 per cent are estimated to exist in the tropics, particularly in the tropical rain forests. Tropical ecosystems are being degraded and/or destroyed at alarming rates (Box 14.1). Estimates suggest that perhaps 50 per cent of tropical rain forests have already disappeared, and at current rates of destruction, only a few forest fragments will remain in 30 years.

The outer circle in the figure represents the present level of global biodiversity. Each inner circle represents the level of biodiversity under different value frameworks. Question marks indicate the uncertainties over where the boundaries exist and therefore the appropriate size of each circle under different value frameworks.

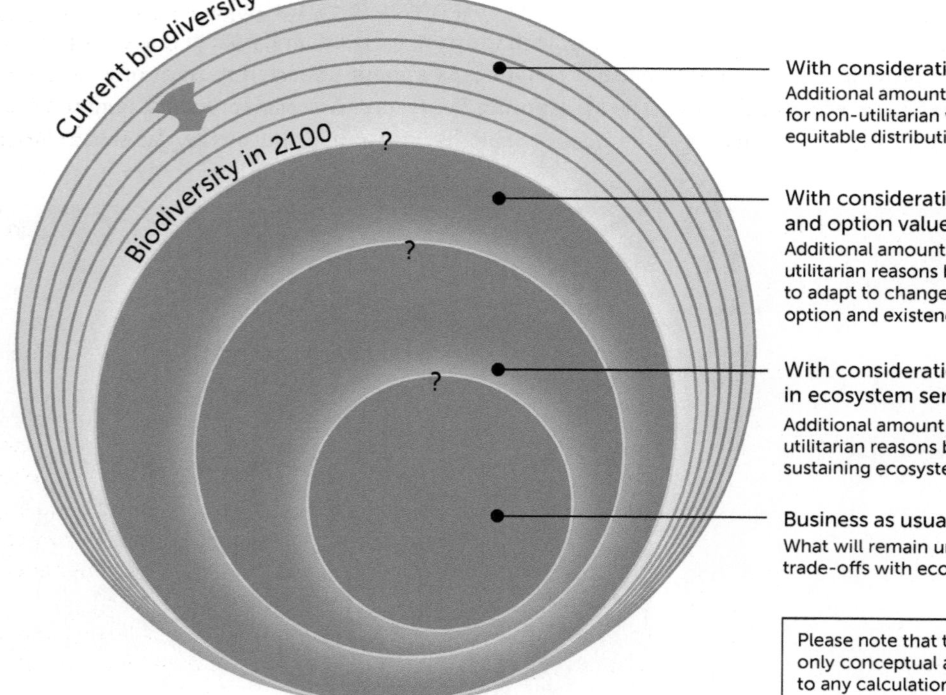

FIGURE 14.1 | How much biodiversity will remain a century from now under different value frameworks?

Source: Millennium Ecosystem Assessment (2005).

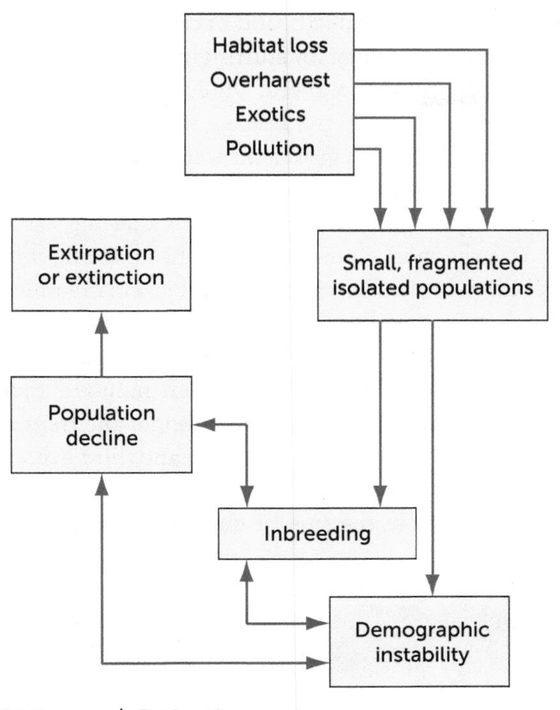

FIGURE 14.2 | Extinction vortex.

Causes of tropical deforestation include:

- Rapidly growing population levels—more people equals less biological diversity, since people use natural resources
- Overconsumption of resources—the rise of industrial capitalism and materialistic modern societies has greatly accelerated demands for natural resources, particularly in developing countries
- Inequality in the distribution of wealth—poor rural people with no land or resources of their own destroy biological communities and hunt endangered species just to stay alive

Aquatic ecosystems are an increasing area of concern (Box 14.2). In both oceans and freshwater ecosystems, our knowledge of species abundance is very limited. As knowledge improves, many species have been found to be threatened, and these numbers will continue to increase. Freshwater fish and amphibians now hold the top two spots for animal species threatened worldwide (Table 14.1).

Extinctions also occur in developed and temperate countries. Since the European colonization of North America,

ENVIRONMENT IN FOCUS

BOX 14.1 | The Global Toll

Through its Species Survival Commission, the International Union for Conservation of Nature (IUCN) evaluates and categorizes species according to their relative level of extinction risk (2014 figures in parentheses):

- extinct (832)
- extinct in the wild (69)
- critically endangered (4,635)
- endangered (6,940)
- vulnerable (10,838)
- near threatened (5,103)
- least concern (34,934)
- data deficient (12,609)

This so-called **Red List** is produced by thousands of scientific experts and is the best source of knowledge on the status of global biodiversity.

Some highlights from recent lists:

- The Red List includes 22,413 species threatened with extinction, falling into the critically endangered, endangered, or vulnerable categories.
- Over 50 per cent of all primate species (257 out of 426) are listed as threatened.
- 10,584 plants were assessed as threatened in 2014. However, with under 5 per cent of the world's described plants evaluated, the true percentage of threatened plant species is likely much higher. Most plant species listed are trees, since they have been relatively thoroughly assessed.
- There are now 832 plant and animal species recorded as extinct, and a total of 901, if species no longer existing in the wild are included. In 2002, the number of species assessed as extinct and extinct in the wild was 811.
- Countries with the most threatened species overall are Ecuador, the US, Malaysia, Indonesia, and Mexico.
- Birds and mammals are increasingly moving toward the higher-threat categories (i.e., more bird and mammal species are entering the critically endangered and endangered categories).
- Habitat loss and degradation affect 89 per cent of all threatened birds, 83 per cent of threatened mammals, and 91 per cent of threatened plants assessed. Habitats with the highest number of threatened mammals and birds are lowland and mountain tropical rain forests. Freshwater habitats are extremely vulnerable, with many threatened fish, reptile, amphibian, and invertebrate species.
- Just over 10 per cent of threatened species have climate change listed as a major pressure (Akcakaya et al., 2014).

Sources: International Union for Conservation of Nature (2011; 2014).

more than 500 species and subspecies of native plants and animals have become extinct. The Committee on the Status of Endangered Wildlife in Canada (COSEWIC) has identified 15 extinctions and 24 extirpations in Canada since the arrival of Europeans (Table 14.2). Most of the following examples have been chosen to illustrate extinction pressures in Canada.

Overharvesting

Many examples exist in Canada of species under pressure due to overharvesting. Several historical examples that took place at least partly in Canadian territory are well known.

The great auk. The great auk, a large flightless bird, inhabited the rocky islets of the North Atlantic. For many years, fishers in these waters used the great auk as a source of meat, eggs, and oil. It was reasonably easy to catch these birds and club them to death, and once the feathers became an important commodity for stuffing mattresses in the mid 1700s, extinction soon followed. On Funk Island off the east coast of Newfoundland, the species was extirpated by the early 1800s. The last two great auks were clubbed to death off the shores of Iceland in 1844.

The passenger pigeon. There are claims that the passenger pigeon was the most abundant land bird on Earth, totalling up to 5 billion birds. These great flocks used to migrate annually from their breeding grounds in southeastern Canada and the American northeast to their wintering grounds in the southeastern US. So great were their numbers that tree limbs would break under the pigeons' weight and trees would die as a result of the large amount of guano (bird excrement) deposited. Many eyewitness accounts tell of flocks so huge that they blotted out the sun for days. The pigeons were an

ENVIRONMENT IN FOCUS

BOX 14.2 | Aquatic Ecosystems in Trouble

Aquatic ecosystems are not only among the least known but also among those most inadequately protected in park systems. You will also see later that many of Canada's most recent extinctions have been from aquatic ecosystems. The following global examples highlight this plight.

- Fifty-six per cent of the 252 endemic freshwater Mediterranean fish are threatened with extinction, the highest proportion in any regional freshwater fish assessment. Seven species are now extinct.
- Of the 564 dragonfly and damselfly species so far assessed, nearly one in three (174) are threatened, including nearly 40 per cent of endemic Sri Lankan dragonflies.
- In East Africa, human impacts on the freshwater environment threaten more than one in four (28 per cent) freshwater fish species. This could have major commercial and dietary consequences for the region. For example, in Malawi, 70 per cent of animal protein consumed comes from freshwater fish. The lake trout, or mpasa, from Lake Malawi is fished heavily during its spawning runs upriver but has suffered a 50 per cent decline in the past 10 years as a result of siltation of its spawning grounds and reduced flows because of water abstraction. It is now listed as endangered.
- Larger freshwater species, such as the common hippopotamus, are also in difficulty. One of Africa's best-known aquatic icons, it is now classified as a **vulnerable species**, primarily because of a catastrophic decline in the Democratic Republic of the Congo (DRC). In 1994, the DRC had the second-largest population in Africa—30,000, after Zambia's 40,000—but numbers have plummeted by 95 per cent. The decline is due to unregulated hunting for meat and the ivory of their teeth.

Philip Dearden

Unregulated hunting has led to a catastrophic decline in the hippopotamus population in the Democratic Republic of Congo, putting this freshwater species on the Red List for the first time.

- As of 2014, 9,608 marine species were on the IUCN Red List. Sharks and rays were among the first marine groups to be systematically assessed, and of the 547 species listed, 20 per cent are threatened with extinction. This confirms suspicions that these mainly slow-growing species are exceptionally susceptible to overfishing and are disappearing at an unprecedented rate across the globe. Curbing demand for shark products is a major step toward enhanced protection and in late 2011, for example, the City of Toronto banned the sale of sharkfin soup.

Sources: IUCN (2011), www.iucnredlist.org (n.d.).

TABLE 14.1 | Number of Threatened Species in Each Major Group of Organisms Worldwide

	2002	2014
Mammals	1,137	1,199
Birds	1,192	1,373
Reptiles	293	927
Amphibians	157	1,957
Fish	742	2,222
Invertebrates	1,932	4,140
Plants	5,714	10,584
Fungi/protists		11
Total	10,767	22,413

Sources: World Conservation Union, 2002, 2014. © International Union for Conservation of Nature and Natural Resources. www.iucnredlist.org

Great auks, painted by John James Audubon.

easy target for hunters, and they were slaughtered in great numbers for food, with more than 1 billion birds killed in Michigan alone in 1869. Hunting took place concurrently with a reduction in their breeding grounds as habitat was converted into agricultural lands. The last passenger pigeon sighted in Canada was at Penetanguishene, Ontario, in 1902; the last pigeon died in a zoo in Cincinnati in 1914. The world will never again experience the sound and sight of millions of passenger pigeons darkening the heavens.

This astonishing tale of a species going from such abundance to extinction is not that unusual. Three fish species of the Great Lakes (blue walleye, deepwater cisco, longjaw cisco) were at one time all very abundant, and millions of kilograms of the fish were harvested commercially. By 1950, they were fished into extinction. Similarly, the northern cod, once one of the most abundant fish on the planet, was fished into commercial extinction by the early 1990s and designated as endangered by COSEWIC in 2003 (see Chapter 8). Overharvesting is the major cause of endangerment for marine species listed by COSEWIC and gives further impetus for Canada to fulfill its international commitments to establish a network of marine protected areas , as discussed in Chapter 8.

Perhaps extinction of the passenger pigeon and the great auk are sufficiently in the past that we can excuse their demise on the grounds of a lack of knowledge. However, such a case cannot be made for more recent extinctions. They stand as the ultimate symbol of the failure of resource managers and decision-makers to understand the natural dynamics of species supposedly being managed.

One aspect of overharvesting generally given little consideration is the demand for captive species. In the past, the

TABLE 14.2 | Summary of COSEWIC's Assessment Results for the Risk Categories

	Extinct	Extirpated	Endangered	Threatened	Special Concern	Total
Mammals	3	3	26	14	32	78 (69)
Birds	3	2	29	26	25	85 (71)
Reptiles		4	17	11	10	42 (38)
Amphibians		2	9	5	9	25 (20)
Fish	7	3	48	37	54	149 (111)
Lepidopterans, arthropods		3	29	6	10	48 (13)
Molluscs	1	3	19	3	8	34 (26)
Plants		3	94	48	44	189 (168)
Mosses	1	1	8	3	5	18 (16)
Lichens			5	3	7	15 (9)
Total	15 (13)	24 (22)	284 (225)	156 (141)	204 (155)	683 (556)

Note: Figures shown are for 2014, with 2007 figures in parentheses.
Source: Adapted from Summary of COSEWIC'S Assessment Results for the Risk Categories: www.cosewic.gc.ca/rpts/Full_List_Species.html

Metropolitan Toronto Reference Library

A pair of passenger pigeons, painted by John James Audubon.

Perspectives on the Environment

The Passenger Pigeon

The noise they made, even though still distant, reminded me of a hard gale at sea, passing through the rigging of a close-reefed vessel. As the birds arrived and passed over me, I felt a current of air that surprised me. Thousands of the Pigeons were soon knocked down by the pole-men, while more continued to pour in. . . . The Pigeons, arriving by the thousands, alighted everywhere, one above another, until solid masses were formed on the branches all around. Here and there the perches gave way with a crash under the weight and fell to the ground, destroying hundreds of birds, beneath, and forcing down the loaded. The scene was one of uproar and confusion. I found it quite useless to speak, or even to shout, to those persons nearest me. Even the gun reports were seldom heard, and I was made aware of the firing only by seeing the shooters reloading.

—John James Audubon

zeal of zoo collectors to exhibit various species, particularly rare species such as pandas and orangutans that visitors would pay to see, was of serious concern. International regulations, such as the **Convention on International Trade in Endangered Species of Wild Fauna and Flora** (CITES), of which Canada is a signatory, make it difficult for this kind of trade to occur. However, despite international regulations, trade in rare and endangered species occurs because of demand from private collectors. Exotic species such as tigers, monkeys, parrots, and tropical fish belong in their native habitats, not in people's homes. Some of the most sought-after Canadian species are falcons, particularly gyr and peregrine falcons; they can fetch thousands of dollars each on the international market. Although an allowable harvest of wild falcons exists in some provinces and territories, poaching is a problem because of the high price tags attached to these birds.

Hunting/fishing and the harvesting of live specimens for captivity can have a significant impact on populations. However, more subtle instances of "non-consumptive" activities have detrimental impacts on species by causing displacement from valuable habitat or even death. For example, research is underway on both the Atlantic and Pacific coasts of Canada to assess the potential impact of whale-watching vessels on the well-being of whales. Such research requires detailed knowledge of a species' natural distribution and behaviour before it can be ascertained whether changes have occurred as a result of disturbance. Impacts associated with the non-consumptive use of natural resources are usually much more difficult to document than the more direct effects of consumptive use. Nonetheless, researchers have detected costs to killer whales in terms of energy use—for example, from boat traffic in BC (Williams et al., 2006).

Predator Control

Several species have been targeted for elimination by humans because they compete directly with humans for consumption of the same resource. One North American example is the Carolina parakeet, the only member of the parrot family native to North America. It was exterminated in the early part of the previous century because of its fondness for fruit crops. Another example is the prairie dog, which was extensively poisoned because of the mortality of horses and cattle after they stepped into prairie dog burrows and broke their legs. This extermination program has been highly successful—prairie dog populations have declined by 99 per cent. Once such a decline occurs, repercussions occur elsewhere in the food chain. In this case, the drastic decline in prairie dogs led to collapse of their main predator, the black-footed ferret, for which prairie dogs made up more than 90 per cent of their diet. Fortunately, the ferrets have been successfully bred in captivity, an example of **ex situ conservation**. The ferrets have been reintroduced to the wild in places where prairie dogs are protected. The swift fox is another example of predator control and ex situ conservation (Box 14.3).

Philip Dearden

Overhunting, especially for valuable products, is a main cause of endangerment for many species, such as this black rhinoceros in Kenya's Maasai Mara National Reserve. Predator species such as the lion are often greatly reduced in numbers and distribution due to competition with humans.

Although not often seen as "predators," deer are sometimes culled to prevent or stop overbrowsing of vegetation. Across parts of their North American range, white-tailed deer populations are literally eating themselves out of house and home—deer populations are in excess of what can be supported by the natural resource base. This is due in large part to reductions in range and population declines of their predators, particularly wolves. In stark contrast, other parts of the country, such as Vancouver Island, do not have enough deer, and provincial governments have considered shooting wolves in order to increase the number of deer that humans can kill for sport (Box 14.4). A similar debate is also underway in Newfoundland, where coyotes, which first invaded the island in the 1980s, are now taking significant numbers of caribou.

Recently, there have been calls in Prince Edward Island and Ontario to kill double-crested cormorants, accused of taking too many fish and threatening endangered plant species. Point Pelee National Park has established a cormorant cull on select islands in Lake Erie as part of an **active management** program to protect endangered plants that exist in few other places. As the human population grows and as our demands increase, conflicts over who will consume another organism will escalate. So far, other species appear to be losing the battle.

Habitat Change

Habitat change is *the* most important factor causing biodiversity loss at national and international scales. For endangered species in Canada, habitat degradation is responsible for 100 per cent of the listed reptiles, amphibians, invertebrates, and lichens, 99 per cent of the listed plants, 90 per cent of the listed birds, 85 per cent of the listed fish, and 67 per cent of the listed mammals. Habitat loss is the most prevalent threat overall, accounting for 84 per cent of listings (Venter et al., 2006).

Human demands are causing both physical and chemical changes to the environment. Physical changes such as deforestation *remove* important habitat components, while chemical pollution may *degrade* habitats to the point that they are no longer able to support wildlife even if the physical structure of the habitat remains. Humans place further pressure on species by the introduction of alien species (Chapter 3).

Physical Changes

Some impacts arising from physical changes in the natural environment have already been discussed relative to forestry and agricultural practices (Chapters 9 and 10). It is difficult

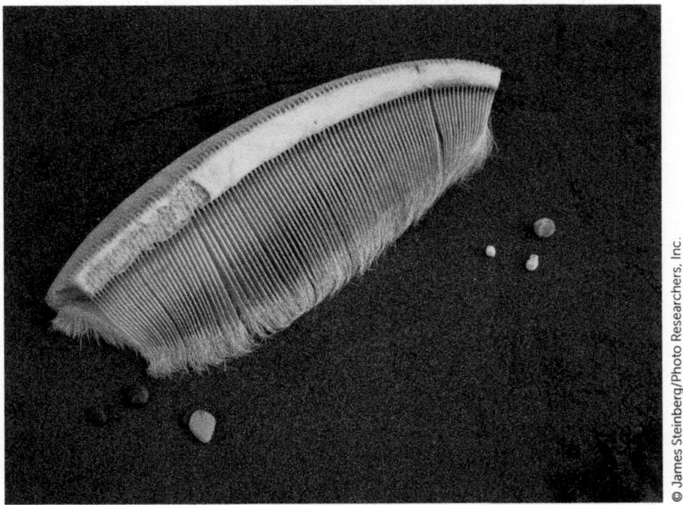

© James Steinberg/Photo Researchers, Inc.

Whales were hunted to the point of extinction around the world because of their commercial value. Baleen, or whalebone, pictured here, is a filter-feeding system inside a whale's mouth. It was used for such "indispensable" things as umbrellas, buggy whips, and ladies' corsets.

ENVIRONMENT IN FOCUS

BOX 14.3 | Ex Situ Conservation at Work

Not all species subject to heavy pressures are pushed to extinction. Some, such as the beaver, may recover in numbers and start to repopulate their old range. The beaver was able to repopulate with relatively little help. The swift fox, on the other hand, was the target of a 20-year, $20 million reintroduction program, emphasizing the difficulties and costs associated with trying to reverse extinction trends.

The swift fox is so called because of its ability to run down rabbits and other prey in its home terrain, the dry, shortgrass prairie. The swift fox is small (about half the size of a red fox), and at one time roamed all the way from Central America to the southern Prairies of Canada. Unlike most other members of the dog family, the swift fox uses dens throughout the year, preferably located on well-drained slopes close to a permanent water body. This may be for protection because of their small size. Natural enemies include coyotes and birds of prey such as eagles and red-tailed and rough-legged hawks.

The last swift fox in the wild was spotted in Alberta in 1938. A combination of factors led to its demise, including habitat degradation, overhunting, and predator control programs. The shortgrass prairie came under heavy pressure from cultivation, leading to a loss of habitat for the swift fox and many other species. In addition, the fox was heavily trapped in the mid and late 1800s for its soft, attractive pelt. The Hudson's Bay Company sold an average of 4,681 pelts per year between 1853 and 1877; by the 1920s, the take had declined to just 500 pelts per year. However, predator control programs against the coyote and wolf finally removed the swift fox from the Canadian Prairies. Predator control programs often relied on extermination methods not species-specific, such as poisoned bait and leg traps. As with many species, more than one factor typically drives a species to extinction, and these factors often interact synergistically.

Since 1978, efforts have been made to return the fox to the Prairies. Foxes were bred in captivity, and wild populations from the United States were relocated to Alberta. The captive breeding program was initiated by two private citizens, illustrating the positive impact that individuals can have on environmental issues. More than 600 swift foxes are now living and breeding in the wild on the Canadian Prairies.

The best strategy for the long-term protection of wildlife species is preservation of populations in the wild—only in natural communities are species able to continue their process of evolutionary adaptation to a changing environment. Conservation strategies focused on the organism within its natural habitat are referred to as **in situ preservation**. The Thelon Game Sanctuary in the Northwest Territories, for example, was established in 1927 to help protect the remaining population of muskox. Since that time, much of the mainland habitat of the animal has been recolonized by outmigration from this sanctuary. However, in situ preservation may not be a viable option for many rare species, including the swift fox. If remnant populations are too small, on-site preservation strategies will be ineffective. In such cases, the only way to prevent extirpation or extinction is to maintain individuals in artificial conditions under human supervision. This strategy is known as **ex situ preservation**. Zoos, game farms, aquariums, private breeders, and botanical gardens are all examples of ex situ facilities. The swift fox is an example of ex situ conservation, where the species is reintroduced to its natural habitat.

David Parsons/iStockphoto

Swift foxes have been successfully reintroduced to the Canadian Prairies using both captive-reared and wild-caught foxes from US Prairie states.

Given the scale of change evident in many species groups, some scientists believe that the only chance for survival for some is through the activities of zoos. One example is Amphibian Ark, which aims to prevent the world's more than 6,000 species of frogs, salamanders, and caecilians from disappearing. Scientists estimate that up to 170 species of frogs have become extinct over the past decade through fungal attack and other causes, and that an additional 1,900 species are threatened. Amphibian Ark wants zoos, botanical gardens, and aquariums in each country to take in at least 500 frogs from a **threatened species** to protect them from the killer fungus, thought to have originated in Africa. The fungus prevents amphibians from breathing through their pores and has wiped out frog populations from Australia to Costa Rica and the US. However, this is only a stopgap measure to buy time and prevent more species from going extinct while researchers figure out how to keep amphibians from dying off in the wild. Unfortunately, given the spread of alien species described in Chapter 3, combined with the effects of global climate change, such catastrophic measures are going to become much more common in the future.

TABLE 14.3 | Examples of Reintroductions of Endangered Species into Canadian National Parks

Species	Park
American beaver	Cape Breton Highlands, Prince Edward Island
American bison	Prince Albert, Riding Mountain
Plains bison	Elk Island
Wood bison	Nahanni National Park Reserve, Jasper, Waterton Lakes, Elk Island
Fisher	Georgian Bay Islands, Riding Mountain, Elk Island
American marten	Fundy, Kejimkujik, Terra Nova, Riding Mountain
Moose	Cape Breton Highlands
Muskox	Ivvavik
Trumpeter swan	Elk Island
Caribou	Cape Breton Highlands
Swift fox	Grassland

Source: Dearden, P. (2001).

historically to separate these influences from the more general impact of colonization in North America. Large areas of forests in central and eastern Canada were cleared to make way for agriculture. Species dependent on these forests, such as the eastern cougar and wolverine, suffered accordingly. Forests are still being replaced by agriculture in some areas. Venter et al. (2006) found that agriculture, followed by urbanization, was the largest cause of endangerment in Canada, although 70 per cent of listed species are under pressure from more than one source.

Before the mid 1850s, some 101 million hectares of longgrass prairie existed in central North America; less than 1 per cent remains. Other prairie ecozones have not fared much better, with only 13 per cent of shortgrass prairie, 19 per cent of mixed-grass prairie, and 16 per cent of aspen parkland remaining. Millions of bison and antelope once grazed these regions, and the land trembled with their migrations. The bison and the antelope have been replaced by cattle. Not surprisingly, one-half of Canada's endangered and threatened mammal and bird species are prairie dwellers. In Canada, an overall loss of 44 per cent of the populations of grassland bird species has happened since the 1970s, with individual species showing declines of up to 87 per cent (Downes et al., 2010).

Accompanying the transformation of the natural prairie grassland for agricultural purposes, thousands of hectares of wetlands have been drained to create more agricultural land. Until the early 1990s, the Canadian Wheat Board Act made it financially attractive for farmers to expand cropland instead of managing their land more effectively, and as a result much marginal land was brought under the plow. It is now estimated that more than 70 per cent of prairie wetlands have been drained. Of the remaining wetlands, 60 to 80 per cent of the habitat surrounding the basins is affected by farming practices. Such changes have been a major factor behind declines in waterfowl breeding on the Prairies, a trend only just being reversed by wildlife management practices (Box 14.5).

Draining of wetlands is not restricted to the Prairies. Eighty per cent of the wetlands of the Fraser River Delta have been converted to other uses, as have 68 per cent of the wetlands in southern Ontario and 65 per cent of the Atlantic coastal marshes. Drainage not only has a negative impact on marsh-dwelling species but also serves to increase pollutant loads and sediment inputs accumulated in drainage water. High pesticide, fertilizer, sediment, and salt levels may negatively affect organisms further downstream. Wetland drainage is recognized as being one of the main pressures on biodiversity declines both nationally and internationally. Canada has no national inventory or monitoring program, but is thought to harbour one-quarter of the world's remaining wetlands (Federal, Provincial, and Territorial Governments of Canada, 2010).

Another ecozone particularly hard-hit by habitat destruction is the Carolinian forests of southwestern Ontario. These southern deciduous forests support a greater variety of wildlife than any other ecosystem in the country, including 40 per cent of the breeding birds. More than 90 per cent of this habitat has now been transformed by forestry, agriculture, and urbanization; less than 5 per cent of the original woodland remains. An estimated 40 per cent of Canada's species at risk are in this zone. Most of the remaining forests are in tracts belonging to regional conservation authorities or in privately owned woodlots potentially open to logging. Landscapes such as these are particularly suited to stewardship initiatives, discussed in greater detail later in the chapter.

The Canadian Prairies have been virtually completely transformed into an agricultural landscape, with the result that many species native to this habitat are now endangered.

ENVIRONMENT IN FOCUS

BOX 14.4 | Wolf Control

Predator control is usually about killing animals that prey upon livestock, but some of the most controversial cases in Canada involve cases where predators, including wolves, are being killed to try to boost the numbers of another, usually endangered, species. The wolf was vilified as a rapacious killer and enemy of humans for centuries. It was shot, poisoned, and extirpated throughout large areas of its range, particularly in parts of the United States, where it became an endangered species. Canada has some of the healthiest wolf populations in the world, numbering around 58,000, and they are being used for reintroductions, such as the transfer of wolves from Alberta to Yellowstone National Park.

However, wolf populations are still threatened in many areas, including in and around parks. In Ontario, for example, in 2004 the government announced a permanent moratorium on wolf hunting and trapping in the 39 townships surrounding Algonquin Provincial Park. A moratorium was first enacted in 2001, designed to protect the largest remaining population of the eastern wolf. However, a loophole allowed traps to be set if coyotes were the intended target species, which led to the death of several wolves. This protection issue is complicated in eastern Canada by the increasing populations of coywolves—hybrid pack animals resulting from wolf–coyote interbreeding that are considerably larger than the western coyote yet, like the coyote and unlike the wolf, do not shy away from heavily human-impacted areas. Also, genetic makeup or ancestry does not appear to distinguish definitively "wolf" from "coyote" or "coywolf"; rather, like many early Aboriginal groups, it is who you run with that defines the individual. In 2010, British Columbia declared an open season on the wolf hunt in ranch country, allowing unlimited year-round trapping in some areas, while other areas are now allowed unlimited trapping on private land from 1 April to 14 October. In 2015, hunting also resumed in the Okanagan region after wolves started making a comeback.

The grey wolf has now been removed from the endangered species list in the US, and an unlikely beneficiary will probably be the pronghorn antelope. In areas where wolves became re-established in Montana, Wyoming, and Idaho, pronghorn antelope numbers grew by more than 50 per cent. Research shows that the increase was due to increased calf survival, since wolves find a pronghorn calf too small to be worth the effort. The same is not true for coyotes, which take a high number of the calves. As the wolves move into an area, they displace the coyotes, and the pronghorns thrive. This relationship illustrates how complex predator control can be, as shown in the next example.

Biologists in BC and Alberta are concerned about the declining numbers of mountain caribou and have identified wolf predation as a main contributing factor. In response, Alberta biologists killed 733 wolves in seven years in west-central Alberta (Hervieux et al., 2014). Wolves were captured by nets from helicopters, fitted with radio collars and released, and subsequently led the biologists to the entire pack which were then all killed by gunshot from the helicopters. In this manner 579 wolves were killed. The remainder of the wolves were killed through eating bait laced with strychnine. A further 91 ravens, 36 coyotes, 31 red foxes, four American martens, three lynx, two weasels, and two fishers also died, although it is highly likely that many undetected animals also died. The BC government in early 2015 announced a similar plan to shoot up to 184 wolves to protect caribou; however they were only able to shoot half that number—the rest could not be found.

Other scientists question this approach. Whether the wolves are the main factor in the caribou decline is open to question, as the Alberta government continues to open up increasing amounts of caribou habitat to industrial exploitation, particularly oil and gas exploration, contrary to the caribou protection policies of the federal government. Developing roads provides easier access for the wolves to prey on the caribou. In BC, a similar destruction of habitat has taken place through logging activities.

Scientists opposed to the kill also raise important questions regarding the moral and ethical approach taken by the biologists involved in reducing wolf numbers (Brook et al., 2015). Shooting animals from helicopters and using non-species-specific poisons are both approaches that cause inhumane suffering to both the target and non-target animals.

Another predator cull was carried out earlier on Vancouver Island, the home of Canada's only endemic endangered

Brad Hill and Raincoast

The Raincoast Conservation Foundation invested in roadside billboards to raise awareness among the public about BC's 2015 wolf kill intended to reduce predator pressure on endangered caribou populations.

mammal, the Vancouver Island marmot. Numbers of the marmot were as low as 30 before ex situ breeding programs were established and began reintroducing animals into their mountain homelands. Released marmots have successfully bred in the wild and there are now an estimated 320–370 animals living in the wild with potential breeding pairs on 28 mountains—up from three mountains in 2006. However, this highly vulnerable population is threatened by predation. In a study conducted in 2002, 6 of 18 fitted with radio-transmitter collars were killed by predators—wolves killed four, an eagle killed one, and a cougar killed the other. A study between 2001 and 2005 showed that as marmot populations declined, their social structure began to disappear, compounding their risk for extinction. In 2003, despite government estimates that pointed to a decline in wolf and cougar populations on the island, a cull of up to 30 wolves and 20 cougars was approved. Some environmentalists suggest that if the government was truly concerned about recovering marmot populations, it would advocate an end to clear-cut logging at higher elevations. Non-lethal predator management techniques are now being tested, such as the use of human shepherds, which has shown some success in deterring cougars and wolves but not golden eagles. New release sites are also being tested to see if predation rates vary from site to site. Similarly, new breeding programs focus on breeding in natural conditions and within colonies in an attempt to help the marmots regain their sociality.

Do you think that it is acceptable to cull one endangered species if it is threatening the survival of an even more endangered species? The marmot case is not unique; the same problem arises on the west coast with the reintroduced sea otter that is feasting on another endangered species, abalone. What would you do?

Concern about the loss of habitat for Canadian species extends beyond the Canadian border. The harsh winters and productive summers that characterize much of Canada mean that many species in Canada, especially birds, are migratory. Over the past few decades, significant population declines have occurred for species that spend most of the year in tropical habitats but migrate to Canada to breed. In BC, for example, significant declines have occurred among northern flickers, Swainson's thrushes, chipping sparrows, yellow warblers, and dark-eyed juncos. These declines probably involve several factors, including loss of winter range through tropical deforestation and increased **fragmentation** within their northern breeding habitat. More long-term data and detailed studies are required to sort out the complexities of these changes.

Sometimes the impact of physical habitat change can be indirect. A good example is the parasitic habit of the brown-headed cowbird. This species lays its eggs in the nests of other species. The unsuspecting parents often lavish more attention on this large interloper and neglect their own young, leading to their death. The cowbird is an indigenous grassland species, but its distribution has expanded dramatically with human disturbance, since it prefers fragmented habitats and is adept at interloping on the forest-edge nesting sites of other birds. Some of its favourite targets are endangered species, such as the Kirtland's warbler, for which rates of up to 70 per cent parasitism have been recorded.

Physical habitat change has usually focused on aspects of the land or water that a species inhabits. An integral component of this habitat is the climate of the area. Ecological theory, as outlined in Chapter 2, tells us that vegetation growth is primarily controlled by climate in most areas and that animal communities depend on the vegetation for their sustenance. Global climate change will have a dramatic effect on these relationships.

The climate change scenarios for Canada show that we will be one of the most affected countries in the world because of our high latitudes, as discussed in Chapter 7. The northern regions are already showing large-scale reductions in snow and ice cover, reductions in permafrost, coastal inundation, and stressed populations of northern species such as polar bears. The US government has listed the polar bear under its Endangered Species Act as a result of thinning ice sheets due to global warming.

Scientists predict that each 1°C rise in temperature will cause biomes to migrate northward some 300 kilometres. Given the predicted minimum increase of 2–5°C in 70 to 100 years, this will translate into 600 to 1,500 metres in elevation and 300 to 750 kilometres in distance. Species will either be able to migrate fast enough to keep up with these changes, evolve to deal with them, or go extinct. Certain biomes, such as Arctic-alpine and the boreal forest, will be very vulnerable to these changes. In Canada, many of the great caribou herds have plummeted in numbers, and there is concern that they may be in danger of extirpation over a large part of their range (Festa-Bianchet et al., 2011). In the High Arctic, the most northerly caribou, Peary's, numbered more than 50,000 in the 1970s and are now down to about 12,000. Warmer weather has caused an increase in freezing rains, creating a surface that the caribou cannot penetrate to access the tundra vegetation beneath it, and they starve to death. Global climate change is not the only problem, but when linked with other causes, such as logging, increased predation due to habitat changes, disturbance by mining and oil exploration, and overhunting, the pressures may well reach a critical threshold for many populations.

Some effects of climate change are subtle. Mismatch between food supply and brood arrival in birds is one example. Many bird species are returning from southern migrations earlier and also producing earlier offspring. These

ENVIRONMENT IN FOCUS

BOX 14.5 | Are Conservation Efforts Paying off for Canada's "Duck Factory"?

Millions of ducks, geese, and swans darken the skies every year as they migrate across the length of the continent and back again. This annual migration evokes a sense of wonder and mystery in the more than 60 million North Americans who watch migratory birds each year. But for some, wonder and mystery is accompanied by anxiety over the future status of the 35 species of waterfowl that spend part of each year in Canada. Waterfowl depend on a complex and increasingly vulnerable chain of habitats extending across international borders, and their numbers fluctuate markedly (Figure 14.3).

Many of the most productive wetlands in Canada have been drained to bring more land under cultivation. Wetlands in the Prairie provinces are particularly productive. The retreat of glaciers that at one time covered all of Canada left behind significant nutrient deposits, which have formed the basis of richly productive ecosystems. Waterfowl such as mallards and pintails feed on the plants and invertebrates that feed on the nutrients. But as farm intensification has increased, prairie wetlands have diminished in number and extent, making it difficult for ducks to secure adequate food supplies and nesting sites along their long migratory routes.

Unfortunately, habitat loss and degradation are not the only pressures on migrating waterfowl. Duck mortality rates also vary in response to weather, climate, competition for resources, environmental contamination, and hunting. In the Canadian and US Prairies, weather has a particularly strong influence on the habitat conditions for waterfowl breeding and consequently on the abundance of waterfowl populations. Drought in the late 1980s and early 1990s created difficult breeding conditions for ducks. Spring habitat conditions improved into the late 1990s from the low levels during the drought of the 1980s but declined again in the early years of this century. In 2002, pond numbers were 58 per cent below the 10-year and the long-term (1961–2002) averages, and total duck populations declined by 33 per cent (to 7.2 million ducks), illustrating the dramatic impact that weather can have on the reproductive potential of waterfowl. By 2009 and 2010, numbers were at all-time lows, with more than 34 per cent of the total ducks that usually settle in the Canadian Prairies staying in the US. Major flooding events in the spring of 2011 saw a record-breaking 45.6 million ducks in the Canadian and US Prairies and this rose to 49.2 million by 2014 with an accompanying record number of ponds (7.18 million).

Hunting regulations were introduced decades ago by the Canadian and American governments to protect waterfowl populations, but governments were slow to recognize the impact of land-use practices on waterfowl habitat and therefore abundance. The issue was not formally addressed until 1986, when Canada and the US signed the North American Waterfowl Management Plan (NAWMP) (Mexico joined in 1994). A distinctive feature was the focus on public–private **stewardship** initiatives, and it remains one of the most successful examples of this kind of stewardship approach to conservation. The priority goals of the plan were to:

- Sustain average waterfowl populations of the 1970s
- Stop further wetland loss
- Stop further loss of native lands, especially native grasslands
- Restore lost wetlands, especially small basins
- Restore the function of upland habitats in landscapes conducive for maintenance of bird populations

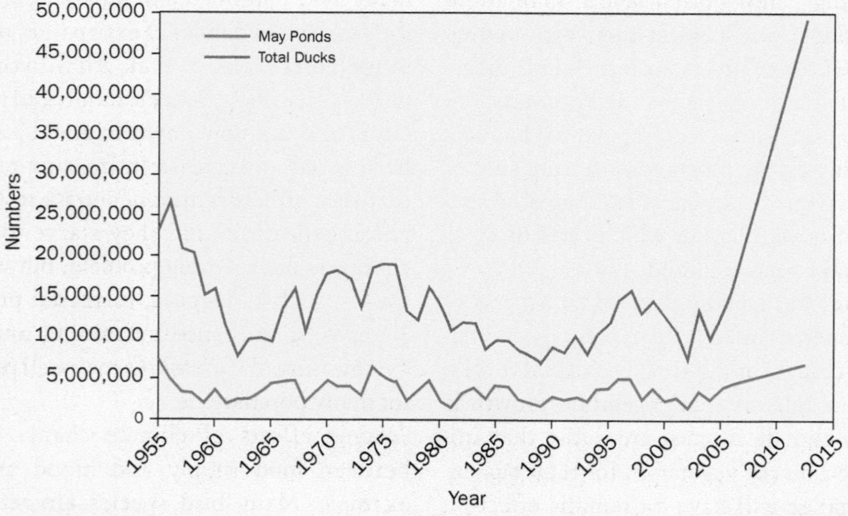

FIGURE 14.3 | Estimates of total ducks and May ponds in the southern Prairie region of Canada.

Source: Adapted from Environment Canada (2007a).

Conservation efforts under the NAWMP include involvement from various stakeholder groups—government agencies at all levels, industry, conservation groups, hunters, farmers, and other landowners. Duck conservation practices include maintaining nesting areas on land close to shallow water for land breeders such as mallards, pintails, teal, gadwalls, wigeons, and shovellors and ensuring that water levels are managed for diving ducks such as redheads and canvasbacks. Encouraging better cropping practices is also important. More than 17,000 landowners participate in habitat conservation programs on their lands. It is perhaps this cooperation and the reduction in the rate of habitat changes that have spawned the increasing numbers of ducks in recent times. However, only time will tell whether these can be sustained.

changes may not be reflected in the abundance of the food supply, which may not be so tightly keyed to climate change. For example, on the west coast several fish-eating birds have declined rapidly in numbers over the last few decades. Their hatching dates have moved earlier by over a month in some species and these dates no longer match peak food supply in their ocean habitat (Gaston et al., 2009).

Hybrids occur in nature, but what happens when hybrids occur much more frequently because of human interference, such as through climate change? Are they to be celebrated as a natural evolutionary adjustment to climate change or despised as the ultimate symbol of human interference with the greatest biological process on Earth, evolution? Animal hybrids are often infertile, as is most often the case, for example, of the mule, the offspring of a donkey and a horse. Even if not, they might have trouble finding a mate. Species with small populations can rarely afford the luxury of wasted reproductive effort, so this is particularly troubling for endangered species. Furthermore, interbreeding may lead to genetic swamping of a rare species by a more common one. Thus, fears exist that the endangered red wolf of eastern Canada may become genetically swamped by interbreeding with the more common coyote.

Interaction among many different changes caused by global climate change is also important. For example, the whitebark pine of the Pacific coast and Rocky Mountains may run out of habitat as temperatures rise. Its population has already fallen by 70 per cent as a result of an infectious fungus called blister rust, mountain beetle infestation, rising temperatures, and fire suppression.

Chemical Changes

As the number of chemicals introduced into the environment continues to increase, concern over chemical degradation of habitats intensifies. Pollution is the second-most important cause of endangerment for freshwater species in Canada. The effects of chemical pollution are often more difficult to assess than those of physical destruction. Unless there is a catastrophic chemical spill, the signs of declining populations often go unnoticed for several years, even decades. Even after population declines have been documented, it may take many years of careful analysis before a conclusive link to chemical pollution can be established. This was the case with the decline in the numbers of birds at the top trophic level (Box 14.6) after pesticide biomagnification (Chapter 10) led to thinner eggshells and ultimately lower breeding success. Bald eagles, for example, had been killed for a long time around the Great Lakes, but it was the total breeding failure due to high chemical levels that led to their extirpation from the Ontario side of Lake Erie by 1980. In 1980, only seven nests existed along the entire Canadian shoreline of the Great Lakes, including Lake Superior, and not one healthy chick was produced.

Bald eagles have now recolonized many areas in the Great Lakes region where they were extirpated as a result of chemical use, but the birds are often dying young—at 13 to 15 years, less than half their normal natural lifespan. Autopsies completed on dead birds show high levels of lead and mercury contamination. The former is likely persisting in the environment from the time when lead was used in the manufacture of bullets and fishing lures; it should decrease over time. The source of mercury, which is highly toxic and accumulates through the food chain, is undetermined, although mercury is a naturally occurring element. It has been eliminated from most products in which it was once used, and discharges from human sources are down about 80 per cent. However, the metal is emitted as a by-product of burning coal to produce electricity. Mercury also tends to build up in fish that live in the reservoirs behind power dams, as discussed in Chapter 11 regarding the James Bay Project. Scientists are now investigating these sources and their links to bald eagles.

Philip Dearden

Bald eagles in the Great Lakes region are dying at half their natural lifespan, often with high levels of lead and mercury in their systems as result of the persistence of these pollutants in the environment.

There are also interesting and disturbing links between contaminant pollution and climate change. For example, in western Hudson Bay, due to declining sea ice, polar bears are feeding more on fish-eating open-water seals rather than on invertebrate-eating ice seals. Fish-eating seals have larger concentrations of contaminants, resulting in larger concentrations in polar bears. One contaminant flame retardant chemical increased in concentration among polar bears sampled by 28 per cent between 1991 and 2007 (Mckinney et al., 2009).

Alien Species

Invasive alien species are responsible for about 40 per cent of animal extinctions for which the cause is known, and globally these species are second only to habitat destruction as a main cause of endangerment. Introduced species have a significant impact by out-competing native species for necessary resources or by direct predation on native species (Chapter 3). The introduction of new species to insular habitats provides graphic examples of the destruction that can be wrought. On Haida Gwaii, for example, the introduction of both raccoons and Norway rats is having a catastrophic impact on ground-nesting seabirds. The breeding population of ancient murrelets on Langara Island off the north coast of Haida Gwaii declined by approximately 40 per cent between 1988 and 1993, leaving the population at less than 10 per cent of its original size. Further south in the new national park reserve of Gwaii Hanaas, the main ancient murrelet colony on Kunghit Island decreased in size by approximately one-third between 1986 and 1993. In both cases, predation by Norway rats appears to be mainly responsible for the declines.

Aside from direct predation, alien species can affect native species in other ways. For example, populations of the Newfoundland crossbill have declined significantly; competition for food (pine cones) with the introduced red squirrel is believed responsible. However, in contrast to the US, Venter et al. (2006) found that, currently, alien species are the least influential causes of endangerment in Canada. This is likely to change as warming climates make for a more hospitable environment for many more potential invaders.

Vulnerability to Extinction

The effects of overhunting and habitat degradation differ among species, since not all species are equally vulnerable to extinction. Ecologists have identified a set of extinction-prone characteristics to identify species most vulnerable to extinction. Using such characteristics, conservationists are better able to anticipate the need for protection. Species with one or more of the following characteristics are more vulnerable to extinction.

- *Specialized habitats for feeding or breeding.* Once a habitat is altered, the environment may no longer be suitable for specialized species. A good example is the northern spotted owl, discussed in Chapter 9. Northern spotted owls require old-growth habitat for survival and reproduction.
- *Migratory patterns.* Many songbirds are experiencing population declines in Canada as a result of their long and hazardous migrations to South and Central America. Species that migrate seasonally depend on two or more distinct habitat types, and if either one of these habitats is damaged, the species may be unable to persist.
- *Insular and local distributions.* Dawson's caribou, endemic to the Haida Gwaii archipelago, became extinct because of the ease with which it could be hunted in such a restricted habitat, with no hope of an emigrating population for replacement.
- *High economic value.* Many organisms are overharvested to the point of extinction because of their high economic value. The American ginseng was once abundant in the forests of eastern North America but is now rare because of demand in Asian countries for dried ginseng roots for medicinal purposes. Similarly, populations of Asian bears have been all but eliminated across their range. Their gall bladders are highly valued in Asian markets, and North American bears are now coming under pressure from the same markets. A single gall bladder can be worth more than $5,000. One illegal dealer in BC was found with 1,125 gall bladders in his possession. BC has passed a law making possession of endangered animal contraband an offence. The recent increases in elephant poaching in Africa, with poachers killing over 100,000 elephants between 2010 and 2012, is driven by the demand for ivory mainly in China.
- *Animals with large body size.* Large animals tend to have large home ranges, require more food, and are more easily hunted by humans. Top carnivores, for example, depend on abundance of many different species lower in the food chain. If the numbers of prey species are disrupted, the impacts are felt at the top of the food chain. Furthermore, animals higher up the food chain are more vulnerable to the concentration of toxic materials (Chapter 10). Killer whales are a good example of this vulnerability.
- *Need for a large home range.* Species that need to forage over a wide area are prone to extinction when part of their range is damaged or fragmented. Grizzly bears, for example, are very sensitive to fragmentation caused by logging and agricultural clearance.
- *Only one or a few populations and/or small population size.* Any one population may "blink out" as a result of chance factors (e.g., earthquakes, fire, disease), increasing the species's vulnerability to extinction. Small populations are also more likely to become extinct locally because of their greater vulnerability to demographic and environmental variation. This is why one of the main goals of the Vancouver Island marmot reintroduction has been to start a number of geographically dispersed different colonies.

ENVIRONMENT IN FOCUS

BOX 14.6 | Raptors as Indicators of Chemical Degradation of Habitat

Sitting as they do at the top of the food chain, birds of prey or raptors are powerful indicator species of ecosystem health. Raptors were discovered to be useful indicators of environmental health during the 1960s when research into drastic population declines in bird- and fish-eating species revealed that eggshell-thinning and reproductive failure were caused by organochlorine pesticides. The decline of peregrine falcon populations is particularly well documented.

Peregrine falcons are powerful birds of prey, catching other birds in flight while attaining speeds as great as 300 kilometres per hour. Favourite prey include songbirds, waterfowl, pigeons, shorebirds, and seabirds, and, especially among the Arctic peregrines, small mammals such as lemmings. Falcons nest on cliffs or in trees where they can look down over water bodies. Tall buildings in cities may serve as a substitute, in which case urban pigeons are the main prey.

The peregrine falcon once bred all across Canada. Populations appeared remarkably stable until the 1940s when they started to crash, linked to the bioaccumulation of pesticides (Chapter 10) such as DDT, DHC, dieldrin, and heptachlor epoxide. Surveys in the 1970s documented the continuing downfall of the peregrine, and by that time the species had been extirpated from large areas of its previous range. In 1978, COSEWIC classified peregrines as endangered.

In the late 1980s, urban populations were established in southern Canada through the reintroduction of captive-raised young (an example of ex situ conservation). The program was expanded, and now more than 700 birds have been released to the wild at more than 20 sites from the Bay of Fundy to southern Alberta and the Okanagan Valley in BC.

Peregrine falcons appear to be recovering. Nevertheless, chemical habitat degradation is not the only stress threatening the long-term viability of peregrine falcons across Canada. In BC, for example, falcon populations are threatened by declines in the raptor's supply of colonizing seabirds due to habitat loss and competition from alien predators such as rats. Alien species are discussed in more detail in a later subsection.

In 1996, the captive breeding station was closed and the peregrine has been downlisted by COSEWIC. In fact, raptors overall have increased by 70 per cent since the 1970s, largely as a function of phasing out use of the chemicals to which they proved to be so vulnerable (North American Bird Conservation Initiative Canada, 2014).

JeremyTolbert/iStockphoto

The peregrine falcon suffered badly as a result of the biomagnification of agricultural chemicals but is now recovering in numbers in many areas.

- *Not effective dispersers*. Species unable to adapt to changing environments must migrate to a more suitable habitat or face extinction. Species that cannot migrate quickly have a greater chance of extinction. This factor will become much more important as the impact of climate change increases.
- *Behavioural traits or feeding needs causing susceptibility*. Some species have behavioural traits that make them particularly vulnerable to clashes with human activities. For example, the red-headed woodpecker flies in front of cars, and the Florida manatee appears to be attracted by motorboats, a main cause of death for the animal. Other species, although not attracted by human activities, may be too slow to get out of the way, such as with right whales off the east coast. Others are caught incidentally when feeding near human harvesting activities. This is often the case with fisheries bycatch where an additional mortality of 4 per cent of the Canadian population of black-footed albatross, and 7 per cent of the Nova Scotia breeding population of common eider (Calvert et al., 2013), are caught. These are both very vulnerable populations.

Although some species are more vulnerable to extinction than others, some species also naturally occur at lower population densities than others. The cougar, for example, was once found all across North America but at very low densities because of its need for an area large enough for each individual to secure sufficient food. How do scientists determine whether a species is just naturally rare or declining and in danger of extinction? How small does a population have to be before it is considered endangered? These and similar questions are answered by scientists on the basis of standardized, quantitative criteria. In Canada, COSEWIC uses criteria based on those suggested by IUCN and used in the global Red List.

The extinction of species may now be occurring roughly 100 to 1,000 times faster than the natural rate of extinction. This rate of extinction is much faster than the evolution of new species, so we are in a period in which the world's biological diversity is in decline. Even high-profile species, such as the tiger, are declining rapidly, despite millions of dollars devoted to their protection, as discussed in the "International Guest Statement" in Chapter 2. What are nations doing to arrest this decline in biodiversity? What are the best strategies for the long-term preservation of biological diversity? In the sections that follow, we will discuss the international and Canadian responses to our biodiversity crisis.

Philip Dearden

Alive or dead, exotic species, such as these porcupine fish made into ornaments in Thailand, do not belong in your home.

Philip Dearden

Philip Dearden

Species that have high economic values are targeted by hunters and poachers. Here a leopard has fallen victim to a poacher's snare in a park in Sri Lanka, and these cobras in Laos are now part of a local drink.

Responses to the Loss of Biodiversity

The International Response

Awareness that we are living in a period of mass extinction unprecedented in human history has led to several international conventions and programs. Some programs have a regional orientation, such as the North American Waterfowl Management Plan with the United States and Mexico (Box 14.5), while others include many different nations. Established in 1973, the Convention on International Trade in Endangered Species of Wild Fauna and Flora (CITES) is one of the longest-standing treaties. Ratified by more than 120 countries (including Canada), this treaty establishes lists of species for which international trade is to be controlled or monitored (e.g., orchids, cacti, parrots, large cat species, sea turtles, rhinos, primates). International treaties such as CITES are implemented when a country passes laws to enforce them. Once CITES laws are passed within a country, police, customs inspectors, wildlife officers, and other government agents can arrest and prosecute individuals possessing or trading in CITES-listed species and seize the products or organisms involved. Countries that ratify CITES also vote on the species that should be protected by the treaty.

Several well-known Canadian species are listed under Appendix II of the convention, such as the lynx, bobcat, cougar, polar bear, river otter, and burrowing owl. These species may only be traded with a valid permit from the Canadian

Wildlife Service. When travelling through international airports in Canada, you will commonly see information on CITES to warn travellers about trying to import listed plants or animals.

CITES has been instrumental in restricting trade in certain endangered wildlife species. Its most notable success has been a global ban on the ivory trade, instituted in 1989. Without this ban, it is unlikely that any elephants would be left in East Africa, although large-scale smuggling is still evident. Despite the treaty's success in protecting some species, Canada's support has been disappointing.

In March 2013 at the CITES Conference of the Parties in Bangkok, Canada made a spectacular statement against international moves to restrict trade in endangered species by filing reservations to virtually every recommendation. Delegates from 180 countries voted to extend protection to a further 76 species. Canada voted against every one, the vast majority of which do not occur at all in Canada. Compared to this record, Iceland has filed 22 reservations, Japan 18, the UK 8, and the US none in the entire history of CITES. There is no rational explanation for this position, other than that it reflects the overall approach of the federal government to conservation issues. Most Canadians will never realize how they are being represented at the international level by our government.

Other international treaties focused on conserving biodiversity include:

- Convention on Conservation of Migratory Species of Wild Animals (the Bonn Convention, 1979)
- Convention on Conservation of Antarctic Marine Living Resources (1982)
- International Convention for the Regulation of Whaling, which established the International Whaling Commission (1946)
- International Convention for the Protection of Birds (1950)
- Benelux Convention on the Hunting and Protection of Birds (1970)

Unfortunately, participation in these treaties is voluntary, and countries can withdraw at any time to pursue their own interests when they find the conditions of compliance too arduous. Canada, for example, withdrew from the Whaling Convention in order to unilaterally permit indigenous whaling in the Arctic. Although Japan still participates, it acts against the spirit of the Convention by continuing to hunt whales under scientific pretenses. The excess whale meat from these putative scientific expeditions is sold commercially.

One of the most important international agreements to protect biodiversity—the **Convention on Biological Diversity (CBD)**—emerged from the World Summit on Sustainable Development held in Rio de Janeiro in 1992 (Chapter 1). The CBD is legally binding and requires signatories to develop biodiversity strategies, identify and monitor important components of biodiversity, develop endangered species legislation and **protected areas** systems, and promote environmentally sound and sustainable development in areas adjacent to protected areas (also see Chapter 2). The Conference of the Parties adopted a motion to achieve by 2010 a significant reduction of the current rate of biodiversity loss at the global, regional, and national levels and met in Japan in 2010 to assess progress. At that time, it became clear that the countries of the world not only had failed to halt biodiversity erosion but had even failed to slow down the rate of biodiversity erosion (Secretariat of the Convention on Biological Diversity, 2010).

The question is why, and what can be done about it? There are many answers to this question, but a main one is shown in Figure 14.4. Tremendous effort has been invested over the last decade in trying to assess the state of biodiversity and in dealing with direct causes of biodiversity loss, such as habitat loss, by setting aside protected areas, as discussed in the next section. However, relatively little attention has been devoted to addressing the main drivers of biodiversity loss, such as poverty, increased spread of invasive species, and climate change. Future strategies must address these challenges as well as documenting and increasing the benefits that humans derive from biodiversity if the required progress is to occur in terms of preventing further biodiversity erosion. New targets for 2020 for the CBD were adopted in Japan as discussed in the "International Guest Statement" later in this chapter.

Canada has been very slow in implementing many strategies required by the Convention. The *Canadian Biodiversity Strategy* (Canada, 1995) was developed as a response to the requirements of the CBD, and other developments, such as the new Species at Risk Act (described below), are also consistent with these requirements. However, not until 2006 was Canada's Biodiversity Outcomes Framework agreed upon and begun to be implemented, and only in 2010 was the first report released on the status of Canada's ecosystems (Federal, Provincial, and Territorial Governments of Canada, 2010). The report is useful, but one of the main lessons was the lack of adequate data on many aspects of biodiversity in Canada to be able to understand trends, let alone design strategies to address the needs. These responses are discussed more in the next section.

The Canadian Response

In 1973, the United States became the first country to pass endangered species legislation. Australia followed some 20 years later, and a host of other countries, including the European Union and Japan, have developed similar legislation. In Canada, most provinces have endangered species legislation, while others, such as BC, Alberta, and Saskatchewan continue to manage endangered species under

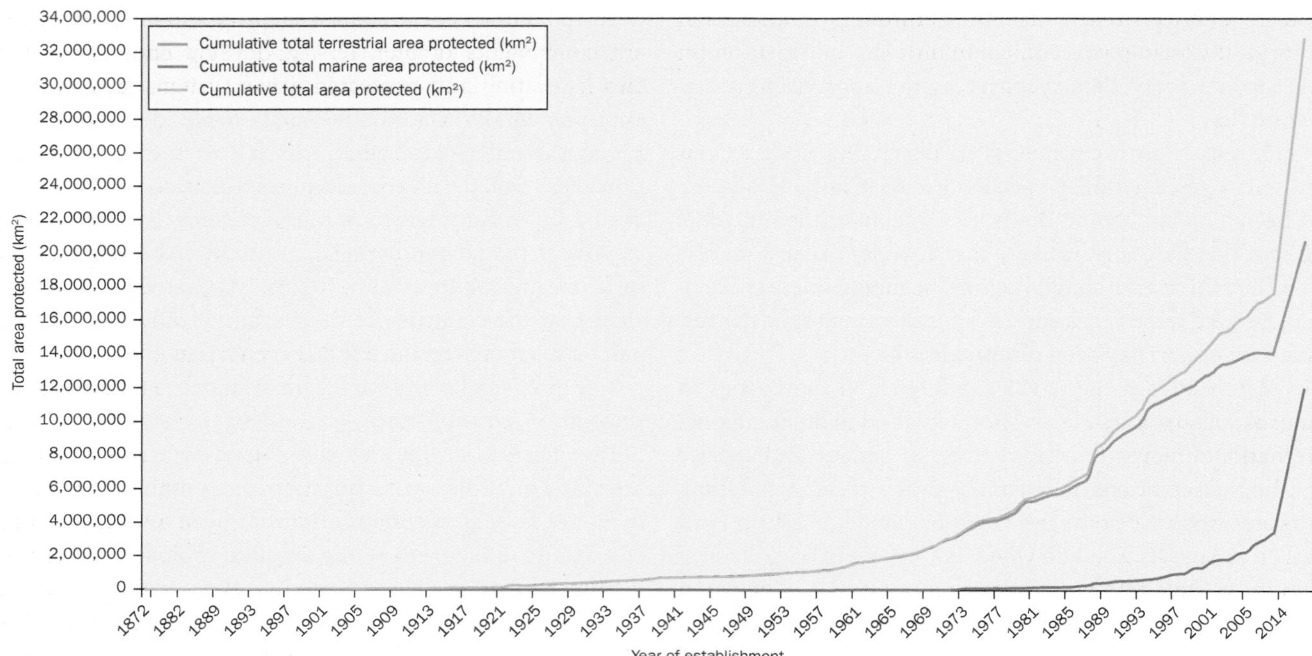

FIGURE 14.4 | Growth in global nationally designated protected areas, 1872–2014.

Source: Adapted from IUCN and UNEP-WCMC (2009) The World Database on Protected Areas (WDPA): January 2009. Cambridge, UK: UNEP-WCMC.

Sariska Tiger Reserve (left) in India is protected by Project Tiger and yet had all 26 tigers poached out of it in the early years of this century. Authorities have now reintroduced tigers to the reserve, and, for the first time, reintroduced tigers have bred successfully and cubs have been born. Tiger reintroductions are very difficult and it is much better to invest in saving tiger populations than trying to reintroduce them after extirpation. The Chinese government is now planning to reintroduce tigers into southern China, as in this reserve in Hunan (right), but first the prey base must be re-established to ensure they have food to eat.

more generic legislation, such as wildlife acts. It took many years for the federal government to respond to the legislative challenge of protecting endangered species. The **Species at Risk Act (SARA)** was finally passed in 2002. The federal government had little choice; as a signatory to the CBD, it was required to enact such legislation.

One reason the government was so reluctant to introduce and pass federal endangered species legislation related to the Canadian Constitution. Unlike the situation in many other countries, most of the land in Canada is publicly owned, with 71 per cent held by the provinces and 23 per cent held by the federal government (see Chapter 1). Most responsibilities are shared by these two levels of government, with the federal government responsible for oceans and freshwater ecosystems, migratory birds, and the management of federal lands, including the Northwest Territories and Nunavut. Yukon now has responsibilities for its own land base, and a similar devolution is underway for the NWT and Nunavut. The federal government also has responsibility for Aboriginal lands in the provinces, although this continues to change as land claim negotiations are settled. Therefore, much of Canada's public lands, and their resources, are under provincial jurisdiction. Federal legislation may not be easily enforced in Canada.

Provincial and territorial legislation differs widely in scope and rigour of application. The New Brunswick approach, in its 2012 Species at Risk Act, closely mirrors the federal process in that determination of endangerment is separated from assessment of the strategies that may be required to address recovery. Ontario, on the other hand, in its 2007 Endangered Species Act divorced the listing process from socio-economic considerations. Species are listed as endangered if they are endangered, irrespective of the socio-economic aspects. The Northwest Territories approach in its 2010 Species at Risk (NWT) Act is interesting in that it includes traditional ecological community and science knowledge at each stage in the listing, recovery, and stewardship process. If your province has legislation, is it effective? Which criteria would you use to judge "effectiveness"? How do we know? If your province does not have explicit nature conservation legislation, why not?

Research consistently shows that ordinary citizens are in favour of species protection, but often government response does not meet that expectation, as illustrated in the "Perspectives on the Environment" box.

The Canadian Endangered Species Conservation Council (CESCC) comprises the three federal ministers responsible for Environment, Canadian Heritage, and Fisheries and Oceans, as well as provincial and territorial ministers responsible for the conservation and management of wildlife. The CESCC coordinates federal, provincial, and territorial government activities related to the protection of species at risk and provides general direction on the activities of COSEWIC and the preparation of recovery strategies and action plans.

Since 1976, COSEWIC has been responsible for determining the status of endangered species. The committee—which includes representatives from relevant federal agencies, provincial and territorial wildlife agencies, and the Aboriginal community, as well eight scientific subcommittees that are species specialist groups—meets annually to consider status reports on candidate species and to assign them to various categories. In 2007, 552 species were designated in five risk categories, and by 2014 this had risen to 721 species (Table 14.2). Ideally, the numbers of threatened species would be falling over time and their category of endangerment becoming less severe.

A recent evaluation was undertaken of the status of species that had been assessed several times by COSEWIC to ascertain whether their status had changed between assessments. The study (Favaro et al., 2014) of 369 species found that 115 species deteriorated, 202 remained unchanged, and 52 improved in status. Twenty species improved their status as they were no longer "at risk"; however, for five of them this was due to improved sampling rather than an increased population. In other words, in Canada, identification of a species as being "at risk" is not very effective as a means to direct effort into reducing that endangerment.

The committee's assessment is the first step in the process for protecting a proposed species at risk under SARA (Box 14.7). However, even if COSEWIC lists a species, this action does not guarantee that the species will receive protection. The ultimate decision is in the hands of the politicians who make up the CESCC, and for this reason SARA has been strongly criticized by many who feel that the process should be scientific, not political.

The influence of politics was clear when the first new species listings under SARA were made in 2004, when the federal fisheries minister delayed by nine months a decision on whether to list 12 aquatic species recommended by COSEWIC. By 2009, while 77 per cent of the species suggested for listing by COSEWIC had been listed under SARA, only 35 per cent of marine fish species recommended for protection on biological grounds were protected.

An analysis of the kinds of species assessed for inclusion on the list found that 93 per cent of non-harvested species recommended by COSEWIC have been listed by SARA, while only 17 per cent of harvested species are listed (Findlay et al., 2010). Schultz et al. (2013) found that no marine fish with an anticipated cost of listing greater than zero received protection.

Species in the North are also less likely to be listed than species in southern Canada. Mooers et al. (2007) suggest that these patterns result from the lack of capacity or willingness on the part of certain agencies, particularly the Department of Fisheries and Oceans (DFO) and wildlife management boards in the North, to accept the additional stewardship responsibilities required by SARA. Delays for further consultation with management boards may lead to the extinction of some species, such as the eastern beluga. A second reason is that

ENVIRONMENT IN FOCUS

BOX 14.7 | The Process for Protecting a Species at Risk

1. COSEWIC assesses and classifies a wildlife species as extinct, extirpated, endangered, threatened, of special concern, data deficient, or not at risk. COSEWIC provides its report to the minister of the Environment and the Canadian Endangered Species Conservation Council, and a copy is deposited in the Public Registry.
2. Within 90 days, the minister indicates how he or she intends to respond to a COSEWIC assessment. Within nine months, the government makes a decision about whether or not to add the species to the List of Wildlife Species at Risk. If no government action is taken, the species is automatically added.
3. When a species is on or added to the List of Wildlife Species at Risk, then extirpated, endangered, or threatened species and their habitats have:
   - immediate protection on federal lands (except for those species in the territories that go through the safety net process described below)
   - immediate protection if it is an aquatic species
   - immediate protection if it is a migratory bird
   - protection through a safety net process if it is any other species in a province or territory
4. For all species included on the List of Wildlife Species at Risk on 5 June 2003:
   - A recovery strategy must be prepared within three years for endangered species and within four years for threatened species or extirpated species (progress regarding such strategies is discussed below).
   - A management plan must be prepared within five years for a special-concern species.

   For all species added to the List of Wildlife Species at Risk after 5 June 2003:
   - A recovery strategy must be prepared within one year for endangered species and within two years for threatened or extirpated species.
   - A management plan must be prepared within three years for a special-concern species.
5. Recovery strategies and action plans, which must include the identification of critical habitat for the species if possible, and management plans are published in the Public Registry. The public has 60 days to comment on these documents.

Five years after a recovery strategy, action plan, or management plan comes into effect, the minister must report on the implementation and the progress toward meeting objectives.

Source: Canada, Species at Risk Act (2004).

each suggested species undergoes a cost–benefit analysis in which very little attention is given to the benefits, both tangible and intangible, whereas the costs are studied in detail. Furthermore, these analyses are not open to peer review.

For species listed under SARA, recovery and management plans must be developed and implemented, unless the minister responsible feels that recovery is not "feasible," a caveat that provides another political opportunity to block action. Under the Act, proposed recovery strategies allow for a 60-day comment period during which any person may file written comments with the minister responsible. Within 30 days of the closing of the public comment period, the proposed recovery strategy must be finalized. Recovery strategies are evaluated every five years and updated as necessary. As emphasized in the "Perspectives on the Environment" box below, Canada is not living up to these legislated requirements.

The Act has been further criticized because even when a species is listed, it receives automatic protection only on federal lands. In southern Canada, where many endangered species live, a significant proportion of federal lands are national parks in which the species are already protected. Therefore, no incremental gain in protection occurs unless provincial jurisdictions agree to provide it. There is a so-called "safety net" whereby the federal government can invoke powers to act if a provincial government refuses to do so and if the case is seen as critical. It has never been used.

This lack of will to influence provincial government's land-use decisions is well illustrated by endangered mountain

Lynn Kent

The northern and southern resident killer whale populations of BC were declared endangered in 2003. A recovery plan has been produced but the action plans to implement it, supposed to be completed in early 2013, have yet to emerge.

caribou in Alberta, which has lost 60 per cent of its numbers over the last decade, largely due to habitat loss through oil and gas development. The federal government had specified that at least two-thirds of the remaining habitat for the critically endangered Redrock–Prairie Creek herd north of Grand Cache should be left undisturbed or restored. In early 2015, about half was undisturbed. Instead of protecting the habitat, Alberta opened up the area to auction for energy exploration. The move followed an earlier sale of 1,000 hectares of habitat of the endangered Narraway herd two weeks after a panel of scientists had recommended upgrading the species to the most threatened category.

Recovery plans that determine critical habitat must be established for listed species. Of 221 species that were required to have critical habitat identified in 2013, only 56 had had recovery plans undertaken (Favaro et al., 2014). If the habitat is not already protected, the minister must order its protection if the habitat is on federal land, and if not, must report on steps taken to protect habitat. In only two cases has SARA been used to protect habitat. One was the protection of killer whale habitat on the west coast and only came about after the agency responsible, DFO, had been taken to court by a consortium of environmental groups. The judge in the case said "DFO behaved in an evasive and obstructionist way and unnecessarily provoked and prolonged the litigation in this case . . . for no other purpose than to thwart attempts to bring important public issues before the court." Taylor and Pinkus (2013) found that only 17 per cent of recovery strategies led by DFO included critical habitat, as opposed to 63 per cent for those led by Environment Canada. It would appear that the government agencies charged with protecting endangered species in Canada are unwilling to comply with their own legislation.

The Species at Risk Act is different from the American approach to endangered species protection in that it lays out a framework for cooperation on the protection of endangered species and relies primarily on volunteerism (see Waples et al., 2013, for a comparison). The federal government has adopted the same approach for habitat protection, establishing the Habitat Stewardship Program to provide information to landowners on how best to manage their lands to protect endangered species. Landowners may receive compensation for any economic losses incurred. However, independent assessments of the Canadian process for endangered species protection and SARA strongly suggest that the approach is not working. In the US, for example, the longer a species is on the endangered list, the greater its chances of getting off it through management improvements (Waples et al., 2013). The reverse is the case in Canada (Favaro et al., 2014). Dawe and Neis (2012) discussed a case study in eastern Canada of the wolffish listing and found that none of the stakeholder groups had given any attention to how to delist the species through improved management.

Fortunately, endangered species legislation is not the only means of protecting biodiversity, and individuals can help in many ways (Box 14.8). This further underlines a key message in the Millennium Ecosystem Assessment (2005) that "science can help ensure that decisions are made with the best available information, but ultimately the future of biodiversity will be determined by society."

Perspectives on the Environment

Recovery Planning for Species at Risk

Environment Canada, Fisheries and Oceans Canada, and Parks Canada have not met their legal requirements for establishing recovery strategies, action plans, and management plans under the Species at Risk Act. While the organizations have made varying degrees of progress since our 2008 audit in completing the recovery strategies they are responsible for, 146 recovery strategies remain to be completed as of 31 March 2013. Out of the 97 required action plans, only seven were in place. The required management plans for species of special concern were not completed in 42 per cent of cases.

We noted that while Fisheries and Oceans Canada and Parks Canada have made notable progress in completing the majority of the recovery strategies they are responsible for, Environment Canada continues to have a significant number of outstanding recovery strategies. Of these, 84 per cent were overdue by more than three years as of 31 March 2013. Of the recovery strategies that the organizations completed, 43 per cent did not identify the critical habitat of the species at risk.

Based on Environment Canada's annual rate for completing recovery strategies since our last audit, we estimate that it will take the Department approximately 10 years to complete its outstanding recovery strategies, including those coming due in the next year. This estimate does not reflect the additional time it will take the Department to complete the subsequent action plans.

—Auditor General of Canada (2013)

Protected Areas

Protected areas have emerged as one of the key strategies to combat the erosion of biodiversity both internationally and in Canada (Box 14.9). Protected areas play different roles in society (Box 14.10), and in many cases their conservation role has been recognized only recently as the dominant one. This is especially true in Canada, where Banff, our first national park (1885), was set aside mainly to promote tourism and generate income rather than to protect species and ecosystems. However, since that time, the crucial role in species and ecosystem protection played by protected areas in Canada has led to both legislation and policy directives that make it clear that biodiversity protection is the prime mandate for the national park system.

Canada's national park system is central to the protection of rare and endangered species. Although the 47 parks cover only about 4 per cent of the land base, they contain more than 70 per cent of the native terrestrial and freshwater vascular plants and 80 per cent of the native vertebrate species. More than 50 per cent of the endangered vascular plant species and almost 50 per cent of the endangered vertebrate species are found in national parks. Canada's national parks have also played a critical and increasingly important role as sites for reintroduction of endangered species (Table 14.3).

Protected Areas: A Global Perspective

The International Union for Conservation of Nature (IUCN) is an international body that draws together governments, non-governmental organizations, and scientists concerned with nature conservation. A protected area, as defined by the IUCN, is "a clearly defined geographical space, recognized, dedicated, and managed, through legal or other effective means, to achieve the long-term conservation of nature with associated ecosystem services and cultural values." There are many different kinds of protected areas, such as national and provincial parks, wilderness areas, and **biosphere reserves**. They all offer some form of protection but with differing degrees of stringency. To help bring some order and understanding to the different types of protected areas, the IUCN has developed a system of classification that ranges from minimal to more intensive use of the habitat by humans (Table 14.4).

The growth of protected areas has been strong, especially over the past decade (Figure 14.5) and now covers almost 16 per cent of the terrestrial area of the planet as discussed in the "International Guest Statement" below.

Protected Areas and the International Agenda | *Stephen Woodley*

Biological diversity underpins ecosystem functioning and the provision of ecosystem services essential for human survival and well-being. The creatures of the world—capelin, sea slugs, pine trees, grizzly bears—are part of an elaborate network of life that keeps us alive. In a world of shocking decline in biodiversity (see Millennium Ecosystem Assessment, http://www.millenniumassessment.org/documents/document.354.aspx.pdf), protected areas are the most common and assured way of conserving nature. They are a key solution to the crises of species loss and ecosystem degradation and are used by all countries in the world. There is an active international agenda to provide standards, targets, and funding for protected areas.

International standards and guidelines for protected areas (Table 14.4) are developed by the IUCN. Established in 1948, the IUCN is the world's oldest and largest global environmental organization, with more than 1,200 government and NGO members and almost 11,000 volunteer experts in some 160 countries. The volunteer experts are organized into commissions, with the protected area standards and guidelines being developed primarily through IUCN's World Commission on Protected Areas (http://www.iucn.org/about/work/programmes/gpap_home/). The IUCN was in instrumental in establishing the Convention on Biological Diversity (see Chapter 2) and advises the convention on matters relating to protected areas.

The use of international treaties and agreements to establish protected area targets has a long history. In 1983, the United Nations established the World Commission on Environment and Development (also known as the Brundtland Commission). Its report on sustainable development, *Our Common Future* (WCED, 1987), suggested that protected areas should cover at least 12 per cent of the Earth. That simple, political target became the first global standard. Because nature is the basis of our survival and our economy, nature conservation, measured by the percentage of a country in protected areas, is also part of the 2002 United Nations Millennium Development Goals with a target completion date of 2015, as discussed in Chapter 1 in this book.

The global plan to slow down biodiversity loss was established under the Convention on Biological Diversity, agreed in Rio in 1992 and now signed by 194 countries (see Chapter 2). Many countries have worked hard under this treaty, and in 2010, adopted a detailed Strategic Plan for Biodiversity that is to be achieved by 2020. The strategic plan outlines 20 targets (named the Aichi Targets) to achieve global biodiversity conservation. Arguably, all 20 Aichi Targets have implications for the establishment and management of protected areas, but only Target 11 addresses them directly:

> By 2020, at least 17 per cent of terrestrial and in land water areas and 10 per cent of coastal and marine areas, especially areas of particular importance for biodiversity and ecosystem services, are conserved through effectively and equitably managed, ecologically representative and well-connected systems of protected areas and other effective area-based conservation measures, and integrated into the wider landscape and seascape.
>
> —Convention on Biological Diversity (n.d.)

Despite containing only 61 words, Target 11 is surprisingly all encompassing. It applies to both marine and terrestrial ecosystems, and sets goals for spatial planning (representivity, ecological connectivity, and areas of importance for biodiversity); protected areas management (including management effectiveness and social equity); and criteria about what counts toward being a protected area under Target 11.

Countries are now working to implement the Aichi Targets. Under the CBD, the mechanism to consider the targets is called the National Biodiversity Strategies and Action Plans. In the so-called "developing world," funding is provided to meet the obligations of the CBD through an independently operating financial organization called the Global Environment Facility (GEF). The GEF is the largest public funder of projects to improve the global environment, providing grants for projects related to biodiversity, climate change, international waters, land degradation, the ozone layer, and persistent organic pollutants.

The global list of protected areas is kept by the United Nations Environment Programme's World Conservation Monitoring Centre (UNEP-WCMC). Using standards from the IUCN, the Monitoring Centre provides online information systems (http://www.protectedplanet.net/) and develops the *Protected Planet Report* on the status of the world's protected areas. The latest *Protected Planet Report* (Juffe-Bignoli et al., 2014) states that protected areas now cover 15.4 per cent of the world's terrestrial area and 8.4 per cent of the coastal marine areas under national jurisdiction, getting close to the numerical targets of Aichi Target 11. However, these simple numerical targets are very misleading. The distribution of protected areas is not representative, being skewed to areas in which no development would have occurred, such as high, dry, and biologically unproductive places. Most importantly, the global protected area system is poorly managed, with inadequate staffing, equipment, and enforcement.

Some countries have already met Aichi Target 11 on protected areas. Examples include Brazil and Costa Rica. In Canada, only 9.6 per cent of the land and less than 1 per cent of the coastal seas were protected as of 2014. There is no completed national plan to meet the Aichi Targets by 2020. Many Canadian protected areas, both federally and provincially, are underfunded and lack staff, current management plans, or even boundary marking. So it appears that, while many countries will honour their international obligations on protected areas, others such as Canada will fall short.

International Union for the Conservation of Nature (IUCN)

Stephen Woodley is co-chair of the WCPA-SSC Joint Task Force on Biodiversity and Protected Areas, International Union for the Conservation of Nature (IUCN).

ENVIRONMENT IN FOCUS

BOX 14.8 | What You Can Do: Helping Protect Endangered Species

Although the challenges created by endangered species can seem daunting to the individual, you can do several things.

1. If you own land, even your own backyard, try to encourage the growth of native species and promote high diversity among these species. Provide the three staples—food, water, and shelter. Plant perennials such as fruit and nut trees, nectar-producing flowers, and berry bushes. Do not use chemicals!
2. Write letters to politicians at all levels encouraging them to adopt specific measures. For example, write to local politicians urging protection for a natural habitat in your area.
3. Join and support an environmental group with a special interest in endangered species.
4. Take part in an active biodiversity monitoring project such as the Christmas Bird Count, the Canadian Lakes Loon Survey, Frogwatch, Project FeederWatch, or one of the other many organized activities that take place across the country. Details on these projects are available from local NGOs and university and college departments.
5. Do not keep exotic pets.
6. If you have a pet, try to make sure that it does not injure or harass wildlife. Put a bell on your cat. Domestic cats kill large numbers of songbirds every year.
7. Do not buy products made of endangered animals or plants.
8. Vote for political candidates who share your views on conservation matters.
9. Keep informed of biodiversity issues by watching nature programs on television, reading books, attending public lectures, and having discussions with local conservationists.
10. Actively learn more about wildlife, not just by reading and watching television but also by becoming more aware of the wildlife in your region through field observation. Encourage others, especially children, to do likewise.

The chance to overnight in spectacular locations such as this is what draws many people to visit protected areas year after year and involves many of the roles outlined in Box 14.10.

Several factors explain the rapid growth in protected area establishment:

1. *Increased realization of the rate of biodiversity loss and the severity of the issue.* In 1990, for example, statistics on endangered wildlife in Canada listed 194 species at risk, compared to over 700 by 2014.
2. *Growing awareness at the political level of the links between environmental and societal health.* When ecosystems collapse, livelihoods and economies collapse too. This interdependency between ecosystem protection and poverty is now recognized by many international development agencies and has helped to spur the worldwide interest in protected area establishment. For example, the Global Environmental Facility (GEF), an international agency formed in 1991 to assist developing countries in undertaking activities that benefit the global environment,

ENVIRONMENT IN FOCUS

BOX 14.9 | People and Protected Areas: A Global Perspective

From the origins of the conservation movement in the US, the idea of having areas protected by government for conservation and public benefit, education, and enjoyment has spread throughout the world. Implementation has differed to reflect local conditions, but one ubiquitous concern for managers is the relationship between protected areas and local populations. As human populations grow, so do pressures for increased use of protected areas. In the UK, this overuse might be mainly recreational, and significant biophysical impacts may result just from the sheer numbers of people enjoying the parks. In many tropical areas, conflicts arise as local people, often driven by poverty and land-use pressures, encroach on the parks in large numbers, hunting wild animals and cutting down trees to make way for agriculture, obtain firewood, and/or sell on international markets.

Park wardens in Thailand receive little pay and risk their lives to protect what remains of the wildlife. Every year, lives are lost in battles with poachers.

Such management problems are challenging. There is little point in trying to manage the area of land officially designated as a protected area if, in fact, it is not protected from resource use. In the past in Thailand, management activities focused on a preventive approach, with armed guards patrolling boundaries. Since most large remaining areas of forest and most wild animal populations are within the protected area system, there have been some benefits to this approach. Nevertheless, large-scale poaching continues in many areas, and shootouts between poachers and park guards are not an ideal management tool. Attention, therefore, has also spread to trying to address underlying motives behind poaching, such as poverty, although here, too, there are substantial challenges. Economic development programs initiated in some villages have triggered an increase in land prices, leading some villagers to sell their lands and encroach further into park lands. Unscrupulous local leaders may also encourage villagers to sell so that they can gain control over more land.

As with many environmental management problems, the answer does not lie in one single solution. Each case is different, and an adaptive management approach (see Chapter 6) to the protected area ecosystem is essential. In the long term, education must play a lead role. Many people are unaware of the vital functions played by protected areas. It is better to achieve voluntary compliance with more flexible management regimes than to have armed standoffs and mass noncompliance, as has often occurred in the past.

ENVIRONMENT IN FOCUS

BOX 14.10 | The Many Roles of Protected Areas

Art gallery: Many parks were designated for their scenic beauty, still a major reason why people visit parks.

Zoo: As one component of the art gallery, parks are usually places to view wildlife easily in relatively natural surroundings. Because it is protected from hunting in most parks, the wildlife is not as shy of humans as wildlife outside parks.

Playground: Parks provide excellent recreational settings for many outdoor pursuits, and recreation should be recognized for its "re-creation" function of renewal of the human body and spirit (e.g., see Lemieux et al., 2015).

Movie theatre: Just like a movie, parks can lift us into a setting different from that of our everyday life.

Cathedral: Many people derive spiritual fulfillment from communing with nature, just as others go to human-built places of worship.

Factory: The first national parks in Canada were designated with the idea of generating income through tourism. Since these early beginnings, the economic role of parks has been recognized, although it is a controversial one because of potential conflict with most other roles.

Museum: In the absence of development, parks serve as museums, reminding us of how landscapes might have looked to early settlers. These museums also perform a valuable ecological function, since they encompass important areas against which ecological change in the rest of the landscape can be measured.

Bank: Parks are places in which we store and protect our ecological capital, including threatened and endangered species. We can use the "interest" from these "accounts" to repopulate areas with species that have disappeared.

Hospital: Ecosystems are not static and isolated phenomena but are linked to support processes all over the planet. Protected areas constitute one of the few places where such processes still operate in a relatively natural manner. As such, they may be considered ecosystem "hospitals" where air is purified, carbon stored, oxygen produced, and ecosystems "re-created." About 15 per cent of the carbon sequestered in North America is in protected areas (LifeWeb, n.d.).

Laboratory: As relatively natural landscapes, parks represent outdoor laboratories for scientists to use in unravelling the mysteries of nature. Killarney Provincial Park in Ontario, for example, was an important laboratory for early research on acidic precipitation in Canada.

Schoolroom: Parks can play a major role in education as outdoor classrooms.

Source: Dearden (1995).

provided approximately $9.5 billion in grants and leveraged about $42 billion in co-financing in support of more than 2,700 biodiversity projects in 165 countries between 1991 and 2011. In addition, a small grants program has started more than 6,500 biodiversity projects at the community level in 120 countries since 1992.

3. *Realization of the value of ecosystem services.* Increased methodological sophistication has allowed monetary values to be placed on ecosystem values. One team of researchers put an average price tag of US$33 trillion a year on fundamental ecosystem services such as nutrient cycling, soil formation, and climate regulation. This figure is nearly twice the annual global GDP of US$18 trillion and demonstrates, in economically understandable terms, the value of the so-called "free" services of functioning environments (Costanza et al., 1997).
4. *Growing evidence of the effectiveness of protected areas in helping to combat environmental degradation.* Many studies demonstrate the effectiveness of protected areas for biodiversity protection. Protected areas are a main cornerstone for biodiversity protection under international treaties, such as the Convention on Biological Diversity, and a main recommendation of the Millennium Ecosystem Assessment (2005).

Although major gains have been seen in terms of terrestrial park systems, greater progress is required in the marine realm. Less than 1 per cent of the total area of freshwater and oceanic ecosystems enjoy any effective protection (Chapter 8).

Protected Areas: A Canadian Perspective

Canada has a large variety of protected areas, ranging from small ecological reserves to vast multiple-use areas, and the growth in protected areas has been strong (Figure 14.4). These areas are protected by a wide range of authorities, from municipal to federal. The most important protected

TABLE 14.4 | IUCN Classification of Protected Areas

Category	Name	Description
Ia	Strict nature reserve	Strictly protected areas set aside to protect biodiversity and also possibly geological/geomorphological features, where human visitation, use, and impacts are strictly controlled and limited to ensure protection of the conservation values.
Ib	Wilderness area	Usually large unmodified or slightly modified areas, retaining their natural character and influence, without permanent or significant human habitation, which are protected and managed so as to preserve their natural condition.
II	National park	Large natural or near-natural areas set aside to protect large-scale ecological processes, along with the complement of species and ecosystems characteristic of the area, which also provide a foundation for environmentally and culturally compatible spiritual, scientific, educational, recreational, and visitor opportunities.
III	Natural monument or feature	Areas set aside to protect a specific natural monument, which can be a landform, sea mount, submarine cavern, geological feature such as a cave, or even a living feature such as an ancient grove.
IV	Habitat/species management area	Areas that aim to protect particular species or habitats and where management reflects this priority. Many category IV protected areas will need regular, active interventions to address the requirements of particular species or to maintain habitats, but this is not a requirement of the category.
V	Protected landscape or seascape	An area where the interaction of people and nature over time has produced a distinct character with significant ecological, biological, cultural, and scenic value, and where safeguarding the integrity of this interaction is vital to protecting and sustaining the area and its associated nature conservation and other values.
VI	Protected areas with sustainable use of natural resources	Areas conserving ecosystems and habitats, together with associated cultural values and traditional natural resource management systems. They are generally large, with most of the area in a natural condition, where a proportion is under sustainable natural resource management and where low-level, non-industrial use of natural resources compatible with nature conservation is seen as one of the main aims of the area.

Source: Dudley et al. (2010: 34).

areas are in our national and provincial park systems, and the total area of land protected overall by these two levels of government is about equal. Parks Canada is the main federal agency in charge of federal protected areas, such as national parks, although Environment Canada has jurisdiction over large areas, such as migratory bird sanctuaries and national wildlife areas, set aside primarily for wildlife. The location of national parks is strongly influenced by Parks Canada's national park **system plan**, which divides the country into 39 physiographic regions representative of Canada's natural heritage. The goal is to have at least one national park in each of these regions (Figure 14.6). All provinces have similar system plans, and the overall total amounts to 486 natural regions across the country. Malcolm (2015) discusses the various provincial park systems in more detail.

In 1969, the federal minister in charge of parks, Jean Chrétien, announced a goal of achieving system completion by 1985. However, by 1985 the system was less than half complete. In 1992, Canada's federal, provincial, and territorial ministers of environment, parks, and wildlife signed a Statement of Commitment to Complete Canada's Network of Protected Areas. Terrestrial systems were to be completed by 2000, whereas marine designation was to be "accelerated." Again, the goal was not met, and in 2002 Prime Minister Jean Chrétien announced a five-year plan to establish 10 new terrestrial parks, increasing representation to 35 of the 39 regions, and five marine protected areas under the 29-region marine system plan. Although some progress was made, again this goal was not achieved.

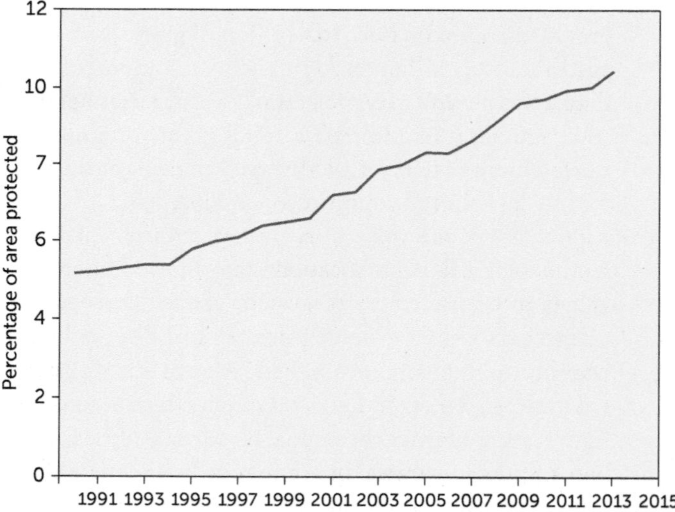

FIGURE 14.5 | Terrestrial protected areas in Canada.

Sources: For Canada, except Quebec: Canadian Council on Ecological Areas (CCEA) (2014) Conservation Areas Reporting and Tracking System (CARTS).

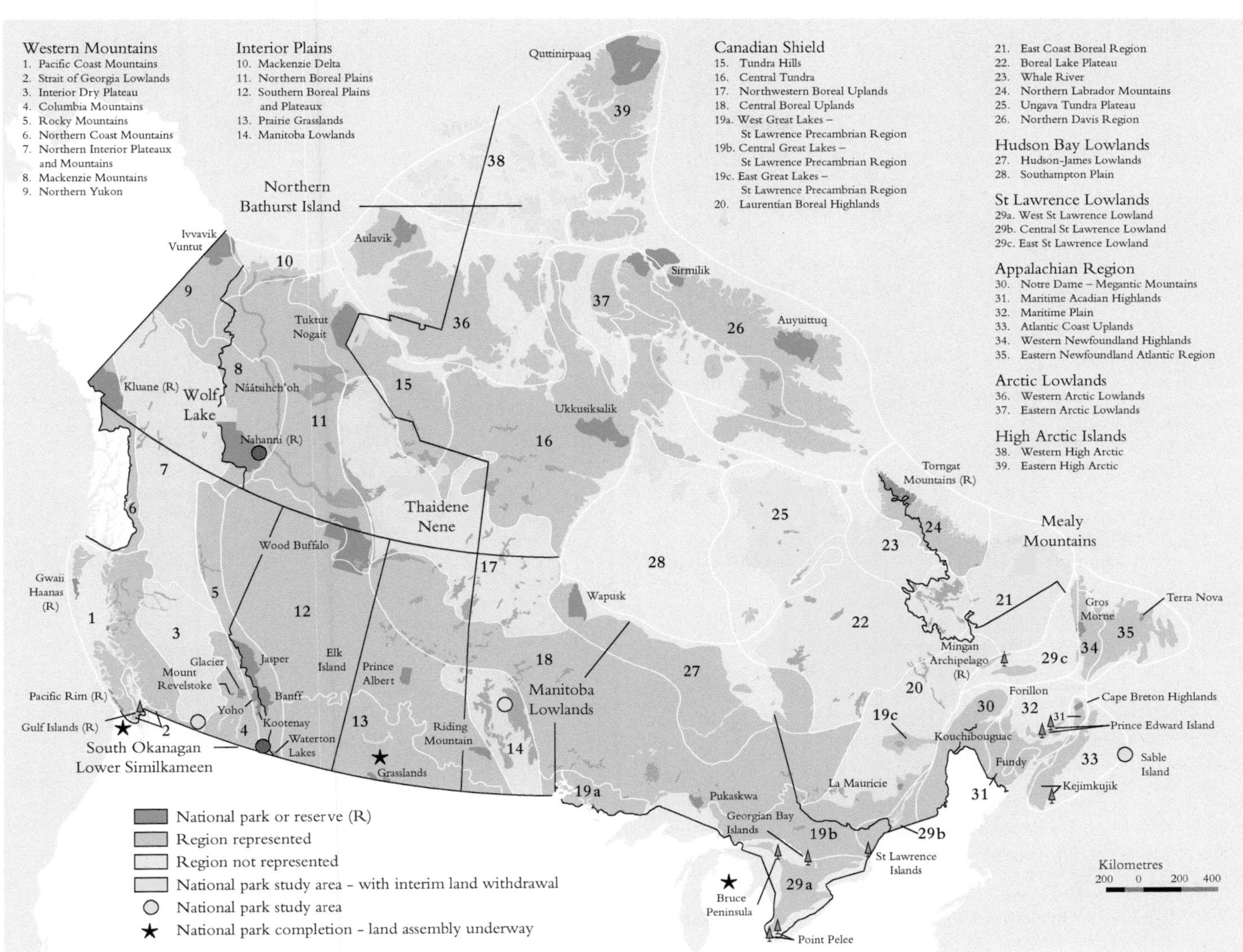

FIGURE 14.6 | Canada's national park system and state of completion as of 2013.

Source: Parks Canada. Adapted from base map: www.pc.gc.ca/eng/progs/np-pn/cnpn-cnnp/index/~/media/docs/pc/plans/rpp/rpp2013-2014/Fig1-eng-large.ashx

Canada is still far from meeting these commitments. Parks Canada has fallen behind in reaching the goal, with about 70 per cent of the terrestrial park system complete (Figure 14.6) and 15 per cent of the marine system (Figure 14.7). Dearden and Canessa (2015) provide a more detailed account on the reasons behind the very slow progress in marine protection, with the most important being a lack of political and bureaucratic leadership. However, there has been major progress at the provincial level. In 1968, Ontario had 90 regulated protected areas totalling 1.6 per cent of the province by area. Currently, Ontario has 631 protected areas totalling more than 9.4 million hectares, or 8.7 per cent of the province. In British Columbia, the area of parkland doubled between 1977 and 2005 and now totals more than 12 million hectares (Figure 14.8). BC and Alberta are the only jurisdictions currently to accomplish the 12 per cent target set by the World Commission on Environment and Development (WCED, 1987), but others are planning to meet this mark. For example Nova Scotia aims to have protected 13 per cent of the province's landmass by 2015—up from 9.3 per cent. This goal is especially challenging since Nova Scotia has relatively little public land and therefore will involve considerable government investment.

Figure 14.9 shows that there is also great variability in the proportions of each ecozone that are protected, with some having up to 40 per cent and others scarcely any. These differences reflect historical perspectives on what to protect. This has been termed the "worthless lands hypothesis," when lands for which there were few resource values for timber, mining or agriculture, were made into parks. Unfortunately, we now know that this was not a good strategy for achieving ecological representation and protecting biodiversity. Some of the most ecologically valuable and unique lands have little representation because of their other values. There are

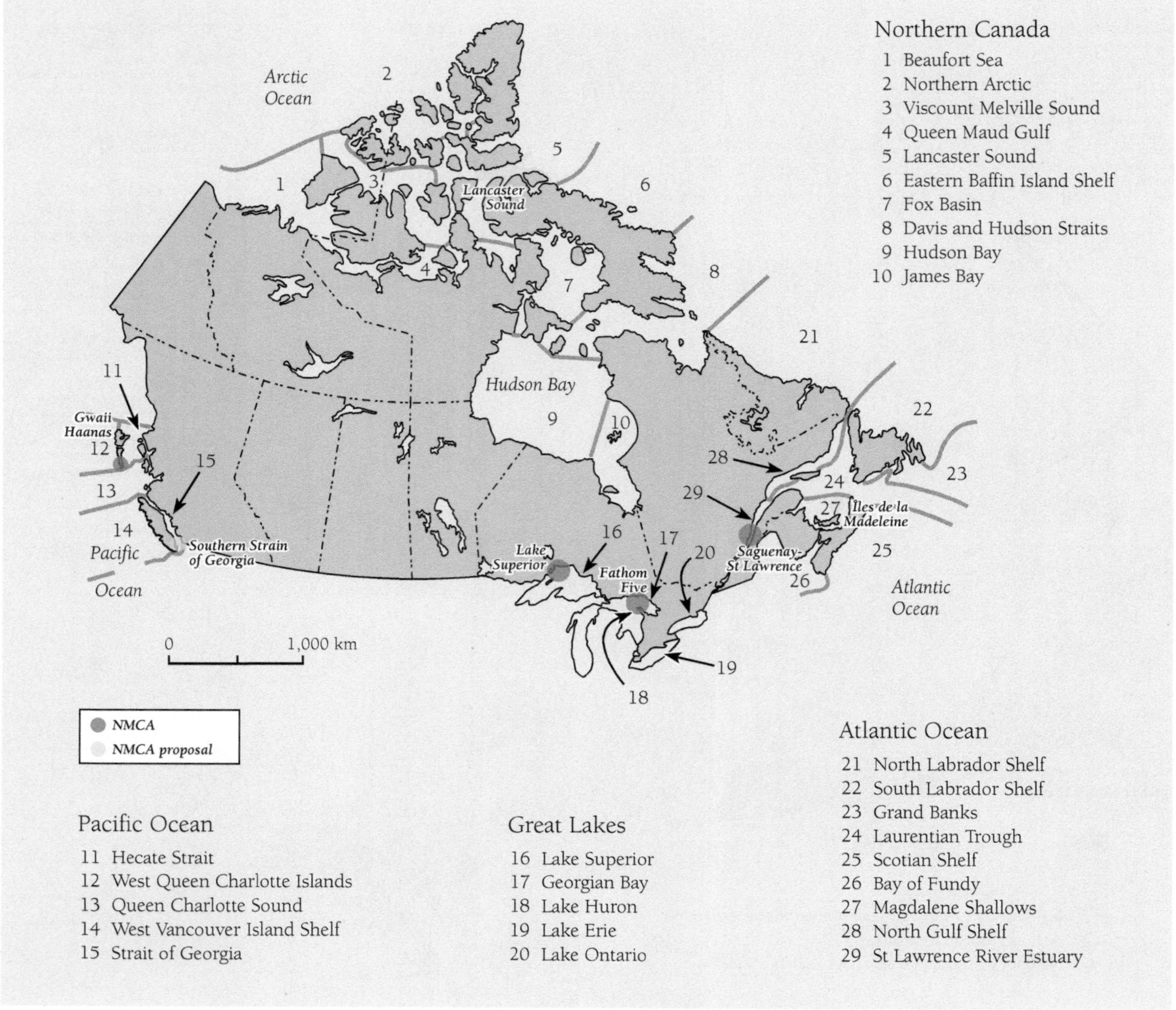

FIGURE 14.7 | Parks Canada's marine system plan and its state of completion.

Source: Parks Canada. Adapted from base map: www.pc.gc.ca/eng/progs/amnc-nmca/cnamnc-cnnmca/index/~/media/progs/amnc-nmca/cnamnc-cnnmca/NMCA-map-large.ashx

also other reasons behind this imbalance in representation, including the willingness of political parties to designate protected areas. Less than 1 per cent of Canada's marine area is set aside in protective designation, and Canada ranks seventieth globally in terms of the percentage of oceans protected (Environment Canada, 2006b).

Environment Canada manages 54 national wildlife areas and 92 migratory bird sanctuaries. These areas were established to protect significant habitat for wildlife, including species at risk and migratory birds. The orientation differs from that of Parks Canada in that the focus is on wildlife and may involve active intervention for this purpose. The performance of the agency was reviewed by the Auditor General in 2013. The audit found that:

- According to Environment Canada's own analysis, more than 70 per cent of national wildlife areas and about 55 per cent of migratory bird sanctuaries are considered to have less than adequate ecological integrity. As such, the Department is not meeting the purpose of its protected areas, which is to maintain the ecological integrity of the site for the benefit of wildlife, including migratory birds and species at risk. Without action to address threats to their ecological integrity, Environment Canada's protected areas may deteriorate.
- Environment Canada has made little progress in monitoring activities, conditions, and threats for the protected areas it manages. The Department's own assessments show a lack of proper inventories and insufficient information on species at risk. Monitoring of sites occurs sporadically. Without regular monitoring, the Department cannot track whether the ecological integrity in protected areas

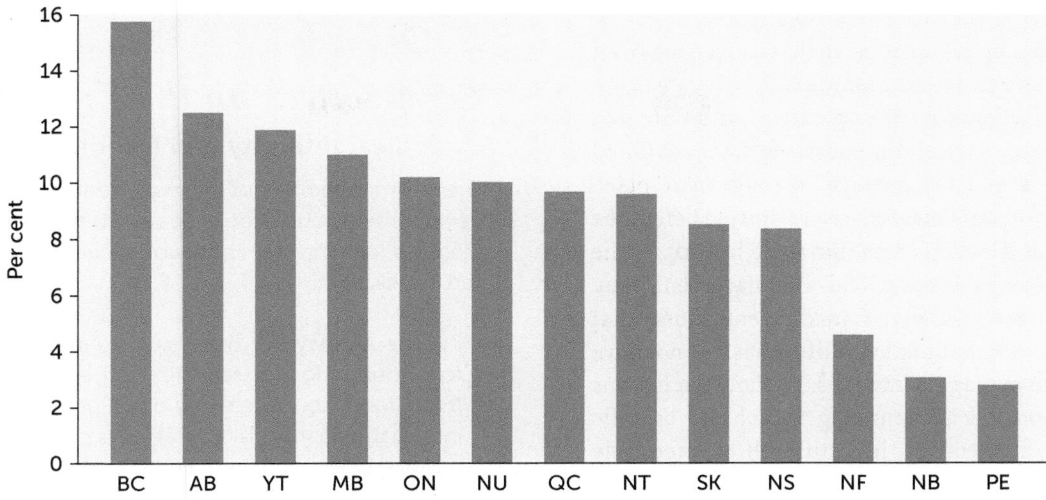

FIGURE 14.8 | Percentage of land and water in protected areas in each province andterritory.

Sources: For Canada except Quebec: Canadian Council on Ecological Areas (CCEA) (2014) Conservation Areas Reporting and Tracking System (CARTS). For Quebec: Ministère du Développement durable, de l'Environnement, de la Faune et des Parcs (2014) Registre des aires protégées au Québec. Data are current as of 31 December 2013. © Her Majesty The Queen in Right of Canada, as represented by the Minister of Environment, 2015. The Environment Canada data is available online, at no cost, by visiting http://www.ec.gc.ca.

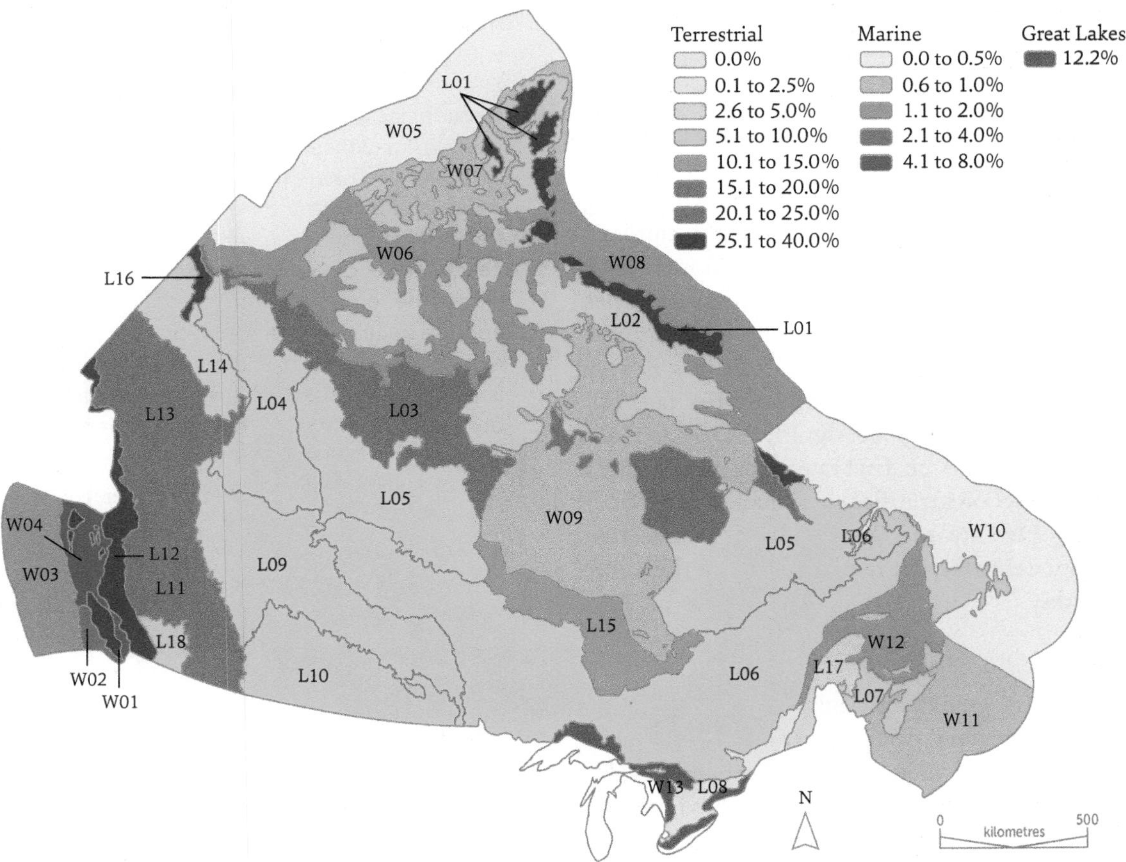

FIGURE 14.9 | Percentage of ecological regions protected, 2013.

Sources: For Canada, except Quebec: Canadian Council on Ecological Areas (CCEA) (2014) Conservation Areas Reporting and Tracking System (CARTS). For Quebec: Ministère du Développement durable, de l'Environnement et de la Lutte contre les changements climatiques (2014) Registre des aires protégées au Québec. Data are current as of 31 December, 2013. © Her Majesty The Queen in Right of Canada, as represented by the Minister of Environment, 2015. The Environment Canada data is available online, at no cost, by visiting http://www.ec.gc.ca.

is changing, nor can it identify any new or potential threats to local species so that it can react in an appropriate and timely manner.

- The Department is still operating with outdated management plans for most of its 54 national wildlife areas. On average, management plans date from 1992. Thirty-one were drafted before the Species at Risk Act came into force in 2003, while eight areas have never had a management plan. In 2011, Environment Canada determined that 90 per cent of national wildlife areas did not have adequate management plans. Without such plans to support decision-making to achieve specific goals and objectives, it is difficult to effectively manage or assess progress in its protected areas. (Auditor General of Canada, 2013)

Just over 10 per cent of Canada's terrestrial area has been awarded protective designation, short of the international goal of 12 per cent first suggested by the WCED (1987) and well short of the average 14.6 per cent protected by OECD countries almost 10 years ago (Environment Canada, 2006b) and the new 17 per cent target established under the CBD. However, 95 per cent of Canada's terrestrial protected areas fall within IUCN categories I–IV (Table 14.4) and hence have a strong protective mandate. Among OECD countries, Canada ranks sixteenth out of 30 in terms of the proportion of land protected. The US protects almost 25 per cent compared to our 10 per cent, yet ranks fourth in terms of proportion of land with strong protection (IUCN categories I–IV). Furthermore, two-thirds of Canada's protected area is situated within a small number of sites that are at least 300,000 hectares in size. Few countries have the opportunity to preserve such large intact landscapes.

The overall quality of Canadian protected areas is very high, with several national parks on the World Heritage list. These sites are of national and global significance. High international accolades depend on first-rate park management practices. The next section identifies some management challenges facing protected areas in Canada. Most of the section is devoted to national parks, but many challenges also apply to provincial parks.

Perspectives on the Environment

Ecological Integrity and National Parks

The Commissioner of Environment and Sustainable Development undertook an audit of Parks Canada's progress on maintaining ecological integrity in 2013 and concluded:

- . . . the Agency has been slow to implement systems for monitoring and reporting on ecological integrity. It has failed to meet many deadlines and targets, and information for decision making is often incomplete or has not been produced. For example, the Agency has not met its own target for establishing, by 2009, a fully functional and scientifically credible monitoring and reporting system for ecological integrity in Canada's national parks. Scientifically credible and up-to-date information on the condition of ecosystems is essential in making informed decisions and to understand and counter threats to ecological integrity. In addition, the Agency either does not know or has not met targets for maintaining ecosystems through the active management of fire in 74 per cent of national parks with fire management targets.
- Spending on Heritage Resources Conservation at Parks Canada has recently decreased by 15 per cent. Overall staffing for conservation has declined by 23 per cent and the number of scientific staff positions has decreased by over a third. Parks Canada has not clarified how and by when, with significantly fewer resources, the Agency will address the backlog of unfinished work, the emerging threats to ecological integrity, and the decline in the condition of 34 per cent of park ecosystems that it has identified. Consequently, there is a significant risk that the Agency could fall further behind in its efforts to maintain or restore ecological integrity in Canada's national parks.

—Auditor General of Canada (2013)

Park Management Challenges

Park management is guided by legislation and relevant policies. Park management plans articulate how requirements will be translated into on-the-ground activities in different parks. However, a national survey by Environment Canada (2006b) on the status of Canada's protected areas found that only 25 per cent had management plans in place. Furthermore, although most park systems in Canada recognize ecological integrity as their main purpose, only two jurisdictions (Parks Canada and Ontario) have measures to monitor changing conditions. Ecosystems are considered to have integrity when they have their native components and processes in place. Several factors make park management a challenging process.

Development within the Parks

Management in national parks is determined by the National Parks Act. Although the first national park was created in Banff, Alberta, in 1885, the first National Parks Act was not passed until 1930. Both this Act and earlier legislation dedicated the parks to "the people of Canada for their benefit, education and enjoyment . . . such Parks shall be maintained and made use of so as to leave them unimpaired for the enjoyment of future generations." Reconciling the balance between "making use of" and maintaining the parks "unimpaired" has been a major topic of debate ever since.

Tourism and income generation were the main reasons behind the establishment of many parks, including Banff. Thus, catering to the demands of tourists was the most important management priority.

By the 1960s, the visitors to Canada's national parks had increased tremendously, as had developments to serve them, including ski hills, golf courses, roads, and hotels. A massive proposal to expand the Lake Louise ski area was rejected in the early 1970s, signifying that the environmental movement was at last starting to be heard in the parks. The next 40 years witnessed many debates about controlling development in protected areas. Although the Lake Louise expansion was thwarted, smaller developments permeated the parks. In 1988, the balance between development and protection was clarified in amendments to the National Parks Act. Protection of ecological integrity became the primary mandate. Despite this legislative mandate, development pressures continued.

In response, in 1998 the federal minister created an Ecological Integrity Panel—to look at development pressures in all of Canada's national parks. The panel's report concurred with an earlier study on Banff, and strongly recommended a more adaptive approach to park management, with greater attention to ecosystem-based management and greater consultation with stakeholders (Chapter 6). The panel's 127 recommendations delivered one central message: *ecological integrity in all the national parks is in peril*. The minister accepted the panel's findings. The proclamation of a new National Parks Act in 2000, which further strengthens the ecological mandate of the parks, was one response.

The findings of the panel and subsequent recommendations emphasized what had already been well known to biogeographers. The theory of **island biogeography** suggests that small islands are unable to support as many species as large islands of similar habitat. Given that many terrestrial parks are separated from colonizing sources from outside the park, they are analogous to islands. Development inside the parks essentially makes them smaller, and smaller parks are more likely to experience extinctions.

Research has shown that development within parks is detrimental to many species, and over the past 15 years the government has revised the National Parks Act twice in favour of a mandate that supports wildlife protection over recreational opportunities. But while these legislative changes are positive (see Dearden and Bennett, 2015a, for a more detailed overview), there have been subsequent developments in the parks, such as the construction of the Skywalk in Jasper National Park, or the resort expansion at Maligne Lake in the

Photawa/iStockphoto

Gros Morne National Park in western Newfoundland is a World Heritage Site.

© Yvette Cardozo/Alamy Stock Photo

Although the environmental lobby was successful in its fight against the construction of an upper and lower village at Lake Louise founded by Imperial Oil and supported by Parks Canada in the early 1970s, many would argue that the subsequent incremental developments have achieved almost the same result. This photograph shows the enlarged Château Lake Louise in front of what is advertised as the largest ski hill in Canada. Is this a national park landscape?

Perspectives on the Environment

On Banff

I do not suppose in any portion of the world there can be found a spot, taken all together, which combines so many attractions and which promises in as great a degree not only large pecuniary advantage to the Dominion, but much prestige to the whole country by attracting the population, not only on this continent, but of Europe to this place. It has all the qualifications necessary to make it a place of great resort. . . . There is beautiful scenery, there are curative properties of the water, there is a genial climate, there is prairie sport, and there is mountain sport; and I have no doubt that it will become a great watering-place.

—Sir John A. Macdonald on Banff, 1887

Philip Dearden

Wildlife overpass built over the Trans-Canada Highway in Banff National Park.

same park, that clearly favour a pro-development philosophy. Furthermore, there has been a growing realization that internal development is not the only threat to ecological integrity within our parks. Many management challenges arise from threats originating beyond park boundaries.

External Threats

Parks do not exist in isolation—they are intimately linked to surrounding and global ecosystems. It is therefore necessary to be aware of any influences from outside park boundaries that may have a detrimental impact on wildlife resources within the park (Box 14.11). This awareness is relatively recent (Figure 14.10). In the early days, boundaries were easily penetrated as society adjusted to the idea of preserving nature. But as time passed, park boundaries became less permeable, and protection of wildlife resources was more assured. However, as development surrounding parks intensified, park managers began to realize that development pressures outside park boundaries were affecting resources within parks. In response, they began to develop integrated management plans that took external threats into account.

Although the creation of integrated management plans is a step in the right direction, external threats to parks are often difficult to eliminate or even control. Invasions by exotic species constitute one of the most challenging problems, and alien species make up to 50 per cent of the flora in some national parks. External threats may originate from private landowners surrounding park boundaries, and it may be difficult or impossible to restrict activities on private land. External threats also come in all shapes and sizes—to tackle them all would require significant human and economic resources. Examples of external threats include mining, logging, agriculture, urbanization, water projects, hunting, exotic species, tourism, acid precipitation, and chemical pollution.

Some external threats can be readily identified and even managed, such as forestry activities along a park boundary. However, in other instances the influences of external factors are too distant and diffuse for park managers to control. Global climate change (see Chapter 7) is a good example, and it will obviously have serious implications for protected areas. On the one hand, protected areas will have a huge role to play in terms of their *hospital role* (Box 14.10) in helping sequester carbon from the atmosphere. On the other hand, the *bank role*, providing refuge for natural populations, will be highly vulnerable to the changes. Protected area networks must be made as resilient as possible against these changes. One main mechanism for doing this is through large-scale bioregional planning illustrated by the Yellowstone-to-Yukon initiative discussed below, which emphasizes connectivity, especially north–south connectivity, among protected areas. We will also require new protected areas that help to facilitate migration, provide source populations, and offer suitable habitat for incoming populations. Including private lands in planning will also be important. The biodiversity implications of climate change are likely to be especially severe in the oceans, yet Canada has created very few marine protected areas, let alone functioning networks of marine protected areas, as discussed in Chapter 8.

Nantel et al. (2014) provide a review of the many interactions between climate change and biodiversity in Canada and the implications for protected area managers. They suggest:

- Protecting more intact ecosystems through establishment of more protected areas
- Connecting protected areas through sustainably managed landscapes and waterscapes
- Restoring degraded ecosystems and species recovery
- Planning for adaptation, for example in designing protected area systems plans
- Building knowledge to support planning, funding research
- Engaging communities in adaptation planning

A survey of protected area jurisdictions in Canada found that three-quarters of the agencies already reported climate

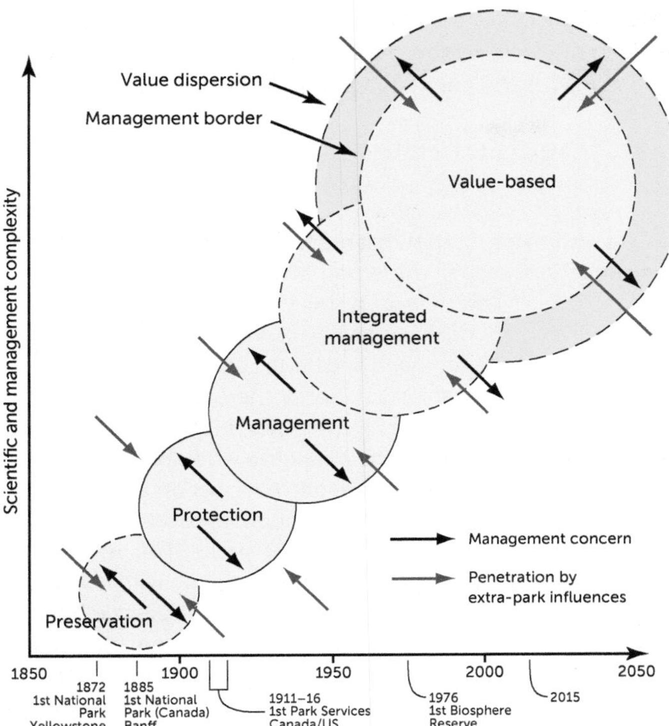

FIGURE 14.10 | Protected areas: evolving relationships from isolation to value-based conservation. The circles represent the growing size of the protected system over time. Boundaries (circle circumferences) were initially of little importance (dashed line) but assumed greater significance in the protection and management phases (solid lines). As the scale of outside threats grew (e.g., climate change, acid rain), these boundaries once more became permeable (dashed lines). The arrows show the threats crossing the borders and the management attention in response. Managers must no longer limit their attention to inside the boundaries as in the "protection" and "management" phases, but cast their attention to the threats coming from outside. The value-based circle represents the need to export conservation values beyond the limitations of the boundary.

Source: Augustine and Dearden (2014).

change impacts and that 94 per cent felt that climate change will significantly alter protected areas planning and policy over the next 20 years. Furthermore, 91 per cent felt that they did not have the capacity to deal with climate change issues (Lemieux et al., 2011). One of the most important steps in dealing with global change in protected areas is to close this management gap before it becomes too wide to bridge. Unfortunately, in almost all provincial jurisdictions in Canada, politicians have been driving things the other way by consistently cutting the funding available to park agencies. One often overlooked role for protected areas in addressing climate change is their *schoolroom role* (Box 14.10), making visitors more aware of the challenges of global change and of the things they can do to help. One of these things is to help persuade politicians to restore funding to park programs.

The idea of park managers actively intervening in park ecosystems rather than leaving change to the vagaries of nature is known as active management. It recognizes that the human forces of change are so prevalent throughout the landscape that even parks are affected. Active management activities include habitat restoration, creation of wildlife corridors, reintroduction of extirpated species (Table 14.3), prescribed burning, and management of hyper-abundant species, such as culling white-tailed deer populations in Point Pelee National Park in Ontario. However, because of limited knowledge of ecosystem processes, considerable debate often occurs among scientists regarding how such programs should be implemented.

Effective management of threats originating from outside parks requires an ecosystem-based approach (Chapter 6), combined with methods that protect wildlife resources along ecosystem rather than legal/political boundaries. Such approaches attempt to mitigate external threats while also counteracting the forces of fragmentation.

Fragmentation

Parks are increasingly becoming islands of natural vegetation totally surrounded by human-modified landscapes, as illustrated by the Riding Mountain case discussed in Box 14.12. Studies of Fundy National Park in New Brunswick showed that only 20 per cent of the surrounding area remained in forest patches large enough to be 500 metres from disturbed areas. This situation creates several problems, since many animal species and some bird species cannot cross modified landscapes. As a result, they become an isolated breeding population, leading to genetic inbreeding and a higher susceptibility to extinction. This raises two questions: (1) How many individuals are necessary to ensure the long-term survival of a species? (2) How large an area of habitat is required to sustain the population?

The first question, related to the **minimum viable population (MVP)** of a species (i.e., the smallest population size predicted to have a very high chance of persisting for the foreseeable future), can be estimated using genetic and demographic models. Estimates of MVP are then multiplied by the area required to support each animal. In western Canada, for example, calculations suggest that 15,000 km^2 would be required to support a viable wolf population. MVP analysis has now been broadened to include a wider range of factors and is being replaced by **population viability analysis (PVA)**, a means of quantifying risk of extinction, elucidating factors contributing to numerical decline, and helping in prioritizing conservation actions among endangered species and populations. These methods enable assessment of extinction risk relative to uncertainty in source data and under a variety of environmental or management scenarios. Theberge et al. (2015) provide a more detailed overview of the main

ENVIRONMENT IN FOCUS

BOX 14.11 | The Role of Parks in Endangered Species Protection: Wood Buffalo National Park

Straddling the Alberta–Northwest Territories boundary, Wood Buffalo covers 44,807 km^2. The park is both a World Heritage Site and a Ramsar Site. Ramsar Sites are wetlands of global significance. Wood Buffalo contains critical habitat for two endangered species: North America's largest terrestrial mammal, the bison, and the tallest bird, the whooping crane.

> We came to places where, as far as the eye could see, untold thousands [of buffalo] were in sight; the country being fairly black with them . . . these immense herds were moving north and there seemed no end to them.
>
> —Cecil Denny in Saskatchewan, 1874

Bison: The image of vast herds of bison ranging back and forth along the Great Plains of North America is one never to be seen again. With up to 60 million animals, bison herds probably constituted the greatest large-mammal congregations that ever existed on Earth and were important in the subsistence lifestyles of many **Aboriginal peoples** in western Canada. But by the 1860s, the bison had been extirpated from the plains of Manitoba. As American Indians flooded into Canada to seek the protection of the Great White Mother (Queen Victoria), the pressure on the remaining herds increased dramatically, and the wild bison herds were extirpated from the Canadian Prairies.

> All through today's journey, piled up at the leading stations along the road, were vast heaps of bones of the earliest owners of the prairie—the buffalo. Giant heads and ribs and thigh bones, without one pick of meat on them, clean as a well-washed plate, white as driven snow, there they lay, a giant sacrifice on the altar of trade and civilization.
>
> —traveller on the Canadian Pacific Railway, 1888

Several remnants remained, however. A small number had been protected by the earlier establishment of Yellowstone National Park. Yellowstone is the only place where wild, free-ranging plains bison have survived since colonial times. Banff also had a growing population kept as a tourist attraction in an animal compound. In addition, two remnants had been brought together by an American rancher. The herd was bought by the Canadian government, and the 703 animals were transported to a national park (created for that purpose) adjacent to the railway near Wainwright, Alberta. In the mid 1920s, the herd, then numbering 6,673, was relocated to Wood Buffalo National Park.

These were plains bison (*Bison bison*). Less well known is their non-migratory, taller, and darker cousin, the wood bison (*Bison athabascae*). This bison was once widely distributed from the aspen parklands of Saskatchewan and Alberta to the eastern slopes of the Rockies and British Columbia and north to the coniferous forests of the Mackenzie Valley. It is endemic to Canada. Estimates suggest that more than 168,000 wood bison were once in Canada. The wood bison was never as abundant as the plains bison, and by 1891 fewer than 300 of them remained. Wood Buffalo National Park was established at least partly to protect this remnant, and by 1922 the herd had grown from 1,500 to 2,000 animals. Shortly thereafter, the herd of plains bison was imported from Wainwright, and interbreeding led to the disappearance of the distinctive wood bison characteristics. Wood bison were believed to have become extinct.

In 1957, however, an isolated group of wood bison was located in a remote area of the vast park. This herd was relocated to guard against further interbreeding within Wood Buffalo. Some animals were removed to the Mackenzie Bison Sanctuary in the North; the herd now numbers more than 200, and individuals have expanded their range outside the sanctuary. Other animals were removed to Elk Island National Park near Edmonton, where their numbers have to be closely controlled because of the small area available. This herd has provided animals for satellite herds in the Yukon, the Northwest Territories, northwestern Alberta, and Manitoba. Some have even been sent to repopulate parks in Russia. An estimated 4,188 wood bison now live in six free-ranging, disease-free herds; 6,216 animals in four diseased, free-ranging herds; and 1,029 animals in captive conservation (public and private) and research herds. Two wild herds exceed the minimum viable population of 400 individuals. In 1988, COSEWIC downlisted the wood bison from endangered to threatened. In 2013, the species was reassessed; its status did not change.

The dangers for the bison are not yet over, however. When the plains bison were imported from Wainwright, they brought with them bovine diseases such as brucellosis and tuberculosis. These diseases have already taken a toll on bison populations—from highs of more than 12,000 animals, they dropped to a quarter of this number by the early 1990s. Diseases afflicting the bison have raised concerns from the agricultural sector. Bison represent the last focus for both diseases in Canada, and as agriculture has impinged on the western boundary of Wood Buffalo, farmers are concerned that domestic stock will become infected. This has led to calls from the agricultural lobby for elimination of the herd.

Several factors besides disease also threaten bison populations. The Peace–Athabasca Delta, for example, supported the highest concentrations of bison during the twentieth century. However, since the completion in 1968 of the Bennett Dam upstream in British Columbia, water levels on the Delta have fallen considerably, causing habitat changes that have negatively affected many animal species, including the bison. A more recent impact on the Delta has been changes in the Athabasca River system as a result of extractions of water for oil production at the oil sands in Alberta, discussed in Chapter 12. This impact from outside Wood Buffalo National

The vast herds of plains bison had been extirpated from Canada until efforts were made to reintroduce them from the US and eventually transport them to Wood Buffalo National Park, where they mixed with the wood bison population.

Park again emphasizes the need for an ecosystem-based perspective on park management (Chapter 6).

Whooping crane: Unlike the bison, the whooping crane (*Grus americana*) was never numerous. Historical accounts suggest a population of 1,500. What it lacked in numbers, it made up for in presence. More than 1.5 metres high and pure white except for black wing tips, black legs, and a red crown, with wing spans in excess of 2 metres, this majestic bird migrates annually from wintering grounds on the Gulf of Mexico coast of Texas to the Northwest Territories. These wintering grounds are all that remain of a winter range that included marshes from southern Louisiana into central Mexico, and at one time this bird had a breeding summer range that stretched from New Jersey in the east to Salt Lake City in the west and as far north as the Mackenzie Delta (see Figure 14.11). Requiring undisturbed breeding habitat, the crane soon declined under the expansion of agriculture. Unrestricted hunting along its long migration routes also contributed to the decline. By 1941, there were only 22 whooping cranes left.

The governments of the US and Canada agreed to a joint program to try to save the species from extinction. They used the 1916 Migratory Bird Treaty between the US and Canada to stop legal hunting. In 1937, the US government bought the Aransas National Wildlife Refuge to protect the wintering habitat on the Gulf coast. In 1954, the only known nesting area was discovered in the northern part of another protected area, Wood Buffalo. Finding the breeding grounds enabled direct human interventions, such as artificial incubation of eggs. The whooping crane generally lays two eggs, but usually only one chick survives. A captive propagation program in the 1960s and 1970s moved one of the eggs for incubation. The North American population of wild whooping cranes is now almost 600 including introduced populations, with over 300 in Canada. The species is listed as endangered by COSEWIC.

If you turn back to the discussion on factors influencing the vulnerability of species to extinction earlier in the chapter, you will see that the whooping crane possesses many of the characteristics that make species vulnerable. It is especially at risk because of its long migration and the vulnerability of its wintering grounds to both natural (e.g., hurricanes) and human-caused destruction.

An interesting dilemma arose with their recovery program. As mentioned above, the crane lays two eggs, and usually only one chick survives. As part of the recovery program, second eggs were removed from the nests and hatched separately. However, Parks Canada, in an effort to maintain natural processes in Wood Buffalo, disallowed the removal of the second egg. This has slowed down the population growth rate. What would you do—maintain natural processes or speed up recovery?

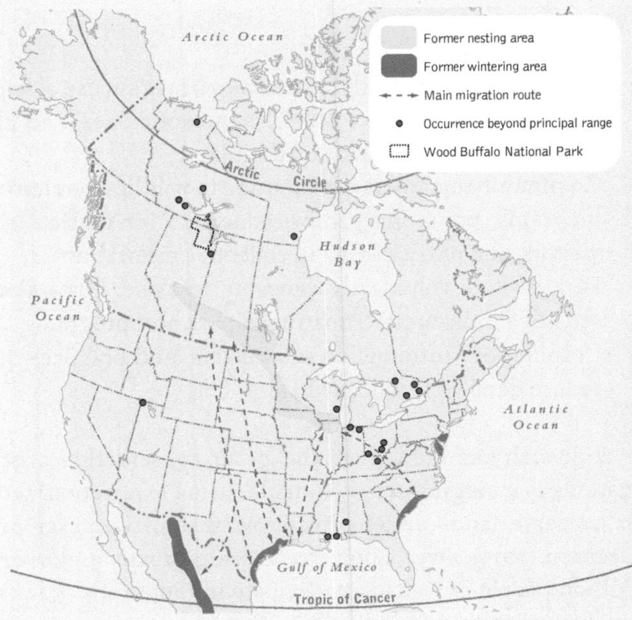

FIGURE 14.11 | The original range of the whooping crane.

The whooping crane, the tallest North American bird and one of the rarest, makes its habitat in muskeg, prairie pools, and marshes.

Building greater awareness among visitors of the role of national parks in society is a central facet of sound management. Parks Canada has developed some of the best interpretive facilities in the world. This is the visitor centre at Greenwich in PEI National Park.

ecological principles and approaches that are used in protected area planning with applications to Canada.

Island biogeography theory also suggests that the number of species surviving on an island represents an equilibrium between species immigration and extinction, and this depends on its distance from a colonizing source. In theory, the number of species on an island will be greater if the island is large and sources of immigration are close. There is some debate as to the veracity of this assertion, but in association with other research it has given rise to principles regarding reserve design. In general, (1) blocks of habitat close together are better than blocks far apart; (2) habitat in contiguous blocks is better than fragmented habitat; and (3) interconnected blocks of habitat are better than isolated blocks.

The Muskwa-Ketchika Management Area in northern BC is a critical piece of the Yellowstone-to-Yukon jigsaw puzzle. Set aside by the BC government in 1998 under a special Act, the 6.4 million–hectare area is managed for sustainable use and contains several provincial parks.

The importance of connectivity can be seen in the efforts of Parks Canada to mitigate the impacts of the Trans-Canada Highway cutting through Banff National Park. The highway was a major sink for wildlife populations, with more than 800 collisions per year. Following the installation of 22 underpasses and two overpasses in the late 1990s, wildlife mortality overall was reduced by 80 per cent. This example shows how connectivity can be improved with enough scientific information and resources to build mitigating structures. However, overall our parks are too small, too few, and too far apart to sustain populations of many species throughout the next century. Attention is being directed toward ways of linking the parks through corridors of natural habitat. One such scheme would extend American parks such as Yellowstone north through the Canadian Rockies and into Yukon and Alaska. There are 11 national parks and dozens of state, provincial, and territorial parks in the Yellowstone-to-Yukon corridor. One wolf marked for tracking in Montana was actually shot on the Alaska Highway along the corridor. Many other threats exist besides hunting along such corridors, including mining, industrial development, and resort and housing developments. It is much easier to maintain connectivity before development starts than to restore it afterward.

These kinds of bioregional schemes explicitly acknowledge the limitations of park systems and encourage a more integrated perspective toward resource management on lands outside the parks that involves other stakeholders, such as landowners and private foundations. This approach is often called stewardship and refers, in general, to many different activities that can be undertaken to care for the Earth. In the context of protected areas, it generally means encouraging landowners to modify their activities to help protect ecosystems. In practice, stewardship takes many forms, including:

- Landowners voluntarily restricting damaging use of land, planting native species rather than exotic ones, and placing protective covenants on their land
- Community members contributing to wildlife monitoring programs, providing passive education for tourists and visitors, and participating in collective restoration
- Park visitors voluntarily choosing to avoid hikes along sensitive trails or participating in park host programs
- Corporations introducing sustainable land practices that reduce damage to wildlife habitat

A diversity of land trust and other conservation organizations is emerging across Canada, using a variety of tools to conserve lands under private ownership (Dempsey and Dearden, 2015). Over 1,000 stewardship groups and over 1 million people in Canada participate in thousands of initiatives on private and public lands. Stewardship Canada is an online portal that provides access to many resources related to stewardship programs in Canada (www.stewardshipcanada.ca/). The Nature Conservancy of Canada—one of many conservation organizations—has protected almost 1 million hectares since 1962 (see the "Domestic Guest Statement" by Joslyn Spurgeon in Chapter 6 regarding the Nature Conservancy of Canada). Ducks Unlimited has been responsible for the protection of more than 2.5 million hectares of Canadian wetlands since 1938. Smaller, provincially based and local land trusts are also increasing. Government agencies such as Environment Canada and various provincial ministries are also embracing stewardship. For example, numerous funding programs exist for community stewardship, and some ministries publish guides or maintain websites to educate and to support local initiatives. Legislative changes, particularly tax deductions, have also been implemented, resulting in incentives and encouragement for ecological gifts and donations.

These initiatives are critically important for the future of conservation in Canada and will play a significant role in restoring connectivity among other protected areas. Private lands will never replace the role played by strictly protected areas, but they do play an essential role in "gluing together" the larger wilderness areas set aside in government parks. The international Biosphere Reserve Program is one of the best-known initiatives promoting greater stewardship surrounding protected areas (Box 14.12). One of the greatest challenges faced by biosphere reserves is to accommodate the views of diverse stakeholders in a constructive manner (Reed et al., 2014).

The totem poles of Ninstints, an abandoned Haida village on Gwaii Hanaas (Moresby Island in the Queen Charlotte Islands), give some impression of the Haida's spiritual connection with the environment. The village is now part of Gwaii Hanaas National Park Reserve and is co-managed by Parks Canada and the Haida.

Stakeholder Interests

Balancing the interests of the range of stakeholders that may be affected by the establishment and/or management of parks is a formidable challenge. Private landowners, local communities, Aboriginal peoples, industry, tourists, conservation organizations, and government agencies all have an influence over how parks are managed. Environment Canada (2006b) reports that 13 out of 15 jurisdictions (which includes two federal agencies) provide opportunities for community involvement in most or all of their protected areas.

Aboriginal Peoples

Aboriginal peoples have a particularly powerful role in the designation and management of many parks and are considered another level of government rather than a stakeholder. An amendment to the National Parks Act in 1972 created a special category of park, the *national park reserve*, which does not prejudice future land claim negotiations. Several large parks have been created in the Arctic as a result. In the south, on the other hand, where the provincial governments have jurisdiction over the land base, progress has been slow. It was not until after protests and several court cases that the legitimacy of Aboriginal claims over land and resources in southern Canada was taken seriously. More than 50 per cent of the land area in Canada's national park system has now been protected as a result of Aboriginal peoples' support for conservation of their lands, and this proportion will only increase in the future as the remaining Native land claims are settled (Dearden and Bennett, 2015b).

There are also significant additions to protection at the provincial level through Aboriginal commitments. In Manitoba, the government announced in 2011 that it would support the efforts of one Aboriginal group, the Poplar River First Nation, which developed a land-use plan for its territory on the east side of Lake Winnipeg that resulted in the protection of 807,650 hectares of boreal forest and wetlands. This brings the total of land protected in that province to over 10 per cent of its land area.

In addition to providing support for other designations of protected areas, Aboriginal peoples are increasingly creating their own designations as discussed by Eli Enns in the "Domestic Guest Statement."

ENVIRONMENT IN FOCUS

BOX 14.12 | Riding Mountain National Park and Biosphere Reserve

Riding Mountain National Park illustrates the kinds of external pressures that threaten the ecological integrity of many of our national parks. The park is located on the Manitoba Escarpment and is an isolated boreal forest area completely surrounded by agricultural land. Nonetheless, the 3,000-km^2 park provides habitat for some 5,000 elk, 4,000 moose, more than 1,000 black bears, and populations of cougars and wolves.

Large-mammal populations have become increasingly threatened by the intensification of agricultural activities surrounding the park. Between 1971 and 1986, the amount of land under agriculture within 10 kilometres of the boundary increased from 77 to 93 per cent. Not only did the amount of farmland increase, the intensity of use did as well, with a 42 per cent increase in cropland area in the same zone over the same period. During the same 15-year period, the area of woodland declined by 63 per cent within a 70-kilometre radius of the boundary, the volume of agricultural fertilizers used quintupled, and pesticide expenditures indicate an increase of 744 per cent in pesticide applications.

Agricultural expansion is not the only challenge confronting park wildlife. Until recently, bear-baiting was permitted directly on the park boundary. Farmers conditioned bears to feed from barrels full of meat. In the hunting season, the bears formed easy targets for "sportsmen." Some 70 "bear-feeding" stations existed around the park, causing unnatural bear distributions, very large bears, irregularities in breeding behaviour, and death. On average, 122 bears are killed each year in this way. Scientists suggest that these mortality levels cannot be maintained if the bear population of the park is to survive. Farmers are now required to move bait barrels back from the park boundary itself. However, bears are highly mobile animals and have little difficulty in locating the barrels.

These types of external pressures can have significant impacts on biodiversity within park boundaries. The Biosphere Reserve Program of the United Nations Educational, Scientific and Cultural Organization (UNESCO) is one of the most highly touted means of dealing with such external threats to protected areas. Biosphere reserves exist to represent global natural regions and should consist of a protected core area, such as a national park, surrounded by a zone of cooperation where socio-economic activities may take place but are modified to help protect the integrity of the core area. The reserves also have important educational and scientific roles. Unfortunately, no legislation ensures cooperation on the privately owned lands in the zone of cooperation. Continued hunting around the park boundary at Riding Mountain National Park, designated as a biosphere reserve in 1986, graphically illustrates the need for landowners to cooperate. Similar challenges face other biosphere reserves, such as Georgian Bay Islands National Park in Ontario, the Niagara Escarpment Biosphere Reserve in Ontario, the Greater Fundy Ecosystem in Nova Scotia, and Waterton Lakes National Park in southern Alberta, Canada's oldest biosphere reserve.

The goals of Aboriginal peoples and conservationists, however, are not always identical. Aboriginal peoples, for example, retain the right to hunt in many parks. At the moment, there are few restrictions on the size or means of harvest, a source of concern for some conservation scientists. Several parks in both northern and southern Canada have some form of co-management arrangement between Parks Canada and Aboriginal peoples. In general, they have worked to the satisfaction of both groups, but the issue of shared responsibility remains an ongoing challenge.

Implications

There is no debate about whether rates of extinction have increased as a result of human activities over recent times. Some uncertainty still exists, however, regarding the impact of the extinctions. Is there ecological redundancy such that the Earth can afford to lose some species without major impacts? Is the loss of any species as a result of human activities ethically and morally acceptable? There are many unanswered questions regarding the implications of reduced biodiversity.

Extinction is commonly viewed as simply a biological problem. Yet there is a need to link the biological process of extinction with the economic and ethical reasons why extinction is undesirable, the reasons why human-caused extinctions are increasing, and the kinds of measures needed to prevent this from happening. In other words, extinction is not just the domain of biologists but involves consideration from a broad range of perspectives, including all the social sciences, geography, law, and ethics.

Canada is certainly not doing very well in terms of meetings its own legislative mandates or those from international conventions. Canada is not lacking in good scientists nor a spirit and commitment to conservation. Historically considered as a global leader, Canada is now regarded with suspicion by many conservation scientists, reflecting some of the international actions reported in this chapter. It will take many years before Canada and Canadians can once more take to the global stage knowing that we are doing our very best at home and overseas to help protect nature.

DOMESTIC GUEST STATEMENT

Tribal Parks in Clayoquot and Beyond: Forwarding Indigenous and Community Conserved Areas in a Canadian Context | *Eli Enns*

The 1993 United Nations Convention on Biological Diversity (CBD) was ratified by over 190 countries to catalyze a global effort to promote the conservation of biological diversity. Among the many directives, the international community called for the recognition of indigenous peoples and local communities as legitimate governors of conservation areas. The International Union for the Conservation of Nature (IUCN) answered this call by establishing a new type of internationally recognized protected areas which would become known as Indigenous Peoples and Community Conserved Territories and Areas (ICCAs).

ICCAs (https://iccaconsortium.wordpress.com) are a modern-day articulation of a very old phenomenon. Traditional cultures the world over have designed sophisticated ways to manage their relationship to place that not only meet their present-day needs but are mindful of future generations needs as well. This is also true in the Canadian context where indigenous peoples have cultivated natural resources at an ecosystem level since time immemorial, and where they are still today asserting their responsibility to continue in this intergenerational relationship. These assertions take many forms, but in terms of ICCAs one of the leading models is known as tribal parks.

At the heart of the Clayoquot Sound Biosphere Reserve on the west coast of Vancouver Island, a new model of tribal parks is emerging as a global leader in social-ecological resiliency (Figure 14.12). While recovering from the brink of extinction and simultaneously adapting their age-old ecological governance system to a series of aggressive foreign influences, the Tla-o-qui-aht peoples of Clayoquot have an ICCA concept that marries the old with the new to form a sustainable livelihoods model that promotes environmental security. The keystone of this approach (http://www.dasiqox.org/) is a fundamentally different conception of humanity which orients individuals within a rich social contract and extends ideas of justice to the environment, as articulated in the following:

> Quu-us: Real live human being. Real as opposed to imagined or dreamt; "Live" as opposed to deceased or unborn; and "human being" as opposed to any other being on Earth. As Quu-us we have access to a full range of emotional language that educates us about ourselves and our environments; no matter what you are feeling, it is okay to feel that way, just don't become fixated on one. As Quu-us we are a link between our past Ancestors, and future Ancestors forming circles in time; as links we have a responsibility to manage our natural inheritance with care for future Ancestors. Our natural inheritance includes an interconnection of everything from air, water, cedar and salmon to names, language, songs and even our own natural selves.
>
> —Nuu-chah-nulth-aht

The quote above is the accumulation of several elders sharing knowledge patterns about the Quu-us crest. "Nuu-chah-nulth-aht" is a general reference to what the Nuu-chah-nulth peoples (aht) have said about this.

This conception of humanity forms the basis of a cultural logic for intergenerational accountability. On 15 May 1914, the Royal Commission on Indian Affairs for British Columbia met with Tla-o-qui-aht hereditary chiefs on Meares Island. The chiefs demonstrated this outlook in the following passages:

> Now listen, gentlemen. I am going to tell you what I think—what is in my heart. I am very glad to see you gentlemen here. . . . I am of a good heart to see you here, and I am feeling pretty high myself about you coming to see me. I am the Chief here. I am going to tell you what I have in my mind. . . . I have 221 Indians and this place is too small. . . . When there is another generation of people, three hundred years from now, there will be no timber for them at all. It is all taken up by . . . settlers who surround the reserve all round, and pretty soon there will be no room.
>
> —Chief Joseph

Eli Enns

A Nuu-chah-nulth totem pole.

Continued

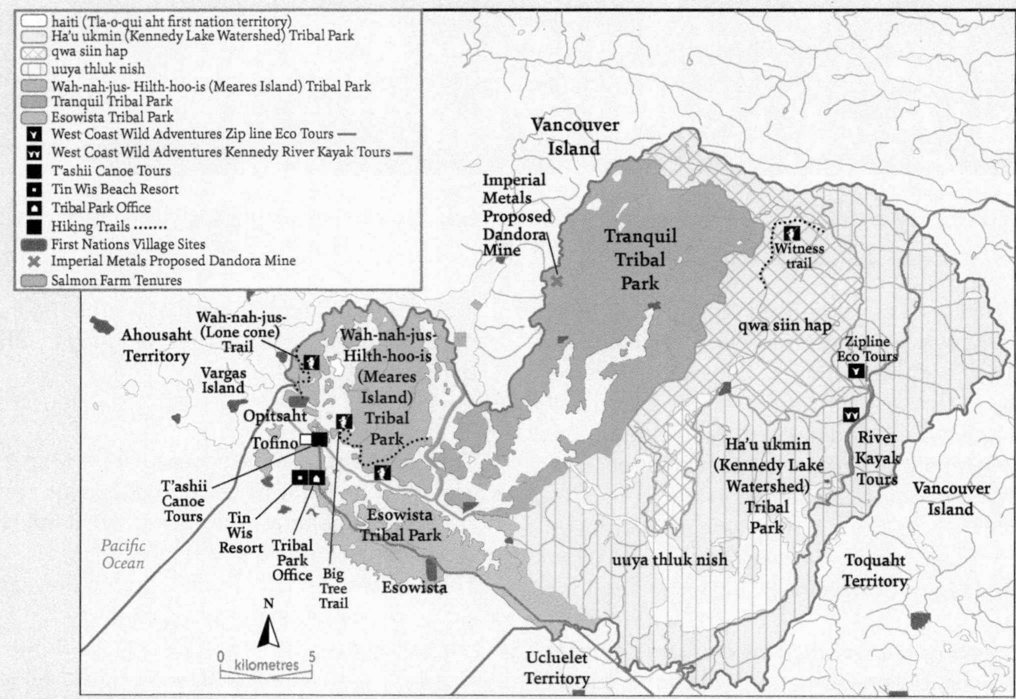

FIGURE 14.12 | Map of Tla-o-quiat Tribal Parks Initiative.

Source: Tla-o-quiat Tribal Parks Initiative. Courtesy of Clayoquot Action and Wilderness Committee.

Chief Jimmy Jim spoke next:

> I am going to tell you that I am very happy to see you here. . . . There are not old people here now. They are all young people here, but we know all about the old people. . . . That was the time when there was no white people here then. And when I was a boy there were no white men here either . . . until the Bishop and Mr Gilliod came. He was the first Agent. . . . Mr Gilliod used to say to the Indians that there would not be any white people here. They will not come here it is too wild, he said, and white people would not use this land. . . . It is full here now; this small place we cannot fall any trees for firewood in because it is too small for generations to come. We are holding the wood for the people who come after us.

The above words were spoken in Opitsaht on Meares Island at the heart of Clayoquot Sound over 100 years ago. Another anniversary celebrated recently was the thirtieth anniversary of the Meares Island Tribal Park declaration in April 1984. A significant shift from 1914 to 1984 was that Tla-o-qui-aht had moved from polite protest to direct action in the form of blockades and successful litigation against the provincial government which had condoned the clear-cut logging of the ancient cedar rain forests of Meares Island. The most significant development from 1984 to 2015 is that the Tla-o-qui-aht have moved from logging blockades to pioneering tribal parks as an alternative to the "business as usual" approach to natural resource management.

The tribal parks model is a manifestation of a dramatically different social contract which extends ideas of justice to the environment on which we all share and depend, and through time to the future ancestors to whom we are ultimately accountable, based on the humanity concept Quu-us. This social contract is captured in works of art such as totem poles. The crests function as symbolic memory devices associated with various knowledge patterns that have been encoded in story. The stories depicted by the totem poles provide a moral education for the listeners, guiding their behaviour toward others in their human community, as well as other beings with whom they share the environment.

This system of "active participation in a social contract" ensures that stories with encoded knowledge patterns about Natural Law are an ever present visual characteristic of the built environment. Far from being just beautiful art, these crests and stories continue to influence ecological governance applications by First Nations in modern times, such as the tribal parks initiative. They ideally lead to effective management outcomes in educational ecotourism, renewable energy projects, ecosystem service programs, and value-added natural resource and non-timber forest product sector development—all with a long-term view of climate change adaptation and what is in the best interests of the future generations three hundred years from now.

Eli Enns

Eli Enns is a Nuu-chah-nulth Canadian political scientist focused in constitutional law, international dispute resolution, and ecological governance. Co-founder of the Ha'uukmin Tribal Park in Clayoquot Sound on the west coast of Vancouver Island and North American coordinator for the ICCA Consortium, Eli is the great-grandson of Nah-wah-suhm, public speaker and historian for Wickaninnish, Tyee Ha'wiih of Tla-o qui-aht.

ENVIRONMENT IN FOCUS

BOX 14.13 | What You Can Do: Supporting Protected Areas

1. Visit parks and other protected areas often throughout the year. Enjoy yourself. Tell others that you have enjoyed yourself, and encourage them to visit.
2. Always follow park regulations regarding use. Feeding wildlife, for example, may seem kind or harmless, but it can lead to death of the animal.
3. If you have questions regarding the park's management or features, do not be afraid to ask. A questioning public is a concerned public.
4. Many park agencies have public consultation strategies relating to topics ranging from park policy to the management of individual parks. Let them know your interests so that you can be placed on the mailing list to receive more information.
5. Join a non-governmental organization, such as the Canadian Parks and Wilderness Society or Nature Canada, with a strong interest in parks issues.
6. Many parks now have cooperating associations in which volunteers can help with various tasks. Find out whether a park near you has such an organization.
7. Write to politicians to let them know of your park-related concerns.

Summary

1. Extinction levels have reached unprecedented levels. There are several reasons why we should be concerned. Life-supporting ecosystem processes depend on ecosystem components. As we lose components through extinction, these processes become more impaired. We also derive many useful and valuable products from natural biota, including medicines. In addition to these utilitarian reasons, there are ethical and moral reasons why we should be concerned about species extinction.

2. Many factors are behind current declines. The underlying factor is human demand as population and consumption levels grow. Much attention has concentrated on the tropics because of the high biodiversity levels and high rates of destruction there. However, Canada has experienced 13 extinctions and 22 extirpations since European colonization.

3. Main pressures causing extinction include overharvesting, predator control, and habitat change. Habitat change includes not only physical changes (e.g., conversion of habitat into agricultural land) but also those caused by chemicals and the introduction of alien species.

4. Not all species are equally vulnerable to extinction. Species with specialized habitat requirements, migratory species, species with insular and local distributions, species valued by humans for commercial reasons, animal species with a large body size, species needing a large home range, species not effective as dispersers, and species with low reproductive potential tend to be the most vulnerable.

5. Canada is party to several international treaties for the protection of biodiversity, including the legally binding Convention on Biological Diversity. None of the CBD goals set for 2010 were met, including the overriding mission of slowing down the rate of biodiversity loss.

6. As a signatory to the CBD, Canada was required to introduce legislation to protect endangered species. In 2002, the federal government passed the Species at Risk Act (SARA).

7. The Committee on the Status of Endangered Wildlife in Canada (COSEWIC) is responsible for determining the status of rare species and categorizing them as extinct, extirpated, endangered, threatened, or vulnerable. As of 2014, 721 species had been classified as at risk. The Committee's assessment is the first step in the process for protecting a proposed species at risk under SARA.

8. For species listed under SARA, recovery and management plans must be developed and implemented, unless the minister responsible feels that recovery is not "feasible." By 2013, only 56 out of 221 plans had been completed.

9. Protected areas are one of the key strategies to combat the erosion of biodiversity, both internationally and in Canada. Protected areas fulfill many roles in society, including species and ecosystem protection, maintenance of ecological processes, and as places for recreation and spiritual renewal, aesthetic appreciation, tourism, and science and education in natural outdoor settings.

10. There are many different kinds of protected areas in Canada, including national and provincial parks, wilderness areas, tribal parks, wildlife refuges, ecological reserves, and regional and municipal parks. The amount of protection given to ecosystem components varies among these different types.

11. National parks are outstanding natural areas protected by the federal government because of their ecological importance and aesthetic significance. There are 47 national parks in Canada. The goal is to have at least one national park in each of the 39 regions of the national system plan. At present, Canada's terrestrial system is about 60 per cent complete and the marine system about 15 per cent complete. The CBD target is to establish 17 per cent of the land base and 10 per cent of the marine area of each country in protected areas by 2020. Canada currently has about 10 per cent and 1 per cent in these categories.

12. Banff, the first national park in Canada, was established in 1885. Since that time, the national parks fulfilled a dual mandate that required protection of park resources in an unimpaired state but also permitted their use. This conflicting mandate was clarified in an amendment to the National Parks Act in 1988 and further clarified in the National Parks Act of 2000, giving first priority to protecting the ecological integrity of the parks.

13. Management challenges to the national parks system include external threats and fragmentation. An ecosystem approach to management is required to address these challenges by embracing stewardship of park lands.

14. Aboriginal peoples have been integral to the development of many protected areas in Canada and constitute a third level of government that needs to be involved in the designation and management of protected areas in most areas of Canada.

Key Terms

Aboriginal peoples
active management
Biosphere Reserves
Convention on Biological Diversity (CBD)
Convention on International Trade in Endangered Species of Wild Fauna and Flora (CITES)
ecologically extinct
endangered
ex situ conservation
ex situ preservation
extirpated
extrinsic values
fragmentation
in situ preservation
intrinsic value
island biogeography
minimum viable population (MVP)
population viability analysis (PVA)
protected areas
Red List
Species at Risk Act (SARA)
stewardship
system plan
threatened species
vulnerable species

Questions for Review and Critical Thinking

1. Why do you think the signatories to the CBD failed to meet all the 2010 targets? What changes do you think need to be made to meet the targets set for 2020?
2. What are the main reasons why we should be concerned about species extinctions?
3. Why are some species more vulnerable to extinction than others?
4. What is being done to protect endangered species in your province?
5. What are some of the strengths and weaknesses of Canada's Species at Risk Act?
6. What do you think should be the relative importance of the various roles played by protected areas?
7. What different classifications of protected areas exist in your province, and what kinds of protection are offered by these different systems?
8. What is your province doing to achieve the 12 per cent protected area that all jurisdictions in Canada have committed to establishing? Are there plans to help meet the 17 per cent terrestrial and 10 per cent marine targets for 2020?

Related Websites

Canadian Council on Ecological Areas
ccea.org

Canadian Environmental Assessment Agency
www.ceaa.gc.ca

Canadian Parks and Wilderness Society
www.cpaws.ca

Committee on the Status of Endangered Wildlife in Canada
www.cosewic.gc.ca

Ducks Unlimited Canada
www.ducks.ca

Environment Canada
www.ec.gc.ca

Environment Canada: Species at Risk
www.ec.gc.ca/nature/default.asp?lang=En&n=FB5A4CA8-1

Global Environment Facility
www.gefweb.org

International Union for Conservation of Nature, Red List
www.iucnredlist.org

Marmot Recovery Foundation
www.marmots.org

Nature Canada
www.naturecanada.ca

North American Waterfowl Management Plan
http://nawmp.wetlandnetwork.ca/

Northwest Territories: Environment and Natural Resources
www.nwtwildlife.com

Ontario Ministry of Natural Resources and Forestry
www.mnr.gov.on.ca

Parks Canada
www.pc.gc.ca

Sierra Youth Coalition
www.syc-cjs.org

Species at Risk Public Registry
www.sararegistry.gc.ca

State of Birds in Canada
www.stateofcanadasbirds.org

United Nations Environment Programme, World Conservation Monitoring Centre
www.unep-wcmc.org

Wilderness Committee
www.wildernesscommittee.org

World Commission on Protected Areas
www.iucn.org/about/work/programmes/gpap_home/

World Wildlife Fund Canada
www.wwf.ca

Further Readings

Note: This list comprises works relevant to the subject of the chapter but not cited in the text. All cited works are listed in the References at the end of the book.

Abbey, E. 1968. *Desert Solitaire: A Season in the Wilderness*. New York: Simon and Schuster.

Alexander, S.M. 2015. "Carnivore management and the role of conservation GIS," in B. Mitchell, ed., *Resource and Environmental Management in Canada*, 5th edn. Don Mills, ON: Oxford University Press, 293–317.

Cardinale, B. J, et al. 2012. "Biodiversity loss and its impact on humanity." *Nature* 486: 59–67.

Carroll, D., 2014. "Native enclosures: Tribal national parks and progressive politics of environmental stewardship in Indian country," *Geoforum* 53: 31–40.

Dearden, P., R. Rollins, and M. Needham. 2015. *Parks and Protected Areas in Canada: Planning and Management*, 4th edn. Toronto: Oxford University Press.

Favaro, B., J.D. Reynolds, and I.M. Côté. 2012. "Canada's weakening aquatic protection." *Science* 337: 154.

Lemieux, C.J. 2015. "Planning and Managing Canada's Parks and Protected Areas in an Era of Rapid Climate Change." In P. Dearden, R. Rollins, and M. Needham *Parks and Protected Areas in Canada: Planning and Management*, 4th edn. Toronto: Oxford University Press.

Lemieux, C.J., T.J. Beechey, D.J. Scott, and P.A. Gray. 2010. *Protected Areas and Climate Change in Canada: Challenges and Opportunities for Adaptation*. Canadian Council on Ecological Areas (CCEA) Technical Report #19. CCEA: Ottawa, Ontario.

McCune, J.L., W.L. Harrower, S. Avery-Gomm, J.M. Brogan, A. Csergo, et al. 2013. "Threats to Canadian species at risk: An analysis of finalized recovery strategies." *Biological Conservation* 166: 254–265.

McNamee, K. 2009. "From wild places to endangered spaces," in P. Dearden and R. Rollins, eds, *Parks and Protected Areas in Canada: Planning and Management*, 3rd edn. Toronto: Oxford University Press, 24–55.

Murray, G., and L. King 2012. "First nations values in protected area governance: Tla-o-qui-aht Tribal Parks and Pacific Rim National Park Reserve." *Human Ecology* 40: 385–395.

Olive, A. 2014. "The road to recovery: Comparing Canada and US recovery strategies for shared endangered species." *The Canadian Geographer* 58: 263–275.

Go to www.oupcanada.com/DeardenMitchell5e to access additional learning tools on your smartphone, tablet, or PC.

PART E

Environmental Change and Challenge Revisited

Be the change you want to see in the world.

—Mahatma Gandhi

We must always change, renew, rejuvenate ourselves; otherwise we harden.

—Johann Wolfgang von Goethe

Change is ubiquitous. This book provides an overview of environmental change and challenge in Canada. Change occurs as a result of both natural and human-induced pressures, and it is often difficult to determine the balance between them. However, human-induced changes frequently are the dominant driving factor for many aspects of environmental change. In many cases, these changes, such as extinction and climate change, are irreversible and serve to impoverish the planet for future generations.

The preceding chapters emphasize the need to understand the ecological aspects of environmental change, along with various management approaches. Reading this book should enable you to understand the background to many environmental problems and also to appreciate the different management approaches to their resolution. In each chapter, we have attempted to make you aware not only of the nature of the challenges but also possible solutions.

This final part contains one chapter, and its main focus is on solutions. We provide an assessment of progress at the global and national levels in addressing environmental change. We also provide a detailed case study which pulls together various perspectives about interacting natural, economic, and social systems related to energy, water, and food. We end with suggestions on actions that you can take. We hope that you will not only read the chapter carefully but also take action to try to improve your balance sheet with, or your footprint on, the environment! Your efforts, combined with those of thousands of others acting individually, can make substantial changes in the environment of tomorrow.

CHAPTER FIFTEEN

Making It Happen

Learning Objectives

- To identify selected global responses to environmental degradation
- To understand some key Canadian responses to environmental degradation
- To place Canada within the global context for environmental response
- To assess how important environment is to the administration of your university
- To make better decisions to minimize your impact on the environment
- To use your influence more effectively to benefit the environment
- To clarify what "the good life" means for you

> When I call to mind my earliest impressions, I wonder whether the process ordinarily referred to as growing up is not actually a process of growing down; whether experience, so much touted among adults as the thing children lack, is not actually a progressive dilution of the essentials by the trivialities of life.
>
> —Aldo Leopold, *A Sand County Almanac* (1949)

Introduction

Aldo Leopold, one of the greatest conservation thinkers and writers, points out that as we get older and our lives get busier, we often get distracted from the important things in life, like protecting the environment. Nearly everyone says that environmental protection is important, but most devote minimal effort to doing anything about it. We are all members

Perspectives on the Environment

The Pattern of Change

When change works, it tends to follow a pattern. The people who change have a clear direction, ample motivation, and a supportive environment.

—Heath and Heath (2010: 255)

of NATO: No Action, Talk Only. And the same is true of our country. On paper, Canada has impressive legislation, policies, strategies, and plans regarding the environment. Sadly, the translation of these into "on-the-ground" improvements is often chronically under-resourced. Many examples have been cited in this book, ranging from lack of resources to implement Canada's Oceans Strategy, as mandated under the Oceans Act (Chapter 8), to the failure to follow through on how to meet our obligations under the Kyoto Protocol (Chapter 7).

This chapter provides a brief overview of global and Canadian responses to environmental change. But governments are only part of the answer. This final chapter rests on the conviction that individuals can make a *significant difference* in how the environmental challenges presented in this book will develop over the next decade, if we are aware of the problems and are willing to do something about them. This chapter provides some ideas about how *you* can become involved in creating change.

Global Perspectives

The previous century may be characterized as an age of diminishing imperial powers, ongoing wars, atomic bombs, the harnessing of the entire globe into an interconnected economic system, rising consumer demands, and an exploding human population. This century will witness the continuation of some of these trends, but many scientists seem convinced that many factors discussed in this book such as global climatic change, water shortages, biological impoverishment, declining food yields per capita, desertification, pollution, and overpopulation will constitute the backdrop for the Anthropocene era discussed in Chapter 1 and Box 15.1.

Many of these trends are driven by consumption of material goods, which emerged over the last decades of the past century as the dominant international ideology. From its heartland in Europe, North America, and Japan, globalization of consumption will be one of the main developments of the next couple of decades, if not the entire century. Although population growth is still a concern, convincing signs point to falling rates of increase and the stabilization of populations, probably within the next 50 years. In contrast, consumption reflects no bounds. Indeed, our whole global economic system is focused on increasing consumption. At the individual level, our psyches often are dominated by images of the consumer goods we hanker for. The shopping mall has become the new place of worship.

Roughly one-quarter of humanity is now within this consumer class, a number divided more or less equally between those in developed countries and the rapidly increasing numbers of consumers in developing countries such as China and India.

The impacts of growing consumer demands are far-reaching. The Millennium Ecosystem Assessment (2005), introduced in Chapter 1, reviewed the state of planetary ecosystems, calculating that 15 of the 24 major ecosystem services supporting humanity, such as climate regulation, water provision, and soil production, have been pushed beyond their limits and are in a degraded state. The UNEP (2010) estimates that the services provided by ecosystems are worth between \$21 and \$72 trillion per year.

Until we find an effective way to incorporate these ecosystem values into the decision-making process, ecosystems will continue to be eroded. Clear scientific evidence exists for the deterioration of global ecosystems, but degradation cannot be seen outside the human context that drives the activities causing degradation. The Millennium Ecosystem Assessment's framework shown in Figure 15.1 illustrates these connections. The box in the bottom left, the ecosystem services provided by functioning ecosystems, is influenced by the direct drivers of change promoting indirect drivers that affect

Philip Dearden

Ninety per cent of children in developing regions attend primary school, according to Millennium Development Goal statistics. Here children in a remote Sea Gypsy village in Myanmar study English. Schoolteachers are held in high regard in Myanmar and education is prized. Note that many of the students are female. However, often this is not the case in many countries, and greater efforts need to be made to secure equal access to education for females.

ENVIRONMENT IN FOCUS

BOX 15.1 | The Anthropocene Revisited

In Chapter 1, we reported that many scientists believe that humans now have such a pervasive effect on the Earth that a new geological era, the Anthropocene, has started. After reading this book, you may be forming your own ideas on this topic. The pictures in this box were all taken by one of the authors on a 400-metre stretch of beach in Ghana and clearly illustrate the global situation.

Picture 1 shows what seems like an idyllic scene, a tropical beach with the pounding surf, but subsequent pictures reveal many concerns. Picture 2 shows that the sea is powerful; in fact, so powerful that decades-old palm trees are getting washed into the ocean, symbolic of rising seas levels associated with global climate change (Chapter 7). Picture 3 also shows erosion, but this time regarding the soil profile. Look carefully and you will see that incorporated into the soil profile are large amounts of plastic. The natural processes of soil-building discussed in Chapter 2 have been replaced by plastic debris of civilization. The very fabric of the Earth now incorporates totally synthetic materials. Picture 4, showing this plastic debris being washed up on the beach from sources near and far (Chapter 8), is symbolic of the widespread pollution of global oceans, mostly unseen until it washes up on shore. Picture 5 reveals a specific kind of debris, so-called ghost nets (see Chapter 8) that have broken free and drift around the oceans, killing as they go, until washing up on some shore somewhere. As they drift their killing is unintentional but pervasive, the fate of many creatures adversely affected by human activities (Chapter 14). Picture 6 epitomizes this tragedy. A broken plastic doll was among the debris washed up. Look carefully. Under the doll's arm is a rabbit. Is this symbolic of the broken trust placed in humanity to be the conscience of nature and protect biodiversity? And finally, the last picture shows the fishermen of the community at the end of the beach trying to secure one of their fishing boats after yet another journey to seek ever-declining numbers of fish to feed their families. As Chief Seattle is oft quoted as saying, "Whatever befalls the Earth, befalls the sons of the Earth."

If all this is occurring in just 400 metres of beach, what does it say for the rest of the world? Can we deny the Anthropocene has arrived?

1

2

3

4

All photos Philip Dearden

ecosystems and reduce human well-being. In turn, the desire for human well-being is the force behind the indirect drivers. The pincers on the arrows show links that are amenable to strategic interventions.

The **Millennium Development Goals (MDGs)** introduced in Chapter 1 are globally accepted. The target date for meeting the goals was 2015. Box 15.2 shows that by 2014 several goals had already been met and others show progress.

At least some progress has been made on all but one of the MDGs. The exception is the environment. We have done quite well in improving the lot of humanity, but not on the environment on which we all depend. So how is it possible that overall human welfare appears to be improving on a global scale and yet ecosystems are degrading?

Changes in drivers indirectly affecting biodiversity, such as population, technology, and lifestyle (upper right corner of figure), can lead to changes in drivers directly affecting biodiversity, such as the catch of fish or the application of fertilizers (lower right corner). These result in changes to ecosystems and the services they provide (lower left corner), thereby affecting human well-being. These interactions can take place at more than one scale and can cross scales. For example, an international demand for timber may lead to a regional loss of forest cover, which increases flood magnitude along a local stretch of a river. Similarly, the interactions can take place across different time scales. Different strategies and interventions can be applied at many points in this framework to enhance human well-being and conserve ecosystems.

To address this question Raudsepp-Hearne et al. (2010) advanced four alternative explanations. First, humans are really worse off than we realize; second, well-being mostly depends on food, and food production has been increasing; third, humans have averted the worst consequences of environmental degradation through technology; and, finally, due to a time lag, the worst is yet to come regarding the full impacts of global degradation. They found little support for the first explanation, although other scientists disagree, pointing out that the data were based almost entirely on the Human Development Index, which might not be the most valid comparison. The other three explanations all had some support, but the main finding was in the last one—the worst yet to come. In other words, humans have not yet felt the true impacts of environmental degradation, but have continued to enjoy benefits from environmental over-exploitation. Refer to Figure 1.12 in Chapter 1 showing the relationship between the global ecological footprint and Earth's biocapacity. It indicates we are now in the space of the biocapacity deficit, and awaiting the full repercussions of the deficit.

ENVIRONMENT IN FOCUS

BOX 15.2 | Millennium Development Goals, 2014

Goals Met

- Extreme poverty was reduced by half.

  In 1990, almost half of the population in developing regions lived on less than $1.25 a day. This rate dropped to 22 per cent by 2010, reducing the number of people living in extreme poverty by 700 million.
- The fight against malaria and tuberculosis has shown results.

  Between 2000 and 2012, an estimated 3.3 million deaths from malaria were averted due to substantial expansion of malaria interventions. About 90 per cent of those averted deaths—3 million—were children under the age of five living in sub-Saharan Africa. The intensive efforts to fight tuberculosis have saved an estimated 22 million lives worldwide since 1995. If the trends continue, the world will reach the MDG targets on malaria and tuberculosis.
- Access to an improved drinking-water source became a reality for 2.3 billion people.

  The target of halving the proportion of people without access to an improved drinking water source was achieved in 2010. In 2012, 89 per cent of the world's population had access to an improved source, up from 76 per cent in 1990.
- Disparities in primary school enrolment between boys and girls are being eliminated in all developing regions.

  Substantial gains have been made toward reaching gender parity in school enrolment at all levels of education in all developing regions. By 2012, all developing regions had achieved, or were close to achieving, gender parity in primary education.
- Political participation by women continues to increase.

  In January 2014, 46 countries had more than 30 per cent female members of Parliament in at least one chamber.
- Development assistance rebounded, the trading system stayed favourable for developing countries, and their debt burden remained low.

  Official development assistance stood at $134.8 billion in 2013, the highest level ever, after two years of declining volumes. However, aid is shifting away from the poorest countries. The debt burden of developing countries remained stable at about 3 per cent of export revenue.

Goals Not Met, More Effort Required

- Major trends that threaten environmental sustainability continue, but with examples of successful global action.

  Global emissions of carbon dioxide (CO_2) continued upward and those in 2011 were almost 50 per cent above their 1990 level. Millions of hectares of forest are lost every year, many species are being driven closer to extinction, and renewable water resources are becoming scarcer. However, international action is on the verge of eliminating ozone-depleting substances and the proportion of protected terrestrial and coastal marine areas has been increasing.
- Hunger continues to decline, but immediate additional efforts are needed to reach the MDG target.

  The proportion of undernourished people in developing regions decreased from 24 per cent in 1990–1992 to 14 per cent in 2011–2013. However, progress has slowed in the past decade.
- Chronic undernutrition among young children declined, but one in four is still affected.

  In 2012, a quarter of all children under the age of five years were estimated to be stunted—having inadequate height for their age. This represents a significant decline since 1990 when 40 per cent of young children were stunted. However, 162 million young children are still suffering from chronic undernutrition.
- Child mortality has been almost halved, but more progress is needed.

  Worldwide, the mortality rate for children under age five dropped almost 50 per cent, from 90 deaths per 1,000 live births in 1990 to 48 in 2012. Preventable diseases are the main causes of under-five deaths and appropriate actions need to be taken to address them.
- Much more needs to be done to reduce maternal mortality.

  Globally, the maternal mortality ratio dropped by 45 per cent between 1990 and 2013, from 380 to 210 deaths per 100,000 live births. Worldwide, almost 300,000 women died in 2013 from causes related to pregnancy and childbirth.
- Antiretroviral therapy is saving lives, but must be expanded.

  Access to antiretroviral therapy (ART) for HIV-infected people has been increasing dramatically, with 9.5 million people in developing regions receiving treatment in 2012. Expanding its coverage can save many more lives.
- Over a quarter of the world's population has gained access to improved sanitation since 1990, yet a billion people still resort to open defecation.

  Between 1990 and 2012, almost 2 billion people gained access to an improved sanitation facility. However, in 2012, 2.5 billion people did not use an improved sanitation facility and 1 billion people still resorted to open defecation, posing a huge risk to communities already often poor and vulnerable.
- In developing regions, 90 per cent of children attend primary school.

  The school enrolment rate in primary education in developing regions increased from 83 per cent to 90 per cent between 2000 and 2012. Most gains were achieved by 2007, after which progress stagnated. In 2012, 58 million school-age children were not in schools.

Changes in drivers that indirectly affect biodiversity, such as population, technology, and lifestyle (upper right corner of figure), can lead to changes in drivers directly affecting biodiversity, such as the catch of fish or the application of fertilizers (lower right corner). These result in changes to ecosystems and the services they provide (lower left corner), thereby affecting human well-being. These interactions can take place at more than one scale and can cross scales. For example, an international demand for timber may lead to a regional loss of forest cover, which increases flood magnitude along a local stretch of a river. Similarly, the interactions can take place across different time scales. Different strategies and interventions can be applied at many points in this framework to enhance human well-being and conserve ecosystems.

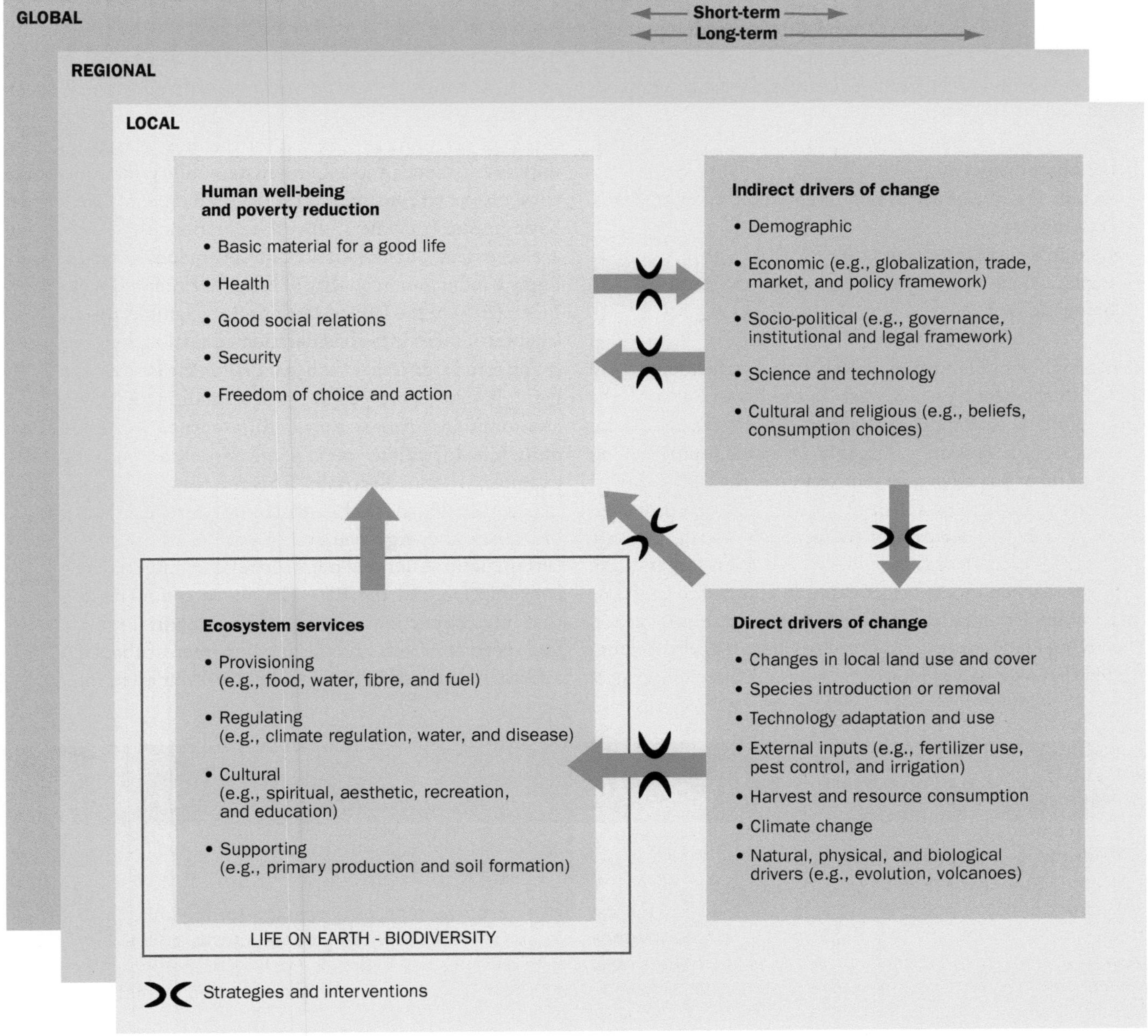

FIGURE 15.1 | Conceptual framework of the Millennium Ecosystem Assessment.

Source: Millennium Ecosystem Assessment (2005: vii).

Some environmentalists have pointed out that, while having Millennium Development Goals is positive, these goals only address the challenge from one perspective, development. However, a main challenge is "over-development" in some areas of the world. What we really need are **Millennium Consumption Goals** that identify the most important and necessary cuts in consumption. Infinite development cannot occur in a finite world without cuts in consumption. Suggested goals include:

- Halve total energy use by 2025
- Cut military spending by 75 per cent by 2025
- Halve fossil fuels used by 2020
- Halve household energy use by 2020

- Halve obesity and overweight rates by 2020
- Produce half of food organically by 2020
- Reduce consumption of animal products by 50 per cent by 2020
- Increase density of suburban housing by 50 per cent by 2020
- Increase local resilience of food supply, producing more crops locally, where appropriate
- Halve the work week from the current 40+ hours per week to 20 hours per week
- Better distribute wealth by raising taxes on the wealthiest members of society
- Double the rate of use of non-motorized transport (bikes, walking, etc.)
- Guarantee access to health care for all
- Replace GNP with a genuine progress indicator or well-being index

Although some landmark international agreements were signed in the past 25 years, such as the Kyoto Protocol, the Convention on Biological Diversity (CBD), and the Stockholm Convention on Persistent Organic Pesticides, progress on many of them has been slow. For example, the CBD required signatory nations to establish networks of marine protected areas covering 10 per cent of the oceans by 2012, yet only 1 per cent was achieved. Indeed, not one main target of the CBD was reached by the target dates. In contrast to this slow speed of implementation, global change is continuing apace. The Living Planet Index, discussed in Chapter 1, also demonstrated that over half of biodiversity has declined since 1970. And the year 2014 was the warmest on record, and Arctic sea ice has declined 35 per cent in the last 35 years.

However, progress is occurring in some areas, such as product certification (see Chapters 8 and 9) as well as development of more integrated approaches to thinking about environment (Box 15.3). The area of certified forest worldwide increased from 3.24 million hectares in 1995 to 180.44 million hectares by July 2013. More than 250 fisheries are now certified worldwide as being sustainable. Obviously, given very different conditions prevailing in various world regions, different solutions are needed for the most effective way to improve resilience and achieve sustainability. For some countries, increased consumption is required if people are to meet basic needs. For others, drastic reductions in consumption are necessary. Such reduction, however, does not necessarily imply a reduction in quality of life. The Human Development Index (HDI) of the United Nations, for example, discussed in Chapter 1, takes into consideration education, longevity, and living standards rather than just GNP as measures of development. For very poor people, even a small increase in energy consumption can make a major difference to their living standard. It is difficult to spend long hours studying at night, for example, without electricity. This retards educational levels, which in turn holds back economic development. The benefits of additional energy availability and income increase up to a certain point. After that point, no relationship exists between consumption and the HDI. The above comments highlight that interconnections among different natural resource systems need attention, and the growing interest about a "nexus" approach, outlined in Box 15.3, deserves our attention.

ENVIRONMENT IN FOCUS

BOX 15.3 | Nexus Thinking

A frequent criticism about trying to address environmental challenges at all levels is that too often government agencies take a "siloed" approach, meaning each focuses only on its own responsibilities and functions. A negative outcome can be initiatives in one agency undermine those by another agency, or opportunities for greater efficiency and effectiveness are lost. To address this challenge, attention is being given to what is termed the **water-energy-food (WEF) nexus**. In other words, it is being recognized that each of water, energy, and food has implications for the other two, and therefore more attention needs to be given to their interconnections. In the words of Barrett (2014), "Ultimately, 'nexus thinking' means implementing integrated solutions at an ecosystem or landscape level that enhance security and sustainability in all three sectors."

Water is needed for extracting and processing fossil fuels. Water is also a key for generating electricity (hydro power), and for growing crops processed for biofuels. Furthermore, fossil-fuel extraction can contribute to pollution of water, with oil sands and hydraulic fracking of shales being prominent examples. And energy is required to extract, move, distribute, and treat water. At a global scale, production of food accounts for about 70 per cent of fresh water use by people, and in some countries this percentage can be as high as 90 per cent. Agricultural production also can lead to water pollution, whether from soil erosion or non-point sources (fertilizers, pesticides, herbicides).

The Stockholm International Water Institute (2014: 6) summarized the needs, opportunities, and challenges in the following way:

> Energy and water are inextricably linked—we need "water for energy" for cooling, storage, biofuels, hydropower, fracking, etc., and we need "energy for water" to pump,

treat and desalinate. Without energy and water we cannot satisfy basic human needs, produce food for a rapidly growing population and achieve economic growth.

Researchers are exploring the nexus approach. In the US, Griffiths-Sattenspiel and Wilson (2009) found that total energy use related to water was the equivalent of 13 per cent of all electricity generated in the US. Earlier, a study in California by Cohen et al. (2004) determined that water-related services accounted for 19 per cent of electricity consumed and 30 per cent of the natural gas demand in that state.

The US Department of Energy (2014), in a report entitled *The Water-Energy Nexus*, recommended six "strategic pillars" to address relationships between energy and water: (1) optimize freshwater efficiency of energy production, electricity generation, and end-use systems, (2) optimize energy efficiency of water management, treatment, distribution, and end-use systems, (3) enhance reliability and resilience of energy and water systems, (4) increase safe and productive use of non-traditional water sources, (5) promote responsible energy operations related to water quality, ecosystem, and seismic impacts, and (6) exploit productive synergies among water and energy systems.

In Ontario, Maas (2010) examined the total energy needed by water-related services to heat, treat, deliver, and remove water for five sectors: residential, commercial/institutional, manufacturing, agriculture, and power generation. She concluded that powering pumps, treatment plants, hot-water heaters, and boilers accounted for 12 per cent of total demand for electricity in the province and for 40 per cent of the demand for natural gas, similar to the situation in California. And, the Alberta WaterPortal (2013) reported that between 1999 and 2008, the average annual virtual water exports from Alberta related to exported crops and livestock was 12.10 Gm^2/year, with the largest importers being Japan, Mexico, the US, China, Iran, and Indonesia.

And, finally, Bizikova et al. (2013), at the International Institute of Sustainable Development in Winnipeg, developed a practical framework to deal with the interrelations among water, energy, and food security. They indicated that attention to the WEF nexus will need to consider the following overlapping challenges: significant quantities of water required for energy-processing activities, (e.g., refining of oil products or manufacturing of synthetic fuels); increasing amounts of water utilized by irrigation systems for food production as well as for industrially produced meat; energy utilized in post-harvest stages of food production; and negative environmental impacts due to deforestation, overgrazing, and frequent low-productivity agricultural practices, which result from trying to ensure sufficient energy and food. Key aspects of the WEF nexus are highlighted in Table 15.1.

Using the information in Table 15.1, reflect on which issues should be addressed to improve effectiveness, efficiency, and equity when managing water, energy, and food in your community, region, or province. What might be initial modifications to current policies and practices to achieve a more integrated approach?

TABLE 15.1 | WEF Security Nexus Elements

Water security	1. water access 2. water safety 3. water affordability in order that every person can experience a clean, healthy, and productive life, while ensuring the natural environment is protected and enhanced
Energy security	1. continuity of energy supplies relative to demand 2. physical availability of supplies 3. supply sufficient to satisfy demand at a given price
Food security	1. food availability, influenced by production, distribution, and exchange of food 2. access to food, including affordability, allocation, and preference 3. utilization, regarding nutritional value, social value, and food safety 4. food stability over time

Source: Bizikova et al. (2013: 5). Reprinted with the permission of the International Institute for Sustainable Development (IISD) www.iisd.org

Consuming more will not, after a certain threshold, improve overall well-being. The challenge at the international level is to enact policies and programs that will see consumption levels raised in needy countries but reduced in over-consuming countries, such as Canada. Reduction in material consumption in wealthier nations will have to be in the order of 90 per cent for some semblance of sustainability and equity to emerge. Thus, people in developed countries need to rediscover the importance of the *quality* of life as opposed to the current emphasis on *quantity* of goods to acquire.

The **Happy Planet Index (HPI)** attempts to provide a different perspective on human well-being and environmental impact and focus on achieving sustainability. The HPI assumes that most people want to live long and fulfilling lives and that the country doing the best is one that allows its citizens to do so while avoiding infringing on the ability of people in the future and in other countries to do the same. Human well-being is assessed as "happy life years" and impacts by measuring ecological footprints per capita, as discussed in Chapter 1. The HPI provides an assessment of the environmental efficiency of supporting well-being in a given country. Such efficiency could emerge in a country with a medium environmental impact and very high well-being, but it could also emerge in a country with only

Philip Dearden

Philip Dearden

Two photos, one world. On the left is a chemical plant in Singapore, a small but wealthy country that imports all its needs and exports processed material around the planet. It depends mainly on finite supplies of stock resources, such as fossil fuels and mineral ores, to fuel its economy, along with advanced technical knowledge. Its impact is worldwide in terms of resource extraction and pollution. On the right is a village in upper Ghana. The village walls are made of mud, the roofs of grass. The village is fuelled by the sun, whether it is the pile of firewood used for cooking, the grass that sustains the goats, or the new solar-powered light in the middle of the village. Its impact is local. When too much wood is taken, or too many goats exist, the community suffers.

mediocre well-being but very low environmental impact (such as Vietnam). Each country's HPI value is a function of its average subjective life satisfaction, life expectancy at birth, and ecological footprint per capita. Conceptually, it approximates multiplying life satisfaction and life expectancy and dividing that by the ecological footprint. High- and medium-development Latin American countries score highest in delivering fairly long and happy lives with a relatively low ecological footprint. In 2012, Costa Rica scored the highest, followed by Vietnam and Colombia, while Botswana, Chad, and Qatar ranked at the bottom of the list. Canada ranked sixty-fourth out of 151 countries, mainly because of our very high ecological footprint.

Perspectives on the Environment

The Good Life

Rethinking what "constitutes the good life" is overdue in a world on a fast track to self-inflicted ill-health and planet-wide damage to forests, oceans, biodiversity, and other natural resources. . . . Indeed, a new understanding of the good life can be built not around wealth but around well-being: having basic survival needs met, along with freedom, health, security, and satisfying social relations. Consumption would still be important, to be sure, but only to the extent that it boosts quality of life. Indeed, a well-being society might strive to minimize the consumption required to support a dignified and satisfying life.

—Gardner and Assadourian (2004: 165)

These kinds of indices are useful, if controversial, because they make us consider different ways of defining progress and re-evaluate what we are trying to achieve. The traditional way of looking at global development along the consumer-based lines that Western societies have "progressed" is simply untenable for the rest of the world. All evidence shows that planetary ecosystems are collapsing under current burdens and can no longer provide services required for future generations. Adding further to these stresses is an option only for the most short-sighted and self-centred of

Philip Dearden

Global challenges require different solutions in different parts of the world. While most of us need to reduce our consumption, some people around the world cannot. The Karen people, who live in this village in western Thailand, have nothing to reduce. They would need to increase their levels of consumption just to meet what many of us would classify as basic needs.

Philip Dearden

"The best things in life aren't things." This Bali rice farmer has none of the mechanical aids of our modern farmers, none of the household appliances that you and I have, but is a happy man.

societies. Unfortunately, as Diamond points out in his book *Collapse* (2005), some societies took exactly that route in the past. It usually occurred where a ruling class benefited greatly from the existing state of affairs and preferred to see it continue even over the short term rather than risk their extravagant lifestyle.

The challenge, then, is to reduce the level of stress below current levels while raising the standard of living of the world's poor to acceptable levels. Although international agencies such as the World Bank do define a "poverty level," analysis shows this level varies remarkably among societies and that a broader range of values should be taken into account. The Happy Planet Index is one example of such an approach, and it applies not only to the so-called underdeveloped nations but to developed nations such as Canada. The goal is to produce as much human well-being as possible for society with minimal environmental impact. The next section discusses some national perspectives on this challenge.

National Perspectives

Canada is a remarkable country—the world's second-largest by area, with some of the largest remaining wilderness areas. Canada is ranked the highest in the world regarding estimated value per capita of natural capital (Statistics Canada, 2011a). Canadians enjoy one of the highest standards of living in the world and rank eighth in the UN's Human Development Index. (UNDP, 2014). We are few in number with a big country and a high standard of living. Most Canadians have no idea of the scope of the various global challenges because of our isolation from global pressures. As a result, our performance in most areas of environmental management, from failing to comply with global treaties or to pass and enforce effective legislation to the everyday statistics that document our excessive per capita global impact, is largely overlooked. Throughout this book, we have cited many examples. The audits undertaken on environmental and sustainability issues by the government's Office of the Auditor General also provide many examples. The audits repeatedly show failures by government departments to comply with their own policies and legislation. We make commitments at international and national levels that we consistently fail to fulfill. To emphasize the seriousness of these shortcomings, the main findings of the commissioner of the Environment and Sustainable Development for 2013 are shown in Box 15.4.

Violations of our commitments under the Kyoto Protocol (Chapter 7) are well known, but many others exist. In terms of marine conservation, projections suggest that we will manage less than a third of our commitments under the Convention on Biological Diversity to establish a network of marine protected areas, and will struggle to make the terrestrial commitment, despite the vision of our forefathers in creating the world's second national park in Banff in 1885. Canada would not support the global moratorium on bottom trawling promoted by George W. Bush, not a conservationist US president; voted against declaring bluefin tuna endangered under the Convention on International Trade in Endangered Species; and filed more objections under this treaty than the rest of the world collectively. Canada also refused to support the US proposal to ban trade in polar bears under the same treaty.

On climate change, we have been charting a course diametrically opposed to that of much of the rest of the world (Chapter 7), and were recognized as a major impediment to progress on climate change regulations through the numerous "Fossil of the Day" awards given by a coalition of hundreds of international non-governmental organizations at climate talks ranging from Poland in 2008 through to Durban at the end of 2011, where Canada held "a virtual mortgage" on this award for obfuscation and delay (Parkinson, 2011). At the 2013 Warsaw conference, Canada won a Lifetime Unachievement Fossil Award, for its long-standing failure to make meaningful contributions at these meetings and consistently blocking progress.

Canada reduced its emissions target from 282 million tonnes in the government's first plan in 2007 to 28 million tonnes in 2010, a drop of approximately 90 per cent. It has also made new commitments set out under the Copenhagen Accord, the 2010 Federal Sustainable Strategy, and the Cancún action plan to reduce its greenhouse gas emissions by 17 per cent, from 2005 levels, by 2020. An audit by the Auditor General (2011) concluded that Canada will not be able to make even these very reduced commitments until there is a clear strategic plan including clear objectives, timelines, interim targets, and expectations with key partners. The world is set to gather in Paris in 2015 to seek a legally binding global accord on climate change. By the time you read this book, you will know what happened at this critical meeting,

Perspectives on the Environment

Global Warming and Leadership

What is really needed is a new consciousness of the threat of global warming, and a shared sense of responsibility toward future generations. We need to get our act together as a society. We need leadership to meet the challenge of our time. Where will it come from?

—E. Frind (2014: A9)

and whether Canada once more swept the awards for doing the most to wreck the agreement, or returned to being the environmentally committed, proactive voice.

The availability of information to interested citizens also seems increasingly restricted in Canada, as already discussed in this book, in contrast to many other countries where growing Internet use has promoted greater citizen access to government data. An international study of the effectiveness of freedom-of-information acts in five parliamentary democracies placed Canada last (Hazell and Worthy, 2010). Canada was criticized for its low political support, weak information commissioner, and antiquated and expensive system for requests that deters many from seeking information. Canada was among the first countries in the world to introduce freedom-of-information legislation, in 1983, but several studies have shown that we are far from a leader in this field.

The lack of good information was highlighted by the Auditor General in 2010, and Canada has been the subject of international condemnation in premier international journals such as *Nature* for federal government scientists being barred from talking openly about their work. These restrictions apply not only to research that might be considered "sensitive," such as on climate change, but also to pure research such as the report in *Nature* by a scientist on a flood that occurred in northern Canada 13,000 years ago (*Nature* 464, 2010: 740–3). Fisheries scientists have also been particularly constrained in their ability to discuss their findings in public. A federal fisheries biologist published a paper in *Science* (Miller et al., 2011), linking the crash in fisheries stocks in the Fraser River to a virus infection. *Science* highlighted the study

ENVIRONMENT IN FOCUS

BOX 15.4 | Commissioner of the Environment and Sustainable Development: Main Findings for 2013

Protecting our natural heritage is an immense challenge, given Canada's geography and the range of species involved, from fish and amphibians to birds, plants, and large mammals such as caribou. As well, the complex interaction among stressors such as climate change, habitat loss, invasive species, and pollution contributes to the difficulty of this task. Despite its long-standing tradition of leadership in conservation, Canada continues to lose ground in key areas as these pressures increase. For example, scientists have documented deteriorating biodiversity conditions in all of the main types of ecosystems in Canada. In some ecosystems there are healthy areas, but in others, the deterioration is quite rapid. According to the federal government, 518 species are at risk of disappearing, and the list is growing. While some bird populations in Canada have increased since 1970, other types of birds, such as grassland birds, have declined dramatically. I see a wide gap between the government's commitments and the results achieved. Our findings include several examples that are particularly striking:

- Legislative requirements under the Species at Risk Act have not been met. At the current rate, it will take Environment Canada approximately 10 years to complete its backlog of recovery strategies required under the Act.
- Environment Canada has assessed ecological integrity to be less than adequate in over one-half of its wildlife protected areas, which together cover an area about the size of New Brunswick and Nova Scotia.
- Although protecting ecological integrity is the first priority for Parks Canada, less than half of the ecosystems it assessed in 2011 were in good condition (with declining trends in the condition of many).
- Environment Canada has completed less than half of the Bird Conservation Region Strategies it committed to finishing by 2010.
- Environment Canada estimates that monitoring for 30 per cent of the bird species in Canada is insufficient to determine whether they are at risk.

These findings are cause for concern. Despite Canadians' deep affinity with nature and the central place it holds in our economy, our history, our culture, and our values, we have been unable to keep up with the challenges. It is time to look for new approaches.

Source: Office of the Auditor General of Canada (2013: 1).

Perspectives on the Environment

International Attention on Canada and the Need for Activist Scientists

Canada's international reputation as a green and gentle nation has long been a matter of national pride. But is that reputation deserved? Canada's actions on environmental issues—from ignoring Kyoto Protocol targets to obstructing progress at United Nations climate change talks—are increasingly raising eyebrows, both at home and abroad. Perhaps nothing is more emblematic of this reality gap than Canada's determination to mine its tar sands at a frantic rate. The sands are a dirty source of oil. They require more energy for oil extraction than do conventional reserves, producing extra greenhouse-gas emissions. The industry has torn up vast swathes of landscape, created toxic ponds of waste, and released pollutants into waterways. Where such issues justify pressure for action, it is crucial that scientists such as David Schindler . . . highlight them.

—Editorial in *Nature* (2010)

and notified over 7,400 journalists worldwide about it, telling journalists to contact a media officer in Fisheries and Oceans Canada. Major media outlets throughout the world requested interviews with Miller but were denied access by the Privy Council Office. This disturbing trend of restricting the flow of scientific data was highlighted and discussed in Chapter 1.

However, some progress is occurring. As noted in Chapter 7, British Columbia initiated a carbon tax on the rationale that people should be rewarded for adopting behaviour less likely to exacerbate the effects of global warming. This means taxing carbon-based activities, such as those using fossil fuels. In BC, people pay such a tax at the gas pump every time they fill up. Evaluations indicate that the tax is effective and that no noticeable loss of quality of life has occurred in the province. Yet there was major opposition to the tax when it was first introduced. Despite such opposition, BC politicians moved ahead with the tax in the belief that it was the right thing to do.

Other provinces are moving forward with innovative ideas. As discussed in Chapter 7, in early 2015, Ontario agreed to join Quebec to implement a cap-and-trade system in their respective provinces. Nova Scotia is hoping to harness the power of the world's largest tides at the Bay of Fundy to develop an electricity supply that could meet up to 15 per cent of the province's needs. The province is also exploring a project to see whether the old coal mines in Cape Breton, some 3,200 kilometres in length, can be used to produce geothermal energy. The mines are flooded with water at a temperature of 9 to 15°C, and the idea is to turn the mines that once supplied half of Canada's coal into a new energy resource. A related example in Marmora in eastern Ontario is a proposed $660 million plan for "pumped storage"—water from the large reservoir in an abandoned open-pit iron mine would be pumped to another reservoir at the surface during off-peak energy hours and then sent back down through turbines.

These examples illustrate two key principles for moving forward. First, enlightened political leadership can play a major role in implementing change at the societal level, and second, human ingenuity is vast but needs to be applied to the key challenges facing society. The bottom line is that Canadians are too often not rising to meet environmental challenges and, in many cases, are falling behind. We are frequently followers and laggards rather than leaders. A global comparison is provided by the Environmental Performance Index (epi.yale.edu/), which ranks 178 countries in terms of overall environmental performance. Canada's overall rank in 2014 was twenty-fourth, a very modest position for a rich, large country. Canada scores well on some attributes, such as human health for which we were ranked first, and water resources where we were twentieth. Unfortunately, for agriculture we were ranked one-hundred-and-fifth, for forestry one-hundred-and-fourth and for fisheries seventy-first in terms of major resource industry performance on environment. Biodiversity protection was ranked ninety-seventh and changes in trends of carbon intensity, something that federal politicians are proud to boast about, eighty-sixth.

Canada's performance in the environmental field is also reflected in the Canadian Index of Wellbeing already discussed in Chapter 1. This index tracks eight factors. From 1994 to 2010, the CIW shows an increase of 5.7 per cent, but "environment" is one of three factors that dropped over this period (−7.8 per cent). (Details are available at https://uwaterloo.ca/canadian-index-wellbeing/.)

The image that many of us have of ourselves—that this country is a leader in global environmental management—is strongly supported by governments, but it is inconsistent with the facts. Macdonald (2009) attributes this to the governmental "search for environmental legitimacy," or what environmentalists might term "greenwashing," that is, controlling the message rather than addressing the problem. This perspective and approach have been noted in numerous places in earlier chapters.

Unfortunately, the longer we delay action to address environmental degradation, the more dramatic (and often more costly) the remedial actions will be if and when they do occur. In some cases, remedial action is delayed so long that the desired environmental conditions cannot be restored. Extinction is the ultimate example, but there are many others. Scientists have found that although we have met agreed-upon targets for reduced sulphate depositions, large areas are still receiving excessive sulphates, pH levels are not improving in many lakes, and biological indicators of recovery are even further behind. Reductions were made, but they were too little and too late to halt the acidification of many lakes in eastern Canada. The real challenge is to identify and mitigate these problems before they develop so far that they become either irreversible or so costly to reverse that they cannot be resolved. A 2011 report on the impacts of global climate change on the Canadian economy, for example, suggested that by 2020 it could cost the economy $5 billion per year and that by 2050, annual costs could range from $21 billion to $43 billion (NRTEE, 2011b).

Despite our poor response as a nation in many areas of environmental management, individual Canadians can take many actions that will have a significant impact not only on the Canadian environment but also globally. If an average Cambodian were to halve his or her consumption of global resources, the incremental gains would be small. But because of the scale of our personal consumption, even individual Canadians can make significant changes. If 35 million Canadians made changes, the cumulative impact would be staggering. The next section discusses some perspectives on environmental change at the personal level, to counter Leo Tolstoy's observation that "Everyone thinks of changing the world, but no one thinks of changing himself," and instead to endorse the view of Norman Vincent Peale that "You change your thoughts and you change your world."

Personal Perspectives

Pick Up That Degree

> The future is increasingly a race between education and catastrophe.
>
> —H.G. Wells

The difficulty with many environmental challenges is the vastness of their scale. They are so widespread that most Canadians do not realize they are out there, especially because we are more sheltered from their effects than people in smaller, more densely populated countries. Most of these problems also have long lag times (the period between the time when the processes are set in motion and when the effects are felt), especially when the effects may have different impacts in different parts of the globe. Global warming, for example, may lead to cooling and increased precipitation in some areas, while the effect may be just the opposite in other areas. Changes of this complexity and magnitude require long-term study before they can be understood. The scale of change also suggests that within the human lifespan, many of these trends may be irreversible.

Urgent actions are required if we are to help defuse these trends, but actions do not occur in a vacuum. They require understanding of the road we are on, where it goes, and how we can get on other, more desirable roads. Educational systems should help to bring about this understanding. Many schools, colleges, and universities graduate students who have little or no idea about how the ecosphere functions and how human activities impair those functions. They shop, travel, eat, drink, work, and play in blissful ignorance of the impact they may be having on life-support systems.

Colleges and universities are frequently accused of not being part of the "real" world. By "real" world, people usually mean the economic realities of today's society. However, that is not the real "real" world; it is essentially a game that humans invented to facilitate barter and exchange. Important? Yes! But is it the real world? Only partly! The real world includes the air we breathe, the water we drink, the organisms that keep the life-support systems going, and the ground we stand on. Without these things, there can be no invented world, however "real" it might seem. We concentrate on balancing these "play" budgets when, in reality, the more significant budgets of energy throughflow and material balance determine the future of society. One major challenge contributing to lack of understanding and action on environmental matters is **nature deficit disorder**. The term was coined by Richard Louv (2006) to describe an increasing gap in understanding of the *real* world on the part of the younger generation. Instead of playing outdoors in fields, woods, streams, lakes, or the ocean, an increasing proportion of the youth of today are glued to their computer or TV screens. They seldom visit the outside world, especially areas dominated by nature rather than human activities. The decline in the number of visitors to national parks and similar areas across North America bears testimony to this trend. A feedback loop develops. The less exposure that young people have to the natural world, the less they understand it and the less comfortable they feel outdoors. As a result, they tend to avoid encounters with nature and become even further estranged.

At a time when it is critical that more people become involved in significant environmental action, we seem to be producing a new generation that is farther than ever from developing any attachment to the environment. This does not bode well for society in the future as this generation matures and becomes the main economic drivers and decision-makers. Concern over this situation has prompted movements across North America to provide opportunities and facilities to encourage outdoor re-engagement by younger people (e.g., see the Kesho Trust in "Related Websites" at the end of the chapter). British Columbia, for example, has articulated four goals to guide its initiative to reconnect children and families with nature and the outdoors (Kesho Trust, 2007):

1. Children have outdoor playtime included in their school and out-of-school lives and have opportunities to freely access the outdoors and/or wild nature with friends and significant adults.

DOMESTIC GUEST STATEMENT

A Generation of Possibility | *Skye Augustine*

There has never been a better time to be a young person in Canada!

Unlike previous generations, we young people have the fortune of being limited only by our imagination. Today, over 3.5 billion people are under the age of 30, comprising more than half the world population. In Canada, we are among the world's wealthiest people. Most young Canadians are no longer limited by gender oppression, by child labour, or by strict family social roles. In addition, we are fortunate to have the most global world view of any generation before us.

Today, youth are looked to as catalysts of innovation and creativity. We have the opportunity to think of solutions that have never been tried. There are more young people in politics, more young CEOs, and more successful young musicians than ever before. This is a generation of possibility!

Many are using their growing voice to make substantial change in the world. Young Canadians serve on youth councils and groups for environmental professionals and attend international negotiations for current world issues. A Quebec youth, Leehi Yona, was recognized as a Canadian champion for the environment based on her contributions addressing climate change on the world stage. In 2015, 22-year-old Caitlyn Baikie from Labrador, was drawing international attention to the impact of climate change on her Inuit community and culture. Raised in British Columbia, Severn Cullis-Suzuki stole the stage at the United Nations Earth Summit in Rio de Janeiro at the age of 12 when she spoke about the importance of the environment to young citizens of the world. In 2012, Sliammon youth Ta'Kaiya Blaney gave a similarly impassioned speech at the UN Rio +20, highlighting our responsibly to be stewards of this planet. In 2014, she sang about the importance of caring for our planet, calling on "generation now" during the closing ceremonies of the World Parks Congress, in Sydney, Australia.

As Canadians of the generation of possibility, we also have a level of responsibility to both our country and the planet. Youth are often marginalized in decision-making processes, and in many cases our future is being decided for us. Changes are occurring more rapidly than ever before, and many of these changes could have dire long-term consequences. It is paramount that we as young people engage and represent our ideas to ensure that we receive an adequate future.

In many instances, young Canadians have banded together to shape policy, stop a company, protect a significant natural space, and raise awareness about important topics. In 2009 and again in 2012, over a thousand youth from across the country gathered in Ottawa for a conference called PowerShift. Together they learned about climate change, inspired one another, and lobbied politicians to take serious action to address climate change and the future of the planet.

Universities such as yours are often hubs of change. They present opportunities to create networks with like-minded people and develop the capacity to influence change in the surrounding communities, and the world.

Now is the time to get involved! What can you do? (1) Get informed. (2) Join a group that represents an issue you care about. (3) Ask your professors difficult questions. (4) VOTE. (5) Get your friends to vote. (6) Take action. (7) Stay inspired!

As Paul Hawken (2009) put it "if you look at the science about what is happening on Earth and aren't pessimistic, you don't understand the data. But if you meet the people who are working to restore this earth and the lives of the poor, and you aren't optimistic, you haven't got a pulse."

Courtesy Skye Augustine

Skye Augustine is from the Stz'uminus Nation and is the associate director of the Salish Sea Research Center at Northwest Indian College in Ferndale, WA. She was a regional coordinator for PowerShift 2009.

2. We design and build neighbourhoods and environments that allow and recognize nature to be nearby, accessible, and attractive to children and their families and seen as friendly, safe, joyful, and beneficial.
3. Children are seen as independent and competent and able to handle and benefit from the challenges of being outdoors and/or in wild nature.
4. We are seen as part of nature and are comfortable with the environment in which we live.

A primary function of our educational system should be to give students a general level of understanding about the nature of our environment and natural resources. We have requirements for general levels of language and mathematical competence but require nothing from our students in terms of this most fundamental challenge of the future. Indeed, pressures grow, especially on universities, to put greater and greater emphasis on meeting the short-term economic demands of society. Business schools and faculties of

Perspectives on the Environment

On Education

. . . without significant precautions, education can equip people merely to be more effective vandals of the Earth. If one listens closely, it may even be possible to hear the Creation groan every year in May when another batch of smart, degree-holding, but ecologically illiterate *Homo sapiens* who are eager to succeed are launched into the biosphere.

—Orr (1994)

One of the main ways to fight environmental degradation is to become aware of the implications of your own actions.

commerce flourish, yet few additional resources are allocated for programs dealing with the environment.

Even in such programs, colleges and universities have seldom done a good job of instilling in students an appreciation for and love of the planet as discussed above. Increasingly, science programs have become a process of learning more and more about less and less. They have produced technically competent scientists, but often miss the mark considerably in terms of maintaining students' wonder about the natural world and combining the rigour of scientific inquiry with deep moral questioning. Science programs often mistake the laboratory for the "real" world and cut students off from a more comprehensive understanding of and passion for their environment.

You can create change on your campus. Are there sufficient courses on the environment? Do these courses cover a wide spectrum from the technical to the philosophical, and more importantly, are students encouraged or even required to select from courses all along this spectrum? You should also remember that campuses are large consumers and processors of matter and energy. How efficient are they? Has anyone undertaken an environmental audit of your campus? How are wastes disposed of? How much recycling occurs? Are chemicals used for landscaping? Does the faculty pension fund invest in businesses with unsound environmental practices (see the "Domestic Guest Statement" below)? You can investigate many questions through course work, in environmental clubs, or as an individual.

So pick up that degree and encourage others to increase their understanding of environmental challenges. Do not be intimidated by people who think that interest in the environment and higher learning is not the "real" world. Challenge your teachers to inspire you. Be interested. Apply what you learn to your life. Do not be misled, however, into thinking that the formal education system is the only source of learning. Keep on reading. Many of the most inspiring works on the environment do not make their way onto college or university reading lists, and most of the rewarding environmental experiences are certainly not part of the curriculum.

DOMESTIC GUEST STATEMENT

The Power of Fossil-Fuel Divestment

James Rowe, Jessica Dempsey, Peter Gibbs, and Kelsey Mech

The fossil-fuel **divestment** movement is the current centre of gravity for Canadian student activism on climate change. In the four years since Bill McKibben outlined the case for divestment in *Rolling Stone* (2012), hundreds of campaigns have sprouted up across the globe. While centred on university campuses, the movement extends to foundations, municipalities, churches, unions, and financial managers. The campaign to divest institutional stockholders from fossil-fuel companies has supporters of many political stripes, all joined together by growing concern over climate change and the slow pace of governmental action.

In January 2014, Kelsey and Peter, then both students at the University of Victoria, approached Jessica and James, two faculty members, and encouraged them to organize University of Victoria faculty to support divestment. In other words, this campaign was initiated by students. Answering the call was easy: faculty who teach about the risks of climate change would be hypocritical not to take action. Later that year, UVic faculty voted by a wide margin to divest our endowment and the faculty pension fund from fossil-fuel companies. Soon after that, UVic students held their own referendum, and similarly voted in favour of divestment (77.3 per cent in favour). With two major constituencies on campus supporting the campaign, it will be difficult for UVic's administration to ignore our collective call for action.

In the meantime, by participating together in this growing movement, students and faculty continue learning from each other. Connections are being forged among faculty, staff, and students that are helpful not only for this particular campaign but for future political organizing as well. Collective problems, such as climate change, can only be confronted through collective action, which itself is only possible by building alliances across differences: geographical, age, cultural, political, and economic. If you are a student concerned about climate change, we cannot recommend the divest movement enough. One of the most inspiring aspects for all of us has been the amazing and passionate individuals with whom we get to work to tackle the systemic change we so need.

Why act on divestment? Three interlocking arguments motivate fossil-fuel divestment: one moral, one political, and one economic. The moral argument is simple: if it is wrong to wreck the climate, then it is wrong to profit from that wreckage. This holds for fossil-fuel companies, but also institutional stockholders such as universities that become part owners of these companies by investing in them. We need to be reducing our reliance on fossil fuels, not profiting from their sale. Climate change is no longer just an environmental issue; it is perhaps the greatest social justice issue of our time, with millions of people around the world already facing severe climate change impacts (see the "International Guest Statement" in Chapter 10, for example). Divestment movements are premised on the notion of climate justice: an approach that foregrounds the entwined nature of ecological and social injustices.

The second rationale underpinning divestment is political. Why has government action on climate change been so slow? Our best climate science warns that global temperature rise must remain below 2°C in order to prevent catastrophic climate change. Countries around the world, including Canada, have agreed to this target, and yet are failing to take action commensurate with the challenge, as discussed in Chapter 7.

Why is there a political deadlock on climate change? A primary reason is that fossil-fuel companies are filthy rich and deploy those riches to protect their self-interest. For example, most fossil-fuel companies in Canada belong to the Canadian Association of Petroleum Producers (CAPP). CAPP has a record of directly engaging in political lobbying against strong climate policy. CAPP was at the centre of lobbying for the 2012 omnibus bills that overhauled and eliminated some of the country's most significant environmental laws. Between 2008 and 2012, CAPP met with the Canadian government 536 times, whereas Canada's largest citizen climate coalition, the Climate Action Network, had six meetings.

The University of Victoria owns $20 million worth of fossil-fuel companies that are members of CAPP. In other words, UVic owns a $20 million stake in companies that belong to an industry group that directly advocates against climate action. How much of an ownership stake does your school have in companies that belong to CAPP, and by proxy facilitate intensive lobbying against the climate action we all need?

The theory behind divestment is that if enough respected institutions such as universities, municipalities, and churches divest from fossil-fuel companies, then this will remove the legitimacy these institutions bestow upon a reckless industry. Divestment aims to remove the social licence from fossil-fuel companies, making it harder for them to exert political influence and gum up the gears of needed climate legislation.

The final argument underpinning the divestment movement is economic. In 2012, the International Energy Agency released a report (IEA, 2012) estimating that two-thirds of known fossil-fuel reserves need to remain in the ground if catastrophic climate change is to be avoided. Recent studies (e.g., Carbon Tracker, 2014) have shown that proportion to be closer to 80 per cent; meaning four-fifths of all the oil, coal, and gas we know about must stay underground, untouched and unburned. Yet fossil-fuel companies attract investments on the assumption that they will exploit their total proven reserves. However, once strong legislative mechanisms to limit emissions kick in, this inflating "carbon bubble" will pop, exposing the fossil-fuel sector and all its investors to trillions of dollars of financial losses. This is partly why Black Rock Inc., the world's largest asset manager, started a fossil fuel–free fund to facilitate coming waves of divestment.

In a world in which the political voices of youth may be marginalized, students have both moral and strategic power in divestment campaigns. Visit gofossilfree.ca to find a campaign near you or to launch your own. In all likelihood, there is already an active campaign on your campus. Go to a meeting and start acting. To address the climate challenge we need to demonstrate collective leadership so that our politicians will follow. Join us in making history, making friends, and making a better world for ourselves and our loved ones: Divest!

Philip Dearden

James Rowe and **Jessica Dempsey** (centre) are assistant professors of Environmental Studies at the University of Victoria. **Peter Gibbs** is lead organizer for Organize BC, and **Kelsey Mech** is national director of the Canadian Youth Climate Coalition.

Challenge society to change, and seek a new kind of relationship between humanity and our home, planet Earth.

It also helps if you have your own personal vision statement, to help clarify your beliefs in and expectations out of life. Fritz et al. (2005) suggest the following:

- List five things you are happy about in your life.
- List five things you are committed to in your life.
- List five things you are doing right now that require you to apply your talents.
- Consider your five most important roles in life right now (e.g., son/daughter, brother/sister, student, roommate, employee) and identify five adjectives that describe your behaviour in each one of these roles.
- Identify five roles you may have in the future (e.g., partner, parent, professional, activist, civic leader, volunteer) and identify five adjectives that describe your behaviour in each of these roles.
- List your five priority values or principles in life.
- List your ten greatest strengths.
- List five things you would like to do to make a difference in the world.
- List five things you really enjoy doing.
- Write a paragraph that you would like someone to read at your funeral.
- Review all your responses above and summarize your ten life-guiding principles (values) or core beliefs (e.g., fairness, hard work, respect).

Light Living

Light living expresses the need to tread as lightly as possible, to minimize our own ecological footprints (Chapter 1). Light living is often characterized by the four R's: refuse, reduce, reuse, and recycle.

Refuse

Our society is geared toward making consumption easy. Newspapers are full of advertisements regarding the best buys. Turn on the radio, and you hear from the sponsor, or you are bombarded with commercials on TV. Estimates suggest that the average American will see 35,000 television ads every year. Most of us are surrounded by shopping opportunities on a daily basis. We can drive to one of several megamalls in most large Canadian cities, park with ease and at little expense, and consume from a wide variety of stores, paying by credit card, ATM, cheque, or even cash. We frequently shop not to fulfill basic needs but to indulge frivolous and petty whims. In 2015, for example, *Forbes* (McCarthy, 2015) reported that global expenditure on luxury goods amounted to just over $1 trillion, with almost half spent on luxury cars. Clothes are discarded when no longer fashionable rather than when they wear out. Gadgets are discarded in favour of newer and shinier models. Christmas as a religious holiday is now the time when we pay homage to our greatest god, **consumerism** (Box 15.5).

> ### *Perspectives on the Environment*
> **Master of Change**
>
> Resolve to be a master of change rather than a victim of change.
>
> —Brian Tracey

Resist and *refuse* to buy anything that you do not really, really *need*. If the purchase is necessary, shop carefully. Buy items that are less harmful to the environment during all stages of the product life cycle, from manufacture to consumption and disposal. There are products certified by the government for their low impacts, as discussed later. Buy one quality item rather than a succession of several shoddy ones to fulfill your needs. Buy organic produce wherever available, or better still and if possible, grow your own. It is difficult, because consuming is easy. All the messages that we receive from society extol the virtues of buying things.

Reduce

Can you reduce your consumption of certain items? Energy is a good place to start and a major contributor to greenhouse gas emissions. More than a quarter of Canada's GHG emissions occur due to everyday activities of Canadians. A lot of energy is used in space heating in Canada, but must you set that thermostat so high? Canadians tend to keep their houses much warmer inside than Northern Europeans do, for example. These cultures (New Zealanders, too) are accustomed to setting a low thermostat and wearing warmer clothing in the house in winter. They would not expect to be comfortable wearing just a T-shirt. Turn down the thermostat, wear warmer clothes, and turn the thermostat down further when you go out or go to bed. Statistics Canada (2013c) reports that in 2011, 60 per cent of Canadian households turned down the thermostat at night in winter, compared with 55 per cent in 2007 and 60 per cent in 2009.

Reduce lighting costs by replacing bulbs with long-life bulbs. They are more expensive to buy, but they last 10 years or longer and use 75 per cent less electricity. An incandescent light bulb converts only about 5 per cent of the energy it produces into light; the rest is wasted heat energy, as you will recall from the discussion of the laws of thermodynamics in Chapter 2. In 2007, calculations suggested that phasing out incandescent bulbs could save as much as 4 million tonnes of carbon dioxide emissions from Canada by 2015. If you want a simple and easy way to make your own contribution, changing your light bulbs is a good place to start. When

ENVIRONMENT IN FOCUS

BOX 15.5 | Dreaming of a "Green" Christmas?

Christmas heralds the biggest consumer bash of the year, although merchants are also trying to persuade us to be equally excessive at other times. Take control of your consumer lifestyle at Christmas. Consider the following gifts:

1. Arrange an event, an outing, or a personal service rather than giving a material item.
2. Increase "green" education by giving a book or subscription to a magazine. You could also buy someone a membership in a "green" organization, such as Pollution Probe, the Canadian Parks and Wilderness Society, or Greenpeace.
3. Give a houseplant, a backyard composting kit, or an unbreakable coffee mug to replace disposable ones. The World Wildlife Fund also enables you to protect an acre of rain forest by making a donation to fund a project started by unemployed students.
4. Give, in your gift recipient's name, a goat, a llama, a water buffalo, or any number of other animals through Heifer International, a 70-year-old NGO with a mission of alleviating hunger, poverty, and environmental degradation by providing food-producing animals and sustainable agriculture education to needy families.
5. Give something that conserves energy, such as a bus pass or an energy-saving showerhead.
6. Give second-hand items.
7. Make your own gifts, such as a sweater, dried flowers, or jam.
8. Give items that display the EcoLogo of three doves.
9. Choose gifts that require little wrapping. Reuse old wrapping paper or use reusable fabric gift bags.
10. Put "Planet Earth" at the top of your list. If we all gave the planet an offering for Christmas that would make it feel better—the Earth would be a little more loved and a little less stressed.

replacing electrical appliances, energy efficiency should be a major consideration. Before you turn on a light or an appliance, think about whether you really need it. Every time you flick the switch or plug in an appliance, you are sending a message of demand. Electricity-producing utilities and governments will react to your message by building new production facilities with all their attendant environmental costs. If you do not want those costs, try not to send as many messages signalling your demand. Of households buying major appliances in Canada in the past five years, almost two-thirds said that water and energy consumption was the biggest factor in their decision-making (Statistics Canada, 2011b).

Transportation is also a big energy consumer, accounting for one-quarter of all energy used in Canada. Road vehicles are responsible for 83 per cent of that share. Canadians' average annual per capita gasoline consumption is 1,100 litres, compared with 350 to 500 litres in European countries. It is also estimated that each kilometre of road or highway takes up about 6.5 hectares of land. In Ontario, which has 160,000 kilometres of highways, roads, and streets, this would add up to 1 million hectares for motorized vehicles. Whenever feasible, walk or ride a bicycle. If you have to use motorized transport, use public transport such as buses and trains. If you have a car, get a small economical one with a standard transmission, use it sparingly, and try to carpool. Most people are aware that larger cars (and SUVs) consume more gasoline. However, since it takes 18 litres of water to produce one litre of gasoline, they also contribute to water deficiencies.

Food choices are second only to transportation in terms of their environmental impacts. Agriculture covers more than 25 per cent of the world's surface and profoundly affects the health of natural ecosystems. A meat-rich meal with ingredients imported from afar generates as much as nine times the carbon emissions of a vegetarian meal made from local produce and requires two to four times the land to produce. It is not only what we choose to eat but how much we eat as well. In Canada, as in other Western countries and in the consumer classes of developing countries, the growing prevalence of obesity is one of the main challenges both to personal and global health. In fact, globally, the number of clinically obese people now exceeds the number of chronically hungry people, and the number of obese people globally has doubled since 1980.

Obese people consume 18 per cent more calories than the average, which overall results in more fuel consumed to produce and transport food. Overeating drives up the cost of food by increasing demand. It also contributes to global warming by boosting food production. We need policies to promote walking and cycling that would help to reduce obesity as well as reduce fuel consumption. Reducing the prevalence of obesity would reduce the global demand for both fuel and food. Decreased car use would reduce greenhouse gas emissions and thus the need for biofuels produced from vegetative matter. It would also mean more physical activity and reduce the risk of injury from traffic accidents as well as air pollution, thereby improving population health.

Eat only as much as your body needs to function in an effective and healthy manner. Become part of the food democracy movement. This means using your purchasing power to help establish connections between consumers and producers in the local area and making sure that you eat the kinds of food you wish to eat, not the kinds promoted by government subsidies and industrial agriculture. See how close you can come to the **100-mile diet** (Chapter 10). Water use is also where individuals and households can make important contributions to conservation, and they appear to be doing so in Canada. Statistics Canada (2013c) reports that between 1991 and 2011 use of low-flow showers in Canada increased from 28 to 63 per cent and low-flow toilets from 9 to 47 per cent. Furthermore, only 22 per cent of households reported drinking primarily bottled water, compared with 30 per cent in 2007. All these statistics show changes in the right direction. However, there is a long way to go. A study of consumer behaviour in 10 OECD countries showed that Canada's household water use was still almost double that of the OECD average (OECD, 2011).

You can also reduce the waste associated with the things you buy. Many products are over-packaged. They may look good on the store shelf but will only add to waste sent to the landfill. When you can, buy groceries in bulk to help reduce packaging. Reduce your waste by starting a compost heap for kitchen wastes. Reduce and if possible eliminate your use of toxic materials. Products that may seem innocuous (paint, solvents, and cleaning agents, for example) become hazardous wastes when disposed. Try to find alternatives. Do not buy more products than you need, and dispose of them in full accordance with the instructions from your local municipality.

Some countries, such as Bangladesh and China, have banned plastic bags while others, such as Ireland, South Africa, and Taiwan, have legislation to discourage plastic bag use, with authorities either taxing shoppers who use them or imposing fees on companies that distribute them. Canada has no such national law, but Leaf Rapids, Manitoba, was the first municipality in North America to propose, pass, and adopt a law forbidding shops to use plastic bags. Many other cities have since followed suit, or stores now charge for plastic bags as a disincentive for their use. Statistics Canada (2011b) reported that 49 per cent of Canadian households used recycled or reusable bags for shopping in 2009, compared with 30 per cent in 2007.

Reuse

Buy products that can be reused, such as rechargeable batteries. Try to find another use for something no longer useful in its original state. Use plastic food containers to store items in your fridge or workshop. Return to the store with the same plastic bags that you used the previous time and use them for your next load of groceries, or better still, use cotton bags. When you are finished with something, it may still be useful to someone else. Organize a garage sale or donate the items to charity rather than throwing them out.

Recycle

Recycling facilities have sprung up across the country over the past 20 years. Recyclable materials include newspaper, cardboard, mixed paper, glass, various metals, some plastics, car batteries, tires, and oil. These materials can be reprocessed into new goods. It takes 30 to 55 per cent less energy, for example, to make new paper from old paper than to start fresh from a new tree. Estimates suggest that if we recycled all the paper used in Canada, we would save 80 million trees annually. Canadians consume more than 50 kilograms of newsprint per person per year—enough to account for one whole mature tree. Similar efficiencies can be obtained by recycling other materials that require less energy for remanufacture. Oil, for example, fuels many industrial processes. Estimates suggest that if 1 per cent of the Canadian population recycled instead of trashing one aluminum can a day, the oil saved by remanufacturing would produce 21 million

Philip Dearden

Philip Dearden

In Europe, few students have cars. Cities are designed for people, and it is easy to get to campus by bicycle or mass transit. Even when people buy cars, they prefer small ones.

litres of gasoline. Recycling one aluminum can saves enough energy to run your TV for three hours. Making steel from recycled material uses only one-quarter of the energy it takes to make steel from virgin ore, while recycling copper results in energy savings of up to 85 per cent.

The vast majority of Canadian households with access to recycling programs use them, regardless of household income, occupants' education levels, or type of dwelling (Statistics Canada, 2007c). Canada has one of the highest levels of recycling on the planet. This is one of the ratings you can find on the Greendex developed by the National Geographic Society to measure and monitor consumer progress toward sustainability. Based on surveys in 18 countries, it focuses on actual behaviour and material lifestyles, including measures such as the relative penetration of green products versus traditional products, household footprint, energy use, transportation habits, and food consumption. Canadians shared the lead in recycling with Australia. Unfortunately, we fared much worse in the other categories; our score has declined since 2008 and Canada ended up ranking second from the bottom, surpassing only the US. India, China, and South Korea topped the list. Among developed countries, average consumers in Germany, Spain, and Sweden received the highest scores. Overall, though, the survey found that most countries surveyed had improved their scores over time, but in many cases the difference was quite small.

You can calculate your own Greendex (see "Related Websites" at the end of this chapter). Consumers can adopt more sustainable consumption habits and help to raise Canada's Greendex score by doing any of the following:

- Eating less meat, more locally produced foods, and more fruits and vegetables and drinking less bottled water
- Improving the energy efficiency of their homes by sealing drafts, upgrading windows, and installing more efficient water heaters and other appliances
- Keeping air heating at lower and cooling at higher settings
- Using only cold water to wash laundry and minimizing water use overall
- Driving alone less often (e.g., carpooling)
- Driving less overall
- Driving smaller and/or more fuel-efficient vehicles
- Having fewer vehicles for their household
- Walking or riding a bicycle when distance allows
- Maximizing the lifespan of household items and minimizing disposal
- Avoiding environmentally harmful products and packaging and seeking out environment-friendly alternatives
- Recycling whenever possible
- Using reusable shopping bags rather than accepting new disposable ones
- Having fewer televisions sets and personal computers in their household

Philip Dearden

Recycling is a major form of employment in some countries, such as India.

Nonetheless, the bottom line remains that while it is better to recycle than not to, reducing consumption levels in the first place is still the preferred option, and significant progress in this area has yet to be achieved.

The Law of Everybody

You can reduce the pressure on the environment in many ways. We have offered just a few suggestions to get you started. The key point is that the accumulated actions of many concerned individuals will make a difference. In this book, we have introduced you to many scientific laws and principles related to understanding and managing the environment. However, if everyone knew and enacted the following law, this would go a long way toward ameliorating our environmental challenges: it is, simply, the **law of everybody**.

"Everybody's Got to Do Something"

If we all did many small things that could be done easily, without having much negative or even noticeable influence on our lifestyle (e.g., drive 10 per cent less a year, buy fewer toys, shower with a friend), many of our environmental challenges would be greatly reduced in scale. It is not important that all people do everything, but everyone has to do something!

Perspectives on the Environment

The Paradox of Change

Only the wisest and stupidest of men [and women] never change.

—Confucius

Several websites can help you to find out more about your own environmental impact and suggest concrete ways to reduce it. For example, try the *personal challenges* on the website of the Canadian environmentalist, David Suzuki (www.davidsuzuki.org), and explore other websites at the end of this and other chapters. Make sure that you do not get trapped by the reasons outlined in Box 15.6 into doing nothing.

Influence

One of the best ways to influence business is through your purchasing power as a consumer. If consumers refuse to buy certain products because of their impact on the environment, the manufacturer will either have to respond to these concerns or go out of business. Many successful examples exist of these kinds of actions. During the 1970s and 1980s, for example, conservationists were able to exert pressure on hamburger chains to change their source of beef supply to ensure that tropical rain forests were not being cut down and replaced by grass to feed cattle for hamburgers. Following boycotts, all the major chains were persuaded to ensure that their sources did not contribute to the destruction of the rain forests. Similar campaigns have been directed at tuna canners to ensure that tuna is not caught by methods that kill dolphins, which often swim with schools of tuna.

Consumer boycotts can be an effective way of influencing business practices and reducing environmental impacts. When choosing fish to eat, for example, check out the websites at the end of Chapter 8. Download Canada's Seafood Guide (www.Seachoice.org) which lists three categories of seafood—best choices, concerns, and avoid—based on independent assessments of the sustainability of that particular fishery. If consumers followed these guidelines, it would alleviate much of the pressure on fishery resources.

Not only should we be sending messages to producers about our environmental standards through purchasing power, we should also let non-conforming producers know why we are not buying their products. If you believe in eating wild rather than farmed salmon, always ask the origin of the salmon before you buy it. If you believe in fair-trade coffee or certified wood products, always let retailers know for what it is you are shopping. Home Depot, for example, is the largest retailer of wood products in the world. Following a consumer boycott organized by a non-governmental organization, Home Depot committed to phase in sale of only certified wood products. This decision, rapidly echoed by two other major retailers, probably did more to protect old-growth forests in BC than all the protests of the past 25 years. However, the change was slow in coming, and opportunity still exists for improvement in Home Depot's purchasing practices. Home Depot argues that one of the main reasons behind its tardy behaviour is simply that customers do not ask for certified wood products and often do not buy them preferentially.

While boycotts can send a strong message and can influence corporations to change their practices, **carrot mobs** developed as a way to support businesses doing a great job. Carrot mobs, like boycotts, are a form of organized consumer purchasing. Members of the public gather to encourage businesses demonstrating environmental and social leadership. By compiling the dollars of many consumers, organized purchasing can provide an economic incentive for businesses to provide energy efficient, socially just, and long-lasting alternatives to mainstream corporate stores.

ENVIRONMENT IN FOCUS

BOX 15.6 | Why Not?

In Chapter 1 we talked about the need for transdisciplinarity in addressing environmental challenges. Understanding the human psyche and why we do or not do things is critical to this discourse. Environmental psychologist Bob Gifford (2013) has distilled the many reasons why people do not take action into eight categories:

Limited thinking: People are tired of hearing the message, do not understand the facts, or discount their relevance because they seem so far away.

Ideology: Action can be limited by belief in political and religious ideas.

Influence: People are influenced by their peers.

Investments: The need for environmental action may conflict with other goals in which the individual is fully invested.

Discredence: Some people will not believe the science, even though they have no training in that area.

Perceived risk: People feel more comfortable continuing to do what they always have done. There is risk in change.

Limited behaviour: People may make a token effort, but not really engage in significant change.

Time is money: People who feel that everything revolves around money are less likely to make environmental changes.

Perspectives on the Environment

Managing Planet Earth

A second myth is that with enough knowledge and technology, we can, in the words of *Scientific American* (1989), "manage planet Earth." Higher education has largely been shaped by the drive to extend human domination to its fullest. In this mission, human intelligence may have taken the wrong road. Nonetheless, managing the planet has a nice ring to it. It appeals to our fascination with digital readouts, computers, buttons, and dials. But the complexity of Earth and its life systems can never be safely managed. The ecology of the top inch of topsoil is still largely unknown, as is its relationship to the larger systems of the biosphere. What might be managed, however, is us: human desires, economies, politics, and communities. But our attention is caught by those things that avoid the hard choices implied by politics, morality, ethics, and common sense. It makes far better sense to reshape ourselves to fit a finite planet than to attempt to reshape the planet to fit our infinite wants.

—Orr (1994: 9)

As a responsible consumer, you should let your preferences be known. This also raises the question of **corporate responsibility** (Box 15.7). Is it the responsibility of the retailer to take part in, or even lead, the switch to a more sustainable and resilient way of doing things by informing its customers about the environmental implications of different products? Or is it sufficient merely to react to customer demands once they are manifest in the marketplace?

Many countries have enacted what are known as **extended producer responsibility** laws that require manufacturers and importers to accept responsibility for their products at the end of their useful lifespan. These laws provide an incentive for companies to design their products so that they can be recycled or reused and to eliminate toxic materials, since they would have to dispose of them. Ultimately, products should be designed to be either biodegradable or disassembled into their components for reuse in the future. Canada has no such laws, but some companies have taken the initiative, as discussed in Box 15.7.

Life-cycle assessments (LCAs) are now gaining greater support from both government and industry. LCAs identify inputs, outputs, and potential environmental impacts of a product or service throughout its lifetime. One industrial example is Volvo, which provides LCAs for the various components involved in vehicle manufacture. Some NGOs, such as Green Seal, provide standards for various products that manufacturers must meet to gain their endorsement. Others have excellent programs to assist consumers, industry, and government in making wise procurement decisions, such as the Center for a New American Dream. Among useful websites are Fair Trade Canada, Ethiquette, and Climate Counts, all listed in "Related Websites" at the end of the chapter. Climate Counts produces a scorecard, rating various companies on their performance in measuring, assessing, and reducing the carbon print of their products and on how supportive of climate change initiatives and policies they are.

In Canada, the product ecolabelling program EcoLogo aims to influence business practices by shifting consumer and institutional purchasing to products and services conforming to stringent environmental standards. A diverse stakeholder committee establishes criteria that each category of product must at minimum meet to obtain certification, signified by the three-doves logo. EcoLogo standards can contain, for example, criteria for recyclability, design of packaging material, product emissions, use of recyclate in manufacturing, effluent toxicity, and energy consumption (http://industries.ul.com/environment).

Governments make many decisions that can promote or retard sustainability and resilience. Public transport can be subsidized instead of private cars, land-use planning and building codes can be designed to minimize energy and material use, and governments can facilitate shared public consumption, such as provision of libraries and swimming pools, rather than encouraging private acquisition. Many municipalities have inherited what has been called the "infrastructure of consumption" from previous generations. However, it is necessary now to redesign the way we live to reflect our increased understanding of planetary limits. Box 15.7 offers several examples of this kind of approach.

What can you do to encourage governments to act? Election campaigns offer a major opportunity. Make a point of asking your local candidates at all levels of government for their views on sustainable development and resilience issues. Help to publicize these views. It is much more difficult for politicians to change their positions if their views are well known. Make sure that politicians follow through on their pre-election promises on environmental matters. Make sure that you express your views on the environment to politicians between elections. Write them letters, call them, go and see them, and organize demonstrations. The position of the commissioner of the Environment and Sustainable Development was specifically created by the federal government within the Auditor General's office to provide a place where *any Canadian* can go with a question about the environmental performance of a particular federal ministry or program and ask to have it audited. If you have such a question, go to the commissioner's website listed in "Related Websites" at the end of this chapter and review the simple process on how to proceed.

ENVIRONMENT IN FOCUS

BOX 15.7 | Corporate Contributions

Large corporations and retailers are highly visible targets for environmental action and have attracted a lot of attention. However, many corporations do much better than we do personally, or than our governments do, in systematically addressing their environmental impacts. For example, McDonald's has the Earth Effort program, which embraces the reduce, reuse, and recycle philosophy. Every year, McDonald's is committed to buying at least $100 million worth of recycled products for building, operating, and equipping its facilities. Carry-out bags are made from recycled corrugated boxes and newsprint; take-out drink trays are made from recycled newspapers. New restaurants have been constructed with concrete blocks made from recycled photographic film and roofs made from computer casings. McDonald's has also reduced the amount of waste produced; for example, sandwich packaging has been reduced by more than 90 per cent by switching from foam packaging to paper wraps. It also uses compostable food packaging made from reclaimed potato starch and other materials.

McDonald's also has a strict policy to not buy the beef of cattle raised on land converted from rain forests. In addition, it has programs to reduce energy consumption and to take part in local initiatives ranging from tree planting to local litter drives. For its efforts, McDonald's in the US has won White House awards and the National Recycling Coalition's Award for Outstanding Corporate Leadership.

Another company that environmentalists love to hate, Walmart, also has tremendous potential to influence sustainability. The chain has over 4,100 stores in the US and more than 300 in Canada. It operates the continent's largest trucking company, is the largest consumer of electricity, and with 1.3 million employees in the US and 75,000 in Canada stands as the biggest employer. More than 100 million customers per week visit Walmart stores. Walmart has introduced some far-reaching programs and demands that its suppliers also achieve sustainability thresholds. It has launched a $30 million Personal Sustainability project that raises awareness among employees of individual measures to live more sustainable lifestyles. The combined impact of these kinds of programs can be many times that of government agencies.

Many other well-known corporations are making contributions. Eddie Bauer, for example, has joined forces with an NGO, American Forests, in a tree-planting effort on damaged forest ecosystems in eight reforestation sites in the US and Canada. Consumers can opt to add a dollar to the price of their purchase at the store, and in turn the store will plant a tree for each dollar and donate another tree. Nike, the shoe, clothing, and sports equipment giant, has not only boosted the proportion of organic cotton in its own products but also helped to launch Organic Exchange, a network of 55 businesses committed to significantly expanding the use of organic cotton. Nike has programs to achieve zero toxics, zero waste, and 100 per cent recovery, recycling, and reuse of the products it sells. The company is designing a running shoe with a biodegradable sole and an upper portion that can be remanufactured into a new shoe. Other companies, such as Texas Instruments, Levi Strauss, and the Ford Motor Company, have banded their purchasing power together to buy recycled paper.

Also consider Valhalla Pure Outfitters of Vernon, BC, makers of high-quality outdoor clothing. Valhalla makes all of its polyester fleece jackets from recycled materials that look, feel, wear, and last the same as new fabric, even though they are made from recycled pop bottles. Each pop bottle diverted from a landfill site for recycling is sent to a factory in South Carolina, where it is separated by colour and then reprocessed before being sent to finishing plants in the US and Quebec. The final cost is similar to that of making new material but has added environmental advantages. Each jacket is equivalent to about 25 pop bottles.

The corporate and business world also has created some substantial foundations to which environmental groups can apply for funding for specific problems. As government coffers are drained, more pressure is put on these sources. The Laidlaw Foundation, for example, used to give $50,000 a year for environmental projects, and requests rarely exceeded this amount. The foundation now disburses $350,000 but has requests exceeding $1 million. The Richard Ivey Foundation in London, Ontario, provides up to 80 per cent of its $2 million budget for environmental projects each year but still manages to meet only 5 per cent of the amount requested.

If there are environmental problems in your area that you think need to be addressed, do not be afraid to approach local businesses for support. They may well agree with you and be happy to make a contribution to a carefully crafted solution.

Governments are often more than willing to adopt environment-friendly, voter-popular measures—as long as they do not involve any significant cost. Issues are often very complex, too complex for the understanding of many individuals who nonetheless care about acting in an environmentally responsible fashion. For this reason, concerned people may band together in **non-governmental organizations (NGOs)**. Such organizations represent the collective concern and resources of many people and consequently are better positioned than an individual to attack a problem. One of the best ways to spend your conservation dollar is to support such a group. They have had significant impacts on government policies in Canada. The online appendix available on this book's companion website lists some of these organizations.

Printed with permission from TerraChoice Environmental Marketing, administer of the EcoLogoProgram

The symbol of three doves in the shape of a maple leaf identifies products certified under Canada's EcoLogo Program. The three doves represent Canada's consumers, industry, and government working together to improve the environment.

Implications

The overall implications raised in this book should be brutally clear by now. Humanity is facing major challenges over the next decade regarding our relationship with the Earth and its life-support systems. So great are our capabilities to affect these systems that human-controlled influences now dominate many natural processes, resulting in the many critical environmental problems described throughout this book. Government programs at the international and national levels continue to emerge, but actions that make a practical difference are few and far between. Still, we are not powerless to change the direction of society. As individuals and as concerned individuals banding together, we can effect many of the changes that need to be made, and we can strive for greater well-being in the future (see the "Domestic Guest Statement" by Skye Augustine earlier in the chapter). So, despite the severity of the challenges, it is important to remain optimistic.

Above all, stay cheerful, stay active, look after yourself, look after others, love this planet, and do not give up! We are on the most beautiful planet we know about. Canada has some

Josh McCulloch/All Canada Photos

A wind farm in Pincher Creek, Alberta.

of the most breathtaking wonders in the universe. We have a responsibility. We can think of no better advice than that offered by Edward Abbey (1977):

> *Do not burn yourselves out. Be as I am—a reluctant enthusiast . . . a part-time crusader, a half-hearted fanatic. Save the other half of yourselves and your lives for pleasure and adventure. It is not enough to fight for the land; it is even more important to enjoy it. While you can. While it's still here. So get out there and . . . ramble out yonder and explore the forests, encounter the grizz, climb the mountains, bag the peaks, run the rivers, breathe deep of that yet sweet and lucid air, sit quietly for a while and contemplate the precious stillness, that lovely, mysterious, and awesome space. Enjoy yourselves, keep your brain in your head and your head firmly attached to the body, the body active and alive, and I promise you this much: I promise you this one sweet victory over our enemies, over those desk-bound people with their ears in a safe deposit box and their eyes hypnotized by desk calculators. I promise you this: you will outlive the bastards.*

Perspectives on the Environment

Ongoing Change

When you're finished changing, you're finished.

—Benjamin Franklin

Perspectives on the Environment

On Well-Being and Accumulation

Societies focused on well-being involve more interaction with family, friends, and neighbours, a more direct experience of nature, and more attention to finding fulfillment and creative expression than in accumulating goods. They emphasize lifestyles that avoid abusing your own health, other people, or the natural world. In short, they yield a deeper sense of satisfaction with life than many people report experiencing today.

—Gardner and Assadourian (2004: 16)

Summary

1. The previous century witnessed the start of a consumer-dominated society in several parts of the world that is rapidly spreading and threatens to engulf most of the world in this century.
2. Population growth rates are showing declines, but consumerism continues to expand. Environmental conditions continue to deteriorate and are likely to do so even more as consumerism spreads.
3. Significant progress has been made in meeting some of the Millennium Development Goals, The only one where things have actually become worse since the year 2000 is environmental sustainability.
4. Important global agreements have been forged, including the Kyoto Protocol and the Convention on Biological Diversity, that set frameworks for global actions, but progress on their implementation has made little impact compared with the scale of the challenges faced.
5. Growing attention is being given to the interconnections among water, energy, and food in order to manage them in an integrated way and avoid a compartmentalized approach.
6. Progress has been made in some areas. The area of certified forest worldwide increased from 3.24 million hectares in 1995 to 180.44 million hectares as of July 2013. More than 250 fisheries are now certified worldwide as being sustainable.
7. Research examining the relationship between consumerism and well-being shows that a positive relationship does exist when incomes are small. However, after a certain point, there is no relationship. Most of the developed world has already attained triple this income level.
8. Only one of the eight global regions is on track to achieve all of the Millennium Development Goals by 2015, with severe shortfalls in many areas such as sub-Saharan Africa.
9. We need Millennium Consumption Goals as well as Millennium Development Goals that indicate where consumption needs to fall and by when.
10. The Happy Planet Index is a measure of human well-being in various countries against the impacts caused. In 2014, Canada ranked 64th out of a total of 151 countries on the scale.
11. Canada is among the highest-ranked countries in the world in terms of estimated value per capita of natural capital.
12. Canada suffers from a lack of sustained leadership for environmental protection, and our response to environmental degradation at both international and national scales continues to be very slow despite clear signals regarding the state of the environment. We are in violation of many international environmental agreements.
13. Canada ranks twenty-fourth out of 178 countries on the international Environmental Performance Index.
14. Poor quality of information and the difficulty of accessing government information are serious challenges to improved environmental management in Canada. Canada ranked at the bottom of an international comparison of freedom-of-information legislation. There has been increased control by the federal government over the ability of government scientists to discuss their research.
15. BC has introduced the most ambitious plan to address global climate change in North America, including carbon taxes. BC has set a target of reducing greenhouse gases by at least 33 per cent below current levels by 2020. This would be 10 per cent lower than the 1990 level, exceeding California's goal of returning to 1990 levels by 2020.
16. Ordinary citizens can have a positive impact on the environmental challenges facing society. A first step is building awareness of these problems. Universities and colleges should be intimately involved in this process by ensuring that all students achieve environmental literacy before they graduate. Universities and colleges are also large consumers of matter and energy and should lead by example in reducing their impact on the environment.
17. There is growing evidence of "nature deficit disorder" among younger people as they spend more time on their computers and less time interacting with nature. This makes building awareness of environmental change and getting people emotionally engaged with change even more challenging.
18. Individuals can help by living in accordance with the four R's: *refuse* to be goaded into overconsumption; *reduce* consumption of matter and energy whenever possible; *reuse* materials whenever possible; and *recycle* those that you cannot reuse.
19. Individuals can also wield influence by taking collective action—for example, through consumer boycotts of products and companies that engage in environmentally destructive practices. One of the most effective ways of doing this is to join a non-governmental organization (NGO) composed of and supported by like-minded individuals. As an individual, you will probably not be able to afford to support an environmental lobbyist in

Ottawa. However, if thousands of people contribute, it can happen.

20. Big corporations have a lot of opportunity to influence sustainability and resilience, and many of them have accepted that responsibility.

21. In spite of the serious nature of many environmental problems described in this book, it is important to remain optimistic that they can be solved and to take time to get out and enjoy the beauty and challenge of one of the most splendid parts of the planet, Canada, our home.

Key Terms

carrot mobs
consumerism
corporate responsibility
divestment
extended producer responsibility
Happy Planet Index (HPI)
law of everybody
life-cycle assessments (LCAs)
light living
Millennium Consumption Goals
Millennium Development Goals (MDGs)
nature deficit disorder
non-governmental organizations (NGOs)
100-mile diet
water-energy-food (WEF) nexus

Questions for Review and Critical Thinking

1. What do you think are the main factors driving global environmental degradation?
2. Which factors are the most serious? Why?
3. Discuss what you think should be the top priorities for global action.
4. Explain how the water-energy-food nexus approach could be applied in specific situations, and what benefits could be expected from such an approach.
5. Outline some of the main responses to environmental degradation at both the international and national levels.
6. Discuss Canada's current and potential role at the international level.
7. What do you think are the main barriers to more effective government response in Canada?
8. Discuss your institution's present and potential role in raising environmental awareness.
9. What are three concrete steps toward "light living" that you are willing to take over the next month?
10. What are some initiatives that you could take as an individual or as part of your community to reduce negative environmental consequences from human activities?
11. Find out the names and mandates of the environmental NGOs in your area. Is there anything you can do to help them?
12. Who is your local MP? What is his or her view on environmental issues? Exercise your democratic right—phone and find out.

Related Websites

Auditor General of Canada
www.oag-bvg.gc.ca

BC Sustainable Energy Association
www.bcsea.org

Better Environmentally Sound Transportation
www.best.bc.ca

Center for a New American Dream
www.newdream.org

Child and Nature Alliance of Canada
www.childnature.ca

City Green Solutions
www.citygreen.ca

Climate Counts
www.ClimateCounts.org

Commissioner of the Environment and Sustainable Development: Environmental Petitions
www.oag-bvg.gc.ca/internet/English/pet_fs_e_919.html

David Suzuki Foundation: What you can do
www.davidsuzuki.org/what-you-can-do

EcoLogo
http://industries.ul.com/environment

Ethiquette
www.ethiquette.ca/en/

Fair Trade Canada
www.transfair.ca

Greendex
http://environment.nationalgeographic.com/environment/greendex/

Happy Planet Index
www.happyplanetindex.org

Kesho Trust: Nature Child Reunion
www.naturechildreunion.ca

Marine Stewardship Council
www.msc.org

Natural Resources Canada, Office Energy Efficiency
www.nrcan.gc.ca/energy/offices-labs/office-energy-efficiency

Nature Serve Canada
www.natureserve.ca

Nature Watch
www.naturewatch.ca

Ocean Wise iPhone App
www.oceanwise.ca/iphone-app

Sierra Youth Coalition
www.syc-cjs.org

United Nations Conference on Sustainable Development
www.uncsd2012.org

United Nations Environment Programme
www.unep.org

United Nations Human Development Index
hdr.undp.org/en/statistics/hdi

The Water, Energy & Food Security Nexus Resource Platform
www.water-energy-food.org/en/home.html

World Summit on Sustainable Development
www.un.org/events/wssd

Further Readings

Note: This list comprises works relevant to the subject of the chapter but not cited in the text. All cited works are listed in the References at the end of the book.

Cross, G. 2002. *An All-Consuming Century: Why Commercialism Won in Modern America*. New York: Columbia University Press.

Thirwell, G.M., C.A. Madramootoo, and I.W. Heathecote. 2007. *Energy-Water Nexus: Energy Use in the Municipal, Industrial and Agricultural Water Sectors*, Canada–US Conference, Washington, DC: Policy Research Initiative of Canada and the Woodrow Wilson Institute.

United Nations. 2014. *The Millennium Development Goals Report 2014*. New York: UN.

Go to www.oupcanada.com/DeardenMitchell5e to access additional learning tools on your smartphone, tablet, or PC.

GLOSSARY

abiotic components Non-living parts of the ecosystem, including chemical and physical factors, such as light, temperature, wind, water, and soil characteristics.

Aboriginal peoples The Indian (First Nations), Inuit, and Métis peoples of Canada.

acid deposition Rain or snow that has a lower pH than precipitation from unpolluted skies; also includes dry forms of deposition, such as nitrate and sulphate particles.

acidification The increased acidic content of waters, notably the world's oceans, making the concentration of available carbonate ions too low for marine calcifiers, such as coral reefs, molluscs, crustaceans, and some algae, to build their shells and skeletons.

acid mine drainage Acidic drainage from waste rock and mine tailings caused by the oxidization of iron sulphides to create sulphuric acid, which in turn dissolves residual metals.

acid shock The buildup of acids in water bodies and standing water over the winter, resulting in higher acidity than experienced through the rest of the year.

active management Purposeful interference by resource and environmental managers in ecosystems, which recognizes that the human forces of change are now so ubiquitous that even protected areas are affected; includes habitat restoration, creation of wildlife corridors, reintroduction of extirpated species, prescribed burning, and management of hyperabundant species.

adaptation Adjustment to different or changing circumstances, such as when insurance companies modify their claims forecasting and setting of premiums with regard to future climate change conditions. The largest challenge for adaptation strategies will occur in the future when the most significant consequences from climate change will appear.

adaptive co-management Management concept including such key attributes as learning-by-doing, integrating different knowledge systems, collaborating and power-sharing among community, regional, and national levels, and managing for flexibility.

adaptive environmental management An approach that develops policies and practices to deal with the uncertain, the unexpected, and the unknown; approaches management as an experiment from which we learn by trial and error.

adaptive phased management Used by the Canadian Nuclear Waste Management Organization; has two components. First, as a technical method it involves centrally containing and isolating used nuclear fuel in a deep geological repository. Second, as a management approach it applies manageable stages, with each stage having explicit decision points as well as ongoing interaction with stakeholders. The intent is to allow approval or disapproval decisions at each stage, thus enabling decision-makers to draw upon new knowledge and/or emerging views of stakeholders.

aerobic Requiring oxygen.

Aichi targets Proportions of terrestrial (and freshwater) and marine ecosystems to be designated as protected areas by the year 2020, agreed under the Convention on Biological Diversity.

albedo The extent to which the surface of the Earth reflects rather than absorbs incoming radiation from the sun. Snow has a high albedo, but as temperatures rise, the area covered in snow will be replaced by areas free of snow, uncovering rocks and vegetation with lower albedo values that absorb radiation and thus add to warming.

alien species Any organism, such as zebra mussels, purple loosestrife, and Eurasian water milfoil in Canada, that enters an ecosystem beyond its normal range through deliberate or inadvertent introduction by humans; also known as exotic, introduced, invader, or non-native species.

allelopathic A plant that directly inhibits the growth of surrounding species through production of chemicals in the soil.

alternative dispute resolution (ADR) A non-judicial approach to resolving disputes that uses negotiation, mediation, or arbitration, with a focus on reparation for harm done and on improving future conduct.

anadromous Aquatic life, such as salmon, that spend part of their lives in salt water and part in fresh water.

anaerobic Lacking oxygen.

annual allowable cut (AAC) The amount of timber that is allowed to be cut annually from a specified area.

Anthropocene Proposed as a new geologic epoch for a period in which important geological conditions and processes have been significantly affected by human activities. Agreement does not yet exist about adoption of this term, nor when it should begin, although the start time most generally suggested is the Industrial Revolution in the late 1700s.

anthropocentric view Human-centred, in which values are defined relative to human interests, wants, and needs.

apex predators Super-predators at the very top of the food chain.

aquaculture Seafood farming, the fastest-growing food production sector in the world.

aquifer A formation of permeable rocks or loose materials that contains usable sources of groundwater and may extend from a few square kilometres to several thousand square kilometres.

arable land Land that can be plowed and can produce crops.

arbitration A procedure for dispute resolution in which a third party is selected to listen to the views and interests of the parties in dispute and develop a solution to be accepted by the participants.

artisanal Small-scale fisheries.

aspirational approach With reference to climate change, an approach emphasizing long-term but unspecific and non-binding targets for reducing greenhouse gas emissions. Advocated by developed countries.

assimilated food energy The proportion of ingested energy actually absorbed by an organism.

atmosphere Layer of air surrounding the Earth.

autotrophs Organisms, such as plants, that produce their own food, generally via photosynthesis.

Bali Conference A UN-sponsored climate change conference held in the first two weeks of December 2007 in Bali, Indonesia, to start a process to create a new framework to replace the Kyoto Protocol, which ended in 2012. There was agreement that both developed and developing countries must participate in reducing greenhouse gas emissions but reluctance from key developed countries to commit to binding targets.

benthic Of or living on or at the bottom of a water body.

bioaccumulation The storage of chemicals in an organism in higher concentrations than are normally found in the environment.

biocapacity The amount of biologically productive area—cropland, pasture, forest, and fisheries—available to meet humanity's needs.

biocentric perspective A view that values aspects of the environment simply because they exist and accepts that they have the right to exist.

biochar Created through pyrolysis of biomass, a type of charcoal used to enhance soil. In addition to sequestering carbon, it increases food security and soil biodiversity.

biocides Chemicals that kill many different kinds of living things; also called pesticides.

bioconcentration The combined effect of bioaccumulation and biomagnification.

biodiversity The variety of life forms that inhabit the Earth. Biodiversity includes the genetic diversity among members of a population or species as well as the diversity of species and ecosystems.

biodiversity hot spots Areas with high numbers of endemic species, as in tropical forests.

biofuels Solid, liquid, or gas fuel derived from relatively recently dead biological material and distinguished from fossil fuels, which are derived from long-dead biological material.

biogeochemical cycles Series of biological, chemical, and geological processes by which materials cycle through ecosystems.

biological oxygen demand (BOD) The amount of dissolved oxygen required for the bacterial decomposition of organic waste in water.

biomagnification Buildup of chemical elements or substances in organisms in successively higher trophic levels.

biomass The sum of all living material, or of all living material of particular species, in a given environment.

biomass pyramid Related to the fact that in terrestrial ecosystems, greater biomass generally exists at the level of primary consumers, with the least total biomass at the highest trophic levels; in marine ecosystems, the reverse is true, and the pyramid is inverted—greater biomass is at the highest trophic level, while the primary consumers, phytoplankton, at any given time comprise much less biomass but reproduce rapidly.

biomes Major ecological communities of organisms, both plant and animal, that are usually characterized by the dominant vegetation type; for example, a tundra biome and a tropical rain forest biome.

biosphere The zone of all living matter on Earth, including animals, vegetation, and the soil layer.

Biosphere Reserves A UNESCO program of land designation containing a protected core, a buffer zone, and a zone of cooperation.

biotic components Those parts of ecosystems that are living; organisms.

biotic potential The ability of species to reproduce regardless of the level that an environment can support, i.e., regardless of the carrying capacity of the environment.

bitumen Any of various minerals that will burn, such as asphalt or petroleum.

blue boxes Blue plastic boxes or bins introduced for curbside collection programs in urban neighbourhoods to divert selected household waste material (e.g., bottles, cans, paper and plastic products) from landfill sites to be recycled.

boreal forest One of the largest forest belts in the world, extending all across North America and Eurasia, encompassing roughly a third of the Earth's forest land and 14 per cent of the world's forest biomass and separating the treeless tundra regions to the north from the temperate deciduous forests or grasslands to the south.

Boreal Shield The largest ecozone in Canada, stretching along the Canadian Shield from Saskatchewan to Newfoundland.

bottom trawling One of the most destructive means of fishing in which heavy nets are dragged along the sea floor scooping up everything in their path.

bottom-up control Ecosystems where the structure is controlled by factors at low trophic levels, such as nutrient flows and productivity.

brownfields Abandoned or active industrial sites. On the surface or underground are soils contaminated through disposal practices accepted in earlier times before people appreciated the long-term consequences.

buffering capacity The factors in an environment, such as carbonate-rich rocks and deep soils, that ameliorate the harms caused by acid deposition.

butterfly effect A central example in chaos theory that postulates the effect of a butterfly flapping its wings in South America might affect weather systems in North America.

bycatch Non-target organisms caught or captured in the course of catching a target species, as in the fisheries, where estimates suggest that 25 per cent of the world's catch is dumped because it is not the right species or size.

calorie A unit of heat energy; the amount of heat required to raise the temperature of one gram of water by 1°C.

Cancún Summit Meeting of representatives from 193 countries and other interested parties held in Mexico in December 2010 to seek to advance mitigative action on climate change. Canada continued to be a laggard, and only incremental progress was made.

carbon balance A balance between the amount of CO_2 in the atmosphere and bicarbonate in the water.

carbon sequestration Reforestation and afforestation to ameliorate carbon dioxide loadings in the atmosphere because trees and shrubs use the excess CO_2.

carbon sink A process or material that removes carbon dioxide from the atmosphere.

carbon tax An approach in which greenhouse gas emissions by individuals or companies are taxed. The purpose is to change human behaviour toward activities that produce fewer greenhouse gas emissions.

carnivore An organism that consumes only animals.

carrot mobs Organized consumer purchasing in support of businesses demonstrating environmental and social leadership.

carrying capacity Maximum population size that a given ecosystem can support for an indefinite period or on a sustainable basis.

cellular respiration Metabolic processes through which living cells produce energy.

certification The confirmation of certain characteristics of an object, person, or organization, as with various forestry programs certifying that wood products have come from sustainably managed forests.

chain-of-custody Procedures for verification of compliance with sustainable practices from product origin through to the final product, as with wood products from the forest to Home Depot.

chemoautotroph A producer organism that converts inorganic chemical compounds into energy.

chlorophylls Pigments of plant cells that absorb sunlight, thus enabling plants to capture solar energy.

clear-cutting A forest harvesting technique in which an entire stand of trees is felled and removed.

climate The long-term weather pattern of a particular region.

climate change A long-term alteration in the climate of a particular location or region or for the entire planet.

climate change deniers Those who, for ideological and economic reasons, use communication tactics to question the science underlying climate change and therefore delay action to mitigate this change.

"Climategate" The controversy surrounding leaked e-mails from a climate research centre at the University of East Anglia, just weeks prior to the Copenhagen Summit, that appeared, incorrectly, to suggest that researchers had manipulated their data to make climate change appear more severe.

climate justice Focuses on the interaction of environmental degradation and social, economic, and racial inequities created by climate change. It calls for resolving the disproportionate impact of climate change on poor and marginalized people.

climate modelling Various mathematical and computerized approaches for determining past climate trends in an effort to build scenarios predicting future climate, which use any or all of the following factors in measurement: incoming and outgoing radiation; energy dynamics or flows around the globe; surface processes affecting climate, such as snow cover and vegetation; chemical composition of the atmosphere; and time step or resolution (time over which the model runs and the spatial scale to which it applies).

climatic climax The situation in a mature or climax community where the vegetative growth is largely influenced by climate.

climax community Last stage of succession; a relatively stable, long-lasting, complex, and interrelated community of organisms.

co-evolution Process whereby two species evolve adaptations as a result of extensive interactions with each other.

collaboration The art of working together.

co-management An arrangement in which a government agency shares or delegates some of its legal authority regarding a resource or environmental management issue with local inhabitants of an area.

commensalism An interaction between two species that benefits one species and neither harms nor benefits the other.

community Populations in a particular environment.

competitive exclusion principle The principle that competition between two species with similar requirements will result in the exclusion of one of the species.

complete-tree harvesting The harvesting of all of the above- and below-ground biomass of a tree.

compound The coming together of two different atoms to form a different substance, such as water (H_2O), a compound made up of two hydrogen atoms (H) and one oxygen atom (O).

condensation nuclei Particles in the atmosphere that provide a starting point for water moving from the gaseous to liquid phase.

consumerism Wasteful consumption of resources to satisfy wants rather than needs.

consumers Organisms that cannot produce their own food and must get it by eating or decomposing other organisms; in economics, those who use goods and services.

consumption Using a good or service. The obtaining and use of consumer goods are often used as the standard or ideal against which individuals or families assess their quality of life. Marketing and promotions encourage individuals to purchase non-essential goods, which often places pressure on the environment and natural resources.

contemporary evolution Evolution that occurs on short time scales.

context Specific characteristics of a time and place.

contour cultivation The cultivation and seeding of fields parallel to the contour of the slope, which serves to reduce the speed of runoff by catching soil particles in the plow furrows.

Convention on Biological Diversity (CBD) International treaty that emerged from the World Summit on Sustainable Development in Rio de Janeiro in 1992 that requires signatories, including Canada, to develop biodiversity strategies, identify and monitor important components of biodiversity, develop endangered species legislation/protected areas systems, and promote environmentally sound and sustainable development in areas adjacent to protected areas.

Convention on International Trade in Endangered Species of Wild Fauna and Flora (CITES) A 1973 treaty currently ratified by more than 120 countries (including Canada) that establishes lists of species for which international trade is to be controlled or monitored (e.g., orchids, cacti, parrots, large cat species, sea turtles, rhinos, primates).

coordination The effective or harmonious working together of different departments, groups, and individuals.

Copenhagen Summit Two-week meeting of world leaders, environment ministers, and other interested parties held in Copenhagen, Denmark, in late 2009, which sought unsuccessfully to advance the agenda for action on climate change. Canada showed itself at this conference to be among the greatest laggards in seeking action for improved GHG emissions standards.

coral bleaching Death of corals caused by water temperatures becoming too warm.

coral polyps Individual biotic members of a coral reef.

corporate responsibility Occurs when corporations systematically examine the environmental impact of their activities, then take action to reduce the negative impacts. Initiatives include reducing, reusing, and recycling, specifying environment-friendly production practices for suppliers, and providing funds to environmental groups.

critical load The maximum level of acid deposition that can be sustained in an area without compromising ecological integrity.

crop rotation Alternating crops in fields to help restore soil fertility and also control pests.

crude birth rate (CBR) Number of births in a population per 1,000 individuals per year.

crude bitumen A thick and heavy oil.

crude death rate (CDR) Number of deaths in a population per 1,000 individuals per year.

crude growth rate (CGR) Produced by subtracting the crude death rate (CDR) from the crude birth rate (CBR).

cryosphere Based on the Greek word *kryos* meaning "cold," those parts of the Earth's surface where water is in solid form as ice or snow. The cryosphere includes sea, lake, and river ice, snow cover, glaciers, ice caps, and ice sheets, as well as frozen ground (permafrost).

culmination age The age of economic maturity of a tree crop, which varies widely but usually falls within the 60- to 120-year range in Canada.

cumulative environmental effects The combined effects of an action with the effects of other past actions and that have implications for the present and future.

custom-designed solutions Management approach in which the specific conditions of a place and time are recognized and the attempt to ameliorate or resolve a problem takes these specifics into account.

cyclic succession Where a community progresses through several seral stages but is then returned to earlier stages by natural phenomena such as fire.

DDT (dichlorodiphenyltrichloroethane) An organochlorine insecticide used first to control malaria-carrying mosquitoes and lice and later to control a variety of insect pests but now banned in Canada because of its persistence in the environment and ability to bioaccumulate.

decomposer food chain A specific nutrient and energy pathway in an ecosystem in which decomposer organisms (bacteria and fungi) consume dead plants and animals as well as animal wastes; essential for the return of nutrients to soil and carbon dioxide to the atmosphere; also called detritus food chain.

demand management Emphasizes influencing human behaviour so that less water or energy is used.

demitarian Someone who aims to halve the amount of meat in their regular diet.

demographic transition Transition of a human population from high birth rate and high death rate to low birth rate and low death rate.

denitrification The conversion of nitrate to molecular nitrogen by bacteria in the nitrogen cycle.

detritus Organic waste, such as fallen leaves.

district heating systems Heating or energy systems create from a central plant one or more of steam, hot water, or chilled water which are conveyed through underground pipes to individual buildings for space heating, hot-water heating, and air conditioning. Buildings connected to a district heating system do not require individual boilers, furnaces, or air conditioners, resulting in higher energy efficiency and improved environmental quality.

disturbances Natural or human-induced events or processes that interrupt ecological succession.

diversions Movements of water from one water system to another in order to enhance water security, reduce flood vulnerability, or generate hydroelectricity.

divestment In contrast to investment, the selling of stocks, bonds, or investment funds viewed as ethically questionable. "Fossil fuel divestment" removes investments associated with companies which extract fossil fuels as one initiative to ameliorate climate change.

dominant limiting factor The weakest link in the chain of various factors necessary for an organism's survival.

double-loop learning Situations for which there is a mismatch between intention and outcome and when such a mismatch is addressed by challenging underlying values and behaviour rather than assuming that the prevailing values and behaviour are appropriate.

drought Condition in which a combination of lack of precipitation, temperature, evaporation, evapotranspiration, and the inability of soil to retain moisture leads to a loss of resilience among flora and fauna in dry conditions.

dyke A wall or earth embankment along a watercourse to control flooding (running dyke), or encircling a town or a property to protect it from flooding (ring dyke), or across a stream so that the flow of water is stopped from going upstream by a sluice gate (cross dyke).

dynamic equilibrium Occurs when two opposing processes proceed at the same rate.

E. coli *Escherichia coli*, a bacterium present in fecal matter that can get into a water supply and pollute it, as happened in Walkerton, Ontario, in May 2000.

ecocentric (biocentric) values The view that a natural order governs relationships between living things and that a harmony and balance reflect this natural order, which humankind tends to disrupt.

ecological footprint The land area a community needs to provide its consumptive requirements for food, water, and other products and to dispose of the wastes from this consumption.

ecologically extinct A species that exists in such low numbers that it can no longer fulfill its ecological role in the ecosystem.

ecological redundancy The situation, as in a tropical rain forest, where there are many times more species than in more northerly ecosystems and the chance of other species combining to fulfill the ecological role of a depleted one is much higher.

ecological restoration Renewing a degraded, damaged, or destroyed ecosystem through active human intervention.

ecological succession The gradual replacement of one assemblage of species by another as conditions change over time.

ecosphere Refers to the entire global ecosystem, which comprises atmosphere, lithosphere, hydrosphere, and biosphere as inseparable components.

ecosystem Short for ecological system; a community of organisms occupying a given region within a biome, including the physical and chemical environment of that community and all the interactions among and between organisms and their environment.

ecosystem-based management Holistic management that takes into account the entire ecosystem and emphasizes biodiversity and ecosystem integrity, as opposed to focusing primarily or solely on a resource or resources, such as water or timber, within an ecosystem.

ecosystem diversity The variety of ecosystems in an area.

ecosystem services Contribution of ecosystems to human well-being.

ecotone The transitional zone of intense competition for resources and space between two communities.

ecotourism Visits to view natural areas or species that contribute to conservation of the environment and involve an explicit educational component.

edaphic climaxes The situation in mature or climax communities where the vegetative growth is principally influenced by underlying geologic features, such as soils.

El Niño A marked warming of the waters in the eastern and central portions of the tropical Pacific that triggers weather changes and events in two-thirds of the world.

emission credits Can be earned by a nation based on land-use or forestry (afforestation, reforestation) initiatives that reduce measurable greenhouse gas emissions.

emissions trading Under the Kyoto Protocol, a system whereby one country that will exceed its allotted limit of greenhouse gas emissions can buy an amount of greenhouse gas emissions from another country that will not reach its own established emissions limit.

endangered An official designation assigned by the Committee on the Status of Endangered Wildlife in Canada to any indigenous species or subspecies or geographically separate population of fauna or flora that is threatened with imminent extinction or extirpation throughout all or a significant portion of its Canadian range.

endemic species A plant or animal species confined to or exclusive to a specific area.

endemism Species with local geographical distributions that occur just in that area.

endocrine disruption The interference of normal bodily processes such as sex, metabolism, and growth by chemicals in such products as soaps and detergents that are released into an ecosystem, as happens among aquatic species, often causing feminization.

energy The capacity to do work; found in many forms, including heat, light, sound, electricity, coal, oil, and gasoline.

energy efficiency Amount of total energy input of a system that is transformed into work or some other usable form of energy.

entropy A measure of disorder. The second law of thermodynamics applied to matter says that all systems proceed to maximum disorder (maximum entropy).

environment The combination of the atmosphere, hydrosphere, cryosphere, lithosphere, and biosphere in which humans, other living species, and non-animate phenomena exist.

environmental impact assessment Part of impact assessment that identifies and predicts the impacts from development proposals on both the biophysical environment and on human health and well-being.

environmental justice The most common definition is from the US Environmental Protection Agency: "Environmental justice is the fair treatment and meaningful involvement of all people regardless of race, colour, national origin or income with respect to the development, implementation and enforcement of environmental laws, regulations and policies."

environmental migration Movement of people motivated to leave their home area as a result of abrupt or long-term negative alterations to their local environment. Drivers of environmental migration include serious droughts, desertification, coastal flooding, and sea-level rise. Environmental migrants may move to another place in their own country, often the nearest largest city, or move to another country.

epidemiological transition Change in mortality rates from high to low in a human population.

epiphytes Plants that use others for support but not nourishment.

estuary Coastal regions, such as inlets or mouths of rivers, where salt water and fresh water mix.

euphotic zone Zone of the ocean to which light from the sun reaches.

eutrophic Pertaining to a body of water rich in nutrients.

eutrophication The over-fertilization of a body of water by nutrients that produce more organic matter than the water body's self-purification processes can overcome; also called nutrient enrichment.

evapotranspiration Evaporation of water from soil and transpiration of water from plants.

evolution A long-term process of change in organisms caused by random genetic changes that favour the survival and reproduction of those organisms possessing the genetic change; organisms become better adapted to their environment through evolution.

exclusive economic zones (EEZs) Areas off the coasts of a nation that are claimed by that nation for its sole responsibility and exploitation, as permitted by the UN Convention on the Law of the Sea.

exponential growth The growth when a population increases by a certain percentage rather than an absolute amount, producing a J-shaped curve.

ex situ conservation The conservation of species outside their natural habitat, including breeding in captivity, so that they can be reintroduced to their natural habitat, as has been done, for example, with the black-footed ferret and swift fox.

ex situ preservation The preservation of representatives of a species, often endangered, outside their natural habitat, as in a zoo, aquarium, or game farm.

extended producer responsibility The concept underlying laws or regulations that require manufacturers and importers to accept responsibility for their products at the end of their useful lifespan. They provide an incentive for companies to design their products so that they can be recycled or reused and to eliminate toxic materials, since they would have to dispose of them.

extinction The elimination of all the individuals of a species.

extirpated An official designation assigned by the Committee on the Status of Endangered Wildlife in Canada to any indigenous species or subspecies or geographically separate population of fauna or flora no longer known to exist in the wild in Canada but occurring elsewhere.

extrinsic values Values that humans derive from other species, including consumptive and non-consumptive values.

facts Refers to something that is real or has occurred. Scientific facts must be able to be verified to be true, often using the scientific method.

falldown effect The lower volume of harvestable timber at the culmination age for second growth on sites where old-growth forest was previously harvested.

fishing down the food chain Harvesting at progressively lower trophic levels as higher trophic levels become depleted.

flood plain Low-lying land along a river, stream, or creek or around a lake that under normal conditions is flooded from time to time.

food chain A specific nutrient and energy pathway in an ecosystem proceeding from producer to consumer; along the pathway, organisms in higher trophic levels gain energy and nutrients by consuming organisms at lower trophic levels.

food miles The distance food must travel from point of production to consumption.

food webs Complex intermeshing of individual food chains in an ecosystem.

forest tenure The conditions that govern forest ownership and use.

fossil fuels Organic fuels (coal, natural gas, oil, oil sands, and oil shale) derived from once-living plants or animals.

fracking Involves drilling into the earth and then injecting a mixture of water, sand, and chemicals under high pressure to release the gas contained within rocks. The released gas then flows to the well head where it is extracted.

fragmentation The division of an ecosystem or species habitat into small parcels as a result of human activity, such as agriculture, highways, pipelines, and population settlements.

frozen core dam Type of dam used in mining in the North, as at the Ekati diamond mine in the Northwest Territories, with a central core of frozen soil saturated with ice and bonded to the natural permafrost and surrounded by granular fill to ensure both stability and thermal protection.

full-tree harvesting Timber-cutting where trees are felled and transported to roadside with branches and top intact.

functional compensation The situation where a given role in an ecosystem, e.g., as decomposer or as prey, can be fulfilled by more than one species within that system.

functional connectivity The behavioural responses of organisms to physical links among habitat patches.

Gaia hypothesis View that the ecosphere itself is a self-regulating homeostatic system in which the biotic and abiotic components interact to produce a balanced state; the ecosphere as Mother Nature.

gaseous cycles Cycles of elements that have most of their matter in the atmosphere.

general circulation models (GCMs) The most prominent and most complex type of climate modelling, which takes into account the three-dimensional nature of the Earth's atmosphere and oceans or both.

generalist species Species, like the black bear and coyote, with a very broad niche where few things organic are not considered a potential food item.

genetically modified organisms (GMOs) Organisms created by humans through genetic manipulation combining genes from different and often totally unrelated species to create a different organism that is economically more productive and/or has greater resistance to pathogens.

genetic diversity The variability in genetic makeup among individuals of the same species.

geo-engineering Various technologies, from as simple as tree planting to as complex as stratospheric aerosols and space mirrors, that are used or have been proposed to mitigate the effects of climate change.

glaciation Period of global cooling when alpine glaciers increase and continental ice sheets cover and scour vast land masses.

global climate change Impacts of accumulation of greenhouse gases on the Earth's climate.

global warming Changes in average temperatures of the Earth's surface, although these changes are not uniform (i.e., some regions experience significantly higher temperatures, others only slight changes upward, and still others might experience somewhat cooler temperatures).

governance The processes used to determine how policy decisions are taken and by whom. Governance arrangements identify how disputes will be resolved and require capacity to identify trade-offs and compromises.

government The formal rules or authority over a country, state, or other jurisdiction, facilitated by people, structures, and processes and designed to provide transparency and accountability for decisions taken.

grasshopper effect Atmospheric transport and deposition of persistent and volatile chemical pollutants whereby the pollutants evaporate into the air in warmer climates and travel in the atmosphere toward cooler areas, condensing out again when the temperature drops. The cycle then repeats itself in a series of "hops" until the pollutants reach climates where they can no longer evaporate.

grazing food chains Energy transfer among organisms that is directly dependent on solar radiation as the primary source of energy and the producers (green plants) are eaten by organisms that are subsequently eaten by other organisms.

green bins The second stage of urban curbside collection programs involving residents placing organic and similar wastes into green plastic boxes or bins with the contents then composted and sold or made available at nominal cost for residents to use as soil.

greenfields Areas not yet developed and known not to have surface or underground soil contamination.

greenhouse effect A warming of the Earth's atmosphere caused by the presence of certain gases (e.g., water vapour, carbon dioxide, methane) that absorb radiation emitted by the Earth, thereby retarding the loss of energy to space.

greenhouse gas (GHG) A gas that contributes to the greenhouse effect, such as carbon dioxide.

green manure Growing plants that are plowed into the soil as fertilizer.

Green Revolution Development in plant genetics (hybridization) in the late 1950s and early 1960s resulting in high-yield varieties producing three to five times more grain than previous plants but requiring intensive irrigation and fertilizer use.

gross national product (GNP) The total value of all goods and services produced for final consumption in an economy, used by economists as an index or indicator to compare national economies or periods of time within a single national economy.

gross primary productivity (GPP) The total amount of energy produced by autotrophs over a given period of time.

groundwater Water below the Earth's surface in the saturated zone.

guano The phosphorus-rich droppings of seabirds that, in quantity, as from offshore islands of Peru, is mined for fertilizer.

habitat The environment in which a population or individual lives.

Happy Planet Index (HPI) An index that attempts to provide a perspective on human well-being and environmental impact and to focus on achieving sustainability. Each country's HPI value is a function of its average subjective life satisfaction, life expectancy at birth, and ecological footprint per capita—it approximates multiplying life satisfaction and life expectancy and dividing that by the ecological footprint.

heat The total energy of all moving atoms.

herbivores Animals that eat plants—that is, primary consumers.

heritage rivers Rivers designated for special protection by the Canadian Heritage Rivers Board because of their historical, cultural, ecological, and recreational significance.

heterotroph An organism that feeds on other organisms.

high-quality energy Energy that is easy to use, such as a hot fire or coal or gasoline, but that disperses quickly.

humus Decomposed organic material found in some soils.

hybridization The crossbreeding of two varieties or species of plants or animals.

hydraulic fracturing (fracking) See *fracking*.

hydrochlorofluorocarbons (HCFCs) Compound containing hydrogen, chlorine, fluorine, and carbon. HCFC is one type of chemical being used to replace chlorofluorcarbons (CFCs) because HCFCs have less impact on reducing ozone in the stratosphere. CFCs are formed by chlorine, fluorine, and carbon and are broken down by ultraviolet light in the stratosphere. When broken down, CFCs release chlorine atoms, which deplete the ozone layer. CFCs are used as refrigerants, solvents, and foam-blowing agents.

hydrological cycle The circulation of water through bodies of water, the atmosphere, and land.

hydrosolidarity An approach that recognizes the interconnections among aquatic, terrestrial, and other resource systems, leading to management that is integrated, participative, collaborative, coordinated, and shared, whether at local, provincial, national, or international levels.

hydrosphere One of three main aspects of the ecosphere, containing all the water on Earth.

hypothesis An educated guess as to the outcome of a particular relationship amongst phenomenon that can be tested.

hypoxic Oxygen-deficient.

ice cap An ice mass covering not more than 50,000 km^2 of land area.

ice shelf An ice mass extending over more than 50,000 km^2 of land area.

illegal, unreported, and unregulated (IUU) fisheries Fisheries that are not included in most catch statistics.

impact and benefit agreements (IBAs) Voluntary agreements between extractive industries and communities that go beyond formal impact assessment requirements and are intended to facilitate extraction of resources in a way that contributes to the economic and social well-being of local people and communities.

impact assessment Thorough consideration of the effects of a project that takes into account its potential and probable impacts on the environment and on society or a community and that assesses the technology proposed for the project as well as the technology available for dealing with any negative impacts.

"implementation gap" The situation that occurs when it becomes difficult or impossible to implement the ideas contained in a strategy or a plan, resulting in a "gap" between intention and action.

incentive-based Generation of inducements encouraging compliance with desired management actions.

indicators Specific facets of a particular system, such as the population of a key species within an ecosystem, that tell us something about the current state of the system but do not help us understand why the system is in that state.

indigenous knowledge Understanding of climate, animals and animal behaviour, soil, waters, and/or plants within an ecosystem based on experiential knowledge of a people who have lived or worked in a particular area for a long period of time; also referred to as traditional ecological knowledge (TEK) or local knowledge.

inertia The tendency of a natural system to resist change.

in situ preservation Conservation strategies that focus on a species within its natural habitat.

in situ recovery Refers to the general practice used at depths greater than 100 metres to remove crude bitumen from oil sands by the specific technique of steam-assisted gravity drainage.

integrated pest management (IPM) The avoidance or reduction of yield losses caused by diseases, weeds, insects, etc., while minimizing the negative impacts of chemical pest control.

integrated plant nutrient systems (IPNSs) Maximization of the efficiency of nutrient use by recycling all plant nutrient sources within the farm and by using nitrogen fixation by legumes.

integrated water resource management (IWRM) An approach that promotes the coordinated development and management of water, land, and related resources in order to maximize the resultant economic and social welfare in an equitable manner without compromising the sustainability of vital ecosystems.

intensive livestock operations (ILOs) Factory farms, feedlots, etc. where large quantities of external energy inputs are required to raise for market larger numbers of animals than the area in which they are raised can support, which can result in problems of disease and dealing with animal waste.

intermediate disturbance hypothesis Hypothesis suggesting that ecosystems subject to moderate disturbance generally maintain high levels of diversity compared to ecosystems with low levels of disturbance or those with high levels of disturbance.

International Joint Commission A bilateral institution, consisting of three Canadian commissioners and three American commissioners, established by the 1909 Boundary Waters Treaty to manage interjurisdictional resource issues between Canada and the United States.

interspecific competition Competition between members of different species for limited resources such as food, water, or space.

intraspecific competition Competition between members of the same species for limited resources such as food, water, or space.

intrinsic value A belief that nature has value in and of itself apart from its value to humanity; a central focus for the preservation of species.

invasive An introduced species that spreads out and causes harmful effects on other species and ecosystems.

island biogeography A field within biogeography that attempts to establish and explain the factors that affect the species richness of natural communities.

James Bay and Northern Quebec Agreement Treaty signed in 1975 by the James Bay Cree and Quebec Inuit with the Quebec government permitting the continuance of the James Bay Project and granting to the Natives, among other things, $232.5 million in compensation and outright ownership of 5,543 km^2, as well as exclusive hunting, fishing, and trapping rights to an additional 62,160 km^2; often considered the first modern Aboriginal land claim settlement in Canada.

James Bay Project A hydroelectric megaproject in northern Quebec, begun in the 1970s, that has involved extensive dams on the La Grande and other rivers and has flooded thousands of square kilometres of the James Bay Cree homeland.

keystone species Critical species in an ecosystem whose loss profoundly affects several or many others.

kimberlite pipes Rare, carrot-shaped igneous rock formations sometimes containing diamonds and found in parts of northern Canada.

kinetic energy The energy of objects in motion.

K-strategists Species that produce few offspring but make considerable effort to ensure that the offspring reach maturity.

Kuznet curve Proposes a relationship between income per capita and environmental degradation. During initial economic growth, it suggests that environmental degradation increases. However, at some level of per capita income this pattern reverses, resulting in enhancement of the environment.

Kyoto Protocol An international agreement reached in Kyoto, Japan, in 1997 that targets 38 developed nations as well as the European Union to ensure that "their aggregate anthropocentric carbon dioxide equivalent emissions of the greenhouse gases [e.g., carbon dioxide, methane, nitrous oxide, hydrofluorocarbons, perfluorocarbons, sulphur hexafluoride] . . . do not exceed their assigned amounts." The Protocol came into effect in 2004 when 55 countries accounting for 55 per cent of 1990 global carbon dioxide emissions had ratified it.

landscape connectivity The degree to which the landscape facilitates or restricts movement between and among habitat patches.

landscape ecology The science of studying and attempting to improve the relationships between spatial patterns and ecological processes on a multitude of spatial scales and organizational levels.

law of conservation of energy Law stating that energy cannot be created or destroyed; it is merely changed from one form to another; also known as the first law of thermodynamics.

law of conservation of matter Law that tells us that matter cannot be created or destroyed, but merely transformed from one form into another.

law of entropy When energy is transformed from one form into another, there is always a decrease in the quality of usable energy.

law of everybody The understanding that if everyone did many small things of a conserving and environmentally aware nature, major environmental problems, threats, and dangers would be ameliorated or alleviated.

leaching The downward movement of dissolved nutrients to the hydrological system.

LEED Acronym for the Leadership in Energy and Environmental Design Green Building Rating System. It is a national standard, established in the US, related to the design, construction, and operation of "high-performance green buildings." LEED provides benchmarks for performance related to five issues regarding human and environmental health: sustainable site development, water savings, energy efficiency, materials selection, and indoor environmental quality.

life-cycle assessments (LCAs) Identification of inputs, outputs, and potential environmental impacts of a product or service throughout its lifetime, from manufacture to use and ultimate disposal.

light living Treading as lightly as possible, to minimize our ecological footprints, often characterized by the four R's: refuse, reduce, reuse, and recycle.

limiting factor A chemical or physical factor that determines whether an organism can survive in a given ecosystem. In most ecosystems, rainfall is the limiting factor.

limiting factor principle Stipulates that all factors necessary for growth must be available in certain quantities if an organism is to survive.

lithosphere The Earth's crust.

Livestock Revolution The shift in production units from family farms to factory farms and feedlots that depend on outside supplies of feed, energy, and other inputs to produce vastly more livestock, a shift that has fuelled the growth in meat consumption worldwide, which has doubled since 1977.

Living Planet Index An index that quantifies the overall state of planetary ecosystems.

loams Soils that contain a mixture of materials of different sizes, including humus.

locavore People who eat locally produced food.

longline Type of commercial fishing using lines with many baited hooks.

long-range sustained yield The yield for an area that is equal to the culmination of mean annual increment weighted by area for all productive and utilizable forest land types in that area; what a given unit of land, such as a forest, should yield in perpetuity.

low-quality energy Energy that is diffuse, dispersed, at low temperatures, and difficult to gather; most of the energy available to us.

LULUs Acronym for "locally unwanted land uses," often the source of a NIMBY ("not in my backyard") reaction.

LUST Acronym for "leaking underground storage tanks," which results in contaminated aquifers.

macronutrient A chemical substance needed by living organisms in large quantities (for example, carbon, oxygen, hydrogen, and nitrogen).

marine protected areas (MPAs) Underwater reserves set aside and protected from normal human exploitation because of the fragility, rarity, or valued biodiversity of their ecosystems.

matter What things are made of—92 natural and 17 synthesized chemical elements such as carbon, oxygen, hydrogen, and calcium.

mature community A collection of plants and associated animal species that, over time, see replacement of individuals by similar species.

mediation A negotiation process guided by a facilitator (mediator).

megaprojects Large-scale engineering or resource development projects that cost at least $1 billion and take several years to complete.

mesosphere Layer of the atmosphere extending from the stratosphere, from about 50 to about 80 kilometres above Earth.

mesotrophic Water bodies with nutrient levels between oligotrophic (low levels) and eutrophic (high levels).

metal toxicity The poisonous or harmful nature of metals and minerals, such as asbestos and lead, both to humans and to ecosystems.

micronutrient An element needed by organisms but only in small quantities, such as copper, iron, and zinc.

migration A movement, often involving a large group of people or animals from one place to another. Migration of people usually is triggered by a desire to achieve greater economic opportunities or to escape violence or conflict. Migration of animals is often motivated to have access to food or for breeding.

Millennium Consumption Goals Identification of consumption targets intended to provide motivation for the globally most wealthy people to consume in a more sustainable manner, in order to reduce the pressure on natural resources and the environment as well as facilitate intra- and inter-generational equity. They are intended to complement the Millennium Development Goals.

Millennium Development Goals (MDGs) Globally accepted goals for development agreed to by member states of the UN. The target date for meeting the goals was 2015. One of the goals is to "ensure environmental sustainability."

Millennium Ecosystem Assessment Program carried out by the UN to assess the consequences of ecosystem change for human well-being and to establish the scientific basis for actions needed to enhance the conservation and sustainable use of ecosystems and their contributions to human well-being.

mineralization The process by which biomass is converted back to ammonia (NH_3) and ammonium salts (NH_4) by bacterial action and returned to the soil when plants die.

minimum viable population (MVP) The smallest population size of a species that can be predicted to have a very high chance of persisting for the foreseeable future.

mitigation Strategies to reduce or minimize the negative consequences from a hazard such as climate change. Mitigation requires action today in order for initiatives to be able to reduce the most serious negative impacts in the future.

monitoring Explicit and systematic checking of outputs and outcomes related to a management initiative in order to understand what works and what does not work and to determine needed modifications to enhance effectiveness.

monoculture cropping Cultivation of one plant species (such as corn) over a large area, which leaves the crop highly susceptible to disease and insects, especially when all the individual plants are genetically identical.

Montreal Protocol Signed in 1987 by 32 nations, established a schedule for reducing use of chlorofluorocarbons and halons to reduce the rate of depletion of the ozone layer.

multi-barrier approach A method of ensuring the quality of a water supply by using a series of measures (e.g., system security, source protection through pollution regulations within a watershed, water treatment and filtration, testing), each independently acting as a barrier to water-borne contaminants through the system.

mutualism Relationship between two organisms having to do with food supplies, protection, or transport that is beneficial to both.

natural selection The selection by nature of that segment of a population whose genetic attributes favour its success in a changing or changed environment.

nature deficit disorder The increasing gap in understanding of the "real world" on the part of the younger generation. Instead of playing outdoors in fields, woods, streams, lakes, or the ocean, an increasing proportion of the children of today are glued to their computer or TV screens. They seldom visit the outside world, especially areas dominated by nature rather than human activities.

negative feedback Control mechanism present in the ecosystem and in all organisms—information in the form of chemical, physical, and biological agents influences processes, causing them to shut down or reduce their activity.

negotiation One of the two main types of alternative dispute resolution when two or more parties involved in a dispute join in a voluntary, joint exploration of issues with the goal of reaching a mutually acceptable agreement.

neo-liberalism A political or policy perspective that places high value on the role of free markets to allocate resources efficiently, leading to a belief that it is best to allow markets to function with minimum intervention by government regulations.

net community productivity (NCP) The rate of accumulation of organic material, allowing for both plant respiration and heterotrophic predation during the measurement period.

net primary productivity (NPP) Gross primary productivity (the total amount of energy that plants produce) minus the energy plants use during cellular respiration.

new forestry A silvicultural approach that mimics natural processes more closely through emphasizing long-term site productivity by maintaining ecological diversity.

niche An organism's place in the ecosystem: where it lives, what it consumes, and how it interacts with all biotic and abiotic factors.

NIMBY "Not in my backyard," a phrase used to describe local people's reactions when a noxious or undesired facility—for example, a landfill site, a sand and gravel pit, or an expressway—is proposed in an area adjacent to or near their property.

nitrogen fixation Conversion of gaseous (atmospheric) nitrogen (N_2) into ammonia (NH_3) by bacteria, such as those that grow on the root nodules of legumes.

non-governmental organizations (NGOs) Organizations outside of the government and private sectors, usually established to address a specific societal issue or need; also referred to as "not-for-profit" or "social profit" organizations. They are one element of "civil society" and when focused on environmental matters can be referred to as ENGOs (environmental non-governmental organizations).

non-point sources Sources of pollution from which pollutants are discharged over a widespread area or from a number of small inputs rather than from distinct, identifiable sources.

non-renewable or stock resources Resources, such as oil, coal, and minerals, that take millions of years to form and thus, for practical purposes, are fixed in supply and therefore not renewable.

non-timber forest products (NTFPs) Forest resources of economic value but not related to the lumber and pulp and paper industries, such as wild rice, mushrooms and berries, maple syrup, edible nuts, furs and hides, medicines, and ornamental cuttings.

no-till/conservation agriculture (NT/CA) Zero, minimum, or low tillage to protect and stimulate the biological functioning of the soil while maintaining and improving crop yields, which includes direct sowing or drilling of seeds instead of plowing, maintenance of permanent cover of plant material on the soil, and crop rotation.

nuclear power Power, usually electric power, produced by atomic energy. Atoms contain atomic energy, which can be released slowly in reactors or rapidly in bombs through alteration of the nuclei of atoms.

nuclear wastes The radioactive wastes remaining from the uranium used to fuel nuclear fuel reactors. Such wastes have an extremely long life and are life-threatening, thereby creating significant storage and containment challenges.

nutrient capital The amount of nutrients within a particular nutrient reservoir.

nutrients Elements or compounds that an organism must take in from its environment because it cannot produce them or cannot produce them as quickly as needed.

old-growth forests Forests that generally have a significant number of huge, long-lived trees; many large standing dead trees; numerous logs lying about the forest floor; and multiple layers of canopy created by the crowns of trees of various ages and species.

oligotrophic Nutrient poor.

omnivores Organisms that eat both plants and animals.

100-mile diet A term introduced in 2005 referring to buying and eating food grown, manufactured, or produced entirely within a 100-mile radius of one's residence.

optimal foraging theory The relationship between the benefit of making a kill and feeding and the cost of the energy expended to make the kill.

optimum range The ideal conditions for the survival of a species.

organic farming An agriculture production management system that focuses on food web relations and element cycling to maximize agro-ecosystem stability and to promote and enhance ecosystem health. It is based on minimizing the use of external inputs.

organism A living entity; one of a population.

oxygen sag curve The drop in oxygen levels in a body of water when organic wastes are added and the number of bacteria rises to help break down the waste.

ozone An atmospheric gas (O_3) that when present in the stratosphere helps to protect the Earth from ultraviolet rays. However, when present near the Earth's surface, it is a primary component of urban smog and has detrimental effects on both vegetation and human respiratory systems.

ozone layer Thin layer of ozone molecules in the stratosphere that absorbs ultraviolet light and converts it into infrared radiation, effectively screening out 99 per cent of the ultraviolet light.

Palliser's Triangle Roughly triangular-shaped semi-arid area of southeast Alberta and southwest Saskatchewan, south of the Saskatchewan River, first identified by Captain John Palliser during an expedition to the Canadian West in 1857–60 sponsored by the Royal Geographical Society and the British Colonial Office.

parasitism Relationship in which one species lives in or on another that acts as its host.

parent material The material from which soil forms, such as sediment or weathered bedrock.

partnerships A sharing of responsibility and power between two or more groups, especially a government agency and a second party, regarding a resource or environmental issue; co-management is an example of a partnership.

pelagic Marine life, such as cod and whales, that live in the upper layers of the open sea.

permaculture Agricultural designs, such as urban farming and organic farming, based on ecological relationships with the fundamental principle of minimizing wasted energy and with the wastes of one component becoming the inputs for another.

permanent cropland Lands where crops (e.g., coffee, tea, fruit) do not require annual replanting.

permanent pastures Lands used primarily for grazing livestock.

persistent organochlorine pesticides (POPs) Chemical substances that persist in the environment.

phenology The study of how time cycles, such as the seasons, influence plant and animal life.

pheromones Volatile compounds, or "scents," used by insects of a given species to communicate with each other.

photosynthesis A two-part process in plants and algae involving (1) the capture of sunlight and its conversion into cellular energy and (2) the production of organic molecules, such as glucose and amino acids from carbon dioxide, water, and energy from the sun.

phototrophs Organisms that produce complex chemicals through photosynthesis.

phytoplankton Single-celled algae and other free-floating photosynthetic organisms.

planetary carrying capacity The ability of Earth and its various systems to sustain the number of people and other organisms on the planet and their effects on these systems.

point sources Easily discernible "end-of-pipe" sources of pollution, such as a factory or a town sewage system.

polar amplification The effect of a positive feedback loop in the North whereby increased temperatures lead to a greater area of snow-free land in summer, which in turn leads to increased temperatures because of the lower albedo.

policy target value A target set as a result of compromise among scientific, social, economic, cultural, and political objectives.

population A group of organisms of the same species living within a specified region.

population age structure The relative distribution of age cohorts in the population.

population density The number of individuals of a population within a certain defined area, such as sea otters per hectare or humans per square kilometre.

population viability analysis (PVA) A process that determines the probability that a population will go extinct within a given number of years.

positive feedback loop A situation in which a change in a system in one direction provides the conditions to cause the system to change further in the same direction.

potential energy Stored energy that is available for later use.

precautionary principle A guideline stating that when there is a possibility of serious or irreversible environmental damage resulting from a course of action, such as a development project, lack of scientific certainty is not an acceptable reason for postponing a measure to prevent environmental degradation or for assuming that damage in the future can be rectified by some kind of technological fix.

predator An organism that actively hunts its prey.

prescribed burning Burning purposely initiated, usually to achieve ecological goals of restoring natural fire regimes.

prey An organism (e.g., deer) that is attacked and killed by a predator.

prey switching A familiar foraging behaviour whereby a predator shifts from its target species after it is depleted or not available in an area to the next most preferred or profitable species until that, too, is depleted and then continuing to move down the food chain, as wolves do in moving from caribou to Arctic hare to small rodents or as humans have done in fishing down the food chain in commercial fisheries.

primary consumers The first consuming organisms in a given food chain, such as a grazer in grazer food chains or a decomposer organism or insect in decomposer food chains; primary consumers belong to the second trophic level.

primary succession The development of a biotic community in an area previously devoid of organisms.

producers Autotrophs capable of synthesizing organic material, thus forming the basis of the food web.

protected areas Areas such as national and provincial parks, wildlife sanctuaries, and game preserves established to protect species and ecosystems.

qualitative An approach to research that does not use measurable quantities but emphasizes qualities that are descriptive, subjective, or difficult to measure.

quantitative An approach to research based on measurement of quantities.

radiant energy Energy from the sun.

rainshadow effect The decrease in precipitation levels as the air warms up in its descent from the mountains and can hold more moisture (i.e., there is considerably less precipitation on the leeward side of a mountain or a mountain range than on the windward side).

range of tolerance Range of abiotic factors within which an organism can survive, from the minimum amount of a limiting factor that the organism requires to the maximum amount that it can withstand.

reclamation The process of bringing an area back to a useful, good condition—similar to rehabilitation.

recovery Involves burning waste in incinerators and then recovering the generated energy to provide heating for homes, offices, and other buildings.

recycling The third stage in waste management, involving the return of used products (glass, plastic, or metal containers; newspapers) to be processed so that the glass, plastic, metal, or newsprint can be used for other products; movement of elements in characteristic repetitive paths through ecosystems.

REDD+ A mechanism for compensating countries for reducing emissions from deforestation and forest degradation.

Red List An annual listing of species at risk prepared by the IUCN and produced by thousands of scientific experts; the best source of knowledge on the status of global biodiversity.

reduction The first stage in waste management, involving using less material or products to meet needs.

relative humidity The amount of moisture held in the air compared to how much could be held if fully saturated at a particular temperature.

renewable or flow resources Resources that are renewed naturally within a relatively short period of time, such as water, air, animals, and plants, as well as solar radiation, wind power, and tidal energy.

renewable water supply Supply based on precipitation that falls, then runs off into rivers, often being held in lakes before draining to the ocean or moving downward into aquifers. The flows associated with precipitation or snowmelt should be identified as the renewable supply.

replacement-level fertility Fertility rate that will sustain a population.

resilience Ability of an ecosystem to return to normal after a disturbance.

resource partitioning A situation in which resources are used at different times or in different ways by species with an overlap of fundamental niches, such as owls and hawks, which seek the same prey but at different times during the day.

resources Such things as forests, wildlife, oceans, rivers and lakes, minerals, and petroleum.

reuse The second stage in waste management, involving the reuse of a product rather than discarding and replacing it.

rewilding Restoring the ecological processes that underlie natural systems, complete with their ecological components.

Richter scale A scale developed in 1935 by C.F. Richter for measuring the magnitude of earthquake severity on a logarithmic scale. Although theoretically open-ended, beginning at zero, no earthquakes have registered higher than 9.0 on the scale.

risk assessment Determining the probability or likelihood of an environmentally or socially negative event of some specified magnitude.

rock cycle The relationship among three rock-forming processes and how each rock type can be transformed into another type.

r-strategists Species that produce large numbers of young early in life in a short time but invest little energy in their upbringing.

salinization Deposition of salts in irrigated soils, making soil unfit for most crops; caused by a rising water table due to inadequate drainage of irrigated soils.

science a systematic field of inquiry that creates and organizes knowledge about the universe that is usually generated through creation of testable hypotheses.

scientific law A scientific law is the highest form of scientific explanation and provides a true statement of fact about the relationship between phenomenon that always occurs under the specified conditions.

scientific target value A target set on the basis of scientific information.

secondary consumers Second consuming organisms in a food chain and belonging to the third trophic level.

secondary succession The sequential development of biotic communities after the complete or partial destruction of an existing community by natural or anthropogenic forces.

second growth A second forest that develops after harvest of the original forest.

second law of thermodynamics Law stating that when energy is converted from one form to another, it is degraded—that is, it is converted from a concentrated to a less concentrated form. The amount of useful energy decreases during such conversions.

sedimentary cycles Those cycles of elements, such as the phosphorus and sulphur cycles, that hold most of their matter in the lithosphere.

seed bank Locations where plant seeds accumulate.

seral Each stage in a successional process.

serial depletion When one stock after another becomes progressively depleted as a result of prey switching, even if the total catch remains the same.

serotiny Behaviour of some plant species that retain their non-dormant seeds in a cone or woody fruit for up to several years but release them after exposure to fire.

shifting baseline When scientists have no other option than to take the current or recent degraded state as the baseline for stock biomass rather than the historical ecological abundance.

Silent Spring A book written by Rachel Carson and published in 1962 that detailed the disastrous effects of biocides on the environment.

silo effect Occurs when a government ministry focuses only on its interests, mandate, objectives, and programs without regard to whether they complement or conflict with those from other ministries or agencies.

silviculture The practice of directing the establishment, composition, growth, and quality of forest stands through a variety of activities, including harvesting, reforestation, and site preparation.

single-loop learning Learning that emphasizes ensuring a match between intent and outcome.

smog Originally, a mixture of smoke and fog in urban areas, mainly due to burning of coal to heat homes and power factories and the subsequent mixing of smoke with the humid air. Now more usually due to photochemical reactions of sunlight with hydrocarbons and nitrogen oxide emitted into the atmosphere from vehicles and industries.

social learning Learning applied not only to individuals but also to social collectives, such as organizations and communities. The implication is that resource and environmental management processes should be designed so that both individuals and organizations are able to learn from their experience and thereby become more knowledgeable and effective in the future.

soft path A management approach to improving water use efficiency by challenging basic patterns of consumption. While demand management emphasizes the question of "how," or how to do the same with less water, the soft path asks why water is even used for a function. The "why" question normally leads to consideration of a broader range of methods.

soil compaction The compression of soil as a result of frequent heavy machinery use on wet soils or the overstocking of cattle on the land.

soil erosion A natural process whereby soil is removed from its place of formation by gravitational, water, and wind processes.

soil horizons Layers found in most soils.

soil permeability The rate at which water can move through a soil, largely determined by soil texture, i.e., the size of the materials that make up the soil.

soil profile A view across soil horizons.

solar power Energy that results from converting sunlight into electricity either directly through photovoltaics or indirectly through concentrated sunlight.

specialist Organism that has a narrow niche, usually feeding on one or a few food materials and adapted to a particular habitat.

speciation Phyletic evolution, i.e., formation of new species when evolution within a population is so great that interbreeding with the original population is no longer possible.

species A group of individuals that share certain identical physical characteristics and are capable of producing fertile offspring.

Species at Risk Act (SARA) Canadian legislation passed in 2002 that mandates the Committee on the Status of Endangered Wildlife in Canada to maintain lists of species at risk and to recommend to the minister responsible that particular species be given special protection in their environment.

species diversity The total number of different species in an area.

stakeholders Persons or groups with a legal responsibility relative to a problem or issue, or likely to be affected by decisions or actions regarding the problem or issue, or able to pose an obstacle to a solution of the problem or issue.

steam-assisted gravity drainage Injection of high-pressure steam into tar sands at depths greater than 100 metres to separate the bitumen from the sand, silt, and clay. Exposed to the steam, bitumen becomes liquefied and can flow to a well from which it can be pumped to the surface.

stewardship Activities undertaken by humans toward caring for the Earth.

strategic environmental assessment Focuses on policies, plans, and programs (PPPs) in order to integrate environmental considerations at the earliest possible stage of decision-making. Such assessment occurs before development decisions are made and when alternative futures and options for development are still open. Emphasis is on opportunities, regions, and sectors as opposed to projects. The objective is to integrate environmental considerations in the development of PPPs and to identify preferred futures and the means to achieve them, rather than focusing on mitigating the most likely outcomes of an already taken development decision.

stratosphere The layer of the atmosphere (about 10 to 50 kilometres above the Earth's surface) in which temperatures rise with increasing altitude.

strip cropping A technique similar to contour cultivation in which different crops are planted in strips parallel to the slope.

structural connectivity The physical relationship among habitat patches.

sublimation The process for direct transfer between the solid and vapour phases of matter, regardless of direction.

subsidiarity A policy and management approach stipulating that decisions should be taken at the level closest to where consequences are most noticeable or have the most direct impact.

subsistence farming The production of food and other necessities to satisfy the needs of the farm household.

sulphur dioxide emissions Release into the atmosphere of huge quantities of sulphur, mainly in the form of dioxides, as a result of smelting sulphide ores and burning fossil fuels, which causes air pollution and climate change.

summer fallow A practice common on the Prairies in which land is plowed and kept bare to minimize moisture losses through evapotranspiration but which leads to increased salinization.

supply management Approach based on manipulating the natural system to create new sources of supply, normally through either augmenting an existing supply or developing a new supply.

sustainability assessment Analysis that seeks to determine the environmental sustainability of a proposed course of action.

sustainable development Economic development that meets current needs without compromising the ability of future generations to meet their needs, a concept popularized by the 1987 World Commission on Environment and Development headed by Norwegian Prime Minister Gro Harlem Brundtland.

sustained yield The amount of harvestable material that can be removed from an ecosystem over a long period of time with no apparent deleterious effects on the system.

synergism An interaction between two substances that produces a greater effect than the effect of either one alone; an interaction between two relatively harmless components in the environment.

system plan An idealized blueprint of the distribution of protected areas within a given jurisdiction.

technocentric perspective The assumption that humankind is able to understand, control, and manipulate nature to suit its purposes and that nature and other living and non-living things exist to meet human needs and wants.

territory A specific area dominated by a specific individual of a species.

tertiary consumers In a food chain, organisms at the top that consume other organisms.

theory A body of knowledge that provides explanatory power for observations.

thermocline Sharp transition in temperature between the warmer surface waters of the ocean and the cooler waters underneath, generally occurring at a depth of 120 to 240 metres.

thermohaline circulation The movement of carbon-saturated water around the globe, mainly as a result of differing water densities.

thermosphere Uppermost layer of the atmosphere, beyond the mesosphere.

threatened species A species designated by the Committee on the Status of Endangered Wildlife in Canada is likely to become endangered in Canada if factors threatening its vulnerability are not reversed.

three waves Distinct ways of thinking about resource and environmental management. The first wave appeared in the late nineteenth century, and focused on rediscovering and protecting wilderness areas, leading to national parks. The second wave began in the twentieth century, and sought to identify and publicize environmental degradation and advocate reduction of such damage through new environmental laws, policies, and ministries. The third wave emerged late in the twentieth century, building on the second wave, and advocated repairing and remediating environmental degradation and seeking sustainable development. International and local coalitions have been created to address environmental problems.

threshold A point or limit beyond which something is unsatisfactory relative to a consideration, such as health, welfare, or ecological integrity.

top-down control Where the structure and/or population dynamics of an ecosystem are dominantly influenced by top level predators.

total allowable catch (TAC) The amount, in tonnage, of a particular aquatic species that the federal Department of Fisheries and Oceans, for example, determines can be landed within a particular fishery in a given year.

total fertility rates Average number of children each woman has over her lifetime.

traditional ecological knowledge (TEK) Belief, knowledge, and practice gained through experience, normally shared and transmitted verbally; often referred to as "indigenous knowledge."

transpiration The loss of water vapour through the pores of a plant.

tree-length harvesting Felling, delimbing, and topping the trees in the cut-over area.

triple bottom line Also called the 3Ps (people, planet, and profit), goes beyond the traditional private sector focus on profits, return on investment, and shareholder value to include attention to both environmental and social considerations.

trophic cascade Where removal of a top predator in a top-down system creates repercussions throughout the ecosystem.

trophic level Functional classification of organisms in a community according to feeding relationships: the first trophic level includes green plants, the second level includes herbivores, and so on.

troposphere Innermost layer of the atmosphere that contains 99 per cent of the water vapour and up to 90 per cent of the Earth's air and is responsible for our weather, extending about 6 to 17 kilometres up from the Earth, depending on latitude and season.

uncertainty A situation in which the probability or odds of a future event are not known and therefore that indicates the presence of doubt.

urban form The type and distribution of infrastructure (e.g., buildings, roads) in communities and a key factor influencing environmental quality in cities.

urban heat island Increased temperatures in core urban areas relative to surrounding areas resulting from heat absorbed and radiated from the built environment (e.g., buildings, roads). It is not uncommon for the temperature of city centres to be 2–6°C higher than that of nearby rural areas.

urban sprawl Urban areas characterized by low population densities and significant travel costs because of the high priority the majority of residents place on living in single-family, detached homes with large properties. Sprawl contributes to loss of, disruption to, or degradation of adjacent agricultural land, environmentally sensitive areas, natural habitats, and water and air quality.

vernacular knowledge A combination of community values and beliefs with local and expert scientific knowledge.

virtual water A concept recognizing that because significant amounts of water are required to grow some foodstuffs, nations can reduce pressure on their water resources by importing such products, allowing use of water for other, higher-value products.

vision A view for the future for a region, community, or group that is realistic, credible, attractive, and attainable.

vulnerable species An official designation assigned by the Committee on the Status of Endangered Wildlife in Canada to any indigenous species or subspecies or geographically separate population of fauna or flora that is particularly at risk, though not at present "threatened," because of low or declining numbers, because it occurs at the fringe of its range or in restricted areas, or for some other reason.

war on science Occurs when government leaders seek to control science and government scientists, and/or dismiss the findings and conclusions of independent scientists, particularly when scientific findings challenge or generate questions about their government's priorities, policies, and programs.

water-energy-food nexus The interactions among water, energy, and food systems, highlighting that each has implications for the other two, and therefore attention should be given to such interconnections.

water ethics A statement of principles or values to guide behaviour by individuals or groups with regard to water.

water footprint An indicator of water consumption that tracks and totals both direct and indirect yearly water use by a consumer or a nation, or of a product over the course of its life cycle.

water rights The view that water is a basic human right, as put forth several times in recent years by the UN Human Rights Council, a view that the Canadian government had strongly opposed, presumably for geopolitical and internal political and administrative reasons.

water table The top of the zone of saturation.

weather The sum total of atmospheric conditions (temperature, pressure, winds, moisture, and precipitation) in a particular place for a short period of time.

wetlands Areas that are hybrid aquatic and terrestrial systems, such as swamps and marshes, where the ground is saturated with water much or all of the time.

wicked problems Issues characterized by changing and complex relationships that are challenging to identify, resulting in difficulty in resolving them because of incomplete and/or contradictory understanding.

wind power The fastest-growing sector in the world's energy market, which uses wind turbines to generate electricity.

windthrow Uprooting and blowing down of trees by wind.

World Summit on Sustainable Development (WSSD) Conference held in Johannesburg in 2002, 10 years after the Earth Summit in Rio, that made various commitments, such as halving the proportion of people without access to adequate sanitation by the year 2015.

zone of physiological stress Upper and lower limits of the range of tolerance in which organisms have difficulty surviving.

zooplankton Non-photosynthetic, single-celled aquatic organisms.

zooxanthellae Unicellular algae.

REFERENCES

Abbey, E. 1977. *The Journey Home: Some Words in Defense of the American West*. New York: Dutton.

Agreement Review Committee. 2007. *Review of the Great Lakes Water Quality Agreement, Volume 1, Final Report to the Great Lakes Binational Executive Committee*. Windsor, Ont.: Environment Canada–Ontario, Great Lakes Office.

Agriculture and Agri-Food Canada. 2003. "Canada's Agriculture, Food and Beverage Industry: Organic Industry." www.ats.agr.gc.ca/pro/fhs-eng.htm.

——. 2008. "An Overview of the Canadian Agriculture and Agri-Food System 2007." www4.agr.gc.ca/AAFC-AAC/display-afficher.do?id=1201291159395&lang=eng.

——. 2010a. "Producers." www4.agr.gc.ca/AAFC-AAC/display-afficher.do?id=1165871799386&lang=eng.

——. 2010b. "Government of Canada invests in organic sector." News release, 6 Mar. http://www.marketwired.com/press-release/government-of-canada-invests-in-organic-sector-1127679.htm

——. 2013. *An Overview of the Canadian Agriculture and Agri-Food System 2013*. Ottawa.

——. 2015. *Certified Organic Production Statistics for Canada 2009*. Accessed 11 Mar. 2015. http://www.agr.gc.ca/eng/industry-markets-and-trade/statistics-and-market-information/by-product-sector/organic-products/organic-production-canadian-industry/certified-organic-production-statistics-for-canada-2009/?id=1312385802597.

Akcakaya, H.R., et al. 2014. "Preventing species extinctions resulting from climate change." *Nature Climate Change* 4: 1048–1049.

Alberta Energy. 2008. "Electricity frequently asked questions." www.energy.gov.ab.ca/Electricity/683.asp#where.

——. 2014. "Oil sands, facts and statistics." Accessed 26 Nov. 2014. http://www.energy.alberta.ca/oilsands/791.asp.

Alberta Environment. 2005. *Report on the Implementation Progress of Water for Life: Alberta's Strategy for Sustainability*. Edmonton: Alberta Environment.

Alberta, Environment and Sustainable Resource Development. 2014. *Greenhouse Gas Reduction Program*. Accessed 3 Jan. 2015. http://esrd.alberta.ca/focus/alberta-and-climate-change/regulating-greenhouse-gas-emissions/greenhouse-gas-reduction-program/default.aspx.

Alberta Food and Rural Development. 2001. "Woodlot harvest." www1.agric.gov.ab.ca/$department/deptdocs.nsf/all/apa3316.

Alberta Government. 2014. *Alberta's Oil Sands*. Accessed 25 Nov. 2014. http://oilsands.alberta.ca.

Alberta WaterPortal. 2013. *Learn: Virtual Water Flows—Conclusions and Impacts*. Accessed 7 Sept. 2014. www.albertawater.com/virtualwaterflows/virtual-water-flows-conclusions-and-impacts.

Aldaya, M.M., P. Martinez-Santos, and M.R. Llamas. 2010. "Incorporating the water footprint and virtual water into policy: Reflections from the Mancha Occidental Region, Spain." *Water Resources Management* 24: 941–58.

Allan, T. 2011. *Virtual Water*. New York: I.B. Tauris.

Alliance to Save Energy. 2012. "Top Ten Energy Efficiency Tips." Accessed 27 Sept. 2015. https://www.ase.org/resources/top-10-home-energy-efficiency-tips.

Amadeo, K. 2014. "How much did Hurricane Katrina damage the US economy?" Accessed 2 Oct. 2014. http://useconomy.about.com/od/grossdomesticproduct/f/katrina.damage.html.

Anderegg, W.R.I. 2010. "The ivory lighthouse: Communicating climate change more effectively." *Climatic Change* 101, 3 and 4: 655–62.

Andrey, J., and L. Mortsch. 2000. "Communicating about climate change: Challenges and opportunities." In D. Scott et al., *Climate Change Communication: Proceedings of an International Conference*. Waterloo, Ont.: University of Waterloo and Environment Canada, Adaptation and Impacts Research Group, wp1–wp11.

Anielski, M., and S. Wilson. 2005. *Assessing the Real Value of Canada's Boreal Ecosystem*. Edmonton: Pembina Institute.

—— and ——. 2009. *Counting Canada's Natural Capital: Assessing the Real Value of Canada's Boreal Ecosystems*. Ottawa: Pembina Institute and Canadian Boreal Initiative.

Apps, C.D., and B.N. McClellan. 2006. "Factors influencing the dispersion and fragmentation of endangered mountain caribou populations." *Biological Conservation* 130: 84–97.

AREVA. 2007. "Uranium in Saskatchewan." www.arevaresources.com/publications/uranium_in_sask_01/environment and safety.html.

Armitage, D., F. Berkes, and N. Doubleday, eds. 2007. *Adaptive Co-management: Collaboration, Learning and Multi-Level Governance*. Vancouver: University of British Columbia Press.

——, ——, and ——. 2007. "Introduction: Moving beyond co-management." In Armitage et al. (2007: 1–15).

Armstrong, A. 2009. "Further ideas towards a water ethic." *Water Alternatives* 2: 138–47.

Arndt, D.S., M.O. Baringer, and M.R. Johnson. 2010. "State of the climate in 2009." *Bulletin of the American Meteorological Society* 91, 7: S1–S224.

Arnstein, S. 1969. "A ladder of citizen participation." *Journal of the American Institute of Planners* 35, 4: 216–24.

Assiniboine Hills Conservation District. n.d. Accessed 18 Aug. 2014. www.assiniboinehillscd.ca.

Associated Press. 2014. "New Orleans since Katrina: Before and after." *Huffington Post*, 27 Aug. Accessed 2 Oct. 2014. http://www.huffingtonpost.com/2012/08/27/new-orleans-since-katrina_n_1834696.html.

Auditor General of Canada. 2002. *2002 Report of the Commissioner of the Environment and Sustainable Development*. Ottawa: Minister of Supply and Services.

——. 2005a. *2005 Report of the Commissioner of the Environment and Sustainable Development*, Chapter 5: "Drinking water in First Nations communities." www.oag-bvg.gc.ca/internet/English/parl_cesd_200509_05_e_14952.html.

——. 2005b. *2005 September Report of the Commissioner of the Environment and Sustainable Development*. Ottawa: Minister of Supply and Services.

——. 2006. *2006 Report of the Commissioner of the Environment and Sustainable Development*. www.oag-bvg.gc.ca/internet/English/parl_cesd_200609_e_936.html.

——. 2013. *Report of the Commissioner of the Environment and Sustainable Development*. Ottawa.

——. 2014. "Commissioner of the Environment and Sustainable Development's Opening Statement." *2014 Fall Report of the Commissioner of the Environment and Sustainable Development*. Accessed 10 Oct. 2014. http://www.oag-bvg.gc.ca/internet/English/osm_20141007_e_39914.html.

Augustine, S., and P. Dearden. 2014. "Changing paradigms in marine and coastal conservation: A case study of clam gardens in the Southern Gulf Islands." *The Canadian Geographer* 58: 305–314.

Augustine S., P. Dearden, and R. Rollins. (In press). "Are changing diver characteristics important for coral reef conservation?" *Aquatic Conservation: Marine and Freshwater Ecosystems*.

Aulakh, R., and J. Spears. 2014. "No definitive link between wind turbines and poor health, says Health Canada study." *Toronto Star*, 7 Nov. Accessed 7 Nov. 2014. http://www.thestar.com/news/canada/2014/11/06/wind_turbine_noise_doesnt_cause_harm_health_canada_finds.html.

Ayers, C.A., P. Dearden, and R. Rollins. 2012. "An exploration of Hul'qumi'num Coast Salish peoples' attitudes towards the establishment of no-take zones within marine protected areas in the Salish Sea, Canada." *The Canadian Geographer* 56: 260–274.

Babbage, M. 2010. "Provinces to take action on climate." *The Record*, 9 Nov., D4.

Bakker, K., ed. 2007. *Eau Canada: The Future of Canada's Water*. Vancouver: University of British Columbia Press.

Balshi, M.S., et al. 2009. "Vulnerability of carbon storage in North American boreal forests to wildfires during the 21st century." *Global Change Biology* 15: 1491–1510.

Ban, N.C., and J. Alder. 2008. "How wild is the ocean? Assessing the intensity of anthropogenic marine activities in British Columbia, Canada." *Aquatic Conservation: Marine and Freshwater Ecosystems* 18: 55–85.

Banff–Bow Valley Study. 1996. *Banff–Bow Valley: At the Crossroads. Summary Report of the Banff–Bow Valley Task Force*. R. Page et al., eds. Ottawa: Ministry of Canadian Heritage.

Bardati, D.R. 1995. "An environmental action plan for Bishop's University." *Journal of Eastern Townships Studies* 6: 19–38.

——. 2006. "The integrative role of the campus environmental audit: Experiences at Bishop's University, Canada." *International Journal of Sustainability in Higher Education* 7, 1: 57–68.

Barlow, M., and E. May. 2000. *Frederick Street: Life and Death on Canada's Love Canal*. Toronto: HarperCollins.

Barnosky, A.D., et al. 2004. "Assessing the causes of late Pleistocene extinctions on the continents." *Science* 306: 70–5.

——et al. 2011. "Has the Earth's sixth mass extinction already arrived?" *Nature* 471: 51–7.

Barrett, K. 2014. "The water-energy-food nexus: Interlinked solutions for interlinked challenges." *Ecosystem Marketplace*, 11 Jun. Accessed 7 Sept. 2014. www.ecosystemmarketplace.com/pages/dynamic.article.page_php?page_id=13099.

Bay of Fundy Ecosystem Partnership. n.d. Accessed 18 Aug. 2014. www.bofep.org/wpbofep/?page_id=8.

Beamish, R., and H. Harvey. 1972. "Acidification of the La Cloche Mountain lakes, Ontario, and resulting fish mortalities." *Journal of the Fisheries Research Board of Canada* 29, 8: 135.

Beanlands, G.E., and P.N. Duinker. 1983. *An Ecological Framework for Environmental Impact Assessment in Canada*. Halifax: Institute for Resource and Environmental Studies, Dalhousie University.

Beardmore, T., K. Forbes, D. Simpson, M. Williams, and B. Arsenault. 2012. *The State of Canada's Forest Genetic Resources*. www.conforgen.ca/stateoftheworldsFGR.html.

Beaudoin, A., et al. 2014. "Mapping attributes of Canada's forests at moderate resolution through kNN and MODIS imagery." *Canadian Journal of Forest Research*. doi : 10.1139/cjfr-2013-0401

Bennett, N., and P. Dearden. 2013. "Why local people do not support conservation: Community perceptions of marine protected area livelihood impacts, governance and management in Thailand." *Marine Policy* 44: 107–116.

Bennett, N.J., P. Dearden, G. Murray, and A. Kadfak. 2015. "The capacity to adapt?: Coastal communities in a changing climate, environment, and economy on the Andaman Coast of Thailand." *Ecology and Society* 19. http://www.ecologyandsociety.org/vol19/iss2/art5/.

Bentley, C.F., and L.A. Leskiw. 1985 *Sustainability of Farmed Lands: Current Trends and Thinking*. Ottawa: Canadian Environmental Advisory Council, Environment Canada.

Benton, T., A. Dougill, E.D.G. Fraser, and D. Howlett. 2011. "The scale for managing production vs the scale required for ecosystem service production." *World Agriculture* 2: 14–21.

Berch, S.M., D. Morris, and J. Malcolm. 2011. "Intensive biomass harvesting and biodiversity in Canada: A summary of relevant issues." *Forestry Chronicle* 87: 479–87.

Berger, T.R. 1977. *Northern Frontier, Northern Homeland: The Report of the Mackenzie Valley Pipeline Inquiry*, 2 vols. Ottawa: Minister of Supply and Services.

Bergeron, Y., et al. 2001. "Natural fire frequency for the eastern Canadian boreal forest: Consequences for sustainable forestry." *Canadian Journal of Forest Research* 31: 384–91.

Berkes, F. 1988. "The intrinsic difficulty of predicting impacts: Lessons from the James Bay hydro project." *Environmental Impact Assessment Review* 8: 201–20.

——, D. Armitage, and N. Doubleday. 2007. "Synthesis: Adapting, innovating, evolving." In Armitage et al. (2007: 308–27).

BHP Billiton. 2001. *Environmental Agreement Annual Report 2001*. www.corporateregister.com/a10723/ekati01-env-ca.pdf.

Birkedal, T. 1993. "Ancient hunters in the Alaskan wilderness: Human predators and their role and effect on wildlife populations and the implications for resource management." In W.E. Brown and S.D. Veirs Jr, eds, *Partners in Stewardship: Proceedings of the 7th Conference on Research and Resource Management in Parks and on Public Lands*, 228–34. Hancock, MI: The George Wright Society.

Biswas, A.K. 2004. "Integrated water resource management: A re-assessment." *Water International* 29: 248–56.

——. 2008. "Integrated water resources management: Is it working?" *Water Resources Development* 24: 5–22.

Bizikova, L., D. Roy, D. Swanson, H.D. Venema, and M. McCandless. 2013. *The Water-Energy-Food-Security Nexus: Towards a Practical Planning and Decision-Support Framework for Landscape Investment and Risk Management*. Winnipeg: International Institute for Sustainable Development.

Blatchford, C. 2010. *Helpless: Caledonia's Nightmare of Fear and Anarchy, and How the Law Failed All of Us*. Toronto: Doubleday Canada.

——. 2014. "Caledonia natives still calling the shots in land dispute." *Financial Post*, May 20. Accessed 16 Jul. 2014. http://fullcomment.nationalpost.com/2014/05/20/christie-blatchford.

Bone, R.M. 2005. *The Regional Geography of Canada*, 3rd edn. Toronto: Oxford University Press.

Boyce, M.S., S.R. Lele, and B.W. Johns. 2005. "Whooping crane recruitment enhanced by egg removal." *Biological Conservation* 126: 395–401.

Boychuk, R. 2008. "Seeing the light." *Canadian Geographic*. www.canadiangeographic.ca/Magazine/jun08/ednotebook.asp.

Boyd, D.R., and S.J. Genuis. 2008. "The environmental burden of disease in Canada: Respiratory disease, cardiovascular disease, cancer, and congenital affliction." *Environmental Research* 106: 240–9

Boyer, M. 2008. *Freshwater Exports for the Development of Quebec's Blue Gold*. Montreal: Montreal Economic Institute.

Branch, T.A. 2008. "Not all fisheries will be collapsed in 2048." *Marine Policy* 32, 1: 38–9.

Brandes, O.M., and D.B. Brooks. 2006. *The Soft Path for Water in a Nutshell*. Ottawa: Friends of the Earth; Victoria: University of Victoria, POLIS Project.

Brandes, O.M., R. Maas, and E. Reynolds. 2006. *Thinking beyond Pipes and Pumps: Top 10 Ways Communities Can Save Water and Money*. Victoria: University of Victoria, POLIS Project.

Bregha, F., et al. 1990. *The Integration of Environmental Considerations into Government Policy*. Prepared for the Canadian Environmental Assessment Research Council. Ottawa: Minister of Supply and Services.

Briggs, D., et al. 1993. *Fundamentals of Physical Geography*, 2nd Canadian edn. Toronto: Copp Clark Pitman.

British Columbia. 2008. "Budget Speech: Turning to the Future, Meeting the Challenge." 19 Feb. Victoria: Ministry of Finance.

——. 2012. "British Columbia outlines requirements for heavy oil pipeline consideration." Victoria: Ministry of Environment. July 23. Accessed 14 Apr. 2013. http://www2news.gov.bc.ca/news_releases_2009-2013/2012ENV0047-001074.html.

British Columbia Ministry of Environment. 2006. *BC Seafood Industry Year in Review*. www.env.gov.bc.ca/omfd/reports/YIR-2006.pdf.

British Columbia Ministry of Finance. 2011a. "How the carbon tax works." www.fin.gov.bc.ca/tbs/tp/climate/A4.html.

———. 2011b. "Myths and facts about the carbon tax." www.fin.gov.bc.ca/tbs/tp/climate/A6.htm.

Brook, B.W., and D.M.J.S. Bowman. 2004. "The uncertain blitzkrieg of Pleistocene megafauna." *Journal of Biogeography* 31: 517–23.

Brook, R.K, M. Cattet, C.T. Darimont, P.C. Paquet, and G. Proulx. 2015. "Maintaining ethical standards during conservation crises." *Canadian Wildlife Biology and Management* 4: 72–78.

Brooks, D.B. 2005. "Beyond greater efficiency: The concept of water soft paths." *Canadian Water Resources Journal* 30: 83–92.

———, O.M. Brandes, and S. Gurman. 2009. *Making the Most of the Water We Have: The Soft Path Approach to Water Management*. London: Earthscan.

——— and S. Holtz. 2009. "Water soft path analysis: From principles to practice." *Water International* 34: 158–69.

Brown, S., H. Schreier, and L.M. Lavkulich. 2009. "Incorporating virtual water into water management: A British Columbia example." *Water Resources Management* 23: 2681–92.

Brown, V.A., J.A. Harris, and J.Y. Russell, eds. 2010. *Tackling Wicked Problems: Through the Transdisciplinary Imagination*. London: Earthscan.

Browne, C.L., and S.J. Hecnar. 2003. "Dwindling turtle populations." *National Park International Bulletin* no. 9 (May).

——— and ———. 2007. "Species loss and shifting population structure in freshwater turtles despite habitat protection." *Biological Conservation* 138: 421–9.

Bruno, J.F., and E.R. Selig. 2007. "Regional decline of coral cover in the Indo-Pacific: Timing, extent, and subregional comparisons." *PLoS ONE* 2, 8: e711. doi:10.1371/ journal.pone.0000711

Bryant, Ben. 2011. "Deepwater Horizon and the Gulf oil spill—The key questions answered." theguardian.com, 20 Apr. www.guardian.co.uk/environment/2011/apr/20/deepwater-horizon-key-questions-answered.

Bryant, R. 2007. "International chronology of environmental justice." www-personal.umich.edu/~bbryant/iejtimeline.html.

Bubb, P.J., et al. 2009. *The IUCN Red List Index: Guidance for National and Regional Use*. Gland, Switzerland: IUCN.

Bullock, R., and K. Hanna. 2008. "Community forestry in British Columbia: Mitigating or creating conflict?" *Society and Natural Resources* 2: 77–85.

Bullock, R., and A. Watelet. 2006. "Exploring conservation authority operations in Sudbury, Northern Ontario: Constraints and opportunities." *Environments* 34, 2: 29–50.

Burck, J., F. Marten, and C. Bals. 2014. *The Climate Change Performance Index*. Berlin: Germanwatch and Brussels: Climate Action Network Europe. https://germanwatch.or/en/dowload/8599.pdf.

Burt, B. 2007a. "Land claim stalls wind project." *The Record*, 12 Aug., B1–B2.

———. 2007b. "Wind farm claim riles Tory." *The Record*, 16 Aug., A1–A2.

Butchart, S.H.M., et al. 2010. "Global biodiversity: Indicators of recent declines." *Science* 328: 1164–8.

Butterworth, J., J. Warner, P. Moriarty, S. Smits, and C. Batchelor. 2010. "Finding practical approaches to integrated water resources management." *Water Alternatives* 3: 68–81.

Calvert, A.M., et al. 2013. "A synthesis of human-related avian mortality in Canada. *Avian Conservation and Ecology* 82: 11. doi: dx.doi.org/10.5751/ACE-00581-080211

Cameron, R.P. 2006. "Protected area–working forest interface: Ecological concerns for protected area management in Canada." *Natural Areas Journal* 26: 403–7.

Cameron, S.D. 1990. "Net losses: The sorry state of our Atlantic fishery." *Canadian Geographic* 110, 2: 28–37.

Canada. 1995. *Canadian Biodiversity Strategy: Canada's Response to the Convention on Biological Diversity*. Ottawa: Minister of Supply and Services.

———. 2004. Species at Risk Act. www.sararegistry.gc.ca/background/process_e.cfm.

Canada and Ontario. 1988. *First Report of Canada under the 1987 Protocol to the 1978 Great Lakes Water Quality Agreement*. Toronto: Environment Canada, Communications Directorate.

Canada Mortgage and Housing Corporation. 2005. *Smart Growth in Canada: A Report Card*. Research Highlight Socio-economic Series 05-036. Ottawa: Canada Mortgage and Housing Corporation.

Canada–Newfoundland and Labrador Offshore Petroleum Board, Terra Nova Development Project Environmental Assessment Panel. 1997. *Terra Nova Development: An Offshore Petroleum Project*. Ottawa: Minister of Public Works and Government Services.

Canadian Academy of Engineering. 2007. *Energy Pathways Task Force Phase 1: Final Report*. Ottawa: Canadian Academy of Engineering.

Canadian Biodiversity Strategy. 2010. "Ecosystem status and trends." www.biodivcanada.ca/default.asp?lang=En&n=560ED58E-1& offset=3&toc=show.

Canadian Boreal Forest Agreement. 2010. http://cbfa-efbc.ca/wp-content/uploads/2014/12/CBFAAgreement_Full_NewLook.pdf.

Canadian Council of Forest Ministers (CCFM). 2006. *Facing the Challenge of Forest Industry Restructuring*. Ottawa.

———. 2007. "Compendium of Canadian Forestry Statistics." www.nfdp.ccfm.org.

———. 2008. *A Vision for Canada's Forests: 2008 and Beyond*. Ottawa: Canadian Council of Forest Ministers. www.ccmf.org/pdf/Vision_EN.pdf.

———. 2014. "National Forestry Database: Silvicultural Statistics by Province/Territory." http://nfdp.ccfm.org/data/compendium/html/comp_61e.html.

Canadian Council of Ministers of the Environment. 2003. *Climate, Nature, People: Indicators of Canada's Changing Climate*. Winnipeg: Canadian Council of Ministers of the Environment.

———. 2005. *Five-Year Review of the Canada-Wide Acid Rain Strategy for Post-2000*. www.ccme.ca/assets/pdf/5_year_review_acid_rain_strategy_e1.0_web.pdf.

———. 2006. *2004–2005 Progress Report on the Canada-Wide Acid Rain Strategy for Post-2000*. www.ccme.ca/assets/pdf/2004_2005_ar_progrrpt_1.0_e_web.pdf.

———. 2008. *2006–2007 Progress Report on the Canada-Wide Acid Rain Strategy*. Ottawa: Canadian Council of Ministers of Environment.

Canadian Council on Ecological Areas. 2014. "Conservation Areas Reporting and Tracking System (CARTS)." http://www.ccea.org/tools-resources/carts/carts-reports/.

Canadian Cryospheric Information Network. 2014. *Canadian Cryospheric Watch*. Accessed 29 Dec. https://www.ccin.ca/home/ccw.

Canadian Environmental Assessment Agency. 1996. *NWT Diamonds Project: Report of the Environmental Assessment Panel*. Cat. En105-53/1996E.

———. 2003. "Federal environmental assessment making a difference: Sable Island offshore gas project." http://www.ceaa.gc.ca/default.asp?lang=En&n=B79A2A7A1&offset=3&toc=show.

Canadian Food Inspection Agency (CFIA). 2004. *Action Plan for Invasive Alien Terrestrial Plants and Plant Pests*. Ottawa: Canadian Food Inspection Agency.

———. 2010. "Imported food sector regulatory proposal." www.inspection.gc.ca/english/fssa/imp/lic/queste.shtml.

Canadian General Standards Board. 2003. *Draft National Standard: Organic Agriculture*. Ottawa: Canadian General Standards Board, Committee on Organic Agriculture.

Canadian Heritage Rivers Board. 2002. *The Canadian Heritage Rivers System: Annual Report 2001–2002*. Ottawa: Minister of Public Works and Government Services.

———. 2010. *Canadian Heritage Rivers System, Annual Report 2009–2010*. Ottawa: Minister of Public Works and Government Services Canada, Apr.

Canadian Heritage Rivers System. 2014. *The Canadian Heritage Rivers System Charter.* Accessed 12 Dec. 2014. http://www.chrs.ca/en/main.php#toe8.

Canadian Infrastructure Report Card. 2012. *Canadian Infrastructure Report Card. Volume 1: 2012 Municipal Roads and Water Systems.* Ottawa: Canadian Construction Association, Canadian Public Works Association, Canadian Society for Civil Engineering, Federation of Canadian Municipalities.

Canadian Institute of Forestry. 2003. "Silviculture systems." web.archive.org/web/20030428183657/http://cif-ifc.org/practices/silviculture.htm.

Canadian Parks and Wilderness Society (CPAWS). 2003. "Boreal forests: For the birds." Boreal Forest Factsheet Series. www.borealbirds.org/resources/factsheet-bsioverview.pdf.

Canadian Press. 2007. "No end in sight to stand-off." *The Record*, 27 Feb., C11.

———. 2008. "Walkerton victims waiting for help." *The Record*, 10 Mar., A1, A3.

Canadian Wildlife Service. "Contaminants levels in double-crested cormorant eggs, 1970–2000." www.ecoinfo.org/env_ind/region/cormorant/pcbs_e.cfm.

Canadian Wind Energy Association. 2008. "Wind energy sets global growth record in 2007." www.canwea.ca/news_releases.cfm?ID=58.

———. 2014. "Installed capacity." Accessed 17 Nov. 2014. http://canwea.ca/wind-energy/installed-capacity/.

Carbon Tracker. 2014. *Unburnable Carbon 2013: Wasted Capital and Stranded Assets.* London: Grantham Research Institute.

Carlson, M., et al. 2010. "Maintaining the role of Canada's forests and peatlands in climate regulation." *Forestry Chronicle* 86, 4: 1–10.

Carpenter, R.A. 1995. "Communicating environmental science uncertainties." *Environmental Professional* 17: 127–36.

Carson, R. 1962. *Silent Spring.* Boston: Houghton Mifflin.

Casselman, A. 2011. "The source of life: Canada's watershed protection action guide." *Canadian Geographic* (Jun.): 69–76.

Casti, J. 2012. *X-Events: The Collapse of Everything.* New York: William Morrow.

CBC News. 2011. "Labrador Innu vote on contentious land claim deal." 30 Jun. www.cbc.ca/news/canada/newfoundland-labrador/story/2011/06/30/nl-innu-labrador-claims-churchill-vote-630.html.

Census of Marine Life. 2010. www.coml.org/coml.htm.

Certification Canada. 2014. http://certificationcanada.org/en/statistics/canadian-statistics/

Chalecki, E.L. 2000. "Same planet, different worlds: The climate change information gap." In D.N. Scott et al., *Climate Change Communication: Proceedings of an International Conference.* Waterloo, Ont.: University of Waterloo and Environment Canada, Adaptation and Impacts Research Group, A2, 15–22.

Challinor, A.J., et al. 2014. "A meta-analysis of crop yield under climate change and adaptation." *Nature Climate Change* 4: 287–291.

Chambers, P., et al. 2001. "Agricultural and forestry land use impacts." In Environment Canada, *Threats to Sources of Drinking Water and Aquatic Ecosystem Health in Canada.* Ottawa: Environment Canada, 57–62.

Chapman, J.D. 1989. *Geography and Energy: Commercial Energy Systems and National Policies.* Harlow, UK: Longman Scientific and Technical.

Chestnut, L.G., and D.M. Mills. 2005. "A fresh look at the benefits and costs of the US acid rain program." *Journal of Environmental Management* 77: 252–66.

Cheung, W.W.L., D. Zeller, and D. Pauly. 2011. *Projected species shifts due to climate change in the Canadian marine ecoregions; A report prepared for Environment Canada.* Accessed 22 Jan 2015. www.seaaroundus.org/researcher/dpauly/PDF/2011/Books_Reports_OrChaptersTherein/ProjectedSpeciesShiftduetoClimateChange.pdf.

Cheung, W.W.L., et al. 2010. "Large-scale redistribution of maximum fisheries catch potential in the global ocean under climate change." *Global Change Biology* 16: 24–35.

Chevalier, G., et al. 1997. "Mercury in northern Québec: Role of the Mercury Agreement and the status of research and monitoring." *Water, Air and Soil Pollution* 97: 75–84.

Chomitz, K.M., et al. 2007. *At Loggerheads? Agricultural Expansion, Poverty Reduction, and Environment in the Tropical Forests.* Jakarta, Indonesia: World Bank.

Churchman, C.W. 1967. "Guest editorial: Wicked problems." *Management Science* 14, 4: B141–B142.

City of Calgary. 2006. *imagineCalgary Plan for Long Range Urban Sustainability 2007.* Sept.

———. 2013. "2020 Sustainability Direction: The City of Calgary's 10-Year Plan Towards imagineCalgary."

City of Greater Sudbury. 2013. *Regreening Program, Annual Report 2013.*

City of Toronto. 2014. "Using salt wisely." Accessed 7 Oct. 2014. http://www1.toronto.ca/wps/portal/contentonly?vgnextoid=9297a84c9f6e1410VgnVCM10000071d60f89RCRD&vgnextchannel=cd3d4074781e1410VgnVCM10000071d60f89RCRD.

Clancy, P. 2014. *Freshwater Politics in Canada.* Toronto: University of Toronto Press.

Clark, W.F., et al. 2010. "Long-term risk for hypertension, renal impairment, and cardiovascular disease after gastroenteritis from drinking water contaminated with *Escherichia coli* 0157:H7: A prospective cohort study." *British Medical Journal* 341. www.bmj.com/content/341/bmj.c6020.

Clarke, A., and C.M. Harris. 2003. "Polar marine ecosystems: Major threats and future change." *Environmental Conservation* 30: 1–25.

Clean Air Sudbury. 2005. *Clearing the Air: Air Quality Trends in Sudbury.* Sudbury, Ont.

Climate Action Network Canada. 2013. "Canada wins 'Lifetime Unachievement' Fossil award at Warsaw climate talks." Accessed 3 Jan. 2015. http://climateactionnetwork.ca/2013/11/22/canada-wins-lifetime-unachievement-fossil-award-at-warsaw-climate-talks/.

Cline, W.R. 2007. *Global Warming and Agriculture: Impact Estimates by Country.* Washington: Center for Global Development.

Cohen, R., B. Nelson, and G. Wolff. 2004. *Energy Down the Drain: The Hidden Costs of California's Water Supply.* New York: Natural Resources Defense Council; Oakland: Pacific Institute.

Collinge, S. 2010. "Spatial ecology and conservation." *Nature Education Knowledge* 1, 8: 69.

Collins, C. and R. Kays. 2011. "Causes of mortality in North American populations of large and medium-sized mammals." *Animal Conservation* 14: 474–483.

Commissioner of the Environment and Sustainable Development. 1997. *Report of the Commissioner of the Environment and Sustainable Development to the House of Commons.* Ottawa: Office of the Auditor General.

———. 2003. "Managing the safety and accessibility of pesticides." *Report of the Commissioner of the Environment and Sustainable Development.* Ottawa: Office of the Auditor General of Canada.

———. 2008. "Selected aspects of managing the safety and accessibility of pesticides." *Status Report of the Commissioner of the Environment and Sustainable Development.* Ottawa: Office of the Auditor General of Canada.

———. 2009. *Spring Report of the Commissioner of the Environment and Sustainable Development to the House of Commons.* Ottawa: Office of the Auditor General of Canada.

———. 2010. *2010 Fall Report of the Commissioner of the Environment and Sustainable Development.* Ottawa: Office of the Auditor General, 7 Dec. www.oag-bvg.ca/internet/English/parl_cesd_201012_00_e_34423.html.

———. 2011. *2011 Report of the Commissioner of the Environment and Sustainable Development.* Ottawa: Office of the Auditor General, 4 Oct.

Commission for Environmental Cooperation. 2008. *Green Building in North America: Opportunities and Challenges.* Montreal: Commission for Environmental Cooperation.

———. 2011. *North American Environmental Outlook to 2030.* Montreal: CEC.

Committee on the Status of Endangered Wildlife in Canada (COSEWIC). 2003. "Canadian species at risk." www.cosewic.gc.ca.

——. 2007. "Canadian species at risk." www.cosewic.gc.ca.

——. 2011. "Canadian species at risk." www.cosewic.gc.ca/rpts/Full_List_Species.html.

Conference Board of Canada. 2007. *Mission Possible*, vol. 2. Ottawa: Conference Board of Canada.

——. 2014a. *How Canada Performs: Environment*. Accessed 28 Dec. 2014. http://www.conferenceboard.ca/hcp/details/environment.aspx.

——. 2014b. *Water Quality Index*. Accessed 8 Dec. 2014. http://www.conferenceboard.ca/hcp/details/environment/water-quality-index.aspx.

Conservation Authorities of Ontario. 1993. *Restructuring Resource Management in Ontario: A Blueprint for Success*. Mississauga, Ont.: Credit Valley Conservation Authority.

Convention on Biological Diversity. n.d. "Aichi Biodiversity Targets." http://www.cbd.int/sp/targets/.

Copenhagen. 2007. *Eco-Metropole: Our Vision for Copenhagen 2015*. Municipality of Copenhagen: Technical and Environmental Centre.

Cornia, G.A. 1985. "Farm size, land yields and the agricultural production function: An analysis for fifteen developing countries." *World Development* 13, 4: 513–34.

COSEWIC. 2014. "Summary of COSEWIC assessment results as of November 2014." www.cosewic.gc.ca/rpts/Full_List_Species.html.

Costanza, R., et al. 1997. "The value of the world's ecosystem services and natural capital." *Nature* 387: 253–60.

Couch, W.J. 2002. "Strategic resolution of policy, environmental and socio-economic impacts in Canadian Arctic diamond mining: BHP's NWT diamond project." *Impact Assessment and Project Appraisal* 20: 265–78.

Cressman, D.R. 1994. "Remedial action programs for soil and water degradation problems in Canada." In T.L. Napier, S.M. Camboni, and S.A. El-Swaify, eds, *Adopting Conservation on the Farm*. Ankeny, Iowa: Soil and Water Conservation Society, 413–34.

Crutzen, P., et al. 2007. "N_2O release from agro-biofuel production negates global warming reduction by replacing fossil fuels." *Atmospheric Chemistry and Physics Discussions* 7: 11191–205.

Cryderman, K. 2014. "What's next: Major hurdles face Enbridge before digging begins." *The Globe and Mail*, Jun. 18, A8.

Csatho, B.M., et al. 2014. "Laser altimetry reveals complex patterns of Greenland ice dynamics." *Proceedings of the National Academy of Sciences* 111, 52: 18478–18483.

Curran, T. 1991. "Forests and global warming." Ottawa: Government of Canada/Science and Technology Division. http://publications.gc.ca/Collection-R/LoPBdP/BP/bp254-e.htm.

Cusack, D.F., et al. 2014. "An interdisciplinary assessment of climate engineering strategies." *Frontiers in Ecology and the Environment* 12, 5: 280–87.

Dale, A., and L. Newman. 2007. "Governance for integrated resource management." In K.S. Hanna and D.S. Slocombe, eds, *Integrated Resource and Environmental Management: Concepts and Practice*. Toronto: Oxford University Press, 56–71.

Darimont, C.T., et al. 2009. "Human predators outpace other agents of trait change in the wild." *Proceedings of the National Academy of Sciences* 106: 952–954.

Darimont C.T., et al. In press. "Trophic hegemony by human predators." *Science*.

Darwin, C. 1859. *On the Origin of Species*. London: John Murray.

——. 2001. *Charles Darwin's Beagle Diary*. London: Cambridge University Press.

David Suzuki Foundation. 2007. "What is carbon offset?" www.davidsuzuki.org/Climate_Change/What_You_Can_Do/carbon_offsets.asp.

——. 2014. *Carbon Tax or Cap-and-Trade?* Accessed 4 Jan. 2015. http://www.davidsuzuki.org/issues/climate-change/science/climate-solutions/carbon-tax-or-cap-and-trade/.

Davis, A., and J. Wagner. 2006. "A right to fish for a living? The case for coastal peoples' determination of access and participation." *Ocean and Coastal Management* 49: 476–97.

Dawe, J.L., and B. Neis. 2012. "Species at risk in Canada: Lessons learned from the listing of three species of wolffish." *Marine Policy* 36: 405–413.

Dawson, D. 2002. "Plant-covered roofs ease urban heat." *National Geographic News*, 15 Nov. news.nationalgeographic.com/news/2002/11/1115_021115_GreenRoofs.html.

Day, J.C., and F. Quinn. 1992. *Water Diversion and Export: Learning from Canadian Experience*. Department of Geography Publication Series no. 36. Waterloo, Ont.: University of Waterloo.

Dearden, P. 1995. "Park literacy and conservation." *Conservation Biology* 9: 1654–6.

——. 2001. "Endangered species and terrestrial national parks." In K. Beazley and R. Boardman, eds, *Politics of the Wild: Canada and Endangered Species*. Toronto: Oxford University Press Canada, 75–93.

——and N.J. Bennett. 2015a. "Parks and protected areas." In B. Mitchell, ed., *Resource and Environmental Management in Canada*, 5th edn. Toronto: Oxford University Press, 318–44.

——and N.J. Bennett. 2015b. "Aboriginal people and national parks." In P. Dearden, R . Rollins, and M. Needham, eds, *Parks and Protected Areas in Canada: Planning and Management*, 4th edn. Toronto: Oxford University Press.

——and R.C. Canessa. 2015. "Marine protected areas." In P. Dearden, R . Rollins, and M. Needham, eds, *Parks and Protected Areas in Canada: Planning and Management*, 4th edn. Toronto: Oxford University Press.

——, R. Rollins, and M. Needham, eds. 2015. *Parks and Protected Areas in Canada: Planning and Management*, 4th edn. Toronto: Oxford University Press Canada.

——, M. Theberge, and M. Yasué. 2010. "Using underwater cameras to assess the effects of snorkeler or SCUBA diver presence on coral reef fish abundance, family richness and species composition." *Environmental Monitoring and Assessment* 163: 531–538.

Debreuil, C. 2006. *The Right to Water: From Concept to Implementation*. Marseilles, World Water Council.

de Groot, W.J., et al. 2013a. "A comparison of Canadian and Russian boreal forest fire regimes." *Forest Ecology and Management* 294: 23–34.

——. 2013b. "Climate change impacts on future boreal fire regimes." *Forest Ecology and Management* 294: 35–44.

de Loë, R.C., S. Di Giantomasso, and R.D. Kreutzwiser. 2002. "Local capacity for groundwater protection in Ontario." *Environmental Management* 29, 2: 217–33.

Dempsey, J., and P. Dearden. 2015. "Stewardship: Expanding ecosystem protection." In P. Dearden, R. Rollins, and M. Needham, eds, *Parks and Protected Areas in Canada: Planning and Management*, 4th edn. Toronto: Oxford University Press.

Department of Fisheries and Oceans Canada (DFO). 2008. "Canadian fisheries statistics 2005." www.dfo-mpo.gc.ca/stats/commercial/cfs/2005/cfs05-eng.htm.

——. 2010. *Canadian Marine Ecosystem Status and Trends Report*. Ottawa: Her Majesty the Queen in Right of Canada.

Department of National Parks, Wildlife and Plant Conservation (DNP). 2010. *Thailand Tiger Action Plan: 2010–2022*. Bangkok: DNP.

——. 2013. *Smart Patrol for Smart Protection*. http://www.wcsthailand.org/publication/SMART_Patrol_opt.pdf.

Desjardins, R.L., et al. 2008. "Moving Canadian agricultural landscapes from GHG source to sink." In H. Hengeveld et al., *Enhancement of Greenhouse Gas Sinks: A Canadian Science Assessment*. Ottawa: Ministry of Environment, 19–37.

de Villiers, M. 1999. *Water Wars: Is the World Running Out of Water?* London: Weidenfeld and Nicolson.

Diamond, B. 1990. "Villages of the dammed." *Arctic Circle* (Nov.–Dec.): 24–34.

Diamond, J. 2005. *Collapse: How Societies Choose to Fail or Succeed*. New York: Viking.

Diduck, A. 2010. "Incorporating participatory approaches and social learning." In Mitchell (2010: 495–525).

——and B. Mitchell. 2003. "Learning, public involvement and environmental assessment: A Canadian case study." *Journal of Environmental Assessment Policy and Management* 5: 339–64.

Dillon Consulting Ltd. 2000. *Wind Turbine Environmental Assessment: Draft Screening Document*. Toronto: Dillon Consulting Ltd.

——. 2011. *Shaping Our Future: City of Moncton Sustainability Plan (An Integrated Community Action Plan)*. Apr. City of Moncton.

Di Prisco, G., et al. 2013. "Neonicotinoid clothianidin adversely affects insect immunity and promotes replication of a viral pathogen in honey bees." *Proceedings of the National Academy of Sciences*. doi:10.1073/pnas.1314923110

Dirzo, R., et al. 2012. "Defaunation in the Anthropocene." *Science* 345: 401–406.

Ditchburn, J. 2014. "Gateway pipeline not a done deal." *The Record*, Jun. 19, A6.

Doelle, M. 2009. "The role of Strategic Environmental Assessments (SEA) in energy governance: A case study of tidal energy in Nova Scotia's Bay of Fundy." *Journal of Energy and Natural Resources Law* 27: 191–225.

Doubleday, W.G. 2000. "Seals & cod." *Isuma* 1, 1. web.archive.org/web/20070422225604/http://www.isuma.net/v01n01/doubleda/doubleda_e.shtml.

Dougill, A., E.D.G. Fraser, and M.S. Reed. 2011. "Anticipating vulnerability to climate change in dryland pastoral systems: Using dynamic systems models for the Kalahari." *Ecology and Society* 15, 2: 17.

Dove, A., and S.C. Chapra. 2015. "Long-term trends of nutrients and trophic response variables for the Great Lakes." *Limnology and Oceanography* 60: 696–721.

Downes, C., P. Blancher, and B. Collins. 2010. *Landbird Trends in Canada, 1968–2006*. Ottawa: Environment Canada.

Dubreuil, C. 2006. *The Right to Water: From Concept to Implementation*. Marseille: World Water Council.

Dudley, N., ed. 2008. *Guidelines for Applying Protected Area Management Categories*. Gland, Switzerland: IUCN.

——, et al. 2010. "The revised IUCN protected area management categories: The debate and ways forward." *Oryx* 44: 485–90.

Duinker, P. 2011. "Advancing the cause? Contributions of criteria and indicators to sustainable forest management in Canada." *Forestry Chronicle* 87, 4: 488–93.

——et al. 1991. "Community forestry and its implications for northern Ontario." *Forestry Chronicle* 67: 131–5.

——et al. 1994. "Community forests in Canada: An overview." *Forestry Chronicle* 70: 711–20.

Dumont, C., et al. 1998. "Mercury levels in the Cree population of James Bay, Quebec, from 1988 to 1993/94." *Canadian Medical Association Journal* 158: 1439–45.

Dunbar, D., and I. Blackburn. 1994. *Management Options for the Northern Spotted Owl in British Columbia*. Victoria: Ministry of Environment.

Durner, G., J. Whiteman, H. Harlow, S. Amstrup, E. Regehr, and M. Ben-David. 2011. "Consequences of long-distance swimming and travel over deep-water pack ice for a female polar bear during a year of extreme sea ice retreat." *Polar Bear* (US government) 34: 975–84.

Dusic, J. 2010. *Recommendation for General Technical Guidance on SEA in Indonesia*. Unpublished paper, presented for the Ministry of Environment, Jakarta.

Dwivedi, O.P., and R. Khator. 2006. "Sustaining development: The road from Stockholm to Johannesburg." In G.M. Mudacumura, D. Mebratu, and M.S. Haque, eds, *Sustainable Development Policy and Administration*. Boca Raton, Fla: Taylor and Francis, 114–33.

Dyer, G. 2007. "Arctic scramble is about seabed resources." *The Record*, 14 Aug., A9.

——. 2009. "A missed opportunity." *The Record*, 22 Dec., A11.

Earth Policy Institute. 2007. *Earthtrends*. www.earth-policy.org/Updates/2006/Update55_data.htm.

Easterling, W.E., et al. 2007. "Food, fibre and forest." In Intergovernmental Panel on Climate Change, *Climate Change 2007: Impacts, Adaptations and Vulnerability*. Cambridge, UK: IPCC.

Eaton, E. 2013. *Growing Resistance: Canadian Farmers and the Politics of Genetically Modified Wheat*. Winnipeg: University of Manitoba Press.

Ebeling, J. 2006. *Tropical Deforestation and Climate Change: Towards an International Mitigation Strategy*. Oxford: Oxford University Press.

Edgar, G.J., et al. 2014. "Global conservation outcomes depend on marine protected areas with five key features." *Nature* 506: 216–220.

Edwards, P., and I. Roberts. 2008. "Transport policy is food policy." *The Lancet* 371: 1661.

ÉEM Inc. 2007. "Environmental paper procurement: A review of forest certification schemes in Canada." marketsinitiative.org/uploads/MI-EEMcert-2.pdf.

Eggertson, L. 2008. "Despite federal promises, First Nations' water problems persist." *Canadian Medical Association Journal* 178: 985.

Ehrlich, P., and A. Ehrlich. 1996. *Betrayal of Science and Reason: How Anti-Environmental Rhetoric Threatens Our Future*. Washington: Island Press.

El Ayoubi, F., and J. McNiven. 2006. "Political, environmental and business aspects of bulk water exports: A Canadian perspective." *Canadian Journal of Administrative Sciences* 23: 1–16.

Elgie, S., and J.A. McClay. 2013. *BC's Carbon Tax Shift after Five Years: Results*. Ottawa: Sustainable Prosperity.

Elkington, J. 1994. "Towards the sustainable corporation: Win-win-win business strategies for sustainable development." *California Management Review* 36, 2: 90–100.

El Lakany, H., M. Jenkins, and M. Richards. 2007. "Background paper on means of implementation." Contribution by PROFOR to discussions at UNFF-7, Apr. Program on Forests (PROFOR).

El-Sadek, A. 2010. "Virtual water trade as a solution for water scarcity in Egypt." *Water Resources Management* 24: 2437–88.

Encyclopedia of Saskatchewan. 2007. Urban Heat Islands. http://www.esask.uregina.ca/entry/urban_heat_islands.html.

Energy.gov. 2014. *Energy Saver Guide: Tips on Saving Money and Energy at Home*, accessed 26 Sept. 2015. http://energy.gov/energysaver/energy-saver-guide-tips-saving-money-and-energy-home.

Energy Informative. 2014. "Where is solar power used the most?" Accessed 18 Nov. 2014. http://energyinformative.org/where-is-solar-power-used-the-most/

Englander, J.G., S. Bharadwaj, and A. Brandt. 2013. "Historical trends in greenhouse gas emissions of the Alberta oil sands (1970–2010)." *Environmental Research Letters* 8: 044036.

Environmental Assessment Panel. 1991. *Rafferty-Alameda Project: Report of the Environmental Assessment Panel*. Ottawa: Federal Environmental Assessment Review Office.

Environmental Commissioner of Ontario. 2003. *2002–2003 Annual Report*. Toronto: Environmental Commissioner of Ontario.

Environmental Protection Agency (EPA). 1997. "About environmental justice." epa.gov/swerops/ ej/aboutej/html.

Environment Canada. 1972. *Canada Land Inventory: Soil Capability Classification for Agriculture*, Report no. 2, Catalogue no. F063-2/1972. Ottawa: Environment Canada.

——. 1985. *Currents of Change: Final Report, Inquiry on Federal Water Policy*. Ottawa: Environment Canada.

——. 1991a. *Toxic Chemicals in the Great Lakes and Associated Effects*. Toronto: Department of Fisheries and Oceans; Ottawa: Health and Welfare Canada.

——. 1991b. *The State of Canada's Environment*. Ottawa. Minister of Supply and Services.

——. 2002a. *Population Status of Migratory Game Birds in Canada*. CWS Migratory Birds Regulatory Report no. 7. Ottawa: Canadian Wildlife Service Waterfowl Committee.

——. 2002b. "Trichloroethylene and tetrachloroethylene in solvent degreasing." www.ec.gc.ca/Publications/C835ECFFD5EA-40A3-9E09-2784A982E525/StrategicOptionsForTheManagementOf ToxicSubstancesTrichloroethyleneAnd TetrachloroethyleneInSolventDegreasing.pdf.

———. 2003a. "Atmospheric science: Acid rain." www.ec.gc.ca/air/default. asp?lang=En&n=7E5E9F00-1.

———. 2003b. "Environmental signals: Canada's National Environmental Indicator Series 2003." Ottawa: Environment Canada. publications.gc.ca/collections/Collection/En40-775-2002E.pdf.

———. 2003c. "Natural disasters on the rise." *Science and Environment Bulletin* (Mar.–Apr.).

———. 2003d. "NPRI: Substance information, dioxins and furans." www.ec.gc.ca/pdb/ npri/npri_dioxins_ecfm.

———. 2004. "Canadian acid deposition science assessment." publications.gc.ca/collections/Collection/En4-46-2004E.pdf.

———. 2006a. *Canada–US Air Quality Agreement Progress Report 2006*. 40. www.ec.gc.ca/Publications/default.asp ?lang=En&xml=4B98B185-7523-4CFF-90F25688EBA89E4A.

———. 2006b. *Canadian Protected Areas Status Report 2000–2005*. Environment Canada, Cat. No.: En81-9/2005E.

———. 2006c. *National Inventory Report*. Ottawa: Environment Canada.

———. 2006d. *Impacts of Sea-Level Rise and Climate Change on the Coastal Zone of New Brunswick*. Ottawa: Minister of the Environment.

———. 2007a. *2006 Prairie Waterfowl Status Report*. Ottawa: Environment Canada.

———. 2007b. Canadian Environmental Sustainability Indicators. Ottawa: Environment Canada.

———. 2009a. "Water conservation—every drop counts." 26 Nov. www.ec.gc.ca/eau-water/default.asp?lang=Eng&n=3377BC74-1.

———2009b. Canadian Environmental Sustainability Indicators, 2008: Freshwater Quality Indicator, Data Sources and Methods. Ottawa: Environment Canada.

———. 2009c. Canada's 4th National Report to the UN Convention on Biological Diversity. Ottawa: Environment Canada.

———. 2010a. "Canada-U.S. Air Quality Agreement Progress Report 2010." 45. www.ec.gc.ca/Publications/default.asp ?lang=En&xml=4B98B185-7523-4CFF90F2-5688EBA89E4A.

———. 2010b. Canada Water Act: Annual Report for April 2008 to March 2009. Ottawa: Environment Canada.

———. 2010c. "Dams and diversions." 30 Jul. www.ec.gc.ca/eau-water/default. asp?lang-Eng&n=9D404A01-1.

———. 2010d. *Groundwater Contamination*. Accessed 4 Feb. 2015. http://www.ec.gc.ca/eau-water/default.asp?lang=En&n=6A7FB7B2-1.

———. 2011a. "Canada's protected areas." www.ec.gc.ca/indicateurs-indicators/default.asp?lang=en&n=478A1D3D-1.

———. 2011b. *2011 Municipal Water Report—Municipal Water Use 2009 Statistics*. Accessed 11 Dec. 2014. https://www.ec.gc.ca/Publications/default.asp?lang=En&xml=B77CE4D0-80D4-4FEB-AFFA-0201BE6FB37B.

———. 2012. *Water: Frequently Asked Questions*. Accessed 5 Dec. 2014. http://www.ec.gc.ca/eau-water/default.asp?lang=En+n+1C100657-1.

———. 2013a. "Greenhouse Gas Emissions Data." https://www.ec.gc.ca/indicateurs-indicators/default.asp?lang=en&n=BFB1B398-1.

———. 2013b. *National Inventory Report 1990–2011: Greenhouse Gas Sources and Sinks in Canada*, Part 3. Accessed 28 Oct. 2014. http://unfccc.int/national_reports/annex_i_ghg_inventories/national_inventories_submissions/items/7383.php.

———. 2014a. "International Comparison of Urban Air Quality." Accessed 2 Oct. 2014. www.ec.gc.ca/indicateurs-indicators/default.asp?lang=en+n=FDBB2779-1.

———. 2014b. *Federal Sustainable Development Strategy*. Accessed 8 Dec. 2014. http:/www/ec.gc.ca/dd-sd/default.asp?lang=Eng&n=CD30F295-1.

———. 2014c. *Freshwater Quality in Canadian Rivers*. Accessed 8 Dec. 2014. http://ec.gc.ca/indicateurs-indicators/default.asp?lang=en&n=1462CE5B-1#wq1.

———. 2015a. "International Comparison of Air Pollutant Emissions." http://www.ec.gc.ca/indicateurs-indicators/default.asp?lang=en&n=0B0E77F5-1.

———. 2015b. "Nitrogen Oxide Emissions." http://www.ec.gc.ca/indicateurs-indicators/default.asp?lang=en&n=0870FFFC-1.

———. 2015c. "Sulphur Oxide Emissions." http://www.ec.gc.ca/indicateurs-indicators/default.asp?lang=en&n=402A9845-1.

———and Alberta Environment. 2012. *Joint Canada-Alberta Implementation Plan for Oil Sands Monitoring*. Gatineau: Environment Canada.

———and Alberta Environmental Monitoring, Evaluation and Reporting Agency. 2014. *Joint Canada-Alberta Implementation Plan for Oil Sands Monitoring: The Implementation Plan, Second Annual Report: 2013–2014*. Gatineau: Environment Canada. http://jointoilsandsmonitoring.ca/default.asp?n=5F73C7C9-1&lang=en.

———, Statistics Canada, and Health Canada. 2006. *Canadian Environmental Sustainability Indicators*. Ottawa: Statistics Canada, Environment Accounts and Statistics Division.

———and US Environmental Protection Agency. 2003. *State of the Great Lakes, 2003*. Ottawa: Environment Canada; Washington: US Environmental Protection Agency.

———and ———. 2007. *State of the Great Lakes 2007*. Ottawa: Environment Canada.

Estes, J.A., D.O. Duggins, and G.B. Rathbun. 1989. "The ecology of extinctions in kelp forest communities." *Conservation Biology* 3: 252–64.

European Commission. 2013. *Copenhagen: European Green Capital, 2014*. Luxembourg: Publications Office of the European Union.

External Advisory Committee on Cities and Communities. 2006. *From Restless Communities to Resilient Places: Building a Stronger Future for All Canadians*. Ottawa: Infrastructure Canada.

Exxon Mobil. 2015. *The Outlook for Energy: A Vision to 2040*. Irving, Texas.

Fa, J.E., C.A. Peres, and J. Meeuwig. 2002. "Bushmeat exploitation in tropical forests: An intercontinental comparison." *Conservation Biology* 16: 232–237.

Fargione, J., J. Hill, D. Tilman, S. Polasky, and P. Hawthorne. 2008. "Land clearing and the biofuel carbon debt." *Science* 319: 1235–8.

Farrell, A.E., et al. 2006. "Ethanol can contribute to energy and environmental goals." *Science* 311: 506–8.

Favaro B., et al. 2014. "Trends in extinction risk for imperilled species in Canada." *PLoS ONE* 9: e113118. doi:10.1371/journal.pone.0113118

Federal Ministry of Lands, Housing and Urban Development, Department of Urban and Regional Development. 2014. *Slum Identification and Needs Assessment Studies of Selected Settlements in Nigeria—Aba, Kaduna and Oshogbo*. Final reports, Aug. Lagos: Polad Technologies.

Federal, Provincial, and Territorial Governments of Canada. 2010. *Canadian Biodiversity: Ecosystem Status and Trends 2010*. Ottawa: Canadian Council of Resource Ministers.

———. 2012. *Canadian Biodiversity: Ecosystem Status and Trends, 2010*. Ottawa: Canadian Councils of Resource Ministers.

Festa-Bianchet, M. 2003. "Exploitative wildlife management as a selective pressure for the life-history evolution of large mammals." In M. Festa-Bianchet and M. Apollonio, eds, *Animal Behavior and Wildlife Conservation*. Washington: Island Press, 191–207.

———, et al. 2011. "Conservation of caribou (*Rangifer tarandus*) in Canada: An uncertain future." *Canadian Journal of Zoology* 89: 419–34.

Field, J.G., G. Hempel, and C.P. Summerhayes. 2002. *Oceans 2020*. Washington: Island Press.

Findlay, C.S., et al. 2010. "Species listing under Canada's Species at Risk Act." *Conservation Biology* 23: 1609–17.

Fischer, G., et al. 2005. "Socio-economic and climate change impacts on agriculture: An integrated assessment." *Philosophical Transactions of the Royal Society B* 360: 2067–83.

Fisher, A.C, J.P. Volpe, and J.T. Fisher. 2014. "Occupancy dynamics of escaped farmed Atlantic salmon in Canadian Pacific coastal salmon streams: Implications for sustained invasions." *Biological Invasions*. doi: 10.1007/s10530-014-0653-x

Fisheries and Oceans Canada, *see* Department of Fisheries and Oceans (DFO).

Flanagan, K., and S. Rasheed. 2002. "Population viability analysis applied to woodland caribou in Jasper National Park." *Research Links* 10: 16–18.

Fleischhauer, M. 2008. "The role of spatial planning in strengthening urban resilience." In H.J. Pasman and L.A. Kirillov, eds, *Resilience of Cities to Terrorist and Other Threats*. Dordrecht, The Netherlands: Springer, 273–98.

Foley, J.A., et al. 2011. "Solutions for a cultivated planet." *Nature* 478: 337–42.

Food and Agriculture Organization (FAO). n.d. http://faostat3.fao.org.

——. 2001. "Conservation agriculture." *FAO Magazine Spotlight*. www.fao.org/ag/magazine.

——. 2003. "Water management: Towards 2030." www.fao.org/ag/magazine.

——. 2006. *The State of World Fisheries and Aquaculture*. Rome: FAO.

——. 2007a. *The State of the World's Animal Genetic Resources for Food and Agriculture*. Rome: FAO.

——. 2007b. *World Food Outlook*. Rome: FAO.

——. 2010. *Global Forest Resources Assessment 2010*. Rome: FAO. www.fao.org/forestry/ fra/fra2010/en/.

——. 2011a. "Global wheat production to increase in 2011." Press release, 23 Mar. www.fao.org/news/story/en/item/53813/icode/.

——. 2011b. *FAO Cereal Supply and Demand Brief.* World Food Situation. Rome: FAO. www.fao.org/worldfoodsituation/en/.

——. 2013. *Implementing the Non-legally Binding Instrument on All Types of Forests*. Rome: Food and Agriculture Organization of the United Nations.

——. 2014a. *State of the World's Forests, 2014*. Rome: Food and Agriculture Organization of the United Nations.

——. 2014b. *The State of the World Fisheries and Aquaculture*. Rome: FAO.

——. 2015. *FAO Food Balance Sheets*. Accessed 1 Mar. 2015. http://faostat3.fao.org/browse/FB/*/E.

Forest Products Industry Competitiveness Task Force. 2007. *Industry at a Crossroads: Choosing the Path to Renewal*. Ottawa: Forest Products Association of Canada.

Foster, H.D. 1997. *The Ozymandias Principles: Thirty-one Strategies for Surviving Change*. Vancouver: University of British Columbia Press.

Foster, H.D., and W.R.D. Sewell. 1981. *Water: The Emerging Crisis in Canada*. Ottawa: Canadian Institute for Economic Policy.

Fox, T.A., T.E. Barchyn, and C.H. Hugenholtz. 2012. "Successes of soil conservation in the Canadian Prairies highlighted by a historical decline in blowing dust." *Environmental Research Letters* 7. doi:10.1088/1748-9326/7/1/014008

Fraser, E.D.G. 2007. "Travelling in antique lands: Using past famines to develop an adaptability/resilience framework to identify food systems vulnerable to climate change." *Climatic Change* 83: 495–514.

——. 2013. "Coping with food crises: Lessons from the American dust bowl on balancing local food, agro technology, social welfare, and government regulation agendas in food and farming systems." *Global Environmental Change* 23: 1662–1672.

Fraser Basin Council. n.d. Accessed 18 Aug. 2014. http://www.fraserbasin.bc.ca/about_charter.html.

——. 1997. *Charter for Sustainability*. Vancouver: Fraser River Basin Council.

Fraser Institute. 1999. *Environmental Indicators for Canada and the United States*. Vancouver: Fraser Institute.

Freedman, B. 1981. *Intensive Forest Harvest: A Review of Nutrient Budget Considerations*. Information Report M–X–121. Fredericton: Maritimes Forest Research Centre.

——, P.N. Duinker, and R. Morash. 1986. "Biomass and nutrients in Nova Scotia forests, and implications of intensive harvesting for future site productivity." *Forest Ecology and Management* 15: 103–27.

Freiwald, A., et al. 2004. *Cold-Water Coral Reefs*. Cambridge, UK: UNEP-WCMC.

Friedmann, H. 2005. "From colonialism to green capitalism: Social movements and the emergence of food regimes." In F.H. Buttel and P. McMichael, eds., *New Directions in the Sociology of Global Development. Research in Rural Sociology and Development*. Oxford: Elsevier, 229–264.

Frind, E. 2014. "We must heed the threat of global warming." *The Record*, 8 Sept., A9.

Fritz, S.M., et al. 2005. *Interpersonal Skills for Leadership*, 2nd edn. Englewood Cliffs, NJ: Pearson Prentice-Hall.

Fulford, R. 1996. *The Accidental City: The Transformation of Toronto*. Toronto: Houghton Mifflin Harcourt.

Gabriel, A.O., and R.D. Kreutzwiser. 1993. "Drought hazard in Ontario: A review of impacts, 1960–1989, and management implications." *Canadian Water Resources Journal* 18: 117–32.

Gardner, A.S., et al. 2011. "Sharply increased mass loss from glaciers and ice caps in the Canadian Arctic Archipelago." *Nature*. doi: 10.1038/nature10089

Gardner. G. 2011. "Roundwood production plummets." In Worldwatch Institute (2011: 84–8).

——and A. Assadourian. 2004. "Rethinking the good life." In Worldwatch Institute (2004: 164–80).

Garshelis, D.L. 1997. "Sea otter mortality estimated from carcasses collected after the *Exxon Valdez* oil spill." *Conservation Biology* 11, 4: 905–16.

Gaston, A.J., et al. 2009. "Changes in Canadian seabird populations and ecology since 1970 in relation to changes in oceanography and food webs." *Environmental Reviews* 17: 267–86.

Gauthier, G., et al. 2001. "Seasonal survival of greater snow geese and effect of hunting under dependence in sighting probability." *Ecology* 82: 3105–19.

Gedalof, Z., and A.A. Berg. 2010. "Tree ring evidence for a limited direct CO fertilization effect." *Global Biogeochemical Cycles* 24: GB3027, doi:10.1029/2009GB003699

Gencer, E.A. 2013. *The Interplay between Urban Development, Vulnerability and Risk Management: A Case Study of the Istanbul Metropolitan Area*. Berlin: Springer.

Geological Survey of Canada. 2013. *State and Evolution of Canada's Glaciers*. pathways.geosemantica.net/collections/documents_folderview.aspx?p=0&coll=0a21b46a-ab5b-4549-8d37-88d9e022ae6f.

Gibbins, J., and H. Chalmers. 2008. "Carbon capture and storage." *Energy Policy* 36, 2: 4317–22.

Gibson, R.B. 2007. "Integration through sustainability assessment: Emerging possibilities at the leading of edge of environmental assessment." In K.S. Hanna and D.S. Slocombe, eds, *Integrated Resource and Environmental Management: Concepts and Practice*. Toronto: Oxford University Press, 72–96.

Gifford, R 2013. "Dragons, mules and honeybees: Barriers, carriers and unwitting enablers of climate change action." *Bulletin of the Atomic Scientists* 69: 41–48.

Gleick, P.H. 2003. "Global freshwater resources: Soft-path solutions for the 21st century." *Science* 302: 1524–8.

Global Water Partnership. 2000. *Integrated Water Resources Management*. Technical Advisory Committee Background Paper no. 4. Stockholm: Global Water Partnership.

Global Wind Energy Council. 2006. *Global Wind 2006 Report*. Brussels: Global Wind Energy Council.

——. 2014. *Global Wind Statistics*. Brussels: Global Wind Energy Council.

Godfray, H., et al. 2010. "Food security: The challenge of feeding 9 billion people." *Science* 327, 5967: 812–818. doi: 10.1126/science.1185383

Godschalk, D.R. 2003. "Urban hazard mitigation: Creating resilient cities." *Natural Hazards Review* August: 136–143.

Goetz, J.N., R.H. Guthrie, and A. Brenning. 2014. "Forest harvesting is associated with increased landslide activity during an extreme rainstorm on Vancouver Island, Canada." *Natural Hazards and Earth System Sciences Discussions* 2: 5525–5574.

Gonsamo, A., J.M. Chen, and C. Wu. 2013. "Citizen science: Linking the recent rapid advances of plant flowering in Canada with climate variability." *Scientific Reports*, 3. doi:10.1038/srep02239

Gore, A. 2006. *An Inconvenient Truth: The Planetary Emergency and What We Can Do about It*. Emmaus, Penn.: Rodale Books.

Gorrie, P. 1990. "The James Bay power project: The environmental cost of reshaping the geography of northern Quebec." *Canadian Geographic* 110, 1: 21–31.

———. 2008. "Green giant." *Toronto Star*, 8 Mar., ID1–ID2.

Gosselin, P., et al. 2010. *Environmental and Health Impacts of Canada's Oil Sands Industry*. Ottawa: Royal Society of Canada.

Gould, S.J. 1989. *Wonderful Life: The Burgess Shale and the Nature of History*. New York: W.W. Norton.

———. 1994. "The evolution of life on the earth." *Scientific American* 271: 84–91.

Government of Canada. 2014a. "Canada delivers its National Statement at the 20th Conference of the Parties to the United Nations Framework Convention on Climate Change." Accessed 15 Dec. 2014. http://news.gc.ca/web/article-en.do?nid=913179.

———. 2014b. *Canada's 5th National Report to the Convention on Biological Diversity*. Ottawa.

———. 2014c. "Government of Canada accepts recommendation to impose 209 conditions on Northern Gateway proposal." Ottawa: Natural Resources Canada. 17 Jun. Accessed 19 Jun. 2014. http://news.ca/web/article-en.do?nid=858469.

———. 2014d. "Next steps on Northern Gateway project." Ottawa: Natural Resources Canada. Accessed 19 Jun. 2014. http://news.gc.ca/web/article-en.do?nid=859479.

Government of Nunavut, Northwest Territories, and Yukon. 2011. *Pan-Territorial Adaptation Strategy: Moving Forward on Climate Change Adaptation in Canada's North*. http://www.anorthernvision.ca/strategy/.

Government of Saskatchewan. 2007. *The Great Sand Hills Regional Environmental Study: Final Report*. Regina: Saskatchewan Ministry of Environment. Accessed 18 Feb. 2015. http//:www.environment.gov.sk.ca/GreatSandHillsRegionalStudy.

Graenfeldt, D. 2010. "The next nexus? Environmental ethics, water policies, and climate change." *Water Alternatives* 3: 575–86.

Gray, B. 1989. *Collaborating: Finding Common Ground for Multiparty Problems*. San Francisco: Jossey-Bass.

Greater Sudbury. 2010. *Living Landscape: A Biodiversity Action Plan for Greater Sudbury*. Sudbury, Ont.: Vegetation Enhancement Technical Advisory Committee.

Greer, A., V. Ng, and D. Fisman. 2008. "Climate change and infectious diseases in North America: The road ahead." *Canadian Medical Association Journal* 178: 715–22.

GRID. 2012. "Greenhouse Gas Intensity of National Economies." Accessed 4 Jan. 2015. http://www.grida.no/graphicslib/detail/greenhouse-gas-intensity-of-national-economies_f729.

Griffiths-Sattenspiel, B., and W. Wilson. 2009. *The Carbon Footprint of Water*. Portland, Ore.: River Network.

Groombridge, B.. 1992. *Global Biodiversity: Status of the World's Living Resources*. London: Chapman and Hall.

Gruber, N., and J.N. Galloway. 2008. "An Earth-system perspective of the global nitrogen cycle." *Nature* 451: 293–6.

Guan, D.B., Z. Liu, Y. Geng, S. Lindner, K. Hubacek. 2012. "The Gigatonne gap in China's CO_2 inventories." *Nature-Climate Change* 2: 672–675.

Gustavsson, J., et al. 2011. "Global food losses and food waste." Study conducted for the International Congress SAVE FOOD! at Interpack 2011, Düsseldorf, Germany. Rome: Food and Agriculture Organization of the United Nations.

Gutberlet, J. 2008. *Recycling Citizenship, Recovering Resources: Urban Poverty Reduction in Latin America*. Aldershot: Ashgate.

———. 2009. "The solidarity economy of recycling co-ops: Micro-credit to alleviate poverty." *Development in Practice* 19, 6: 737–51.

———. 2010. "Waste, poverty and recycling." *Waste Management* 30, 2: 171–3.

———. 2012. "Informal and cooperative recycling as a poverty eradication strategy." *Geography Compass* 6: 19–34.

———and A. Baeder. 2008. "Informal recycling and occupational health in Santo André, Brazil." *International Journal of Environmental Health Research* 18, 1: 1–15

Hall, J. 2004. "Hazel's gift wrapped in green." *Toronto Star*, 15 Oct., B1–B2.

Hallmann, C.A., et al. 2014. "Declines in insectivorous birds are associated with high neonicotinoid concentrations." *Nature*. doi:10.1038/nature13531

Halweil, B. 2002. *Home Grown: The Case for Local Food in a Global Market*. Worldwatch Paper 163. Washington: Worldwatch Institute.

Hambler, C., M.A. Speight, and P.A. Henderson. 2011. "Extinction rates, extinction-prone habitats and indicator groups in Britain and at larger scales." *Biological Conservation* 144, 2: 713–21.

Hangs, R.D., J.D. Knight, and K.C.J. Van Rees. 2003. "Nitrogen uptake characteristics for roots of conifer seedlings and common boreal forest competitor species." *Canadian Journal of Forest Research* 33: 156–63.

Hannah, L. 2003. "Protected areas management in a changing climate." In N.W.P. Munro et al., eds, *Making Ecosystem-Based Management Work*. Proceedings of the Fifth International Conference on Science and Management of Protected Areas, Victoria, BC, May 2003. Wolfville, NS: Science and Management of Protected Areas Association. www.sampaa.org/publications.

Hansen. M.C., et al. 2013. "High-resolution global maps of 21st-century forest cover change." *Science* 342: 850–853. doi: 10.1126/science.1244693

Harden, A., and H. Levalliant. 2008. *Boiling Point: Six Community Profiles of the Water Crisis Facing First Nations within Canada*. Ottawa: Polaris Institute.

Hare, F.K., and J.C. Ritchie. 1972. "The boreal bioclimates." *Geographical Review* 62: 333–365.

Harris, Michael. 1998. *Lament for an Ocean: The Collapse of the Atlantic Cod Fishery, A True Crime Story*. Toronto: McClelland & Stewart.

Hartig, J.H., and M.A. Zarull. 1992. *Under RAPs: Towards Grassroots Ecological Democracy in the Great Lakes Basin*. Ann Arbor: University of Michigan Press.

Hauzer, M., P. Dearden, and G. Murray. 2013. "The effectiveness of community-based governance of small-scale fisheries, Ngazidja island, Comoros." *Marine Policy* 38: 346–354.

Hawken, Paul. 2009. "Commencement: Healing or stealing?" Accessed 5 Jun. 2015. http://www.up.edu/commencement/default.aspx?cid=9456.

Hazell, R., and B. Worthy. 2010. "Assessing the performance of freedom of information." *Government Information Quarterly* 27: 352–9.

Health Canada. 2007. *Canada's Health Concerns from Climate Change and Variability*. Ottawa: Health Canada. www.taiga.net/nce/resources/newsletters/NCE_Newsletter_Winter2003.pdf.

———. 2008. *Canada's Food Guide: Food and Nutrition*. Ottawa: Government of Canada.

———. 2010. *First Nations, Inuit and Aboriginal Health: Drinking Water and Wastewater*. www.hc-sc.gc.ca/fniah-spnia/promotion/public-publique/water-eau-eng.php.

———. 2014. "Wind turbine noise and health study: Summary of results." Accessed 7 Nov. 2014. http://www.hc-sc.gc.ca/ewh-semt/noise-bruit/turbine-eoliennes/summary-resume-eng.php.

———. 2015. *First Nations and Inuit Health, Drinking Water Advisories in First Nations Communities*. 10 Sept. Accessed 24 Sept. 2015. http://www.hc-sc.gc.ca/fniah-spnia/promotion/public-publique/water-eau-eng.php.

Hearnden, K.W., et al. 1992. *A Report on the Status of Forest Regeneration*. Toronto: Ontario Independent Forest Audit Committee.

Heath, C., and D. Heath. 2010. *Switch: How to Change Things When Change Is Hard*. Toronto: Random House Canada.

Heck, N, P. Dearden, and A. McDonald. 2012. "Insights into marine conservation efforts in temperate regions: Marine protected areas on Canada's West Coast." *Ocean and Coastal Management* 57: 10–20.

Heimann, M., and M. Reichstein. 2008. "Terrestrial carbon ecosystem dynamics and climate feedbacks." *Nature* 451: 289–92.

Hengeveld, H. 1991. *Understanding Atmospheric Change: A Survey of the Background Science and Implications of Climate Change and Ozone Depletion*. SOE Report no. 91–2. Ottawa: Minister of Supply and Services.

——. 2006. *CO_2/Climate Report*. Toronto: Environment Canada, Atmospheric Science Assessment and Integration Branch.

——, E. Bush, and P. Edwards. 2002. *Frequently Asked Questions about Climate Change Science*. Ottawa: Minister of Supply and Services.

——, B. Whitewood, and A. Fergusson. 2005. *An Introduction to Climate Change: A Canadian Perspective*. Toronto: Environment Canada, Atmospheric Science Assessment and Integration Branch.

——et al. 2008. *Enhancement of Greenhouse Gas Sinks: A Canadian Science Assessment*. Ottawa: Ministry of Environment.

Herkenrath, P., and J. Harrison. 2011. "The 10th meeting of the Conference of the Parties to the Convention on Biological Diversity—a breakthrough for biodiversity?" *Oryx* 45: 1–2.

Hervieux, D., et al. 2014. "Managing wolves (*Canis lupus*) to recover threatened woodland caribou (*Rangifer tarandus caribou*) in Alberta." *Canadian Journal of Zoology* 92: 1029–1037.

Hilborn, R.C. 2004. "Sea gulls, butterflies, and grasshoppers: A brief history of the butterfly effect in nonlinear dynamics." *American Journal of Physics* 72, 4: 425–427.

Hilson, G. 2000. "Sustainable development policies in Canada's mining sector: An overview of government and industry efforts." *Environmental Science and Policy* 3: 201–11.

Hilson, G., and V. Nayee. 2002. "Environmental management system implementation in the mining industry: A key to achieving cleaner production." *International Journal of Minerals and Processes* 64: 19–41.

Himmelman, A.T. 1996. "On the theory and practice of transformational collaboration: From social service to social justice." In C. Huxham, ed., *Creating Collaborative Advantage*. Thousand Oaks, Calif.: Sage, 19–43.

Hipfner, J.M. 2008. "Matches and mismatches: Ocean climate, prey phenology and breeding success in a zooplanktivorous seabird." *Marine Ecology Progress Series* 368: 295–304.

Hirsch Hadorn, G., et al. 2008. *Handbook of Transdisciplinarity Research*. Dordrecht: Springer.

Hites, R.A., et al. 2004. "Global assessment of organic contaminants in farmed salmon." *Science* 303: 226–9.

Hobson, K.A., E.M. Bayne, and S.L. Van Wilgenburg. 2002. "Large-scale conversion of forest to agriculture in the boreal plains of Saskatchewan." *Conservation Biology* 16, 6: 1530–41.

Hockstra, A.Y., and A.K. Chapagain. 2007. "Water footprints of nations: Water use by people as a function of their consumption pattern." *Water Resources Management* 21: 35–48.

Hodgkins, S.B., et al. 2015. "Changes in peat chemistry associated with permafrost thaw increase greenhouse gas production." *PNAS Early Edition*. doi: 10.1073/pnas.1314641111

Hofmann, N., and M.S. Beaulieu. 2006. *A Geographical Profile of Manure Production in Canada, 2001*. Report 21–601–MIE–N.07. Ottawa: Statistics Canada.

Hofmann, N., G. Filoso, and M. Schofield. 2005. *The Loss of Dependable Agricultural Land in Canada*. Rural and Small Town Canada Analysis Bulletin 6. Catalogue no 21–006– XIE. Ottawa: Statistics Canada.

Hoggan, J., with R. Littlemore. 2009. *Climate Cover-up: The Crusade to Deny Global Warming*. Vancouver: Greystone Books.

Holling, C.S., ed. 1978. *Adaptive Environmental Assessment and Management*. Chichester: John Wiley.

——. 1986. "The resilience of terrestrial ecosystems: Local surprise and global change." In W.C. Clark and R.E. Munn, eds, *Sustainable Development in the Biosphere*. Cambridge: Cambridge University Press, 292–317.

——. 2007. *The Upside of Down: Catastrophe, Creativity and the Renewal of Civilization*. Toronto: Vintage Canada.

Holmes, M., and A. Macey. 2014. "Organic Agriculture in Canada." In H. Willer and J. Lernoud, eds., *The World of Organic Agriculture. Statistics and Emerging Trends 2014*. FiBL-IFOAM Report. Revised version of 24 Feb. Frick: Research Institute of Organic Agriculture (FiBL); Bonn: International Federation of Organic Agriculture Movements (IFOAM), 247–251.

Holt-Gimenez, E. 2014. "Feeding nine billion: Five steps to the wrong solution." *Huffington Post*, April 25. Accessed 1 May 2014. http://www.huffingtonpost.com/eric-holt-gimenez/feeding-nine-billion-five_b_5208388.html.

Hoornweg, D., L. Sugar, and C.L.T. Gómez. 2011. "Cities and greenhouse gas emissions: Moving forward." *Environment and Urbanization* 23: 207–227.

Howard, K.W.F., and H. Maier. 2007. "Road deicing salt as a potential constraint on urban growth in the Greater Toronto Area, Canada." *Journal of Contaminant Hydrology* 91, 1 and 2: 146–70. Human Development Resource Office. 2007.

Hull, J., et al. 2004. *Report of the Expert Panel on Science Issues Related to Oil and Gas Activities, Offshore British Columbia*. Ottawa: Royal Society of Canada.

Human Development Report 2007/2008: *Fighting Climate Change*. Houndmills, UK: Palgrave Macmillan.

Huntington, H.P., et al. 2005. "The changing Arctic: Indigenous perspectives." In L. Arris, ed., *Arctic Climate Impact Assessment*. Cambridge: Cambridge University Press, 61–98.

Hutchings, J.A., et al. 2012. "Climate change, fisheries, and aquaculture: Trends and consequences for Canadian marine biodiversity." *Environmental Review* 20: 220–311.

Hutchings, J.A., and R.A. Myers. 1994. "What can be learned from the collapse of a renewable resource? Atlantic cod, *Gadus morhua*, of Newfoundland and Labrador." *Canadian Journal of Fisheries and Aquatic Sciences* 51: 2126–46.

Hutchings, J.A., and J.R. Post. 2013. "Gutting Canada's Fisheries Act: No fishery, no fish habitat protection." *Fisheries* 38: 497–501.

Hutchings, J.A., C. Walters, and R.L. Haedrich. 1997. "Is scientific inquiry incompatible with government information control? *Canadian Journal of Fisheries and Aquatic Sciences* 54, 5: 1198–1210.

Hyde, D., H. Hermann, and R.A. Lautenschlager. 2010. *The State of Biodiversity in Canada*. Ottawa: Natureserve Canada.

Hydro-Québec and Genivar. 2013. *Environmental Monitoring at the La Grande Complex—Evolution of Mercury Levels in Fish—Summary Report 1978–2012*. Quebec City: Hydro-Québec.

Independent Environmental Monitoring Agency (IEMA). 2007. *Plain Language Annual Report 2006–07*. www.monitoringagency.net/AgencyDocumentsPresentations/AnnualReports/tabid/64/Default.aspx.

——. 2010a. "Independent Environmental Monitoring Agency: Why was it created?" www.monitoringagency.net/AboutUs/WhytheAgencywascreated/tabid/61/ Default .aspx.

——. 2010b. *Plain Language Annual Report 2009–10*. Yellowknife, NWT: Independent Environmental Monitoring Agency.

Indian and Northern Affairs Canada. 1997a. *Highlights of the Canadian Arctic Contaminants Assessment Report: A Community Reference Manual*. Ottawa: Minister of Public Works and Government Services.

——. 1997b. "Pathways of transportation of persistent organics and metals to Arctic freshwater and marine ecosystems." In Indian and Northern Affairs Canada (1997a).

Intergovernmental Panel on Climate Change (IPCC). 2001a. *Climate Change 2001: Impacts, Adaptation, and Vulnerability*. Contribution of Working Group II to the Third Assessment Report of the Intergovernmental Panel on Climate Change. J.J. McCarthy et al., eds. Cambridge: Cambridge University Press.

———. 2001b. *Climate Change 2001: The Scientific Basis*. Contributions of Working Group I to the Third Assessment Report of the Intergovernmental Panel on Climate Change. J.T. Houghton et al., eds. Cambridge: Cambridge University Press.

———. 2001c. *Climate Change 2001: Synthesis Report*. A Contribution of Working Groups I, II and III to the Third Assessment Report of the Intergovernmental Panel on Climate Change. R.T. Watson and the Core Writing Team, eds. Cambridge: Cambridge University Press.

———. 2007a. *Climate Change 2007: Impacts, Adaptation and Vulnerability*. Paris and Geneva: IPCC Secretariat.

———. 2007b. *Climate Change 2007: The Physical Science Basis*. Working Group I Contribution to the Fourth Assessment Report of the Intergovernmental Panel on Climate Change, Figure SPM.2. Cambridge: Cambridge University Press.

———. 2007c. "Summary for policy makers of the synthesis report of the IPCC fourth assessment report." www.ipcc.ch.

———. 2014a. "Summary for Policymakers." *Climate Change 2014 Synthesis Report*. Accessed 20 Dec. 2014. http://www.ipcc.ch/pdf/assessment-report/ar5/syr/AR5_SYR_FINAL_SPM.pdf.

———. 2014b. "Summary for Policymakers." In O. Edenhofer et al., eds, *Climate Change 2014: Mitigation of Climate Change*. Contribution of Working Group III to the Fifth Assessment Report of the Intergovernmental Panel on Climate Change. Cambridge and New York: Cambridge University Press.

International Energy Agency. 2010. *Key World Energy Statistics*. Paris: OECD/IEA.

———. 2012. *World Energy Outlook 2012*. Paris. OECD.

International Joint Commission. 2012a. *Great Lakes Water Quality Protocol, 2012*. Accessed 15 Dec. 2014. http://www.ijc.org/en_/Great_Lakes_Water_Quality.

———. 2012b. *16th Biennial Report on Great Lakes Water Quality: Assessment of Progress Made towards Restoring and Maintaining Great Lakes Water Quality since 1987*. Windsor: Great Lakes Regional Office.

International Organization for Migration. 2010. "Facts and figures: Global estimates and trends." www.iom.int/jahia/Jahia/about-migration/facts-and-figures/lang/en.

International Reference Group on Great Lakes Pollution from Land Use Activities. 1978. *Environmental Management Strategy for the Great Lakes System: Final Report to the International Joint Commission*. Windsor, Ont.: IJC.

International Strategy for Disaster Reduction. 2005. *Hyogo Framework for Disaster Reduction 2005–2015: Building Resilience of Nations and Communities to Disaster*. Report of the World Conference on Disaster Reduction, 18–21 Jan. Kobe, Hyogo, Japan.

International Water Resources Association. 2000. "Towards hydrosolidarity." *Water International* 25, 2 (special issue).

IUCN, *see also* World Conservation Union.

IUCN. 2011. www.iucn.org/en/news/archive/2006/05/02_pr_red_list_en.htm.

———. 2011. "IUCN Red List of Threatened Species." IUCN Species Survival Commission. Gland, Switzerland.

———. 2014. "IUCN Red List of Threatened Species." IUCN Species Survival Commission. Gland, Switzerland, and Cambridge, UK.

Jachmann, H., P.S.M. Berry, and H. Imae. 1995. "Tusklessness in African elephants: A future trend." *African Journal of Ecology* 33: 230–5.

Jackson, J., et al. 2014. *Status and Trends of Caribbean Coral Reefs: 1970–2012*. Washington, DC: Global Coral Reef Monitoring Network.

Jackson, J.B.C., et al. 2001. "Historical over-fishing and the recent collapse of coastal ecosystems." *Science* 293: 629–38.

Jacob, A.L. 2014. "Conserving and restoring biodiversity and ecosystem services in African tropical rainforest." PhD thesis. Montreal: McGill University, Department of Biology.

Jacques Whitford Engineering, Scientific, Planning and Management Consultants. 2006. *Final Report: 100% Design Report, Demolition and Disposal of the Old SYSCO Cooling Pond*. Prepared for the Sydney Tar Ponds Agency. Dartmouth, NS: Jacques Whitford.

James, C. 2006. *Global Status of Commercialized Biotech/GM Crops: 2006*. ISAAA Brief no. 35. Ithaca, NY: International Service for the Acquisition of Agri-biotech Applications.

———. 2010. *Global Status of Commercialized Biotech/GM Crops: 2010*. ISAAA Brief no. 42. Ithaca, NY: ISAAA. www.isaaa.org/resources/publications/pocketk/16/default.asp.

———. 2014. *Global Status of Commercialized Biotech/GM Crops: 2014*. ISAAA Brief No. 49. Ithaca, N.Y.: ISAAA.

Jayyousi, O.A. 2007. "Water as a human right: Towards civil society globalization." *Water Resources Development* 23: 329–39.

Jeffries, D.S., et al. 2003. "Assessing the recovery of lakes in southeastern Canada from the effects of acidic deposition." *Ambio* 32: 176–83.

———, I. Wong, I. Dennis, and M. Sloboda. 2010. "Terrestrial and aquatic critical loads map." Ottawa: Environment Canada, Water Science and Technology Branch, unpublished.

———, ———, and M. Sloboda. 2010. "Boreal Shield steady-state exceedances for forest soils or lakes map." Prepared for Boreal Shield Ecozone status and trends report. Ottawa: Environment Canada, Water Science and Technology Branch, unpublished.

Jeziorski, A., et al. 2008. "The widespread threat of calcium decline in fresh water." *Science* 322: 1374–7.

Jeziorski, A., et al. 2014. "The jellification of northern temperate lakes." *Proceedings of the Royal Society B*: 282. doi: 10.1098/rspb.2014.2449

Johnstone, B. 2014. "Clean coal best bet to stop climate change." *Leader-Post*, 4 Oct. Accessed 20 Nov. 2014. http://www.leaderpost.com/technology/JOHNSTONE+Clean+coal+best+stop+climate+change/10262940/story.html.

Joint Review Panel for the Enbridge Northern Gateway Project. 2013a. *Connections*, vol. 1. Calgary: National Energy Board.

———. 2013b., *Considerations*, vol. 2. Calgary: National Energy Board.

Jones, C.G., R.S. Ostfield, M.P. Richard, E.M. Schauber, and J.O. Wolff. 1998. "Chain reactions linking acorns to gypsy moth outbreaks and Lyme disease risk." *Science* 279: 1023–6.

Jørgensen, C., et al. 2007. "Managing evolving fish stocks." *Science* 318: 1247–8.

Joseph, C., T.I. Gunton, and J.C. Day. 2006. "Implementation of resource management plans: Identifying keys to success." *Journal of Environmental Management* 88: 594–606.

Juffe-Bignoli, D., et al. 2014. *Protected Planet Report 2014*. Cambridge, UK: UNEP-WCMC.

Kanninen, M., et al. 2007. *Do Trees Grow on Money? The Implications of Deforestation Research for Policies to Promote REDD*. Bogor, Indonesia: Center for International Forestry Research.

Katz, D. 2010. *Making Waves: Examining the Case for Sustainable Water Exports from Canada*. Vancouver: Fraser Institute.

Kay, C.E. 1994. "Aboriginal overkill: The role of Native Americans in structuring western ecosystems." *Human Nature* 5: 359–98.

KBM Forestry Consultants. 2007. *National Forest Strategy (2003–2008) Evaluation: Final Report*. Ottawa: Canadian Council of Forest Ministers.

Kedron, P. 2014. "Environmental governance and shifts in Canadian biofuel production and innovation." *The Professional Geographer*. doi:10.1080/00330124.2014.983589

Keith, H., et al. 2014. "Managing temperate forests for carbon storage: Impact of logging versus forest protection on carbon stocks." *Ecosphere* 56. http://dx.doi.org/10.1890/ES14-00051.

Keith, L.B., et al. 1984. "Demography and ecology of a declining snowshoe hare population." *Wildlife Monographs* 90: 1–43.

Kelley, B. 2009. *Sustainable Community Design: Introduction to Principles and Practices for Conservation Design "Municipal Tool Kit."* Jan. Bathurst, N.B.: Bathurst Sustainable Development.

Kelly, E.N., et al. 2010. "Oil sands development contributes elements toxic at low concentrations to the Athabasca River and its tributaries." *Proceedings of the National Academy of Sciences* 107, 37: 16178–83.

Kenworthy, J.R. 2006. "The eco-city: Ten key transport and planning dimensions for sustainable city development." *Environment and Urbanization* 18, 1: 67–85.

Kesho Trust. 2007. "Reconnecting children and families with nature." Report of workshops sponsored by ActNow BC, 28 June and 17 July, Royal Roads University, Victoria, BC.

Khadka, A.K. 2010. "The emergence of water as a 'human right' on the world stage: Challenges and opportunities." *Water Resources Development* 26: 37–49.

Kimmins, J.P. 1977. "Evaluation of the consequences for the future tree productivity of the loss of nutrients in whole-tree harvesting." *Forest Ecology and Management* 1: 169–83.

Kitasei, S. 2011. "Wind power growth continues to break records despite recession." In Worldwatch Institute (2011: 26–8).

Klironomos, J.N., M.F. Allen, M.C. Rillig, J. Piotrowski, S. Makvandi-Nejad, B.E. Wolfe, and J.R. Powell. 2005. "Abrupt rise in atmospheric CO_2 overestimates community response in a model plant–soil system." *Nature* 433: 621–4.

Knight, W.A., and T. Keating. 2010. *Global Politics: Emerging Networks, Trends, and Challenges.* Toronto: Oxford University Press.

Krantzberg, G., and J.P. Manno. 2010. "Renovation and innovation: It's time for the Great Lakes Regime to respond." *Water Resources Management* 24: 4273–85.

Krebs, C.J., et al. 2001. "What drives the 10-year cycle of snowshoe hares?" *Bioscience* 51: 25–35.

Kreutzwiser, R., and R. de Loe. 2004. "Water security: From exports to contamination of local water supplies." In B. Mitchell, ed., *Resource and Environmental Management in Canada: Addressing Conflict and Uncertainty.* Toronto: Oxford University Press, 166–94.

Krkošek, M., et al. 2007. "Declining wild salmon populations in relation to parasites from farm salmon." *Science* 318: 1772–5.

Krugel, L. 2010. "U.S. group hopes to tar Alberta with image of oily ducks." *The Record*, 15 Jul., B3.

Kurz, W.A., et al. 2008. "Mountain pine beetle and forest carbon feedback to climate change." *Nature* 452: 987–90.

Kuvlesky, W.P., et al. 2007. "Wind energy development and wildlife conservation: Challenges and opportunities." *Journal of Wildlife Management* 71: 2487–98.

Kyoto Protocol to the United Nations Framework Convention on Climate Change. 1997. unfccc.int/resource/docs/convkp/kpeng.pdf.

Lahey, A. 1998. "Black lagoons: They're ugly. They stink. But are the tar ponds really killing the people of Sydney, Nova Scotia?" *Saturday Night* 113, 8: 37–40.

Land Reclamation Program. 2007. *Land Reclamation Program Annual Report, 2007.* Sudbury, Ont.: Environmental Planning Initiatives.

Landry J-S., and N. Ramankutty. 2015. "Carbon cycling, climate regulation, and disturbances in Canadian forests: Scientific principles for management." *Land* 4: 83–118.

Landry, M., V.G. Thomas, and T.D. Nudds. 2001. "Sizes of Canadian national parks and the viability of large mammal populations: Policy implications." *The George Wright Forum* 18, 1: 13–23.

Lasserre, F. 2007. "Drawers of water: Water diversions in Canada and beyond." In Bakker (2007: 143–62).

——. 2009. "Transferts massifs d'eau au Canada: Entre mythe et réalité." *Policy Options* (Jul.–Aug.): 53–9.

Lautenbach, W.W. 1985. *Land Reclamation Program 1978–1984.* Sudbury, Ont.: Vegetation Enhancement Technical Advisory Committee.

—— et al. 1995. "Municipal land restoration program: The regreening process." In J.M. Gunn, ed., *Restoration and Recovery of an Industrial Region: Progress in Restoring the Smelter-Damaged Landscape near Sudbury, Ontario.* New York: Springer-Verlag, 109–22.

Lautenschlager, R.A., and T.P. Sullivan. 2002. "Effects of herbicide treatments on biotic components in regenerating northern forests." *Forestry Chronicle* 78: 695–731.

Lawrence, D.P. 2013. *Environmental Impact Assessment—Practical Solutions to Recurrent Problems.* Hoboken, N.J.: John Wiley and Sons.

Lebeuf, M., et al. 2007. "Temporal trends (1987–2002) of persistent, bioaccumulative and toxic (PBT) chemicals in beluga whales (*Delphinapterus leucas*) from the St Lawrence estuary, Canada." *The Science of the Total Environment* 383: 216–31.

Lee, K.N. 1993. *Compass and Gyroscope: Integrating Science and Politics for the Environment.* Washington: Island Press.

Leeder, J. 2010. "As nations squabble, bluefin is fished closer to extinction." *Globe and Mail*, 26 Nov., A8.

Leggett, W.C., and K.T. Frank. 2008. "Paradigms in fisheries oceanography." *Oceanography and Marine Biology: An Annual Review* 46: 331–63.

Leip, A., et al. 2013. "The nitrogen footprint of food products in the European Union." *The Journal of Agricultural Science* 152, S1: 20–33.

Lemieux, A. 2005. "Canada's global mining presence." In *Canadian Minerals Yearbook, 2005.* Ottawa: Minister of Public Works and Government Services.

Lemieux, C., T. Beechey, and D. Scott. 2007. "A survey on protected areas and climate change (PACC) in Canada: Survey update." *ECO* 16: 2–3.

——, ——, ——, and P. Gray. 2011. "The state of climate change adaptation in Canada's protected area sector." *Canadian Geographer* 55: 301–17.

Lemieux, C.J., et al. 2015. *Healthy Outside–Healthy Inside: The Human Health and Well-Being Benefits of Alberta's Protected Areas—Towards a Benefits-Based Management Agenda.* Canadian Council on Ecological Areas (CCEA). Occasional Paper No. 20. Ottawa: CCEA Secretariat.

Lemos, M.C., and A. Agrawal. 2006. "Environmental governance." *Annual Review of Environment and Resources* 31: 297–325.

Lenton, R., and M. Muller, eds. 2009. *Integrated Water Resources Management in Practice.* London: Earthscan.

Leopold, A. 1949. *A Sand County Almanac.* Oxford: Oxford University Press.

Le Prestre, P.G., and P. Stoett. 2001. "International initiatives, commitments, and disappointments: Canada, CITES, and the CBD." In K. Beazley and R. Boardman, eds, *Politics of the Wild: Canada and Endangered Species.* Toronto: Oxford University Press, 190–216.

Lesieur, D., S. Gauthier, and Y. Bergeron. 2002. "Fire frequency and vegetation dynamics for the south-central boreal forest of Quebec, Canada." *Canadian Journal of Forest Research* 32: 1996–2002.

Leslie, K. 2014. "Ontario says federal government to blame if dispute with Six Nations leads to unrest in Caledonia this summer." *Financial Post*, Jul. 11. Accessed 16 Jul. 2014. http://news.nationalpost.com/2014/07/22/ontario-says-federal-government-to-blame.

LifeWeb. n.d. www.cbd.int/lifeweb/carbon/.

Lin, B. 2011. "Resilience in agriculture through crop diversification: Adaptive management for environmental change." *Bioscience* 61, 3: 183–93.

Liu, J., A.J.B. Zehnder, and H. Yang. 2007. "Historical trends in China's virtual water trade." *Water International* 32: 78–90.

Liu, Z., et al. 2012a. "Embodied energy use in China's industrial sectors." *Energy Policy* 49: 751–758.

Liu, Z., et al. 2012b. "Uncovering China's GHG emission from regional and sectoral perspectives." *Energy* 45: 1059–1068.

Llamas, R.M., Martinez Cortina, L. and Mukherji, A. (eds). 2009. *Water Ethics.* Boca Raton: CRC Press.

Longhurst, A. 2002. "Murphy's law revisited: Longevity as a factor in recruitment to fish populations." *Fisheries Research* 56: 125–31

Los F. 2014. "Boreal truce." *Canadian Geographic* Jan/Feb. http://www.canadiangeographic.ca/magazine/jf14/canadian-boreal-forest-agreement.asp.

Louv, R. 2006. *Last Child in the Woods.* Toronto: Algonquin Books.

Lovelock, J.E. 1988. *The Ages of Gaia.* New York: W.W. Norton.

Low-Level Radioactive Waste Management Office. 2012. *Inventory of Radioactive Waste in Canada.* March. Ottawa: Low-Level Radioactive Waste Management Office.

Lunn, K.E., and P. Dearden. 2006. "Fisher's needs in marine protected area zoning." *Coastal Management* 34: 183–198.

Lynam, A.J. 2010. "Securing a future for wild Indochinese tigers: Transforming tiger vacuums into tiger source sites." *Integrative Zoology* 5: 324–34.

Maas, C. 2010. *Ontario's Water-Energy Nexus: Will We Find Ourselves in Hot Water . . . or Tap into Opportunity?* Polis Research Report 10–01, Victoria: University of Victoria, POLIS Water Sustainability Project.

McBean, G., and D. Henstra. 2003. *Climate Change, Natural Hazards, and Cities.* Paper Series no. 31. Toronto: Institute for Catastrophic Loss Reduction.

McCarthy, N. 2015. "How the rich spend their money: The global luxury goods market in 2014." *Forbes*, 15 Jan.

Macdonald, D. 2009. "The Government of Canada's search for environmental legitimacy: 1971–2008." *International Journal of Canadian Studies* 39 and 40: 191–210.

MacDougall, A.H., C.A. Avis, and A.J. Weaver. 2012. "Significant contribution to climate warming from the permafrost carbon feedback." *Nature Geoscience* 5: 719–721.

McGinnity, P., et al. 2003. "Fitness reduction and potential extinction of wild populations of Atlantic salmon (*Salmo salar*) as a result of interactions with escaped farm salmon." *Proceedings of the Royal Society: Biological Sciences* 270: 2443–50.

McIver, J.D., A.R. Moldenke, and G.L. Parsons. 1990. "Litter spiders as bio-indicators of recovery after clear-cutting in a western coniferous forest." *Northwest Environmental Journal* 6: 410–12.

McKibben, B. 2010. "Science under siege: Climate change skeptics have presented their case too well." *The Record*, 3 Mar., A9.

McKibben, B. 2012. "Global Warming's Terrifying New Math." *Rolling Stone*, 19 Jul. http://www.rollingstone.com/politics/news/global-warmings-terrifying-new-math-20120719.

Mckinney, M.A., E. Peacock, and R.J. Letcher. 2009. "Sea ice-associated diet change increases the levels of chlorinated and brominated contaminants in polar bears." *Environmental Science and Technology* 43: 4334–9.

Mackintosh, W.A. 1934. *Prairie Settlement: The Geographic Background*. Toronto: Macmillan.

Maclaren, V.W. 2010. "Waste management: Moving up the hierarchy." In Mitchell (2010: 382–406).

McLeman, R., and B. Smit. 2003. *Climate Change, Migration and Security*. Commentary no. 86. Ottawa: Canadian Security Intelligence Service.

MacRae, R. 2011. "A joined-up food policy for Canada." *Journal of Hunger & Environmental Nutrition* 6: 424–457.

MacRae, R., B. Frick, and R.C. Martin. 2007. "Economic and social impacts of organic production systems." *Canadian Journal of Plant Science* 87: 1037–1044.

Magnan, A. 2011. "The limits of farmer control: Food sovereignty and conflicts over the Canadian Wheat Board." In Wittman, Desmarais, and Wiebe (2011: 114–133).

Malcolm, C. 2003. "The current state and future prospects of whale-watching management with special emphasis on whale-watching in BC, Canada." PhD dissertation, University of Victoria.

———. 2015. "Provincial parks." In Dearden, Rollins, and Needham (2015).

Malcolm, J.R., et al. 2006. "Global warming and extinctions of endemic species from biodiversity hotspots." *Conservation Biology* 20: 538–48.

Mandryk, M. 2014. "CO_2 project sequesters tax dollars." *Leader-Post*, 4 Oct. Accessed 20 Nov. 2014. http://www.leaderpost.com/technology/project+sequesters+dollars/10261713/story.html.

Manitoba. n.d. Accessed 4 Sept. 2014. www.gov.mb.ca/conservation/susresmb/principles-susdev.index.html.

Manitoba. 2014. The Sustainable Development Act. Accessed 4 Sept. 2014. https://web2.gov.mb.ca/laws/statutes/ccsm/s270e.php?ccsm=s270.

Manitoba, Public Utilities Board. 2014. *Report on the Needs for and Alternatives to (NFAT): Review of Manitoba's Preferred Development Plan – Final Report*. 20 Jun. Winnipeg: Public Utilities Board.

Manitoba Round Table on Environment and Economy. 1992. *Sustainable Development: Towards Institutional Change in the Manitoba Public Sector.* Winnipeg: Manitoba Round Table on Environment and Economy.

Manitoba Water Stewardship. 2006. "About us, and minister's message." www.gov.mb.ca/waterstewardship/misc/about.htm.

———. 2007. "Potential transboundary water projects." www.gov.mb.ca/waterstewardship/water_info/transboundary/potential.html.

Marshall, G. 2014. *Don't Even Think about It: Why Our Brains Are Wired to Ignore Climate Change*. New York: Bloomsbury.

Martellozzo, F., et al. 2014. "Urbanization and the loss of prime farmland: A case study in the Calgary–Edmonton corridor of Alberta." *Regional Environmental Change*. doi:10.1007/s10113-014-0658-0

Martin, P.S. 1967. "Prehistoric overkill." In P.S. Martin and H.E. Wright Jr, eds, *Pleistocene Extinctions: The Search for a Cause*. New Haven: Yale University Press, 75–120.

Mascarenhas, M. 2007. "Where the waters divide: First Nations, tainted water and environmental justice in Canada." *Local Environment* 12: 565–77.

Masters, M., A. Tikina, and B. Larson. 2010. "Forest certification audit results as potential changes in forest management in Canada." *Forestry Chronicle* 86: 455–60.

Mastny, L. 2004. "Purchasing for people and the planet." In Worldwatch Institute (2004a: 122–42).

——— and H. French. 2002. "Crimes of (a) global nature." *Worldwatch* (Sept.–Oct.): 12–23.

Matthews, C., R.B. Gibson, and B. Mitchell. 2007. "Rising waves, old charts, nervous passengers: Navigating toward a new water ethic." In Bakker (2007: 335–58).

May, E., and M. Barlow. 2001. "The tar ponds." *Alternatives Journal* 27, 1: 7–11.

Mayhew, P.J., G.B. Jenkins, and T.G. Benton. 2008. "A long-term association between global temperature and biodiversity, origination and extinction in the fossil record." *Proceedings of the Royal Society of London B* 275: 47–53.

Meadows, D.H., et al. 1972. *The Limits to Growth*. London. Earth Island.

Ménard, M. 2009. "Canada, a big energy consumer: A regional perspective." Statistics Canada, 12 Nov. www.statcan.gc.ca/pub/11-621-m/11-621-m2005023-eng.htm.

Mercredi, O., and M.E. Turpel. 1993. *In the Rapids: Navigating the Future of First Nations*. Toronto: Viking. Copyright © Ovide Mercredi and Mary Ellen Turpel, 1993. Reprinted by permission of Penguin Group (Canada), a Division of Pearson Canada Inc.

Millennium Ecosystem Assessment. 2003. *Ecosystems and Human Well-being: A Framework for Assessment*. Washington: Island Press.

———. 2005. *Ecosystems and Human Wellbeing: Synthesis*. Washington: Island Press.

Miller, G. 2002. *Climate Change: Is the Science Sound?* Special Report to the Legislative Assembly of Ontario. Toronto: Environmental Commissioner of Ontario.

———. 2003. *2002–03 Annual Report of the Environmental Commissioner of Ontario*. www.eco.on.ca/uploads/Reports%20-%20 Annual/2002_03/03ar.pdf.

Miller, K., et al. 2011. "Genomic signatures predict migration and spawning failure in wild Canadian salmon." *Science*, 14 Jan., 214–17.

Mills, T.J., T.M. Quigley, and F.J. Everest. 2001. "Science-based natural resource management decisions: What are they?" *Renewable Resources Journal* 19, 2: 10–15.

Ministère du Développement durable, de l'Environnement, de la Faune et des Parcs. 2014. "Registre des aires protégées au Québec." Montreal.

Ministry of Natural Resources and Forestry (MNRF). 2008. "Partnerships Protect Greenspace." Mar. 3. http://news.ontario.ca/archive/en/2008/03/03/Partnerships-Protect-Greenspace.html.

Mitchell, B. 2009. "Implementation gap." *IWRA Update* 22, 3: 7–12.

———, ed. 2010. *Resource and Environmental Management in Canada: Addressing Conflict and Uncertainty*, 4th edn. Toronto: Oxford University Press.

——. 2014. "Addressing implementation deficits related to IWRM in Canada." In V.R. Squires, H.M. Milner, and K.A. Daniell, eds., *River Basin Management in the Twenty-first Century: Understanding People and Place*, Boca Raton, Fla.: CRC Press, 42–59.

——. 2015. "Conflict and uncertainty: Context, challenges, and opportunities." In B. Mitchell, ed., *Resource and Environmental Management in Canada*, 5th edition. Don Mills, ON: Oxford University Press, 3–10.

Mittelstaedt, M. 2007. "Pollution causing premature deaths." *Globe and Mail*, 3 Oct., A1. www.theglobeandmail.com/servlet/story/LAC.20071003.TOXIC03/TPStory/TPNational/BritishColum.

Molle, F. 2007. "Scales and power in river basin management: The Chao Phraya River in Thailand." *Geographical Journal* 173: 358–73.

Moncton. n.d. "Green City." http://www.moncton.ca/Residents/Environment/Green_City.htm.

Montreal. 2010. *Montreal: Community Sustainable Development Plan, 2010–2015*. Montreal: Environment and Sustainable Development.

Mooers, A.O., et al. 2007. "Biases in legal listing under Canadian endangered species legislation." *Conservation Biology* 21: 572–5.

Moore, D. 2012. "Timeline restricts review of oil pipeline." *The Record*, Aug. 20, B5.

Moore, D. 2014. "No quick-fix solution for climate change, study says." *Globe and Mail*, Jun. 4. Accessed 28 Mar. 2015. http://www.theglobeandmail.com/news/british-columbia/no-quick-fix-solution-for-climate-change-study-says/article 18996060/.

Moreno-Sánchez, R.D.P., and J.H. Maldonado. 2006. "Surviving from garbage: The role of informal waste-pickers in a dynamic model of solid-waste management in developing countries." *Environment and Development Economics* 11: 371–91.

Morris, T.J., et al. 2007. *Changing the Flow: A Blueprint for Federal Action on Freshwater*. Toronto: The Gordon Water Group of Concerned Scientists and Friends.

Morrison, D. 2011. "Indigenous food sovereignty: A model for social learning." In Wittman, Desmarais, and Wiebe (2011: 97–113).

Morrison, K., T. Nelson, and A. Ostry. 2011. "Methods for mapping local food production capacity from agricultural statistics." *Agricultural Systems* 104: 491–9.

Mosquin, T., and P.G. Whiting. 1992. *Canada Country Study of Biodiversity*. Ottawa: Canadian Museum of Nature.

——, ——, and D.E. McAllister. 1995. *Canada's Biodiversity: The Variety of Life, Its Status, Economic Benefits, Conservation Costs and Unmet Needs*. Ottawa: Canadian Museum of Nature.

Mulkins, L.M., et al. 2002. "Carbon isotope composition of mysids at a terrestrial-marine ecotone, Clayoquot Sound, British Columbia, Canada." *Estuarine, Coastal and Shelf Science* 54: 669–75.

Mulvahill, P., M. Winfield, and J. Etcheverry. 2013. "Strategic Environmental Assessment and advanced renewable energy in Ontario: Moving forward or blowing in the wind?" *Journal of Environmental Assessment Policy and Management* 15, 2: 1.

Munro, M. 2008. "Environment Canada 'muzzles' scientists' dealings with media." *Ottawa Citizen*, 1 Feb.

Murphy, S.D., and L.R.G. Martin. 2001. "Urban ecology in Ontario, Canada: Moving beyond the limits of city and ideology." *Environments* 29, 1: 67–83.

Muskett, H. 2014. "Earthquake studies: GCSE." Accessed 9 Oct. 2014. http://exploregeography.net/earthquake-case-studies-gcse/.

Mustapha, I. 2013. *Composting by Households in Canada*. Ottawa: Statistics Canada, Environment Accounts and Statistics Division. Accessed 2 Oct. 2014. http://www.statcan.gc.ca/pub/16-002-x/2013001/article/11848-eng.pdf.

Myers, R.A., and B. Worm. 2003. "Rapid worldwide depletion of predatory fish communities." *Nature* 423: 280–3.

Myers-Smith, I.H., et al. 2011. "Shrub expansion in tundra ecosystems: dynamics, impacts and research priorities." *Environmental Research Letters* 6: 045509.

Nakashima, D.J. 1990. *Application of Native Knowledge in EIA: Inuit, Eiders and Hudson Bay Oil*. Prepared for the Canadian Environmental Assessment Research Council. Ottawa: Minister of Supply and Services.

Nantel, P., M.G. Pellatt, K. Keenleyside, and P.A. Gray. 2014. "Biodiversity and protected areas." In F.J. Warren and D.S. Lemmen, eds, *Canada in a Changing Climate: Sector Perspectives on Impacts and Adaptation*. Ottawa: Government of Canada, 159–190.

Nanus, B. 1992. *Visionary Leadership*. San Francisco: Jossey-Bass.

NASA, Global Climate Change. 2014. "Graphic: Global Warming from 1880 to 2013." Accessed 29 Dec. 2014. http://climate.nasa.gov/climate_resources/28/.

National Commission on the BP Deepwater Horizon Oil Spill and Offshore Drilling. 2011. *Deep Water: The Gulf Oil Disaster and the Future of Offshore Drilling: Report to the President*. Jan. Washington: National Commission on the BP Deepwater Horizon Oil Spill and Offshore Drilling.

National Energy Board (NEB). 2009a. "Global and Canadian context for energy demand analysis—energy brief." www.neb-one.gc.ca/clf-nsi/rnrgynfmtn/nrgyrprt/nrgdmnd/glblcndncntxt2008/glblcndncntxtnrgbrf-eng.html.

——. 2009b. *Canadian Energy Demand: Passenger Transportation*. Energy Briefing Note. Calgary: NEB, Publications Office.

——. 2014. *Canada's Energy Future 2013—Energy Supply and Demand Projections to 2035—An Energy Market Assessment*. Accessed 16 Nov. 2014. https://www.neb-one.gc.ca/nrg/ntgrtd/ftr/2013/index-eng.html.

National Forest Strategy Coalition (NFSC). 2005. *Highlights of Accomplishments: Advancing the National Forest Strategy*. Ottawa: Canadian Council of Forest Ministers.

National Geographic Society. 2008. *Greendex 2008: Consumer Choice and the Environment: A Worldwide Tracking Survey*. Washington: National Geographic Society.

National Oceanic and Atmospheric Administration (NOAA). n.d. International Tree Ring Data Bank. www.ncdc.noaa.gov/paleo/treering.html.

National Oceanic and Atmospheric Administration, National Climate Data Center. 2010. *State of the Climate Global Analysis, Annual 2010*. www.ncdc.noaa. gov/sotc/global/2010/13.

National Research Council, Division of Earth and Life Studies, Committee on the Science of Climate Change. 2001. *Climate Change Science: An Analysis of Some Key Questions*. Washington: National Academy Press.

National Round Table on the Environment and the Economy (NRTEE). 2003a. *2003 Environment and Sustainable Development Indicators for Canada*. Ottawa.

——. 2003b. *Securing Canada's Natural Capital: A Vision for Nature Conservation in the 21st Century*. Ottawa.

——. 2003c. *State of the Debate: Environmental Quality in Canadian Cities: The Federal Role*. Ottawa.

——. 2006. *The State of the Debate on the Environment and the Economy: Environmental Quality in Canadian Cities: The Federal Role*. Ottawa.

——. 2010. *Degrees of Change: Climate Warming and the Stakes for Canada*. Ottawa.

——. 2011a. *Parallel Paths: Canada–U.S. Climate Policy Choices*. Ottawa.

——. 2011b. *Paying the Price: The Economic Impacts of Climate Change for Canada*. Ottawa.

National Snow and Ice Data Center. 2014. "Glaciers and Climate Change." Accessed 31 Dec. 2014. http://nsidc.org/cryosphere/glaciers/questions/climate.html.

Natural Resources Canada. 1995. "Silviculture terms in Canada." cfs.nrcan.gc.ca/pubwarehouse/pdfs/24216_e.pdf.

——. 2005a. "Canadian vehicle survey 2005." oee.nrcan.gc.ca/Publications/statistics/cvs05/index.cfm?attr=0.

——. 2005b. *The State of Canada's Forests: Annual Report 2004–5: The Boreal Forest*. Ottawa:

Canadian Forest Service, Natural Resources Canada.

——. 2005c. "Technologies and applications: About solar energy." canmetenergy.nrcan.gc.ca/renewables/solar-photovoltaic/2438.

——. 2006a. "Canadian minerals yearbook." Minerals and Mining Statistics Online. web.archive.org/web/20071026150232/http://mmsd1.mms.nrcan.gc.ca/mmsd/intro_e.asp.

——. 2006b. "Energy efficiency trends in Canada 1990–2004." oee.nrcan.gc.ca/ publications/statistics/trends06/chapter6.cfm?attr=0.

——. 2006c. "Technologies and applications: About wind energy." canmetenergy.nrcan. gc.ca/renewables/wind/2171.

——. 2007a. "Employment in Canada's mining and mineral processing industries remains robust in 2006." Information Bulletin. publications.gc.ca/collections/collection_ 2009/nrcan/M31-6-2007E.pdf.

——. 2007b. *The State of Canada's Forests: Annual Report 2007.* Ottawa: Canadian Forest Service, Natural Resources Canada.

——. 2007c. "Strong growth expected for Canada's mining sector." Natural Resources Canada's News Room. web.archive.org/web/20080221193508/http://www.nrcan-rncan.gc.ca/media/ newsreleases/2007/200789a_e.htm.

——. 2009a. "Canadian mining industry: 2009 general review." *Canadian Minerals Yearbook—2009.* www.nrcan.gc.ca/minerals-metals/business-market/canadian-minerals-yearbook/4033.

——2009b. "Partnership agreements." *Ekati Diamond Mine. Partnership Agreements.* www.nrcan.gc.ca/minerals-metals/aboriginal/bulletin/3719.

——. 2010a. "Non-timber forest products." canadaforests.nrcan.gc.ca/article/borealntfp.

——. 2010b. *State of Canada's Forests: Annual Report 2010.* Ottawa: Natural Resources Canada.

——. 2010c. "Energy efficiency: Energy use." web.archive.org/web/20101227104424/http://www.nrcan.gc.ca/eneene/effeff/transuse-eng.php.

——. 2011. *The State of Canada's Forests: Annual Report 2011.* Ottawa: Natural Resources Canada.

——. 2013. *The State of Canada's Forests, 2013.* Ottawa, Canadian Forest Service.

——. 2014a. *The State of Canada's Forests, 2014.* Ottawa, Canadian Forest Service.

——. 2014b. "Canada is a Global Mineral Exploration and Mining Giant." Accessed 23 Oct. 2014. http://www.nrcan.gc.ca/media-room/backgrounders/2013/1851.

——. 2014c. "Mineral Trade." Accessed 24 Oct. 2014. http://www.nrcan.gc.ca/mining-materials/publications/16466.

——. 2014d. "Canadian Mineral Production." Accessed 24 Oct. 2014. http://www.nrcan.gc.ca/mining-materials/publications/8772.

——. 2014e. *About Renewable Energy.* Accessed 17 Nov. 2014. http://www.nrcan.gc.ca/energy/renewable-electricity/7295.

——. 2014f. "Offshore British Columbia: Review of the Federal Moratorium on Oil and Gas Activities Offshore British Columbia." Accessed 19 Nov. 2014. http://www.nrcan.gc.ca/energy/offshore-oil-gas/5843.

Nature. 2010. "Citizen scientists" (editorial). *Nature* 468: 476.

——. "Editorial: Frozen out." *Nature* 483: 6.

Nature Saskatchewan. n.d. "Operation Burrowing Owl." http://www.naturesask.ca/what-we-do/stewards-of-saskatchewan/operation-burrowing-owl.

Neave, D., et al. 2002. "Forest biodiversity in Canada." *Forestry Chronicle* 78, 6: 779–83.

Neilson, E.T., et al. 2007. "Spatial distribution of carbon in natural and managed stands in an industrial forest in New Brunswick, Canada." *Forest Ecology and Management* 253: 148–60.

Nellemann, C., S. Hain, and J. Alder, eds. 2008. *In Dead Water: Merging of Climate Change with Pollution, Over-harvest, and Infestations in the World's Fishing Grounds.* Arendal, Norway: UNEP/GRID-Arendal. www.grida.no.

Newman, P.W.G. 2006. "The environmental impact of cities." *Environment and Urbanization* 18, 2: 275–95.

Newmark, W.D. 1995. "Extinction of mammal populations in western North American national parks." *Conservation Biology* 9: 512–26.

Nikiforuk, A. 2007. *On the Table: Water, Energy and North American Integration.* Toronto: University of Toronto, Munk Centre for International Studies, Program on Water Issues, Sept.

NOAA. National Climatic Data Center. 2013. *State of the Climate: Global Analysis for Annual 2013.* December. Accessed 29 Dec. 2014. http://www.ncdc.noaa.gov/sotc/global/2013/13.

Nobel, P.G. 1990. *Contaminants in Canadian Seabirds.* SOE Report no. 90–2. Ottawa: Environment Canada.

Nobelprize.org. 2007. "The Nobel Peace Prize, 2007." Accessed 30 Dec. 2014. http://www.nobelprize.org/nobel_organizations/nobelmedia/nobelprize_org/copyright/index.html.

Noble, B. 2008. "Strategic approaches to regional cumulative effects assessment: A case study of the Great Sand Hills, Canada." *Impact Assessment and Project Appraisal* 26, 2: 78–90.

North American Bird Conservation Initiative Canada. 2014. *The State of Canada's Birds, 2012.* Ottawa: Environment Canada. Accessed 17 Jan. 2015. www.stateofcanadasbirds.org/index.jsp.

Northwest Territories Ministry of Environment and Natural Resources. 2014. *Barren-ground Caribou: Bathurst Herd.* Accessed 3 Nov. 2014. http://www.enr.gov.nt.ca/programs/barren-ground-caribou-bathurst-herd.

Nova Scotia Department of Environment and Labour. 2002. *A Drinking Water Strategy for Nova Scotia: A Comprehensive Approach to the Management of Drinking Water.* Halifax: Nova Scotia Environment and Labour.

Nova Scotia Tourism Partnership and Nova Scotia Tourism, Culture and Heritage. 2007. *Nova Scotia Strategy for Sustainable Coastal Tourism Development.* Halifax: Nova Scotia Tourism, Culture and Heritage.

Nuclear Energy Institute. 2014. *Top 10 Nuclear Generating Countries.* Accessed 24 Nov. 2014. http://www.nei.org/Knowledge-Center/Nuclear-Statistics/World-Statistics/Top-10-Nuclear-Generating-Countries.

Nuclear Waste Management Organization (NWMO). 2005. Choosing a Way Forward: The Future Management of Canada's Used Nuclear Fuel: A Summary. Toronto: NWMO.

——. 2013. *Learning More Together: Summary, Triennial Report 2011 to 2013.* Toronto: Nuclear Waste Management Corporation.

——. 2014a. "Moving Forward Together: Canada's Plan for the Long-Term Management of Used Nuclear Fuel, Site Selection Process, Step 1. Overview: Canada's Plan." Accessed 25 Nov. 2014. http://www.nwmo.ca/sitingprocess-overview3.

——. 2014b. "Moving Forward Together: Canada's Plan for the Long-Term Management of Used Nuclear Fuel, Site Selection Process, Step 1. Overview: Review the Steps." Accessed 25 Nov. 2014. http://www.nwmo.ca/sitingprocess_theprocess

——. 2014c. "Moving Forward Together: Canada's Plan for the Long-Term Management of Used Nuclear Fuel, Site Selection Process, Step 1, Guiding Principles." Accessed 25 Nov. 2014. http://www.nwmo.ca/sitingprocess_overview5

Obokata, R., L.Veronis, and R. McLeman. 2014. "Empirical research on international environmental migration: A systematic review." *Population and Environment* 36: 111–135.

O'Connor, D.R. 2002a. *Report of the Walkerton Inquiry: Part One, The Events of May 2000 and Related Issues.* Toronto: Ontario Ministry of the Attorney General.

——. 2002b. *Report of the Walkerton Inquiry: Part Two, A Strategy for Safe Drinking Water.* Toronto: Ontario Ministry of the Attorney General.

Odum, E.P. 1969. "The strategy of ecosystem development." *Science* 164: 262–70.

——. 1971. *Fundamentals of Ecology,* 3rd edn. Toronto: Holt, Rinehart and Winston, CBS College Publishing.

OEER. 2008. *Fundy Tidal Energy Strategic Environmental Assessment Final Report.* Halifax: Nova Scotia Department of Energy.

Office of the Auditor General (OAG). 2011. "Report of the Commissioner of the Environment and Sustainable Development." In *A Study of Managing Fisheries for Sustainability.* Ottawa.

Office of the Auditor General of Canada 2013. *2013 Fall Report of the Commissioner of the Environment and Sustainable Development*. Ottawa.

Office of the Auditor General. 2013. "Recovery planning for species at risk." Chapter 6 in *Report of the Commissioner of Sustainable Development and Environment*. Ottawa.

Office of the Auditor General of Canada. 2013. *Report of the Commissioner of the Environment and Sustainable Development*. Ottawa.

O'Hara, K. 2010. "Canada must free scientists to talk to journalists." *Nature* 467: 501.

Oil Sands Advisory Panel. 2010. *A Foundation for the Future: Building an Environmental Monitoring System for the Oil Sands*. A report submitted to the Minister of Environment. Dec.

Oldreive, M. 2013. "The role of Strategic Environmental Assessments for emerging marine renewable energy sectors: The Nova Scotian example." *Journal of Environmental Assessment Policy and Management* 15, 2: 1.

Oliver, Joe. 2012. "An open letter from the Honourable Joe Oliver, Minister of Natural Resources, on Canada's commitment to diversify our energy markets and the need to further streamline the regulatory process in order to advance Canada's national economic interest." Natural Resources Canada, 9 Jan. 2012. http://www.nrcan.gc.ca/media-room/news-release/2012/1/1909.

Olsson, P. 2007. "The role of vision in framing adaptive co-management processes: Lessons from Kristianstads Vattenrike, southern Sweden." In Armitage et al. (2007: 168–85).

Omeja, P.A., A.L. Jacob, M.J. Lawes, J.S. Lwanga, J.M. Rothman, C. Tumwesigye, and C.A. Chapman. 2014. "Do changes in elephant abundance affect forest composition or regeneration?" *Biotropica* 46: 704–711.

O'Neill, D. 2004. "Threats to water availability in Canada: A perspective." In *Threats to Water Availability in Canada*. NWRI Scientific Assessment Report Series no. 3 and ACSD Science Assessment Series no. 1. Ottawa and Burlington, Ont.: Environment Canada and National Water Research Institute, xi–xvi.

Ontario Ministry of Energy. 2006. "Ontario leads Canada in wind power generation." Press release. news.ontario.ca/archive/en/2006/11/22/Ontario-Leads-Canada-InWindpower-Generation.html.

Ontario Power Generation. 2010. "Nuclear power." www.opg.com/power/nuclear/.

Organisation for Economic Co-operation and Development (OECD). 2002. *Towards Sustainable Consumption: An Economic Conceptual Framework*. Paris: OECD Environment Directorate.

———. 2011. *Greening Household Behaviour*. Paris.

O'Riordan, T. 1976. *Environmentalism*. London: Pion.

Orr, D.W. 1992. "The problem of education." *New Directions for Higher Education* 77 (Spring): 3–8.

———. 1994. *Earth in Mind: On Education, Environment and the Human Prospect*. Covelo, Calif.: Island Press.

Palen, W.J., et al. 2014. "Consider the global impacts of oil pipelines." *Nature* 510: 465–467.

Panetta, A. 2015. "Keystone bills stalled again with veto." *The Record*, 25 Feb., A4.

Pappas, S. 2011. "Global chronic hunger rises above 1 billion." In Worldwatch Institute (2011: 92–5).

Paquette, M., et al. 2015. "Rapid disappearance of perennial ice on Canada's most northern lake." *Geophysical Research Letters*. doi:10.1002/2014GL062960

Parkinson, G. 2011. "Durban talks off to a bad start." *Climate Spectator*, 28 Nov. www.climatespectator.com.au/commentary/durban-talks-bad-start.

Parks Canada Agency. 2011. *Corporate Plan 2011/2012 to 2015/2016*. Ottawa: Her Majesty the Queen in Right of Canada.

Parmesan, C. 2006. "Ecological and evolutionary responses to recent climate change." *Annual Review of Ecology and Systematics* 37: 637–69.

Parson, E.A. 2000. "Environmental trends and environmental governance in Canada." *Canadian Public Policy* 26 (supplement): S123–S143.

Partidario, M.F., and R. Clark, eds. 2000. *Perspectives on Strategic Environmental Assessment*. Boca Raton, Fla: Lewis Publishers.

Pauly, D. 2006. "Major trends in small-scale fisheries, with emphasis on developing countries, and some implications for the social sciences." *Maritime Studies* 4, 2: 7–22.

Pedlar, J.H., et al. 2012. "Placing forestry in the assisted migration debate." *BioScience* 62: 835–842.

People's Food Policy Project. 2011. *Resetting the Table: A People's Food Policy for Canada*. People's Food Policy Project. Food Secure Canada, 36.

Perkel, C. 2011. "War over fresh water possible, meeting told." *The Record*, 23 Mar., A8.

Peterson, C.H., et al. 2003. "Long-term ecosystem response to the *Exxon Valdez* oil spill." *Science* 302: 2082–6.

Phillips, D. 1990. *The Climate of Canada*. Ottawa: Minister of Supply and Services Canada.

Plummer, R., and J. FitzGibbon. 2007. "Connecting adaptive co-management, social learning, and social capital through theory and practice." In Armitage et al. (2007: 38–61).

Pollution Probe. 2007. *Towards a Vision and Strategy for Water Management in Canada*. Toronto: Pollution Probe.

Popkin, B.M., L.S. Adair, and S.W. Ng. 2012. "Global nutrition transition and the pandemic of obesity in developing countries." *Nutrition Reviews* 70: 3–21. doi: 10.1111/j.1753-4887.2011.00456.x

Population Reference Bureau. 2007. "World population highlights." *Population Bulletin* 62: 2.

Potash Investing News. 2014. "2013 Top 10 Potash Producing Countries." Accessed 24 Oct. 2014. http://potashinvestingnews.com/10219-2013-top-potash-producing-countries.html.

Potts, S.G., et al. 2010. "Global pollinator declines: Trends, impacts and drivers." *Trends in Ecological Evolution* 25: 345–353.

Pradhan, P., et al. 2013. "Embodied crop calories in animal products." *Environmental Research Letters* 8: 044044.

Prescott-Allen, R. 2001. *The Well-being of Nations: A Country by Country Index of Quality of Life and the Environment*. Washington and Ottawa: Island Press and IDRC.

Prince Edward Island Environmental Advisory Council. 2013. *Principles of Sustainable Development*. Charlottetown. Accessed 4 Sept. 2014. www.gov.pe.ca/photos.original/elj_susdeve_eacpdf.

Priscoli, J.D., J. Dooge, and M.R. Llamas. 2004. *Water and Ethics: An Overview*. Series on Water and Ethics, Essay 1. Paris: UNESCO.

Puxley, C. 2014. "'Canada is Indian land:' chief." *The Record*, 11 Dec., A3.

Qualman, D. 2011. "Advancing agriculture by destroying farms? The state of agriculture in Canada." In Wittman, Desmarais, and Wiebe (2011: 20–42).

Quebec. 2013. *Government Sustainable Development Strategy 2008–2013: A Collective Commitment*. Jan. Quebec City: Government of Quebec.

Quinn, F. 2007. *Water Diversion, Export and Canada–US Relations: A Brief History*. Toronto: University of Toronto, Munk Centre for International Studies, Program on Water Issues, Aug.

——— et al. 2004. "Water allocation, diversion and export." In *Threats to Water Availability in Canada*. NWRI Scientific Assessment Report Series no. 3 and ACSD Science Assessment Series no. 1. Ottawa and Burlington, Ont.: Environment Canada and National Water Research Institute, 1–8.

Quoden, J. 2010. "Multi-instrumental EU environmental policy." presentation at conference on Europe Environment Policy: What's Next? . . . Towards a 7th Environment Action Program, Brussels, 25–6 Nov. www.eapdebate.org/files/files/Session4-Joachim-Quoden.pdf.

Rahman, M.M., and O. Varis. 2005. "Integrated water resources management: Evolution, prospects and future challenges." *Sustainability: Science, Practice and Policy* 1: 15–21.

Rainham, D. 2002. "Risk communication and public response to industrial chemical contamination in Sydney, Nova Scotia: A case study." *Journal of Environmental Health* 65, 5: 26–32.

Raudsepp-Hearne, C., et al. 2010. "Untangling the environmentalists' paradox: Why is human well-being increasing as ecosystem services are degrading?" *BioScience* 60, 8: 576–89.

RBC. 2011. "2011 Canadian Water Attitudes Study: Three quarters of Canadians using toilet as garbage can." smr.newswire.ca/en/rbc-financial-group/canadian-water-attitudes-study.

RBC Bluewater Project. 2014. *2014 RBC Canadian Water Attitudes Study*. Accessed 5 Dec. 2014. http://www.rbc.com/community-sustainability/environment/rbc-blue-water/water-attitude-study.html.

Reed, M.G., et al. 2014. "Building a community of practice for sustainability: Strengthening learning and collective action of Canadian biosphere reserves through a national partnership." *Journal of Environmental Management* 145: 230–239.

Rees, J. 1985. *Natural Resources: Allocation, Economics and Policy*. London: Methuen.

Rees, W.E. 2010. "Getting serious about urban sustainability: Eco-footprints and the vulnerability of twenty-first-century cities." In T. Bunting, P. Filion, and R. Walker, eds, *Canadian Cities in Transition: New Directions in the Twenty-First Century*, 4th edn. Toronto: Oxford University Press, 70–86.

Reeves, H.W. 2010. *Water Availability and Use Pilot: A Multiscale Assessment in the U.S. Great Lakes Basin*. Professional Paper 1778. Reston, Virginia: US Geological Survey.

Reguly, E. 2009. "We're in the doghouse—but we can buy our way out." *Globe and Mail*, 16 Dec., A16.

Reichel, J. 2011. "New oil sands extraction method cheaper, more sustainable." *Epoch Times*, 22–8 Sept., A5.

Reid, E. 2015. "BIXI: Montreal's Public Bike System." Accessed 6 Feb. 2015. http://montreal.about.com/od/gettingaroundtown/a/public_bikes.htm.

Reig, P., A. Maddocks, and F. Gassert. 2014. *World's 36 Most Water-Stressed Countries*. World Water Institute. Accessed 4 Feb. 2014. http://www.wri/blog/2013/12/world's-36-most-water-stressed-countries.

REN21. 2014. *Renewables 2014: Global Status Report*. Paris. REN21 Secretariat.

Renewable Energy World.Com. 2014. "Advantages and disadvantages of solar photvoltaic—Quick pros and cons of solar PV." Accessed 18 Nov. 2014. http://www.renewableenergyworld.com/rea/blog/post/2012/12/advantages-and-disadvantages-of-solar-photovoltaic-quick-pros-and-cons-of-solar-pv.

Resilient Earth. 2014. Accessed 31 Dec. 2014. http://theresilientearth.com/??=content/nasa-satellite-debunks-melting-glacier-myth.

Reynolds, M. 2010. "Who sets climate policy? The U.S.?" *The Record*, 9 Feb., A11.

Richardson, N.H., B.I. Savan, and L. Bodnar. 1989. *Economic Benefits of a Clean Environment: Sudbury Case Study*. Prepared for the Department of Environment, Canada. Toronto: N.H. Richardson Consulting.

Rittel, H.W.J., and M.M. Webber. 1973. "Dilemmas in a general theory of planning." *Policy Sciences* 14, 2: 155–169.

Rivers, N., and D. Sawyer. 2008. *Pricing Carbon: Saving Green—A Carbon Price to Lower Emissions, Taxes and Barriers to Green Technology*. Vancouver: David Suzuki Foundation.

Roberts, C.M. 2003. "Our shifting perspectives on the oceans." *Oryx* 37: 166–77.

Rochette, P., et al. 2008. "Estimation of N_2O emissions from agricultural soils in Canada, II: 1990–2005 inventory." *Canadian Journal of Soil Science* 88, 5: 655–69.

Rockström, J., et al. 2009. "A safe operating space for humanity." *Nature* 461: 472–5.

Rode, K., S. Amstrup, and E. Regehr. 2010. "Reduced body size and cub recruitment in polar bears associated with sea ice decline." *Ecological Applications* 20, 3: 768–82.

Rode, K.D., et al. 2006. "Nutritional ecology of elephants in Kibale National Park, Uganda, and its relationship with crop-raiding behaviour." *Journal of Tropical Ecology* 22: 441–449.

Rode, K.D., et al. 2012. "A tale of two polar bear populations: Ice habitat, harvest, and body condition." *Population Ecology* 54: 3–18.

Roman, G., P. Dearden, and R. Rollins. 2007. "Application of zoning and 'limits of acceptable change' to manage snorkeling tourism." *Environmental Management* 39: 819–830.

Ross, N. 2001. *Healing the Landscape: Celebrating Sudbury's Reclamation Success*. Sudbury, Ont.: Vegetation Enhancement Technical Advisory Committee.

Ross, P.S., et al. 2000. "High PCB concentrations in free-ranging Pacific killer whales, *Orcinus orca*: Effects of age, sex and dietary preference." *Marine Pollution Bulletin* 40: 504–15.

Rowe, S. 1993. "In search of the holy grass: How to bond with the wilderness in nature and ourselves." *Environment Views* (Winter): 7–11.

Rowell, P., G.L. Holroyd, and U. Banasch. 2003. "Summary of the 2000 Canadian peregrine falcon survey." In J. Kennedy, ed., *Bird Trends: A Report on Results of National Ornithological Surveys in Canada*. Ottawa: Canadian Wildlife Service, 52–6.

Royal Commission on the Future of the Toronto Waterfront. 1992. *Regeneration: Toronto's Waterfront and the Sustainable City, Final Report*. Ottawa and Toronto: Minister of Supply and Services Canada and Queen's Printer of Ontario.

Roy-Dufresne, E., T. Logan, J.A. Simon, G.L. Chmura, V. Millien. 2015. "Poleward expansion of the white-footed mouse (*Peromyscus leucopus*) under climate change: Implications for the spread of Lyme disease." *PLOS One* 8: 11 e80724.

Ruddiman, W.F. 2003. "The anthropogenic greenhouse era began thousands of years ago." *Climatic Change* 61: 261–93.

Rushton, R.J. 2012. *The Efficacy of Environmental Impact Assessment in Saskatchewan's Forest Resource Sector*. MA thesis, Saskatoon: University of Saskatchewan, Department of Geography and Planning.

Rylatt, M.G. 1999. "Ekati diamond mine background and development." *Mining Engineer* 51: 37–43.

Sadler. B., ed. 2005. *Recent Progress with Strategic Environmental Assessment at the Policy Level*. Prague: Czechoslovakian Ministry of the Environment.

St Clair Conservation. 2013. *Annual Report: Working Together for a Healthy Environment*. Accessed 18 Aug. 2014. https://www.scrca.on.ca/wp-content/uploads/2013/11/Pub-Annual-Report-2012.pdf.

Sanchez, L.E. 1998. "Industry response to the challenge of sustainability: The case of the Canadian nonferrous mining sector." *Environmental Management* 22: 521–31.

——. 2001. "The climate change: Soil fertility–food security nexus." Address at the Sustainable Food Security for All by 2020 Conference, Bonn, Sept.

Sandford, R., and M.-A. Phare. 2011. "A new water ethic." *Alternatives Journal* 37, 1: 12–14.

Sandom, J.C., S. Faurby, B. Sandel, and J.-C. Svenning. 2014. "Global late Quaternary megafauna extinctions linked to humans, not climate change." *Proceedings of the Royal Society B: Biological Sciences* 281: 1787.

Santas, A. n.d. *Environmentalism's Fourth Wave: A Reimagination*. Valdosta, Georgia, Valdosta State University, Department of Philosophy and Religious Studies.

Sargeant, T. 2014. "Cost of Montreal's BIXI bike sharing program still unknown." Global News, Aug. 14. Accessed 6 Feb. 2015. http://globalnews.ca/news/1508171/cost-of-montrealstill-unknown/.

Saskatchewan. 2008. "Mineral resources of Saskatchewan." www.er.gov.sk.ca/mineralsandenergy.

Saskatchewan Community Wind. "Cost of generation, wind and coal compared." Accessed 26 Nov. 2014. http://www.saskwind.ca/blogbackend/2014/10/9/cost-of-generation-wind-and-coal-compared.

Saskatchewan Energy and Resources. 2009. "Mineral resources of Saskatchewan, uranium." www.er.gov.sk.ca.

Saskatchewan Round Table on Environment and Economy. 1992. *Conservation Strategy for Sustainable Development in Saskatchewan*. Regina: Saskatchewan Round Table on Environment and Economy.

SaskPower. 2012. "Boundary Dam integrated carbon capture demonstration project." Accessed 28 Nov. 2014. http://www.saskpower.com/wp-content/uploads/clean_coal_information_sheet.pdf.

Saumure, R.A., T.B. Herman, and R.D. Titman. 2007. "Effects of haying and agricultural practices on a declining species: The North American wood turtle (*Glyptemis insculpta*)." *Biological Conservation* 135: 565–75.

Savard, D. 2013. *Building Sustainable Communities with Design, or How to Build Healthier Communities*. Fredericton: New Brunswick Department of Environment and Local Government.

Sawin, J.L. 2004. "Making better energy choices." In Worldwatch Institute (2004: 24–43).

Scheinberg, A., D.C. Wilson, and L. Rodic. 2010. *Solid Waste Management in the World's Cities*, 3rd edn. In UN-Habitat's State of Water, UN Human Settlements Programme.

Schindler, D., and P. Lee. 2010. "Comprehensive conservation planning to protect biodiversity and ecosystem services in Canadian boreal regions under a warming climate and increasing exploitation." *Biological Conservation* 143: 1571–86.

Schueler, F.W., and D.E. McAllister. 1991. "Maps of the number of tree species in Canada: A pilot project GIS study of tree diversity." *Canadian Biodiversity* 1: 22–9.

Schultz J.A., E.S. Darling, and I.M. Côté. 2013. "What is an endangered species worth?: Threshold costs for protecting imperilled fishes in Canada." *Marine Policy* 42: 125–132.

Scialabba, N.E. 2003. *Organic Agriculture: The Challenge of Sustaining Food Production While Enhancing Biodiversity*. Rome: Food and Agriculture Organization.

——and C. Hattam, eds. 2002. *Organic Agriculture, Environment and Food Security*. Rome: Food and Agriculture Organization.

Science Daily. 2011. "World population to surpass 7 billion in 2011." 28 Jul. www.sciencedaily.com/ releases/2011/07/110728144933.htm.

Scientific Review Panel. 2002. *British Columbia Offshore Hydrocarbon Development: Report of the Scientific Review Panel*. Submitted to the BC Minister of Energy and Mines, 15 Jan.

Scott, D., B. Jones, J. Andrey, L. Mortsch, and K. Warriner, eds. 2000. *Climate Change Communication: Proceedings of an International Conference*, Waterloo, Ont.: University of Waterloo and Environment Canada, Adaptation and Impacts Research Group.

Scott, D., R. Steiger, M. Rutty, and P. Johnson. 2014. "The future of the Olympic Winter Games in an era of climate change." *Current Issues in Tourism*. doi: 10.1080/13683500.2014.887664

Seattle Organic Restaurants. n.d. "37 millions bees found dead in Ontario, Canada after planting large GMO corn field treated with neonicotinoid class of pesticides." http://seattleorganicrestaurants.com/vegan-whole-food/neonicotinoids-pesticides-colony-collapse-of-honeybees-suppressing-immune-system.php.

Seaweb. 2003. "Danger at sea: Our changing ocean." http://www.seaweb.org/resources/documents/reports_dangeratsea.pdf.

Secretariat of the Convention on Biological Diversity. 2010. *Global Biodiversity Outlook 3*. Montreal: Convention on Biological Diversity.

Selbourne, Earl of. 2000. *The Ethics of Freshwater Use: A Survey*. Paris: UNESCO.

Selin, S., and D. Chavez. 1995. "Developing a collaborative model for environmental planning and management." *Environmental Management* 19: 189–95.

Sen, A. 1981. *Poverty and Famines: An Essay on Entitlement and Deprivation*. Oxford: Oxford University Press.

Seymour, D. 2007. "Executive Summary," *The Urban Heat Island Effect in Winnipeg*. Frontier Centre for Public Policy, 26 Sept. Accessed 27 Sept. 2015. http://archive fcpp.org/posts/the-urban-heat-island-effect-in-Winnipeg.

Shaftoe, D., ed. 1993. *Responding to Changing Times: Environmental Mediation in Canada*. Waterloo, Ont.: Conrad Grebel College.

Shang, E.H., R.M.K. Yu, and R.S. Wu. 2006. "Hypoxia affects sex differentiation and development, leading to a male-dominated population in zebrafish." *Environmental Science and Technology* 40: 3118–22.

Sharp, M., et al. 2011. "Extreme melt on Canada's Arctic ice caps in the 21st century." *Geophysical Research Letters* 38, L11501. doi:10.1029/2011GL047381

Shaw, R.W., and CCAF A041 Project Team. 2001. *Coastal Impacts of Climate Change and Sea-Level Rise on Prince Edward Island: Synthesis Report*. Climate Change Action Fund Project CCAF A041. Ottawa: Ministry of Supply and Services.

Shiklomanov, I.A. 2000. "Appraisal and assessment of world water resources." *Water International* 25: 11–32.

Shrubsole, D. 2001. "The cultures of flood management in Canada: Insights from the 1997 Red River experience'," *Canadian Water Resources Journal*, 26(4): 461–79.

Sierra Club of Canada. 2006. *National Forest Strategy 2003–2008: An Assessment in 2006—Is It Making a Difference?* Toronto: Sierra Club of Canada.

Simpson, C.G. 1964. "Species density of North American recent mammals." *Systematic Zoology* 13: 15–73.

Simpson, H.C., and R.C. de Loë. 2014. "A collaborative approach to groundwater protection: The Rural Water Quality Program for Waterloo Region." *Canadian Water Resources Journal* 39, 2: 228–239.

Sinclair, A.J., and M. Doelle. 2010. "Environmental assessment in Canada: Encouraging decisions for sustainability." In Mitchell (2010: 462–94).

Slaper, T.F., and T.J. Hall. 2011. "The triple bottom line: What is it and how does it work?" *Indiana Business Review* 86, 1: 4–10.

Slocombe, D.S. 2010. "Applying an ecosystem approach." In Mitchell (2010: 409–33).

Smith, A., and J.B. MacKinnon. 2007. *The 100-Mile Diet: A Year of Local Eating*. Toronto: Random House Canada.

Smith, J.N.M., et al. 1998. "Population biology of snowshoe hares II: Interactions with winter food plants." *Journal of Animal Ecology* 57: 269–86.

Smith, K., and M. Rosano. 2014. "Energy rich." *Canadian Geographic* 134, 3: 34–40.

Smith, L.C. 2010. *The World in 2050: Four Forces Shaping Civilization's Northern Future*. New York: Dutton Books/Penguin.

——and L. Haddad. 2015. "Reducing child undernutrition: Past drivers and priorities for the post-MDG era." *World Development* 68: 180–204.

Splawinski, A. 2015. "The failure that is food policy in Nunavut." *Rabble*, Feb. 12. Accessed 15 Feb. 2015. http://rabble.ca/news/2015/02/failure-food-policy-nunavut.

Sprague, J.B. 2007. "Great Wet North: Canada's myth of water abundance." In Bakker (2007: 23–35).

Springer, G., and C. Burda. 2014. *Fast Cities: A Comparison of Rapid Transit in Major Canadian Cities*. Sept. Calgary: Pembina Institute.

Standing Committee on Environment and Sustainable Development. 2000. *Pesticides: Making the Right Choice for the Protection of Health and the Environment*. Ottawa: House of Commons.

Statistics Canada. 2001. "2001 Census of agriculture." www.statcan.gc.ca/ca-ra2001/index-eng.htm.

——. 2003a. *Farming Facts 2002*. Ottawa: Ministry of Industry.

——. 2003b. *Human Activity and the Environment: A Statistical Compendium*. Catalogue no. 16-201-XIE. Ottawa: Minister of Supply and Services.

——. 2007a. *2006 Census of Agriculture*. Ottawa.

——. 2007b. "Households and the environment survey 2006." www.statcan.gc.ca/daily-quotidien/070711/dq070711b-eng.htm.

——. 2007c. "Recycling in Canada." *EnviroStats* 1, 1: 3–7.

——. 2009. *Food Statistics*. Catalogue no. 21–020–X. Ottawa.

——. 2010. "Agriculture." In *2010 Annual Report*. Ottawa.

——. 2011a. *Human Activity and the Environment 2010*. Ottawa.

——2011b. *Households and the Environment 2009*. Ottawa.

——. 2013a. *Canada, Urban Wastewater Treatment*. Accessed 8 Dec. 2014. http://www.statcan.gc.ca/pub/16-201-x/2012000/part-partie4-eng.htm.

——. 2013b. *Farm Environmental Management Survey, 2011*. Catalogue no. 21-023-X. Ottawa: Ministry of Industry.

——. 2013c. *Households and the Environment, 2011*. Ottawa.

——. 2014a. *Human Activity and the Environment: Agriculture in Canada 2014*. Ottawa: Ministry of Industry.

——. 2014b. *Report on Energy Supply and Demand in Canada*. Feb. 10. Accessed 16 Nov. 2014. http://www5.statcan.gc.ca/olc-cel/olc.action?objId=57-003-X&objType=2&lang=en&limit=0http://www5.statcan.gc.ca/olc-cel/olc.action?objId=57-003-X&objType=2&lang=en&limit=0.

——, Agriculture Division. 2003. "Food statistics, 2003." publications.gc.ca/Collection/Statcan/21-020-X/21-020-XIE2003002.pdf.

Steele, D.H., R. Andersen, and J.M. Green. 1992. "The managed commercial annihilation of northern cod." *Newfoundland Studies* 8, 1: 34–68.

Stewart, E.J., et al. 2007. "Sea ice in Canada's Arctic: Implications for cruise tourism." *Arctic* 60: 370–80.

Stinchcombe, K., and R.B. Gibson. 2001. "Strategic environmental assessment as a means of pursuing sustainability: Ten advantages and ten challenges." *Journal of Environmental Assessment Policy and Management* 3: 343–72.

Stirling, A., et al. 2008 "Unusual predation attempts of polar bears on ringed seals in the southern Beaufort Sea: Possible significance of changing spring ice conditions." *Arctic* 61: 14–22.

Stirling, I., and A.E. Derocher. 2012. "Effects of climate warming on polar bears: A review of the evidence." *Global Change Biology* 18: 2694–2706.

Stocker, T.F., et al., eds. IPCC. 2013. *Climate Change 2013: The Physical Science Basis.* Contribution of Working Group I to the Fifth Assessment Report of the Intergovernmental Panel on Climate Change. Cambridge and New York: Cambridge University Press.

Stockholm International Water Institute. 2014. "Thematic scope: Energy and water." *World Water Week: 2014 Programme and Call for Registration*. Stockholm, Stockholm International Water Institute, 6–7.

Stockton, A.S., et al. 2005. "A natural experiment on the impacts of high deer densities on the native flora of coastal temperate rain forests." *Biological Conservation* 126: 118–28.

Stockwell, C.A., P. Hendry, and M.T. Kinnison. 2003. "Contemporary evolution meets conservation biology." *Trends in Ecology and Evolution* 18: 94–101.

Stokes, K., and R. Law. 2000. "Fishing as an evolutionary force." *Marine Ecology Progress Series* 208: 307–9.

Stuart-Smith, J., et al. 2002. "Conserving whitebark pine in the Canadian Rockies." *Research Links* 10: 11–14.

Suffling, R., and D. Scott. 2002. "Assessment of climate change effects on Canada's national park system." *Environmental Monitoring and Assessment* 74: 117–39.

Sumaila, U.R., et al. 2007. "Potential costs and benefits of marine reserves on the high seas." *Marine Ecology Progress Series* 345: 305–10.

——and D. Pauly, eds. 2007. *Catching More Bait: A Bottom-up Re-estimation of Global Fisheries Subsidies* (2nd version). Fisheries Centre Research Reports 14, 6. Vancouver: Fisheries Centre, University of British Columbia.

Swain, H., S. Louttit, and S. Hrudey. 2006. *Report of the Expert Panel on Safe Drinking Water for First Nations*, vol. 1. Nov. Ottawa: Department of Indian Affairs and Northern Development,.

Sydney Tar Ponds Agency. n.d. *Sydney Tar Ponds Project: Focus on the Future.* Sydney, NS: Sydney Tar Ponds Agency. www.tarpondscleanup.ca.

Tahera Diamond Corporation. 2008. "Mining—Jericho Diamond Mine." web.archive.org/web/20080915022408/http://www.tahera.com/Operations/Mining/ JerichoDiamondMine/default.aspx.

Taylor, E.B., and S. Pinkus. 2013. "The effects of lead agency, nongovernmental organizations, and recovery team membership on the identification of critical habitat for species at risk: Insights from the Canadian experience." *Environmental Review* 21: 93–102.

Taylor, L. 2009. "Water challenges in oil sands country: Alberta's Water for Life strategy." *Policy Options* (Jul.–Aug.): 44–7.

Taylor, P.D., et al. 1993. "Connectivity is a vital element of landscape structure." *Oikos* 68, 3: 571–2.

Taylor, S. 1984. *Making Bureaucracies Think: The Environmental Impact Statement Strategy of Administrative Reform*. Stanford, Calif.: Stanford University Press.

Theberge, J.C., J.T. Theberge, and P. Dearden. 2015. "Protecting park ecosystems: The application of ecological concepts and active management." In P. Dearden, R. Rollins, and M. Needham, eds, *Parks and Protected Areas in Canada: Planning and Management*, 4th edn. Toronto: Oxford University Press.

Theobold, M. 2009. "Fish production reaches a record." *Vital Signs*, 3 Dec. vitalsigns.worldwatch.org/vs-trend/ fish-production-reaches-record.

The Record (Kitchener–Waterloo). 2004. "Harvesting the wind: Local farmers say they can provide power—if regulations let them." 9 Aug., A1–A2.

——. 2007. "Six Nations can't dictate new laws." 15 Sept., A16.

——. 2010. "Hopeful progress out of Cancun." 14 Dec., A10.

Thérival, R. 1993. "Systems of strategic environmental assessment." *Environmental Impact Assessment Review* 13, 3: 145–68.

Thibault, S., and S. Payette. 2009. "Recent permafrost degradation in bogs of the James Bay area, northern Quebec, Canada." *Permafrost and Periglacial Processes* 20: 383–389.

Thirlwell, G.M., C.A. Madramootoo, and I.W. Heathcote. 2007. *Energy-Water Nexus: Energy Use in the Municipal, Industrial and Agricultural Water Sectors*. Canada-US Conference. Washington, D.C.: Policy Research Initiative of Canada and the Woodrow Wilson Institute.

Thompson, I.D., J.A. Baker, and M. Ter-Mikaelian. 2003. "A review of the long-term effects of post-harvest silviculture on vertebrate wildlife, and predictive models, with an emphasis on boreal forests in Ontario, Canada." *Forest Ecology and Management* 177: 441–69.

Thomson Reuters. n.d. "Haiti earthquake." Accessed 9 Oct. 2014. http://www.trust.org/spotlight/Haiti-earthquake-2010/?tab=background.

Tinker, J. 1996. "Introduction." In J.B. Robinson et al., eds, *Life in 2030: Exploring a Sustainable Future for Canada*. Vancouver: University of British Columbia Press, ix–xv.

Tomalty, R. 2013. *Sustainable Cities: The Role for Philanthropy in Promoting Urban Sustainability*. Toronto: Canadian Environmental Grantmakers' Network.

Tomlinson, I. 2010. "Doubling food production to feed the 9 billion: A critical perspective on a key discource on food security in the UK." *Journal of Rural Studies* 29: 81–90.

Toronto, City of. 2011. "2010 residential waste diversion rates." www.toronto.ca/garbage/residential-diversion.htm.

Toronto and Region Conservation Authority. 2006. *Moving toward the Living City*. Toronto: Toronto and Region Conservation Authority.

Toronto Public Health. 2007. *The State of Toronto's Food: Discussion Paper for Toronto Food Strategy*. Toronto: Toronto Public Health.

Tremblay, C., and J. Gutberlet. 2011. "Empowerment through participation: Assessing the voices of leaders from recycling cooperatives in São Paulo, Brazil." *Community Development Journal* 46: 282–302. doi: 10.1093/cdj/bsq040

Tremblay, C., J. Gutberlet, and A.M. Peredo. 2010. "United we can: Resource recovery, place and social enterprise." *Resources, Conservation & Recycling* 54, 7: 422–8.

Trewartha, G.T. 1954. *An Introduction to Climate.* New York: McGraw-Hill.

Trist, E. 1980. "The environment and system-response capability." *Futures* 12, 2: 113–27.

Trites, A.W., et al. 2007. "Killer whales, whaling, and sequential megafaunal collapse in the North Pacific: A comparative analysis of the dynamics of marine mammals in Alaska and British Columbia following commercial whaling." *Marine Mammal Science* 23, 4: 751–65.

Trostel, K., et al. 1987. "Can predation cause the 10-year hare cycle?" *Oecologia* 74: 185–92.

Turner, C. 2013. *The War on Science: Muzzled Scientists and Wilful Blindness in Stephen Harper's Canada*. Vancouver: Greystone Books.

Tynan, C.T., and J.L. Russell. 2008. "Assessing the impacts of future 2°C global warming on Southern Ocean cetaceans." Paper presented to the International Whaling Commission Scientific Committee, Chile, June.

UNAIDS. 2007. *AIDS Epidemic Update 2007*. Geneva.

UNAIDS. 2010. *Report on the Global AIDS Epidemic*. www.unaids.org/globalreport/Global_report.htm.

UNDP. 2014. *Human Development Report 2014: Sustaining Human Progress: Reducing Vulnerabilities and Building Resilience*. Nairobi.

UNEP. 2012. *Global Environment Outlook 5: Environment for the Future We Want*. Nairobi.

UNEP. 2012. *Global Environmental Outlook 5*. Nairobi.

UNFPA. 2014. *State of the World Population* 2014. Geneva: UN.

UN-HABITAT. 2010. *State of the World's Cities 2010/2011: Bridging the Urban Divide*. London: Earthscan.

United Nations. 2012. "At Rio event, secretary-general says 'Sustainable energy is the golden thread' that weaves together economy, environment, and equity." June 12. http://www.un.org/press/en/2012/sgsm14363.doc.htm.

——. 2014a. "Further Advancing the Durban Platform." Accessed 2 Jan. 2015. http://www.unfccc.int/files/meetings/lima-dec-2014/in-session/applicatioin/pdf/cpl14.pdf.

——. 2014b. *The Millennium Development Goals Report 2014*. New York.

United Nations Development Programme (UNDP). 2005. *Human Development Report 2005: International Cooperation at a Crossroads: Aid, Trade and Security in an Unequal World*. New York.

——. 2010. *Human Development Report 2010. The Real Wealth of Nations: Pathways to Human Development*. New York.

——. 2011. *Human Development Report 2011. Sustainability and Equity: A Better Future for All*. New York.

United Nations Environment Programme (UNEP). 2002. "Global environmental outlook 3 (GEO 3)." www.unep.org.geo/geo3.asp.

United Nations Environment Programme, Division of Technology, Industry and Economics. 2002. *Melbourne Principles for Sustainable Cities*. Nairobi.

——. 2007. *Global Environment Outlook: Environment for Development (GEO-4)*. Nairobi: UNEP.

——. 2008. "Meltdown in the mountains." www.unep.org/Documents.Multilingual/Default.asp?DocumentID=530&ArticleID.

——. 2010. *Annual Report 2009: Seizing the Green Opportunity*. Nairobi: UNEP.

——. 2011. *Annual Report 2010*. Nairobi: UNEP.

United Nations General Assembly. 2010. "General Assembly adopts resolution recognizing access to clean water, sanitation as a human right, by recorded vote of 122 in favor, none against, 41 abstentions." www.un.org/News/Press/docs/2010/ga10967.doc.htm.

United Nations International Strategy for Disaster Reduction. 2004. *Living with Risk: A Global Review of Disaster Reduction Initiatives*. 2 vols. Geneva: UN.

United Nations Population Division. 2014. "World population to reach 10 billion by 2100 if fertility in all countries converges to replacement level." esa.un.org/unpd/wpp/Other-Information/Press_Release_WPP2010.pdf.

United Nations Population Fund. 2007a. *State of the World Population 2007*. New York.

——. 2007b. *World Population Prospects: The 2006 Revision*. Geneva: UN.

United Nations Statistics Division. 2009. "Agricultural support estimate for OECD countries from OECD database 2009." Millennium Development Goal Indicators. unstats.un.org/unsd/mdg/SeriesDetail.aspx?srid=601.

United States Agency of International Development (USAID). 2011. "USAID Fact Sheet 2011. Food for Peace 2010 Programs." News release. Washington.

United States Department of Energy. 2011. *Biomass Energy Data Book: Energy Efficiency and Renewable Energy*. Washington: US Government.

United States Geological Survey. 2013. "The Severity of an Earthquake." http://pubs.usgs.gov/gip/earthq4/severitygip.html.

US Department of Energy. 2014. *The Water-Energy Nexus: Challenges and Opportunities*. DOE/EPSA-0002, June. www.energy.gov.

U.S. Energy Information Administration. 2014. "Canada." Accessed 21 Oct. 2014. http://www.eia.gov/countries/cab.cfm?fips=ca.

Vaiciulis, R., and S. Fluker. 2013. "Linking the California and Québec Emissions Trading Schemes." Accessed 3 Jan. 2015. http://ablawg.ca/2013/12/03/linking-the-california-and-quebec-emissions-trading-schemes/.

Vancouver, City of. 2009a. *Greenest City: Quick Start Recommendations*. Vancouver: City of Vancouver.

——2009b. *Vancouver 2020: A Bright Green Future—An Action Plan for Becoming the World's Greenest City by 2020*. Vancouver.

Vancouver Sun. 2003. "Spotted owl survival threatened." 11 Jul.

Van Damme, L., et al. 2014. *Status Report on Ecosystem- based Management (EBM): Policy Barriers and Opportunities for EBM in Canada*. Prepared for the Canadian Boreal Forest Agreement. Thunder Bay, Ont.: KBM Resources Group.

Vanderploeg, H.A., T.H. Johengen, and J.R. Liebig. 2009. "Feedback between zebra mussel selective feeding and algal composition affects mussel condition: Did the regime changer pay a price for its success?" *Freshwater Biology* 54: 47–63.

Vegetation Enhancement Technical Advisory Committee (VETAC). 2005. *Annual Report*. Sudbury, Ont.: Greater Sudbury Land Reclamation Program.

——. 2007. *Annual Report*. Sudbury, Ont.: Greater Sudbury Land Reclamation Program.

——. 2009. *Land Reclamation Program Annual Report 2009*. Sudbury, Ont.: City of Greater Sudbury.

Venter, O., et al. 2006. "Threats to endangered species in Canada." *BioScience* 56, 11: 903–10.

Viewpoint: Perspectives on Modern Mining. 2008, issue 4. "The reclamation of Sudbury: The greening of a moonscape." Caterpillar Global Mining. https://mining.cat.com/cda/files/2785515/7/Sudbury_Eng.pdf.

Volpe, J.P., et al. 2000. "Evidence of natural reproduction of aquaculture escaped Atlantic salmon (*Salmo salar*) in a coastal British Columbia river." *Conservation Biology* 14, 3: 899–903.

von Braun, J. 2007. *The World Food Situation: New Driving Forces and Required Actions*. Washington: International Food Policy Research Institute.

Voynick, S. 1999. "Diamonds on ice." *Compressed Air* 104: 60–8.

Vyn, R.J., and R.M. McCullough. 2014. "The effects of wind turbines on property values in Ontario: Does public perception match empirical evidence?" *Canadian Journal of Agricultural Economics* 62, 3: 365–392.

Wada, Y., et al. 2010. "A worldwide view of groundwater depletion." *Geophysical Research Letters* 37, L20402. doi:10.1029/2010GL044571

Wagner, F.H. 2001. "Freeing agency research from policy pressures: A need and an approach." *Bioscience* 51, 6: 445–450.

Wakefield, S., K. Fredrickson, and T. Brown. 2014. "Food security and health in Canada: Imaginaries, exclusions and possibilities." *The Canadian Geographer* 59: 82–92. doi:10.1111/cag.12139

Walker, B., and D. Salt. 2006. *Resilience Thinking: Sustaining Ecosystems and People in a Changing World*. Washington: Island Press.

——. 2012. *Resilience Practice: Building Capacity to Absorb Disturbance and Maintain Function*. Washington, DC: Island Press.

Walker, I.J., and R. Sydneysmith. 2008. "British Columbia." In D.S. Lemmen et al., eds, *From Impacts to Adaptation: Canada in a Changing Climate 2007*. Ottawa: Government of Canada, 329–86.

Walsh, J.E., et al. 2004. "Cryosphere and hydrology." In *Arctic Climate Impact Assessment: Impacts of a Warming Climate*. New York: Cambridge University Press, 183–242.

Walston, J., et al. 2010. "Bringing the tiger back from the brink—The six percent solution." *PLoS Biology* 8, 9: e1000485.

Walters, C.J. 2007. "Is adaptive management helping to solve fisheries problems?" *Ambio* 36, 4: 304–7.

Waples R.S., et al. 2013. "A tale of two acts: Endangered species listing practices in Canada and the United States." *Bioscience* 63: 723–734.

Warner, J.F., and C.L. Johnston. 2007. "Virtual water—real people: Useful concept or prescriptive tool?" *Water International* 32: 63–77.

Warnock, R.G., and M.A. Skeel. 2004. "Effectiveness of voluntary habitat stewardship in conserving grassland: Case of Operation Burrowing Owl in Saskatchewan." *Environmental Management* (25 Mar.). wwwspringerlink.com.

Warren, F.J., and D.S. Lemmen, eds. 2014a. *Canada in a Changing Climate: Sector Perspectives on Impacts and Adaptation*. Ottawa: Government of Canada.

——. 2014b. "Synthesis." In F.J. Warren and D.S. Lemmen, eds., *Canada in a Changing Climate: Sector Perspectives on Impacts and Adaptation*. Ottawa: Government of Canada, 1–18.

Wasiuta, V., M.J. Lafrenière, and A. Norman. 2015. "Atmospheric deposition of sulfur and inorganic nitrogen in the Southern Canadian Rocky Mountains from seasonal snowpacks and bulk summer precipitation." *Journal of Hydrology*. doi: 10.1016/j.jhydrol.2015.01.073

Water Footprint Network. 2011. www.waterfootprint.org.

Waters, M.R., T.W. Stafford, B. Kooymanc, and L.V. Hills. 2015. "Late Pleistocene horse and camel hunting at the southern margin of the ice-free corridor: Reassessing the age of Wally's Beach, Canada." *Proceedings of the National Academy of Sciences of the United States of America*, 23 Mar. doi: 10.1073/pnas.1420650112

Watson, R., and D. Pauly. 2001. "Systematic distortion in world fisheries catch trends." *Nature* 414: 534–6.

Watt-Cloutier, S. 2000. "Wake-up call." www.ourplanet.com/imgversn/124/watt.html.

Weber, B. 2011. "Nobel Peace Prize winners urge less oilsands growth." *The Record*, 20 Sept., A8.

Weiss, W., I. Bergmann, and G. Faninger. 2007. *Solar Heat Worldwide: Markets and Contribution to the Energy Supply 2005*. Paris: International Energy Agency.

Wells, J., et al. 2010. *A Forest of Blue—Canada's Boreal Forest: The World's Waterkeeper*. Seattle: International Boreal Conservation Campaign. Courtesy of Pew Environment Group, 2011.

Werniuk, J. 1998a. "Great Canadian diamonds." *Canadian Mining Journal* (Oct.): 8–22.

——. 1998b. "Where the smart mining is going." *Canadian Mining Journal* (Dec.): 14–18.

Westhoek, H. et al. 2014. "Food choices, health and environment: Effects of cutting Europe's meat and dairy intake." *Global Environmental Change* 26: 196–205.

Whitelaw, G.S., and P.E.J. Eagles. 2007. "Planning for long, wide conservation corridors on private lands in the Oak Ridges Moraine, Ontario, Canada." *Conservation Biology* 21: 675–83.

Whitfield, C.J., et al. 2014. "Beaver-mediated methane emission: The effects of population growth in Eurasia and the Americas." *Ambio*. doi:10.1007/s13280-014-0575-y

WHO. n.d. "Food Security." www.who.int/trade/glossary/story028/en/.

Wichelns, D. 2010. "Virtual waters: A helpful perspective, but not a sufficient policy criterion." *Water Resources Management* 24: 2203–19.

Wiebe, N., and K. Wipf. 2011. "Nurturing food sovereignty in Canada." In Wittman, Desmarais, and Wiebe (2011: 1–19).

Wielgus, R.B., and P.R. Vernier. 2003. "Grizzly bear selection of managed and unmanaged forests in the Selkirk Mountains." *Canadian Journal of Forest Research* 33: 822–9.

Wiklund, J.A., et al. 2014. "Use of pre-industrial floodplain lake sediments to establish baseline river metal concentrations downstream of Alberta oil sands: A new approach for detecting pollution of rivers." *Environmental Research Letters* 9, 12. doi:10.1088/1748-9326/9/12/124019

Wiley-Blackwell. 2008. "Birds migrate earlier, but some may be left behind as climate warms rapidly." *Science Daily*, 22 Jun. www.sciencedaily.com/ releases/2008/06/080620115925.htm.

Wilkinson, C.J.A. 2008. "Protected areas law in Ontario, Canada: Maintenance of ecological integrity as the management priority." *Natural Areas Journal* 28: 180–6.

Willer, H., and J. Lernoud, eds. 2014. *The World of Organic Agriculture: Statistics and Emerging Trends 2014*. FiBL-IFOAM Report. Revised version. 24 Feb. 2014. Frick: Research Institute of Organic Agriculture (FiBL); Bonn: International Federation of Organic Agriculture Movements (IFOAM).

Williams, R., D. Lusseau, and P.S. Hammond. 2006. "Estimating relative energetic costs of human disturbance to killer whales (*Orcinus orca*)." *Biological Conservation* 133: 301–11.

Wilson, D., et al. 2012. "Comparative analysis of solid waste management in 20 cities." *Waste Management and Research* 30: 237–254.

Wilson, J., and M. Anielski. 2005. *Ecological Footprints of Canadian Municipalities and Regions*. Prepared for The Canadian Federation of Canadian Municipalities. Calgary.

Wittman, H., A.A. Desmarais, and N. Wiebe, eds. 2011. *Food Sovereignty in Canada: Creating Just and Sustainable Food Systems*. Black Point, N.S.: Fernwood.

Wolfe, B.B., et al. 2005. "Impacts of climate and river flooding on the hydro-ecology of a floodplain basin, Peace–Athabasca Delta, Canada, since A.D. 1700." *Quaternary Research* 64: 147–62.

——et al. 2006. "Reconstruction of multi-century flood histories from oxbow lake sediments, Peace–Athabasca Delta, Canada." *Hydrological Processes* 20, 4: 131–53.

——, et al. 2011. "A 5200-year record of freshwater availability for regions in western North America fed by high-elevation runoff." *Geophysical Research Letters* 38: L11404. doi:10.1029/2011GL047599,2011.

Wong, P.Y., and I. Brodo. 1992. "The lichens of southern Ontario." *Syllogeus* 69: 1–79.

Woo, M.K., K.L. Young, and L. Brown. 2006. "High Arctic patchy wetlands: Hydrologic variability and their sustainability." *Physical Geography* 27: 297–307.

Woods, A. 2014. "Montreal bike-share program BIXI files for bankruptcy protection." *The Toronto Star*, 20 Jan. Accessed 6 Feb. 2015. http://www.thestar.com/news/canada/2014/01/20/montreal_bikeshare_program_bixi_files_for_bankruptcy_protection.html.

Woods, A.J., et al. 2010. "Forest health and climate change: A British Columbia perspective." *Forestry Chronicle* 86, 4: 412–22.

World Bank. 2008. *World Development Indicators 2008*. Washington: World Bank.

World Bank. 2014. "World Development Indicators." Dec. accessed 17 Jan. 2015. http://data.worldbank.org/data-catalog/world-development-indicators.

——. 2015. *World Bank Data Base*. http://data.worldbank.org/indicator/.

World Commission on Environment and Development (WCED). 1987. *Our Common Future*. Oxford: Oxford University Press.

World Conservation Union (IUCN—International Union for the Conservation of Nature and Natural Resources). 2002. "2002 IUCN Red List of Threatened Species." www.redlist.org.

——. 2003. "Release of the 2003 IUCN Red List of Threatened Species." press release. www.iucn.org.

——. 2007. "2007 IUCN Red List of Threatened Species." www.redlist.org.

——. 2011. "The IUCN Red List of Threatened Species." www.iucnredlist.org.

——and UNEP-WCMC. 2009. *The World Database on Protected Areas (WDPA)*. Cambridge: UNEP-WCMC, Jan.

World Health Organization. 2014. "Ambient and Household Air Pollution and Health." Accessed 2 Oct. 2014. http://www.who.int/phe/health_topics/outdoorair/databases/en/.

World Health Organization, Public Health and Environment. 2011. "Database: Outdoor air pollution cities." www.who.in/phc/ health_topics/outdoorair/databases/en.

World Nuclear Association. 2014a. "Uranium in Canada." Accessed 24 Nov. 2014. http://www.world-nuclear.org/info/Country-Profiles/Countires-A-F/Canada-Uranium/.

——. 2014b. "Nuclear Power in Canada."

Accessed 24 Nov. 2014. http://www.world-nuclear.org/info/Country-Profiles/Countries-A-F/Canada--Nuclear-Power/.

World Resources Institute. 2014. "New analysis finds over 100 million hectares of intact forest area degraded since 2000." www.wri.org/news/2014/09/release-new-analysis-finds-over-100-million-hectares-intact-forest-area-degraded-2000#sthash.GGjyduzq.QqxYkL0R.dpuf.

Worldwatch Institute. 2004. *State of the World 2004*. New York: W.W. Norton.

——2007. *Vital Signs: The Trends That Are Shaping Our Future, 2007*. New York: W.W. Norton.

——. 2011. *Vital Signs 2011: The Trends That Are Shaping Our Future*. Washington: Worldwatch Institute.

World Weather Online, Toronto's Climate. n.d. http://www.worldweatheronline.com/Toronto-weather-averages/Ontario/CA.aspx.

World Wildlife Fund. 2010. *Living Planet Report 2010*. wwf.panda.org/about_our_earth/all_publications/living_planet_report/2010_ lpr/. Some rights reserved.

——, Zoological Society of London, and Global Footprint Network. 2006. *Living Planet Report 2006*. Gland, Switzerland: World Wildlife Fund.

Worm, B., et al. 2006. "Impacts of biodiversity loss on ocean ecosystem services." *Science* 314, 7: 87–90.

Wotton, B.M., C.A. Nock, and M.D. Flannigan. 2010. "Forest fire occurrence and climate change in Canada." *International Journal of Wildland Fire* 19: 253–271.

Woynillowicz, D., and C. Severson-Baker. 2006. *Down to the Last Drop: The Athabasca River and Oil Sands*. Drayton Valley, Alta: Pembina Institute.

——, ——, and M. Raynalds. 2005. *Oil Sands Fever: The Environmental Implications of Canada's Oil Sands Rush*. Drayton Valley, Alta: Pembina Institute. Courtesy of the Pembina Institute.

Wu, J., and R. Hobbs, eds. 2007. *Key Topics in Landscape Ecology*. Cambridge: Cambridge University Press.

WWF. 2014. *Living Planet Report 2014*. Toronto.

Yates, J.S., and J. Gutberlet. 2011. "Enhancing livelihoods and the urban environment: The local political framework for integrated organic waste management in Diadema, Brazil." *Journal of Development Studies* 47, 4: 1–18.

Yona, L. 2014. "Opinion: Canada's position on climate change is an embarrassment." *Montreal Gazette*, December 5. Accessed 15 Dec. 2014. http://montrealgazette.com/news/national/opinion-canadas-position-on-climate-change-is-an-embarrassment.

Yuntao Z., et al. 2015. "Record-breaking Lake Erie hypoxia during 2012 drought." *Environmental Science & Technology* 49, 2: 800–807. doi: 10.1021/es503981n

Zhang, M., et al. 2014 "Response of surface air temperature to small-scale land clearing across latitudes." *Environmental Research Letters* 9: 034002

Zhang, X., and X. Cai. 2011. "Climate change impacts on global agricultural land availability." *Environmental Research Letters* 6: 1–8.

Zhu, Y., et al. 2000. "Genetic diversity and disease control in rice." *Nature* 406: 718–22.

Zickfeld, K., M. Eby, and A.J. Weaver. 2008. "Carbon-cycle feedbacks of changes in the Atlantic meridional overturning circulation under future atmospheric CO_2." *Global Biogeochemical Cycles* 22: GB3024.

Zickfeld, K., et al. 2011. "Nonlinearity of carbon cycle feedbacks." *Journal of Climate* 24: 4254–4274.

Zickfeld, K., et al. 2013. "Long-term climate change commitment and reversibility: An EMIC intercomparison." *Journal of Climate* 26: 5782–5809. doi: 10.1175/JCLI-D-12-00584.1

INDEX